D0294866

THE BEST FRENCH WINES

Editions Vintage

Series created and published under the direction of
Patrick DUSSERT-GERBER and Gilles TEMIME

Author and Director of the Editorial Staff:

Patrick Dussert-Gerber

General Director and Manager:

Gilles Temime

14, rue Rennéquin 75017 Paris
ISBN : 2-907506-01-3

EDITIONS VINTAGE
LEADER IN FRANCE
FOR THE PROMOTION
OF THE FRENCH WINES

SOMMAIRE

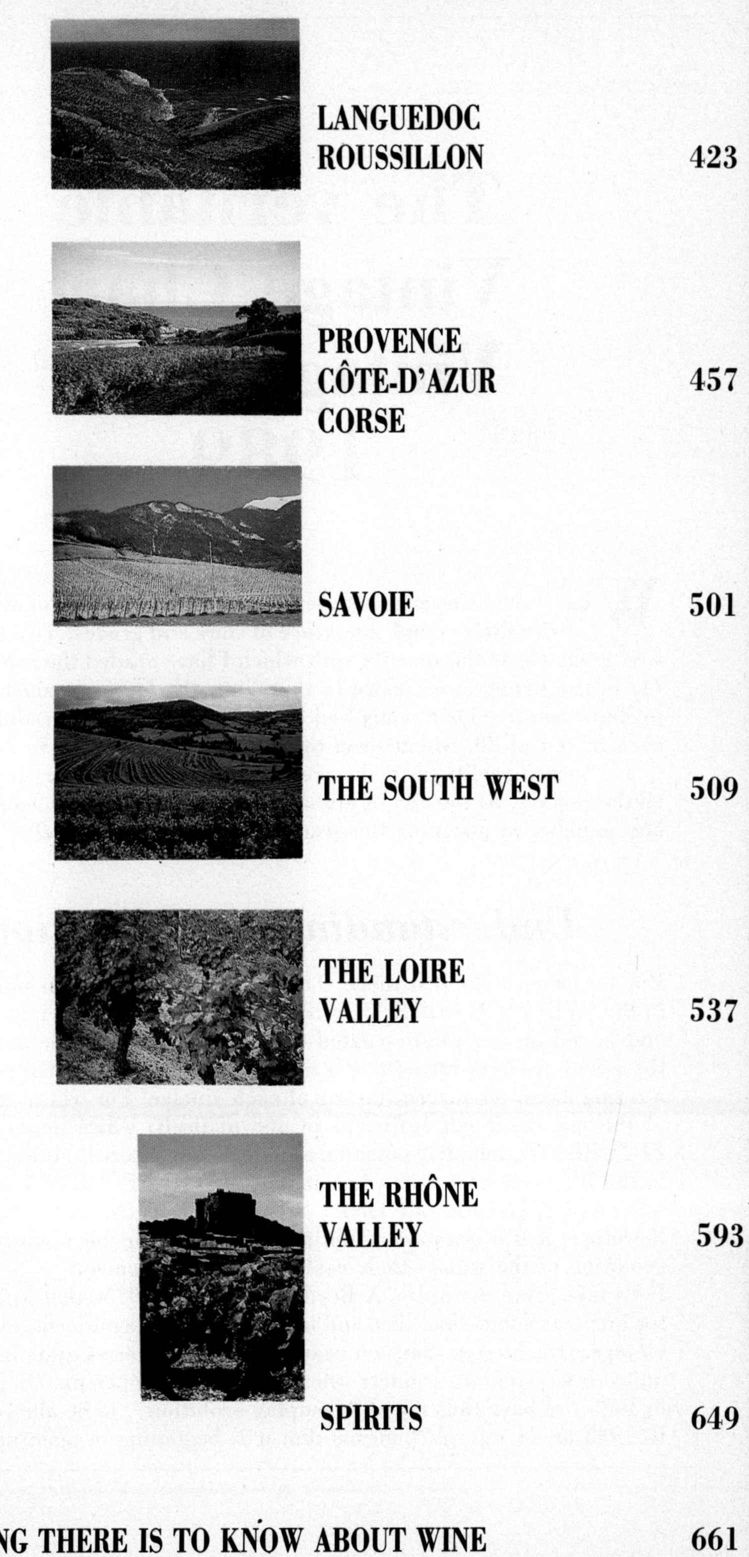

The veritable Vintage Chart Vintage Code© 1989

What is the difference between this and the multitude of other charts with their complex mixture of stars and grades? Two things: the first is the rigor, the severity with which I have graded the intrinsic quality of the vintages, or, more to the point, the harvests, since 1970. As professionals, we have really had enough of extravagant grading, 18, 19, even 20 out of 20, which seem to us much too flattering to correspond to any sort of reality, as if the great vintages were an everyday affair in all the regions. At the risk of offending some, we have decided not to pull any punches in assigning the grades in lightface, lower left.

Understanding the Evolution

But we haven't stopped there. The second thing, the enormous "plus" in the "VINTAGE CODE©", is the second grade (upper right, in Italics and in red on our plastic coated cards). For the first time anywhere in the world, we have introduced a new and absolutely essential parameter: a rating based on current tasting of each vintage! For wines, the quality of the vintage is not sufficient in and of itself; whats important is its FUTURE, its qualitative potential as time passes. There is always a moment in the life cycle of a wine when it is good. THERE AREN'T ANY BAD VINTAGES, THERE ARE ONLY "DELICATE" VINTAGES! Every year, therefore, it is a question of noting—differently or not according to the evolution of the wines—their real value at the moment.
Let's take some examples. A Bordeaux, vintage 1975—that we gave a 16 for intrinsic value—has been and is considered a magnificent, exceptional vintage. OK. Except that, ten years later the '75 tastes quite bad, is still quite closed and one wonders whether it will ever open up. On our chart, in 1985, we have thus noted "Complex evolution", to be allowed to age. In 1988 an 11 out of 20 means that it is beginning to open up.

Another example, also a red Bordeaux. The 1980 vintage has the reputation of being a minor vintage, even a "bad" vintage, according to some professionals. As far as the intrinsic value of the vintage is concerned, they are not wrong (we gave it 7 out of 20). On the other hand, this vintage has evolved in an entirely unexpected way and, at present, tastes quite good (we gave it 10 out of 20). Herein lies the significance of our second grade, which corresponds to the evaluation of its taste "now". Thanks to the second grade, we can immediately tell which are the best vintages in 1988, those for which we must wait, those which have lost some value. For winelovers, consumers, as well as for professionals (proprietors, buyers, restaurant managers, dealers. . .) it is a real working tool which permits the choice of a wine, a vintage, without risk of error. I hope that you will find it useful.

VINTAGE CODE

For your copy, write to
"L'AMOUR DU VIN", 94, rue Saint-Dominique, 75007 PARIS

Notes in Italics (above): value at the most recent tasting (1989).

Notes in Roman type (below): intrinsic value of the vintage, of the harvest (graded from 0 to 20).

VINTAGE CODE 1989 ©	1988	1987	1986	1985	1984	1983	1982	1
BORDEAUX ROUGES (crus)	▬ ★ / 14	╲ *9* / 9 (2)	▬ *13* / 16	▬ *12* / 17	▮ *11* / 10 (1)	╲ *14* / 17	▬ *11* / 18	13
BORDEAUX BLANCS	▬ ★ / 15	╲ *12* / 10	╲ *14* / 15	╲ *12* / 12	▮ *8* / 11	▮ *16* / 16	▮ *15* / 15	13
BORDEAUX LIQUOREUX	▬ ★ / 13	╲ *10* / 11	▬ ★ / 15	▬ *11* / 13	▮ *10* / 11	▬ *14* / 17	╲ *15* / 15	15
BOURGOGNES ROUGES	▬ ★ / 14	╲ *9* / 10	▬ ★ / 14	▬ *12* / 14		╲ *16* / 16	▮ *11* / 10	11
BOURGOGNES BLANCS	▬ ★ / 13	╲ *11* / 12	▬ *14* / 15	╲ *11* / 12	▮ *8* / 10	╲ *18* / 15	▮ *16* / 15	10
BEAUJOLAIS (crus)	▬ ★ / 14	╲ *10* / 11	╲ *15* / 14	╲ *15* / 13		▮ *18* / 15	▮ *12* / 11	13
COTES-DU-RHONE (crus)	▬ ★ / 14	╲ *10* / 10	╲ *13* / 13	╲ *14* / 14	▮ *9* / 11	╲ *16* / 17	▮ *11* / 11	13
ALSACES (crus)	▬ ★ / 13	╲ *11* / 11	╲ *14* / 14	╲ *15* / 16		╲ *16* / 14	▮ *10* / 12	14
VINS DE LOIRE	▬ *10* / 13	╲ *11* / 11	╲ *14* / 14	╲ *14* / 15	▮ *12* / 14	▮ *12* / 17	▮ *11* / 15	11
SUD-OUEST (Cahors...)	▬ ★ / 14	╲ *9* / 9	▬ *13* / 17	╲ *12* / 15		╲ *14* / 14	╲ *13* / 16	12
CHAMPAGNES (millésimés)					▮ *13* / 13	▮ *15* / 12	▮ *14* / 12	

▲ Complex evolution.
★ Tasting still difficult, wait.
▬ To be left to age in the cellar, their bouquet is still undeveloped.
╲ About ready to drink, soft bouquet, reaching maturity.
▮ To be drunk, full aromas present.
(1): Only in the Médoc; better elsewhere.
(2): Coulure in the Merlot: watch out for the wines from the Libourne region (Saint-Émilion, Pomerol...) and from the October harvest.
(3): A vintage not to be trusted... Don't buy any, for the moment.

80	1979	1978	1976	1975	1971	1970	Millésimes renommés	Température de dégustation
10	13 **16**	14 **16**	14 **16**	▲ 16 **11** (3)	14 **18**	15 **13**	1966-1964 1961-1955 1949-1947 1945-1929	(Degrés (°)) 15/16°
	11 **10**			16 **10**				10/12°
8	13 **13**		16 **17**	17 **19**	14 **17**			8/10°
8	13 **12**	18 **18**	16 **14**		15 **13**		1969	14/15°
	17 **16**	15 **14**	15 **10**		15 **8**	18 **14**		11/13°
		11 **12**						11/13°
	14 **12**	17 **16**	14 **13**	13 **8**	13 **8**	17 **11**	1967-1961	14°
	15 **14**	13 **15**	18 **19**	13 **10**	17 **13**			8/10°
	13 **10**	15 **15**	17 **15**				1961-1959 1955-1921	B : 8/10° R : 11/13°
	11 **11**	13 **14**	10 **9**	14 **12**.				14/15°
	14 **14**		15 **14**					7/9°

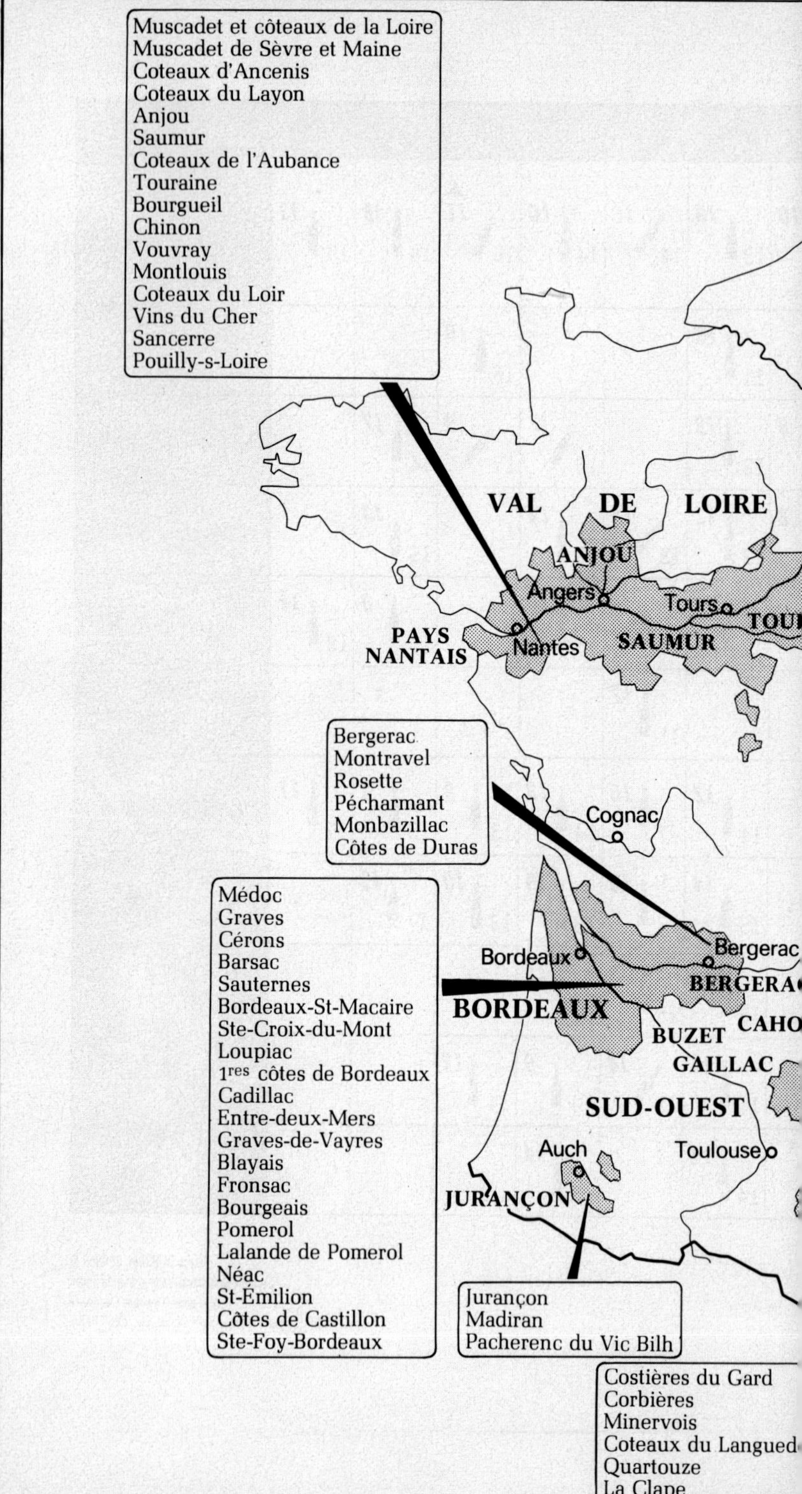
Muscadet et côteaux de la Loire
Muscadet de Sèvre et Maine
Coteaux d'Ancenis
Coteaux du Layon
Anjou
Saumur
Coteaux de l'Aubance
Touraine
Bourgueil
Chinon
Vouvray
Montlouis
Coteaux du Loir
Vins du Cher
Sancerre
Pouilly-s-Loire
VAL DE LOIRE
ANJOU
Angers
Tours
PAYS NANTAIS
Nantes
SAUMUR
Bergerac
Montravel
Rosette
Pécharmant
Monbazillac
Côtes de Duras
Cognac
Médoc
Graves
Cérons
Barsac
Sauternes
Bordeaux-St-Macaire
Ste-Croix-du-Mont
Loupiac
1res côtes de Bordeaux
Cadillac
Entre-deux-Mers
Graves-de-Vayres
Blayais
Fronsac
Bourgeais
Pomerol
Lalande de Pomerol
Néac
St-Émilion
Côtes de Castillon
Ste-Foy-Bordeaux
Bordeaux
Bergerac
BORDEAUX
BUZET
GAILLAC
SUD-OUEST
Auch
Toulouse
JURANÇON
Jurançon
Madiran
Pacherenc du Vic Bilh
Costières du Gard
Corbières
Minervois
Quartouze
La Clape

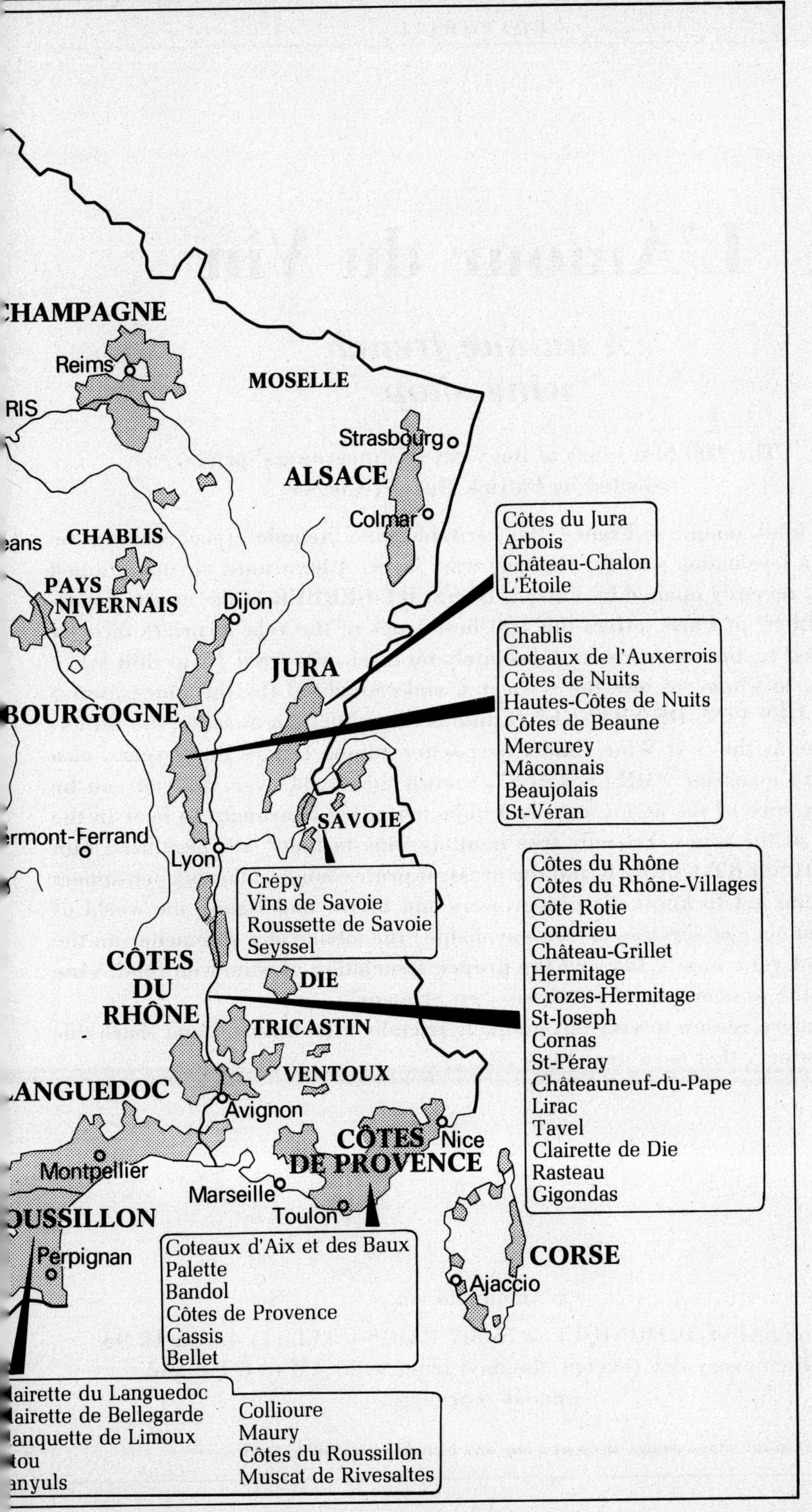

CHAMPAGNE
Reims
RIS
MOSELLE
Strasbourg
ALSACE
Colmar
CHABLIS
PAYS NIVERNAIS
Dijon
JURA
BOURGOGNE
SAVOIE
Lyon
CÔTES DU RHÔNE
DIE
TRICASTIN
VENTOUX
LANGUEDOC
Avignon
Montpellier
Marseille
Toulon
Nice
CÔTES DE PROVENCE
ROUSSILLON
Perpignan
CORSE
Ajaccio
Côtes du Jura
Arbois
Château-Chalon
L'Étoile
Chablis
Coteaux de l'Auxerrois
Côtes de Nuits
Hautes-Côtes de Nuits
Côtes de Beaune
Mercurey
Mâconnais
Beaujolais
St-Véran
Crépy
Vins de Savoie
Roussette de Savoie
Seyssel
Côtes du Rhône
Côtes du Rhône-Villages
Côte Rotie
Condrieu
Château-Grillet
Hermitage
Crozes-Hermitage
St-Joseph
Cornas
St-Péray
Châteauneuf-du-Pape
Lirac
Tavel
Clairette de Die
Rasteau
Gigondas
Coteaux d'Aix et des Baux
Palette
Bandol
Côtes de Provence
Cassis
Bellet
Collioure
Maury
Côtes du Roussillon
Muscat de Rivesaltes

L'Amour du Vin

A unique french wine shop

The 100 best wines of the year, at winegrowers' prices, selected by Patrick Dussert-Gerber.

One of a kind, unique in France, this veritable wine "temple" (according to the press) is a fascinating spot for the true wine lover. A luxurious, air-conditioned boutique, recently opened by Patrick DUSSERT-GERBER in the moste beautiful "quartier" of Paris, offers the 100 best wines of the year at prices directly determined by the winegrowers (absolutely no mark-uf!) from 15 to 300 F.F. Our man, to whom we owe the respected and redoubted (by the winegrowers) "GUIDE DES VINS DE FRANCE" (Editions Albin Michel), awarded the Gutenberg Prize as the best Wine Guide, best-seller among Guides for 9 years, also directs the magazine "MILLESIMES", known the world over. So you can be absolutely sure of the seriousness and objectivity that is brought to bear in the selection of the wines. Friendly free monthly wine-tastings* are organized with Patrick DUSSERT-GERBER and the greatest professionals, allowing consumers to meet and get to know the winegrowers and better understand the world of wine. A number of services are also available: the advice of a sommelier on the creation of your wine cellar and the proper association of wine with food, wine delivery, the possibilities of purchases "en primeur"...
Just one more reason to visit this uniquely friendly establishment and share this "love of wine", that is so dear to us all...

L'Amour du vin

94, rue SAINT-DOMINIQUE – 75007 PARIS – TEL (1) 45 56 12 94
Open every day (except Monday) from 9:30 AM to 8 PM and Sunday mornings.

***To take part in the wine-tastings, drop us a line and include your visiting card.**

Éditorial

The heritage

This second edition of our Guide comes at a turning point in the wine world.
For several years now, the world of wine has been increasingly internationalized. In chile, South Africa, Australia and in California, vineyards are flourishing and are producing more and more reputable wines (not all). If, in addition, those countries "historically" associated with wine (Spain, Italy, Germany, Portugal...) and the émergence of the European Common Market are taken into account, it is evident that competition for French wines in becoming, and will become, more and more "savage".
That's the way it is, and it would be a mistake for our producers to rest on their present laurels.
Already, some of the great French appellations, because of excessive production or an indecent pricing policy, are beginning to suffer in the international marketplace.
However, the great majority of French vineyards have two exceptional adventages which make them unique:

Soil

Except for certain wines from "historic" vineyards (see above), it is very difficult for the other foreign vineyards to compete with the typical nature of our soil. In Alsace as in Burgundy, in Champagne as in Armagnac, in the Loire as in the great South-West, wherever they are produced, our wines benefit from this extraordinary symbiosis between the soil and the climate which it is virtually impossible to find elsewhere.
If Chardonnay was planted in the Côte-de-Beaune, Mourvèdre in Provence, Cabernets or Sémillon in Bordeaux, Sauvignon in the Loire or Gamay in Beaujolais, there were good reasons, that time and experience have confirmed.
The most conclusive proof is that, in order to "make" great wines, white or red, Chardonnay or Cabernet-Sauvignon were quite naturally planted in California and in Australia.
No one can deny that that is our great strength.
However, as the standard bearer and reference point for the other foreign vineyards, our style is relatively easy to "copy" or, at least, to approximate. this is particularly true of the whites, for which modern vinification techniques (cryo-extraction cold fermentation...) have significantly facilitated the production of good wines.

Which leads me, quite naturally, to the second fundamental "plus" that is ours, one which we must learn to take better advantage of.

Reputation

A great wine, or just a good one, is tasted not only with the palate but with the mind. It is the only "product" in the world that is tasted this way, objectively, with love.

Our strength is to have always known how to combine myth and quality, dreams and gustatory gratification. When one savors one of our wines (I mean, of course, a good, typical wine), one also savors its authenticity and its character. At that very moment, each French vineyard becomes "the Madeleine"* of its region and can pride itself on its role as ambassador of its country.

To consolidate and preserve our reputation we must:

1. *Persist in the raising of authentic wines*, typical of their sub-soil and their historical past, consistent with usage and custom, responding to the winemaker's skill and that "je ne sais quoi" which makes all the difference. It is a common heritage, not only of the French, but of all those foreigners, amateur and professional, who are drawn to the intrinsic values of the fruit of the vine.

2. *Spread the word* and make the facts known, once and for all, throughout the world.

It is not enough, nowadays, to make a good wine. It must be talked about, explained, its quality proven.

And for that, we have to get together. That's what we are doing in Paris at "L'AMOUR DU VIN" (94, rue Saint-Dominique – 75007 Paris) and that's what we are doing also in our magazine "MILLESIMES" (which is going international), in my "GUIDE DES VINS DE FRANCE" (Albin Michel) and in this second edition of "THE BEST FRENCH WINES«

Help us spread the "world".

I hope that, through our word and our various projects and publications more people will "hear" it...

Patrick DUSSERT-GERBER

ALSACE

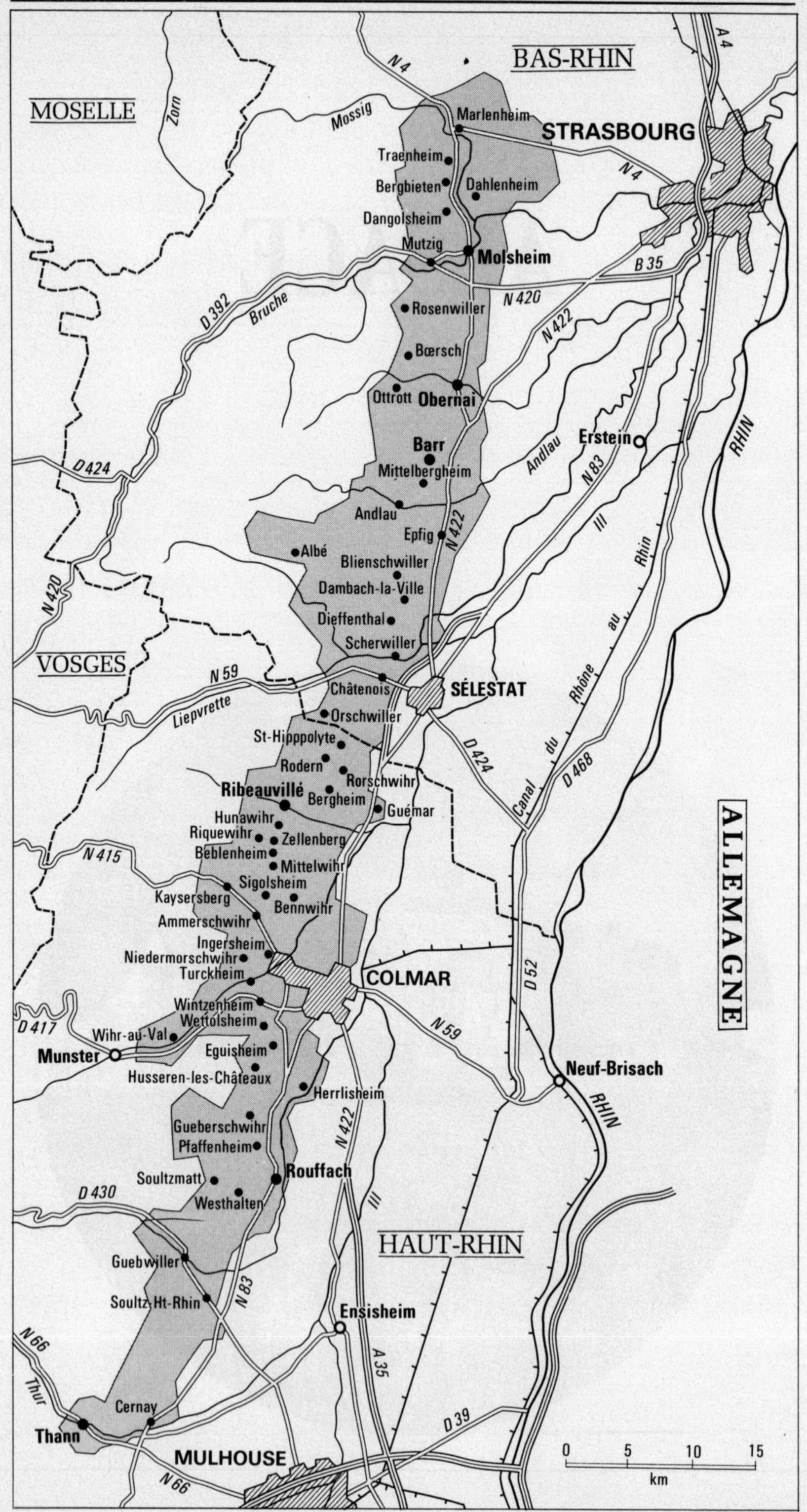
BAS-RHIN
MOSELLE
STRASBOURG
Marlenheim
Traenheim
Bergbieten
Dahlenheim
Dangolsheim
Mutzig
Molsheim
Rosenwiller
Bœrsch
Ottrott
Obernai
Barr
Mittelbergheim
Andlau
Epfig
Albé
Blienschwiller
Dambach-la-Ville
Dieffenthal
Scherwiller
Châtenois
SÉLESTAT
Orschwiller
St-Hippolyte
Rodern
Rorschwihr
Ribeauvillé
Bergheim
Guémar
Hunawihr
Riquewihr
Zellenberg
Beblenheim
Mittelwihr
Sigolsheim
Kaysersberg
Bennwihr
Ammerschwihr
Ingersheim
Niedermorschwihr
Turckheim
COLMAR
Wintzenheim
Wettolsheim
Wihr-au-Val
Munster
Eguisheim
Husseren-les-Châteaux
Herrlisheim
Gueberschwihr
Pfaffenheim
Rouffach
Soultzmatt
Westhalten
HAUT-RHIN
Guebwiller
Soultz-Ht-Rhin
Ensisheim
Cernay
Thann
MULHOUSE
Erstein
Neuf-Brisach
VOSGES
ALLEMAGNE
RHIN
Canal du Rhône au Rhin
Ill
Andlau
Bruche
Mossig
Zorn
Liepvrette
Thur
A 4
N 4
B 35
N 420
N 422
D 392
D 424
N 83
N 59
D 424
D 468
N 415
D 417
D 52
D 430
N 66
A 35
D 39
0
5
10
15
km

The soil above all

Ah, the grands crus of the Alsatian vineyard! Of course, with so considerable a production (140 million bottles, nearly 20% of the French production of AOC whites), it is always possible to find some inexcusably bad bottles on the market, at prices that do no good for the image of Alsatian wines and tend to discredit the real winemakers of the region. These, the exemplary winemakers, jovial yet serious, produce bottles that are far from ordinary, incomparable wines, marked by an exceptional soil, with an aromatic complexity bewitching to the nose and to the taste. They have the right, since 83, to the "Grand Cru" appellation, similar to the Burgundy classification (remarkably precise and complex at the same time), which is of great help to the consumer in distinguishing the great Alsatian wines from the others.

HISTORICAL BACKGROUND

Grapes were cultivated in Alsace prior to the Roman Conquest. The vines no doubt originally came from Provence at the time of the Gauls, traveled through the Rhône and Saône valleys and took root along the golden shores of the Rhine and the Moselle. Syrian and Greek immigrant gardeners and winegrowers from Massila (the former name of Marseilles) planted the vines there. From the way some of the stakes are arranged, ampelography—the study of vines—suspects that winegrowing in the region dates back to ancient Greek and Oriental times. The Gauls added the use of wooden barrels. Evidence thus points to the existence of vines prior to the invasion by the Romans and Alsace is said to have been a wine-producing region throughout Antiquity.

During the Middle Ages, Alsace produced enormous quantities of wines which were in great demand. Ships and chariots brought the wines to the Swabians, the Bavarians, the Batavians, and even as far as Sweden. In England at the time of Edward III, Alsatian wines were known by the name of "Aussay" (the name of Alsace during the Middle Ages).

The very first winegrowers cultivated vineyards for the many all-powerful abbeys and seigniorial domains at a time when Alsace was mainly a feudal and religious region. When the *communes* or free towns were set free, the winegrowers earned the right to work the plots of land set aside for them; much later, they were able to purchase the plots from the lords. Although the vineyards did not become "plebian"—to use one local historian's expression—they were, however, split up into smaller portions.

Of all the Alsatian confraternities, the most unusual was the *Corne*. To be admitted to the Corne, an individual had to drink down in a single gulp the contents of a wild ox horn, the equivalent of two tankards or in today's terms two liters. The noble families of Alsace coveted the honor of being part of the ceremony. Heros like Christophe de Wangen and François de Landsperg were admitted only once they had emptied their ox horn twice in a row, not just once. This is how the name "wiedercome" (come back) was given to the huge tankard.

These customs continued over the years. For instance, to seal a pact of peace between the episcopal soldiers, defenders of the Catholic League, and Richelieu's soldiers, allies in the Protestant Union, Isaac de Saint-Simon (uncle of the Duc de Saint-Simon, author of *Mémoires* of life under Louis XIV and Louis XV), first governor of Hoh Barr, made the ox horn statement of devotion, exhibiting every bit of the seriousness required. For the solemn circumstance, the quality of the wines was overseen by "gourmets," key personalities who were sworn, officially-recognized elected magistrates of the vine. They kept a watch over the wine trade and imposed a code of straight-forwardness and honor. They themselves could not sell wine from their own cellar without the cooperation of another gourmet.

An entire ritual surrounded the buyer; the gourmet was the intermediary between the winegrower and the wineseller. The function of "gourmet" has now disappeared, but the term continues to be associated with those brokers who still proudly bear the name.

THE WINES

- **RIESLING:** The Prince of Alsatian grapes. It produces dry, fruity and firm wines, with subtle bouquet—and the best of them are wines of great distinction.

Riesling thrives near Turckheim, Dambach-la-Vieille, Ribeauvillé, Riquewihr, Kaysersberg, Mittlewihr and Guebwiller. It is the last vine variety of the region to reach maturity.

- **GEWURZTRAMINER:** Higher in alcohol than the Riesling, better balanced, spicy and very aromatic, the Gewurztraminer is a wine that ages remarkably well. Late harvesting, that is to say, the gathering of over ripe grapes, produces wines of astonishing fragance and unctuosity. Good soils: Bergheim, Turckheim, Siglosheim, Wintzenheim, Barr. . .
- **PINOT GRIS OR ALSATIAN TOKAY:** Rather heavy, even thick wine, of a beautiful yellow color, as elegant as the Riesling and the Gewurztraminer, maybe even more powerful, heady and aromatic. Late harvesting. Wines of excellent quality. The best come from Riesling and Cleebourg, Rouffach or Wintzenheim.
- **MUSCAT D'ALSACE:** A dry, fresh and fruity wine, with a musky taste, very grapey.
- **SYLVANER:** Most are too neutral and light. The others are quite refreshing and fruity.
- **CHASSELAS:** More and more replaced by other varieties, the Chasselas produces unpretentious wines that are light and easy to drink.
- **PINOT BLANC:** Much fuller and more supple than the Sylvaner, delicate bouquet and rather well-balanced. Very refreshing when drunk cool.
- **PINOT NOIR:** Rare Alsatian rosés from this famous Burgundy variety, characterized by a very pleasant fruitiness, demand to be tasted.

THE CHARACTERISTICS OF THE VINEYARD

The region of Alsace lies between the Vosges Mountains and the Black Forest, extending over two French administrative districts—called *départements*—the Haut-Rhin and the Bas-Rhin. The region's plains and hills border the Rhine River.

Soil

The region is in a valley and has a complex geographic composition. The soil is mainly granite but there is also alluvial soil.

Climate

Alsace has a continental climate. The nearby Vosges Mountains protect the region and shelter the vineyards from rain which otherwise would come in from the Atlantic. In fact, several microclimates resulting from the effect of the terrain explain the large number and wide variety of Alsatian vineyards. Temperatures may reach as high as 96.8°F (36°C) in summer and as low as 32°F (0°C) in winter. Although precipitation is heaviest in Alsace in the summertime, the region has the lowest rainfall in France, with in. (700 mm) in Strasbourg and in. (502 mm) in Colmar.

VINS D'ALSACE PIERRE ADAM

Domaine Pierre Adam
8, rue du Lieutenant Louis-Mourier
68770 Ammerschwihr
89 78 23 07

Type of vineyard: Family-owned. **Established:** A the beginning of the Century. **Vine stocks:** Sylvaner, Pinot Blanc, Riesling, Tokay, Pinot Noir, Muscat, Gewurztraminer. **Soil:** Clay with calcium carbonate and sand. **Exposure:** Hillsides. **Average annual production in hectoliters:** 600.

Appellation: A.O.C. Vins d'Alsace. **Type:** White. **Technique:** Traditional. **Maturing:** In Oak casks. **Characteristics:** Gewurztraminer Kaefferkopf: white wine, rich and well-balanced, rich fragrance, lots of elegance and finesse. Pinot Noir: (red) Gold Medal – Salon de l'Agriculture, dry with raspberry aromas. **Serving temperature:** Cool, approx. 10°. **Served with:** Riesling: fish, seafood, oysters, Lobster, Salmon. Gewurztraminer Kaefferkopt: as an aperitif or with exotic cooking, pastry. Pinot Noir: red meat, wild boar stew or leg of venison. **Vintages available in 89/90:** 1987, 1988.

Characteristics of vintages

1988: Remarkable year – Wines of exceptional quality. Pinot Auxerrois: made from old vines, delicate and flowery bouquet, honey overtones. Very harmonious. Riesling Grand Cru Schlossberg: grown on dominantly granitic soil, dry and fruity, long keeping. Riesling Grand Cru Mandelberg: breed and harmony, typical of the vintage, to be consumed as of 1990. Pinot Noir: ruby color, delicate, elegant, violet aroma, great future ahead. Gewurztraminer Kaefferkopf: grown on chalky clay, great finesse, full-bodied, complex aromas, to be consumed at all times, for pleasure. **1987:** Tokay Pinot Gris, Réserve Personnelle: harvested verripe. Forthcoming, dry fruit fragrance. To be tasted now. Good year, particularly for the Riesling and the Gewurztraminer.

MAISON LEON BAUR

Jean Louis Baur
71, rue du Rempart Nord 68420 Eguisheim
89 41 79 13

Type of vineyard: Family-owned. **Established:** 1738. **Vine stocks:** Sylvaner, Riesling, Pinot Blanc, Tokay, Muscat, Gewurztraminer, Pinot Noir. **Soil:** Chalky clay. **Exposure:** South.

Appellation: AOC Alsace. **Type:** White, rosé. **Technique:** Traditional. **Alcohol content:** 12.5 to 13%. **Characteristics:** Riesling: Dry, fruity, masculine, delicate bouquet. Muscat: Fruity and penetrating fragrance. Tokay: Heady, full, balanced. Gewurztraminer: Well-bred, rich, well-balanced and spicy. **Serving temperature:** 8 to 10°. **Served with:** Gewurztraminer: Dessert, cakes. Muscat: excellent aperatif wine. Tokay: Patés, foie gras. Riesling: Fish, seafood, sauerkraut specialties. **Vintages available in 89/90:** 1987, 1988.

Characteristics of vintages

1988: Exceptional year. Heady wines with graceful and delicate aromas. **1987:** Agreeably fruity, very typical wines.

Sales volume:
– Retail: 40%. – Restaurants: 20%. – Other: 40% (importers).

Sales in France: 60%.

Export sales: 40%.

Main trading partners: Germany, Denmark, Belgium, Netherlands.

Comments

Eguisheim, cradle of the Alsacian vineyard, is a well-preserved medieval fortified city. Here, the house of Léon Baur, founded in 1738, has passed on the winemaking tradition, from father to son, for 7 generations. The vines of the property form a remarkable mosaic all around this marvelous village. For the most part, the wines come from the Eichberg and Pfersighberg hillsides. The countless wine-tastings won in recent years are a testimonial to the quality of the product. The Riesling Cuvée Elisabeth Stumpf, 1988, was awarded a Gold Medal at the Concours Général Agricole in Paris.

DOMAINE BARMES BUECHER

François Barmes
30 & 23 rue Sainte Gertrude 68920 Wettolsheim
89 80 62 92 our 89 80 61 82

Type of vineyard: Family-owned agricultural association. **Number of employees:** 2. **Vine stocks:** Sylvaner, Pinot Blanc, Riesling, (Tokay – Pinot Gris), Pinot Noir, Muscat, Gewurztraminer. **Soil:** Chalky clay, clay marl. **Exposure:** South, South-East. **Average annual production in hectoliters:** 1,100.

Appellation: Alsace, Alsace Grand Cru, Alsace Vendanges Tardives, Alsace Crémant Controlée. **Type:** Red, white, other: Champagne Method: Crémant. **Technique:** Traditional, with temperature control. **Maturing:** In stainless steel tanks and oak casks. **Characteristics:** Our wines are produced from vines grown on chalky clay hillsides. They are rich and well-balanced, expressive, typical of their vinestock, but also of the soil in which they are grown. HENGST & STEINGRUBLER: They keep well and are particularly fruity. **Serving temperature:** 8-10°. **Served with:** Riesling: fish, seafood, shellfish, Pinot Gris, Pinot Noir (Hengst): game, (wild boar, venison, hare...) Gewurztraminer: Cheese – (Roquefort cheese, Pont l'Évèque, Munster) – exotic cuisine, dessert. Muscat or Gewurztraminer: As an aperitif – Sylvaner Pinot Blanc: First course, hors d'œuvres. **Vintages available in 89/90:** 1988/1987, and 1986 depending on stocks.

Characteristics of vintages

1988: Wine for keeping, exceptional maturation and over maturation, concentration, complexity, lingering taste, very successful. A great Gewurztraminer: The Steingrubler Grand Cru made by selection of Noble Grapes – still undeveloped, while others are beautifully balanced and go well with different types of food. **1986:** Open, pleasant, very easy drinking, starting to be typical of their soil. The Streingrubler Vendanges Tardives (made from old vines) deserves to be aged a little longer. **1985:** Very supple, full-bodied, some varieties are beginning to show their hydrocarbons, because of the chalky clay soil. Very concentrated, complex, great wines. **Other:** A great success: The Gewurztraminer Cuvée des Premières Neiges 1985, a wine made from grapes growne of the Wettolsheim hillsides, harvested 30/11/85. Natural extraction. A wine as fruity as possible, suggesting exotic fruits: kiwi, litchi, pineapples. Price range (pre-tax, ex-warehouse): 20 to 30 F.F. – Riesling, Tokay, Gewurztraminer Pinot Noir, A.O.C 30 to 50 F.F. – Riesling, Muscat, Tokay, Pinot Noir, Gew. Grands Crus. 80 to 120 F.F. – Gewurztraminer Vendanges Tardives.

Sales volume: – Wholesale: 2%.
Retail: 58%. – Restaurants: 40%. – Other: delicatessens, wine cellars (mostly in Germany).
Sales in France: 60%. **Export sales:** 40%.
Main trading partners : Germany, Netherlands, Belgium, Denmark.

References in France

Restaurant: Restaurant with Michelin Stars, 16 Restaurants recommended by Gault & Millau.

VIN D'ALSACE
Appellation Alsace Contrôlée
Mise en bouteille au domaine
Produce of France
MARQUE DÉPOSÉE
Domaine Barmès Buecher
13%vol.
GEWURZTRAMINER
750ml
BARMÈS-BUECHER PROPR.-VITICULTEURS A WETTOLSHEIM (HAUT-RHIN)

Shops: Cave Saint Antoine – Chais du Roy. Cave du Rouet (Marseille).

Abroad

Germany

Exklusiv/ Auslieferungslager: Margret MICHELY, Saarland) – Two agents: PILET D 6334 ASSLAR BERGHAUSEN – Pielorz D. 8650 KULMBACH – LuitpoldstraBe 13.

Comments

Specialties: the Grands Crus Hengst & Streingrubler in particular, the Gewurztraminer, reserved for connaisseurs. Tastings arranged by appointement. To be discovered: the Crémant d'Alsace 1986 – made by the champagne method on the estate.

J. BECKER

Martine and Jean-Philippe Becker
4, route d'Ostheim à Zellenberg
68340 Riquewihr BP 24
89 47 90 16 or 89 47 87 56 – Telex: 871 083 F
Propriétaire de la marque commerciale
Gaston Beck

Type of vineyard: Family Corporation. **Established:** 1610 (corporation since 1848). **Number of employees:** 10. **Vine stocks:** All of the Alsatian varieties: Riesling, Gewurztraminer, Muscat, Pinot gris, Sylvaner, Pinot Blanc, Pinot Noir. **Soil:** Middle Jurassic: chalky and sandy marl clay untill 40% sometimes. **Exposure:** Southeast. **Average annual production in hectoliters:** 3,000.
Appellation: Alsace A.O.C., Alsace Grand Cru Froehn de Zellenberg. **Type:** Red, white, rosé. **Technique:** Traditional – temperature regulation of the alcoholic fermentation. **Maturing:** 50% Oak, 50% glass-lined vats. **Alcohol content:** From 11% (Sylvaner) to 15% (Vendanges Tardives-late harvests). **Characteristics:** Heavy wines when too young. Soil known mainly for Riesling and Muscat and Gewurstraminer. Grand Cru Froehn has a fine Rose smelling. Wines with interesting ageing possibilities, notably the Riesling, Gewurztraminer and the Tokay. **Serving temperature:** White: cool but not cold. Pinot Noir: room temperature or cool. **Served with:** Regional Alsatian specialties, all fish, seafood, first courses and hors-d'œuvre, white meat. With Pinot Gris and Gewurztraminer, exotic cuisine. Strong cheese with Gewurztraminer and Pinot Noir for dessert, Muscat, Gewurztraminer and Crémant d'Alsace. **Vintages available in 89/90:** 1987, 1986, 1985 and old wine for collectors.

Characteristics of vintages

1988: Record for 1988 vintage in Alsace. Muscat of 1.174° on Grand Cru as a selection de grains nobles. **1987:** Well balance, elegant, some, late harvest available, riche and fruity. **1986:** Very fruity, fragrant, goes down well. **1985:** Firm, to be aged. Quality very interesting.

FRÉDÉRIC BERGER ET FILS

Claude Berger
8, rue de Riquewihr – 68630 Mittelwihr
89 47 90 79

Type of vineyard: Family-owned. **Vine stocks:** All of the Alsatian varieties. **Soil:** Clay with calcium carbonate and silica-clay. **Exposure:** Southwest. **Average annual production in hectoliters:** 350.
Appellation: A.O.C. Alsace. **Type:** White, rose, Crémant d'Alsace. **Technique:** Traditional. **Maturing:** In Oak casks. **Characteristics:** Delicately fruity, flowery and long. **Serving temperature:** 11° to 13°. **Served with:** Riesling: seafood and fish. Tokay and Gewurztraminer: white meat and foie gras. Pinot Noir: red meat or steaks. Muscat, Crémant: as an aperitif or at the end of the meal. **Vintages available in 89/90:** 1988.

Characteristics of vintages

1988: Reminiscent of the 1983, supple, well balanced, fruity, developing fresh fruit aromas, lingering taste, seductive. Price range (pre-tax, ex-warehouse): Between 20 F.F. and 30 F.F.
Sales volume:
– Retail: 85%. – Restaurants: 15%.
Sales in France: 90%.
Export sales: 10%.
Main trading partners : Belgium, Germany.

References in France

Restaurants: Local and regional restaurants.

Comments

Family enterprise whose principal concern is to produce very high class wines, well-bred and fruity, perfectly typical, closely linked to the character of Alsatian Wines.

LÉON BEYER

Léon Beyer
2, rue de la 1e Armée – 68420 Eguisheim
89 41 41 05 – Telex: ALEXA 880 908 F
Fax 89 23 93 63

Type of vineyard: Family-owned. **Established:** 1580. **Vine stocks:** Riesling, Tokay, Gewurztraminer, Pinot Noir, Muscat. **Soil:** Clay with calcium carbonate. **Exposure:** South by Southeast.
Appellation: Alsace. **Type:** Red, white. **Technique:** Traditional. **Maturing:** Wooden casks, glass-lined vats. **Characteristics:** Fresh and fruity, rich, well-balanced and robust. **Serving temperature:** 8° to 10°. **Vintages available in 89/90:** 1988, 1987, 1986, 1985, 1983, 1982, 1981.

Characteristics of vintages

Sales in France: 25%. **Export sales:** 75%.
Main trading partners : European Common Market, North America, Japan.

Abroad

United States

W.J. Deutsch, 400 King Street, Chappaqua, New York 10514.

United Kingdom

Michael Druitt Wines 9 Deanery Street Park Lane, London W1Y 5LF.

Germany

Frankhof Kellerei, Burgeffstrasse 19, 6203 Hochheimam Main.

Canada

Liquor Boards of Alberta, British Columbia, Ontario, Québec.

The Netherlands

Heeren Van Heusden, Vismarkt 1A Postbus 66, Heusden.

Denmark

H.J. Hansen Vinhandel als Vestergade 97-101, Postbus 355, 5100 Odense C.

Far East

Japan: Izumi Trading Co. Ltd., 12-8 Itabashi 1, Chome, Itabashi Ku, Tokyo 173.

DOMAINE PAUL BLANCK & FILS

Blanck
32, Grand rue, 66240 Kientzheim

Type of vineyard: Agricultural Association. **Established:** 1923. **Number of employees:** 6. **Soil:** Gravel, sand, chalky clay, clay, granite. **Exposure:** East, South. **Average annual production in hectoliters:** 2,000.
Appellation: Alsace, Alsace Grand Cru, Vendanges Tardives, Sélection de Grains Nobles, Crémant. **Type:** Red, White. Other: Crémant. **Technique:** Temperature control. **Maturing:** In stainless steel and enammelled tanks. **Alcohol content:** Between 11 and 12%. **Characteristics:** Dry, balanced, good keeping matured in air-tight containers. **Serving temperature:** 12°. **Vintages available in 89/90:** 1983, 1984, 1985, 1986, 1987, 1988.

Characteristics of vintages

1988: Very aromatic, well balanced, good keeping. **1987:** Very delicate, aromatic, fragrant. **1986:** Vintage requiring good winegrowers – austere wines for long keeping, great finesse, rich and good acidity balance. **1985:** Very elegant, not yet opened up, very well balanced, long keeping, complex. Price range (pre-tax, ex-warehouse): 20 to 30 F.F. – 50 to 80 F.F.
Sales volume:
– Retail: 70%. – Restaurants: 30%.
Sales in France: 45%. **Export sales:** 55%.
Main trading partners : Belgium, Germany, UK, Netherlands.

References in France

Restaurants: Tour d'Argent, Le Lutetia, (Paris), Westminster Concorde, (Nice), Hôtel La Présidence, (Dieppe), Haeberlin et E. Junp, (Illhaursern Alsace).
Shops: Retrou, (Paris).

Abroad

United Kingdom

Layet Wheeler, Colchester. Adnams, Southwold. Tanners, Shrewsbury.

Germany

Weinwolf, Bonn. Hawesko, Hamburg.

Switzerland

Fischeret Rihs, Bienne. Fischer et Rihs

Belgium

Bleuze-Barrière, Brussels. Lambert, Brussels.

The Netherlands

Jean Arnaud, Tilburg. Groupe Gastrovino.

Comments

In the Blanck family, winemaking tradition goes back to the 18th century. As early as 1842, a member of the family received an award at the Paris competition. Under the management of Paul and Eugène Blanck, the Schlossberg vineyard achieved a certain notoriety in the region. As winebrokers, Paul Blanck's children very quickly realized (in the 1950's) the importance of the soil in Alsace, and now, in 1989, a new generation is taking over to finish the job. The Blanck family has always been devoted to the Grands Crus of Alsace.

EMILE BOECKEL

Émile Boeckel
67140 Mittelbergheim
88 08 91 02 - 88 08 91 91 - Telex: 890555 F

Type of vineyard: Agricultural Association, Corporation. **Established:** For 400 years. **Vine stocks:** Mostly Riesling, Gewürztraminer, Pinot. **Soil:** Variable – sand on sandstone, chalky clay, silica and chalk. **Exposure:** South. **Average annual production in hectoliters:** 60 to 65 hl/ha.
Appellation: Alsace. **Type:** White. Other: Crémant d'Alsace. **Technique:** Traditional. **Maturing:** In oak casks. **Characteristics:** Delicate, typical of the Alsatian soil. **Vintages available in 89/90:** 1986, 1987, 1988 and a few 1983 and 1985.

Characteristics of vintages

1988-1987-1986-1985: Good years – beautiful wines. **Other:** Excellent Wibelsberg Grand Cru Riesling 1983. Price range (pre-tax, ex-warehouse): 20 to 40 F.F. – 80 to 120 F.F. "Vendanges Tardives".
Sales in France: 25%. **Export sales:** 75%.
Main trading partners : Germany, Belgium, Netherlands, UK, USA, Luxemburg.

References in France

Restaurants: Le Crocodile, (Strasbourg), Buerchisel, (Strasbourg), etc.

Abroad

United States

Banfi Vintners. Cedar Swamp Road, Old Brookville N.Y 11545. Garrret's Youngs, Long Island (Tel: (516) 626 92 00).

United Kingdom

Churton Cousins Ltd. Machine House. Chester Road. Rosset. Wrexham LWYD LL12 OHW (Tel: (0244) 571333).

Germany

FA. Franz Strebel 6530 Bingen Am Rhein – Prof Hoepke Str. 12 (Tel: (06721) 17051.

Switzerland

Walther S.A., place de la Gare, 3960 Sierre (Tel: 027 55 10 93). Stucki, Bâle.

Belgium

Jean-Marie Velu Vins SPRL, 215, rue Bollinckx, 1070 Brussels (Tel: 520 60 68).

Canada

Alberta Liquor Control Board, 50 Corriveau Avenue, St. Albert, Alberta T8N 3T5 (Tel: 403/458 4311).

DOMAINE MARCEL DEISS

Jean-Michel and Clarisse Deiss
15 route de Vin - 68750 Bergheim
89 73 63 37

Type of vineyard: Agricultural Association. **Established:** 1955. **Number of employees:** 10. **Vine stocks:** All of the Alsatian varieties. **Soil:** Vineyard extending over 9 communes. **Exposure:** Very varied. **Average annual production in hectoliters:** 1,200.
Appellation : AOC Alsace and AOC Alsace Grand Cru. Type: Red, white. **Technique:** White: slow pressing of whole grapes, alcoholic fermentation. **Maturing:** Natural, temperature 18 to 20°, kept on lees, racking. **Alcohol content:** 11 to 13.5%. **Characteristics:** Related more to the soil than the vinestocks. **Serving temperature:** Between 8 and 10°. **Served with:** Very variable. **Vintages available in 89/90:** 1983, 1985, 1986, 1987, 1988.

Characteristics of vintages

1988: Very great year marked by the noble rot. **1987:** Beautiful year, fresh, well-bred wines, very complete. **1986:** Late year saved by the noble rot. **1985:** Very beautiful year, very healthy grapes, rather austere wines. Price range (pre-tax, ex-warehouse): Vins de Cépage: between 20 and 30 F.F. Vins de Terroir: between 30 and 50 F.F. Grands Crus: between 50 and 80 F.F. Vendages Tardives: between 80 and 120 F.F. Sélection de Grands Nobles "Quintescence": over 160 F.F.
Sales volume:
– Retail: 1/3. – Restaurants: 1/2. – Other: various.
Sales in France: 50%. **Export sales:** 50%.

Main trading partners : Netherlands, Germany, Belgium, United States, Japan, U.K., Denmark.

References in France

Restaurants: Principal restaurants with Michelin stars and the best Alsatian establishments.

Abroad

United States

Importers: Robert Kacher Selections.

United Kingdom

Wine, Food and Beer. Bacchus. Les Vignobles de France.

Belgium

Yves Catulle, Jean Swolf.

The Netherlands

Verbunt, Tilburg.

Comments

The Domain Marcel Deiss was founded by Marcel Deiss in 1950. Starting from almost nothing, he built a 20 hectare vineyard covering 9 communes, thus realizing his dream to offer to the consumer a range of wines defined, not only by the 7 Alsatian vinestocks, but mostly by a great diversity of soil.

CAVE DE LA DÎME

Hubert Metz

57, route du Vin 67650 Blienschwiller

88 92 43 06 - 88 92 40 39

Type of vineyard: Family-owned. **Established:** From father to son. **Vine stocks:** A variety of Alsatian vinestocks. **Soil:** Granite and chalky clay. **Exposure:** South - South-East. **Average annual production in hectoliters:** 500.
Appellation: Sylvaner, Klevner, Riesling, Muscat, Tokay, Pinot Noir, Gewurztraminer, Gewurztraminer Grand Cru Winzenberg, Crémant d'Alsace. **Type:** Red, White. **Technique:** pneumatic pressing, temperature control. **Maturing:** In oak casks. **Characteristics:** Very typical, fruity (Sylvaner, Klevner Riesling) flowery aromas (Muscat) rich and well balanced (Tokay, Gewurztraminer). Red made from Pinot Noir; Sparkling wine from (Crémant d'Alsace). **Serving temperature:** 10 to 12°. **Vintages available in 89/90:** 1987, 1988.

Characteristics of vintages

1988: Excellent, very rich aromas, very good year. **1987:** Very typical, fresh, and delicate wines, a good year. Price range (pre-tax, ex-warehouse): 20 to 30 F.F.
Sales volume:
- Retail: 85%. - Restaurants: 5%. - Other: 10% (export - specialized shops).
Sales in France: 85%.
Export sales: 15%.
Main trading partners : Germany, Denmark.

References in France

Restaurants: Chez La Mère Michel, rue Rennequin, (Paris), Le Green, (Strasbourg), Hôtel des Vosges, (Klingenthal).
Shops: Crus Choisis, (Mulhouse).

Abroad

Denmark

Importer: Mr. Torben Matthes.

Comments

Very old family enterprise located in a typical winegrowing village. Very beautiful domed cellar from 1728, with magnificent oak casks decorated with sculptured barrel staves.

STÉ DOPFF & IRION

Jacques Ricard

Au Château - 68340 Riquewihr

89 47 92 51 - Telex : 880 980 F

Type of vineyard: Corporation. **Established:** 1946. **Number of employees:** 52. **Vine stocks:** Riesling, Gewurztraminer, Tokay Pinot Gris, Muscat, Pinot Noir. **Soil:** Clay with calcium carbonate. **Exposure:** South, Southeast. **Average annual production in hectoliters:** About 21,000.

Appellation: Alsace controlée, Vendanges Tardives, Crémant d'Alsace. **Type:** White, rosé, red. **Technique:** Traditional. **Maturing:** Stainless steel tanks. **Characteristics:** Very fruity, dry, lively, rare elegance and pleasant lightness, very long. The great years age well. **Serving temperature:** 8 to 10°. **Served with:** Riesling: first courses, fish, sauerkraut. Gewurztraminer, Tokay Pinot Gris: foie gras. Muscat and Gewurztraminer: as an aperitif. Pinot Noir (rosé and red) d'Alsace: poultry. **Vintages available in 89/90:** 1981, 1983, 1984, 1985, 1986.

Characteristics of vintages

1986: Characteristic of the year, good balance, fresh, light and lively. **1985:** Very round and full, will age very well. Superb Riesling and Tokay. **1984:** Average year, very fruity wines to be drunk young. Very successful vinification.

1983: Exceptional vintage, especially for the Vendanges Tardives and Grains Nobles. **Other:** 1981: Very great year. The wines are now reaching their peak. Prince range (pre-tax, ex-warehouse): Between 30 and 80 F.F.
Sales volume: – Wholesale: 11%. – Retail: 17%. – Restaurants: 25%. – Other: 47% (export).
Sales in France: 53%.
Export sales: 47%.
Main trading partners : Germany, Canada, Sweden, Belgium, Denmark, Netherlands, U.K.

References in France

Restaurants: Auberge de l'Ill (Illhauesern), Blanc (Vonnas), l'Alsace (Paris) and many other restaurants with stars.
Shops: Fauchon (Paris), Galeries Gourmandes (Strasbourg), Vignon (Paris).

Abroad

United Kingdom
J.B. Reynier Ltd., 16-18 Upper Tachbrook Street, London SWIV 1SL.

Germany
Firma Reidemeister & Ulrichs, Postfach 102 320, D – 2800, Bremen.

Canada
SAQ/LCBO/ALCB/BCLDB.

The Netherlands
Wilmerink & Muller, Jan ter Gouwweg 147, Postbus 301, 1400 AH Bussum, NL – 1412 Naarden.

Far East
Sanyo, Japan. Ser-Olivier, Singapour. Caves de Frances, Hong Kong.

Others
Velier: Italy, Fourcroy: Belgium, Rothe: Denmark.

PIERRE FRICK
Jean Pierre Frick
5, rue de Baer 68250 Pfaffenheim
89 49 62 99

Type of vineyard: Family owned. **Vine stocks:** Sylvaner, Pinot Blanc, Riesling, Muscat, Pinot Gris, Gewurztraminer, Pinot Noir. **Soil:** Mostly chalky clay. **Exposure:** South – South-East. **Average annual production in hectoliters:** 500.
Appellation: Alsace & Alsace Grand Cru, Steinert. **Type:** White. **Technique:** Dry white wine, except for the "Vendanges tardives" and S.G.N. **Maturing:** In oak casks (6 to 9 months). **Characteristics:** Subtle and light wines, excellent evolution. **Serving temperature:** 10°. **Vintages available in 89/90:** 1986, 1987.

Characteristics of vintages

1987: Good wine, fruity, delicate and lingering. **1986:** Excellent year.

Sales in France: 50%.
Export sales: 50%.
Main trading partners : Germany, UK, Belgium, USA, Japan, Italy.

ROLLY-GASSMANN
2, rue de l'Église, 68590 Rorschwihr
89 73 63 28

Type of vineyard: Family-owned. **Established:** 1676. **Soil:** Chalky clay. **Average annual production in hectoliters:** 1,200.

Appellation: Alsace AOC. **Type:** Red, white. **Technique:** Traditional. **Maturing:** In casks for 11 months. **Characteristics:** Typical Alsatian wines, marked by the various vinestocks. **Serving temperature:** 11°. **Vintages available in 89/90:** 1985, 1986, 1987, 1988.

Characteristics of vintages

1988: Great year, successful wines, fragrant, good evolution. **1987:** Good year. **1986:** Good year, successful wines, lively and full-bodied. **1985:** Exceptional year, dense, aromatic wines, good keeping.
Sales volume: – Retail: 90%. – Restaurants: 10%.
Sales in France: 80%.
Export sales: 20%.
Main trading partners : UK, Germany, Belgium, Japan, Netherlands.

Comments

Family enterprise for generations, since 1676.

• *Please note that all temperatures in this book are expressed in degrees Centigrade.*

WILLY GISSELBRECHT ET FILS

Willy Gisselbrecht and Family
Route du Vin - 67650 Dambach-la-Ville
88 92 41 02 - Telex: 870 902 F

Type of vineyard: Family-owned. **Established:** For several generations. **Vine stocks:** All vinestocks of Alsace. **Soil:** Granitic and chalky clay. **Exposure:** South-East. **Average annual production in hectoliters:** 850.

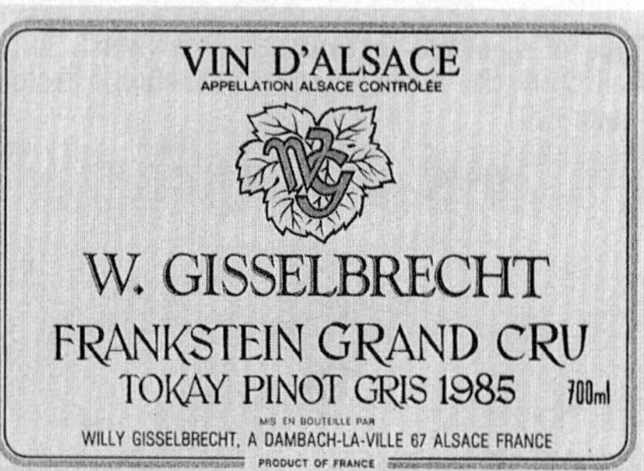

VIN D'ALSACE
APPELLATION ALSACE CONTRÔLÉE
W. GISSELBRECHT
FRANKSTEIN GRAND CRU
TOKAY PINOT GRIS 1985
700ml
MIS EN BOUTEILLE PAR
WILLY GISSELBRECHT, A DAMBACH-LA-VILLE 67 ALSACE FRANCE
PRODUCT OF FRANCE

Appellation: Appellation "Alsace contrôlée". **Type:** White. **Technique:** Traditional. **Maturing:** In wooden casks and stainless steel tanks. **Characteristics:** Pinot: fine and lively, subtle. Gewurztraminer: deep color, beautiful bouquet with a touch of mellowness. Riesling: typical, slightly mellow, musk scent, elegant, rich and well balanced. **Serving temperature:** 8 to 10°. **Served with:** Riesling: shellfish, delicatessen. Gewurztraminer: as an aperitif or with foie gras, dessert. Pinot: delicatessen. **Vintages available in 89/90:** 1986, 1985, 1987, 1988.

Characteristics of vintages

1987: Beautiful wines, flowery, supple, harmonious and fruity. **1986:** The whole range of Alsatian wines beginning with September 1987. **1985:** Whole range available, excellent Pinot, Riesling and Gewurztraminer. All have won Gold Medals at Colmar. Price range (pre-tax, ex-warehouse): 20 to 30 F.F. - 30 to 50 F.F.

Sales volume:
- Wholesale: 25 %. - Retail: 35 %. - Restaurants: 25 %.
- Other: 15% (works councils, cellars, etc.).

Sales in France: 60%. **Export sales:** 40%.

Main trading partners : Germany, Netherlands, UK, Belgium, Switzerland, Denmark, Australia, Canada, USA.

References in France

Restaurants: Many restaurants with Michelin stars and Gault & Millau chef's hats.

Abroad

Switzerland

Boissons Tivoli (previously Gauss Brothers), Route des Jeunes 4, Case Postale 390, CH 1211 Geneva 26.

Belgium

Regional importers.

Canada

Toronto Trading, 92 Colborne Street P.O. Box 844, Bradford, Ontario L3Z 2B3.

The Netherlands

N.C.K., Willem Kloosstraat 66, NL Hazerswoude (Rijndijk).

Others

Denmark: Logismose-Vinimport Skolevj 4, DK5683 Haarby.
Australia: Inter-Europe Olsen-Agencies, 2 McGlone St-Mitcham, Victoria.

Comments

In 1936, winemaker Willy Gisselbrecht added a new commercial dimension to his enterprise. A wholesale outlet which, since the 1950's, has been operated by his three children. The family operates a vineyard of about 15 hectares in the best terrain of Dambach and the neighboring villages of Deiffenthal-Scherviller and Chatenois. In addition to their own production, at harvest time, Willy Gisselbrecht and sons buy grapes from other vineyards which are selected, vinified and matured with the same great care that is devoted to their own harvest.

DOMAINE ANDRÉ & RÉMY GRESSER

Rémy Gresser
2, rue de l'École - F - 67140 Andlau
88 08 95 88 - 88 08 00 65

Type of vineyard: Family-owned. **Established:** 1667. **Vine stocks:** Sylvaner, Pinot d'Alsace, Riesling, Muscat d'Alsace, Tokay d'Alsace, Gewurztraminer, Pinot Noir. **Soil:** Very great geological diversity. **Average annual production in hectoliters:** 500.
Appellation: Alsace, Alsace Grands Crus, Alsace Andlau, Alsace Vendange Tardive. **Type:** Red, white. **Technique:** Traditional with temperature control. **Maturing:** In Oak casks. **Characteristics:** Typical Alsatian wine, well-bred, with very complex aromas in minerals which guarantees the longevity of the Grands Crus. They are regarded as wines with a long lifetime. **Serving temperature:** White: 12°. **Served with:** Riesling: fish. Sylvaner: sea-food. Muscat: asparagus. Tokay: foie gras, game. Gewurztraminer: foie gras, Munster cheese. **Vintages available in 89/90:** 1986, 1985, 1984, 1983.

Characteristics of vintages

1986: Very fruity, typical ot the grape variety. **1985:** Lots of character, mineral, well-bred, good for ageing. **1984:** Fine, delicate, vigorous. **1983:** Full-bodied, long, rich and well-balanced. **1982** Fruity, light, great aromatic finesse. Price range (pre-tax, ex-warehouse): between 17 F.F. and 95 F.F. according to the appellation.

• To help us improve our next edition, please send in your suggestions and answer our questionnaire.

HEIM

Henri Delarbre, Directeur
Vins d'Alsace et Eaux de Vie
68250 Westhalten
89 47 00 45 – Telex: 880 273 F
Télécopie: 89 47 63 77

Type of vineyard: Corporation. **Established:** 1765. **Number of employees:** 12. **Vine stocks:** Sylvaner, Pinot Blanc, Riesling, Tokay, Pinot Gris, Muscat, Gewurztraminer, Pinot Noir. **Soil:** Oolitic and Tertiary chalk. **Exposure:** South, South-East. **Average annual production in hectoliters:** 10,000 hl.
Appellation: Alsace Contrôlée, Alsace Contrôlée Grand Cru, Crémant d'Alsace Appellation Contrôlée, Eaux de vie Marc de Gewurztraminer Appellation Contrôlée. **Type:** White, Rosé. Other: Crémants White and Rosé, Eaux de vie. **Technique:** White: with temperature control. **Maturing:** In stainless steel tanks ans oak casks. **Alcohol content:** 11° and 14° (for the late harvests). **Characteristics:** Spicy note and aromatic character of Alsatian Winestocks accentuated by the chalky sub-soil, while the Mediterranean micro-climate imparts roundness, suppleness and richness to the wines. **Serving temperature:** Crémants: 8°. White: 10°. Pinot Noir "vieilli en fûts de chêne": 14°. **Served with:** As an aperitif and with fish and shellfish, poultry, red meat and game, white meat, cheese and desserts. **Vintages available in 89/90:** 1987, 1986, 1985, 1983, 1979, 1976, 1973, 1971, 1969.

Characteristics of vintages

1988: Promising despite its impetuous youth. **1987:** Characteristic freshness which gives this vintage a much appreciated originality. **1986:** Lots of roundness from sun drenched grapes. **1985:** Rich and well balanced, the wines in this vintage have only one defect: their scarcity! **1983:** The successor vintage to the 1959 on the list of the best vintages of the century. Price range (pre-tax, ex-warehouse): 19 to 26 F.F. (Vins de Réserve) – 22 to 34 F.F. (Vins de Cuvée Réservée) – 25 to 50 F.F. (Cuvée particulière et lieux dits) – 32 to 45 F.F. (Crémants) – 80 to 85 F.F. (Vendanges Tardives).
Sales volume:
– Wholesale: 20%. – Retail: 8%. – Restaurants: 5%. – Other: 27% (dealers), 40% large scale distributors.
Sales in France: 70%.
Export sales: 30%.
Main trading partners : Belgium, Netherlands, Denmark, Germany, Switzerland, Luxemburg, UK, Japan, Canada, U.A.E.

References in France

Restaurants: Les Violettes (63360 Thierenbach), Au Cheval Blanc (Westhalten), A la ville de Lyon (Rouffach), Baumann Marbeuf (Paris), Le Richelieu (Paris), Auberge du Haut-Koenigsbourg (Paris), Le Petit Victor Hugo (Paris).

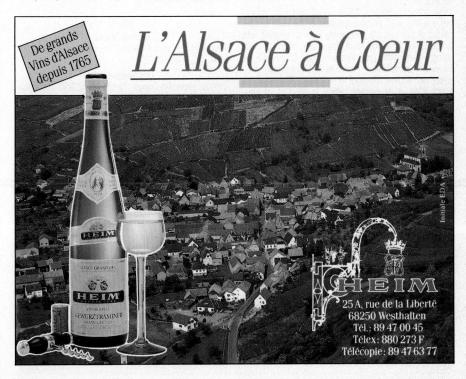

Abroad

United Kingdom

Irvine Robertson, Edimburg – Market Vintners, London.

Germany

Weindepot Dieter Franze, Frankfurt am Main – Bartels Langness, Kiel – Lavpris Suderlugum – Weinagentur Jacobi, Saarbrucken – Wein Kurt Schneider, Dusseldorf.

Switzerland

Bourgeois, Ballaigues.

Belgium

Maison des Vins Fins, Mons – Leroy Prevot, Binches.

The Netherlands

DGS Wijnkopers, Waddinxveen.

Denmark

Sorensens, Hellerup. Axelsen, Slagelse.

Comments

The *Maison Heim* is one of the oldest winemaking establishments in Alsace, going back to 1765, when the little enterprise was known as Hirtz-Koehler. At various times, they were winemakers, distillers, brokers and wholesalers. Some years later, Alfred Heim married Anne-Marie Koehler, sole heir in the line of descendants, and took over the management of the house to which he gave his name. Since then the Heim wines have been among the greatest in Alsace and are very much appreciated in France and abroad.

Wine growers, distillers, brockers and merchants cultivated a golden rule: produce the best of the best Alsatian Wines. A rule that the generations were to transmit with pride. Since then, the Heim House has taken its place along with the other great alsatian names, from where the wines are appreciated in France as much as abroad.

Every care is taken to ensure its personality. The result is a Heim Wine at its pinnacle which is the fruit of time, patience and much care: a generous, proud wine.

HARTMANN

Gérard & Serge Hartmann

13, rue R. Frémeaux 68420 Voegtlinshoffen

89 49 30 27

Vine stocks: Sylvaner, Pinot Blanc, Riesling, Muscat, Tokay, Gewurztraminer, Pinot Noir. **Soil:** Chalky marl, creeping surface deposits and chalky alluvium, deep and well-drained. **Exposure:** South, South-East. **Average annual production in hectoliters:** 65 to 74.

Appellation: Alsace AOC, Alsace Grand Cru Hatschbourg. **Type:** Red, White – other: Crémant d'Alsace. **Technique:** Traditional. **Maturing:** In vats and casks. **Alcohol content:** 12.5% to 14.5%. **Characteristics:** Dry, full-bodied, soft and rich, pronounced bouquet. **Serving temperature:** White: 10 to 12°. Pinot Noir: 14 to 15°. Crémant: 5.7°.

Characteristics of vintages

Price range (pre-tax, ex-warehouse): 10 to 20 F.F. 30 to 50 F.F. 50 to 80 F.F.

Sales volume:

– Retail: 85%. – Restaurants: 5%. – Other: 10% (shops).

Sales in France: 85%.

Export sales: 15%.

Main trading partners: Denmark, Belgium, USA, Germany, Switzerland, Netherlands.

References in France

Restaurants: Altea-Frantel, Fer Rouge, (Colmar), La Providence, (Paris).

Shops: La Bouteille, Aux Amis (Toulouse), Le Pavillon du Vin (56890 Saint Ave).

Abroad

United States

Importers: Weygandt-Metzler Importing, Unionville PA 1937 (Tel: (215) 486 0165).

The Netherlands

Probus Vinimport-Glerup, Parkhovej 42/2760 Glanglose (Tel: 02 36 82).

Comments

Winemakers from father to son for generations, their reputation is not due to a stroke of luck. Already in the 13th century the Augustins of Marbach praised the wines from the monastic vineyard of Voegtlinshoffen. In 1929 the locale was awarded a Model Vineyard diploma. The Grands Crus Hatschbourg wines are very typical of the appellation, with a well developed aroma and a capacity for long ageing.

• *Classification of the great Bordeaux wines in 1988. The ratings of Châteaux Lascombes (Margaux), Mazeris-Bellevue (Canon-Fronsac) and Haut-Maco (Côtes-de-Bourg) are improving, as well as those of certain other surprising crus (Châteaux Trocard, Melin, Gazin, Chantegriue, Gloria, La Croix-Saint-André, Fombrauge...). See the 1988 Classification in the Chapter on Bordeaux wines.*

HUGEL & FILS

68340 Riquewihr
88 47 92 15 – Telex: 880 873 HUGLVIN
Fax: (33) 89 49 00 10

Type of vineyard: Family Corporation. **Established:** 1639. **Number of employees:** 34. **Vine stocks:** All Alsace grapes.
Appellation: Alsace A.O.C. **Type:** Red, white. **Technique:** Traditional. **Characteristics:** Rich and typical (Riesling, Gewurztraminer, Tokay) specializing in the "vendanges tardives", particularly long lasting wines. **Vintages available 1989/90:** 1988, 1987, 1986, 1985, 1983.

Characteristics of vintages

1988: Ripe vintage, rich and opulent wines. **1987:** Very pleasant wines, some great Rieslings. **1986:** A fine classic vintage, very elegant wines. **1985:** Beautiful vintage, rich, soft and supple, strong fragrance, quite long. Price range (pre-tax, ex-cellars): From 20 F.F. to more than 160 F.F.
Sales in France: 13%.
Export sales: 87%.
Main trading partners: UK, Germany, Canada, USA, Netherlands, Belgium, Japan...

Abroad

United States
Dreyfus Ashby & Co – New York, N.Y. 10165. Tel: (212) 818 0770, Sherry-Lehmann, Morell – New York; Calvert Woodley – Washington D.C.; Restaurants: Lutèce, Prunelle, La Caravelle – New York.

United Kingdom
Dreyfus Ashby & Co – London. Tel: 01 378 7581, Harrods, Selfridges, Fortnum + Mason, Justerini + Brooks – London; Le Gavroche, The Waterside Inn – London.

Germany
A. Segnitz & Co – Bremen. Tel: 04 21 38 80 07, Grasshof – Bremen; Feinkost Kaefer, Dalimayer – Munich; Aubergine, Tantris – Munich; Goldener Pflug – Koln; Kurhotel Traube Tonbach, Kurhotel Mitteltal – Baiersbronn.

The Netherlands
Jacobus Boelen – Amsterdam. Tel: 020 114701 – Wijnboetiek De Ware Jacob – Amsterdam, Theo Hendriks – Arnhem, Hellebrekers – Delft. Restaurants: De Klepperman – Hoevelaken, Dehammert-Wallerlooi.

Far East
Japan: Jardine Wines & Spirits KK – Tokyo. Tel: (03) 434 1961. Mitsukoshi, Shibu, Takashimaya – Tokyo: Daimaru, Hankyu – Osaka; Okura, Imperial, Apicius – Tokyo; Hilton – Osaka.

Other:
Australia: Negociants Australia – Adelaide. Tel: 08 231 3963. Crittendens – Melbourne; Hayes – Sydney; Vintage Cellars – Adelaide; Hilton – Adelaide; Regent – Melbourne; Intercontinental – Sydney. Exclusive importers in over 100 countries.

BRUNO HERTZ

Bruno Hertz
9, place de l'Église, 68420 Eguisheim
89 41 81 61

Established: 1980. **Number of employees:** 1. **Vine stocks:** Riesling, Gewürztraminer, Pinot Blanc, Tokay, Syrah, Muscat, Crémant. **Soil:** Chalky clay. **Exposure:** South – South-East. **Average annual production in hectoliters:** 400.

Mise d'Origine
ALSACE GRAND CRU
Produit en France
Appellation Alsace Grand Cru Controlée
GEWURZTRAMINER
1985
RANGEN DE THANN
70 cl
HERTZ Bruno Vigneron Récoltant à Eguisheim (Ht-Rhin)

Appellation: AOC Alsace, Grand Cru Pfirsigberg – Rangen de Thann, Vendange Tardive, Crémant. **Type:** Red, White. **Technique:** Traditional. **Maturing:** In oak vats and casks. **Alcohol content:** 12%. **Characteristics:** Aromatic. **Serving temperature:** 8 to 10°. **Vintages available in 89/90:** 1985, 1986, 1987.

Characteristics of vintages

1988: Excellent. **1987:** Aromatic, well balanced. **1986:** Well balanced, full bodied, remarkable Vendanges Tardives. **1985:** Great wine. Price range (pre-tax, ex-warehouse): 10 to 20 F.F. (generic). 20 to 30 F.F. (Gewürztraminer, Riesling, Tokay). 30 to 50 F.F. (Grand Cru). 80 to 120 F.F. (Vendanges Tardives).
Sales volume:
– Retail: 80%. – Restaurants: 10%. – Other: 10% (winecellars).
Sales in France: 60%.
Export sales: 40%.
Main trading partners: Belgium, Netherlands, USA, Denmark.

Abroad

United States
Weyganot M. Unionville PA 19375 (Tel: (215) 486 0165).

Belgium
"Aux Côteaux", 227, rue de Tinelmatr 5241 Vinalmont 85/21 1561.

The Netherlands
Horsch Léonard, Steltperstraat 5, 6311 GK SCH...

Comments

At Eguisheim, in the heart of the "cradle of Alsatian wines", 7 km South of Colmar, the Hertz family's six hectare vineyard turns golden in the sun. On this generous, mostly chalky clay soil, flourish all of the basic Alsatian vinestocks, in particular the prestigious Riesling and Gewürztraminer. Here, the traditional vinification methods combine perfectly with the newest techniques, preserving the personality of each vinestock. Oak casks, then vats shelter the first fermentation and the maturation of these fine great wines.

CAVE VINICOLE D'INGERSHEIM

Joël Sutter
45 rue de la République, 68040 Ingersheim
89 27 05 96 - Telex: 871 188

Type of vineyard: Cooperative. **Established:** 1926. **Number of employees:** 20. **Vine stocks:** Sylvaner, Riesling, Pinot Blanc, Gris Noir, Gewurtztraminer, Muscat. **Soil:** Chalky and granitic clay. **Exposure:** South, South-East. **Average annual production in hectoliters:** 20,000.

Appellation: AOC Alsace. **Type:** Red, white, Crémant d'Alsace. **Technique:** Traditional. **Maturing:** Concrete and stainless steel tanks. **Alcohol content:** between 11 and 14%. **Characteristics:** Dry, fruity, rich and well-balanced. **Serving temperature:** between 8 and 10°. **Served with:** First courses, fish, white meats. **Vintages available in 89/90:** 83, 85, 86, 87, 88.

Characteristics of vintages

1988: Very beautiful vintage for all varieties. Fruity and full-bodied. **1987:** Agreeable and easy to drink. **1986:** Riesling and Gewurtztraminer: Lovely, full wines, ready to drink now. **1985:** Still beautiful Gewurtztraminer and Riesling, fully mature. **Other:** 1983: A few bottles of Gewurtztraminer, Pinot Noir and Tokay and a very exceptional Vendanges Tardives. Average pre-tax, ex-warehouse price: between 20 F.F. and 130 F.F.

Sales voulume:
– Wholesale: 50%. – Retail: 5%. – Restaurants: 5%. – Other: 40% (distributors).
Sales in France: 70%.
Export sales:30%.
Main trading partners: UK, Germany, Denmark, Benelux, Countries, USA, Japan.

References in France

Shops: Nicolas.

Abroad

United States

Importers: Parliament Import, 3303 Altantic Avenue, Atlantic City, New Jersey 08401.

United Kingdom

Davies and Son, 7 Aberdeen Road, Croydon, Surrey CRO IEQ. Joh, Harvey, Whitechurch Lane, GB Bristol BS 14 OJZ. Waverley Vintners Ltd, PO Box 22, Creiff Road, Perth, Scotland.

Germany

Vif Weinwelt, Mack SS Schule GmbH, Postfach 1147, D7311 Owen, Dallmayer Diennerstrasse D8000 Munich 70. De Grinisch Wienkellerei, Frühlingsweg 2 D 8950 Kaufbevren.

Switzerland

Willy Rauss, Route des 4 Communes, CH 1180 Rolle, Tel: 218 254 385.

Belgium

Godaert et Van Beneden, 15 Rue Lessines, B 1080 Brussels. Tel: 25 225 293.

Comments

The Cave Vinicole d'Ingersheim, founded in 1926, has been developing, over the last decade, a policy of quality based on respect for the soil and a quest for the best possible harmony between vinestock and soil. Great vinestocks, the locality, late harvesting and selection of noble grapes constitute the major lines of research. The most recent beautiful successes are the Riesling Steinweg and Sommerberg 88 as well the GI Grand Cru Florimont 88.

JOSMEYER

Jean Meyer
76, rue Clemenceau - Wintzenhein
68000 Colmar
89 27 01 57 - Fax: 89 27 03 98

Type of vineyard: Family-owned. **Established:** 1854. **Number of employees:** 12. **Vine stocks:** All of the Alsatian varieties: Riesling, Tokay, Gewurztraminer, etc. **Soil:** Various: Alluvium, gravel, limestone, sandstone. **Exposure:** Various. **Average annual production in hectoliters:** 2500.
Appellation: Alsace. **Type:** White. **Technique:** Traditional, without yeast. **Maturing:** In large Oak casks – very old Oak. **Alcohol content:** 12%. **Characteristics:** Elegant wines, expressive, reflecting the characteristics of the grapes and the soil from which they come. **Serving temperature:** 10°. **Served with:** Depends on the type, but there is always one to go with every dish. **Vintages available in 89/90:** 1985, 1986 and, in small quantities, 1982, 1983 and 1984.

Characteristics of vintages

1986: Elegant, seductive. **1985:** Substantial, full of character. Excellent Tokay and Riesling. **1984:** Wellb–red and typical, a bit austere, successful vinification. **1983:** Ripe, elegant, with lots of Class. **1982:** Has kept its lovely youth, pleasant to drink. Price range (pre-tax, ex-warehouse): Between 20 F.F. and 120 F.F.
Sales volume:
– Retail: 10%. – Restaurants: 15%.
Sales in France: 25%.
Export sales: 75%.
Main trading partners : Germany, Belgium, Netherlands, Sweden, Denmark, UK, Switzerland, USA, Japan, Mexico, Canada.

DOMAINE KLEIN AUX VIEUX REMPARTS

Jean-Marie Klein
Route du Haut-Kœnigsbourg
68590 Saint-Hippolyte
89 73 00 41

Type of vineyard: Agricultural Association. **Number of employees:** 2. **Vine stocks:** Gewürztraminer, Riesling, Tokay, Pinot Blanc, Muscat, Chardonnay, Sylvaner, Pinot Noir. **Soil:** Granitic. **Exposure:** South-East – South. **Average annual production in hectoliters:** 70.
Appellation: AOC Alsace. **Type:** Red, white. Other: Crémant d'Alsace. **Technique:** Traditional. **Maturing:** In oak casks (for about 50 years) Pinot Noir: in new casks. **Characteristics:** Marked by the soil, typical of the appellation. **Serving temperature:** White: 10°. Red (Pinot Noir): 15°. **Served with:** Fresh and salt water fish, white meat, game. **Vintages available in 89/90:** Riesling, Tokay and Gewürztraminer: 1988, 1987, 1986, 1985, 1983. Riesling and Gewürztraminer: 1979 and 1981.

Characteristics of vintages

1988: Rich and well balanced, yellow fruit aroma, exotic, great wine for keeping. **1987:** Youthful aromas, very supple, seductive, developing well. **1986:** Great finesse, harmonious, still undeveloped aromas, full, wait 5 years or so. **1985:** Very great vintage, exotic aromas, a certain mineral character (Riesling) full-bodied, will reach its peak towards 1995. Price range (pre-tax, ex-warehouse): 20 to 50 F.F.
Sales volume:
– Retail: 60%. – Restaurants: 15%. – Other: 25% (agent).
Sales in France: 70%.
Export sales: 30%.
Main trading partners : Denmark, Germany, Belgium, Netherlands.

• *Want to know more about wine, its vinification, its nature and its vocabulary? See Chapter "The Chemistry of Wine".*

DOMAINE KLIPFEL

Mr. Lorentz
6, Avenue de la Gare 67140 Barr
88 08 94 85 – Telex: 870 525

Type of vineyard: De Facto Corporation. **Established:** 1824. **Number of employees:** 12. **Vine stocks:** Sylvaner 5%, Pinot Blanc 10%, Riesling 30%, Tokay 5%, Gewürztraminer 35%, Pinot Noir 10%, Muscat 5%. **Soil:** Chalky clay. **Exposure:** South (50%). **Average annual production in hectoliters:** 1 500.
Appellation: GW – Clos Zisser 1976. GW – Clos Sisser AOC Grand Cru Kircheberg. **Type:** White. **Technique:** Traditional. **Maturing:** In oak casks. **Characteristics:** Vendanges Tardives and Sélection de Grains Nobles. **Serving temperature:** 10°. **Served with:** Foie gras, dessert and as an aperitif. **Vintages available in 89/90:** 1976, 1983, 1985, 1986.

Characteristics of vintages

1988: Sélection de Grains Nobles, not yet available. **1987:** Still quite firm but very well balanced. **1986:** Typical Gewürztraminer, well developed and harmonious. **1985:** Vendanges Tardives, still a bit young. **Other: 1976:** Sélection de Grains Nobles, with the characteristic richness of the vintage. Price range (pre-tax, ex-warehouse): 120 to 160 F.F. (1985) over 160 F.F. (1976).
Sales volume:
– Retail: 30%. – Restaurants: 30%. – Other: 40% (agents).
Sales in France: 70%.
Export sales: 30%.
Main trading partners : Germany, UK, Belgium.

Abroad

United Kingdom

Ee May 69 Great Queen St, London WC 25 BU (Tel: (01) 405 62 49).

Switzerland

Tempia Cie 42, rue de Lyon, 1211 Geneve 7 (Tel: 44 70 74).

Belgium

Grafe Lecocq 9, Place St Aubin, Namur (Tel: (081) 22 43 15).

Canada

Drung PO BOX 2364 Station B, Kitchener, Ontario (Tel: (519) 884 76 00).

The Netherlands

Beeres-Dude Int Katsstraat 47-53 Groninggen 9701 (Tel: 050 13 22 41). Thiessen, Grote Gracht, 18 Mastricht (Tel: (043) 25 13 55)

Others

Italy: Sutti, Via Bartolomo Panizza 5, 20144 Milano, (Tel: 46 40 36).

Comments

The Klipfel family is presently in its fifth generation. More than 50% of the vineyard, which now covers more than 35 hectares, is planted in three Grands Crus: Kirchberg de

Barr, Kastelberg, Wiebelserg. All vinification is done in oak casks in a cellar with a capacity of 3 000 hl. The "spécialité de la maison" is the great Gewurztraminer. Some wines from the 30s and 40s are still available.

VINS D'ALSACE KUEHN

Richard Juchert
3 Grande Rue – 68770 Ammerschwihr
89 78 23 16 – Telex: 880 666 KUEHN

Type of vineyard: Corporation. **Established:** 1675. **Number of employees:** 13. **Vine stocks:** All of the Alsatian varieties. **Soil:** Clay with calcium carbonate. **Exposure:** Various. **Average annual production in hectoliters:** 600.
Type: White, rosé. **Technique:** Traditional Alsace. **Maturing:** Large wooden casks. **Characteristics:** Traditional wines, typical of the region. **Vintages available in 89/90:** 1986, 1985, 1984, 1983, 1979.

Characteristics of vintages

Price range (pre-tax, ex-warehouse): between 30 F.F. and 50 F.F.
Sales volume:
– Wholesale: 20%. – Retail: 40%. – Restaurants: 40%.
Sales in France: 57%.
Export sales: 43%.
Main trading partners : European Common Market.

GUSTAVE LORENTZ S.A.

Messrs. Charles & George Lorentz
35 Grand Rue – 68750 Bergheim
89 73 63 08 – Telex: 880 610 F

Type of vineyard: Family-owned. **Established:** 1836. **Number of employees:** 50. **Vine stocks:** All Alsatian wines grapes. **Soil:** Clay with calcium carbonate. **Exposure:** South. **Average annual production in hectoliters:** 2.5 million (bottles).
Appellation: Alsace. **Type:** White, rosé. **Technique:** Traditional. **Characteristics:** Typical Alsatian wines. Tokay, Riesling, Pinot Blanc, Sylvaner: dry. Gewurztraminer, Muscat, etc. fruity. **Serving temperature:** Riesling, Sylvaner: 10°. Gewurztraminer, Tokay: 12°. **Served with:** Riesling & Sylvaner: seafood and typical Alsatian dishes (Sauerkraut, delicatessan products). Tokay: as an aperitif or with foie gras. Gewurztraminer: for receptions, with foie gras, Munster cheese and desserts calling for wine. **Vintages available in 89/90:** 1976, 1983, 1984, 1985, 1986, 1987.

Characteristics of vintages

1988: Very rich, extremely concentrated wines. Very great year, to be kept. **1987:** Great finesse, to be drunk rather young. **1986:** For keeping – very successful. **1985:** Very special lot, Grand Cru Altenberg, Vendanges Tardives. **1984:** Grand Cru Altenberg, Vendanges Tardives. **1983:** Grand Cru Altenberg, Vendanges Tardives. Price range (pre-tax, ex-warehouse): From 20 F.F. to over 160 F.F.
Sales volume:
– Retail: 20%. – Restaurants: 30%. – Other: Export.
Sales in France: 50%.
Export sales: 50%.
Main trading partners : Germany, UK, Australia, Belgium, Denmark, Netherlands, Switzerland, USA.

References in France

Restaurants: Auberge de L'Ill (Illha eusern), Schillinger (Colmar), Armes de France (Ammerschwihr), Blanc (Vonas), Laurent (Paris), Lucas Carton (Paris), Le Crocodile (Strasbourg).
Shops: Hédiard (Paris), Duty Free Shop (Charles-de-Gaulle, Roissy).

DOMAINE MITTNACHT KLACK

Mr. and Mrs. Mittnacht
8, rue des Tuileries 68340 Riquewihr
89 47 92 54

Type of vineyard: Family owned. **Vine stocks:** All Alsatian vine stocks. **Average annual production in hectoliters:** 500 to 600.
Appellation: AOC Alsace. **Type:** White, rosé. **Technique:** Traditional. **Maturing:** In casks. **Alcohol content:** 12%. **Serving temperature:** 11°. **Served with:** Because of the variety of the vinestocks used, you can find an Alsacian to go with everything. **Vintages available in 89/90:** 1983, 1985, 1986, 1987.

Characteristics of vintages

1988: Excellent year – wille be put on the market in Autumn 1990. **1987:** Good year. **1986:** Good Year. **1985:** Excellent year. **Other:** Some of the superb 1983 vintage is still in stock. Price range (pre-tax, ex-warehouse): 20 to 30 F.F. – 30 to 50 F.F. – 80 to 120 F.F.
Sales volume:
– Retail: 70%. – Restaurants: 10%. – Other: 20% (agents).
Sales in France: 80%.
Export sales: 20 %.
Main trading partners : Germany, Netherlands.

References in France

Restaurants: Cheval Blanc, (lembach), Beau Site, (Oitrott) l'Arnsbourg, (Muhlthal Baerenith).
Shops: Les Crus des Vignerons, (56 Auray).

Abroad

Germany
Metzger Weni 7832 Kenzingen (Tel: 0 7644 581).

The Netherlands
Wijnimport "Bouquet" 9152 La Haren (Tel: 050 343690).

Comments

The Domain is the result of the fusion of two family vineyards, which now extends over 5 communes: Risevulie, Hunowih,, Sehenberg, Rifieuwihn and Kieutzheim.

CAVE VINICOLE DE PFAFFENHEIM GUEBERSCHWIHR

Mr. Alex Heinrich (Director)
5, rue du Chai, BP 33, 68250 Pfaffenheim
89 49 61 08 – Telex: 880682

Type of vineyard: Cooperative. **Established:** 1955. **Number of employees:** 20. **Vine stocks:** Sylvaner 20%, Pinot Blanc 20%, Riesling 15%, Tokay 10%, Muscat 5%, Gewürztraminer 25%, Pinot Noir 5%. **Soil:** Chalky clay. **Exposure:** South – South-East. **Average annual production in hectoliters:** 16 000.
Appellation: AOC Alsace. **Type:** White, Rosé. **Technique:** Traditional, fermentation with temperature control. **Maturing:** In stainless steel tanks. **Characteristics:** White (dry): fruity or smoky, depending on the vine stock, goes down well. Rosé (dry): special taste, very delicate, light and velvety texture. **Serving temperature:** 8-10°. **Served with:** According to the vinestocks, the Alsatian wines go with everything, from first courses to dessert. **Vintages available in 89/90:** 1983, 1985, 1986, 1987, 1988, 1989.

Characteristics of vintages

1988: One of the best (comparable to the 1971 – 1976 – 1983 – 1985 vintages). **1987:** Light and fresh. **1986:** Goes down smoothly. **1985:** Probably amongst the best of the Alsatian vineyard. Price range (pre-tax, ex-warehouse): 20 to 30 F.F. – 30 to 50 F.F.
Sales volume:
– Wholesale: 45%. – Retail: 20%. – Restaurants: 5%. – Other: 30% (export).
Sales in France: 70%.
Export sales: 30%
Main trading partners : Belgium, Germany, UK, Netherlands, Norway, Finland, Sweden, Denmark, USA, Japan, Canada.

Comments

The cooperative of Pfaffenheim was created in 1957 and merged with the Gueberschwihr cooperative in 1968. The enterprise cultivates 200 hectares of vineyard in the communes of Pfaffenheim and Gueberschwihr and in the neighbouring communes. The harvest is selected by type of soil and quality of the grapes. The winecellar has won more awards at the Concours Général Agricole de Paris than any other Alsatian winemaker for the 1967 to 1988 vintages.

DOMAINE JOSEPH RIEFLÉ ET FILS

11, place de la Mairie, 68250 Pfaffenheim
89 49 62 82

Type of vineyard: Family-owned. **Established:** 1965. **Number of employees:** 9. **Vine stocks:** All of the Alsacian vinestocks. **Soil:** Chalky clay. **Exposure:** East, South-East. **Average annual production in hectoliters:** 1800.

Vin d'Alsace
APPELLATION ALSACE CONTROLÉE
13% Vol.
Rieflé
750 ml
Tokay-Pinot Gris
Mise en bouteille au
Produce of France
DOMAINE JOSEPH RIEFLÉ & FILS VIGNERONS A 68250 PFAFFENHEIM

Appellation: Alsace, Grand Cru, Crémant d'Alsace, Vendange Tardive. **Type:** White. **Technique:** Traditional method with control of the temperature of fermentation. **Maturing:** On fine lees. **Characteristics:** Very rich and well balanced wines, characterized by the chalky terrain. They increase in distinction with age. **Vintages available in 89/90:** 1986, 1987, 1988.

Characteristics of vintages

1988: Very beautiful year marked by a considerable maturity. **1987:** Remarkably balanced and fine. **1986:** Excellent aromatic richness. Price range (pre-tax, ex-warehouse): between 20 and 50 F.F.
Sales volume:
– Wholesale: 40%. – Retail: 40%. – Restaurants: 20%.
Sales in France: 50%.
Export sales: 50%.
Main trading partners : Belgium, Netherlands, Germany, Denmark.

References in France

Restaurants: Several great restaurants.
Shops: L'Amour du Vin.

Abroad

Germany
Fr. Bremer, Barfüsserstrasse, D-3400 Göttingen.

The Netherlands
Vos Wijnimport, Jellinghaustraat 3, Tilburg 5004 BD.

Comments

Remarkable family exploitation, attached to the great tradition of Alsatian wines. Not to be missed: The Grands Crus and the Vendanges Tardives.

EDGARD SCHALLER & FILS

Patrick Schaller
1, rue du Château 68630 Mittelwihr
89 47 90 28

Vine stocks: Alsatian varieties. **Soil:** Chalky clay. **Exposure:** South – East. **Average annual production in hectoliters:** 500.

Appellation: AOC Alsace. **Type:** White. Other: Crémant. **Technique:** Traditional. **Maturing:** In casks. **Characteristics:** Dry. **Serving temperature:** 10°. **Vintages available in 89/90:** 1986, 1987, 1988.

Characteristics of vintages

1988: Very great vintage, very typical wines, long keeping. **1987:** Good year, wines that go down smoothly. **1986:** Good year, very pleasant after ageing. Price range (pre-tax, ex-warehouse): 20 to 30 F.F. – 30 to 50 F.F.
Sales volume:
– Retail: 50%. – Restaurants: 20%. – Other: 30% (export).
Sales in France: 70%.
Export sales: 30 %.
Main trading partners : USA, Belgium, Germany, Switzerland.

References in France

Restaurants: Armes de France, (Ammerschwihr) Chambaan (Kaysersberg), Auberge de l'Ill (Vosges Ribeauvillé).

Abroad

United States
Robert Kacher, Washington DC.

Switzerland
Schaller Russwill.

Belgium
France Vins, Brussels.

Comments

The first family vineyard go back to 1609. The production was sold in bulk until 1925, at which time selling in bottles was begun. Production of Crémant, now half of the output, was begun in 1975.

CHARLES SCHLERET

Charles Schleret
1-3, route d'Ingersheim – 68230 Turckheim
89 27 06 09

Type of vineyard: Family-owned. **Established:** 1948. **Vine stocks:** Sylvaner, Pinot Blanc, Riesling, Muscat d'Alsace, Tokay Pinot Gris, Gewurztraminer, Pinot Noir. **Soil:** Essentially alluvial, but sandy, pebbly and rich in clay (easy to warm up at the end of the season for good maturation). The soil is sufficiently sandy to store a maximum of heat in poorer years. The rains are the lighest in Alsace. **Exposure:** South. **Average annual production in hectoliters:** 400.
Appellation: AOC. **Type:** White, rosé. **Technique:** Destemming, appropriate pressing, centrifuging of the must, temperature regulation, carbonic maceration for the Pinot Noir. **Alcohol content:** 12.5%. **Characteristics:** Expressive and fruity, can be drunk young or kept for several years. The grapes (mostly from old vines) attain a great maturity and generally provide more aroma and distinction than elsewhere. **Serving temperature:** 8 to 10°. **Served with:** Many dishes: See folders Gastronomie et Vins d'Alse du Civa. **Vintage available in 89/90:** 1986, 1987, 1988.

Characteristics of vintages

1988: Great maturity. Full-bodied, forthcoming wines. **1987:** Aromatic, well balanced wines. **1986:** Good year. Distinguished, harmonious wines. Price range (pre-tax, ex-warehouse): between 20 and 30 F.F.
Sales volume:
– Retail: 60%. – Other: 40% various importers.
Sales in France: 60%.
Export sales: 40%.
Main trading partners: United States, United Kingdom, Netherlands, Belgium, Germany.

Abroad

United States
Neal I. Rosenthal, Wine Merchant – Select Vineyards LTD. 56-31 56th Drive Maspeth, New York 11378.

United Kingdom

Yapp Brothers, Mere Wiltshire.

Belgium

Caves Michel Arnould, 147, avenue de la Gare, B 6800, Bertrix.

The Netherlands

Louis Bogaers B.V., Grootvenstraat 8, 5048 At Tilburg, Postbus 922.

Comments

A good producer, known in France and abroad for the top quality of his wines that have received national and international prizes at wine competitions. Recommended for the good quality/price ratio. Very successful Gewurztraminer, Muscat and Tokay Pinot Gris in recent years, as demonstrated by the 83 and 88 vintages.
Vins provenant essentiellement de vieilles vignes.

DOMAINES SCHLUMBERGER

100, rue Théodore Deck 68500 Guebwiller
89 74 27 00 – Telex: DVS 881449 F

Type of vineyard: Family-owned. **Established:** 1810. **Vine stocks:** Sylvaner, Chasselas, Pinot Blanc, Pinot Noir (33%), Muscat, Pinot Gris, Riesling, Gewurztraminer (67%). **Soil:** Mostly infertile light sand, some chalk with schistic sand on a combination of Lower Triassic pink sandstone and volcanic greywacke. **Exposure:** East – South-East – South-West. **Average annual production in hectoliters:** 45 hl/ha.
Appellation: Alsace AOC, Alsace Grands Crus, Saering, Kitterle, Kessler, Spiegel, Vendanges Tardives, Sélection des Grains Nobles. **Type:** White, red (Pinot Noir). **Technique:** Traditional, no temperature control. **Maturing:** In old oak casks (3 000 to 17 000 liters) and glass lined, enamelled or stainless steel tanks. **Characteristics:** Pinot Blanc: full-bodied, long, rich and well balanced. Riesling: typical, well bred, dry and fruity, great elegance. Gewurztraminer: combination of finesse and balance, very full. Small yields produce wines of great concentration, rich in flavor and aroma. Excellent keeping. **Serving temperature:** 8-10°. **Served with:** Everything that goes with white wine. **Vintages available in 89/90:** 1985, 1986.

Characteristics of vintages

1986: Excellent year, full-bodied, good keeping. **1985:** Excellent year, rich, very well balanced, fruity wines. **Other: 1983:** Magnificent year, very rich wines, exceptional keeping.
Sales in France: 40%.
Export sales: 60%.
Main trading partners: Belgium, USA, Germany, Canada, UK, Japan, Denmark, etc.

Abroad

United States

Importers: Mayfair Vintners Inc, Domecq Importers Inc, 2 Madison Avenue, suite 101, Larchmont NY 10538, USA (Telex: 426 544). Martignetty Grocery Co, Carolina Wines Co. 99, Rivermoore Street, West Roxbury, Mass, 02132 (Telex: 025000/7103206549).

United Kingdom

Maison Marques & Domaines, 212, St. Ann's Hill, London SW 18, (Tel: (1) 871 39 55).

Germany

D.V. Schlumberger K.G., Seves Deutschland, Buchstrasse Industrigebiet, D. 5309 Meckenheim/RHLD (Tel: (0225) 880 90 – Telex: 041000/8869940).

Belgium

Ets Mampaey, Gossetlaan 21, 1720 Groot Bijgaarden (Tel: (02) 466 58 58 – Telex: 046000/24795). Ets. Delhaize "Le Lion", 53, rue Osseghem, 1080, Brussels, (Tel: (02) 428 0010 – Telex: 046000/21976).

Canada

La Rochelle Inc. M. Guy Laurendeau, C.P. 26. Ile des Sœurs, Verdun Québec 1J8 (Telex: 021000/5562430).

Other

Danemark: Italo Lena, 15, Astrupvej, Bronshoj 2700 BRH (Tel: (1) 28 36 74).

Far East

Japan: UNEXPA, Japan Co Ltd 3-6-24 Jingumae Shibuya-Ku, Tokyo 150 (Tel: (03) 470 53 90 - (03) 470 34 85).

ROLAND SCHMITT

35, rue des Vosges
67310 Wasselonne Bergbieten
88 38 20 72

Type of vineyard: Family-owned. **Established:** 1610. **Vine stocks:** 35% Riesling, 25% Gewurztraminer, 15% Sylvaner, 15% Pinots, 10% Muscat and Tokay. **Soil:** Multicolored marl with dolomitic pebbles on the surface. **Exposure:** Full South. **Average annual production in hectoliters:** 60 hl. per hectare.
Appellation: Alsace and Alsace Grand Cru (Altenberg de Bergbieten). **Type:** White. **Technique:** Traditional. **Maturing:** Stainless steel tanks. **Characteristics:** Very flowery fragrance, light, supple and subtle in their youth. Very persistent aroma, admirably accentuated by a freshness characteristic of the region. These wines achieve their best balance after several years of ageing, revealing the bouquet specific to the chalky clay soil. **Serving temperature:** 10° to 12°. **Served with:** Sylvaner: cold plates, Quiches, stew. Riesling: fish, shellfish, poultry. Gewurztraminer: spicy dishes, cheese, exotic cuisine, fois gras. **Vintages available in 89/90:** Altenberg Grand Cru: 1985. Alsace: 1986.

Characteristics of vintages

1988: (available end of 1989) – Full-bodied, complex. Rich aromas, lingering taste. Good keeping. **1987:** Fresh and fruity – very promising. **1986:** Very fruity with beautiful

freshness, already seductive. **1985:** Perfect balance its between rich, virile body and aromatic fragrance. Subtle, very good capacity for ageing. Price range (pre-tax, ex-warehouse): A.O.C. Alsace: between 18 F.F. to 30 F.F. Grand Cru: between 30 F.F. and 50 F.F.
Sales in volume:
– Wholesale: 15%. – Retail: 75%. – Restaurants: 10%.
Sales in France: 90%.
Export sales: 10%.

MAISON ALSACE SELTZ

Mr. Pierre Seltz
21, rue Principale – Mittelbergheim – 67140 Barr
88 08 91 77

Number of employees: 5. **Vine stocks:** All Alsatian vine varietals.
Appellation: Tokay, Riesling, Gewurztraminer, Pinot. **Type:** Red, white. **Technique:** Traditional. **Characteristics:** Regularly well-made wines typical of their appellation. **Serving temperature:** 12°. **Vintages available in 89/90:** 1988, 1987, 1986.

Characteristics of vintages

1988: Promising. Wait. **1987:** Fruity, lively, light and subtle wines. **1986:** Excellent year, good development. Price range (pre-tax, ex-warehouse): 20 to 30 F.F. – 30 to 50 F.F.
Sales in France: 60%.
Export sales: 40%.

Abroad

United States
The Franco American wine Company, Mr. Gerard Toth, 332 S. Virginia Avenue, Pasadena, CA 91107.

United Kingdom
Waterloo Wine Company LTD. 6 Vine Yard, Borough, London Sel QL.

Germany
La Petite France, Weinhander. M. Sindezingue, Florentiusgraben, 5300 Bonn 1.

Belgium
Club D.I.V.O., Quai au Foin 37, 1000 Brussels.

The Netherlands
Wijnkoperij prosper Van Nieulande, Baronielaan 159, 4818 PG Breda.

Others
Denmark: Taster wine A/S, Molestien 11/23 – DK 2450 Kobenhavn.

Comments

Winegrowers from father to son since 1576.

DOMAINE SICK-DREYER

Pierre Dreyer
17 route de Kientzheim 68770 Ammerschwihr
89 47 11 31 – Telefax: 89 47 32 60

Type of vineyard: Agricultural Association. **Established:** Winegrowers from father to son for several generations. **Vine stocks:** White: 95%. Red: 5%. **Soil:** Chalky and silica clay. **Exposure:** South, South-East. **Average annual production in hectoliters:** 900.

Appellation: Alsace A.O.C., Kaefferkopf (classified locality). **Type:** White. **Technique:** Traditional. **Maturing:** In wooden casks. **Alcohol content:** 12.5%. **Characteristics:** Dry white wine, fruity, typical. **Serving temperature:** 12°. **Served with:** Tokay: hors d'œuvres and first course, seafood, fish sauerkraut (choucroute), white meat. Vendanges tardives: with foie gras. **Vintages available in 89/90:** 1987, 1988 an 1985 (Vendanges Tardives).

Characteristics of vintages

1988: Excellent, rich and well-balanced, fine and fruity. **1987:** High quality, light, fruity and harmonious. **1986:** Out of stock. **1985:** Excellent Vendange Tardives (Tokay, Gewurztraminer Kaefferkopf). **Other:** 1983 – exceptional – (Gewurztraminer, Sélection de Grains Nobles, Tokay, Vendanges Tardives). Price range (pre-tax, ex-warehouse): 20 to 30 F.F. 50%. 30 to 50 F.F. 25%. 50 to 120 F.F. 15%. 120 to 160 F.F. 10%. of the harvest.
Sales volume:
– Wholesale: 80%. – Retail: 20%.
Sales in France: 85%.
Export sales: 15%.
Main trading partners : Netherlands, Belgium, Germany, England, USA.

References in France

Restaurants: Le Crocodile (Strasbourg), Aux Armes de France (Ammerschwihr), Baumann (Paris), L'Arpège (Paris), etc.

Abroad

United States
Maison Weygandt-Metzler Unionville PA 19375.

Germany
Maison Schneil 8011 Neukeferloh.

Belgium

Wijnkeldermeester Verbraeken 9821 Gent Afsnee.

The Netherlands

Wijnkoperij H.F.A. Okhuysen 2011 GE Haarlem.

Comments

The Sick-Dreyer estate is 8 km from Colmar, in Ammerschwihr, one of the most important winegrowing centers in Alsace. The estate comprises more than 12 hectares of vineyards, primarily in the best districts of the region, of which at least 2 hectares are included in the area designated by the "Appellation d'Orignie Contrôlée Kaefferkopf", the first to be officially recognized in Alsace. The estate has been in the family from father to sons for several generations. All of the wine is produced and bottled on the estate.

PIERRE SPARR ET FILS

René and Charles Sparr
2 rue de la Première-Armée - 68240 Sigolsheim
89 78 24 22
Telex: 880 825 – Telefax: 89 47 32 62

Type of vineyard: Agricultural Association. **Established:** 1953. **Number of employees:** 30. **Vine stocks:** Sylvaner, Pinot Blanc, Riesling, Pinot Gris, Pinot Noir, Gewurztraminer, Muscat. **Soil:** Chalky clay on the hillsides, sand on the plain. **Exposure:** South, South-West. **Average annual production in hectoliters:** 12,000 to 15,000. **Appellation:** AOC Alsace. **Type:** Red, white, rosé. **Technique:** traditional. **Maturing:** Burgundy barrels, oak casks, stainless steel and glass-lined tanks. **Alcohol content:** 11 to 14%. **Characteristics:** Dry wines, supple, well-balanced, harmonious with lots of character. Very elegant. **Serving temperature:** 8 to 10°. **Vintages available in 89/90:** 1983, 1985, 1986, 1987.

Characteristics of vintages

1988: Very promising. Complete, elegant, well-balanced wines with complex aromas. **1987:** Good year. Good acidity, fruity, dry, agreable. Pleasant surprises. **1986:** Very successful, rich, well-balanced fragrance, fine and distinguished wines. **1985:** Rich, very fragrant, elegant, full, superb Muscat and Gewurztraminer. Prestigious Pinot Noir, Riesling, Tokay Pinot Gris and Gewurtztraminer. **Other:** 1983: One of the greatest vintages since the war. Beginning to arrive at an extraordinary maturity. Opulent, rich, complete wines with superb acidity, complex aromas. For long keeping. Hurry, there is not much left. Price range (pre-tax, ex-warehouse): between 25 F.F. and 140 F.F.

Sales volume:
– Wholesale: 35%. – Retail: 5%. – Retaurants: 20% in France.

Sales in France: 60%.

Export sales: 40%.

Main trading partners: Germany, Canada, Benelux Countries, UK, USA, Denmark, Japan, Ivory Coast, Spain, Luxemburg, Hong Kong.

References in France

Restaurants: Auberge de l'Ill (Illhaeusern), Aux Armes de France (Ammerschwihr), Chambard (Kaysersberg), le Crocodile (Strasbourg). Le Cheval Blanc (Lembach), Café Runtz (Paris).
Shops: Hédiard, L'Amour du Vin, Les Caves d'Edgar, Les Caves de Passy.

Abroad

United States

Importers: Paramount Brands, Port Chester, N.Y. Hand Picked Selections, Washington D.C.. Silenus Wines, Waltham Mass.. Evergreeen Imports, Tukwila, Wash. Morrell & Co., N.Y.. Garnet Wines, N.Y. Restaurants: La Grenouille, N.Y., L'Acajou, N.Y.

United Kingdom

Barwell & Jones, Ipswich.

Belgium

A. Delhalle & Sons, Liège.

Canada

Saq Montreal. LCBO – Toronto.

The Netherlands

Hic, Breukelen. Otto Lenselink, BE Hilversum.

Far East

Hong Kong: F.P.F. Dransfield & Co., Ltd. Japan: Daiei Sangyo Kaisha Ltd., Nagoya.

Comments

The Pierre Sparr estate produces the following grands crus: Schlossberg, Brand and Mambourg. In great years, Sparr vinifies some fabulous late harvests in Riesling, Pinot Gris and Gewurztraminer as well as a great Gewurztraminer. Selection of noble grapes.

DOMAINE WEINBACH

Colette Faller
25 route du vin, Clos des Capucins
68240 Kaysersberg
89 47 13 21

Type of vineyard: Agricultural Association. **Established:** 1898. **Number of employees:** 14. **Soil:** Sandy clay, alluvium, silica, colluvial soils, sand with biotite granite. **Exposure:** Full South. **Average annual production in hectoliters:** 1 000 to 1 300.
Appellation: AOC Vin d'Alsace. **Type:** White. **Technique:** Traditional in oak casks lined with tartar – no new casks. **Maturing:** In oak casks, none new. **Alcohol content:** 12-14% – Vendanges Tardives and Grains Nobles: 15-18%. **Characteristics:** Riesling: typical, fruity, fine and delicate, firm – Gewürztraminer: rose and jasmine fragrance, velvety texture – Tokay: full-bodied and forthcoming, smoky – Sylvaner: fresh, goes down smoothly – Pinot: deep and supple – Muscat: grapy. All of the wines have a beautiful lingering aftertaste and a harmonious acidity. **Serving temperature:** 8-10°. **Served with:** There is an Alsatian wine for all dishes and all circumstances. **Vintages available in 89/90:** 1988, 1987, 1986, 1985.

Characteristics of vintages

1988: Great year, fruity, rich and well balanced, promising. **1987:** Wine with breed, very fruity, well balanced. **1986:** Superb Vendanges Tardives (Gewürztraminer), great, rich and full wines. **1985:** Magnificent Vendanges Tardives (Tokay, Riesling, Gewuztraminer). **Other: 1983:** Sumptuous "Grains Nobles". Price range (pre-tax, ex-warehouse): 20 to 30 F.F. – 30 to 50 F.F. – 120 to 160 F.F. and over 160 F.F.
Sales volume:
– Retail: 60%. – Restaurants: 40%.
Sales in France: 65%.
Export sales: 35%.
Main trading partners: USA, Germany, UK, Denmark, Japan, Belgium.

References in France

Restaurants: Taillevent, Lucas Carton, Guy Savoye, Chez Laurent, Baumann Ternes, Le Louis XIX, La Marée, La Tour d'Argent, Chez Pierre, Le Dôme.
Shops: Hediard, Le Repaire de Bacchus, Steven Spurrier.

Abroad

United States

Vineyard Brands, Robert Haas, P.O. Box 160, Chester Vermont 05143 (Tel: (802) 875 1239).

United kingdom

Maison Loeb & Company Ltd, 64 Southwark Bridge, London SEI OAS (Tel: 01 928 7750).

Germany

Alpina Maison Starosky & Sohn GMBH Postfach 510701, 8000 Hannover 91 – Alpenstraasse 35-37, 8938 Buchloe (Tel: 19 49 824 15 0050).

Switzerland

Maison Reichmuth – Les Vins Classiques, Stauffacherstrasse 145a, 8026 Zurich (Tel: 01 241 56 38).

Belgium

Les Courtiers Vinicoles, Kempische Steenweg 140, 3500 Hasselt (Tel: 32 11 21 20 10).

The Netherlands

Vos Wynimport, Jellinghausstraat 3, 5004 Bd Tilburg (Tel: 013 674918).

Denmark

Imp'Gamel Habihoj Bakke Allé 1, DK 8130, Aabihoj Arhus, (Tel: 19 45 615 77 33).

Comments

Facing full South, at the foothills of the Vosges Mountains, the Domaine Weinbach or Clos des Capucins was a Capucine convent until the Revolution. It was purchased by the Faller family in 1898 and now covers 23 hectares. The diversity of the Weinbach soils allows the cultivation of all of the vinestocks, with something of a predilection for the Riesling, Gewürztraminer, Tokay and Muscat. Their adaptation to the soil accentuates their typical character and allows them to develop perfectly. Quality is assured by short pruning which limits yields. Cultivation without manure and late harvesting, which results in very mature grapes, help develop the individual bouquet of each variety and increase their concentration and richness.

CAVE VINICOLE DE TURCKHEIM

Jean-Paul Ritzenthaler
16, rue des Tuileries 68230 Turckheim
89 27 06 25 – Telex: 871 060 – Fax: 89 27 35 33

Type of vineyard: Cooperative. **Established:** 1955. **Number of employees:** 30. **Vine stocks:** All Alsatian vinestocks. **Soil:** Chalky clay and granite. **Exposure:** South-East, South-West. **Average annual production in hectoliters:** 25,000.
Appellation: AOC Alsace. **Type:** Red, White, Rosé. **Technique:** White (dry): temperature control. Red: fermentation on skins for 7 days. Rosé: fermentation on skins for 3 days. **Maturing:** In glass-lined stainless steel tanks. Pinot Noir in new casks. **Alcohol content:** 12%. **Characteristics:** White (dry): fruity, delicate. Rosé (dry): fruity, light and supple. Red: elegant bouquet. **Serving temperature:** White and Rosé: 8 to 10°. Red: 15°. **Vintages available in 89/90:** 1988, 1987, a few 1985 and 1983.

Characteristics of vintages

1988: Fruity, full-bodied, supple. **1987:** Fruity, very harmonious, delicate. **1985:** Aromatic, forthcoming, rich. Price range (pre-tax, ex-warehouse): 20 to 50 F.F. A few special wines are sold between 50 and 120 F.F.
Sales volume:

- Wholesale: 20%. - Retail: 20%. - Restaurants: 10%. - Other: 50% large scale distribution.
Sales in France: 80%. **Export sales:** 20%.
Main trading partners: UK, Switzerland, Netherlands, Germany, Belgium.

References in France

Restaurants: Crocodile, (Strasbourg), Buerehiesel, (Strasbourg), Cerf, (Marlenheim), Les Trois Marches, (Versailles), Le Tastevin, (Maisons-Laffitte), etc.
Shops: Hediard (Paris), Nicolas, Caves du Château (Versailles), Magnum (Perpignan).

Comments

"Quality is fundamental; it's what makes faithful clients". This slogan was adopted by the managers of the Cave Vinicole de Turckheim in 1955, when the cooperative was established and they have not departed from it since. Rightly so, because they have had continuous relationships with the most demanding distributor for over 30 years.

FRÉDÉRIC-ÉMILE TRIMBACH

Bernard, Hubert, Pierre and Jean Trimbach
15, route de Bergheim - 68150 Ribeauville
89 73 60 30 - Fax: 89 73 89 04

Type of vineyard: Private grower and dealer. **Established:** 1626. **Number of employees:** 20. **Vine stocks:** Riesling, Gewurztraminer, Pinot Gris, Pinot Blanc, Muscat, Sylvaner. **Soil:** Clay with calcium carbonate. **Exposure:** South, East, Southeast. **Average annual production in hectoliters:** 5000 to 6000.
Appellation: Alsace Controlée. **Type:** White, rosé, Vendanges Tardives, Grains Nobles. **Technique:** Traditional, dry wines, temperature control during fermentation. **Maturing:** 6 to 10 months in large casks, glass-lined concrete vats, stainless steel tanks, then 6 months to 3 years in bottles. **Characteristics:** Dry and fruity, typical of their grape varieties. Wines very well known for their long life. **Serving temperature:** 10°. **Served with:** All dishes requiring a dry white wine, particularly the traditional Alsatian cuisine. **Vintages available in 89/90:** 1985, 1986, 1987.

Characteristics of vintages

1988: Vintage similar to 1985. **1987:** Vintage similar to 1986. **1986:** Fruity wines, typical of their grape varieties, good year with a plus for the Riesling. **1985:** Really great wines, rich, well-balanced and fruity, for long ageing. **1984:** Average year - ready to drink. **1983:** Great wines with magnificent Vendanges Tardives and Sélection de Grains Nobles. **1982:** Good year - wines ready to drink. **Other:** 1979 and 1981: the Rieslings are at their peak.
Sales in France: 20%. **Export sales:** 80%.
Main trading partners: USA, Canada, UK, Netherlands, Belgium, Germany, Denmark.

LA CAVE DE WESTHALTEN

Gérard Schatz, Président
52, rue de Soultzmatt - 68250 Westhalten
89 47 01 27 - Telex: 880 273 - Télécopie: 89 47 63 77

Type of vineyard: Producer's Association. **Established:** 1955. **Number of employees:** 15. **Vine stocks:** Sylvaner, Pinot-Blanc, Riesling, Tokay-Pinot-Gris, Muscat, Gewurztraminer, Pinot-Noir, Crémant d'Alsace Blanc and Rosé. Each wine is available in a "reserve" quality and in a "cuvée réservée" quality. Besides we offer "Cuvées particulières", "Lieux-dits" and "Vendanges tardives". **Soil:** Oolitic and tertiary calk. **Exposure:** South, South-East. **Average annual production in hectoliters:** 20,000.
Appellation: Alsace Contrôlée, Alsace Contrôlée Grand Cru, Crémant d'Alsace Appellation Contrôlée. **Type:** White, rosé. **Technique:** White: with temperature control. **Maturing:** In stainless steel tanks and oak casks. **Alcohol content:** 11 to 14° (for the late harvests). **Characteristics:** Full-bodied, complex aromas, the slow evolution characteristic of a chalky sub-soil, aromatic vinestocks, for keeping (Tokay, Gewurztraminer). **Serving temperature:** Crémants: 8°. White and rosé: 10°. Pinot-Noir "vieilli en fûts de chêne": 14°. **Served with:** Perfect companions when dining with friends - there is an Alsation wine for everything.

Characteristics of vintages

1988: Promissing. **1987:** Characteristics freshness provides the vintage with a much appreciated originality. **1986:** Very well balanced, very fruity, capable of slow ageing while developing tertiary aromas. **1985:** Very rich and concentrated, great body, very round and velvety. **1983:** The *Cave de Westhalten* is well-known for the Crémant d'Alsace Brut Cuvée Madame Sans Gêne, vintage 1983, bottled in engraved bottles. This Cuvée Tradition, a rigourous selection among the cuvées Pinot Blanc from the vintages 1983, a grape-variety of choice, fine and delicate, was chosen among the Crémants d'Alsace by the ingeniors and technicians from the National Institut of Wine and Brandy Appellations of Origin on the occasion of his 50th Jubilee. Price range (pre-tax, ex-warehouse): Vins de Réserve: between 19 and 24 F.F. Cuvée Réservée: between 21 and 30 F.F. Cuvées Particulières & lieux-dits: between 80 and 85 F.F.
Sales volume:
- Wholesale: 2%. - Retail: 15%. - Restaurants: 10%. - Other: 73% (large scale distribution).
Sales in France: 60%.
Export sales: 40%.
Main trading partners: Belgium, Netherlands, Denmark, Germany, Hong Kong, Switzerland, Luxemburg.

References in France

Restaurants: Baumann Marbeuf (Paris), Auberge du Cheval Blanc (68250 Westhalten).

Abroad

United Kingdom
Bugmars Ltd Reading Berks.

L'Alsace à Fleur de Coteaux
Westhalten
52, rue de Soultzmatt
68250 Westhalten
Tél.: 89 47 01 27 - Télécopie: 89 47 63 77
Télex: 880 273 F
Initiale EDA

Germany

Jacques Wein dépôt Dusseldorf. Weinagentur Aloïs Henkel – Augsburg.

Switzerland

Landolt Zurich.

Belgium

GB INNO Brussels.

The Netherlands

D.G.S. Wijnkopers, Waddinxveen.

Others

Danemark: Magasin Vin Hvidovre, Kobenhav.

Comments

The *Cave de Westhalten* was established in 1955 by a group of winemakers in an raid, hilly region with steep slopes. Between three well-known hills, – Bollenberg, Strangenberg and Zinnkoepflé – rests the vineyard of Westhalten with 227 hectares. This vineyard is the highest situated in Alsace (410 meters) with the lowest rain gauge. The slopes are turned south and south – east and profit by an exceptional sunshining, which grants them a microclimate comparable to the mediterranean climate. This microclimate, unexampled in Alsace, is confirmed by the presence of particular fauna and flora in the area.
La *Cave de Westhalten* produces wines about the 7 grape-varieties: Sylvaner, Pinot Blanc, Riesling, Gewurztraminer, Tokay Pinot Gris, Muscat and Pinot Noir. A very strict qualitative policy was adopted, notably through the winegrowers participation to produce quality wines. Reputed for its Wines, the *Cave de Westhalten* produces Grands Crus Zinnkoepflé and Vorburg, Lieux-Dits Strangenberg and Bollenberg plus a number of specific specialities such as "Pinot Noir Cuvée à l'Ancienne" (aged for more than two years in oak barrels) or "Riesling Vendanges Tardives". The Crémant d'Alsace is equally as important in the wine product range.
The wines have been awarded with numerous medals, which only verifies the constant efforts employed around the quality.

ALSACE WILLM

Pierre Husherr (director)

32, rue Docteur Sultzer – 67140 Barr (B.P. 13)

88 08 19 11 – Telex: 871 357

Type of vineyard: Corporation. **Established:** 1896. **Vine stocks:** Riesling, Gewurztraminer, Tokay, Sylvaner. **Soil:** Clay with calcium carbonate. **Exposure:** South, Southeast. **Appellation:** Alsace, Riesling Kirchberg de Barr Grand Cru, Gewurztraminer Clos Gaensbroennel. **Technique:** Stainless steel tanks for the selected wines; large wooden casks for the "Grands Crus" and the Cuvée Émile Willm. **Maturing:** 1 year for the Grands Crus, Cuvée E. Willm and Vendanges Tardives. **Vintages available in 89/90:** Grands Crus: 1986 and 1988. Vins de Sélection: 1988.

Characteristics of vintages

1988: Early flowering and harvesting have resulted in rich, well-balanced wines. The Riesling Kirchberg de Barr and the Gewurztraminer Clos Gaensbroennel, two grands crus of the estate, were harvested at the same level of maturity as in 1983. Part of the Clos Gaensbroennel was harvested late (in November). An excellent, expressive vintage. **1987:** Lively, fruity wines, pleasant to drink now; the Riesling and Pinot Noir are excellent. **1986:** Fruity and supple. **1985:** Beautiful year, especially for the Tokay and Gewurztraminer. **1983:** Excellent vintage. Full, will age very well. Superb Riesling Grand Cru Kirchberg de Barr and a First Class Gewurztraminer Clos Gaensbroennel.
Export sales: 75%.
Main trading partners : USA, Canada, UK, Netherlands, Denmark, Belgium, Japan, Switzerland, Luxemburg, Portugal, Germany.

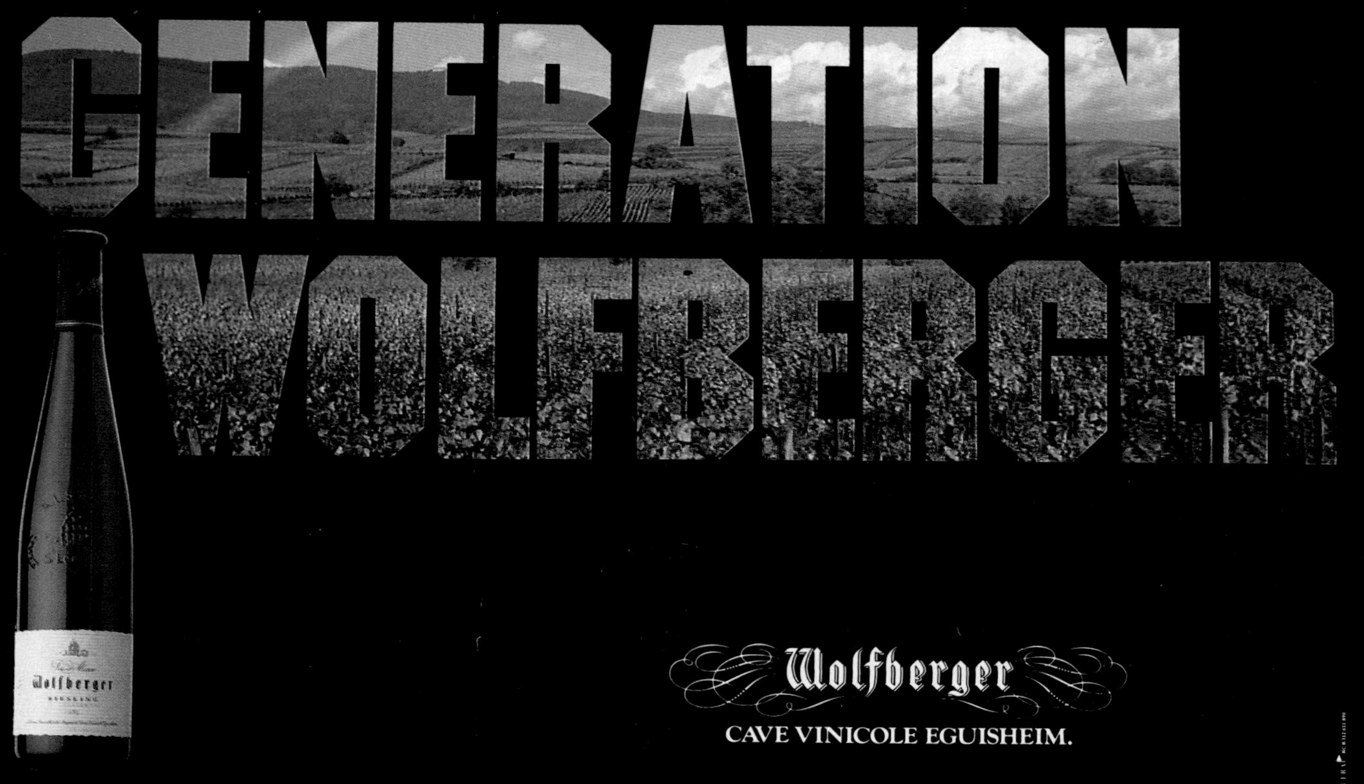

GENERATION
WOLFBERGER
Wolfberger
CAVE VINICOLE EGUISHEIM.

WOLFBERGER
CAVE VINICOLE EGUISHEIN 68420
89 41 11 06 – Telex: 880 211

Established: 1902. **Vine stocks:** Sylvaner, Pinot Blanc, Gris & Noir, Riesling, Muscat, Gewurtztraminer. **Soil:** Chalky clay. **Exposure:** South – South-East. **Average annual production in hectoliters:** 85,000.
Appellation: Alsace AOC **Type:** White, red, other: Crémant d'Alsace (Traditional method). **Technique:** Traditional (dry white). **Maturing:** In vats and oak casks (dating from 1902). **Alcohol content:** 12%. **Characteristics:** Very fruity, aromatic and supple. **Serving temperature:** 8-10°. **Served with:** Everything (fish and seafood in general, white meat, game, delicatessen, desserts, etc.). **Vintages available in 89/90:** 1985-1986 (Reserves), 1987-1988.

Characteristics of vintages

1988: Very rich, goes down well, silky texture, delightfully fruity. **1987:** Delicate, light and fresh. **1985:** Full-bodied, rich, goes down smoothly. Price range (pre-tax, ex-warehouse): 20-30 F.F. specially selected wines and wines awarded a medal, 30-50 F.F. Grandes Réserves, Lieux-dits Grands Crus, Crémants, 50-80 F.F. Vins Armories, 80-120 F.F. Vendanges Tardives.
Sales volume:
– Wholesale: 31% (large distribution), 25% (dealers). – Retail: 12.5%. – Restaurants: 3.5%. – Other: 6.2% (Fairs, Exhibitions), 1.8% (Mail-order Sales).
Sales in France: 79%. **Export sales:** 21%.
Main trading partners : Germany, Netherlands, UK, Denmark, Belgium.

References in France

Restaurants: Brasserie Lipp (Paris), Chez Baumann (Paris), Chez Schillinger (Colmar), Le Rendez-vous de Chasse (Colmar), etc.
Shops: La Maison d'Alsace (Paris & Nice).

Comments

The Cave Vinicole Equisheim was established in 1902. Regrouping three wine cellars, it is the number one cellar specializing in Alsace wines: 750 Winegrowing members, 1,000 hectare vineyard under production, 11 million bottles sold (including 2.5 million bottles of Crémant) (1987-1988). Turnover 87-88: 170 million F.F. Projected turnover (88-89): 200 million F.F.

WUNSCH & MANN
Mann Family
2, rue des Clefs – 68920 Wettolsheim
89 80 79 63

Type of vineyard: Family Corporation. **Established:** 1948. **Number of employees:** 12. **Vine stocks:** All of the Alsatian Varieties. **Soil:** Clay with calcium carbonate. **Exposure:** South, Southeast. **Average annual production in hectoliters:** 5000.
Appellation: Alsace A.O.C. **Type:** Red, white, rosé. **Plus:** Champagne Method. **Technique:** Natural fermentation, temperature control. **Maturing:** Wood and glass. **Alcohol content:** 11.5%. **Characteristics:** The Wettolsheim wines benefit from the particularly fine exposure of the vineyards. Fleshy wines, fruity, very rich grapes are grown. On the richest terrain to make excellent ageing wines (Tokay, Gewurztraminer). **Serving temperature:** Between 8° to 12°. **Served with:** Sylvaner: fish, seafood. Riesling: fish, seafood, Sauerkraut, poultry. Tokay and Gewurztraminer: wines for receptions or foie gras. Pinot Noir: white meat or poultry. **Vintages available in 89/90:** 1988, 1987, 1986.

Characteristics of vintages

1988: Very rich and well-balanced, full bodied, lingering taste. A great vintage. To be kept in the cellar. (Export: 12%). **1987:** Typical of the Alsatian grape varieties, pleasantly fruity, to be watched. **1986:** Fleshy, very well-balanced, typical of the Alsatian grape varieties. Worth watching. **1985:** Rich and well-balanced, lots of fruit. A great vintage. **1984:** More firm and vigorous, dry. Drink now. Average pre-tax, ex-warehouse price: 15 F.F. (1st selection), 21 F.F. (reserve wines). Price range (pre-tax, ex-warehouse): Between 10 F.F. and 30 F.F.
Sales volume:
– Retail: 80%. – Restaurants: 5%. – Other: 15% (wholesale, shops, etc).
Sales in France: 93%.
Export sales: 7%.
Main trading partners : Switzerland, Germany, Netherlands, Denmark, Belgium.

PREISS ZIMMER
Jean-Paul Ritzenthaler
40 rue du Général de Gaulle 68340 Riquewihr
89 47 86 91

Established: For a 100 years. **Number of employees:** 3. **Vine stocks:** All of the Alsatian varieties. **Soil:** Chalky clay. **Exposure:** East to South. **Average annual production in hectoliters:** 2 000.
Appellation: AOC Alsace. **Type:** White, Rosé. **Technique:** White: temperature control. Rosé: fermentation on skins (2 to 3 days). **Maturing:** In glass lined and stainless steel tanks. **Alcohol content:** 12%. **Characteristics:** White (dry): fruity, lively, goes down well. Rosé (dry): aromatic, light and supple. **Serving temperature:** 8 to 10°. **Vintages available in 89/90:** 1988, 1987, 1986, 1985.

Characteristics of vintages

1988: Fruity, full-bodied, supple. **1987:** Fruity, harmonious, delicate. **1986:** Fruity, supple. **1985:** Full-bodied, aromatic,

rich. Price range (pre-tax, ex-warehouse): 30 to 50 F.F. – 50 to 80 F.F. & 80 to 120 F.
Sales volume:
– Retail: 50%. – Restaurants: 20%. – Other: 30% (dealers).
Sales in France: 70%.
Export sales: 30%.
Main trading partners : Netherlands, Belgium, Germany.

Comments

The Preiss Zimmer House, at the sign of the star, is one of the oldest wine establishments in Alsace, specializing in the sale of top quality wines, grands crus and specialities like the "Vendanges Tardives" (from a late, overripe harvest) or selections of "Grains Nobles".

DOMAINE ZIND HUMBRECHT

Léonard Humbrecht
34, rue Maréchal-Joffre – 68000 Wintzenheim
89 27 02 05 – Telex: CHAMCO 880 979

Type of vineyard: Family-owned. **Established:** 1959. **Vine stocks:** All of the Alsatian varieties. **Average annual production in hectoliters:** 250,000 bottles. **Appellation:** Alsace and Alsace Grands Crus: Rangen, Goldert, Brand and Hengst. **Type:** White. **Technique:** Hand Picking, pressing ot the whole grapes, fermentation under temperature control, 2 rackings. **Maturing:** Entirely in oak casks. **Vintages available in 89/90:** 1985, 1986, 1987, 1988.

Characteristics of vintages

1988: Oustanding quality. Superb balance and great concentration with some exceptional vendanges – tardives wines. **1987:** Typical Alsace vintage: dry, fruity wines with a lot of charm. **1986:** Good year, one of the best vintages we have ever made. **1985:** Very complex, rich and heady. **1983:** Rich and heady. Price range (pre-tax, ex-warehouse): Between 10 F.F. and 160 F.F.
Sales volume:
– Retail: 15%. – Restaurants: 15%. – Other: 70% (export).
Sales in France: 30%.
Export sales: 70%.
Main trading partners : European Common Market, USA, Sweden.

BEAUJOLAIS

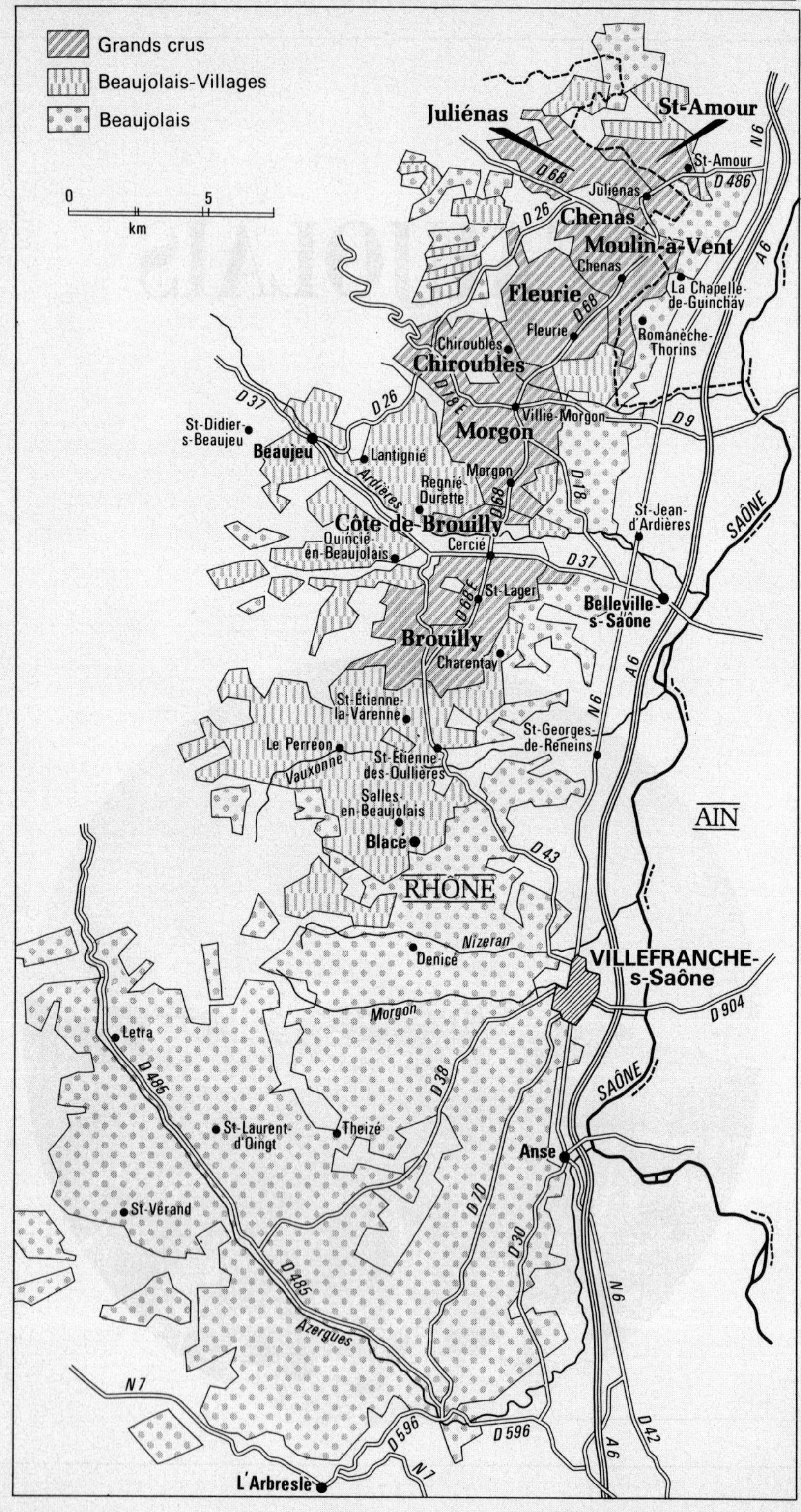

Grands crus
Beaujolais-Villages
Beaujolais
0
5
km
Juliénas
St-Amour
St-Amour
D 486
N 6
D 68
Juliénas
D 26
Chenas
Moulin-à-Vent
Chenas
A 6
La Chapelle-de-Guinchay
Fleurie
D 68
Fleurie
Romanèche-Thorins
Chiroubles
Chiroubles
D 37
D 26
D 18E
Villié-Morgon
D 9
St-Didier-s-Beaujeu
Beaujeu
Lantignié
Morgon
Morgon
Regnié-Durette
Ardières
D 68
D 18
St-Jean-d'Ardières
SAÔNE
Côte-de-Brouilly
Quincié-en-Beaujolais
Cercié
D 37
St-Lager
D 68E
Belleville-s-Saône
Brouilly
Charentay
A 6
N 6
St-Étienne-la-Varenne
St-Georges-de-Reneins
Le Perréon
Vauxonne
St-Étienne-des-Oullières
Salles-en-Beaujolais
AIN
Blacé
D 43
RHÔNE
Nizeran
Denicé
VILLEFRANCHE-s-Saône
Morgon
D 904
Letra
D 485
D 38
SAÔNE
St-Laurent-d'Oingt
Theizé
Anse
St-Vérand
D 70
D 30
D 485
N 6
Azergues
N 7
D 596
D 596
N 7
D 42
A 6
L'Arbresle

Just for the pleasure

In addition to the "primeurs" or "new wines" that we all know, some of which are entirely successful, Beaujolais is brimming with exceptional grands crus (Morgon, Juliénas, Moulin-à-Vent...) which deserve a special place in your cellar, so uniformly great is their quality. The vintage here has, perhaps, less importance than elsewhere. The 87 tastings, for example, have proven the strength of each vineyard and the talent of each winemaker even if, of course, they have not achieved the same heights as in the 86 or the 88 vintages (see the "VINTAGE CODE 89"). And then the omnipresent joie de vivre, the good wine and the generosity of the people gathered round their "flasks", make it abundantly clear that Beaujolais is worth the detour.

DOMAINES SARRIAU

HARVEST TIME AT THE CHATEAU DES CAPITANS

A MORAL PHILOSOPHY: THE TRUTH ABOUT WIN

The Sarrau family owns a château and a winegrowing estate in the Beaujolais region: the Château des Capitans with its appellations Juliénas ans Fleurie, and the Domaine de la Chapelle de Vâtre with its Beaujolais-Villages, its Fleurie "Grand Pré" and its Morgon "Château Gaillard".

Robert and Pierre Sarrau prefer to employ traditional vinification methods which yield rich, well-balanced wines that are quite tannic, very fragant and, when properly stored, can age for several years.

Sarrau in Beaujolais is synonymous with quality. " a Beaujolais to ge good", explains Pierre Sarrau, must be perfect, because it is the most difficult win vinify successfully". While it is true that Robert Pierre Sarrau are madly in love with the Beaujolais N veaux, they can also offer their clientele a comp range of wines matured in oak casks that are very m appreciated by gastronomes and connoisseurs.

Domaines Sarrau - 69220 Saint-Jean-d'Ardières - France - Tel. 74.66.19.43 - Telex 370 361

DISCOVERY THE LATEST BEAUJOLAIS APPELLATION

After Chiroubles, Chenas or Brouilly, the commune of Régnié is now asking to be assigned an appellation in its own name. Is its reputation solid enough?

A formal request for classification as a communal appellation put forth by the winegrowers union in 1980 may well be soon satisfied. On paper as well as on the ground, it is true that conditions are right for this "village" to become the tenth Beaujolais cru. The setting first. Its exposure, due to the orientation of the slopes, is such that it benefits from sunshine from morning to noon, thanks to its rather typical rolling terrain. Whether on the East, South or West, all the plantations are bathed in sunshine. As far as irrigation is concerned, Régnié-Durette is flanked by two rivers with similar names: the Ardeval, at the Villié-Morgon border, and the Ardières, a major link between the Saone and the Loire. In regard to its soil, the commune of Régnié belongs, for the most part, to the granitic block known as "de Fleurie". The technically oriented reader will like to know that it is a pink granite of average granulation, locally porphyritic, and of low mica content. The paragenesis is this rock—made up of quartz, hypidiomorphe plagioclases, and Carlsbad macled orthoclase, is relatively simple. I won't bore you with details concerning the area's agro-pedology, the soil structure of the upper or middle hillside, or its climatology which compares favorably with that of the best wine growing sectors of Morgon or Brouilly.

THE COMMUNE AND ITS HISTORY

From the historical point of view, a multitude of tales and anecdotes round out the folklore of the Régnié commune. From the Cluny Charter to François Myad, Doctor of law and eminent specialist of Beaujolais customs ("Le Vigneronnage en Beaujolais" Imprimeries réunies, Lyon, 1907) several quotations dating back even to the Gallo-Roman Era testify to the reputation of the Régnié vines. In 1938, Messrs David and Foillard drew up a very precise map and classification table of the Beaujolais wines, placing the Régnié wines in the Morgon group: "firm and well-balanced wines that keep well". In 1904, on the Frères Loron price lists, the price of a 216 liter container of 1903 Régnié is more or less the same as that of a Morgon, Brouilly or Juliénas (110 FF compared to 120 FF), placing it above the Saint Amour and the Chiroubles which were less expensive. More recently, on the traditional market of the region, the superior quality of the Régnié wines over those from other "villages" has been confirmed. From Louis Tête to Georges Dubeuf, houses like Loron, Fessy or Vermorel all agree on this point. They are backed up by the powerful Union Interprofessionnelle des Vins du Beaujolais, and Mr. Bréchard, head of the Union Viticole du Beaujolais points out: "their originality, due to good balance between body and fruitiness should qualify them to complete the gamut of Beaujolais crus. These quality wines will appeal to a clientele that appreciates subtle fragrances combined with complex tastes that are the hallmark of all Beaujolais crus."

The Right Honorable Georges Dubeuf, "King" of the Beaujolais Wines, personally supports the request of the Régnié Union. Connoisseur without equal of wines, even those of the smallest grower, he is well aware of the high quality of the wines of Régnié and has been promoting them for a long time. But the present success of the "village" makes him wonder whether it is appropriate to rush into becoming the tenth cru now. In his opinion, the priority for the winegrowers of Régnié should be to make themselves known as such. Is it better to be the first Beaujolais-Villages or the latest Beaujolais cru? A good question which can be overshadowed by petty parochialism. It is not always necessary to be classified—even when it is justified—to build up one's reputation. Stay tuned. . .

THE WINES

- **SAINT-AMOUR:** very light wines, fruity, pleasant, easy to drink.
- **JULIÉNAS:** better balanced and structured than the Saint-Amour, the Juliénas keeps its youthful fruitiness quite a long time. A full-bodied second category Beaujolais, it keeps rather well.
- **CHENAS:** the appellation covers the major part of the commune. The East and South comes under the Moulin-à-vent A.O.C. Robust, rather tannic and forthcoming wines.
- **MOULIN-A-VENT:** considered to be the best wines of the region. Planted mostly in the communes of Romanèche-Thorins and around Chénas, the reds produced in decomposing pink granite soil are full, rich, well-balanced and fragrant; good keeping wines.
- **MORGON:** dense, robust wines that generally improve in the bottle. The stronger wines come from halfway down the hill, particularly when they are vinified in the traditional way using grapes from old vines.
- **CHIROUBLES:** obtained by quick maturation, very fruity and velvety. It should either be drunk "en primeur" within two to three months after harvesting, or allowed to age.
- **FLEURIE:** the most elegant of the Beaujolais. Finer and more distinguished than the Moulin-à-vent or the Chénas, extremely fruity, it is a charming and seductive wine.
- **BROUILLY AND CÔTES DE BROUILLY:** light, good color. The Brouilly wines are light and supple, fruity, complete and well made.

THE CHARACTERISTICS OF THE VINEYARD

The Beaujolais region covers the largest area in Burgundy 55 mi. long (80 km) by 12-15 mi. wide (19-24 km). It is bordered on the north by the Mâconnais vineyards and on the south by the Monts du Lyonnais. The Monts du Beaujolais stand as a barrier to the west, and the Saône River lies to the east.

Soil

Beaujolais' soil is of two distinct types. The northern part of the region is a mixture of granite and sedimentary soil. Clay is the main component of the soil in the south.

Climate

The climate in Beaujolais is temperate because of wind shifts originating from marine, continental and Mediterranean climates. The vineyards of the region face southeast, benefitting from both a microclimate and the heat-regulating effect of the Saône River. The average amount of sunshine is good, so too, is the average temperature, 53.6°F (12°C). In summer storms are frequent and in winter heavy fog covers the region.

THE DUBŒUF SAGA

In the heart of the Beaujolais vineyards, at Romanèche-Thorins, Georges Dubœuf, acknowleded "king", respected by everyone in his profession, extends his wine empire to the four corners of the globe. A salutary tale, in character with the man.

If not for Georges Dubœuf, it is uncertain that winelovers in Tokyo or Valparaiso would be able, every year, to delight their taste buds with the freshness of Beaujolais. With several others, he has participated in one of the greatest commercial successes of all time, the Beaujolais primeur, a veritable national and international madness, which has been a shot in the arm to other crus of the region. There have been two contributing factors: the style of the wines, fresh, seductive, "gouleyants" (said of wines that go down well) as proclaimed in the villages of Cercié or Lantigné, wines mostly to be drunk among friends, symbolized by the hale and hearty winegrowers, welded together as nowhere else, with an enthousiasm for life's freshness. Bend an elbow with them and you will be left with no doubts. The other reason for Beaujolais' sucess is an agressive commercial policy, based on a very real selection among the wines—notwithstanding the claims of some of the regions detractors who probably have not had the pleasure of local wine tasting. After all, if the Beaujolais weren't good, it wouldn't sell!

And every year, vintage by vintage, according to the whims of Mother Nature, our dear Georges tastes thousands of wines, sampling each lot. Is it the commune of Odenas that, in a given year, produced the best Brouilly, or is it the Côtes de Brouilly vineyard, with its Southern exposure and late harvest that came up with the best wine? You have to know the region. History doesn't leave anything to chance and Georges Dubœuf, on his mother's side, comes from one of the oldest winegrowing families in this part of the Mâcon-Beaujolais region, going back to the 15th century. Atavism, combined with a passion for the local soil, has done the rest. The result is the "trademark" of confidence with which the lots are signed, from the lightest and most supple to the most robust, with a permanent insistance on quality. Louis Orizet in associating Beaujolais with fashion states: "Their arts are derived from the same inspiration—to free the silhouette, accentuate curves, encourage effervescence, leave something to be imagined behind a décolletage (. . .). They are, one and the other, essentially family crafts, fighting against the uniformity of our epoch". A quotation perfectly adapted to the Dubœuf saga, because, in the world of wine, it is the men who tend the vines and mature the wine who underlie everything.

SAINT-AMOUR

DOMAINE DE LA CAVE LAMARTINE

Paul Spay
71570 Saint-Amour Bellevue
85 37 12 88

Type of vineyard: family-owned. **Established:** 1929. **Number of employees:** 2. **Vine stocks:** Gamay Noir (white juice). **Soil:** schist and granite. **Exposure:** East, South-East. **Average annual production in hectoliters:** 650.

Appellation: Saint Amour – Julienas – Beaujolais St Amour Blanc. **Type:** Red, White. **Technique:** traditional with temperature control. **Maturing:** in vats. **Alcohols content:** 13%. **Characteristics:** soft tannins, fruity, ruby color, average acidity, typical. **Serving temperature:** Red: around 15°. White: 8-10°. **Served with:** St. Amour Julienas: all meats. Beaujolais St. Amour white: fish, shellfish. **Vintages available in 89/90:** White: 87-88. Red: 88.

Characteristics of vintages

1988: well developed aromas, intense ruby color, balanced and harmonious, rich, great finesse. Price range (pre-tax, ex-warehouse): 20 F.F. to 30 F.F.
Sales volume: – Retail: 40%. – Restaurants: 10%.
Sales in France: 50%. **Export sales:** 50%.
Main trading partners : Switzerland, Belgium, Netherlands, Germany, UK, USA.

References in France

Restaurants: Le Cep (Fleurie – Château de Pizay – La Tassee (Lyon) – Château de Bonneval (Perignat les Sarlièves) – Le Maconnais (Paris) etc.
Shops: La Marmite (Paris) – Le Comptoir (Lyon).

Abroad

United States
Importers: Julienne Importing – Chicago Illinois.

United Kingdom
Vins Simone Weterham – Kent.

Germany
Import Gerard Dubois 6500 – Mainz 1.

Switzerland
A. Reichmuth (Zurich) – Les Caves du Palais de Justice, Geneva.

Belgium
Mirovin (Liege) – Velu Vins (Brussels) Qualivino (Lier).

The Netherlands
P. Turkenburg (Bodegraven).

Comments

The Domaine de la Cave Lamartine once belonged to the family of the French poet and politician Alphonse de Lamartine. Located on hillsides facing East and Sout-East, it enjoys perfect sun exposure. Its granitic pebbly and schistic soil is only suited to the culture of the vine. The altitude is ideal for perfect maturity. All these blessings of Mother Nature are evident in the tasting: the eye is delighted by its shimmering color, the nose signals a bed of flowers and while the palate is roused by all of the fruitiness the tongue and the throat respond to the light touch of this carressing wine.

DOMAINE DES DUC

Duc Frères
La Piat – 71570 Saint-Amour Bellevue
85 37 10 08

Type of vineyard: Family-owned. **Established:** XIIth Century. **Number of employees:** 2. **Vine stocks:** Gamay (white juice). **Soil:** Schistic, silica-clay. **Exposure:** South, Southeast. **Average annual production in hectoliters:** 650.
Appellation: Saint-Amour, Beaujolais-Villages. **Type:** Red. **Technique:** Traditional. **Maturing:** In large casks. **Alcohol content:** 13%. **Characteristics:** – Saint-Amour: good keeping wine. – Beaujolais-Villages: stands up well. **Serving temperature:** 14 to 15°. **Served with:** – Beaujolais-Villages: First course, vegetables. – Saint-Amour: Meat and cheese. **Vintages available in 89/90:** 1986.

Characteristics of vintages

1986: Deep color, transparent and limpid. Aroma of currants and Raspberries. Altogether very supple with soft and full tannins, moderate acidity. A successful vintage ready for adequate ageing with full confidence. Average pre-tax, ex-warehouse price: – Saint-Amour: 23.60 F.F. – Beaujolais-Villages: 16 F.F.
Sales volume:
– Wholesale: 30%. – Retail: 30%. – Restaurants: 10%. – Ohter: 30%.
Sales in France: 30%. **Export sales:** 70%.
Main trading partners : Switzerland, Belgium, Netherlands, Germany, USA, UK.

JULIÉNAS

CLOS DU FIEF

Michel Tete
Les Gonnards - 69840 Juliénas
74 04 41 62

Type of vineyard: Agricultural Association (since 1987). **Established:** Family-owned for 100 years. **Vine stocks:** Gamay Noir (white grape juice). **Soil:** Silica-clay. **Exposure:** Southeast. **Average annual production in hectoliters:** 350.

Appellation: Juliénas and Saint-Amour. **Type:** Red. **Technique:** In the Beaujolais tradition, maceration partly under carbon dioxide with temperature regulation. **Maturing:** From 4 to 6 months in the vat (wood, enamel, concrete) before bottling. **Alcohol content:** 13.3%. **Characteristics:** Juliénas: tannic, well-balanced wine, ages well taking on a Burgundy quality, can be consumed within 4 to 6 years. Saint-Amour: fruity wine which goes down smoothly, typical Beaujolais, can be consumed within 2 to 3 years. **Serving temperature:** Saint-Amour: 12°, Juliénas: 17°. **Served with:** Juliénas: Red meat, game, cheese. Saint-Amour: pleasant under all circumstances, a favorite with the ladies, goes well with everything. **Vintages available in 89/90:** only 1986.

Characteristics of vintages

1986: Good year, well-balanced wine, good tanin/acidity balance, keeps well. Average pre-tax ex-warehouse price: 24.50 F.F. Price range (pre-tax, ex-warehouse): between 20 F.F. and 30 F.F.

Sales volume:
- Wholesale: 10%. - Retail: 75%. - Restaurants: 5%.
- Other: 10% export.

Sales in France: 90%.
Export sales: 10%.
Main trading partners: Netherlands, Switzerland, Belgium, Germany, UK.

• *Glycerine – wine component responsible for its unctuosity. It appears in the course of the alcoholic fermentation but, in the case of mellow and naturally sweet wines, can also come from the favorable action of noble rot on the grapes. See Sauternes.*

• *To better understand the evolution and adherence to type of the various vintages, consult our "Vintage Code" chart.*

CHÂTEAU DE JULIÉNAS

François Condemine
69840 Juliénas
74 04 41 43

Type of vineyard: Family-owned. **Established:** 1907. **Vine stocks:** Gamay Noir (white grape juice). **Soil:** Granitic. **Exposure:** South, Southeast. **Average annual production in hectoliters:** 1,000.

Appellation: Juliénas. **Type:** Red. **Technique:** Stainless steel tanks, thermo-regulation, no addition of carbon dioxide. **Maturing:** For 6 to 8 months before bottling. **Characteristics:** Deep ruby color, fruit fragrance – peach, raspberry. Firmness, vinosity, can age well. **Served with:** Everything. **Vintages available in 89/90:** 1985, 1986.

Characteristics of vintages

1988: Fruity, round, seductive, good vinification. Typical of the appellation. Price range, (pre-tax, ex-warehouse) 25 F.F.

CHÉNAS

VINS PAUL BEAUDET

Jean Beaudet
Pontanevaux 71570 La Chapelle-de-Guinchay
85 36 72 76 - Telex 351 923 F
Fax: 85 36 72 02

Established: 1869. **Vine stocks:** Gamay. **Soil:** Granitic sand. **Exposure:** South-East. **Average annual production in hectoliters:** 700.

Appellation: Chenas Château Desvignes. **Type:** Red. **Technique:** Carbonic maceration. **Maturing:** Early bottling. **Alcohol content:** 12.8%. **Characteristics:** Full, character, complex flavor, long finish, can age 4-5 years. **Serving temperature:** 15°. **Served with:** Poultry, grilled meat, cheese. **Vintages available in 89/90:** 1988.

Characteristics of vintages

1988: Lovely vintage, good color, fruity, full, will age well. **Other:** Beaujolais crus also available: Regnie, Morgon, Chiroubles, Brouilly, Côte de Brouilly, Fleurie, Saint-Amour, Juliénas, Moulin-à-Vent.

DOMAINE JEAN BENON

Jean Benon
Route de Juliénas
71570 La Chapelle de Guinchay
85 36 71 92

Type of vineyard: Family-owned. **Established:** 1965. **Vine stocks:** Gamay. **Soil:** Poor, light and pebbly, subsoil granitic clay. **Exposure:** South. **Average annual production in hectoliters:** 160.
Appellation: Chenas and Beaujolais Villages. **Type:** Red. **Technique:** Beaujolais technique (semi-carbonic maceration). **Maturing:** Enamel tanks. **Alcohol content:** 13%. **Characteristics:** Chenas: round, robust, good color (deep ruby). Fruity, goes down well, will age well (4 to 6 years). Beaujolais Villages: light, round and fruity, goes down well. Beautiful, lively red color, very pleasant, can age 1 or 2 years. **Serving temperature:** Chenas: 13° to 15° – Beaujolais Villages: 10° to 12°. **Served with:** Chenas: Game, roasts, white meat and cheese – Beaujolais Villages: Delicatessen, terrines, white meat and light meals. **Vintages available in 89/90:** Chenas (1987-1988) – Beaujolais Villages (1988).

Characteristics of vintages

1988: Chenas: Fleshy, rich, full-bodied, fruity, very pleasant, supple, easy to drink, remarkable finesse. First Prize at the Concours de Villefranche. Can be kept 3 to 4 years. (20 to 30 F.F.) Beaujolais Villages: Lively, bright, light and fruity, pleasant, goes down well, elegant cuvée, red berry overtones. Can be kept 1 to 2 years. (Less than 20 F.F.) **1987:** Beautiful deep ruby color, round, well-balanced, firm, can be kept 4 to 5 years. (20-30 F.F.) **1985:** Chenas robust, and tannic, pleasant taste, develops an interesting fragrance with age. Can age a long time. Price range (pre-tax, ex-warehouse): between 20 F.F. and 30 F.F.
Sales volume:
– Retail: 65%. – Restaurants: 10%. – Other: 25% (export).
Sales in France: 70%.
Export sales: 30%.
Main trading partners : UK, Belgium, Switzerland.

DOMAINE DES BRUREAUX

Daniel Robin
Cave Robin "Domaine des Brueaux"
69840 Chenas
85 36 72 67 – Telex: 351 004

Type of vineyard: Family-owned. **Number of employees:** 4. **Vine stocks:** Gamay (white juice). **Soil:** Granitic. **Exposure:** South-West. **Average annual production in hectoliters:** 45 hl/ha.

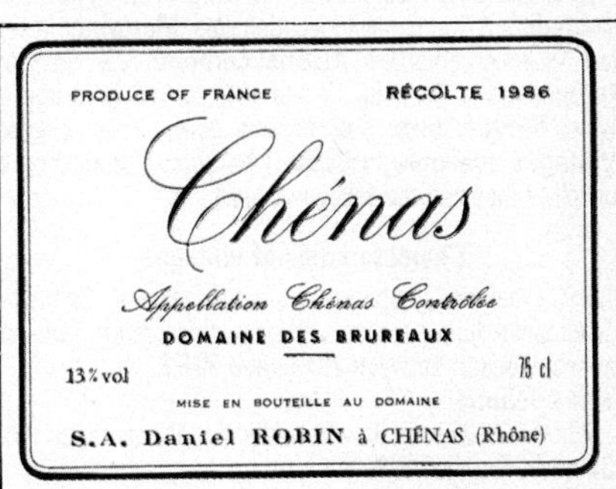

PRODUCE OF FRANCE
RÉCOLTE 1986
Chénas
Appellation Chénas Contrôlée
DOMAINE DES BRUREAUX
13% vol
75 cl
MISE EN BOUTEILLE AU DOMAINE
S.A. Daniel ROBIN à CHÉNAS (Rhône)

Appellation: Chenas. **Type:** Red. **Technique:** Traditional. **Alcohol content:** 13%. **Characteristics:** Tannic, rich and well balanced. **Serving temperature:** 15°. **Served with:** Poultry, red meat. **Vintages available in 89/90:** 1986, 1987, 1988 (in the Spring).

Characteristics of vintages

1988: Rich. **1987:** Elegant. **1986:** Well bred. Price range (pre-tax, ex-warehouse): 20 to 30 F.F.
Sales volume:
– Wholesale: 50%. – Retail: 40%. – Restaurants: 10%.
Sales in France: 75%.
Export sales: 25%.
Main trading partners : Switzerland, Belgium, Germany, Netherlands.

References in France

Restaurants: Le Chapon Fin (Thoissey), Orsi (Lyon), Greuze (Tournus), Hôtel Le Bas Rupts (Gerardmer), le Manoir d'Hastings (Benouville).
Shops: Cave Valmy (Lyon), La Cave de Saint Priest.

Abroad

United States
Mr Alain Junguenet, 28 Baubery Lane Mountiside.

Switzerland
Lers planteurs réunis, Vevey

Belgium
Les Grands Domaines, Brussels.

The Netherlands
Heisterkamp Wijnkopers, Ootmarsum.

G.A.E.C. DU DOMAINE CHAMPAGNON

Champagnon
Les Brureaux Chenas - 69840 Juliénas
85 36 71 32

Type of vineyard: Family-owned. **Established:** for 2 generations. **Number of employees:** 4. **Vine stocks:** Gamay (white grape juice). **Soil:** Sandstone with clay. **Exposure:** On all sides, except West. **Average annual production in hectoliters:** 750.
Appellation: Chenas, Fleurie, Moulin à Vent. **Type:** Red. **Technique:** Traditional, in wooden vats. **Maturing:** In cellars, wooden containers. **Alcohol content:** 13%. **Serving temperature:** Between 15 and 18°, according to age of wine. **Served with:** Delicatessen, game, meat, cheese. **Vintages available in 89/90:** (the annual production is usually exhausted the following year).

Characteristics of vintages

1986: Excellent, good color, smooth tannins, Character developing during the second year. Price range (pre-tax, ex-warehouse): between 20 F.F. and 30 F.F.
Sales volume:
– Wholesale: 25 to 35%. – Retail: 50%. – Restaurants: 10%.
Sales in France: 70%.
Export sales: 30%.
Main trading partners : Netherlands, Beligium, UK, USA, Germany.

DOMAINE DES PENELLES

Roger Delmas
71570 La Chapelle de Guinchay
85 36 74 60

Type of vineyard: Family-owned. **Established:** 1974. **Soil:** Beaujolais-village: granitic. Saint-amour: granitic, schistic an pebbly. Chénas: essentially granitic. **Exposure:** South, Southeast. **Average annual production in hectoliters:** 300.
Appellation: Chénas (red), Saint-Amour (red), Beaujolais-Villages (red). **Technique:** Carbonic vinification. **Maturing:** Concrete, stainless steel and enamelled tanks. **Alcohol content:** 13.3 – 13.5 %. **Characteristics:** Chénas: ruby color, peony fragrance, a delicate and agreeable wine. Saint-Amour: red wine full of finesse and elegance. It is one of the lightest of the Beaujolais. Beaujolais-Villages: very pleasant, delicate, goes down well. **Serving temperature:** Beaujolais-Villages: slightly cool, 11 to 12°. Saint-Amour: the new wine at 15 to 16°, closer to room temperature for older wines. Chénas: 15 to 16°. **Served with:** Beaujolais-villages: delicatessen, meat, cheese. Saint-Amour: game, poultry. Chénas: red meat. Vintages available: 1988: 1986.

Characteristics of vintages

1986: Good Chénas, supple, rich and well-balanced at the same time, good color, keeps well. Successful Saint-Amour, finesse, fragrance. Price range (pre-tax, ex-warehouse): between 20 and 30 F.F. **Sale volume:** – Wholesale: 10 %. – Retail: 90 %. – Restaurants: 2 %.
Sales in France: 99 %.
Export sales: 1 %.
Main trading partners: Belgium, Netherlands, Switzerlanded.

DOMAINE GEORGES TRICHARD

Georges Trichard
Route de Juliénas
71570 La Chapelle de Guinchay
85 36 70 70

Type of vineyard: Family-owned. **Established:** 1965. **Number of employees:** 1. **Vine stocks:** Gamay (white juice). **Soil:** Light, thin, formed by the decomposition of rocks. Sub-soil sandy and pebbly. **Exposure:** Southwest. **Average annual production in hectoliters:** 570.
Appellation: Chenas. **Type:** Red. **Technique:** Semi-carbonic. **Maturing:** In large casks. **Alcohol content:** 13%. **Characteristics:** Pleasant wine, first year with peony and raspberry fragrance. Ages very well. Quite tannic and robust. **Serving temperature:** First year 12° to 14°. Later 16° to 18°. **Served with:** Game, red meat and cheese. **Vintages available in 89/90:** 1986.

Characteristics of vintages

1986: Lovely wine, very fragrant, dense, supple, seductive. Good for ageing. Average pre-tax, ex-warehouse price: 29 F.F. (retail). Price range (pre-tax, ex-warehoue): Between 20 F.F. and 30 F.F.
Sales volume:
– Retail: 40%. – Restaurants: 30%. – Other: 30% (abroad).
Sales in France: 70%.
Export sales: 30%.
Main trading partners : Germany, USA, UK, Netherlands, Canada.

• In 1985, the wines of the following regions received the A.O.C. (Appellation d'Origine Contrôlée) classification: Minervois, Coteaux-des-Baux, Coteaux-d'Aix-en-Provence, Coteaux-du-Lyonnais and Coteaux-du-Languedoc.

• Watch out for wines that lose their authenticity, most often because of carbonic maceration (see Roussillon, Southwest, Périgord...).

MOULIN-A-VENT

S.C.E.R.T. - CHÂTEAU DES JACQUES

Jean-Paul Thorin
71570 Romaneche-Thorins
85 35 51 64 or 85 36 70 43

Number of employees: 12. **Vine stocks:** Moulin à Vent: Gamay. Beaujolais white: Chardonnay. **Average annual production in hectoliters:** Moulin à Vent: 1800. Beaujolais white: 550.

Appellation: Moulin à Vent (red), Beaujolais (white). **Type:** Red, white. **Characteristics:** Moulin à Vent: to be aged, rich and well-balanced, elegant. Beaujolais: dry, white wine, very fruity. **Serving temperature:** Moulin à Vent: 16° to 18°. Beaujolais white: 12° to 14°. **Served with:** Moulin à Vent: roasts, meat in sauce, game, cheese. Beaujolais white: first courses, fish, delicatessen products and as an aperitif. **Vintages available in 89/90:** 1984, 1985, 1986.

Characteristics of vintages

1988: Exceptional year. **1987:** Moulin à Vent: very elegant, rich and well-balanced, bouquet of ripe fruit and woody essences, great for ageing. Beaujolais white: dry, fruity, Hazel Nut bouquet, very fragrant, typical Chardonnay. Price range (pre-tax, ex-warehouse): between 30 F.F. and 50 F.F.
Sales volume:
- Wholesale: 30%. - Retail: 10%. - Restaurants: 20%.
- Other: 50% (export).

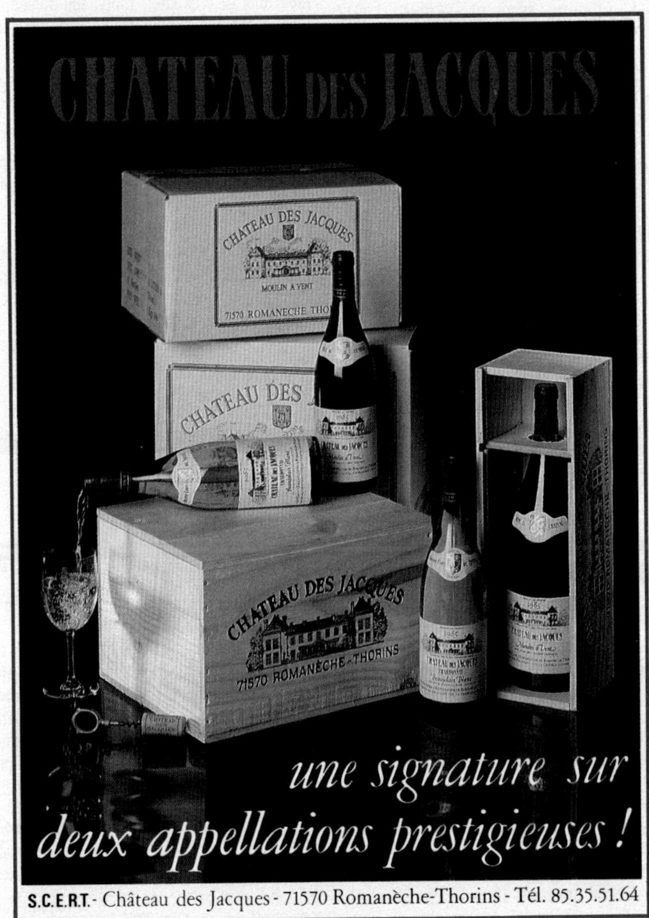

CHATEAU DES JACQUES
CHATEAU DES JACQUES
MOULIN A VENT
71570 ROMANECHE THO
CHATEAU DES
CHATEAU DES JACQUES
71570 ROMANÈCHE-THORINS
une signature sur
deux appellations prestigieuses !
S.C.E.R.T. - Château des Jacques - 71570 Romanèche-Thorins - Tél. 85.35.51.64

Sales in France: 50%.
Export sales: 50%.
Main trading partners : Switzerland, USA, UK, Germany, Belgium, Canada, Austria.

References in France

Restaurants: Cochon d'Or (Paris), Ledoyen (Paris), George Blanc (Vonnas), Oustau de Baumanière, Miramar (Biarritz), Auberge du Cep (Fleurie), Bateau Ivre (Bourget du Lac), Pharamond (Paris), Chabichou (St-Tropez), Espérance Meneau (Vézelay).

Abroad

United States
Buena vista Inc Po Box 182, 27000 Ramal Road. Sonoma CA. 95476 USA. Fax (707) 252 0392

United Kingdom
Rache UK Stone House Farm Ashby Rd. Boundary MR. Woodville Burton on Tront Staffs. Tél. 283 217 703.

Germany
A. Rache Gmbhx Co D. 6530 Bingen/Rhein. Tél. (06721) 188 0.

The Netherlands
Van Ouverkerk, Zuiterhuis, 1, 4201 EK Gorinchem. Tel: 1830 31150.

Others
Switzerland: Maison Bataillard, Hasenmoostrasse 33, 6023 Rothenburg. Tel: 4150 3355. Belgium: S.O.C.E.D. S.A., 49 bld Léopold 2, 1080 Brussels. Tel: 2 428 19 99. Austria: Weinkellerei E.u.M. Muller Ges. M.B.H., 8522 Gross ST., Florian. Tel: 3464/234.

Comments

The very special character of Moulin à Vent today comes form its vinification in the Burgundy style. Its traditional maturing in casks of the best Oak, renewed every second year, proves, as if it were necessary to do so, that it is possible, with Gamay grapes to make just such a fine wine produce a wine worthy of the best Brugundy they wines. Many tastings have proven it.

DOMAINE DE LA BRUYÈRE

R. & M. Siffert
La Bruyère – 71570 Romanèche-Thorins
85 35 50 28

Type of vineyard: Family-owned. **Established:** 1926. **Vine stocks:** Gamay. **Soil:** Sand and clay on granitic and manganese sub-soil. **Exposure:** South, South-East. **Average annual production in hectoliters:** 450. **Appellation:** Moulin à Vent. **Type:** Red. **Technique:** Beaujolais style, completely submerged grapes, long fermentation on skins. **Maturing:** In wooden vats and stainless steel tanks. **Alcohol content:** 13 to 13.2%. **Characteristics:** Deep ruby color, fruity, tannic, typical long

keeping. **Serving temperature:** 16 to 18°. **Served with:** Red meat, game, cheese. **Vintages available in 89/90:** 1987, 1988.

Characteristics of vintages

1988: Full of character, fruity, full-bodied, good keeping. **1987:** Light and supple, fruity, very pleasant. Price range (pre-tax, ex-warehouse): 30 to 50 F.F.
Sales volume:
– Retail: 35%. – Restaurants: 15%. – Other: 50% (export).
Sales in France: 50%.
Export sales: 50%.
Main trading partners : USA, UK, Denmark, Belgium, Netherlands, Luxemburg, Germany and Switzerland.

References in France

Restaurants: Paris/Suburbs: Auberge du Capucin Gourmand, Le Bougnat, L'Apollinaire, L'Argonne, Le Laffitte, L'Ambroisie, Pavillon Baltard, Le Tastevin, La Poularde, Le Piré, Chez Michel, etc.
Shops: Caves Royales (Versailles).

MOMMESSIN

La Grange St-Pierre
B.P. 504 – 71009 Mâcon
85 34 47 74 – Telex: 800 886 – Fax: 85 29 28 74

Vine stocks: Gamay Noir (white juice), Pinot Noir, Chardonnay.
Appellation: Moulin à Vent, Pouilly-Fuissé, Beaujolais, Gevrey-Chambertin. **Type:** Red, white. **Technique:** Traditional. **Maturing:** In oak casks for 6 months to 1 year. **Characteristics:** Reds: Beautiful, red garnet color. Flowery and fruity fragrances, dominant touch of violet. Whites: Lots of aroma, freshness and finesse. **Served with:** Meat. **Vintages available in 89/90:** 1986 and 1985.

Characteristics of vintages

1986: Very fruity wines, white as well as red. **1985:** Some very nice vats of red, particularly the Gevrey-Chambertin, full and well-balanced. Price range (pre-tax, ex-warehouse): Between 30 an 50 F.F.

Sales volume:
- Retail: 40%. - Restaurants: 60%.
Sales in France: 40%.
Export sales: 60%.

References in France

Restaurants: In all the better restaurants in France with Michelin ou Gault & Millau Stars.
Shops: Fauchon (Paris) and other quality wine boutiques.

Abroad

United States
William Grant & Sons, 130 Fieldcrest Avenue, Edison, N.J. 08837.

United Kingdom
Field's Mommessin UK, 29 Rowan Avenue Cheadle Hulme Cheshire SK8 7DH.

Germany
Fa Muehlensiepen, Postfach 5733, Bonnerstrasse 177 - 4000 Dusseldorf 1.

Canada
William Mara, 4950 2 Algona Street Toronto Ontario M8Y 1B9. Mark Anthony Wine merchants, 1290 Homer Street, M2N 6K1, Vancouver V6B 2Y5. Charton Hobbs, 9393 Louis H. Lafontaine, Montreal HIJ 1Y8.

The Netherlands
Kerstens, P.O. Box 732, 5000 AS Tilburg.

Far East
Importers: Parry Pacific, 9F Yat Sun House, 55 Wong Chuk Road, Aberdeen Hong Kong. Godo Shusei Co. Ltd. 6.2.10 Ginza, Chou Ku, Tokyo 104, Japan.

JEAN MORTET
Jean Mortet
Le Bourg - 71570 Romanèche-Thorins
85 35 55 51

Vine stocks: Gamay Noir (white juice). **Soil:** Granitic. **Exposure:** South, South-East. **Average annual production in hectoliters:** 380.

PRODUCE OF FRANCE
750 ML
GRAND VIN DE
BOURGOGNE
Moulin à Vent
APPELLATION
CONTRÔLÉE
MIS EN BOUTEILLES A LA PROPRIETE
Jean MORTET - 71570 Romanèche-Thorins (S.-&-L.) FRANCE

Appellation: Moulin à Vent, Beaujolais Villages. **Type:** Red. **Technique:** Traditional, Beaujolais style. **Maturing:** Moulin à Vent in wooden vats. Villages in concrete tanks. **Alcohol content:** 12.5% to 13%. **Serving temperature:** Villages: 12 to 13°. Moulin à Vent: 16 to 18°. **Served with:** Moulin à Vent: red meat and cheese. Beaujolais Villages: with entire meal. **Vintages available in 89/90:** 1987, 1988.

Characteristics of vintages

1988: Rich and very well balanced, tannic, very good keeping, somewhere between the 1985 and the 1983, Bacchus Award in (March 1988). Janvier 89 avec un Moulin à Vent de la Récolte 1988, (Concours Saint-Vincent). **1987:** Lighter, very typical Beaujolais. Price range (pre-tax, ex-warehouse): 17 F.F. Beaujolais Villages. 29 F.F. Moulin à Vent.
Sales volume:
- Wholesale: 20%. - Retail: 40%. - Restaurants: 10%.
- Other: 30%.
Sales in France: 65%.
Export sales: 35%.
Main trading partners : Belgium, Luxemburg, Netherlands, Denmark, Switzerland, UK.

References in France

Restaurants: Chevalier (Lyon), Restaurant de la Gare (Divonne-les-Bains).
Shops: Chais Saint-François, 36 Vannes, Le Cellier Lorrain, 54 Chenière, Ets Le Tire-Bouchon (Chambéry).

Abroad

United Kingdom
Hicks & Don, Wiltshire BA13 3EA (Tel: 86 47 23).

Switzerland
Ets Danzeisen Payerne (Tel: (037) 612177).

Belgium
N.V. Wynhandel de Probandere, 8781 Wilesbeke (Tel: 05666022). SPRL Vin Herner, Cimbernaim-au-Pont.

The Netherlands
S.A. Peerdemans, 1611 Al Bovenkaisel (Tel: 02285-11 521).

Others
Denmark: Philipson Wine APS, DK 2920 Charlottenlund (Tel: (45) 1645081). Luxemburg: Restaurant Saint-Laurent, 4412 Belvaux (Tel: 591080).

• Watch out for wines that lose their authenticity, most often because of carbonic maceration (see Roussillon, South-west, Périgord...).

• The quality of the 1987 vintage, particularly in Bordeaux, is questionable. Much of the Merlot suffered from coulure and a good bit of the harvesting was done in the rain. Only a few vineyards will produce a good vintage (see the Chapter on Bordeaux wines and the "Vintage Code").

MORGON

CHÂTEAU DE PIZAY

Pascal Dufaitre
Saint-Jean d'Ardières,
69220 Belleville-sur-Saône
74 66 26 10 - Telex: 305 772 - FAX: 74 69 60 66

Type of vineyard: Agricultural Association. **Established:** 1981. **Number of employees:** 9. **Vine stocks:** Gamay, Chardonnay. **Soil:** Granitic. **Exposure:** South, South-East. **Average annual production in hectoliters:** 2, 000.

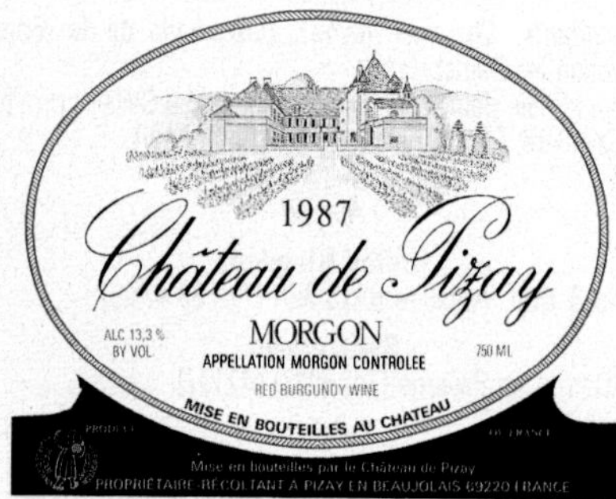

Appellation: Beaujolais Rouge, Rosé, Blanc and Morgon. **Type:** Red, White, Rosé. **Technique:** In the Beaujolais style - semi-carbonic. **Maturing:** Wood and stainless steel. **Alcohol content:** 12.5%. **Serving temperature:** Beaujolais: 14°. Morgon: 16°. **Vintages available in 89/90:** 1987, 1988.

Characteristics of vintages

1988: Very rich and well-balanced, for keeping. **1987:** Lighter and more delicate. Price range (pre-tax, ex-warehouse): between 10 and 30 F.F.

Sales volume:
- Wholesale: 10%. - Retail: 40%. - Restaurants: 10%.
- Other: 40% (export).

Sales in France: 60%.
Export sales: 40%.
Main trading partners: Japan, Germany, Switzerland, UK.

References in France

Restaurants: Mère Brazier (Lyon), Frantel, Ti Al Lannec (22 Trébeurden), Les Prateaux (85 Noirmoutier), Attalaya (66 Llo), Hôtel de Printemps (26 Montélimar), Auberge Cévenole (30 La Favède), Sky d'Or (Tignes).

Abroad

United States
Importers: I.W.S.I., New York.

United Kingdom
Connolly's Wines, Birmingham.

Germany
Haus Saarbrück.

Switzerland
Berthoud, Corcelles. Escher, Geneva.

Belgium
GB Inno BM, Brussels. Mirovin, Liège.

Canada
Herman, Vancouver. Yukon. D. Campbell, Montreal.

The Netherlands
Van Heijst, Tilburg.

Far East
Japan: Seiwa, Tokyo.

Others
Puerto Rico: Alégria. Bermuda: Gosling.

DOMAINE DES PILLETS

Gérard Brisson
Les Pillets 69910 Villié Morgon
74 04 21 60 - Telex: 340 777 Brisson

Type of vineyard: Agricultural Association. **Established:** 1751. **Vine stocks:** 100% Gamay. **Soil:** Granite with manganese. **Exposure:** Slopes facing South. **Average annual production in hectoliters:** 950.
Appellation: Morgon AOC, Morgon les Charmes AOC, Regnié. **Type:** Red. **Technique:** Traditional with long fermentation. **Maturing:** new oak casks. **Alcohol content:** 12.5 to 13%. **Characteristics:** Very marked red berry fragrance when young; ripe fruit with cacao, vanilla and grilled coffee fragrances after 1 1/2 to 2 years. Rich, well-balanced wines, full and high in alcohol. **Serving temperature:** Young wine: 10 to 12°. Older wine: 13 to 16°. **Served with:** Young wine: white meat, fish in sauce, poultry and cheese. **Vintages available in 89/90:** 1986, 1987, 1988.

Characteristics of vintages

1988: Very sustained ruby color with violet glints, violet and cherry fragrance, full and fleshy. **1987:** Comparable to the 86. Iridescent ruby color, floral nose, long, well made. **1986:** Superb vintage, Vielle Vigne still a bit closed, very rich, subtle nuances. **1985:** Very beautiful deep color, full. Vielle Vigne still a bit closed. Price range (pre-tax, ex-warehouse): between 20 F.F. and 30 F.F.

Sales volume:
- Wholesale: 60%. - Retail: 20%. - Other: 20% (export).

Sales in France: 60%.
Export sales: 40%.
Main trading partners: UK, Switzerland, Netherlands, Germany, USA.

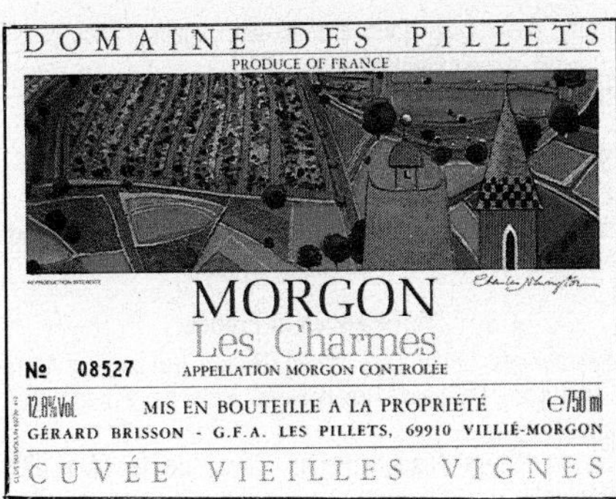

DOMAINE DES PILLETS
PRODUCE OF FRANCE
MORGON
Les Charmes
Nº 08527 APPELLATION MORGON CONTROLÉE
12,8%Vol. MIS EN BOUTEILLE A LA PROPRIÉTÉ e750 ml
GÉRARD BRISSON - G.F.A. LES PILLETS, 69910 VILLIÉ-MORGON
CUVÉE VIEILLES VIGNES

References in France

Restaurants: Auberge Grand Maison (Mur de Bretagne 22), Château Hôtel de Coatguelen (Lanvollon 22).
Shops: L'Amour du Vin (Paris).

Abroad

United States

Georgia Crown, Atlanta.

United Kingdom

Simon Finch Noyes, Herfordshire. John Harvey & Sons Ltd, Bristol. Pugson's, Burton. Thompson Cook Wines, Liverpool.

Germany

Baus and Provost, Neuweiller.

Switzerland

Ets Charles Amoiel, Geneva.

Belgium

Lambert, Brussels.

The Netherlands

Les Compagnons, Hoorn Wenneker, Roosendal.

Others

Australia: Farmer Bros., Manuka.

Comments

Winegrowers for generations, the Brisson's have been known since 1431. Crossed by the ancient Roman Lyon-Autun road, the property enjoys a privileged mid-hillside location facing South. In 1974, Gérard Brisson joined the vineyard and developed direct sales of its production, after having obtained his Œnologists Diploma from the Faculté des Sciences of Dijon. He grows, bottles and distributes the Morgon Domaine des Pillets. Enthousiastic about his profession, he is, above all, a great lover of wine.

• *The naturally sweet wines of the Loire region, such as Quarts-de-Chaume or Coteau-du-Layon, offer the possibility of some very lovely wine tastings. Very fruity, full, supple and harmonious, they will keep well. (See the Chapter on the Loire Valley).*

CHIROUBLES

DOMAINE DE "LA COMBE AU LOUP"

Gérard-Roger Meziat
Le bourg - 69115 Chiroubles - Beaujolais France
74 04 24 02

Type of vineyard: Family-owned. **Established:** 1969. **Number of employees:** 1. **Vine stocks:** Gamay. **Soil:** Granitic. **Exposure:** Hillsides facing South-West. **Average annual production in hectoliters:** 460.

Appellation: Chiroubles, Morgon, Régnié.
Type: Red. **Technique:** Traditional with precise control of temperature during vinification. **Maturing:** Wood and cement. **Alcohol content:** 13°. **Characteristics:** Aromatic, rich and well balanced. **Serving temperature:** 14°. **Served with:** White meats, certain types of game, cheese. **Vintages available in 89/90:** 1987, 1988.

Characteristics of vintages

1988: Aromatic, rich and well balanced, very long, classic.
1987: Aromatic, very well balanced and harmonious, fine and dense, very successful. Price range (pre-tax, ex-warehouse): between 30 and 50 F.F.
Sales volume:
- Retail: 80%. - Restaurants: 20%.
Sales in France: 75%.
Export sales: 25%.
Main trading partners: Switzerland, Germany, United Kingdom, Belgium, Luxemburg, Netherlands.

References in France

Restaurants: La Maison Blanche (Paris), Hôtel le Tilleul (Évian 74), Auberge du Bois Prin (Chamonix 74) and many others.

Abroad

United Kingdom

Roger Harris Wines, Norfolk. Thorman Hunt and Co. Ltd.. London.

Switzerland

Les Planteurs Réunis, S.A.C.H., Vevey. Magnin Louis Importateur, Rieix C.H.

Comments

Family domain in the old Beaujolais family tradition, nestled in the heart of one of the best known Beaujolais vineyards. The wines produced at the Domaine de La Combe Au Loup are the result or fine maturing and a well conducted vinification, combining tradition, experience and progress illustrated by the rigid control of temperatures during vinification. Every year, medals and certificates are awarded in recognition of the know-how and dedication of the winemaker.

DOMAINE CHÂTEAU DE RAOUSSET

Bernard & René Passot
69115 Chiroubles
74 04 24 71

Type of vineyard: Family-owned. **Established:** 1850. **Vine stocks:** Gamay Noir (white juice). **Soil:** Granitic, fine gravel and pebbles. **Exposure:** Mostly East, South-East. **Average annual production in hectoliters:** 50 to 58 hl/ha.

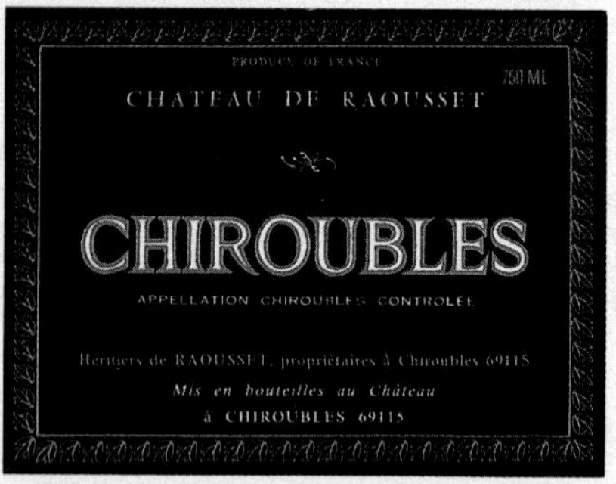

Appellation: Chiroubles, Fleurie, Morgon. **Type:** Red. **Technique:** Traditional Beaujolais style. **Maturing:** In oak casks (6 to 9 months) before bottling. **Alcohol content:** 13%. **Characteristics:** Fruity and aromatic, flowery (violet, rose), red berry fragrance (raspberry, cherry). **Serving temperature:** 14-16°. **Served with:** Regional delicatessen, meat, cheese depending on the wines and vintages. **Vintages available in 89/90:** 1988, 1989.

Characteristics of vintages

1988: Beautiful color, good constitution, long. **1987:**Fruity, supple and elegant. **1986:** Very well constituted, not overly fruity, developing good aromas with ageing. Price range (pre-tax, ex-warehouse): 30 to 50 F.F.

Sales volume:

– Wholesale: 60%. – Retail: 20%. – Restaurants: 20%.

Sales in France: 45%.

Export sales: 55%.

Main trading partners: Switzerland, UK, Ireland, Netherlands, Belgium, Germany, Japan.

References in France

Restaurants: Le Drainak (Paris), Dufour (Rouen), La Mère Guy (Lyon), L'Escale (Aubervilliers), Hôtel de l'Europe (Avignon).

Shops: Caves Fesger (Paris), Caves de la Côte d'Or (Melun).

Abroad

United States

Importers: Grand Cru Inc Hartley and Parker.

United Kingdom

The French wines people matlock, Justerine and Blook London.

Germany

Restaurant Golfier Berlin – Lager Baden-Baden.

Switzerland

La vieille Rolle – Ullrich – Bale

Belgium

Bigodte, Brussels – Schalsech Thueux.

The Netherlands

VPS Vojhnimport – Tilburg.

Far East

Japan: Toya Menka Vaisha, Yokohama.

Comments

Estate created by a silk merchant from Lyon between 1820 and 1850. Clearing of poor, pebbly soil yields wines of exceptional quality. Medals awarded for the Chiroubles: Silver Medal, Paris, 1867. Gold Medal, Lyon, 1869. Silver Medal, Lyon, 1861.

• *Scandal in Saint-Émilion. To find out all about his appellation and the real quality of its wines, from the least pretentious to the greatest, see "Open Letter" in the Chapter on Bordeaux wines.*

• *Blending – a method consisting of mixing different wines from different lots or different vintages in order to obtain a more homogeneous product.*

• *Paulée – traditional meal which brings winelovers and winegrowers together after the harvest, particularly in Burgundy.*

FLEURIE

BERROD

René Berrod
Les Roches du Vivier 69820 Fleurie
74 04 13 63

Type of vineyard: Agricultural Association (family owned). **Established:** 1980. **Vine stocks:** Gamay. **Soil:** Granite. **Exposure:** South – South-East. **Average annual production in hectoliters:** 875.

Appellation: Fleurie, Moulin à Vent, Beaujolais Villages. **Type:** Red. **Technique:** Traditional Beaujolais style. **Maturing:** In oak vats and casks. **Characteristics:** Fleurie: fruity, light and fragrant. Moulin à Vent: matured in oak vats, full-bodied, good keeping. Beaujolais-Villages: pleasant, supple, very fruity. Serving temperature: 13-15°. **Served with:** Delicatessen, meat and cheese. **Vintages available in 89/90:** 1988, 1989.

Characteristics of vintages

1988: Fruity, rather tannic, should age well. Price range (pre-tax, ex-warehouse): 20 to 30 F.F. - 30 to 50 F.F.
Sales volume:
– Wholesale: 20%. – Retail: 40%. – Restaurants: 15%. – Other: 25% (dealers).
Sales in France: 50%.
Export sales: 50%.
Main trading partners: Switzerland, UK, USA, Netherlands, Denmark, Germany.

References in France

Restaurants: Auberge du Cep, (69820 Fleurie), Pascal Saunier 12, rue Belvédère, (76130 Mont-Saint-Aignan), Lassausaie (69380 Chasselay). Le Saint-Vincent 26, rue de la Croix Nivert 75015 Paris.

Abroad

United States

Alain Junguenet Wines of France, P.O. Box 1003, 28 Bayberry Lane Mountainside NJ 07092.

United Kingdom

Le Tire Bouchon 6 Upper James Street, London Wl. Tante Claire 68 Royal Hospital Road SWB, London. Harrods Limited, Wine department, Knightsbridge London SWIX 7XL.

Switzerland

Agent: M. Pultier A., Résidence St. Jacques 14, av. Charles de Gaule 21200 Beaune.

Others

Denmark: Restaurant Gammel Aabyhoj Bakkealle 1 DK 8230 Aabyhoj Aarhus. Restaurant Bagatelle I Hellerup.

Comments

The 22 hectare estate in the commune of Fleurie is operated by the Berrod family. Harvesting is always done by hand, in accord with the principle of "vinification of the entire crop", an essential process for obtaining the typical fruitiness of the Beaujolais Gamay.

• *Read labels carefully – An indication to watch out for: "Bottled in the 'region' of production", which often refers to a blend of wines from several producers and not just one.*

• *For an ideal wine cellar, find out what to do and what not to do (see chapter "Organizing a Wine Cellar")*

MICHEL CHIGNARD-LES MORIERS

Michel Chignard
Le Point du Jour - 69820 Fleurie
74 04 11 87

Type of vineyard: Family-owned. **Established:** 1900, 3 generations. **Vine stocks:** Gamay. **Soil:** Granitic. **Exposure:** South-East. **Average annual production in hectoliters:** 350.

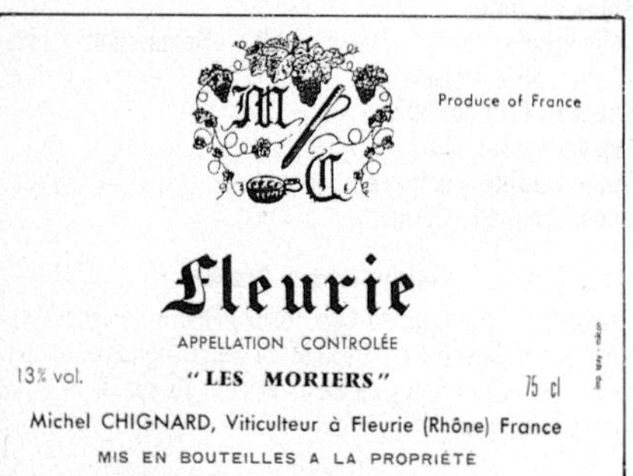

Produce of France
Fleurie
APPELLATION CONTROLÉE
13% vol.
"LES MORIERS"
75 cl
Michel CHIGNARD, Viticulteur à Fleurie (Rhône) France
MIS EN BOUTEILLES A LA PROPRIÉTÉ

Appellation: Fleurie-Les-Moriers. **Type:** Red. **Technique:** Traditional, 5 to 8 days before pressing. **Maturing:** Aged in casks before bottling. **Alcohol content:** 13%. **Characteristics:** Can be drunk young by those who like fruity wines and typical Beaujolais, but also ages well, retaining for a long time the qualities which do honor to a great cellar. **Serving temperature:** 15°. **Vintages available in 89/90:** 1988.

Characteristics of vintages

1988: Very good year, well balanced, fruity and distinguished, characteristic of its appelation, excellent evolution possible. Price range (pre-tax, ex-warehouse): between 30 and 50 F.F.

Sales volume:
- Retail: 20%. - Restaurants: 30%. - Other: 50% export.

Sale in France: 50%.
Export sales: 50%.
Main trading partners: United Kingdom, United States, Switzerland, Netherlands.

References in France

Restaurants: Auberge du Cep (Fleurie), Le Tastevin, Allard, Le Port Alma, Le Bellecour, Le Quai des Ormes, Le Grenadin, La Maison Blanche, Bistro des Augustins (Paris), La Côte St. Jacques (Joigny), La Saulir (Courchevel), Les Crayères, Le Chardonnay (Reims), Le Balandre (Cahors), La Bonne Étape (Château Arnoux), La Taupinière (Pont Aven), etc.

Abroad

United States
Kermit Lynch, 1605 San Pablo Ave., Berkeley, Cal. 94702. Tel: (415) 524-1524.

United Kingdom
Fields Wine Merchants LTD, 55 Sloane Ave., Chelsea, London. Tel: 01 589 5753. Morris and Verdun, 28 Churton Street, London SWIV 2LP. Tel: 01 630 8888. Viticulteur, The Vintner LTD, Winefare House, 5 High Road Byfleet, Weybridge, Surrey KT147QF. Tel: 093 23 51585.

Switzerland
Paul Ulrich, 4051 Bazel. Tel: 061255866. Divo, rue des Terreaux 2, 1003 Lausanne. Tel: 021232742.

Belgium
Branellec, 25 Driesdreef 9910. Gent. Tel: 091266983,

The Netherlands
Gebr Heisterkamp Wijnkopers, Oostwal 5, 7631 EG Ootmarsum. Tel: 05419 2222.

Others
Norway: Riis Gruppen Sondregt 14, 7001 Trondheim. Tel: 07531510.

Comments

Excellent enthusiastic winemaker who regularly produces one of the best Fleurie wines (super 83 and 86 vintages, in particular).

BROUILLY

JEAN LATHUILLIÈRE

La Pisse-Vieille - Cercle Rhône 69220
74 66 13 23

Type of vineyard: Family-owned. **Established:** From father to son. **Number of employees:** 1 permanent. **Vine stocks:** Gamay (colorless juice). **Soil:** Clay and pebbly, sub-soil granitic. **Exposure:** Full South. **Average annual production in hectoliters:** 550.
Appellation: Brouilly Pisse-Vieille. **Type:** Red. **Technique:** Traditional with whole grapes. **Maturing:** Large wooden casks. **Alcohol content:** 13%. **Characteristics:** Considerable red fruit fragrance, bouquet. **Serving temperature:** 15°. **Served with:** White meat (veal, poultry). **Vintages available in 89/90:** 1986 and 1987.

Characteristics of vintages

1986: Beautiful color, good bouquet, a well-made wine. Price range (pre-tax, ex-warehouse): between 20 F.F. and 30 F.F.

Sales volume:
- Wholesale: 5%. - Retail: 50%. - Restaurants: 30%.
- Other: 15% (wine cellars).

Sales in France: 85%.
Export sales: 15%.
Main trading partners : Belgium, Netherlands, UK.

CÔTES-DE-BROUILLY

SABLES D'OR

Olivier Ravier
En "Descours" 69220 BELLEVILLE
74 66 12 66
Telefax: 74 66 57 50

Type of vineyard: Agricultural association. **Established:** 3 generations. **Number of employees:** 2.

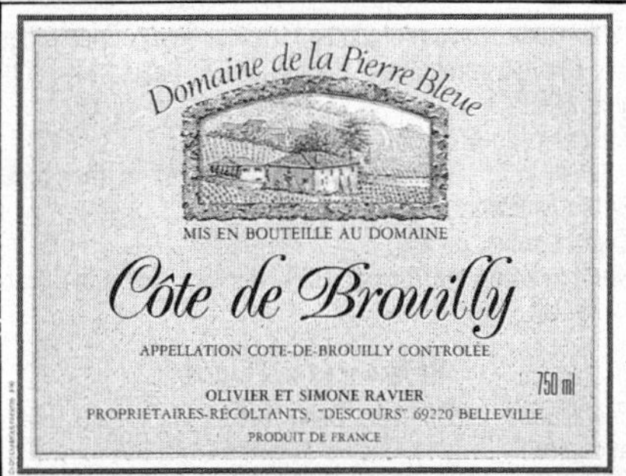

Vine stocks: Gamay. **Soil:** Sand for the Beaujolais, granite for the Brouilly and Côte de Brouilly. **Exposure:** South, South-East. **Average annual production in hectoliters:** 700.
Appellation: Beaujolais, Brouilly, Côte de Brouilly. **Type:** Red, rosé. **Technique:** Semi-carbonic maceration. **Maturing:** Oak casks. **Alcohol content:** 12.5 to 12.8%. **Characteristics:** Beaujolais: light, fruity, red berry (strawberry, raspberry) fragrance. Brouilly: good balance, sustained color, violet nuance. Côte de Brouilly: very typical, violet and peony perfume, slightly peppery, very good keeping. **Serving temperature:** 13 to 15°. **Served with:** Beaujolais: delicatessen. Brouilly and Côte de Brouilly: red meat, game, cheese. **Vintages available in 89/90:** 1987, 1988, 1989.

Characteristics of vintages

1988: Côte de Brouilly: good balance, dominant fruit falvor, promising, ready in 6 months. Brouilly: very round, good tannin/alcohol balance. Beaujolais: good constitution, sustained color, very fruity. Price range (pre-tax ex-warehouse): between 10 and 30 F.F.
Sales volume:
– Wholesale: 20% – Retail: 50% – Restaurants: 15% – Other: 15% (fine winecellars).
Sales in France: 60%
Export sales: 40%.
Main trading partners: UK, Belgium, Germany, Netherlands.

References in France

Restaurants: Machonnerie (Lyon), Josephine "chez Dumonet" (Paris), Le Suffren (Paris), Le Montegrosso (Paris).
Shops: Caves de la Croix-Blanche (95 Argenteuil), Mauduit (Paris).

Abroad

United Kingdom
Oddbins, London.

Germany
Henninger, Munich.

Belgium
Benevins, Brussels.

The Netherlands:
Eric Sauter, Maastrich.

Others
Greece: Kouniakis, Athens. Austra: Régélé, Ehrenhausen.

Comments

The winecellars of the Domaine de la Pierre-Bleue, located on the Southern slopes of the Brouilly hills, was built in 1840 with walls made of blue stones. Today, fixed up as a reception room for Beaujolais evening affairs, it retains its typical regional character, with its wooden vats and its old wine press.

DOMAINE DES FOURNELLES

Alain Bernillon
"Godfroy" – 69220 Saint-Lager
74 66 81 68

Type of vineyard: Family-owned. **Established:** 1947. **Vine stocks:** Gamay. **Soil:** Silica-clay. **Exposure:** Southeast. **Average annual production in hectoliters:** 240. **Appellation:** Côte-de-Brouilly. **Type:** Red. **Technique:** Beaujolais style, semi-carbonic maceration. **Maturing:** Stainless steel and wood. **Characteristics:** Rich and well-balanced, with body, lots of finesse, fruitness, fragrance remain dominant. **Serving temperature:** 12° to 14°. **Served with:** Almost everything. **Vintages available in 89/90:** 1988.

Characteristics of vintages

1988: Very fruity, great finesse, red fruit aromas, typical of the Côte de Brouilly. Recently awarded the distinction of a Gold Medal at the Concours Général Agricole, Paris.

• *Read labels carefully – An indication to watch out for: "Bottled in the 'region' of production", which often refers to a blend of wines from several producers and not just one.*

RÉGNIÉ

DOMAINE DU PLATEAU DE BEL-AIR

Serge & Henry Fessy
69220 Saint-Jean-d'Ardières
74 66 00 16 - Telex: 380 786 - FAX 74 69 61 67

Type of vineyard: Agricultural Association. **Vine stocks:** Gamay Noir. **Soil:** Granitic. **Exposure:** Plateau. **Average annual production in hectoliters:** 600.

Appellation: Bouilly, Beaujolais. **Type:** Red. **Technique:** Traditional. **Alcohol content:** 14%. **Vintages available in 89/90:** 1988.

Characteristics of vintages

1988: Full, very fruity and aromatic. Price range (pre-tax, ex-warehouse): 20 to 30 F.F. Beaujolais. 30 to 50 F.F. Brouilly.

Sales volume:
- Retail: 10%. - Restaurants: 90%.

Sales in France: 80%.
Export sales: 20%.

References in France

Restaurants: Brasserie Flo.
Shops: Flo Prestige, Inter-Caves.

Abroad

United Kingdom
Gaujon & Fils, 1 Monza Street, Waping Hall, London.

Switzerland
Bourgeois Frères, 1338 Ballaignes.

Belgium
Chacalli de Decker, 2220 Wormmelgem 0335315G1.

CHÂTEAU DU BASTY

Gilles Perroud
Lantignie - 69430 Beaujeu
74 04 85 98

Type of vineyard: Family-owned. **Established:** 1482. **Number of employees:** 3. **Vine stocks:** Gamay. **Soil:** Granitic. **Exposure:** Hillsides facing East and Southeast. **Average annual production in hectoliters:** 900. **Appellation:** Regnié and Beaujolais Lantignié. **Technique:** Traditional, long fermentation with skins. **Maturing:** In Oak casks. **Characteristics:** Rich and well-balanced, developing after 5 or 6 months. Bottling in the spring, following the harvest. **Serving temperature:** Room temperature. **Vintages available in 89/90:** 1988.

Characteristics of vintages

1988: Quite successful vintage, typical, lively. Price range (pre-tax, ex-warehouse): Regnié 30 F.F. Beaujolais Lantignié 24 F.F.

Sales volume:
- Retail: 15%. - Restaurants: 30% (+cellars). - Other: 55%.

Sales in France: 45%.
Export sales: 55%.
Main trading partners: USA, Benelux Countries, Germany, UK.

References in France

Restaurants: La Flambée, Deauville; Le Vieux Puits, Pont-Audemer.
Shops: Chez Mélac, Caves des Gobelins, La Tour d'Argent, Opéra, Bastille, Paris.

GAEC DE LA TOUR-BOURDON

Michel et Jean-Paul Rampon
69430 Régnie-Durette
74 04 32 15 and 74 04 36 32

Type of vineyard: Family-owned. **Established:** 1981. **Vine stocks:** Gamay (white grape juice). **Soil:** Sandy, pebbly hillsides, granitic (pink). **Exposure:** South. **Average annual production in hectoliters:** 800. **Appellation:** Beaujolais-Régnie (Beaujolais Villages). **Type:** Red. **Technique:** Semi-carbonic. **Maturing:** Concrete vats. **Alcohol content:** 13.3%. **Characteristics:** Round and fruity, very well developed aroma, sufficiently tannic for keeping. **Serving temperature:** 15°. **Served with:** Everything except fish. **Vintages available in 89/90:** 1985 until depletion of stock and 1986.

Characteristics of vintages

1986: Supple and very fruity, to be drunk in the next 2 years. **1985:** Good colored and more tannic, long, keeps well, typical of its appellation. Price range (pre-tax, ex-warehouse): between 10 F.F. and 20 F.F.

Sales volume:

– Wholesale: 40%. – Retail: 40%. – Restaurants: 20%.
Sales in France: 95%.
Export sales: 5%.
Main trading partners : Germany and Switzerland.

References in France

Restaurants: La Route du Beaujolais at Fontainebleau.

BEAUJOLAIS-VILLAGES

VINS DESSALLE

"Les Villards" 69823 Belleville Cedex
74 69 69 21 – Telefax: 74 69 69 49

Established: 1978. **Number of employees:** 6. **Vine stocks:** Gamay. **Soil:** Schist and granite. **Exposure:** South. **Average annual production in hectoliters:** 10,000.
Appellation: Vin du Beaujolais, Maconnais. **Type:** Red, White. **Technique:** Semi-carbonic. **Maturing:** In stainless steel tanks. **Alcohol content:** 13%. **Characteristics:** Fruity, supple, ruby color. **Serving temperature:** 15°. **Served with:** Red meat. **Vintages available in 89/90:** 1988.

Characteristics of vintages

1988: Substantial, slightly tannic, aromatic. **1987:** Very supple – not to be missed. **1985:** Super wines. Price range (pre-tax, ex-warehouse): 20 to 30 F.F. Beaujolais Villages. 30 to 50 F.F. Crus du Beaujolais.
Sales volume:
– Wholesale: 14%. – Retail: 1%. – Restaurants: 85%.
Sales in France: 34%.
Export sales: 66%.
Main trading partners : Japan, USA, Australia, UK, Switzerland, Benelux countries.

References in France

Restaurants: Troisgros (Roanne), Chez Philippe, Bistrot de Paris, Le Petit Zinc, Le Stella.
Shops: Layrac Boutique, Picnic, Drugstore des Champs Élysées.

Abroad

United States

(Dealer): USA, Wineburg CA 95487. Lauber Import, New Jersey. Garnet (G. String). Window of the World.

United Kingdom

Atkinson Baldwin St Mary's House, 42 Vicarage Crescent, London SW11 SLB.

Switzerland

Ets. Pierre Vallade, route des Franchisés, Geneva.

Belgium

Robert Goffard, rue Eggericky 28 1150, Brussels.

Canada

Le Marchand de vin 1938 Ouest, rue Sherbrooke, suite 590 Montreal, Québec.

The Netherlands

Levert et Schudel BV PO Box No. 3 AA Vijemuizen.

Far East

Japan: Jardine Wine and Spirit, Onarimon, Minatoku, Tokyo.

Others

Australia: (Dealer) Australia, 205 Grove Street, Adelaide SA 5000.

Comments

Sylvain Fessy represents the fifth generation of Beaujolais producers and dealers. In 1978, at the age of 26, after six years of apprenticeship with his father, he bought his own company called Vins Dessale. In 10 years he has provided the enterprise with ultra-modern equipment, exported his Beaujolais all over the world and multiplied his turnover by a factor of 10. He takes great pleasure in choosing the most beautiful Beaujolais wines, to everyone's taste, for the pleasure of all.

LES VINS LOUIS TETE

Les Dépôts - 69430 St. Didier-sur-Beaujeu
74 04 82 27 - Telex: 370 866

Type of vineyard: Family-owned. **Vine stocks:** Gamay. **Soil:** Caly with calcium carbonate. **Average annual production in hectoliters:** 520.
Appellation: Beaujolais Villages and Château des Alouettes, Moulin à Vent and Regnié. **Type:** Red. **Technique:** Semi-carbonic. **Maturing:** Concrete vats for Beaujolais villages, Oak casks for Moulin à Vent. **Alcohol content:** Beaujolais Villages: 12.5% to 13%. Moulin à Vent and Regnié: 13% to 13.5%. **Characteristics:** Beaujolais Villages: very fruity, goes down well, lovely ruby color. Moulin à Vent: rich and well-balanced, spicy flavor. **Serving temperature:** Beaujolais Villages and Regnié: 13° to 14°. Moulin à Vent: 15° to 16°. **Served with:** Beaujolais Villages: with all first courses (fish); a well-balanced wine for beginning or ending a meal. Moulin à Vent: with red meat, game, cheese.

Characteristics of vintages

1986: Moulin à Vent: excellent, finesse, structure, fragrance, keeps well. Beaujolais Villages: a successful vintage. Price range (pre-tax, ex-warehouse): between 10 F.F. and 30 F.F.
Sales volume:
- Retail: 20%. - Restaurants: 80%.
Sales in France: 50%. **Export sales:** 50%.
Main trading partners: USA, Switzerland, Belgium, Japan, Luxemburg, UK, Neterlands, Germany.

References in France

Restaurants: Nandron (Lyon), Lameloise (Chagny).

DOMAINE DALICIEUX

Bernard Dalicieux
Lavernette - 71570 Leynes
85 35 60 79

Type of vineyard: Family-owned. **Established:** 1975. **Number of employees:** 2. **Vine stocks:** Gamay and Chardonnay. **Exposure:** Mostly South. **Average annual production in hectoliters:** 500.
Appellation: Beaujolais-Villages Rouge, Beaujolais Blanc, Mâcon-Villages Blanc. **Technique:** Traditional with temperature control. **Maturing:** Red: large casks and vats. White: enamel tanks. **Characteristics:** Red: aromatic, rich and well-balanced. White: Fruity, dry, very elegant. **Serving temperature:** Red: 16 to 17°. White: 9 to 11°. **Vintages available in 89/90:** 1986.

Characteristics of vintages

1986: Very good aroma/richness balance. Taste and aroma in harmony. White Beaujolais: light, supple and fragrant. Mâcon: good vinification. Price range (pre-tax, ex-warehouse): between 20 F.F. and 35 F.F.

DOMAINE DES TERRES DESSUS

Jean Floch
Les Terres Dessus - 69220 Lancie
74 04 13 85

Type of vineyard: Family-owned. **Established:** 1950. **Vine stocks:** Gamay Noir (white juice). **Soil:** Clay with calcium carbonate. **Exposure:** South. **Average annual production in hectoliters:** 620.
Appellation: Beaujolais-Villages. **Type:** Red. **Technique:** Traditional. **Maturing:** In vats. **Alcohol content:** 13%. **Characteristics:** Fruity, for ageing. **Serving temperature:** 14°. **Served with:** Poultry, game. **Vintages available in 89/90:** 1986.

Characteristics of vintages

1986: Light and pleasant. Average pre-tax, ex-warehouse price: 17 F.F. Price range (pre-tax, ex-warehouse): Between 10 F.F. and 20 F.F.
Sales volume:
- Wholesale: 80%. - Retail: 20%.
Sales in France: 50%. **Export sales:** 50%.
Main trading partners : Canada, Switzerland.

CHÂTEAU DE CORCELLES

M. Richard
Corcelles-en-Beaujolais
69220 Belleville-s/Saône
74 66 00 24 - Telex: CHAMVIL 340 777 F

Established: 1986. **Number of employees:** 22. **Vine stocks:** 100% Gamay. **Soil:** Clay and calcium carbonate (Beaujolais), granitic and schist (Brouilly). **Average annual production in hectoliters:** 5 000.
Appellation: Beaujolais, Beaujolais-Villages, Brouilly, Beaujolais Rosé. **Type:** Red, rosé. **Technique:** Typical Beaujolais, carbonic maceration. **Alcohol content:** 12.5%. **Characteristics:** Give the impression on entering into an enchanted garden of floral and fruity fragrances. Beaujolais and Beaujolais-Villages, when young, have a dominant banana fragrance. Brouilly, aroma of fresh grapes and red fruit (black and red currants). **Serving temperature:** Cool but not cold. **Served with:** The Beaujolais cuisine goes with its frankness and friendliness. It is the country of all kinds of sausages and goat cheese. **Vintages available in 89/90:** 1987, 1988.

GAEC MIOLANE RENÉ ET CHRISTIAN

René Miolane
Le Cellier - Salles en Beaujolais
69830 St. Georges de Pieneins
74 67 52 67

Established: 1977. But the (Vineyard goes back 3 Centuries). **Vine stocks:** Gamay Noir (White juice). **Soil:** Granitic. **Exposure:** South, South-West and Southeast. **Average annual production in hectoliters:** 900 to 1,200.
Appellation: Beaujolais Villages. **Type:** Red, rosé. **Technique:** Traditional. **Maturing:** In large Oak casks. **Alcohol content:** 12% to 13%. **Characteristics:** There are several lots, bottled separately, which gives a complete line of wines. Classic Beaujolais Villages: Beautiful cherry-red color; wines with character. In general they have a fruity taste (mulberry, red currant, rapsberry). Other lots are more supple. **Serving temperature:** Beaujolais Villages: 14° to 15°; La Cuvée des Chasseurs: 15° to 16°; Rosé: 12°. **Served with:** La Cuvée des Chasseurs: red meat or game. **Vintages available in 89/90:** 1985 and 1986.

Characteristics of vintages

1988: Very fruity, bright color, very pronounced raspberry, red currant and blackcurrant flavor. **1987:** Wine with exeptional quality. This is a wine with character, a fruity taste and fragrance. We specially recommend this wine. Price range (pre-tax, ex-warehouse): between 10 F.F. and 20 F.F.
Sales volume: - Wholesale: 33%. - Retail: 33%. - Restaurants: 34%.
Sales in France: 50%. **Export sales:** 50%.
Main trading partners: UK, Belgium, Netherlands, Luxembourg, Germany, Switzerland.

References in France

Restaurants: Les Vieux Métiers de France (Paris), Taverne Henri IV (Paris), Le Panorama (69 Dardilly), La Fontaine Bleue (69 Dardilly), Restoberge (75 Paris).
Shops: 15 shops in France and abroad.

CHÂTEAU DE LACARELLE

Louis Durieu de Lacarelle
69460 Saint Étienne-des-Oullières
74 03 40 80

Type of vineyard: Family-owned. **Established:** Over two hundred years ago. **Number of employees:** 24. **Vine stocks:** Gamay Noir (white juice). **Soil:** Decomposed and rocky granite. **Exposure:** 1/4 East 1/2 South, 1/4 North. **Average annual production in hectoliters:** 8,000.

Appellation: Beaujolais Village. **Type:** Red. **Technique:** Traditional, semi-carbonic maceration, temperature controlled fermentation. **Alcohol content:** 12.5% and 13%. **Characteristics:** Aromatic, very supple, easy to drink. **Serving temperature:** 17°. **Served with:** Almost everything. **Vintages available in 89/90:** 1987, 1988, 1989.

Characteristics of vintages

1988: Rich and well balanced, can only improve with ageing. **1987:** Very delicate, rich bouquet, has reached its peak. **Other:** 1989: quality not yet known.
Sales in France: 30%.
Export sales: 70%.
Main trading partners: Switzerland, USA, Germany, Benelux countries, UK, Japan, Denmark, Italy.

References in France

Restaurants: Le Train Bleu (Paris), Relais & Châteaux.

Abroad

United States

Château and Estate Wine Company - 365 Park Avenue, New-York.

Switzerland

Gebruder Nauer Bremgarten.

Belgium

Mrs. Breuval, Zellik near Brussels.

The Netherlands

Jacobus Boelen, Amsterdam.

Far East

Meida-Ya Company 28 Kyobashi, Tokyo.

Others

Denmark: Steuwer Risgukde. Italy: Graziano Fecchio Bruino, Torino.

Comments

Lacarelle is one of the oldest Beaujolais winegrowing estates and has remained to this day the largest and most important of the family properties of the appellation. Although the Château de Lacarelle is located in the heart of the region primarily producing Beaujolais Primeur, they have concentrated on the production and bottling of wine for longer keeping and have been encouraged to continue in this direction by the qualitative results obtained in recent years.

CHÂTEAU DU CHATELARD

Robert Grossot

Lancie - 69220 Belleville-sur-Saône

74 04 12 99

Type of vineyard: Family-owned. **Established:** Estate bought on April 1, 1979. **Number of employees:** 2. **Vine stocks:** Gamay for red Beaujolais Villages and Chardonnay for white Beaujolais. **Soil:** Sand and clay with calcium carbonate. **Exposure:** Several vineyards situated on several plots. **Average annual production in hectoliters:** 600 (100 white).
Appellation: Red Beaujolais Villages - White Beaujolais - La Fleurie. **Technique:** Maceration partly under carbon dioxide for the red wine; treading and immediate pressing for white wine. **Alcohol content:** 12.5%. **Characteristics:** Red: supple and very fuity, typical Beaujolais, beautiful purple color. White: grace and distinction, fruity because of the age of the vines (about 75 years). **Serving temperature:** about 14°. **Served with:** Whites suitable for first courses and very pleasant with fish and seafood. Reds suitable for all types of food. **Vintages available in 89/90:** 1988.

Characteristics of vintages

1988: Good quality, light and pleasant red wines - excellent white wines. Ready to be enjoyed. Le Fleurie, very seductive. Price range (pre-tax, ex-warehouse): Red Beaujolais Village - between 15 F.F. and 20 F.F. Fleurie and white - between 25 F.F. and 35 F.F.

BEAUJOLAIS A.O.C.

VIGNOBLE CHARMET

La Ronze - Le Breuil - 69620 Le Bois d'Oingt

74 71 64 83

Type of vineyard: Family-owned. **Established:** From father to son since 1718. **Vine stocks:** Gamay Noir (white grape juice) Chardonnay (white Baujolais). **Exposure:** Southeast, East. **Average annual production in hectoliters:** 700.

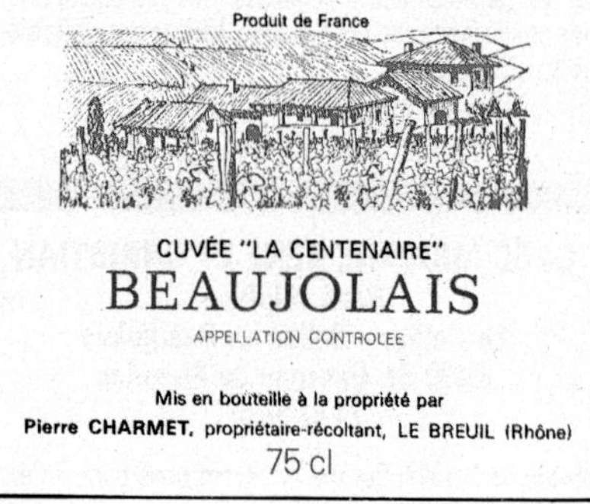

Produit de France
CUVÉE "LA CENTENAIRE"
BEAUJOLAIS
APPELLATION CONTROLEE
Mis en bouteille à la propriété par
Pierre CHARMET, propriétaire-récoltant, LE BREUIL (Rhône)
75 cl

Appellation: Beaujolais. **Type:** Red, white. **Technique:** Semi-carbonic vinification - temperature control for fermentation at low temperature to preserve the aroma. **Maturing:** In temperature controlled vats. **Characteristics:** The taste is round, light and supple, very fruity, red fruit aroma. **Serving temperature:** 13° to 15°. **Served with:** Goes with everything; may be served throughout the meal. Start with "La Ronze" and "Masfraise" choose "Centenaire" with meat and cheese. **Vintages available in 89/90:** 1986, 1987.

Characteristics of vintages

1985: Generous, robust, balanced, will probably age well. **1985:** Very nice white. Price range (pre-tax, ex-warehouse): between 20 to 30 F.F.
Sales volume:
- Wholesale: 10%. - Retail: 80%. - Restaurants: 10%.
Sales in France: 70%.
Export sales: 30%.
Main trading partners: UK, Germany, Netherlands, Switzerland, Belgium.

References in France

Restaurants: Restaurants Jean Brouilly at Tarare (Rhône).

Abroad

United Kingdom

Roger Harris Wines – Loke Farm Weston Longville Norfolk NR9 5LG.

Germany

Bauss & Provot – Dudweilerstrasse 57 – 6603 Sulzbach Neuweiler.

The Netherlands

Cees Van Noor – Mgr. Van de Wetering-straat 27 3581 Ed Utrecht.
Shops: Gebr. Heisterkamp – Oostwal 5 – 7631 eg Ootmarsum.

Comments

In 1961 Charmet received the "Best Beaujolais Trophy" trophy in competion with the 9 Grands Crus of the Beaujolais (Moulin à Vent, Fleurie, Côtes de Brouilly, Morgon etc.) The first Beaujolais Villages and the first of the Beaujolais appellation. Since then this super competition has been eliminated. This is unfortunate because they would once more have been able to compare themselves with their friends for the 1966, 1969, 1973, 1982 and 1983 vintages. These vintages won the Paradise-Cup for the charmets which is the first prise for the best Beaujolais. At any rate, they are eminently qualified.

GARLON JEAN

Garlon
Beauvallon – Theizé – 69620 Bois d'Ouyt
74 71 72 52

Type of vineyard: Family-owned. **Established:** Very old. **Vine stocks:** Gamay (white juice). **Soil:** Clay with calcium carbonate. **Exposure:** Southeast. **Average annual production in hectoliters:** 600.
Appellation: Beaujolais. **Type:** Red. **Technique:** Semi-carbonic maceration, temperature control. **Alcohol content:** 12.5%. **Characteristics:** Fresh, supple, fruity. **Serving temperature:** 15°. **Served with:** The Beaujolais may be drunk throughout the meal, but goes especially well with delicatessen products, meat and cheese. **Vintages available in 89/90:** 1986, 1987 (in 1988).

Characteristics of vintages

1986: Gold Medal in Paris; a very successul vintage. Average pre-tax, ex-warehouse price: Between 10 F.F. and 20 F.F.
Sales volume:
– Wholesale: 30%. – Retail: 50%. – Restaurants: 20%.
Sales in France: 90%.
Export sales: 10%.
Main trading partners : UK.

• *Want to know more about wine, its vinification, its nature and its vocabulary? See Chapter "The Chemistry of Wine".*

LES VINS GEORGES DUBŒUF

Georges Dubœuf
Romanèche Thorins
71570 La Chapelle-de-Gunchay
85 35 51 13 – Telex: 800 772 – Fax: 85 35 56 58

Type of vineyard: Corporation. **Established:** 1964. **Number of employees:** 85. **Vine stocks:** Gamay, Pinot, Chardonnay. **Average annual production in hectoliters:** 100000.
Appellation: Beaujolais/Mâconnais/Pouilly-Fuissé/St-Véran. **Type:** Red, white. **Technique:** Traditional. **Alcohol content:** 13%. **Characteristics:** Typical Beaujolais, marked by this soil. Rigorous selection, color, concentration of aromas, firmness. **Served with:** The entire meal, delicatessen products, etc. **Vintages available in 89/90:** 1985 - 1986 - 1987 - 1988.

Characteristics of vintages

1988: Charming wines with a lot of finesse a little less fruity than 1987 but more complete and vinus wine. **1987:** Great vintage with an abundance of red-berry fruit and appealing floral tones. **1986:** Good year. Riche color, firm and fragrant. Excellent whites. **1985:** Excellent year. Remarkable Morgon, Moulin-à-Vent and Chenas. Good for ageing.

DOMAINE DU COLOMBIER
DOMAINE DE LA SORBIÈRE

Jean-Charles Pivot
"Montmay" Quincie-en-Beaujolais
69430 Beaujeu
74 04 30 32

Type of vineyard: Family-owned. **Established:** 1963. **Number of employees:** 1. **Vine stocks:** Gamay. **Soil:** Clay with silice. **Exposure:** South, Southeast. **Average annual production in hectoliters:** 55 to 60.
Appellation: Beaujolais. **Type:** Red. **Technique:** Semi-carbonic maceration. **Maturing:** Concrete tanks and large wooden casks. **Alcohol content:** 12.8%. **Characteristics:** Wine bottled as "primeur" – new wine, extremely fruity with later bottling fruity, stands up well. **Serving temperature:** 11 to 15°. **Served with:** Delicatessen, red meat, cheese. **Vintages available in 89/90:** 1986.

Characteristics of vintages

1986: Supple and fragrant, very pleasant. Average pre-tax ex-warehouse price: 17.50 F.F. **Sales volume:**
– Wholesale: 10%. – Retail: 40%. – Restaurants: 50%.
Sales in France: 80%. **Export sales:** 20%.
Main trading partners : Switzerland, Belgium, UK.

References in France

Restaurants: Le Fouquet's, le Vivarois, Les Trois Marches, Pavillon Baltard (Paris), Taillevent. *Shops:* Petrissan.

THORIN S.A. PONTANEVAUX

Michel Sauzey
71570 La Chapelle-de-Guinchay
85 36 70 43 - Telex: 800802 Burgond

Type of vineyard: Production and sales. **Established:** 1843. **Number of employees:** 50. **Average annual production in hectoliters:** 70,000.
Appellation: Chablis, Côte-de-Beaune, Côte-de-Nuits, Côte Chalonnaise, Mâconnais, Beaujolais, Côtes-du-Rhône.
Type: Red, White, Rosé. **Technique:** Traditional (Burgundy). **Maturing:** Quite typical, structured, round. **Vintages available 89/90:** 1987, 1988.

Characteristics of vintages

1988: Good vintages for reds and whites, supple but still rich and well balanced. **1987:** Excellent results, particularly for very aromatic whites.
Sales in France: 50%. **Export sales:** 50%.
Main trading partners: UK, Germany, USA, Canada, Switzerland, Scandinavian countries.

References in France

Restaurants: Georges Blanc, Cochon d'Or, Cep in Fleurie, Pharamond.

Abroad

United States

Importers: Racke USA, P.O. Box 182, 27000 Ramal Road Sonoma, California 95476. Tel: (707) 938-8504.

United Kingdom

Importers: Racke UK Ltd. Stonehouse Farm, Ashby Rd. Boundary, Nr Woodville, Burton-on-Trent. Tel: 0283-217703.

Importers and agents in over 50 countries.

ETS PIERRE DUPOND

339, rue de Thizy
69653 Villefranche-sur-Saône Cedex
74 65 24 32 – Telex: 305 730 F

Type of vineyard: Corporation. **Established:** 1860.
Appellation: Beaujolais, Mâconnais, Côtes-du-Rhône.
Technique: In the Beaujolais tradition. **Characteristics:** Good color, fruity, combining finesse, richness and balance. **Serving temperature:** 14° to 16°. **Served with:** All white meats and delicatessen. **Vintages available in 89/90:** 1986, 1987.

Characteristics of vintages

1986: Successful year, good color, aromatic, dense wines.

References in France

Restaurants: Lipp, La Lorraine, La Coupole Montparnasse, etc. Paris.

CLOS DE LA PLATTIÈRE

Jean-François Garlon
Theize - 69620 Le Bois d'Oinet
74 71 20 95

Type of vineyard: Family-owned. **Established:** Early 18th Century. **Vine stocks:** Gamay Noir (white juice). **Soil:** Clay with calcium carbonate. **Exposure:** South. **Average annual production in hectoliters:** 100. **Appellation:** Beaujolais. **Type:** Red. **Technique:** Semi-carbonic maceration with temperature control. **Alcohol content:** 12.5%. **Characteristics:** Fruity, light and pleasant to drink. **Serving temperature:** 14°. **Served with:** Delicatessen products, meat, cheese. **Vintages avaible in 89/90:** 1986.

Characteristics of vintages

1986: Bronze Medal Paris: Lovely wine, typical of the region fruity, goes down well, well made. Price range (pre-tax, ex-warehouse): between 10 F.F. and 20 F.F.
Sales in France: 70%.
Export sales: 30%.
Main trading partners : Belgium, Netherlands.

S.A. PIERRE FERRAUD ET FILS

Pierre, Jean-Michel and
Yves-Dominique Ferraud
31 rue Maréchal Foch 69823 Belleville Cedex.
74 66 08 05 - Telex: 330 270 F
Fax: 74 66 05 50

Type of vineyard: Corporation. **Established:** 1882. **Number of employees:** 15. **Vine stocks:** Red and rosé: Gamay Noir (white juice). White: Pinot, Chardonnay. **Soil:** Silica, granite, manganese, chalky clay. **Average annual production in hectoliters:** 1,400000 bottles. **Appellation:** Beaujolais (red), Mâcon (white). **Type:** Red, white, rosé. **Technique:** Red: carbonic maceration. **Maturing:** All wines in wooden casks. Modern methods of filtration and bottling. **Characteristics:** Each appellation has its typical personality. **Serving temperature:** White: 8 to 10°. Red: 10 to 14°. **Served with:** Young red: Salads and light cooking. Older red: Red meat and game. White: Fish and as an aperitif. **Vintages available in 89/90:** Red: some 87 and the whole range of 88. White: some 86 and the whole range of 88.

Characteristics of vintages

1988: Red: Deep color, character. Vintage to be taken seriously and discovered in the course of time. White: fruity and supple. **1987:** Red: fruity and elegant.
Sales volume:
- Retail: 5%. - Restaurants: 85%. - Other: 10% (fine groceries and winecellars).
Sales in France: 65%.
Export sales: 35%.
Main trading partners : Japan, UK, Germany, Benelux Countries, USA.

References in France

Restaurants: All gastronomic levels. Many restaurants with Michelin stars, Inns, Châteaux and Parisian Brasseries.
Shops: Fine groceries and winecellars in various regions.

Abroad

United States

Domecq Importers, 2 Madison Avenue, Larchmont, N.Y. 10538. Tel: (914) 834 4127.

United Kingdom

London and Greater London: Ken Butler, The Birches Industrial Estate, East Grinstead, Sussex RH19 1XZ. Tel: (342) 313 955.

Switzerland

Maison Banchet, 73 rue des Vollandes, 1211 Geneva 6. Tel: 22 35 98 42.

Belgium

Maison Pirard, 1 rue du Glabais, 1470 Genappe. Tel: 67 77 31 01.

Canada

Nihco Gyaki International, 25 Golden Gate Court, Scarborough, Ontario M1P 3A4. Tel: (416) 299 5080.

The Netherlands

Intercaves BV, Marsweg 43, 8013 PE Zwolle. Tel: 38 69 69 69.

Far East

Japan: Jal Wine House Co., Ltd., Tokyo Ryutsu Center Bldg., 6-1-1 Heiwajima, Ohta-Ku, Tokyo 143. Tel: 3 767 6400.

Comments

Family establishment, in direct line of descent for 5 generations, working the same soil for more than a century. One of the rare Beaujolais houses using wooden casks. With respect for their exclusive clientele, they have always concentrated on the breed, typical character and personality of each of the appellations rather than on sales volume.

- *A great naturally sweet wine with Roquefort? Try a Sauternes, of course, a Grand Cru from a late Alsacian harvest, a mellow Anjou or a Banyuls.*

- *The 1980 vintage is badly understood. In Bordeaux the wines are already quite surprising and will do quite well while waiting for the development of the other vintages. See "The last five vintages" in the Chapter on Bordeaux wines.*

CÔTEAUX DU LYONNAIS

LA PETITE GALLÉE

Robert Thollet
69390 Millery
78 46 24 30

Type of vineyard: Family-owned. **Established:** 1944. **Vine stocks:** Gamay, Chardonnay, Aligoté. **Soil:** Clay and glacial pebbles. **Exposure:** South-East. **Average annual production in hectoliters:** 400.
Appellation: Côteau du Lyonnais. **Type:** Red, white. **Technique:** Semi-carbonic. **Maturing:** In wooden casks and concrete tanks. **Alcohol content:** 12.5%. **Characteristics:** Red: Fruity, goes down well. White: Fragrant, dry, and long. **Serving temperature:** Red: 14°. White: 10°. **Served with:** Red: specialties of the Lyon region. White: fish and shellfish. **Vintages available in 89/90:** 1989.

Characteristics of vintages

Price range (pre-tax, ex-warehouse): 10 to 20 F.F.
Sales volume: – Retail: 100%.
Sales in France: 90%. **Export sales:** 10%.
Main trading partners : Belgium.

References in France

Restaurants: Mercure Hôtel (Chasse-sur-Rhône – 38).

Abroad

Belgium

Clairenbourg Cellars (Opprebais).

Comments

Louis the XIVth drank La Gallée wines. The oldest vines of the estate, planted in 1896, are to be found on hillsides

P. JOMARD

P. Jomard
Le Morillion 69210 Fleurieux
74 01 02 27

Type of vineyard: family-owned. **Established:** from father to son since 1620. **Vine stocks:** Gamay – Chardonnay. **Soil:** granitic. **Exposure:** East. **Average annual production in hectoliters:** 1,000.

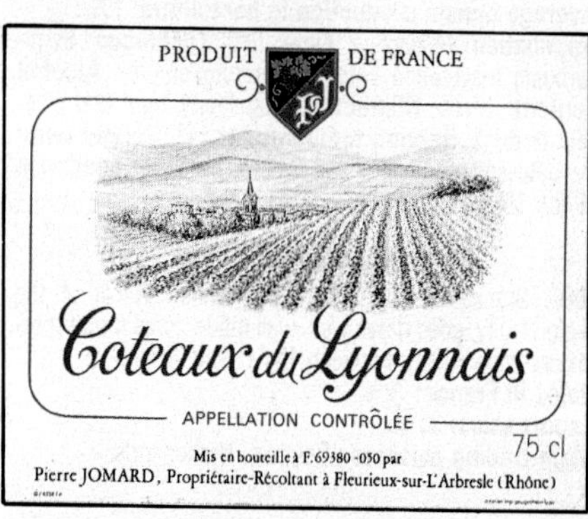

Appellation: Coteaux du Lyonnais. **Type:** Red, White. **Technique:** Carbonic maceration. **Maturing:** in Oak casks. **Characteristics:** very fruity. **Serving temperature:** 16°. **Served with:** with the entire meal. **Vintages available in 89/90:** 1988-1989.

Characteristics of vintages

1988: aromatic and very fruity. **1987:** out of stock. **1986:** out of stock. **1985:** out of stock. Price range (pre-tax, ex-warehouse): 10 F.F. to 20 F.F.
Sales volume:
– Wholesale: 50%. – Retail: 25%. – Restaurants: 25%.
Sales in France: 70%.
Export sales: 30%.
Main trading partners : Netherlands, Germany, Denmark, Belgium.

Comments

Enterprise established at Morillon in 1620 by P. Jomard and operated from this time on, form father to son. Family enterprise made up 15 hectare vineyard planted with Gamay (red wines) and Chardonnay (white wines).

> • *Watch out for wines that have lost their authenticity, "with neither soul nor virtue", most often the result of specific vinification techniques (carbonic maceration, too long maturing in casks...). See the various Regions: Bordeaux, Languedoc, South-West, Provence...*

CAVE DE VIGNERONS RÉUNIS A SAIN-BEL

Mr. Levrat (President), Mr. Sothier (Cellarman)
Les Ragots - 69210 Sain-Bel
74 01 11 33

Type of vineyard: Cooperative Agricultural Association. **Established:** 1956. **Number of employees:** 3. **Vine stocks:** Gamay Noir (white juice), Chardonnay, Aligoté. **Soil:** Red: granitic. White: clay. **Exposure:** South, Southeast. **Average annual production in hectoliters:** 12000 hl.

Appellation: Beaujolais (red), Coteaux du Lyonnais (white, rosé, red). **Type:** Red, white, rosé. **Technique:** Beaujolais, vinification at low temperature. **Maturing:** Stainless steel or lined cement tanks, bottling in the Spring. **Alcohol content:** 12° to 12.8°. **Characteristics:** White: fruity, light and fragrant, thirst-quenching, to be drunk anytime. Very good quality/price ratio. Red Beaujolais ('86): fresh, goes down well. Red Coteaux Lyonnais ('86): first of the young 1986 A.O.C. of France. **Serving temperature:** Red: 12° to 14°. White: 12°. **Served with:** White: as an aperitif or with first courses, fish. Red: delicatessen products, poultry, white meat or simply with snacks. May be drunk at any time of day with friends. **Vintages available in 89/90:** 1986, 1987, 1988 (Beaujolais and Coteaux du Lyonnais "Primeurs").

Characteristics of vintages

1986: Good quality despite excessive yiels, very sunny year, especially at the time when the grapes ripened. Good quality/price ratio for the Côteaux du Lyonnais. Average pre-tax, ex-warehouse price: Côteaux Lyonnais (red, rosé and white): 11.40 F.F. Beaujolais (red, white): 14.40 F.F. Price range (pre-tax, ex-warehouse): Between 10 F.F. and 20 F.F.

Sales volume:
- Wholesale: 80%. - Retail: 12%. - Restaurants: 8%.

Sales in France: 98%.
Export sales: 2%.
Main trading partners : UK, Germany, Belgium.

DESCOTES ETIENNE ET FILS

Pierre Descotes
Rue de Gres
78 46 26 09 - 78 46 18 38

Type of vineyard: family-owned. **Established:** 1880. **Vine stocks:** Gamy Noir (white juice). **Soil:** granite and clay. **Exposure:** East-West. **Average annual production in hectoliters:** 50 hl/ha.

Appellation: Coteaux du Lyonnais. **Type:** Red. **Technique:** semi-carbonic maceration. **Maturing:** in casks. **Alcohol content:** 12-12.5%. **Characteristics:** light, pleasant, to be drunk young. **Serving temperature:** 10-13°. **Served with:** delicatessen and other Lyon specialties.

Characteristics of vintages

1988: Paris Gold Medal. Price range (pre-tax, ex-warehouse): 20 F.F. to 30 F.F.

References in France

Restaurants: (Paris): Le Beaujolais Comptoir, Le Vin des Rues, Le lance Pierre, L'Amphitryon, La Providence, Hotel le Crillon. (Lyon): le Sully.
Shops: Euro-Marché, Caves de Genas.

Comments

For peace and contentment, fill your cellar with Coteaux du Lyonnais.

BORDEAUX

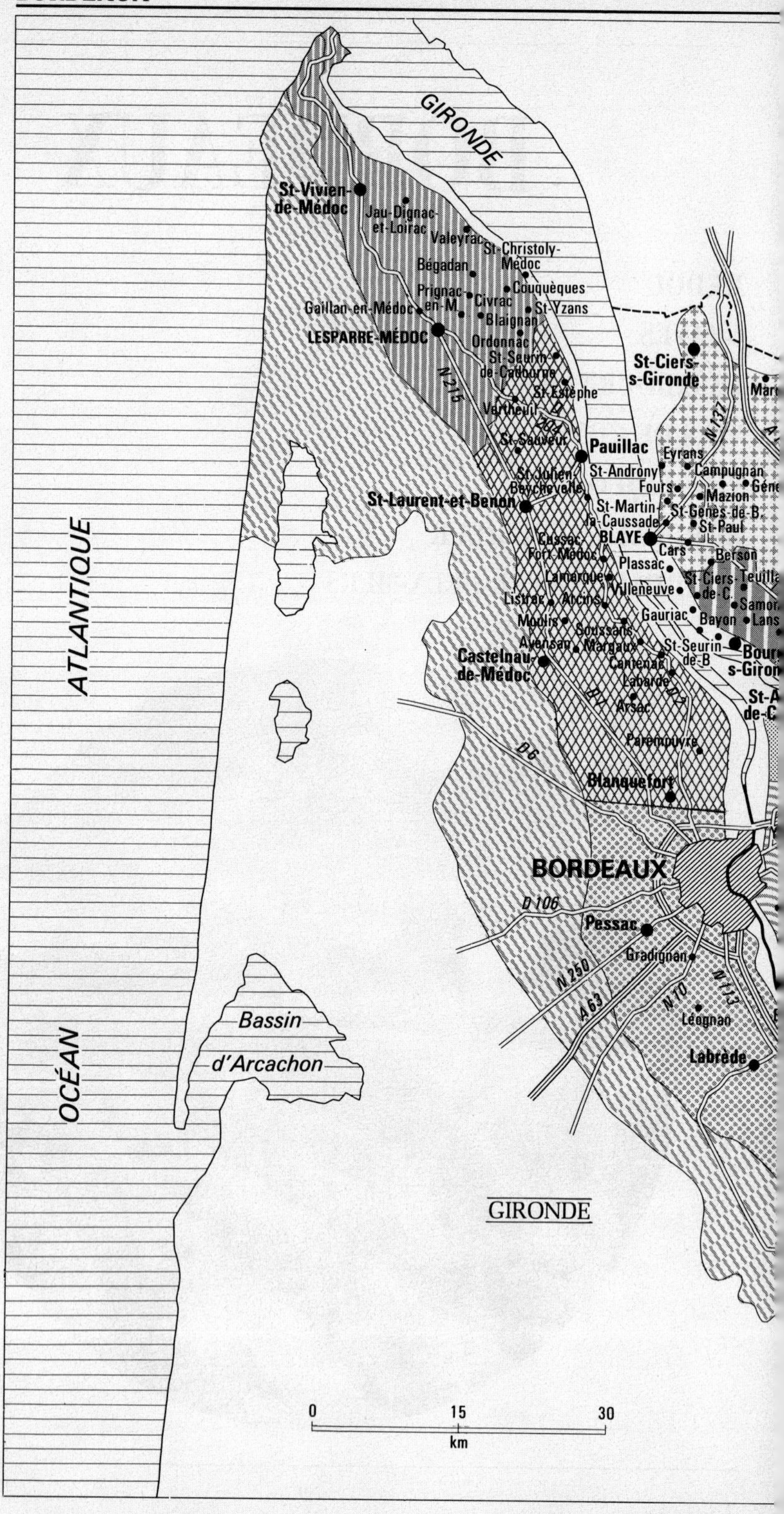

GIRONDE
St-Vivien-de-Médoc
Jau-Dignac-et-Loirac
Valeyrac
St-Christoly-Médoc
Bégadan
Couquèques
Prignac-en-M.
Civrac
Gaillan-en-Médoc
St-Yzans
Blaignan
LESPARRE-MÉDOC
Ordonnac
St-Seurin-de-Cadourne
St-Estèphe
Vertheuil
N 215
D 204
St-Sauveur
Pauillac
St-Julien-Beychevelle
St-Laurent-et-Benon
St-Ciers-s-Gironde
N 137
Mar
Eyrans
St-Androny
Campugnan
Fours
Gène
Mazion
St-Martin-la-Caussade
St-Genès-de-B.
St-Paul
BLAYE
Cars
Berson
Cussac-Fort-Médoc
Plassac
Lamarque
St-Ciers-de-C.
Teuilla
Villeneuve
Listrac
Arcins
Samon
Moulis
Gauriac
Bayon
Lans
Soussans
Avensan
Margaux
St-Seurin-de-B
Bour-s-Giron
Castelnau-de-Médoc
Cantenac
Labarde
St-A de-C
D 1
D 2
Arsac
D 6
Parempuyre
Blanquefort
ATLANTIQUE
BORDEAUX
D 106
Pessac
Gradignan
N 250
A 63
N 10
N 113
Léognan
Labrède
Bassin d'Arcachon
OCÉAN
GIRONDE
0 15 30
km

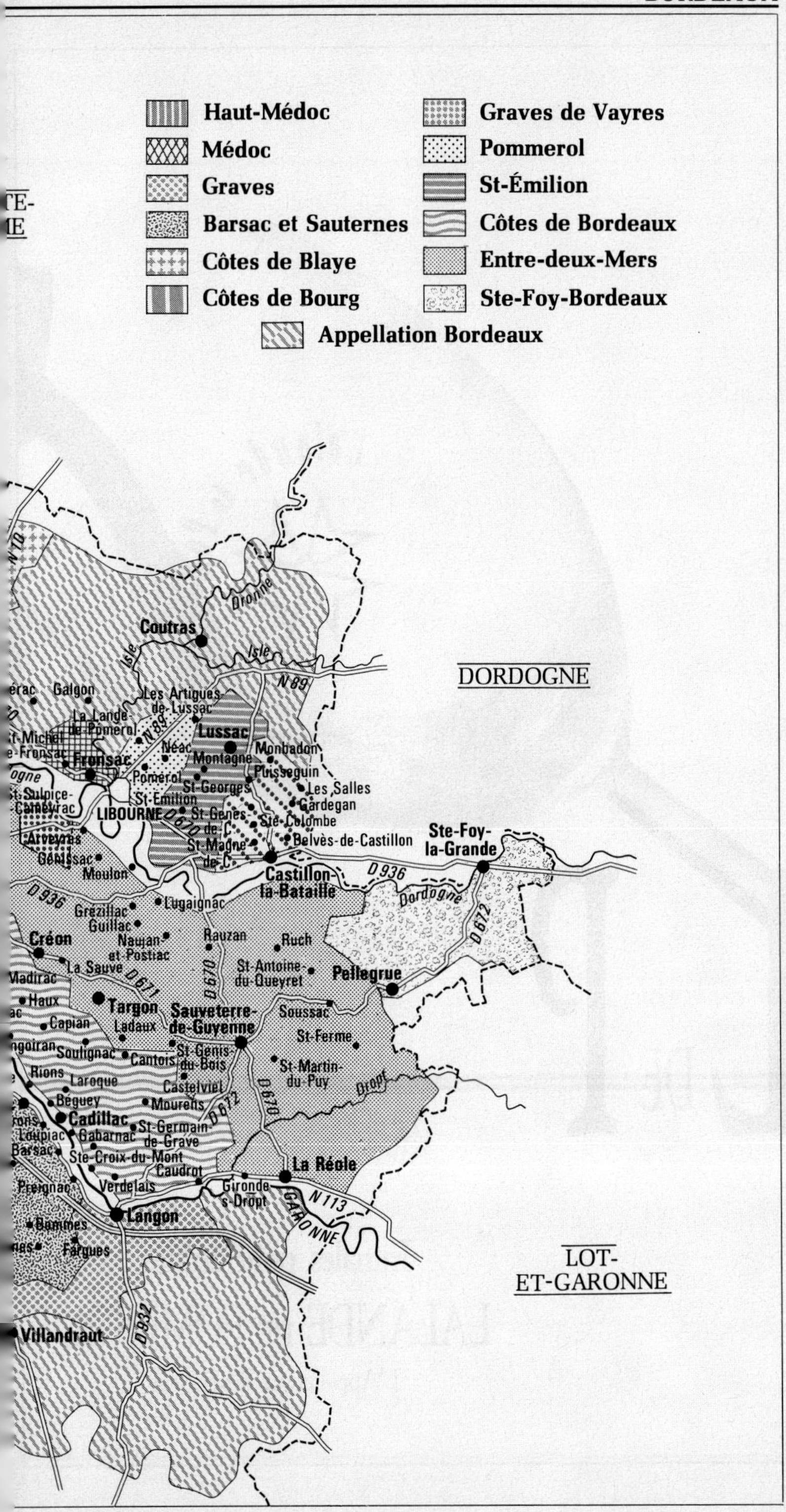

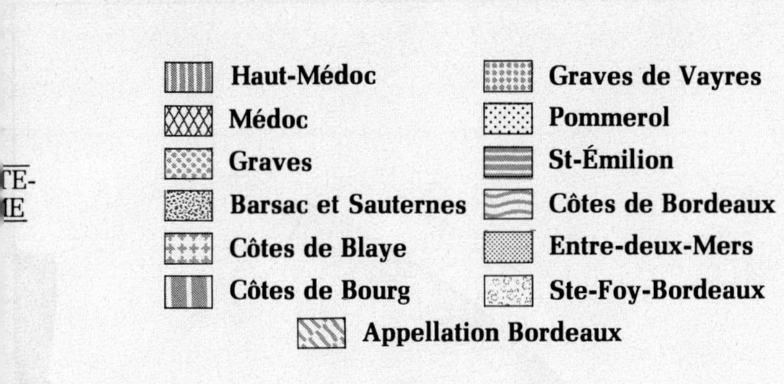

Haut-Médoc
Médoc
Graves
Barsac et Sauternes
Côtes de Blaye
Côtes de Bourg
Graves de Vayres
Pommerol
St-Émilion
Côtes de Bordeaux
Entre-deux-Mers
Ste-Foy-Bordeaux
Appellation Bordeaux
DORDOGNE
LOT-
ET-GARONNE
Coutras
Dronne
Isle
N 89
N 10
Galgon
Les Artigues-
de-Lussac
La Lande-
de-Pomerol
Lussac
Néac
Montagne
Monbadon
Puisseguin
Fronsac
Pomerol
St-Georges
Les Salles
Gardegan
St-Émilion
LIBOURNE
D 670
St-Genès-
de-C.
Ste-Colombe
Belvès-de-Castillon
St-Magne-
de-C.
Arveyres
Génissac
Moulon
Castillon-
la-Bataille
Ste-Foy-
la-Grande
D 936
Dordogne
D 672
Lugaignac
Grezillac
Guillac
Nauian-
et-Postiac
Rauzan
Ruch
Créon
La Sauve
D 671
St-Antoine-
du-Queyret
Pellegrue
Madirac
Haux
Targon
Sauveterre-
de-Guyenne
Soussac
Capian
Ladaux
St-Ferme
Soulignac
Cantois
St-Genis-
du-Bois
St-Martin-
du-Puy
Rions
Laroque
Castelviel
Dropt
Beguey
Mourens
Cadillac
St-Germain-
de-Grave
Loupiac
Gabarnac
Barsac
Ste-Croix-du-Mont
Caudrot
La Réole
Preignac
Verdelais
Gironde-
s-Dropt
N 113
Langon
GARONNE
Bommes
Fargues
D 932
Villandraut

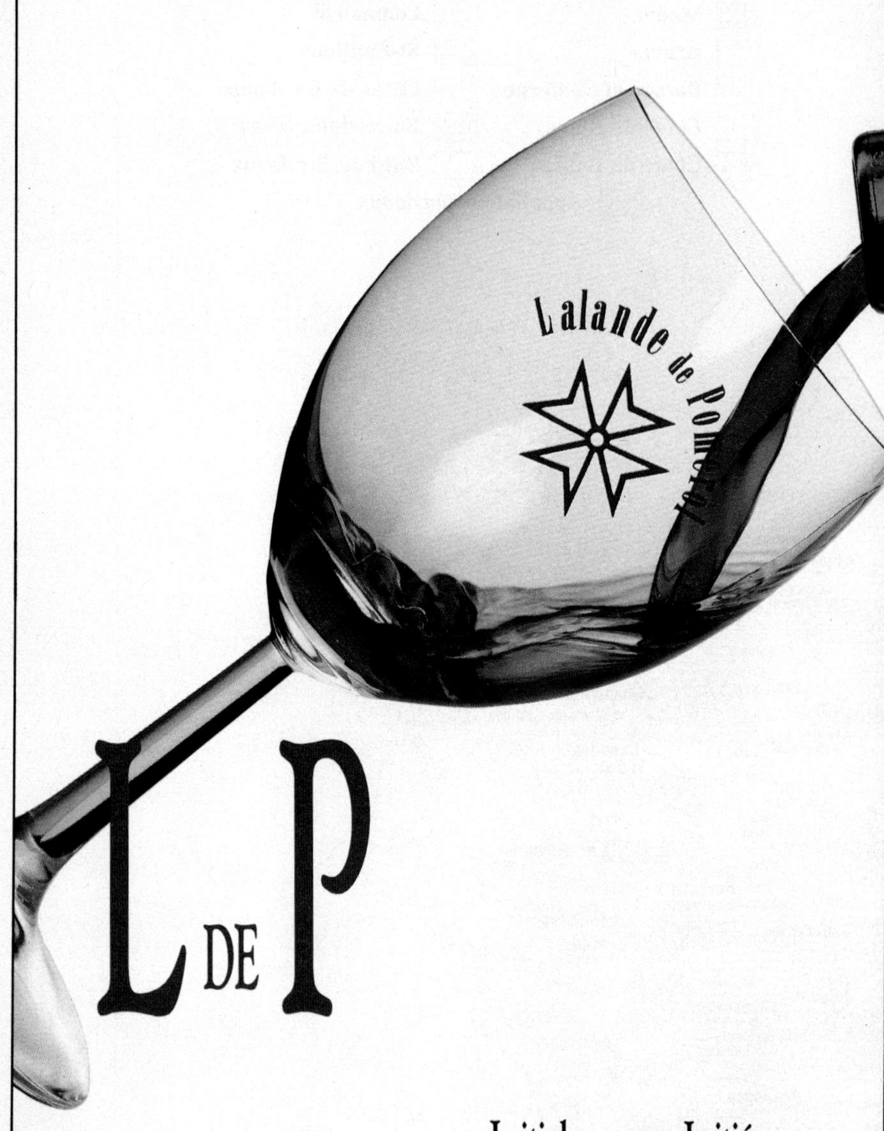

Lalande de Pomerol
L DE P

No holding back the reds

Bordeaux will always be Bordeaux, although it is clear that, recently, a certain restructuration has been taking place. One is suddenly aware that a number of producers of the Bordeaux grands crus (you will recognize them in the Guide) have either been very successful with their 87 vintage or have been able to establish a well publicized (justifiably so) balance between quality and price, or (rarely) both at the same time. Also apparent is a veritable groundswell in the vineyards of the Gironde, with the emergence of exceptional wines, with excellent quality/price ratios, in Médoc, in Libourne, in the Graves, the Vins de Côtes or the "modest" Bordeaux Supérieurs. Bordeaux is an extensive vineyard where all kinds of wines can be found, at all prices. It is more important than ever to "knock on the right door", to question what should properly be questioned (see "Classification 89"). In this way one gains access to the most exceptional wines, the real grands crus which are among the greatest red wines in the world (and certain whites, the Sauternes, in particular) a panoply of quality wines with an exceptional future.

HISTORICAL BACKGROUND

In the mid-12th Century, Bordeaux—called Burdigalia by the Romans—became the capital of Guienne prior to being taken over by the English who retained possession of it for two hundred years. In 1152, the second marriage of Princess Eleanor of Aquitaine and Henry Plantagenet, Duke of Normandy and Count of Anjou, strengthened the ties between the English and the inhabitants of Bordeaux. In 1154, the Count of Anjou, who became Henry II, ascended to the throne of England.

The inhabitants of Bordeaux thus became English subjects, the French language was extolled at the Court of England and wine trading with England developed. Richard I, known as "Richard the Lion-Hearted," the elder son of Eleanor of Aquitaine and Henry II, lived in Bordeaux and was a connoisseur of vintage wines. His brother, John Lackland, placed the merchants of Bordeaux under his protection and established a regulatory period for the sale of wine: November and December.

At that time there was no procedure for keeping wine stored in barrels, so the wine that sold the best was the youngest wine. Older wine was given to the poor. English decrees began to strongly support Bordeaux, to such an extent that merchants from other cities asked to be admitted into the Aquitaine elite.

During the Hundred Years' War, the bourgeoisie of Bordeaux took the side of the English—because they valued the privileges the English enjoyed. But Guienne tried not to lend its support. The English General Talbot, whose family was of Norman origin, attacked and took Bordeaux, but was killed in the battle at Castillon on July 17, 1453. The century of wars came to an end and Bordeaux was French once again.

Vineyards blossomed around Bordeaux and the city acquired wealth which enabled it to use its power to stop Médoc winegrowers from loading their wines along the Gironde River. Before the economic blockade or "Bordeaux privilege" was abolished in 1776, many great wines unfortunately disappeared.

Wine consumption grew and grew, as did both discriminate and excessive use of it. Consequently in 1536, François I. decreed that "anyone found intoxicated will immediately be imprisoned and fed nothing more than bread and water." A second infraction was punishable by whipping. Upon a third infraction, the individual was whipped again, but this time in public. If the transgressor was caught a fourth time in infraction of the decree, his ear was cut off.

Drinking as an art began in the 16th Century under Henry III. According to the custom of the time, a toasted crouton was placed in the bottom of a glass which was filled with wine. The glass was passed from hand to hand until it reached the person who was to be honored. The honored individual then drank the contents of the glass and ate the crouton called "a toasted." The origin of the word toast comes from this custom.

The Bordeaux wine trade underwent a period of calm when exports to England stopped.

The Methuen Treaty between England and Portugal heavily taxed French wines. (A duty of £55 per ton was livied, whereas the amount was only £7 per ton for Portuguese wines.) As a result of the heavy taxation, *claret* wines were exported via Dutch boats which arrived every year by the hundreds to load new wine.

Preserving wine became easier when cork plugs and hand-blown glass bottles came into use. Exports to more distant countries began, including to the French Antilles, India and North America. The prosperity Bordeaux enjoyed encouraged the English, the Danish, the Irish and the Dutch to set up offices along Quai des Chartrons and engage in wine trading much more extensively.

The French Revolution and the wars under the Empire put an end to Bordeaux's economic expansion. And when Napoleon came into power, the situation worsened further because of his great preference for Burgundy wines. The Bordeaux wine trade recovered full expansion only when Napoleon was exiled to Sainte Hélène.

THE WINES

- **MEDOC:** The vineyard extends, from north to south, over approximately 80 kilometres. It is sheltered from the Atlantic Ocean by a large pine forest and bordered by the huge Gironde estuary. Its relatively warm and humid microclimate is ideally suited to the cultivation of the vine.
- **PAUILLAC:** This 950 hectare vineyard, located between Saint-Estèphe and Saint-Julien, produces three of the best grands crus classés of the Médoc (Lafite, Latour and the recent Mouton, born in 1973). Generally strong, elegant, well-bred and vigorous wines.
- **MARGAUX:** (1,000 hectares). Five villages (Arsac, Cantenac, Labarde, Margaux and Soussans) have a right to the Margaux appellation. They produce the most delicate wines of all.
- **SAINT-ESTÈPHE:** ((1,300 hectares). Richer, better-balanced and fuller than most of the great Médoc appellations, the Saint-Estèphe wines only come into their own with ageing.
- **SAINT-JULIEN:** (695 hectares). Somewhere between the finesse of the Margaux and the robustness of the Pauillac. Generally dense and full, they also have a fine bouquet.
- **MOULIS:** (300 hectares). Between Saint-Julien and Margaux, produces fragrant, soft and rich wines.
- **LISTRAC:** (480 hectares). The most robust, full-bodied, and well-balanced of the Médoc wines.
- **HAUT-MEDOC:** (2,100 hectares) and **MEDOC** (2,300 hectares). Two "simple" appellations whose names do not do them justice. A fine opportunity to discover great Bordeaux in these two A.O.C.S.
- **SAINT-EMILION:** Appellation covering 1,000 crus extending from the Premier Grand Cru Classé to the simple Saint-Emilion A.O.C., including the Grand Cru Classé and the Grand Cru. The beautiful commune of Saint-Emilion, in the heart of the Libournais, literally surrounded by vineyards, is regarded as one of the oldest French winegrowing areas. There are good and lesser quality Saint-Emilions, depending on the growing area (plain or hillside), the soil and exposure and, of course, the proprietor.
- **FRONSAC and CANON-FRONSAC:** Neighboring Saint-Emilion and Pomerol, a few kilometres from Libourne, Fronsac produces reds that are robust and forthcoming, very tannic, with a particular spicy flavor.

• **POMEROL:** Deep ruby color, full-bodied, robust and velvety wines.

• **GRAVES:** A natural extension of the Médoc, to which it has always been attached, from both the historical and geographical point of view. Its gravelly soil (from which its name is derived) is poor but helped by exceptionnal climatic conditions and the art of the Bordeaux winegrowers. The red wines are better-balanced and easily distinguishable from the other Médocs. The dry white Graves need a bit of ageing.

SWEET WHITE WINES

• **SAUTERNES:** Appellation covering five communes (Barsac, Bommes, Fargues, Preignac and Sauternes) whose originality stems from the harvesting method used. Grapes must reach full maturity under the action of Botrytis Cinerea, also called "noble rot". The degradation process causes the grape to loose its water and increase its alcohol content, giving the wine a heavy concentration of liqueur.

• **BARSAC:** If produced from vines grown in the Sauternes region, the Barsac wines can take the Sauternes appellation and/or keep their own.

• **CERONS, LOUPIAC, CADILLAC, GRAVES SUPERIEUR, SAINTE CROIX DU MONT:** Less sweet and delicate than those from Barsac-Sauternes. Matured with utmost care, often very fruity.

OTHERS APPELLATIONS

• **VINS DE COTES:** 400,000 hectolitres of wine are made from the superior grapes of Bordeaux (CABERNET, MERLOT, MALBEC for reds, SEMILLON, MUSCADELLE and SAUVIGNON for whites) grown on the hillsides on the right bank of the Garonne, Dordogne and Gironde, mostly facing the Médoc and Graves regions.

• **PREMIERES COTES DE BORDEAUX:** Made from vines planted in clay and limestone, sometimes over gravel, the red Premières Côtes de Bordeaux are rich and very fruity wines.

• **COTES DE BLAYE:** 10,000 hectares vineyard facing the Médoc. The dry white wines are fruity and the reds very fine (A.O.C. Premières Côtes de Blaye).

• **COTE DE CASTILLON:** At the outermost limits of the Gironde, with Saint-Emilion on the West and Bergerac on the East. Mainly red wines.

• **COTES DE BOURG:** Baptized the "Suisse Girondine" because of its hilly, undulating soil, the Bourg Region, situated on the banks of the Gironde, offers beautifully structured, fragrant and round red wines. The whites are fresh, fine and easy to drink.

• **COTES DE FRANCS:** 8,000 hectoliters of Côtes de Francs A.O.C. (70% red) are produced north of Castillon-la-Bataille.

• **ENTRE-DEUX-MERS:** The Entre-Deux-Mers region extends from the Dordogne to the Garonne, opposite the Graves area, from the tip of the Ambès headland to the borders of the Dordogne and of the Lot-et-Garonne. It produces dry, fruity and lively white wines.

CHARACTERISTICS OF THE VINEYARD

Bordeaux contains the widest variety of winegrowing regions, each contributing to the richness and uniqueness of the Bordeaux wine country.

THE MÉDOC

The name Médoc means "the country in the middle." Shaped like a fat wedge of cheese, the region lies northwest of Bordeaux and is flanked on the west by the Atlantic Ocean and on the east by the estuary of the Gironde River. Vineyards extend for 80 mi. (129 km), but the area is small in width—only about 5 mi. wide (8 km)—because to the west pine forests have been planted along the shore to protect the vineyards from the ocean. The Médoc is divided into two regions, the Médoc and the Haut-Médoc, which share six appellations in two communes : Saint-Estèphe, Pauillac, Moulis, Saint-Julien, Margaux and Listrac.

Soil

Paradoxically, the Médoc's poor quality and porous quaternary soil is a blessing for the vineyards. Primarily composed of sand, gravel and pebbles, it makes the ideal mixture for great vineyards. This mixture allows the roots to grow as deep as ?? feet (six meters) underground and helps the growth of the grapevine at both the soil and subsoil levels.

Climate

Because the Bordeaux winegrowing region is situated on the 45th parallel, the Médoc has a warm and humid marine climate. Weather conditions are further improved by its geographic location. Situated between the Atlantic Ocean and the Gironde River, these two bodies of water serve as heat regulators, creating the best microclimate vines could ever hope for. The amount of sunshine is not impressive, nor is the temperature which remains stable at about 53.6°F (12°C). Annual rainfall varies, averaging only 170 days of precipitation a year. But this is good because the small amount of rain has no trouble trickling down the many tiny hills where the Médoc vineyards are scattered.

GRAVES

The region of Graves, to the south of the Médoc, covers an area 50 mi. (80 km) long by 15 mi-20 mi wide (24-32 km). It is bordered on the west by forests and on the east by plains. To the north, the vineyards extend into the Bordeaux winegrowing region. Graves' greatest claim to fame is that it produces both vintage reds and whites.

Soil

Like the Médoc, the soil in Graves is a mixture of gravel, sand and clay—the kind of mixture that allows grapevines to thrive.

Climate

Graves also has a marine climate, but unlike the Médoc, there is heavy mist at dawn. The sun shines on Graves ?? days a year; annual rainfall averages 833 ??; the average temperature of 53.6°F (12°C) makes for mild weather.

ENTRE DEUX MERS

Literally "between two seas," the region is so-named because it is located between two rivers, the Garonne and the Dordogne. Another unique feature is the region's size: Entre Deux Mers is vast. Vineyards are planted up and down its many slopes. The region produces both red and white wines.

Soil

The soil of Entre Deux Mers is especially complex. Along the bank of the two rivers, the composition is mainly alluvial soil; the inland areas are a mixture of clay, silica and limestone.

Climate

Like the Médoc and Graves, Entre Deux Mers also has a marine climate as well as comparable annual rainfall and temperature.

POMEROL, FRONSAC AND CANON-FRONSAC

The commune of Pomerol, located on the right bank of the Dordogne River, borders two other giant winegrowing areas: Saint-Emilion and Libourne. The village of Fronsac and the tiny area of Canon-Fronsac lie in the hills near the town of Libourne. In recent years, Fronsac wines have carved out a place of honor despite the great fame enjoyed by its neighbors Pomerol and Saint-Emilion.

Soil

Pomerol is located on a plateau which is composed mainly of gravel, except to the west where the soil is a mixture of clay and sand. The subsoil composition in the north and center is clay; the south is

Château Petrus, the tiny yet greatly renowned wine estate, is unique in terms of its soil which contains heavy deposits of clay. Toward the end of winter, because the soil becomes extremely hard, the vine roots die. But the Château is on a hill, so water drains off easily and this is a key factor in the Chateau's classification.

BARSAC AND SAUTERNES

The commune of Barsac and the small region of Sauternes are both part of the region of Graves. They are bordered on the northeast by the Garonne River and on the south by a pine forest. The production is white wine exclusively, especially dessert wines, including the famed Sauternes.

Soil

The soil of Barsac and Sauternes is a mixture of gravel and sand. Terrace cultivation along the Garonne continues to be used today.

Climate

Like all of the Bordeaux region, Barsac and Sauternes have a marine climate. The temperature averages 55.4°F (13°C); the sun rarely shines intensely. Rainfall in winter is heavy yet unpredictable. Heavy local precipitation sometimes produces extremely destructive hailstorms.

1988 CLASSIFICATION
Patrick DUSSERT-GERBER
RED BORDEAUX ©

Classification by appellation in alphabetical order.

Because of the soil, and micro-climate, and a greater or lesser proportion of such and such a vinestock, the age of the vines, their exposure, the skill of the winemaker, a special something that sometimes can't be explained, the Grand Crus of Bordeaux should not, by any sense of obligation, be put in the same category. It is often said, for example, that the Pauillac wines tend to be hard, the most tannic, the longest to develop and open up, whereas, the Margaux wines are said to be the most delicate, the most "feminine". Château Margaux is often thought of in this way. In fact, if you follow their evolution, you find that there is no typical Pauillac, St-Estèphe, Margaux or St-Julien. Two striking examples: Château Margaux, which is a concentrated wine, rich in tannins not at all "feminine" and Château Lafite (Pauillac), which has never been a fleshy wine, but always fine and distinguished. I would tend to say, therefore, that one should rather consider two types of wines, irrespective of appellation: a category A, more "traditional" and a category B in which the wines are more supple, being careful, all the while, not to lose track of the differences... The most recent vintages for which the two categories can be "compared" are the 1981 and, more particularly, the 1979. The 1983 vintage now also appears to be a likely candidate.

Category A

Priority to richness and balance. Great traditional wines, deeply colored, concentrated, to be kept (20 years or more), soft and full, very tannic, they only acquire their finesse and suppleness, their fullness, with the passage of time.

Category B

Priority to elegance over richness and balance. Great, very aromatic wines, fine, more supple, soft and subtle structure, less robust, better after ten years than after thirty, but quite capable of going the distance.

P.S.: Certain crus are, obviously, hard to classify, like Lafite, Petrus or Léoville-Las-Cases, Lamarque, Sigognac, Biston-Brillette, Beychevelle, Haut-Brion.

BORDEAUX ROUGES
(Alphabetical order)

BEYOND CLASSIFICATION NORMS:
CHÂTEAU PÉTRUS, *Pomerol****
CHÂTEAU MARGAUX (A), depuis 1978

1.	CATÉGORIE A	CATÉGORIE B
Premiers Grands Vins Classés *****	Châteaux AUSONE *St-Émilion* COS D'ESTOURNEL *St-Estèphe** CLOS FOURTET *St-Émilion* GISCOURS *Margaux* (2) LATOUR *Pauillac* LYNCH-BAGES *Pauillac** (2) MAGDELAINE *St-Émilion* LA MISSION-HAUT-BRION *Graves* MONTROSE *St-Estèphe** MOUTON-ROTHSCHILD *Pauillac* (1) PAVIE *St-Émilion** TROTANOY *Pomerol*	Châteaux BEAUSÉJOUR-BÉCOT *St-Émilion* BRANE-CANTENAC *Margaux* CHEVALIER *Graves* (2) DUCRU-BEAUCAILLOU *St-Julien* FIGEAC *St-Émilion* (2)* (1) HAUT-BRION *Graves* LAFITE *Pauillac*** (1) (P.S.) LÉOVILLE-LAS-CASES *St-Julien* (2) (P.S.) PICHON-LONGUEVILLE *Pauillac* ● Comtesse-de-Lalande*
Deuxièmes Grands Vins Classés **	**Châteaux** **L'ARROSÉE** ***St-Émilion**** **CANON** ***St-Émilion*** **DURFORT-VIVENS** ***Margaux*** **L'ÉVANGILE** ***Pomerol irrégulier*** **FIEUZAL** ***Graves**** **(3) (2)** **LA GAFFELIÈRE** ***St-Émilion*** **GLORIA** ***St-Julien**** **GRAND-PUY-LACOSTE** ***Pauillac*** **HAUT-BAILLY** ***Graves*** **HAUT-BATAILLEY** ***Pauillac*** **LAFLEUR** ***Pomerol**** **LARCIS-DUCASSE** ***St-Émilion*** **LASCOMBES** ***Margaux*** **LÉOVILLE-BARTON** ***St-Estèphe*** **MALARTIC-LA-GRAVIÈRE** ***Graves*** **PALMER** ***Margaux*** **PETIT-VILLAGE** ***Pomerol*** **PONTET-CANET** ***Pauillac*** **SMITH-HAUT-LAFITE** ***Graves*** **SOUTARD** ***St-Émilion*** **TROPLONG-MONDOT** ***St-Émilion*** **VIEUX-CHÂTEAU CERTAN** *(3)*	**Châteaux** **BEAUSÉJOUR (Duffau-Lagarosse)** ***St-Émilion*** **BEYCHEVELLE** ***St-Estèphe*** **(3)** **BRANAIRE-DUCRU** ***St-Julien*** **CALON-SEGUR** ***St-Estèphe*** **CHEVAL BLANC** ***St-Émilion*** **(4)** **LA DOMINIQUE** ***St-Émilion**** **L'ÉGLISE-CLINET** ***Pomerol*** **LA FLEUR PETRUS** ***Pomerol*** **HAUT-MARBUZET** ***St-Estèphe*** **LÉOVILLE-POY-FERRÉ** ***St-Julien*** **LA LOUVIÈRE** ***Graves*** **PAPE CLÉMENT** ***Graves*** **RAUSAN-SEGLA** ***Margaux*** **TROTTEVIEILLE** ***St-Émilion***

1.	CATÉGORIE A	CATÉGORIE B
Troisièmes Grands Vins Classés ***	Châteaux BEAUREGARD *Pomerol* LA CABANNE *Pomerol* CAMENSAC *Haut-Médoc** (3) CANTEMERLE *Haut-Médoc** CERTAIN DE MAY *Pomerol* CLERC-MILON *Pauillac* CLOS RENÉ *Pomerol* LA CONSEILLANTE *St-Émilion* Irr. CURE-BON *St-Émilion* FOMBRAUGE *St-Émilion* GOMBAUDE-GUILLOT *Pomerol* (3) LA GRAVE *Pomerol* LA LAGUNE *Haut-Médoc* LE GAY *Pomerol* MALESCOT-SAINT-EXUPÉRY *Margaux* (3) MARQUIS DE TERME *Margaux* (PICHON-LONGUEVILLE- BARON *Pauillac*)	Châteaux BOUSCAUT *Graves* BOYD-CANTENAC *Margaux* (3) CANTENAC-BROWN *Margaux* CARBONNIEUX *Graves* CLINET *Pomerol* CLOS DU PÈLERIN *Pomerol** COS-LABORY *St-Estèphe* LA CROIX-DE-GAY *Pomerol* LES FORTS DE LATOUR *Pauillac* GAZIN *Graves** GRUAUD-LAROSE *St-Julien* D'ISSAN *Margaux* LARMANDE *St-Émilion** LOUDENNE *Médoc* MOULINET *Pomerol* LA POINTE *Pomerol* SAINT-GEORGES-CÔTES-PAVIE *St-Émilion* SAINT-GEORGES *St-Georges – St-Émilion** (3) (2) SIRAN *Médoc** SOCIONDO-MALLET *Ht-Médoc* LA TOUR-POMEROL *Pomerol* VRAIE-CROIX-DE-GAY *Pomerol**
Quatrièmes Grands Vins Classés **	Châteaux BELLEVUE *Montagne-St-Émilion* BEL-ORME-TRONQUOY-DE- LALANDE *Ht-Médoc* BON PASTEUR *Pomerol* CROIZET-BAGES *Pauillac* LA CROIX *Pomerol* LA CROIX-SAINT-ANDRÉ *Lalande-de-Pomerol* (3) LE-CROCK *St-Estèphe* Irrégulier DEPEZ *St-Estèphe* (DUHART-MILON *Pauillac*) (4) FOURCAS-HOSTEN *Listrac** GRAND-PUY-DUCASSE *Pauillac* MAZERIS-BELLEVUE *Canon-Fronsac* (3)* OLIVIER *Graves* (POUJEAUX *Moulis*) PRIEURÉ-LICHINE *Margaux* SOLEIL *Puisseguin-St-Émilion* TALBOT *St-Julien* (LA TOUR-DE-BY) TRONQUOY-LALANDE *St-Estèphe* TOURNEFEUILLE *Lalande-de-Pomerol**	Châteaux BATAILLEY *Pauillac** BISTON-BRILLETTE *Ht-Médoc** CHANTEGRIVE *Graves** CLOS DES JACOBINS *St-Émilion* (DALEM) *Fronsac* (4) FONBADET *Pauillac* FOURCAS-DUPRÉ *Listrac** HANTEILLAN *Ht-Médoc** HAUT-BAGES-LIBERAL *Pauillac* HAUT-SIMARD *St-Émilion* LABEGORGE-ZEDE *Margaux* LAFON-ROCHET *St-Estèphe* (3) LALANDE-BORIE *St-Julien** LAMARQUE *Ht-Médoc* (3) LANESSAN *Ht-Médoc* (MAGENCE *Graves*)* (4) MAZEYRES *Pomerol* MEYNEY *St-Estèphe* LES ORMES DE PEZ *St-Estèphe** (3) PONTOISE-CABARRUS *Ht-Médoc** POTENSAC *Médoc** (3) RAMAGE-LA-BATISSE *Ht-Médoc** (3) LA TOUR-DU-PIN-FIGEAC- MOUEIX *St-Émilion* LA TOUR-FIGEAC *St-Émilion* LA TOUR-MARTILLAC *Graves* VILLARS *Fronsac*

1.	CATÉGORIE A	CATÉGORIE B
Cinquièmes **Grands Vins Classés** *	**Châteaux** **D'ANGLUDET *Margaux*** **BEL-AIR *Lalande-de-Pomerol* (3)** **LE BOURDIEU *Ht-Médoc**** **CLOS DU NOTAIRE *Côtes-de-Bourg**** **FONROQUE *St-Émilion* Irrégulier** **GUIONNE *Côtes-de-Bourg** (3)** **HAUT-MACO *Côtes-de-Bourg** (3)** **KIRWAN *Margaux* Irrégulier** **MARCHESSEAU *Lalande-de-Pomerol** (3)** **MARTINIENS *Margaux*** **MOULIN-A-VENT *Moulis** (3)** **PATACHE D'AUX *Médoc**** **PEYROR *Côtes-de-Bourg**** **SOCIONDO-MALLET *Ht-Médoc*** **TAYAC/LA TOUR-HAUT-CAUSSAN *Médoc*** **VIEUX-ROBIN *Médoc***	**Châteaux** **BRETHOUS *Premières Côtes de Bordeaux*** **(CITRAN) *Ht-Médoc*** **COUFRAN *Ht-Médoc*** **DILLON *Ht-Médoc**** **FAYAU *Bordeaux supérieur**** **LACHESNAYE *Ht-Médoc*** **LAFITTE-CARCASSET *St-Estèphe*** **LAROSE-TRINTAUDON *Ht-Médoc*** **LESTAGE *listrac*** **MALESCASSE *Ht-Médoc*** **MELIN *Premières-Côtes**** **MONBOUSQUET *St-Émilion*** **PEYRABON *Ht-Médoc*** **REYNON *Premières-Côtes-de-Bordeaux*** **SIGOGNAC *Médoc** (3)** **SOCIONDO *Premières Côtes-de-Blaye** (3)** **SUAU *Premières-Côtes*** **TROCARD *Bordeaux supérieur**** **VILLEGEORGE *Ht-Médoc** (3)**

P.S. Certain wines are very difficult to categorize A or B. The best example is LAFITE, as rich and well-balanced as it is seductive, young, as well as aged, and, of course, according to the vintages. This is the case with Pomerol and even Saint-Émilion wines. Watch out, but don't neglect the nuances.
Certain wines which do not appear in this classification could not be tasted in enough different vintages to be included this year. Stay tuned. . .

MÉDOC

HORS-CLASSE
CHÂTEAU MARGAUX (A), depuis 1978

1.	CATÉGORIE A	CATÉGORIE B
Premiers Grands Vins Classés *****	COS D'ESTOURNEL GISCOURS LATOUR LYNCH-BAGES MONTROSE MOUTON-ROTHSCHILD	BRANE-CANTENAC DUCRU-BEAUCAILLOU LAFITE LÉOVILLE-LAS-CASES PICHON-LONGUEVILLE- COMTESSE-DE-LALANDE
Deuxièmes ****	DURFORT-VIVENS GLORIA GRAND-PUY-LACOSTE HAUT-BATAILLEY LASCOMBES LÉOVILLE-BARTON PALMER PONTET-CANET	BEYCHEVELLE BRANAIRE-DUCRU CALON-SÉGUR HAUT-MARBUZET LÉOVILLE-POYFERRÉ RAUZAN-SEGLA
Troisièmes ***	CAMENSAC CANTEMERLE CLERC-MILON LA LAGUNE MALESCOT-ST-EXUPÉRY MARQUIS-DE-TERME (PICHON-LONGUEVILLE- BARON)	BOYD-CANTENAC CANTENAC BROWN COS-LABORY GRUAUD-LAROSE D'ISSAN LES FORTS DE LATOUR LOUDENNE SIRAN SOCIANDO-MALLET
Quatrièmes **	BEL-ORME-TRONQUOY-DE- LALANDE CROIZET-BAGES (DUHART-MILON) FOURCAS-HOSTEN GRAND-PUY-DUCASSE (LA TOUR DE BY) LE CROCK (POUJEAUX) DE PEZ PRIEURÉ-LICHINE TALBOT TRONQUOY-LALANDE	BATAILLEY BISTON-BRILLETTE FONBADET FOURCAS-DUPRÉ HANTEILLAN HAUT-BAGES-LIBÉRAL LABEGORCE-ZÉDÉ LAFON-ROCHET LALANDE-BORIE LAMARQUE LANESSAN MEYNEY LES ORMES DE PEZ PONTOISE-CABARRUS POTENSAC RAMAGE-LA-BATISSE
Cinquièmes *	D'ANGLUDET KIRWAN LE BOURDIEU MARTINENS MOULIN-A-VENT PATACHE-D'AUX (TAYAC) TOUR-HAUT-CAUSSAN VIEUX ROBIN	(CITRAN) COUFRAN DILLON LACHESNAYE LAFITTE-CARCASSET LAROSE-TRINTAUDON LESTAGE MALESCASSE PEYRABON SIGOGNAC VILLEGEORGE

SAINT-ÉMILLION

1.	CATÉGORIE A	.CATÉGORIE B
Premiers Grands Vins Classés *****	AUSONE CLOS FOURTET MAGDELAINE PAVIE	BEAUSÉJOUR-BÉCOT FIGEAC
Deuxièmes ****	L'ARROSÉE CANON LA GAFFELIÈRE LARCIS-DUCASSE SOUTARD TROPLONG-MONDOT	BEAUSÉJOUR (Duffau-Lagarosse) (CHEVAL BLANC) LA DOMINIQUE TROTTEVIEILLE
Troisièmes ***	CERTAN DE MAY CURE-BON FOMBRAUGE	ST-GEORGES-COTE-PAVIE LARMANDE SATELLITE ST-GEORGES-ST-ÉMILLION
Quatrièmes **	SATELLITES BELLEVUE SOLEIL	CLOS DES JACOBINS HAUT SIMARD LA TOUR-DU-PIN FIGEAC-MOUAIX LA TOUR-FIGEAC
Cinquièmes *	FONROQUE	MONBOUSQUET

POMEROL

HORS-CLASSE :

CHÂTEAU PÉTRUS

1.	CATÉGORIE A	CATÉGORIE B
Premiers Grands Vins Classés *****	TROTANOY	
Deuxièmes ****	LAFLEUR L'ÉVANGILE GOMBAUDE-GUILLOT PETIT-VILLAGE VIEUX-CHÂTEAU-CERTAN	L'ÉGLISE-CLINET LA FLEUR-PÉTRUS
Troisièmes ***	BEAUREGARD CLOS RENÉ LA CABANNE LA CONSEILLANTE LA GRAVE	CLINET CLOS DU PÈLERIN LA CROIX-DE-GAY LA POINTE LA TOUR-POMEROL MOULINET VRAIE-CROIE-DE-GAY LE GAY
Quatrièmes **	BON PASTEUR LA CROIX	MAZEYRES
	SATELLITES	
	A	B
	Lalande-de-Pomerol LA CROIX-ST-ANDRÉ TOURNEFEUILLE Canon-Fronsac MAZERIS-BELLEVUE	Fronsac : VILLARS
Cinquièmes *	SATELLITES (et vins de « Côtes »)	
	A	B
	Lalande-de-Pomerol BEL-AIR MARCHESSEAU Côtes-de-Bourg : CLOS DU NOTAIRE GUIONNE HAUT-MACO	Premières Côtes-de-Bordeaux : BRETHOUX MELIN REYNON SUAU Premières Côtes-de-Blaye : SOCIONDO Bordeaux supérieur : FAYAU TROCARD Fronsac : DALEM

GRAVES
(Red and White)

1.	CATÉGORIE A	CATÉGORIE B
Premiers Grands Vins Classés *****	LA MISSION-HAUT-BRION	CHEVALIER HAUT-BRION
Deuxièmes *****	FIEUZAL HAUT-BAILLY MALARTIC-LA-GRAVIÈRE SMITH-HAUT-LAFITE	LA LOUVIÈRE PAPE-CLÉMENT
Troisièmes ***		BOUSCAUT CARBONIEUX GAZIN
Quatrièmes **	OLIVIER	CHANTEGRIVE (MAGENCE) LA-TOUR-MARTILLAC

THE 1855 CLASSIFICATION

MÉDOC
Appellation Margaux

First Cru
Château Margaux (Margaux)

Second Crus
Château Rausan-Ségla (Margaux)
Château Rauzan-Gassies (Margaux)
Château Lascombes (Margaux)
Château Durfort-Vivens (Margaux)
Château Brane-Cantenac (Cantenac)

Third Crus
Château Kirwan (Cantenac)
Château d'Issan (Cantenac)
Château Giscours (Labarde)
Château Malescot-Saint-Exupéry (Margaux)
Château Boyd-Cantenac (Cantenac)
Château Cantenac-Brown (Cantenac)
Château Palmer (Cantenac)
Château Ferrière (Margaux)
Château Desmirail (Margaux)
Château Marquis d'Alesme Becker (Margaux)

Fourth Crus
Château Prieuré-Lichine (Cantenac)
Château Pouget (Cantenac)
Château Marquis-de-Terme (Margaux)

Fifth Crus
Château Dauzac (Labarde)
Château du Tertre (Arsac)

MÉDOC
Appellation Saint-Julien

Second Crus
Château Léoville-Las-Cases
Château Léoville-Poyferré
Château Léoville-Barton
Château Gruaud-Larose
Château Ducru-Beaucaillou

Third Crus
Château Lagrange
Château Langoa-Barton

Fourth Crus
Château Talbot
Château Saint-Pierre (Sevaistre)
Château Beychevelle
Château Branaire-Ducru

Appellation Pauillac

First Crus
Château Lafite-Rothschild
Château Latour
Château Mouton-Rothschild (since 1973)

Second Crus
Château Pichon-Longueville (Baron)
Château Pichon-Longueville (Comtesse de Lalande)

Fourth Cru
Château Duhart-Milon-Rothschild

Fifth Crus
Château Batailley
Château Haut-Batailley
Château Clerc-Milon
Château Croizet-Bages
Château Grand-Puy-Ducasse
Château Grand-Puy-Lacoste
Château Haut-Bages-Libéral
Château Lynch-Bages
Château Lynch-Moussas
Château Mouton-Baronne-Philippe
Château Pédesclaux
Château Pontet-Canet

Appellation Saint-Estèphe

Second Crus
Château Cos d'Estournel
Château Montrose

Third Cru
Château Calon-Ségur

Fourth Cru
Château Lafon-Rochet

Fifth Cru
Château Cos Labory

Appellation Haut-Médoc

Third Cru
Château La Lagune

Fourth Cru
Château La Tour Carnet

Fifth Crus
Château Cantemerle
Château Belgrave
Château de Camensac

GRAVES

Red
Château Haut-Brion (Pessac)
Château Pape-Clément (Pessac)
Château La Mission-Haut-Brion (Talence)
Château La Tour Haut-Brion (Talence)
Château Malartic-Lagravière (Léognan)
Château Olivier (Léognan)
Château Smith-Haut-Lafite (Martillac)
Château Latour-Martillac (Martillac)
Château Bouscaut (Cadaujac)
Château Haut-Bailly (Léognan)
Château Carbonnieux (Léognan)
Domaine de Chevalier (Léognan)
Château de Fieuzal (Léognan)

White
Château Laville Haut-Brion
Château Malartic-Lagravière
Château Olivier
Château La-Tour-Martillac
Château Bouscaut
Château Couhins
Château Carbonnieux
Domaine de Chevalier

POMEROL

Château Pétrus

SAINT-ÉMILION

First Grands Crus Classés

Class A :
Château Ausone
Château Cheval-Blanc

Class B :
Château Beauséjour (Duffau-Lagarrosse)
Château Beauséjour (Bécot)
Château Belair
Château Canon
Château Figeac
Clos Fourtet
Château La-Gaffelière
Château Magdelaine
Château Pavie
Château Trottevieille

CLASSEMENT 1988 BARSAC/SAUTERNES ©

HORS-CLASSE:

CHÂTEAU YQUEM, *Sauternes*

1.	BARSAC	SAUTERNES
Premiers Grands Vins Classés *****	Châteaux CLIMENS (1) COUTET	Châteaux FILHOT (1) GILETTE (2) LAFAURIE-PEYRAGUEY SIGALAS-RABAUD SUDUIRAUT
Deuxièmes Grands Vins Classés ****	Châteaux NAIRAC	Châteaux D'ARCHE-PUGNEAUX (**) CLOS HAUT-PEYRAGUEY RAYMOND-LAFON (*)
Troisièmes Grands Vins Classés ***	Châteaux BROUSTET CAILLOU (*) DOISY-DUBROCA GRAVAS (**) LATREZOTTE PIADA ROUMIEU (*)	Châteaux D'ARMAJANDES ORMES DE MAILLÉ (*) HAUT-BOMMES (*) HAUT-BERGERON LAFON LAMOTHE (*) LAVILLE (*) RAYNE-VIGNEAU SAINT-AMAND (**) TOUR BLANCHE (*)
Quatrièmes Grands Vins Classés **	Châteaux CARLES (*) DU MAYNE GRILLON MENOTA	Châteaux BASTOR-LAMONTAGNE BOMMES CLOS DU PAVILLON LAMOURETTE (*) LARIBOTTE MAURAS (*) PROST

(1) CLIMENS and FILHOT deserve this distinction: they remain the great classics of their appellation and become, in the great years, the first among firsts, approaching the Lord and Master, Yquem. As proof – these great naturally sweet wines develop their vigor and body with time – their qualitative level reaches its peak in vintage years such as 1929 or 1937, or even 1953 or 1955. The 1983 vintage is of comparable quality.

(2) GILETTE is a special case: only commercialized are the superb crus more than 20 years old (splendid 1955 and surprising 1953 and 1950). An "antique" Sauternes which really deserves an accolade.

(*) Deserves better some years (notably 1983 and 1982, even 1981).

(**) Well deserves its rank if quality/price ratio is taken into consideration.

N.B. Certains crus are – undergoing a complete "restructuring" – Rieussec, for example-recently taken over by LAFITE. It is preferable to wait before comparing them with what they were or what they should have been, all the more so since the current "masters" are not really inclined to open their doors, which justifies their exclusion from the Guide this year. Other crus (GUIRAUD, SUAU, DOISY-VEDRINES, HAIRE, JANY, JUGE, ROUQUETTE, LIOT, LANGE, BOUYOT, BRIATTE, DUDON, LAMOTHE-GUIGNARD, D'ARCHE...) have not been sufficiently tasted to be included in our 1988 classification.
Any others, finally, don't derserve to be included at present. Stay tuned.

Update on the Vintages since 1970

1970

Still a beautiful year, but uneven success. Certain red wines are already mature, others evolving in a complex manner, are closed and not very attractive. Great ageing potential, due to high tannin concentration, but a flagrant lack of suppleness, for the moment.

1971

Beautiful year. Red wines that are magnificent today, combining vigor and firmness with aromatic richness and balance. The best vintage for tasting at this time, in its mature phase. The naturally sweet wines are progressing well.

1972

Minor year with respect to the quality of the harvest. Surprising evolution of the red wines many of which (but not all) are fine for tasting now. The naturally sweet wines lack unctuosity.

1973

A small step down. Can be drunk without regrets.

1974

Debatable year. Forget the naturally sweet wines. Red wines falling fast. Don't try anything except the grands crus.

1975

Great year, complex evolution. Very promising intrinsic potential of the harvest, but the wines are closed. No telling if they will open up one day. Good dry whites and remarkable naturally sweet wines, which are not yet ready.

1976

Beautiful year, marked by the dry weather. High quality red wines, quite soft, to be drunk as of now.
Excellent year for naturally sweet wines, balanced, harmonious and well-structured—really regal wines.

1977

Minor year for reds as well as whites. Wines without much breadth. Certain Libournais reds are not bad.

1978

Good year, especially for reds. Tasting now is quite difficult. You will have to wait awhile. Some are disappointing. Average year for dry white and naturally sweet wines, which should be drunk immediately.

1979

Beautiful year. Quite comparable to 1981, although perhaps a shade less good. Not for long ageing, but very seductive, delicious, useful with soft aromas. A wine that will give pleasure.

1980

Badly understood vintage. Bad intrinsic quality of the harvest, but often surprising wines, very agreeable today. A commercial year, allowing one to wait for the development of the surrounding vintages.
Wines which certainly have a tendency to improve while ageing in the bottle—something that could not be done on the vine. Good quality/price ratio.

1981

Very great year. Fine vintage, well-bred, elegant. Quite often superior to the 1983. Well-structured wines, ideally constituted. A charming vintage as of now, but with an ageing potential that promises all the harmony that the best wines know how to develop.

1982

Exceptional year in all respects. Classic vintage. Richness, balance, complexity, the quality of evolved tannins, mature, graded colors. At the top of the list. An early maturity produced ripe grapes, rich in sugar and alcohol. Because of high temperatures, the vinification was difficult to control. Generous vintage par excellence, average acidity, grapes rich in sugar, fermentation difficult to control: the best winemakers produced a marvellous vintage; the others will make wines to be drunk sooner but which will be, nevertheless, excellent.
The Libournais is superbly successful.

1983

Beautiful year. Curious and original vintage, marked by an isolation of the grapes with respect to the vine stalk, a drying of the peduncle, even if, overall, the vegetative cycle remained more or less normal.
Mild and humid Spring, warm and dry month of June, a practically tropical Summer, hot and humid with the appearance of rot, hail. . . Happily the stabilizing month of September, sunny and dry, allowed a concentration of the must. Exceptional vintage for the Cabernet-Sauvignon, rich and concentrated. Good acidity and magnificent color. The 1983 will probably evolve

more slowly than the 1982 and several of the 1983 wines are superior to the 1982 in certain Médoc crus. A "masculine" vintage, typical of the Médoc. The Libournais is less successful. Some of the 1983 is, moreover, inferior to the 1981.

1984

Qualitatively, a particularly ambiguous year. The Merlot, which is responsible for roundness and suppleness and tends to compensate for the hardness of the very tannic Cabernet, was struck down by coulure and could really not be harvested under decent conditions.

At Saint-Émilion and at Pomerol, where the Merlot is dominant, the quantity gathered was dramatically small (as little as a quarter of the normal harvest). The grapes were mal-nourished, with very little concentration and most of the wines of these appellations will be without real richness and balance.

In the Médoc, the situation is entirely different. Here, the Cabernet is dominant and the influence of the Merlot is much more limited (from 10 to 30%) in the composition up of the wines. The vines did not suffer in the same way and they have a beautiful, healthy, deep color, combined with strong primary aromas. They are also hard, tannic wines, marked by the Cabernet-Sauvignon whose richness, sometimes attenuated by the suppleness of the Cabernet franc, yields quite unusual wines far from lacking in interest; quality wines, in fact, even if it is too soon to foretell their future. It is absolutely necessary to wait.

The dry white and naturally sweet wines are about average, no better.

1985

Climatic conditions:

— Winter: very cold month of January, more rigorous than in 1956.

— Springtime: temperature near normal during the entire season, with little sunshine in May and June. Rainfall: heavier than usual in April and May, rather light in June with, however, some very violent hail storms in May and June.

— Summer: temperatures higher than normal, very high in September (hot and very dry month). Total absence of rain as of August 10. Sunshine progressively greater than normal.

— Autumn: very high temperatures, no rain.

Conclusion: professionals, after the very rigorous Winter, the rainy Spring and the hail storms of May and June, were worried about their harvest. However, the flowering took place under good conditions and the September weather allowed the grapes to retain a remarkable, healthy quality. It should be noted that the exact dates of half-flowering, color change of the grapes and maturation correspond, within one or two days, to the average of these dates over the last 30 years.

The character of the wines:

With the initial naturally high sugar level in the must, the dry white wines have a sound taste foundation. The aromas are fine and pleasant but will be much more in evidence in the Spring of 1986.

The white naturally sweet wines come from good raw materials on which the noble rot, considering the climatic conditions, did not develop until the

end of the cycle. The wines are quite full, with lasting aromas. The last selections presage great wines.
The red wines already have a very beautiful richness: a very great intensity of color, lasting fruity aromas, normal and balanced acidity, rich and well-balanced tannins. This ensemble is the result of a well-developed maturity before the harvest, whose evolution surprised the specialists.

1986

Reds: Excellent vintage, very promising. Wines rich in color as well as body, strong tannins, concentrated aromas, for keeping.
Dry white and naturally sweet wines: Beautiful year. Lots of fruit and structure, full and distinguished wines. The naturally sweet wines have a beautiful future.

1987

Reds: Because the Merlot was attacked by coulure, this is a very difficult vintage for the Libournais (Saint-Émilion. . .). Average vintage, unpretentious. The wines resulting from a harvest in the rain are light and lacking in structure. Only the harvests selected very severly will make relatively good wines.
Dry white and naturally sweet wines: Average year. Quite neutral wines, except for certain naturally sweet wines produced from late harvests.

1988

Reds: Excellent vintage. Tannic, quite classic wines combining aromatic concentration with richness and balance, that are well worth keeping.
Naturally sweet whites: Beautiful vintage. A sound, late harvest resulting in complex wines, rich in aroma with a promising futures.

Writing about Pomerol

by Jean-Claude Berrouet

Discussing a wine one has just drunk among friends is a pleasant experience; communication is established very easily since it is just a matter of sharing one's pleasure.

Writing on wine, on a blank page, without feedback is a much more difficult task. I could try to make you believe that I have a monopoly on truth. Nothing of the sort, since wines are as full of contradictions as those who drink them and can teach us a great deal about humility.

My purpose is thus simply to lead you through the Pomerol appellation and to offer a few remarks on the wines of this region.

This 730 hectare wine growing area is divided among 180 châteaux. They are linked by an infinity of little winding roads, forming a real labyrinth which tends to confuse tourists.

It won't take us long, but it is necessary, for those who take a real interest in wine and who want to fully understand the differences between them, to take the time to examine the diversity of the soils of which this region is made.

The Bordeaux gravel myth must not be taken too literally. The gravel exists, of course, but clay, alluvial and gravelly sands are also much in evidence.

Man's creations bear the imprint of his personality and originality; so has it been with nature since time immemorial. The type of soil determines the characteristics of the wine produced by each vineyard. In other words, different geological formations in the same appellation will not yield one but several "Pomerols". There will be one to suit everybody's taste: some will be supple and light, some robust and dense, others, rich and full-bodied. But if the diversity of the soil is the major differentiating factor, vinestocks also come into play and give to Pomerols their distintive character which distinguishes them from other classical Bordeaux. The Merlot, which, on the average occupies 3/4 of the Bordeaux vineyard, is the major vinestock. It thrives on the acid soil made up, very often, of clay and alluvium. It is complemented by the Carberbet Franc, called Bouchet in this region. These two vinestocks are not uniformly distributed within each estate, and this adds to the diversity of the wines produced. There are, thus, vineyards planted solely with Merlots, or else with 60% Merlots and 40% Bouchets. For the winegrower, the art consists of making the most of the soil in order to produce the most harmonious, the best balanced wine, which means the best possible wine, by appropriately dosing the vinestock components. As a rule, where the soil is mostly clay, the Merlot is dominant. While on the other hand, if the soil is on the gravelly side, there is a higher Bouchet percentage.

Man makes his presence felt through his art, his originality, his temperament—during the cultivation of the vine which produces the raw material, the grape, and then, during the vinification. But each year—surprise—something new comes up, which bears the mark of the climatic conditions of the year, and we have to take into consideration the idea of vintage as well.

Forgive me for this long preamble, but it was necessary to stress the complexity of the subject matter.

Now let's continue with a general description of the Pomerol characteristics:

— deep, dark purple color.

— powerful nose, a harmonious blend of creamy cocoa scents, truffles, grilled almonds, liquorice and blackcurrant.

— round and supple to the taste, but also fleshy and velvety, masking the sharp tannins of the young wines.

Now let's look at some of the environmental influences:

— When the soil is predominantly sandy, the color is lighter, the nose firmer, the wine is more fluid and develops a bit more quickly. We often find these features in the North, in the Western part and in the South of the appellation.

— On deep gravel, that is found in the neighborhood of the plateau running from the North-East to the South-East via the East, the wine is a beautiful ruby color, with touches of cooked and dry fragrances, particularly in the warmer years. To the taste, the wine structure is classic, with somewhat more rigor, good length and a lot of subtlety.

— Finally, on the plateau surrounding the Church, clay is found in abundance. The color of the wine turns deeper, its nose is more generous, powerful, with a very strong presence of truffles. To the taste, the wine becomes firmer, more dense, and more unctuous. In good years, in particular, one finds overtones of grilled almonds and blackcurrant in the aftertaste. These wines are for keeping.

Weather fluctuations can accentuate or attenuate all of these effects. For example, maturing under difficult conditions can give more flowery wine or even more vegetal scents and tastes. On the other hand, extreme maturation yields strong prune, crystallized fruit, and coffee flavors and often a very pleasant tarry taste.

All this is making me very thirsty and I will call a halt to this literary effort, which may prove a bit too subjective for being essentially intellectual. I hope, however, to have awakened your curiosity and encouraged you to become better acquainted with this mosaic, the wines of Pomerol.

INTERVIEW

Suffice it to say that Jean-Claude Berrouet is the man who makes Pétrus. A disciple of Peynaud, a great specialist of the Libourne area, he takes pleasure in discussing the development of wines, their style and how they should be drunk. An enlightening interview with the best oenologist of his time:

Patrick DUSSERT-GERBER: In what ways are the patterns of wine drinking evolving?

Jean-Claude BERROUET: This is a huge and difficult question. Let's just talk about fine wines, wines with an appellation. In the past you had commercial châteaux wines, plus a few other brand name wines, widely distributed. Well, the market for these wines, whether we're referring to the château-bottled wines (which had a certain personality) or to wines bought on the property and often sold as is, seems to be vanishing. The parties concerned, the trade houses (I mean here those from Bordeaux, Calvet, Cruz, Deluze, Ginestet. . .) have disappeared as family concerns and have been taken over by consortiums. They are now producing wines for mass distribution, blends, Bordeaux brand name products. The brand is defined in relation to the commercial policy of the house, which means that the product is presented in a certain way. It becomes a blended product, made from beginning to end to suit a taste defined a long time in advance. It is "marketed." It is not wine that leads the way but people. All these middle-quality products, with a traditional appearance that are distributed by wine merchants, are being replaced by estate bottled wines and blends. Thus we have two different markets. This is my first point. So, what is the kind of wine that we are heading for? It is somewhat linked with the house personality. We are in a period of observation and reflection. It so happens that, recently, I organized a tasting of brand name wines. There are, obviously, different schools: you've got drinking wines, light, supple, very fluid, refreshing, with no distinctive character, and others which follow a different path. They are traditional in aspect, tannic, almost like wine made for keeping whereas wines in the first category are for immediate drinking. You get the feeling that these wines are more structured, better-balanced. They are more representative of the traditional Bordeaux wine technology.

P. D.-G.: Wine is for pleasure. Is the 1981, for example, good for drinking now?

J.-C. B.: Yes, '81 wines are delicious, surprising wines. They are interesting and useful wines. All the vintages are useful. That's what our judgement should be based on.

P. D.-D.: There's always a particular time when wine is good. . .

J.-C. B.: This is true, in its life time, and in the period during which it is consumed, summer and winter alike. The '78 will be, for me, a summer wine. It's not overly tannic. All vintages which are a bit sharp and vegetal, which have a nip of freshness, will make very pleasant summer drinking, and the great rich and powerful vintages are for winter. Right now, traditional wine growing areas are wondering what to do. Once confined to one particular area, the wine growing problems have become international: the wine market, tastings, publicity—all have become international. There are new wine growing sectors which are looking for room for large-scale production, like California, Australia, South Africa, as well as traditional wine growing areas like Italy, Spain or France. Certain production areas will be subdivided, mass production will become commonplace, since high technology is here to stay and is becoming standard procedure all over the world. In the case of exceptional products and soils, the technology has adapted itself to the products in these new wine growing areas. Whether it can adapt to local problems, or whether it is reproducible under other conditions, remains to be seen.

P. D.-G.: With regard to Grand Crus of a great vintage, let's say 1982, what's the difference between one very great wine and another? Does that mean that the wine has more ageing potential or rather that it is better from the start?

J.-C. B.: You've got two questions in one: whether the wine is good from the start (or thought to be) and whether it will age well?

P. D.-G.: Let's take Pétrus. When it came out in '82, was there a difference, at the time, in quality in relation to other châteaux? Will this difference be maintained, or shall we discover it in twenty years time?

J.-C. B.: The answer is simple and straightforward. The difference in quality always increases with ageing. It is less striking for a young wine than for an aged one. For wine connoisseurs, the art consists in anticipating the quality that a wine will have after it has aged. There are not too many people who can do it. That's why I so much admire Jean-Pierre Moueix who can predict the future of a young wine. That's the trouble with all of the international tastings that are organized today, where wines are judged for what they are. This is how mistakes are made. It must be stressed that wine should be tasted several times over the years, and not only once. I must say that, in good years, the difference is less important than in lesser years, when Grands Crus always stand out with respect to the others. What is judged when great wines, "classic wines," are tasted young, is the richness, the complexity, the potentiality and the texture of the product. Obviously, a very rich wine will tend to be very dense, and this to the detriment of its subtlety and maturing potential. Lighter wines which develop more quickly will give more immediate pleasure. Some are starting to "expand" others to "become firmer," depending on their state of development. The choice of criteria for appreciation is not very sure and accurate. It's different for the consumer. He may select a wine of the lowest category in the hierarchy, which develops quickly, in order to drink it at its peak. There are, in fact, different aspects. You can choose more ordinary wines for hedonistic reasons or because they must be drunk earlier, whereas you have to wait for the others. Often these two get mixed up. One should refrain from making value judgements, but, rather, judgements of appreciation at a specific time in relation to the product's life cycle.

P. D.-G.: Which brings us to the heart of the problem. Since it is common knowledge that wine is drunk more and more quickly and that grands crus only come into their own much later, isn't there a danger that grands crus may one day lose their originality for never being drunk at their peak?

J.-C. B.: Thats's the problem. It is a matter of information. The question needs to be raised. Will the modern wine consumption pattern and its inadequate conservation be somewhat detrimental to the quality of the Grands Crus? In other words will we not tend, more and more, to drink great wines while they are developing, in less than their best condition?
I have always thought that, as opposed to medicines, wine labels should read "not to be consumed before. . . etc."
I'm kidding, of course, but in the present circumstances, it might be quite useful.
I am a stickler for ageing. I make all sorts of discoveries. For example, the '64 wines are just coming out. Well that's a year that has been widely discredited, and God knows that the climatic conditions were good! I remember it well. It was my first vintage year. Well, it met with a number of technical problems. There were a few accidents. If you don't count all those accidents, or all those wines that suffered from under-equipment, they are great today. We missed the 1964 vintage, and we gave it a false image, because it was not drunk right. In my opinion the '78 will not pose the same problem, because it is not a wine that must be aged, it is not fruity. The same goes for the '79 and '80.
The problem years are those which have the early features of the great wines: '70, '75. They are just coming into their own. The '75 is not there yet. We have to wait a bit more, and we are impatient. . . .

P. D.-G.: And then to taste them under the best conditions. . . .

J.-C. B.: Aeration causes wine to lose some of its firmness. It's classic. It's a question of how the wine is served. Aeration and decanting have two important functions: on the one hand, one must get rid of the sediment. This is basic. On the other hand, one must know how long a wine should be allowed to "breathe."

P. D.-G.: Since we are on the subject, I must say that it upsets me, and amuses me as well, when a '76 is decanted in a restaurant. Am I wrong?

J.-C. B.: The '76 is perhaps the only vintage that I do not decant. Though I do decant the '75, '77 and '78. I'll tell you why. 1977 is known as a rather sharp year, and what decanting is supposed to do is to "aerate" the wine, to let it breathe. This means that the tannins will pick up oxygen and lose some of their aggressivity or astringency. They will get softer. The aroma will also develop; the bouquet will expand.
In the case of young wines with rather sharp tannins, I decant at least an hour, as much as an hour and a half to two hours, before serving. If the tannins are very mature, I decant

only at the last minute. I'd rather dispense with decanting, since I am anxious to preserve whatever freshness is left. The '76 is a perfect exemple; if there's no sediment, I do not decant.

P. D.-G.: We're talking here of more or less recent years. Is decanting mandatory for older vintages, let's say for 20 to 30 years old wines?

J.-C. B.: The older the wine, the more it needs decanting; it's absolutely essential.

P. D.-G.: Does this also go for the decanting time?

J.-C. B.: Whatever the year, it's the sharpness and vigor of the tannins that are to be taken into consideration. If the wine is still very tannic, it will be decanted a bit earlier. If the tannins have mellowed, decanting should be done only at the last minute. It is the richness of the tannins that determine when decanting should be done.

P. D.-G.: Let's come back to the evolution of wine drinking patterns, of imported wine, from Spain for example, since this country's entry in the EEC. . .

J.-C. B.: Some are going crazy; others insist that it's not a problem.

P. D.-G.: Do you think that the taste of people used to wines like ours, for example, readily adjust to wines of another style?

J.-C. B.: I don't think so. Taste is something that develops over a long period of time. There are shocks that lead to discoveries, but not very often, and not for products consumed in large quantities. Behavioral patterns are artificially created; all agro-business specialists know that. Today people drink less and less wine and try to be more and more selective. And what do they ask for? Originality, authenticity, that is to say, products that have personality.

P. D.-G.: Which really means that they are willing to try more "difficult" wines?

J.-C. B.: I have often noticed that people like to identify with a product. What I mean that is that the fringe of consumers who drink quality wine, is on the increase. And the younger generations tend to have a more "scientific" approach to wine, a bit like the Anglo-Saxons. . . .

P. D.-G.: Don't you think that foreign wines are at least as good as the 15 to 20 Bordeaux Grands Crus on the top twenty list?

J.-C. B.: I'm afraid I can't answer that question. I know that you've got people who do very good work in certain parts of the world. You referred just now to Spain. Potentially this is one of the regions that is the most serious threat to us. It is still unexploited. The Spanish people are rethinking their traditional behavioral pattern. It's true that their wines are not for tasting, but drinking is another matter. And this is, after all, the first quality to look for. Wine is not always for tasting, but to be enjoyed.

P. D.-G.: Let's talk about the Libournais. I've often been disappointed this year by the Saint Emilions or pleasantly surprised by the Lalande de Pomerols. . . .

J.-C. B.: There are two things to be said about Saint Emilion: first it's a prestigious, magical name and secondly, a very touristic region. The problem is that, at Saint Emilion, the vines are rather recent, which is rather important. This is quite a drawback for the appellation in general, and leads to internal strife. At a time when we are talking about working on a world-wide scale, when we are wondering whether we should worry about world competition, we are not capable of self-discipline within a single appellation.
There are remarkable productions in Lalande. There will always be, within an appellation, a fringe of top level wines and one of mediocre wines. What's important is what percentage of the wines belong to each category. If you have 50% of top level wines in an appellation, it means that this appellation is not properly classified. If it were really that good, chances are people would know it. Lalande de Pomerol is an old Pomerol appellation. There's a Pomerol fringe which is going to come under pressure; the lower and upper fringes always tend to

recombine and superimpose on each other, as happens with the Saint Emilion and its satellites. The best satellites can sometimes be among the lesser Saint Emilions. Obviously. This will always be. That's the problem with fringe production. One would have hoped that it would be wine of lesser quality that would suffer, but that's not always so. More control should have been exercised in Saint Emilion so as not to penalize middle quality wines of the production. There are not too many people capable of enforcing such regulations. There was a remarkable man at Cap de Moulin, Saint Emilion, who participated in the 1944 classification. He was a very rigorous man and made many enemies because of the interests at stake. It's a matter of choice. Grands Crus are always where they belong. Some people want to protest, organize competitions etc., but when it's done by non-professionals it's not to be taken seriously. You have to keep on your toes to make the best possible product.

P. D.-G.: There's a new generation of oenologists, more honest, in so far as they have fewer ties with the winemaking houses. . . .

J.-C. B.: It's a new profession. And this new family hasn't stopped growing since its inception in 1955. In their deliberations on wine, these oenologists set aside all commercial considerations. One of my friends, Marc Dubernet, who lives in Narbonne, belongs to this group of great French oenologists. He is much younger than I and a specialist in Corbières and Minervois. He is a brillant chap, and has a Doctorate in Œnology from the University of Bordeaux.

His father is, with Emile Peynaud, one of my mentors. You know, there are two ways of making your way in this profession. One is to start from a region with a relatively modest potential and make original products that demand recognition. Another, to start from a growing area with a solid reputation, supposedly the best, and to prove to oneself that it is "the" best. It's more difficult because everybody is watching. One has everything to gain in the first place, and everything to lose in the second. At any rate, it is a matter of establishing the quality of a product, since one can't win every year. It is not a question of value added to the raw materials, but of making the most of the materials available, something which is not always possible.

The Entre-Deux-Mers is right on course

The Maison Mau, a leading and powerful wine producing establishment, has its headquarters in Gironde-sur-Dropt. It specializes in under-rated Bordeaux appellations and is one of the first dealers in the new breed of white wines, Entre-Deux-Mers. M. Jean-François Mau, heir to a secular tradition, is a true representative of the wine merchant of the future; a master of the art of marketing, he remains firmly rooted in his native soil...

Question: Four generations in the service of the vine and of wine! It's been a long time since your grandfather used to criss-cross the roads of the region on his bicycle to ferret out the best wines. Where do you stand today?

Answer: It's true that the Maison Mau has come a long way, but we do not disown our orgins, nor certain traditions. On the contrary, we are very anxious to preserve a personal contact with our soil. We are "deeply rooted". The Bordeaux area is a patchwork of small wine-growing vineyards with an average production of 250 hectoliters per vineyard. Yvon Mau is a big producer in the Bordeaux region, and his production, depending on the year, is in the range of 3,000-4,000 hectoliters of red Bordeaux and Entre-Deux-Mers. The Entre-Deux-Mers is a new product for us since our Château Ducla, a white Entre-Deux-Mers, only goes back four years. And it's clearly a success, for the Entre-Deux-Mers wines and the Château Ducla have progressed in quite an unexpected way. This is due to the quality of the product and to its price. It is true that in Bordeaux, red wines are a bit ahead of whites, but a lot has been done as far as quality is concerned. With respect to the vinification of red Bordeaux, there has been little progress during the last five of ten years. The problem was solved a long time ago. As for the whites, methods are still being perfected. It is true that we are large volume producers, but, unfortunately, the Château Ducla is situated at Saint-Exupéry. I would have much preferred it to be located in the upper Gironde, in the neighborhood of Margaux. It would certainly be more profitable for us, and for our image as well. The Entre-Deux-Mers wines do not yet have a solid reputation, but things could change. It the coming years, we expect to make the white Bordeaux a leader in its category by improving its quality. At the same time, statistics show a regular increase of the production of red Bordeaux, while that of whites seems to be regressing. We seem to be heading towards an equilibrium of price and production. We will make more and more red wine, and less white wine, but it will be of excellent quality.

Question: Why?

Answer: As far as red wine is concerned, little has been done, except that its production is of more even quality than before. There is less and less difference between vintages, more to the point, fewer bad years. In Bordeaux we've successfully eliminated the lesser vintages, and our vintages are more uniform, our wines easier to drink, our technique less time consuming. This does not mean that the wines cannot be aged, but they can be drunk younger than in the past. There is another way to improve the red wines of our area-using a harvesting machine. In a vineyard like ours, which covers something like 40 hectares, we used to have a lot of difficulty doing the harvesting by hand. As the harvests extended over three weeks, the tendency was to start too early, with grapes not yet fully ripe, and to end up sometimes much too late, the grapes then being too ripe. With the machine, the harvesting period is cut short, and it is possible to harvest all the plots when the grapes are at their optimum maturity. Most people claim that harvesting machines are not an improvement, but it certainly isn't true for the wines we produce, and for other types as well, since they are used for certain great crus. When the grapes are thought to be at maximum maturity, harvesting is done in one day. As far as our red wines are concerned, harvesting machines ensure the security and the regularity of the production. For white wines and Entre-Deux-Mers in particular, the harvesting machine contributes to the quality of the wine, since white wines more than reds, require quality grapes. It is absolutely indispensable to the making of a good white wine to have ripe grapes, but with no trace of rot whatsoever. Now we have more control over the quality of the grapes that are being harvested and their degree of maturity—which is vital for the quality of the wine.

Question: Have the methods used for fermentation changed too?

Answer: The second great revolution in the Bordeaux region concerns the fermentation techniques. This is nothing new. It had been observed long ago that the vineyards of the North produced wines that had more bouquet and were fruitier that those of the South. Wines of the North fermented naturally, at low temperature. The further South you went, the more the harvesting was done in hot climatic conditions, the wines fermented at higher temperatures, and much too quickly. The wines fermented at 35°C lost all their fruitiness, the esters evaporating with fermentation. The result was neutral wines, quite uninteresting. Little by little, cold fermentation techniques were perfected. Producers started introducing this method in Bordeaux four to five years ago. If you were to compare two wines from the same vineyard, one fermented in the traditional fashion and the other at low temperature, you would find them extremely different, like night and day. We are now convinced that cold fermentation, if it is well done, is more important for the quality of a white wine than the vinestocks or even the soil, for that matter. Only climatic conditions matter more.

Question: Let's talk about supplies. Are you a faithful client?

Answer: Whenever possible, this is our policy. In principle, we buy wines from the same producers and we will keep doing so as long as these producers are serious in their techniques and realistic in what they expect from us. Our role is also to make a selection of the wines of the area that are underrated. The Bordeaux area is the largest A.O.C vineyard in the world. The Grands Crus Classés represent but a very small minority of the production, which is made up essentially of a huge variety of underrated wines. The selector's role is certainly changing at just the right time. People are looking for cheaper wines, wines which are good value for the money. This has always been our policy. As a trader, it's difficult to imagine how we could help consumers, distributors, restaurant owners, if we were out for Château X or Y, Grands Crus Classés. . . These wines are institutions in themselves. Our role could be that of a distributor. We could be financiers. But that's not the way it's done anymore in the trade world. The value added by a dealer is relatively modest and financing must be ensured by production or banks. A wine merchant should be able to select wines and to distribute them at competitive prices. In the 20 th Century, one should be able to use a computer as well as one's palate.

Question: Do you mean that your role as a wine merchant is no longer to put on the market wines that have made it?. . .

Answer: No, because this is just speculation. For these wines we are passive middlemen, our profit margin, as small as it is, is totally unjustified. This is not the case for lesser known wines.

Question: How do you proceed? And, how do you select these lesser known wines?

Answer: By tasting and analyzing daily, dozens of samples brought to us either by wine producers or wine brokers. This is how we estimate the quality/price ratio of the product. If it seems interesting, we decide to promote the product. We taste and analyze each year 25% of the total production of the Gironde area. It's delicate work, of course. One must keep in mind that, each year, the hierarchy of values can be completely reversed. We are against special privileges and of course, for us, classifications made ten years ago are obsolete.

Question: And yet these wines are much in demand. . .

Answer: Correct. If you look at the wine market, you will find that, in France, ordinary wine (vin de table) does not sell. The market for very expensive wines, which fluctuates more, works well but is not stable. You also have wines selling for 10 to 30 francs which make up the bulk of the market. It is a voluminous market in full expansion. The problem is that, in France, one keeps thinking in terms of mass markets, in spite of the fact that a drop in consumption is expected sooner or later. It would be wise to cut down on production and to improve quality, but conversion of production is a political decision that requires a lot of courage.

Question: Do you sell wines "en primeur"?

Answer: Grands Crus are not sold "en primeur". It doesn't make much sense.

Question: And what about the lesser crus?

Answer: In my opinion, selling white wines en primeur is an absolute necessity. Their bouquet is at its best when young. They must thus be bottled very quickly, under inert gas, in order to keep their freshness. They must also be put on the market and drunk as early as possible. It's a bit different with red wines. There is no disputing that all red Bordeaux improve with ageing. The new wine making techniques help produce wines that are extremely fruity, that go down smoothly, and that can be consumed very rapidly. These wines can be aged, but they are "charming" even in their early youth.

Question: How do you place yourself in relation to the traditional Bordeaux wine trade which has been expanding progressively for the last ten years or so? You are often referred to as something of a marginal figure in the wine world. . .

Answer: It is difficult to place oneself! Undeniably, we are among the leaders in our category. We have a branch office in England, another in the States and both are doing quite well. We've just created a third one in Germany. Stay tuned for further developments. . . We are very well placed on the French market. We are thought of as a dynamic group, bordering on aggressivity, sometimes even going a bit over the limit. Although we are a typical Bordeaux family enterprise, we were never part of the general herd of merchants in the wine market place. Yes, you could say we are marginal in relation to the trade—if only by being wine selectors, by being a family concern and by our genuine Gironde roots. Bordeaux has its "peasant" crus; we are "peasant" wine merchants. On the other hand, we have entered the circle of Bordeaux wine trade by the "white wine" door. There was a time when the Bordeaux estates had established their power and reputation on red Bordeaux, on grands crus. . . The "whites" were really looked down upon. These white wines, as far as production and bottling are concerned, are a source of serious problems with regard to quality. We were the first ones to deal with this situation. We have invested in new equipment, conducted research on production, wine making techniques, filtration, bottling, etc. We are, therefore, way ahead in the profession, in Bordeaux, which used to be quite happy just making red wine. The number

of vineyards which have the know-how for making white wine, which are well equipped, and have always had an interest in white wine can be counted on the fingers of one hand. There are two or three white wine specialists like us in Bordeaux. What was a weak position fifteen years ago has now become a position of strength and is a definite plus for exports. Overcoming the technical problems associated with the production of white wine has greatly simplified our task in so far as it has made the production of red wines—which does not raise any major technical problems—easy for us. The white Bordeaux is to the red Bordeaux what duck liver cooked with grapes is to a soft boiled egg! Our present strength derives from the difficulties we have had to overcome.

Question: Could Yvon Mau become an institution one day, in Bordeaux?

Answer: We are proud of our roots and of course, we remain specialists in Bordeaux wines. Diversification is out of the question for us. Our future is linked to that of the wines we produce. There's no danger that we will rest on our laurels. In our profession, you can never be sure. We are, and will remain, in a permanent state of insecurity. . . Security is death. . . particularly for business!

Rencontres

The Chartron, one of the great wines

In Bordeaux, the House of Eschenauer faces the year 2000 without any complexes, combining the traditional know-how of the great Bordeaux Chartrons with a dynamism whose end product is quality. Something sufficiently rare to be worth mentioning.

One of the first Bordeaux business affairs is doing very well, thank you. Its first advantage is that the Maison Eschenauer is privileged by being not only a dealer but also a winegrower. This means that it can perfectly control the quality of its great wine, from the vine to marketing, thus assuring its status as one of the leaders in Bordeaux wine. In the vineyards, there are two exceptional crus, the Château Rausan Segla and Smith-Haut-Lafitte, which Professor Émile Peynaud watches over like a mother hen, selecting the harvests, seeing to the vinification, year after year, making beautiful wines where the strength of the soil and the skill of the winemaker impart the structure and flavor with which they abound. Nearby are the Château la Garde (Graves) and the Château de la Tour (Bordeaux).

PROGRESS AND TRADITION

Second trump, experience. More than 160 years in the business commands a certain respect all over the world, and earns confidence in an establishment and its trademark. As proof, consider the Bordeaux Oliver de France, whose sales to the United States exceed 100,000 cases, backeband sustained by large scale advertizing campaigns which extol Bordeaux know-how. The same goes for the Cuvée des Girondins which supports the Bordeaux soccer team at all of its games.

Inclined towards traditionalism, endowed with a remarkable production facility, the Maison Eschenauer, with an amazing performance record since the arrival of its new Director General, is resolutely concentrating on export, on the future. Jacques Théo himself is well aware of the role that a great local dealer ought to play and how this role should evolve, but, above all, of the necessity to create an effective symbiosis between yesterday and tomorrow, maintaining a respect for quality while looking to the future, so that progress and tradition can go hand in hand to create a great enterprise.

JACQUES THEO - THE MAN

Combining professionalism with his own personal touch of humor, Jacques Théo, 53 years old, successor to Jean Roureau, began his career in banking. In 1965 he started in the wine business and, for 20 years was president of Alexis Lichine et Cie.

After having been rotating President of the C.I.V.B. from June 1980 to June 1982, he is now the Associate Secretary General as well as the President of the Commission on Promotion.

Member of the Board of Directors of the Syndicat des Négociants en Vins et Spiritueux (Association of Dealers in Wines and Spirits) of Bordeaux and of the Gironde, he is also administrator of the National Institute of Appellations d'Origine and a member of the Board of Directors and of the Permanent Commission.

More and more concerned with the export market, he has just hired a marketing director and a top export sales agent who will shortly join his present team, consisting of Annick Coucharrière (Financial Director), Yves Fourault and Anne-Marie Vivier (Export Sales Directors), Lylian Mazoyer (Marketing Director for France) and René Baffert (Vineyard Manager).

The Petrus myth

"No founder can hope to see his work continue if his successors do not receive his message in a spirit of fidelity to the tradition that he has created".
(Extract from the Moueix "motto")

Everyone dreams of Petrus... Colleagues who talk about it without ever having tasted it, jealous winemakers (and rightly so) who take unwholesome pleasure in criticizing both the men and the wine, others who scream about the scandalous prices (enough said), and those – finally – who bless this incredible nectar, unique and fabulous. Here is the story of the most envied wine in the world, where reason competes with passion, desire with mysticism...
To understand Petrus, you have to love wine, the strenght of those who make it, strange odyssees. You have to accept that humility exists, and fidelity too, and that a grand cru is, above all, synomous with an abstract conception, a performance that is both real and theatrical, whose principal actors (soil, man and nature) "play for real" according to Pirandello.
The story begins (we will skip the ancient history) with an unusual woman, also something of a legend, Madame Loubat. There is no telling where she found the strenght – during the 30's – to "dare" to stand up to the great Médoc wines, but she was able to prove that "her" Petrus was easily able to hold its ground against the greatest, by combining a policy of ultra-high quality with an innate sense of public relations. Bravo.
During the 40's, Jean-Pierre Moueix, a dealer from Corrèze, recently settled in Libourne, signed an exclusive commercial contract with this "Great Lady of Pomerol". At Madame Loubat's death, her niece, Madame Lacoste and her nephew inherited the estate. Somewhat later, in 1964, Jean-Pierre Moueix bought up their shares. Until now, the story is banal – it is going to become extraordinary.
But first, you have to understand the determination of the Moueix family and the mentality of the time. You have to understand that, during the 60's, the stars among the Bordeaux wines were the Chartrons and the Médocs. Certainly not the Libourne wines, and still less, those of Corrèze which, for a long time, were just not considered at all. So much so that, at the time, very few of the great Libourne

wines were really taken seriously and adequately commercialized by the local dealers.
With hindsight – and here is where the story becomes interesting – you can't avoid a great feeling of respect for this man who, discretely, little by little, in his own little "corner", will not only create the greatest of the Bordeaux wine empires and impose his sensitivity with his Petrus, but will, moreover, become the "prime mover" of the great Pomerol, Saint-Emilion and Fronsac wines and, finally, make it possible for a number of producers to "come out from the shadow"... Don't you think that that merits admiration in the Médoc and elsewhere? History loves justified revenge against malice. So do we.
Moreover, the Moueix family will become (it is) a real family. Along side Jean-Pierre (not to mention his nephew, Jean-Jacques), his two sons, Jean-François (Etablissements Duclot, Bordeaux) and Christian (who presently directs the company), will show themselves to be worthy of this incredible reversion to type, each in his own way. I know that neither of them cares for flattery but, frankly, I can't help but "tip my hat" to them for their unusual accomplishments. But enough of that now, in respect for their humilty.
But remember that if Petrus exists today, it is only because it existed before (thank you, La Palice). The wine was magnificent and hightly respected and Madame Loubat deserves all the credit. But it is important to keep in mind that, if Petrus was able to retain its position of primacy at the time of a veritable "explosion" in the grand cru market, it is also thanks to Jean-Pierre Moueix, to Christian, to their remarkable associates (the oenologist Jean-Claude Berrouet is an excellent example), to this atmosphere of "one of a kind" which makes a family, from the "simplest" grape picker to the most capable cellar master.
A truly grand cru – lest one forget – is the result of a shared passion for caring for the vines, paying attention to their growth, knowing how to take advantage of the qualitative potential of the soil, how to push it to the limit. In short, it is to live as you ought to live, from the cultivation of the vines to the maturing of the wines, from the selection of the harvest of the vinification, to put everything in question, year after year, to accept the vicissitudes of nature, adapt to them and, quite simply, to strive wholeheartedly to reach the top.
A great wine is a creation and producing it requires a special state of mind.
For the grands crus, Christian Moueix is right to criticize excessive yields per hectares, the "degradation" of the vines because of the over-use of fertilizers and pesticides... Jean-Claude Berrouet is also right to distrust the excessive use of new casks which tends to "depersonalize" the wine.
When one observes the constant effort expended to raise Petrus to the top, when one is privileged to allow the taste buds to salivate over so subtle a potion, when one yields to the passion of this "Blood of Heaven and Earth", the insignificant has been set aside and we know that the "dream" exists because we are part of it. Heaven and Saint Peter (see the label) can be satisfied. On earth, also, we have what we need to satisfy those who share this incomparable, magic, true love for wine. Petrus is not the greatest wine in the world (there is no such wine), but it can well serve as an archetype. So be it.

The great tasting

Petrus is rare, but the ability to objectively evaluate the last fifteen or so vintages of this unique cru, including the most recent, is rarer still. Thanks to Christian Moueix, to several of our Bordeaux dealer friends, to the private collections of English, French, Belgian and Swiss wine-lovers (including the private collection of yours truly), this exceptional evaluation, which took place in stages, from March, 1988 to January, 1989, was possible.

1988: The tasting in January, 1989 – let's be frank – was difficult and delicate. It is a vintage that has just been put into casks, far from being "done", of course, in which one can already detect a definite structure. Very promising. To be tasted again after several months in the cask, which will soften the tannins, before we can really talk about it.

1987: Still in casks. Tasting done on samples. Vintage remarkably – and anecdotally (*) – successful, with a beautiful color, morello cherry fragrance, full and firm, evolving well.

1986: Tasting of recently bottled wine (six months ago). Beautiful wine with its own style, rather more oriental and exotic fragrances, great aromatic concentration, dense and supple but still quite firm, very persistent, well worth waiting for.

1985: Magnificent, highly seductive vintage, in another style, typical of what one expects from a Petrus. Exceptionnally rich and well-balanced, superb, where a lacelike finesse combines with exceptional concentration, a veritable chasm of ripe fruit aromas. Purple color, great persistence, for long keeping, very charming, very elegant.

1983: A more "secret" vintage, quite surprising, combining richness and balance, more supple, good evolution. To be retasted in a few years.

1982: Fantastic success where all of the elegance and richness of Petrus are accentuated. Very beautiful, sustained color, a rich wood-land fragrance, still a bit young and closed, certainly, but with an enchanting charm, truly classical. Along with the 85, our favorite vintage of the 80's.

1981: Excellent vintage, typical of the year, quite classic. Rich in color and flavor, a harmonious, subtle wine, already very pleasant, but for keeping.

1980: Perfectly controlled vintage, thanks to an ultra-rigourous selection and appropriate vinification. Lovely wine already ready to drink, very supple and fragrant, pleasing, with a beautiful richness and balance, evolving well.

1979: Excellent mellow wine, characteristic of this vintage which accords priority to charm and a velvety texture. Lots of finesse, very full, persistent, quite lovely evolution. Nevertheless, not very much in the classic "Petrus" style.

1978: Good year, perhaps a bit more closed but quite good for drinking already. Balanced, complex nose dominated by wood-land and truffles, combining richness and unctuosity, good keeping.

1975: Tasted in Paris in October, 1988. One of the greatest Petrus successes at a time when one is often very disappointed by the majority of other great wines of this vintage. Deep color, substantial, great, complex aromatic persistence, rich and balanced. A wine that is soft and full and firm at the same time, great evolution.

1971: Remarkable wine, combining color, richness and structure, with soft, but definite tannins, very supple, full and rich. Beautiful, long persistence. One of the most beautiful vintages which we enjoyed in Belgium in May of 1988. Later, Christian Moueix confessed that it is currently one of his favourite vintages.

1966: Tasted in magnums. Very great bottle, superb color, very rich, fragrant wine with a distinctly oriental perfume, beautiful depth, solid, full and persistent.

1964: Also tasted in magnums. Very beautiful wine with its own character. Still rather complex nose, beautifully rich and balanced, beginning to arrive at maturity. The first vintage vinified by Jean-Claude Berrouet.

PDG

(*)

An "anecdote" which (perhaps) smacks of genius. It rained heavily during the harvest of the 87 vintage. You know that it is unthinkable to "take in" good grapes under such conditions. Christian Moueix had the strange idea to fly over his vineyard in a helicopter, about fifty meters above the vines. The result: the movement of the "bird's" wings dried the drenched grapes almost immediately. The pickers then harvested the dry and shiny grapes. For the "sceptics", the "bird" then flew over the greatest Libourne and Médoc crus (Mouton...) with similar effect...

MÉDOC

MARGAUX

CHÂTEAU MARQUIS D'ALESME BECKER

Jean-Claude Zuger
33460 Margaux
56 88 70 27

Type of vineyard: Family-owned. **Established:** 1616. **Number of employees:** 6. **Vine stocks:** Cabernet Sauvignon 30%, Cabernet Franc 30%, Merlot 30%, Petit Verdot 10%. **Soil:** Gravel and silica. **Average annual production in hectoliters:** 500.

Appellation: Margaux 3^{e} Cru Classe. **Type:** Red. **Technique:** Traditional, stainless steel tanks. **Maturing:** In casks. **Alcohol content:** 12.5%. **Serving temperature:** 17°. **Served with:** Duck in the Margaux style. **Vintages available in 89/90:** 1980, 1984, 1986, 1987, 1988 (en primeur).

Characteristics of vintages

1988: Not yet tasted. **1987:** Rather successful vintage, beautiful color, supple and fruity wines. **1986:** Excellent vintage, rich and well colored wines, full bodied and lingering taste, good keeping. Price range (pre-tax, ex-warehouse): 80 to 120 F.F., 120 to 160 F.F.

Sales volume:
– Wholesale: 90% (export). – Retail: 10%.

Sales in France: 10%.

Export sales: 90%.

Main trading partners : UK, Belgium, Netherlands, Denmark, Switzerland, Germany, Austria, USA, Japan, Canada.

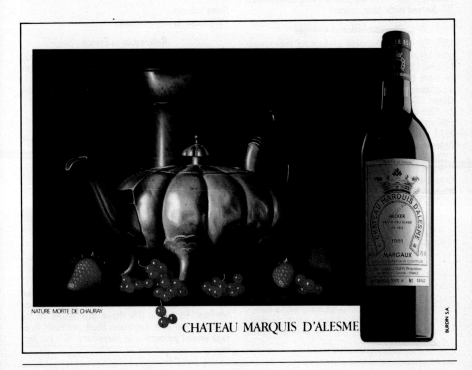

CHÂTEAU D'ANGLUDET

Mr. Peter A. Sichel
33460 Cantenac
56 88 71 41

Type of vineyard: Family-owned. **Established:** A long time ago. **Number of employees:** 11. **Vine stocks:** Cabernet Sauvignon 55%, Merlot 35%, Cabernet Franc 5%, Petit Verdot 5%. **Soil:** Gravelly. **Average annual production in hectoliters:** 1, 500.

Appellation: Margaux. **Technique:** Traditional. **Maturing:** In casks (35% new). **Characteristics:** Rich and well balanced, fruity, typical Margaux. **Serving temperature:** 20°. **Served with:** Meat, cheese.

Characteristics of vintages

1988: Rich and well balanced, forthcoming, rather tannic, good keeping. **1987:** Light, fruity, pleasant. To be drunk between 1990 and 1993. **1986:** Long, elegant, classical. To be drunk between 1995 and 2000. **1985:** Concentrated, exceptional balance. To be drunk between 1995 and 2005. **Other:** 1984: Long, delicate, classical – less structure than the 1985 and 1986, but character. To be drunk between 1990 and 1995. Price range (pre-tax, ex-warehouse): 50 to 80 F.F.
Sales volume:
– Wholesale: 95%. – Retail: 5%.
Sales in France: 5%.
Export sales: 95%.
Main trading partners : UK, Belgium, USA.

Abroad

United States
Importers: Sebastiani Estate Group.

• *Glycerine – wine component responsible for its unctuosity. It appears in the course of the alcoholic fermentation but, in the case of mellow and naturally sweet wines, can also come from the favorable action of noble rot on the grapes. See Sauternes.*

BRANE-CANTENAC

Lucien Lurton
33460 Margaux
56 88 70 20

Type of vineyard: Family-owned. **Established:** Owned by Lucien Lurton since 1956. **Vine stocks:** 70% Cabernet Sauvignon, 15% Cabernet Franc, 13% Merlot, 2% Petit Verdot. **Soil:** Deep Pyrenean gravel. **Exposure:** Southwest. **Appellation:** Margaux. **Type:** Red. **Technique:** Traditional fermentation with skins for 20 days. **Maturing:** 20 months in barrels (30 to 50 per cent renewed each year). **Characteristics:** Finess of structure, complex, aromatic, elegant. **Serving temperature:** 18° to 20°. **Served with:** Pheasant (wild fowl), white meat, sweetbreads, giblets. **Vintages available in 89/90:** 1986, 1985, 1984, 1983, 1982.

Characteristics of vintages

1988: Good fruit – deep and concentrated. **1987:** Subtle and fine aromas – delicate wine to be drunk in the next five years. **1986:** Deep color "black", exceptionally tannic, very promising. **1985:** Full bodied, very long, rich and fine, subtle. **1984:** Spicy – strict and elegant – not to be aged. Not yet tasted. **1983:** Rich and well-balanced, very aromatic, very elegant, full and yound. **1982:** Full, round, tannic, keeps well. **Other: 1980:** Round, fruity, very nice balance. Average pre-tax, ex-warehouse price: between 90 F.F. to 120 F.F. Price range (pre-tax, ex-warehouse): between 80 F.F. to 160 F.F.
Sales volume:
– Wholesale: 100% (Bordeaux).

References in France

Restaurants: Lucas-Carton, La Tour d'Argent, Guy Savoy, La Marée, Le Doyen, Jean Ramet, Guérard, Le Pré Catelan, etc.
Shops: Hédiard, Nicolas, Besse, great Parisian cellars (Petrissans, Movenpick).

Comments

Production of a second wine after a meticulous selection: the "Château Notton".

CHÂTEAU BOYD-CANTENAC

Pierre Guillemet
Cantenac, 33460 Margaux
56 88 30 58

Type of vineyard: Agricultural Association. **Established:** 1987. **Vine stocks:** 67% Cabernet Sauvignon, 7% Cabernet Franc, 6% Verdot, 20% Merlot. **Soil:** Gravel, for the most part, and sand. **Exposure:** South and West. **Average annual production in hectoliters:** 35 hl per hectare.

Appellation: Margaux. **Type:** Red. **Technique:** Classic (destemming, fermentation with temperature control, maceration). **Maturing:** Oak casks. **Characteristics:** Grace, elegance, beautiful ruby color. Wine to be aged. **Serving temperature:** 16 to 17°. **Served with:** Poultry, red meats, fine cheeses. **Vintages available in 89/90:** 1987, 1988.

Characteristics of vintages

1988: Very high class wine, grace, delicacy, beautiful structure, soft tannins, very promising, worth reserving. **1987:** Very typical wine, natural, clean and pleasant, harmonious character, a very successful vintage, thanks to an appropriate selection from the harvest. Price range (pre-tax, ex-warehouse): between 80 and 120 F.F.

Sales volumes:
– Wholesale: 90%. – Retail: 10%.
Sales in France: 20%.
Export sales: 80%.
Main trading partners : United Kingdom, Belgium, Switzerland, Netherlands, Germany.

Comments

"Boyd-Cantenac" goes back to the middle of the 18th century and owes its name to "Sir" Jacques Boyd, squire in the order of the nobility, residing in the city of Bordeaux, in the Chartrons neighborhood. On August 11, 1754, he bought, in the presence of Master Deyrem, notary at Castenau-de-Médoc, the land of a certain Sainvincens, former treasurer of France and citizen of Bordeaux. A beautiful Margaux, regularly successful, classic, combining structure, distinction, and excellent ageing potential.

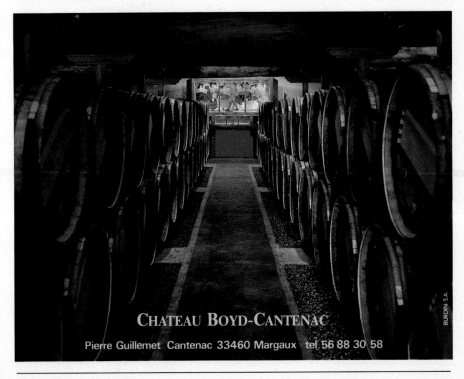

CHATEAU
BOYD-CANTENAC

Appellation Margaux Contrôlée

1985

MIS EN BOUTEILLE AU CHATEAU

75 cl

G.F.A. P. GUILLEMET, GÉRANT A CANTENAC, 33460 MARGAUX

PRODUCE OF FRANCE ALC. 12 % VOL.

CHÂTEAU LABÉGORCE ZÉDÉ

Luc Thienpont
Soussans
56 88 71 31

Type of vineyard: Agricultural Association. **Established:** 1979. **Number of employees:** 7. **Vine stocks:** Cabernet Sauvignon 50%, Merlot 35%, Cabernet Franc 10%, Petit Verdot 5%. **Soil:** Gravelly. **Exposure:** Plateau. **Average annual production in hectoliters:** 45 hl/ha.

Appellation: AOC Margaux. **Type:** Red. **Technique:** Traditional – 40% new casks. **Maturing:** In casks, 14 months. **Alcohol content:** 12%. **Characteristics:** Deep red color, fruity, tannic and long. To be kept at leat 5 years, even for minor vintages. **Serving temperature:** 17°. **Served with:** Red meat. **Vintages available in 89/90:** 1986-1987.

Characteristics of vintages

1988: Rich, very promising. **1987:** Beautiful color, elegant tannins, well balanced, successful year. **1986:** Very beautiful color, flowery bouquet marked by Cabernet Sauvignon, very fine tannins, very long. Exceptional. Price range (pre-tax, ex-warehouse): 50 to 80 F.F.
Sales volume:
– Wholesale: 95%. – Retail: 5%.
Sales in France: Sold exclusively on the Bordeaux market.
Export sales: 80% of which is exported.
Main trading partners : Belgium, UK, Netherlands, USA.

Comments

Beautiful estate (27 hectare vineyard) producing a classic Margaux, rich and fine, combining structure and elegance. (See "Classification 89").

CHÂTEAU DESMIRAIL

Lucien Lurton
33460 Margaux
56 88 70 20

Established: 1981. **Vine stocks:** 80% Cabernet Sauvignon, 9% Cabernet Franc, 10% Merlot, 1% Petit Verdot. **Soil:** Deep quaternary gravel.
Appellation: Margaux. **Type:** Red. **Technique:** Bordeaux tradition. **Maturing:** 20 months in Oak barrels, 1/3 renewed each year. **Characteristics:** Seductive, round, aromatic, lovely structure. **Serving temperature:** 128° to 20°. **Served with:** White meat. **Vintages available in 89/90:** 1986, 1985, 1984, 1983.

Characteristics of vintages

1988: Fruity, full-bodied, complex. **1987:** Balanced and delicate, to be drunk in the next five years. **1986:** Good concentration of tanins, well balanced, good length – to be aged. **1985:** Classic wine, seductive and structured. **1984:** Highly successful vintage, fine and flowery. **1983:** Balanced vintage, with a complex aroma associated with fine tannins, to be aged. Price range (pre-tax, ex-warehouse): between 80 F.F. to 120 F.F.
Sales volume:
– Wholesale: 100%.

References in France

Shops: Hédiard, good Parisian cellars.

Comments

Second wine: Domaine de Fontarney.

CHÂTEAU LASCOMBES

Alain Maurel
33460 Margaux
56 88 70 66

Type of vineyard: Corporation. **Number of employees:** 43. **Vine stocks:** Merlot 35%, Cabernet-Sauvignon 60%, Cabernet Franc 2%, Petit Verdot. **Soil:** Gravelly Hilltop consisting of quartz, coarse sand and gravel on a clay and limestone base. **Exposure:** North. **Average annual production in hectoliters:** 45 hectoliters/hectare.
Appellation: A.O.C. Margaux. **Technique:** Traditional with temperature control. **Maturing:** 12 to 18 months in less than 3 year old barrels (50% renewed each year). **Alcohol content:** 12.5%. **Characteristics:** Well-balanced wine, soft, rich and fine at the same time, full-bodied, firm, great ageing potential, red berry fragrance, flowery with spicy overtones. **Serving temperature:** 14°. **Served with:** All dishes that go with the finesse of Médoc wines and the characteristic feminity of Margaux. **Vintages available in 89/90:** 1969-1970-1976-1977-1979-1981-1982-1983-1984-1985.

Characteristics of vintages

1985: Beautiful vintage. Rich color, light tobacco aroma mingled with the scent of reb berries. Dense, vigorous wine. **1984:** Resin and wild plus nose, round, very successful. **1983:** Well-balanced, the scent of wax, a spicy touch. **1982:** Very round and fleshy – musky – leather and apricot fragrances, long finish. Average pre-tax, ex-warehouse price: 120 F.F.-350 F.F. depending upon the year.
Sales volume:
– Retail: 20%. – Restaurant: 80%.
Sales in France: 25%.
Export sales: 75%.

References in France

Restaurants: Paul Bocuse/Tour d'Argent/Orsi/Chiberta/Relais Gourmands/Relais-Châteaux chain, etc.
Shops: Comtesse du Barry – Fauchon – L'Amour du Vin – Paris.

Comments

A very great Bordeaux Establishment whose renown, is based on the quality of the Château Lascombes. Its director, Alain Maurel, combines efficiency with a passion for wine.

CHÂTEAU LA GALIANE

René Renon
Soussans, 33460 Margaux
56 88 35 27

Type of vineyard: Agricultural Association. **Established:** July 1987. **Number of employees:** 4. **Vine stocks:** Merlot 45%, Cabernet Sauvignon 50%, Petit Verdot 5%. **Soil:** hill tops, fine gravel. **Average annual production in hectoliters:** 180.

1982
CHATEAU LA GALIANE
GRAND VIN
MISE EN BOUTEILLES AU CHATEAU
MARGAUX
75cl
APPELLATION MARGAUX CONTROLEE
R. ET J. RENON · PROPRIÉTAIRES A MARGAUX (GIRONDE)
PRODUCE OF FRANCE

Appellation: Margaux. **Type:** Red. **Technique:** Fermentation on skins, controlled and prolonged if necessary, in the old style. **Maturing:** In oak casks. **Alcohol content:** 12%. **Characteristics:** Beautiful color, fruity nose, rich and well balanced, very pleasant. **Serving temperature:** 16-17°. **Served with:** Grilled meat, roasts (white and red meat) poultry, and certain cheeses. **Vintages available in 89/90:** 1983, 1984, 1985, 1986, 1987, 1988.

Characteristics of vintages

1988: Already very pleasant, quite promising. **1987:** Fine and fruity, will be very pleasant in 4 to 5 years. **1986:** Balanced and harmonious, very delicate bouquet, rich in flavor and round. **1985:** Excellent vintage, well balanced, rich and full. **Other: 1983:** Very good vintage. Price range (pre-tax, ex-warehouse): 30 to 50 F.F.
Sales volume:
– Wholesale: 80%. – Retail: 10%. – Restaurants: 10%. – Other: 10% (cellars).
Sales in France: 70%.
Export sales: 30%.
Main trading partners: Belgium, Switzerland, Luxemburg, Germany.

References in France

Restaurants: La Tupina (Bordeaux), Grand Ecuyer (Cordes), Hotel Restaurant Terminus Reine (Chaumont), L'Escalier (Brou).

Abroad

Germany

Pfeffer, Hamburg.

Switzerland

Zanchi, Lausanne.

Belgium

Helbevino, Hertsberge – De Gauw Leuven.

Others

Luxemburg: Becker, Rombach – Martelange.

Comments

The Château La Galiane owes its name to the English General "Galian" who used it as his headquarters to command the English troops during the occupation of the Aquitaine in the 15th century. Cultivated for several generations, it produces between 15 and 20 casks.

• Would you like to know to recognize the caracteristic fragrances of certains wines, their woodland, fruity, flowery or leather aromas, the evaluate the level of acidity or the presence of tannins, to ascertain the mellowness or the color of a wine...? See the Chapter entitled "The Art and Manner of Wine Tasting".

CHÂTEAU MALESCOT ST-EXUPERY

Roger Zuger
33460 Margaux
56 88 70 68

Type of vineyard: Corporation. **Established:** 1955. **Number of employees:** 18. **Vine stocks:** Cabernet Sauvignon 50%, Merlot 35%, Cabernet Franc 10%, Petit Verdot 5%. **Soil:** Deep Gravels. **Exposure:** Hilltops facing the Gironde. **Average annual production in hectoliters:** 1,400 hl.

Appellation: Margaux. **Type:** Red. **Technique:** Tanks, long fermentation, 2 to 4 weeks. **Maturing:** Barrels, 1/4 new. **Alcohol content:** 11.5° to 13°. **Characteristics:** Elegant, well-balanced (normal for Margaux) typical. **Serving temperature:** 16° to 18° according to age (the older the wine, higer the temperature). **Vintages available in 89/90:** 1979 to 1986.

Characteristics of vintages

1986: Very close to the 1985, juste the same: full, meaty, subtle tannins, very promising. **1984:** Successfull vintage, round and flowery flavor, supple. **1982 & 1983:** Two complete vintages, full, harmonious, great of finesse, well-structured, tenace. **1979:** Very beautiful wine, start to open. Price range (pre-tax, ex-warehouse): Between 120 and 160 F.F.

Sales volume:
– Wholesale: 95%. – Retail: 5%. – Restaurants: Borie Manoux.

Sales in France: 15%. **Export sales:** 85%.

References in France

Restaurants: La Tour d'Argent...
Shops: Fauchon...

Abroad

United States

Kobrand Corp. 134 East 40th Street, N.Y. 10016.

United Kingdom

Percy Fox Gilbey House, Harlow CH20 IDX.

Germany

Casino Gesellschaft Haidelweg 22 8 Munchen 60.

Switzerland

Albert Reichmuth AG. Stauffacherstr 145 8036 Zurich.

The Netherlands

Robbers & VD Hoogen Velperweg 23 6824 Arnhem. Verlinden 5201 Hertogenbosch.

Belgium

Sovex 22 Rue Émile Combe, 33270 Floirac.

Denmark

Vingros Ronneber Allee 3000 Helsingor.

Japan

Unexpa 3-6-24 Shibuya-Ku, Tokyo 150.

• *A great naturally sweet wine with Roquefort? Try a Sauternes, of course, a Grand Cru from a late Alsacian harvest, a mellow Anjou or a Banyuls.*

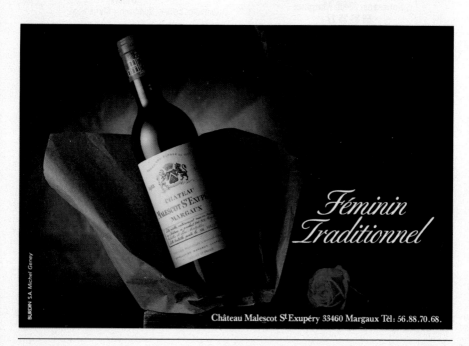

Château Martinens

Membre de l'Union des Grands Crus de Bordeaux

CHÂTEAU MARTINENS

Jean-Pierre Seynat-Dulos
Cantenac 33460 Margaux
56 88 71 37

Type of vineyard: Family-owned. **Established:** 1776. **Number of employees:** 10. **Vine stocks:** Merlot 40%, Cabernet Sauvignon 30%, Petit Verdot 20%, Cabernet Franc 10%. **Soil:** Chalky clay. **Exposure:** East-West. **Average annual production in hectoliters:** 800 to 1, 000. **Appellation:** Margaux AOC. **Type:** Red. **Technique:** Traditional, fermentation for 3-4 weeks. **Maturing:** 18 months. **Alcohol content:** 12.2%. **Characteristics:** Pleasant, fruity, supple, very aromatic. **Serving temperature:** 15° to 18°. **Served with:** Game, red meat. **Vintages available in 89/90:** 1987 and a number of old vintages.

Characteristics of vintages

1988: Rich, balanced and harmonious, deep color, tannic, rich and well balanced. **1987:** Supple, very pleasant, beautiful color. **1986:** Very fruity and delicate. Price range (pretax, ex-warehouse): 50 to 80 F.F.

Sales volume:
– Wholesale: 80%. – Retail: 15%. – Restaurants: 5%.

Sales in France: 50%. **Export sales:** 30%.

Main trading partners : Belgium, Switzerland, USA, Germany, Japan.

References in France

Shops: Maison du Tourisme, Margaux – Pauillac.

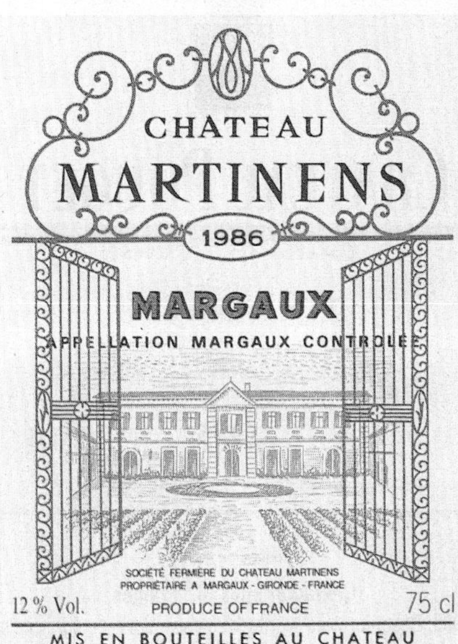

CHATEAU
MARTINENS
1986
MARGAUX
APPELLATION MARGAUX CONTROLÉE
SOCIÉTÉ FERMIÈRE DU CHATEAU MARTINENS
PROPRIÉTAIRE A MARGAUX - GIRONDE - FRANCE
12 % Vol.
PRODUCE OF FRANCE
75 cl
MIS EN BOUTEILLES AU CHATEAU

Abroad

United States

Bordeaux Agents

Comments

The Château Martinens was built in 1776 by the White family, originally from England. Subsequently, it became the property of Count Jean-Philippe de Sautter, Consul General of Tuscany, Chamberlain of the French Empire, descendant of an old Swiss family.

CHÂTEAU POUGET

Pierre Guillemet
Cantenac, 33460 Margaux
56 88 30 58

Type of vineyard: Agricultural Association. **Established:** 1987. **Vine stocks:** 66% Cabernet Sauvignon, 4% Cabernet Franc, 30% Merlot. **Soil:** Gravel, for the most part, and sand. **Exposure:** Southern rim of the very beautiful, gravelly plateau of Cantenac. **Average annual production in hectoliters:** 32 hl per hectare.
Appellation: Margaux. **Type:** Red. **Technique:** Classic (destemming, fermentation with temperature control, maceration). **Maturing:** Oak casks. **Characteristics:** Typical Margaux, fine, elegant, fragrant, harmonious. **Serving temperature:** 16 to 17°. **Served with:** Poultry, red meats, light cheeses. **Vintages available in 89/90:** 1987, 1988.

CHATEAU POUGET
GRAND CRU CLASSÉ
MARGAUX
Appellation Margaux Contrôlée
1985
75 cl
G.F.A. P. GUILLEMET, GÉRANT A CANTENAC, 33460 MARGAUX
MIS EN BOUTEILLE AU CHATEAU
PRODUCE OF FRANCE

Characteristics of vintages

1988: Beautiful wine worthy of its soil. Lovely color, round and tannic, will keep well. **1987:** Floral nose, complex and lively, full, great delicacy and distinction. Price range (pre-tax, ex-warehouse): between 80 and 120 F.F.
Sales volume: – Wholesale: 95%. – Retail 5%.
Sales in France: 45%. **Export sales:** 55%.
Main trading partners : Belgium, Switzerland, Netherlands, Germany.

Comments

Three centuries ago, in 1650, the present domain of Pouget belonged to Etienne Monteil, Canon of St-Emilion, who was entitled, because of his position, to an annual revenue from the cathedral of Bordeaux. Etienne ceded the domain to his brother Martin Monteil whose grand-daughter, Térèse Dorlhiac, made François Etienne Pouget her sole heir, according to an act deposed April 9, 1748 by Master Sejourne, notary at Bordeaux. In 1771, Claire, Pouget's daughter, married Pierre-François de Chavaille, Lord of the Parc (Mérignac parrish), lawyer, secretary-general of the city of Bordeaux. This family remained proprietor of Pouget until 1907 at which time the Elie-Guillemet family took over.

CHÂTEAU DURFORT-VIVENS

Lucien Lurton
33460 Margaux
58 88 70 20

Established: Owner since 1961. **Vine stocks:** 82% Cabernet Sauvignon, 10% Cabernet Franc, 8% Merlot. **Soil:** Quaternary from the Pyrenees Mountains gravel.
Appellation: Margaux. **Type:** Red. **Technique:** In the Bordeaux tradition. **Maturing:** 20 months in oak barrels. **Alcohol content:** 12.5%. **Characteristics:** Full-bodied, slow ageing. **Serving temperature:** 18° to 20°. **Served with:** Red meat. **Vintages available in 89/90:** 1986, 1985, 1984, 1983, 1982.

Characteristics of vintages

1988: Complex and concentrated – good length. **1987:** Elegant and delicate – to be drunk. **1986:** Very beautiful tannin, very promising. **1985:** Mature, rich. **1984:** Balance. To be drunk during the next 2 to 3 years while waiting for the others to open up. Supple and flowery. **1983:** Beautiful vintage, velvety, full-bodied with complex aroma, dense. **1982:** Rich and well-balanced, with ripe tannins, to be aged. **Note: 1980:** open, extraordinary nose and good balance. Price range (pre-tax, ex-warehouse): between 80 and 160 F.F.
Sales volume: – Wholesale: 100%.

References in France

Restaurants: Lucas-Carton, Le Doyen, Le Divellec, etc. – Paris. *Shops:* Hédiard, Pétrissans, Caves de la Côte d'Or, etc. – Paris.

Comments

Second wine: Domaine de Cure-Bourse.

CHÂTEAU PRIEURÉ-LICHINE

Mr. Alexis Lichine
Cantenac - 33460 Margaux
56 88 36 28 - Telex: 550 234 PRILICH
Fax: 56 88 36 28

Type of vineyard: Corporation. **Established:** 1951. **Vine stocks:** Cabernet-Sauvignon 52%, Merlot 33%, Cabernet Franc 8%, Petit Verdot 7%. **Soil:** Gravel. **Average annual production in hectoliters:** 2,000.
Appellation: Margaux. **Type:** Red. **Technique:** in stainless steel and concrete tanks. **Maturing:** In oak barrels for 18 months (70% renewed each year). **Alcohol content:** 12.5%. **Characteristics:** Typical wines, combining structure and finesse. Supple. **Serving temperature:** 16-18°. **Served with:** Meat, cheese, game. **Vintages available in 89/90:** 1983, 1984, 1986.

Characteristics of vintages

1986: Richness in tannin and flavor due to the Cabernet-Sauvignon, and roundness due to the Merlot. **1985:** Velvety texture due to the Merlot (harvested very ripe). Supple. **1984:** Very fine and fruity, light and supple. Delicious right now! **1983:** Very great wine for the Margaux commune. History making. **1982:** Very great vintage. Have patience. **Other:** 1981: A very good vintage. Ready now. Price range (pre-tax, ex-warehouse): 50 F.F.-120 F.F.
Sales volume:
- Wholesale: 87%. - Retail: 12%. - Restaurants: 1%.

Sales in France: 25%.
Export sales: 75%.
Main trading partners : USA, UK, Belgium, Germany.

CHÂTEAU RAUSAN SEGLA

Holt Frères et Fils
(marketed by Louis Eschenauer)
33460 Margaux
56 88 70 30

Vine stocks: 45 hectares. Cabernets 69%, Merlot 31%. **Soil:** Silica gravel with gravel sub-oil. **Appellation:** Margaux. **Type:** Red. **Technique:** Traditional. **Maturing:** Traditional, in oak barrels. **Characteristics:** Remarkable Margaux, typical combination of finesse and richness, overtones of ripe red berries and undergrowth, well-balanced, fine tannic structure, good for ageing (see classification). **Serving temperature:** 16°. **Served with:** Roasts and game. **Vintages available in 1989:** 1982, 1983, 1984, 1985 and 1986. **Vintages available in 1990:** 1983, 1984, 1985, 1986. N° 1987 (all crop sold as second wine: Château de Lamouroux 1987).

Characteristics of vintages

1987: Château de Lamouroux: powerfull nose, volatil and complex. Supple mouth, well-balanced with round tannins. Pleasant final with good aromatic persistence. **1986:** Great year, very well-structured wine, most promising. **1985:** Exceptional year. Very successfull wine, well-balanced, full, good for ageing. **1984:** Perfectly mastered vintage. **1983:** Rich wine, deep colour, fruity bouquet, dense and supple. Good for ageing.

CHÂTEAU SIRAN

W.A.B. Miailhe
6, quai Louis XVIII - B.P. N° 35
Labarde, 33460 Margaux
56 81 35 01 - Telex: 540 655 F Code 405

Type of vineyard: Family-owned. **Established:** Property of a veryu old family. **Vine stocks:** Merlot 25%, Cabernet Sauvignon 50%, Cabernet Blanc 10%, Petit Verdot 15%. **Soil:** Gravel and sand-gravel agglomerate. **Average annual production in hectoliters:** 1 200.
Appellation: Margaux. **Type:** Red. **Technique:** Fermentation with skins (15 to 20 days) in Oak vats. **Maturing:** 1/3 new vats each year. **Alcohol content:** 12.5% to 13%. **Characteristics:** Well-balanced, fragrant, supple, beautiful structure, rich, with finesse and elegance, typical of Margaux. **Serving temperature:** 16° to 18°. **Served with:** Capon (roasted), red, meat, steaks. **Vintages available in 89/90:** 1979, 1981, 1982, 1983, 1984, 1985.

Characteristics of vintages

1985: Beautiful structure, rich and well-balanced, finesse, a great wine for ageing. **1984:** Very pleasant, rather rapid development. **1983:** Fragrant and supple, very "Margaux". **1982:** Great wine, rich and well-balanced. Hold. **Other:** 1981: very balanced, to be watched. 1979: successful, pleasant. Price range (pre-tax, ex-warehouse): between 80 F.F. and 120 F.F.
Main trading partners : UK, Germany, Belgium, Netherlands, Luxemburg, Switzerland, USA, Denmark.

References in France

Restaurants: Chez Paul Bocuse, L'Auberge de l'Ill, Restaurant Les Crayères, Jacques Cagna, L'Orangerie, Maxim's, Le Pré Catalan, Vanel, etc.

CHÂTEAU TAYAC

André Favin
Tayac Soussans - 33460 Margaux
56 88 33 06

Type of vineyard: Family-owned. **Number of employees:** 13. **Vine stocks:** 70% Cabernet, 25% Merlot, 5% Petit Verdot. **Soil:** Gravel. **Average annual production in hectoliters:** 1 600.
Appellation: Margaux. **Type:** Red. **Technique:** Cement

vats, stainless steel tanks. **Maturing:** Casks. **Characteristics:** A standard of its appellation, combines richness and elegance, with fine tannins, keeps well. **Serving temperature:** 18° . **Served with:** Red and white meat, poultry, cheese. **Vintages avialable in 89/90:** 1984, 1985, 1986.

Characteristics of vintages

1986: Great year, to keep, probably or 20 years and more. **1985:** Great year, to keep, probably 20 year or more. **1984:** Average year, to be drunk young, and to keep probably for 10 to 15 years. Price range (pre-tax, ex-warehouse): Between 30 F.F. and 50 F.F.
Sales volume:
- Wholesale: 70%. - Retail: 25%. - Restaurants: 5%.
Sales in France: 70%. **Export sales:** 30%.
Main trading partners: England, Belgium, Germany, Canada, Switzerland, USA, Japan.

CHÂTEAU-LA-TOUR-DE-MONS

Clauzel
33460 Margaux - Soussans
56 88 33 03

Appellation: Margaux. **Type:** Red. **Technique:** Traditional. **Maturing:** In casks (1/5 new). **Alcohol content:** 12%. **Characteristics:** Well developed, rich, well balanced, tannic, typical Margaux - good keeping. **Serving temperature:** 17 to 18°. **Served with:** Red meat, cheese. **Vintages available in 89/90:** 1984, 1985, 1987.

Characteristics of vintages

1988: Still in casks - Wait. **1987:** Good wine, to be consumed rather soon. **1986:** Very beautiful wine, for long keeping. **1985:** Very great vintage, starting now to develop. **Other:** 1983-1982: Very good also, start drinking, very good keeping. Price range (pre-tax, ex-warehouse): 50 to 80 F.F.

Sales volume:
- Wholesale: almost exclusively to the Bordeaux wine.
- Retail: dealers.

References in France

Restaurants: Alain Chapel (Mionnay) and others.
Shops: Aux Vignes Pasquier (Paris), Chez Demost & Bourland (Rambouillet).

CHÂTEAU DU TERTRE

Philippe Capbern Gasqueton
6 Arsac, 33460 Margaux
56 59 30 08

Type of vineyard: Agricultural Association. **Established:** Since the 18th century. **Vine stocks:** Cabernet 85%, Merlot 15%. **Soil:** Gravelly. **Exposure:** East, West. **Average annual production in hectoliters:** 1,800.

Appellation: Margaux. **Type:** Red. **Technique:** Traditional, in steel tanks. **Maturing:** 2 years in wooden casks (30% new). **Alcohol content:** 12.5%. **Characteristics:** Special aroma and flavor characteristic of the soil.

Characteristics of vintages

1988: Great success after a small harvest. **1987:** Finesse and breed. **1986:** Very great wine, lots of distinction, for keeping. **1985:** Excellent, long keeping.
Sales volume:
- Wholesale: 100%.
Sales in France: 20%.
Export sales: 80%.
Main trading partners: European countries, USA, Japan.

Comments

The vineyard, created in 1720, belonged previously to an Irish family which built the first glass works in Bordeaux (Mitchell).

MOULIS

CHÂTEAU BISTON BRILLETTE

Michel Barbarin
Cidex 07/09 – 33480 Moulis-en-Médoc
56 58 22 86

Type of vineyard: Family-owned. **Established:** Beginning of the 19th century. In the family since 1930. **Vine stocks:** 55% Cabernet Sauvignon, 40% Merlot, 5% Petit Verdot. **Soil:** 60% chalky clay, 40% gravelly. **Exposure:** hillsides. **Average annual production in hectoliters:** 800 on 18 hectares.

Appellation: Moulis Cru Bourgeois. **Type:** Red. **Technique:** Harvested when overripe, long maceration (15 to 21 days) under temperature control, racking and traditional fining. **Maturing:** In casks 15 to 20 months (20% new). **Alcohol content:** 12%. **Characteristics:** Colorful wines, fragrant, tannic and balanced, with considerable aromatic distinction which needs 4 to 6 years to develop fully. Remarkable aptitude for ageing. **Serving temperature:** 16°. Open the bottle 2 to 3 hours in advance. **Served with:** Game, red meats, mushrooms, cheese. **Vintages available in 89/90:** 1983, 1984, 1986, 1987, 1988 (end of 1990).

Characteristics of vintages

1988: Very beautiful deep color, great aromatic complexity, rich, well balanced and supple. **1987:** Beautiful color, finely perfumed, woody, fruity, supple and round. **1986:** Very beautiful intense color, woody nose still a little closed. Forthcoming wine, very balanced, round and full, great distinction. **Other: 1984:** Fresh color, well developed nose, supple attack still marked by the fruit, this quite light but very fine wine is very agreeable. **1983:** Brilliant red color, intense cherry fragrance, very fine and fresh, fruity a smoky nuance, feminine, good tannic constitution. Price range (pre-tax, ex-warehouse): between 30 and 50 F.F.

Sales volume:
– Retail: 70%. – Restaurants: 15% (including winecellars).
– Other: 15% export.

Sales in France: 85%. **Export sales:** 15%.
Main trading partners: Countries of the European Economic Community.

References in France

Restaurants: Moulin du Roc (Dordogne), Le Grand Ecuyer (Cordes), various Parisian restaurants...

Abroad

United Kingdom

Laytons Wine Merchants, 20 Midland Road, London NW1. Whiclar Wines, Bridge near Canterbury, Kent. Brown Wine Import, 14 The Garth, Miles Lane KT 11 2DZ Cobham, Surrey. Tel: (0932) 65790. Richmond Wine Warehouse, 138 c Lower Mortlake Road, Richmond, Surrey. Shops: Bibendum Wine Ltd, 113 Regents Park Rd, London. Haughton Fine Wines, Chorley, Nantwich Cheshire CW5 8JR. Tel : 0270 74 537.

Germany

Shops: W. Durselen, Stresemannstrasse 42, 4050 Monchengladbach 2. Tel: (02166) 42576.

Canada

SAQ CP 1058 Place d'Armes, Montreal H2Y3J8. Telex: 05560780 SAQ MTL.

Far East

EGE Export, 32 rue Gabrielle, 94220 Charenton (France). Telex: 26 07 17 FEXT341.

Others Africa

France Afrique Import Export, 53 rue Henri Wallon, 33130 Bordeaux Begles. Telex: FRAFRIQ 541 135 F.

Comments

At the beginning of the 19th century, Mr. Biston, winegrower in the commune of Moulis, gave his name to the locality known as Brillette in order to personnalize his production. After several successions, M. Lagarde, father-in-law of the current proprietor acquired the vineyard in 1930. In 1932 Château Biston Brillette was promoted to the rank of Cru Bougeois. In 1963, M. Michel Barbarin took over the property, reconstituted the vineyard and modernized the installations. Since then, there has been a regular progression of quality, as can be confirmed by tasting the most recent vintages (see "Classification 89").

CHÂTEAU DUTRUCH GRAND-POUJEAUX

François Cordonnier
33480 Moulis-en-Médoc
56 58 02 55

Type of vineyard: Family-owned. **Established:** Turn of the century. **Number of employees:** 7 + seasonal workers. **Vine stocks:** Cabernet 50%, Merlot 40%, Petit Verdot 10%. **Soil:** Gravel, chalky clay. **Exposure:** South, South-West. **Average annual production in hectoliters:** 1,050.

Appellation: AOC Moulis Cru Bourgeois. **Type:** Red. **Technique:** Traditional, fermentation on skins (10 days average). **Maturing:** In casks for 18 months (1/4 new). **Alcohol content:** 12.5%. **Characteristics:** Beautiful deep color, very fine bouquet, slight raspberry overtones. Referred to in E. Penning's book on "The Wines of Bordeaux" as "the roundest and the least austere of the Moulins wines". **Served with:** Duck filet with greeen peppercorn sauce, steaks grilled on vine shoots, mushrooms Bordeaux style. **Vintages available in 89/90:** 1988,1987 and 1986.

Characteristics of vintages

1988: Rich and well balanced, tannic, good ageing potential. **1987:** Lighter than the 1988, red berry aroma. **1986:** Very rich like the 1988, elegant and warm. Price range (pretax, ex-warehouse): 30 to 50 F.F.
Sales volume:
– Wholesale: 70%. – Retail: 30%. – Restaurants (generally through wholesale dealers).
Sales in France: 30%. **Export sales:** 70%.
Main trading partners: Belgium, Switzerland, Finland, UK, Canada.

Abroad

United Kingdom

La Vigneronne, E.J.R. Berry M.W., 105 Old Brompton Road, London S.W.7.

Germany

Firma Poullig Am Bermeshau 4D, 4000 Dusseldorf. Firma Alfred Boehm Weinimport, WE1 Kesselstrasse 13, 7000 Stuttgart Wangen 60.

Switzerland

O.E. Tritten S.A., Borex Soleil, 1261.

Belgium

J.B. Cordonnier & Sons, 17 avenue Colonel Daumerie – 1150 Brussels.

Canada

Liquor Control Board of Ontario, 55 Lake Shore Boulevard, East Toronto Mse 1A4. St Des Alcools du Québéc, 905, avenue de Lorimier, Montreal QC H2K 3V9.

The Netherlands

Winjnkoperij H.F.A. Okhuysen, B.V. Gierstraat, 34-38, 2011 Ge Harlem. Winjnkoperij Prosper Van Nieulande, B.V. Baronielaan, 159, 48 18 PG Breda.

CHÂTEAU DUPLESSIS-FABRE

Patrice Pages, administrator
33480 Moulis en Médoc
56 58 01 07

Type of vineyard: Family Agricultural Association. **Established:** Winecellar and fermenting room built in 1689. **Vine stocks:** Cabernet Sauvignon 42%, Cabernet Franc 8%, Merlot 45%, Petit Verdot 5%. **Soil:** Chalky clay on subsoil of chalk with asteriated opal. **Average annual production in hectoliters:** 650.
Appellation: Moulis en Médoc. **Type:** Red. **Technique:** Traditional. **Maturing:** In oak casks for 12 to 18 months. **Alcohol content:** 12.5%. **Characteristics:** Beautiful ruby colored wines, developing a harmonious bouquet. The tan-

nin balance gives them a remarkably elegant taste. **Serving temperature:** 18°. **Vintages available in 89/90:** 1983, 1984, 1986, 1987,1988.

Characteristics of vintages

1988: Not yet tasted. **1987:** Ruby color, tannins well inevidence, well controlled vintage. **1986:** Beautifull sustained color, very balanced wine, beautiful ripe tannins, fruity and substantial, will evolve well. Price range (pre-tax, ex-warehouse): between 30 and 50 F.F.
Sales volume:
- Wholesale: 70%. - Retail: 20%. - Restaurants: 10%.
Sales in France: 40%. **Export sales:** 60%.
Main trading partners : Denmark, Belgium, Netherlands.

References in France

Restaurants: Hôtel Negresco, Gray d'Albion, Hôtel de Paris (Monte-Carlo).
Shops: Centre de Distribution de Vins de Propriétés, etc.

Comments

This very old vineyard was the property of Armand du Plessis, Marshal and Duke of Richelieu, when he was governor of Guienne in the 18th century. Testimony to the long winemaking tradition are the wine warehouse and the fermenting room which were built in 1689. Since 1975, the Château Duplessis-Fabre wines have won a number of awards at various agricultural competitions: 7 Gold Medals, 6 Silver Medals and 4 Bronze Medals.

CHÂTEAU FRANQUET GRAND POUJEAUX AC MOULIS EN MÉDOC

Pierre Lambert et Fils, Propriétaires
Grand Poujeaux, Moulis en Médoc
33480 Castelneau-Médoc
56 59 04 94

Type of vineyard: Family-owned. **Established:** Since the 19th century - family owned since 1986. **Number of employees:** 2. **Vine stocks:** Cabernet Sauvigon 35%, Francs 25%, Merlot 30%, Petit Verdot 8%, Malbec 2%. **Average annual production in hectoliters:** 40 to 50 hl/ha.
Appellation: AC Moulis-en-Médoc. **Type:** Red. **Maturing:** In wooden casks (new), 1/2 Merlot, 1/2 Cabernet, Sauvignon and Franc. **Alcohol content:** 12.6%. **Serving temperature:** 15° and 17°. **Served with:** Young & full-bodied wines: red meat, sauces, game and mushrooms (cèpes). Aged or lighter wines: grilled meat, white meat. **Vintages available in 89/90:** 1979, 1984, 1985, 1986 (Cuvée Europe), 1986, 1987 and 1988 (en Primeur).

Characteristics of vintages

1988: Surprisingly rich, harmonious and noble even at the beginning of the vinification. Well structured and masculine. **1987:** A very successful though difficult year. Soft and rich wines with a spring fragrance, surprising. **1986:** A typical Grand-Poujeaux vintage - very tannic, rich and well

balanced. Bordeaux Silver Medal (1987) - Cuvée Europe: flowery nose, fruity, round, very well balanced, fresh. Matured in wood, 1/2 new. Half Merlot and half Cabernet Sauvignon and Cabernet Franc. **1985:** Great year, very promising, deep color, soft and full, full-bodied, fruity. Bordeaux Gold Medal (1986). Price range (pre-tax, ex-warehouse): 30 to 50 F.F. - 50 to 80 F.F.
Sales volume:
- Wholesale: 50% export (mainly winecellars). - Retail: 40% France (winecellars). - Other: 10% private clientele.
Main trading partners : Belgium 50%, Germany 15%, Netherlands 10%, Switzerland 5%, Denmark 5%, Canada 5%, etc.

References in France

Shops: A number of reputed winecellars in Western France.

Abroad

Germany
Hanseatische Weinhandelsges 2800 Bremen.

Switzerland
Cretigny S.A. 1165 Allaman, etc.

Belgium
Lambrecht 9830 St Martens-Latem, Uccle Vins 1180 Brussels, etc. (environ 15 importateurs).

Canada
Liquor control board of Ontario, Toronto.

The Netherlands
Verbunt Winjnkopers 500L CAA Tilburg.

Others
Denmark: Vinhandel-Jacobsens 2100 Copenhagen.

Comments

The property is situated on a gravelly hillcrest in the village of "Grand Poujeaux", an excellent location in the commune of Moulis. Some of the vines face South on a chalky clay slope. The meeting of these two soils is responsible for the essential qualities of the wines. While the permeable, poor Quaternary gravel provides liveliness, brilliance, grace and delicacy, the gravel, clay and marine limestone provide body, fleshiness and tannin.

CHÂTEAU LA MOULINE

Jean-Louis Coubris
Moulis, Haut-Médoc
72, avenue Pasteur - 33600 Pessac
56 45 07 89 - Telex: 540495 ITAG Code D82
Fax: 56 45 59 80

Type of vineyard: Family corporation. **Vine stocks:** Cabernet Sauvignon 49%, Merlot 45%, Cabernet 3%, Petit Verdot 2%. **Soil:** 1/2 chalky clay, 1/2 sandy and gravelly plateau. **Exposure:** Very sunny, very little frost. **Average annual production in hectoliters:** 525.
Appellation: Floc Moulis. **Type:** Red. **Technique:** Traditional in stainless steel tanks, long fermentation on skins, temperature control, maximum extraction of solid matter. **Maturing:** 18 to 24 months (half in new oak casks). **Alcohol content:** 12.5%. **Characteristics:** Rich and well balanced, full-bodied and supple. **Serving temperature:** 18°. **Served with:** All red meats, duck filet, even game depending on the year. **Vintages available in 89/90:** 1983, 1984, 1985, 1986.

Characteristics of vintages

1988: Particularly promising, small harvest suggests a great vintage. **1987:** Average wine, likely to be very much appreciated in its youthful vigour. **1986:** Harmonious, and well balanced, ripe fruit nose, full bouquet still developing,

GRAND VIN DU MEDOC
DOMAINE DE LAGORCE
DU
CHÂTEAU LA MOULINE
Moulis-en-Médoc
APPELLATION MOULIS CONTROLEE
ALC. 12,5 %
BY VOL.
750 ML
COUBRIS J.L.C. PROPRIETAIRE A MOULIS-MEDOC-FRANCE
MIS EN BOUTEILLES AU CHATEAU
RED BORDEAUX WINE PRODUCT OF FRANCE CONTAINS SULFITES

long keeping - great future ahead. **1985:** Beautiful intense red color, with ruby glint, rich bouquet (ivy, pepper, cherry) - lively and fresh taste. Well-balanced. Strong wild cherry aroma. Slightly bitter finish due to its youth. Will reach full maturity towards 1992. Warming but not agressive. **Other:** 1984: All of the attraction of a light youth which is already showing suppleness and distinction. Sustained color, cha-

racteristic of the vintage because of its ripe fruit fragrance. Quite fleshy, a bit firm, quite long. 1983: Beautiful wine. Finesse and liveliness, rich aromas. Agreeable now, it will blossom out in the years to come. Price range (pre-tax, ex-warehouse): between 25 and 35 F.F.
Sales in France: 80%.
Export sales: 20%.
Main trading partners : USA.

References in France

Restaurants: L'Épicerie, La Dent Creuse, La Coquille d'Œuf, Au Chiopot, Le Pont Bernet, Le Cellier Bordelais, etc.
Shops: Vignobles de France, Paris.

Abroad

United States

Borvin Wines, Alexandria (Virginia). Bordeaux Wines, San Francisco.

Others

Denmark: Fransk Vinimport M. & Mme Moeller, Silkeborg.

Comments

The Château la Mouline estate, located between a windmill and a watermill, from which the name is derived, is located on the southern slope of a hillcrest, well exposed to the sun and almost frost free. The vineyard is made up of vines planted on chalky soil, some of them over 70 years old. More than half of the harvest is vinified in new oak casks for about 18 months.

GRANINS GRAND POUJEAUX

André Batailley
33480 Moulis en Medoc
56 58 02 99

Type of vineyard: Family-owned. **Established:** 1959. **Vine stocks:** Merlot 50%, Cabernet 35%, Petit Verdot 10%, Malbec 5%. **Soil:** Pyrenean gravel 50%, chalky clay 50%. **Exposure:** South. **Average annual production in hectoliters:** 250.
Appellation: Moulis en Medoc. **Type:** Red. **Technique:** Traditional. **Maturing:** In oak casks. **Alcohol content:** 12%. **Characteristics:** Light, delicate bouquet but rather tannic. **Serving temperature:** 16°. **Served with:** White and red meat, game, cheese. **Vintages available in 89/90:** 1985-1986-1987-1988.

Characteristics of vintages

1988: Very well colored, supple, very promising. **1987:** Light, supple, can be tasted before the 1985 and 1986. Price range (pre-tax, ex-warehouse): 30 to 50 F.F.
Sales volume:
– Retail: 50%. – Restaurants: 10%.
Sales in France: 60%.
Export sales: 40%.
Main trading partners : Belgium, Germany, UK.

CHÂTEAU POUJEAUX

Philippe & François Theil
33480 Moulis-en-Médoc
56 58 02 96

Type of vineyard: Family-owned. **Established:** 18th Century. **Vine stocks:** 45% Cabernet Sauvignon, 35% Merlot, 10% Cabernet franc, 10% Petit Verdot. **Soil:** Sand and gravel, porous. **Average annual production in hectoliters:** 1 200 barrels.
Appellation: Moulis-en-Médoc. **Type:** Red. **Technique:** Traditional. **Maturing:** 12 months in barrels (25% new each year). **Alcohol content:** 12.5%. **Characteristics:** Soft and rich, race given from the Cabernet Sauvignon, and delicacy from the Merlot. **Serving temperature:** 18°. **Served with:** Game, meat and cheese. **Vintages available in 89/90:** 1980, 1981, 1983, 1984, 1985, 1986.

Characteristics of vintages

1988: Intense, deep purple color implies positive richness. Round, almost soft attack with a remarkable fleshiness and density. Tasty tannins, with absolutely no aggressivity, are responsible for the richness and balance. **1987:** Very beautiful, deep, intense, sustained purple color. Rich, well-balanced, soft, full and structured, with tannins whose flavor is dominated by the fruit. Quite exceptional youthfull harmony combined with a surprising elegance ensure great promise for this vintage. It will certainly be a great Médoc success. **1986:** Not yet tasted. **1985:** Deep, fruity, plum aroma, harmonious, velvety tannins. **1984:** Aromatic, vanilla overtones, well-balanced. **1983:** Flowery aroma, touch of plum, rich in alcohol and color, well-balanced, harmonious tannins, forthcoming. Price range (pre-tax, ex-warehouse): Between 50 F.F. and 80 F.F.

LISTRAC MÉDOC

CAVE DE VINIFICATION DES GRANDS VINS DE LISTRAC-MÉDOC

Maurice Meyre (Président)
Listrac-Médoc, 33480 Castelnau-Médoc
56 58 03 19

Type of vineyard: Agricultural Association. **Established:** May 1935. **Number of employees:** 8. **Vine stocks:** Merlot 60%, Cabernet 30%, Petit Verdot 10%. **Soil:** Gravel and chalky clay. **Average annual production in hectoliters:** 8,000.

Appellation: Listrac-Médoc. **Technique:** Fermentation in stainless steel tanks, debourbage, maceration for 2 to 3 weeks. **Maturing:** In concrete tanks and casks. **Alcohol content:** 12.5%. **Characteristics:** Beautiful ruby color, fruity, full-bodied, soft and rich, fragrant with a robust finish. **Serving temperature:** 17°. **Served with:** Red meat, game, cheese. **Vintages available in 89/90:** 1979, 1983, 1984, 1985, 1986.

Characteristics of vintages

1988: Available in 1991. **1987:** Available in the second semester of 1988 – light, pleasant nose and taste, can be drunk in the coming months. **1986:** Great year, ruby color, ripe fruit aroma, keep for a few years. **1985:** Rich tannins, very long.

Sales volume:
– Wholesale: 10%. – Retail: 65%. – Restaurants: 10%. – Other: 15% (Supermarkets).
Sales in France: 68%.
Export sales: 32%.
Main trading partners: Switzerland, Denmark, Germany, UK, Netherlands.

Comments

The history of the Cave de Vinification de Listrac Médoc goes back to 1935. On May 23 of that year, several winemakers acquired property in the commune on which a fermenting room with a 5,000 hl capacity was built. The Cave de Listrac vinifies the harvest of 72 members, some of whom have been members of the cooperative since its inception. Five of the proprietors, whose vineyards are particularly well known, have their harvest vinified separately.

CHÂTEAU FONREAUD

Jean Chanfreau
33480 Listrac-Médoc
56 58 02 43

Type of vineyard: Family-owned. **Established:** 15th Century. **Vine stocks:** 49% Cabernet Sauvignon, 31% Merlot, 17% Cabernet Franc, 3% Petit Verdot. **Soil:** Gravel on chalky and clay. **Exposure:** South. **Average annual production in hectoliters:** 1 800.
Appellation: Listrac-Médoc. **Type:** Red. **Technique:** Traditional Médoc. **Maturing:** Vats and barrels (30% new). **Alcohol content:** 12.5%. **Characteristics:** Very fruity; vanilla, red fruit and grilled almond fragrances. Soft tannins make a wine which is supple and long at the same time. **Serving temperature:** 18°. **Served with:** meat, dishes served with sauce, cheese. **Vintages available in 89/90:** 1983, 1984, 1985, 1986.

Characteristics of vintages

1986: Rich and well-balanced, fruity, supple tannins, promises a brilliant future. **1985:** Red fruit and grilled almond aromas, very long, its fullness and richness make it a remarkable wine. **1984:** Supple and fruity very pleasant right now. **1983:** Elegant and well-bred, rich tannins, balanced and distinguished. **1982:** Subtle blackcurrant and grilled almond fragrances, pleasant, considerable potential. Price range (pre-tax, ex-warehouse): between 30 F.F. and 50 F.F.
Sales in France: 40%.
Export sales: 60%.
Main trading partners: Belgium, Netherlands, Denmark, UK, USA.

CHÂTEAU ,FOURCAS-DUPRE

Patrice Pages, administrator
33480 Listrac Médoc
56 58 01 07

Type of vineyard: Family Agricultural Association. **Established:** 1843. **Number of employees:** 20. **Vine stocks:** 50% Cabernet Sauvignon , 38% Merlot, 10% Cabernet Franc, 2% Petit Verdot. **Soil:** Pyrenean gravel on clay and iron pan. **Average annual production in hectoliters:** 2,000.

Appellation: Listrac-Médoc. **Type:** Red. **Technique:** Traditional vinification, long fermentation on skins with frequent pumping over during fermentation to extract color and tannins. **Maturing:** In oak casks for 12 to 18 months. **Alcohol content:** 12.5%. **Characteristics:** Characterized by a deep ruby color, developing balance and a soft, supple harmony with time due to the softness and elegance of the tannins. **Serving temperature:** 18°. **Vintages available in 89/90:** 1984, 1986, 1987, 1988.

Characteristics of vintages

1988: Concentrated wine with rich and well balanced tannins. **1987:** Sustained color, balanced wine with an excellent aromatic persistance, very successful. **1986:** Very dense color, graceful and delicate nose with an elegant woody touch, not yet fully developed but very concentrated with harmonious tannins. Price range (pre-tax, ex-warehouse): between 30 and 50 F.F.

Sales volume:
– Wholesale: 60%. – Retail: 25%. – Restaurants: 15%.
Sales in France: 50%.
Export sales: 50%.
Main trading partners : Belgium, Denmark, Germany, United Kingdom, Netherlands, Switzerland.

References in France

Restaurants: Auberge de l'Ill, Hôtel de Paris (Monte-Carlo), Gray d'Albion (Cannes), Hôtel des Pyrénées (St Jean Pied de Port), Negresco (Nice), l'Aubergade (Michel Trama), Chez Vanel (Toulouse), Le Chapon Fin (Bordeaux), etc.
Shops: Paris: Centre de Distribution de Vins de Propriétés, Hediard, Caves Legrand, Grands Millésimes, etc.

Abroad

United Kingdom
Thorman Hunt & Co Ltd, 4 Pratt Walk, Lambeth, London SE11 6AR.

Germany
Jacques Wein Depot, Bilker Allée 49 D., 4000 Dusseldorf.

Switzerland
Denner Ag Postfac 263, Grubenstrasse 10, CH-8045 Zurich.

Belgium
Chacalli de Decker, Nijverjeidsstraat 54 A, 2220 Wommelgem.

The Netherlands
Allied Spirits Wines Nederland B.V., Nijverheidsweg 7-11, Postbus 142, Ettenleur 4780 Ac.

Others
Vingaarden A.S., Klostervej 5-13 DK 5000 Odense.

Comments

The Château Fourcas-Dupre domain occupies an especially privilieged location in the Listrac commune. The Fourcas vineyard is to be found on a map made by Belleyme, engineer and surveyor to King Louis XV. Today, the vineyard covers 40 hectares. The average age of the vines is 25 years and the plantation density varies between 8,000 and 10,000 stands per hectare. The Château Fourcas-Dupre wines, known as a Cru Bourgeois Supérieur in 1932, were awarded the title of Cru Grand Bourgeois Exceptionnel in 1977. The Château is a member of the Académie du Vin de Bordeaux and the Union des Grands Crus de Bordeaux.

CHÂTEAU LALANDE

Mrs. Georgette Darriet
Château Lalande 33480 Listrac-Médoc
56 58 19 45

Established: 1800. **Number of employees:** 5. **Vine stocks:** Merlot 50%, Cabernet 35%, Petit Verdot & Malbec 15%. **Soil:** Gravel (80%) – chalky clay (20%). **Exposure:** North-South. **Average annual production in hectoliters:** 450 to 500.

Appellation: AOC Listrac-Médoc. **Type:** Red. **Technique:** Long vinification. **Maturing:** Oak casks. **Alcohol content:** 12%. **Characteristics:** Tannic, very fruity, dark ruby color, made from old vines, hand harvesting. **Serving temperature:** 15°. **Served with:** Red meat, game, cheese. **Vintages available in 89/90:** 1983, 1984, 1985, 1986, 1988.

Characteristics of vintages

1988: Very great year, will be excellent in 5 years time. **1986:** Beautiful ruby color, ripe berry aroma, goes down well. **1985:** Very tannic, dark ruby color, blackcurrant aroma, lingering taste. **Other: 1983:** Very good right now, like eating ripe grapes 1979, 1981, 1982 (in magnums). Price range (pre-tax, ex-warehouse): 30 to 50 F.F. – 80 to 120 F.F. (magnums).

Sales volume:
– Wholesale: 35%. – Retail: 50%. – Restaurants: 15%.
Sales in France: 80%.
Export sales: 20%.

Abroad

Belgium
Bogeda, rue Pierre Van Humbeekstraat, 5 – Brussels (Tel: 02/521 54 55).

Comments

Gold Medal: Paris 1900, Brussels 1910. Cru Bourgeois 1932.

CHÂTEAU LESTAGE
Jean Chanfreau
33480 Listrac-Médoc
56 58 02 43

Type of vineyard: Family-owned. **Established:** 15th Century. **Vine stocks:** 30% Cabernet Sauvignon, 52% Merlot, 16% Cabernet Franc, 2% Petit Verdot. **Soil:** Gravel on a gravel and clay-calcareous sub-soil. **Exposure:** South. **Average annual production in hectoliters:** 2000.
Appellation: Listrac-Médoc. **Type:** Red. **Technique:** Traditionally Medocain. **Maturing:** Vats and barrels, 25% new each year. **Alcohol content:** 12.5%. **Characteristics:** Very fruity and round during the first few years. Its solid structure develops during the course of time, becoming very long. The fruity, with vailla, evolve fragrances evolve toward more smokey aromas. **Serving temperature:** 18°. **Served with:** Meat, dishes served with sauces, cheese. **Vintages available in 89/90:** 1982, 1983, 1984, 1985, 1986.

Characteristics of vintages

1986: Finesse and fruitiness balance the rich tannins and promise a brilliant future. **1985:** Elegant, harmonious wine, with fruit and vanilla fragrances. Excellent. **1984:** Soft tannins, a vintage to be drunk now. **1983:** An imposing wine, rich and structured, which will age marvelously. **1982:** Very rich and well-balanced, lots of volume. Price range (pre-tax, ex-warehouse): Between 30 and 50 F.F.
Sales in France: 50%.
Export sales: 50%.
Main trading partners : Belgium, Netherlands, Denmark, UK, USA.

CHÂTEAU SARANSOT-DUPRE
Yves Raymond
Listrac-Médoc – 33480 Castelnau-de-Médoc
56 58 03 02

Type of vineyard: Individually owned. **Established:** 1735. In the family since 1875. **Vine stocks:** Red: 50% Merlot, 50% Cabernet Sauvignon. White: 70% Semillon, 20% Sauvignon, 10% Muscadelle. **Soil:** Clay with calcium carbonate. **Average annual production in hectoliters:** 500.
Appellation: Rouge: Listrac-Médoc. Blanc: Bordeaux Sec. **Type:** Red, white. **Technique:** Fermentation with temperature control (red: 30° – white: 18°). **Maturing:** In new casks (less than 5 years old). **Alcohol content:** Red: 12.5%. White: 12%. **Characteristics:** Red: supple but full, intense aroma. White: aromatic, likely to age well. **Serving temperature:** Red: 18°. White: 7-8°. **Served with:** Red: red meat, cheese (St-Nectaire or Roblochon). White: fish and seafood. **Vintages available in 89/90:** Red: 1983, 1986, 1987, 1988. White: 1987, 1988.

Characteristics of vintages

1988: Red: very good vintage, delicate and distinguished, fine aromas. White: as delightful to the nose as to the palate. **1987:** Red: good well-balanced wine, undervalued year. White: excellent, aromatic and long. **1986:** Red: excellent, supple and fragrant. White: excellent. **1985:** Red: very traditional, great vintage. **1984:** Red: very pleasant right now, but will age vey quickly. **1983:** Red: fully developed now, but will keep a long time.

CHÂTEAU PEYREDON LAGRAVETTE
Paul Hostein
Médrac – 33480 Listrac-Médoc
56 58 05 55

Type of vineyard: Family-owned. **Established:** 1546. **Number of employees:** 1. **Vine stocks:** Cabernet Sauvignon 65%, Merlot 30%, Malbec 5%. **Soil:** 80% Quaternary gravel of the Garonne Basin, 20% clay with calcium carbonate. **Exposure:** South, Southwest. **Average annual production in hectoliters:** 275.
Appellation: A.O.C. Listrac, Médoc Cru Bourgeois. **Type:** Red. **Technique:** Fermentation – maceration (25 days). **Maturing:** 18 months in barrels (25% new) – fining with egg whites. **Alcohol content:** 12%. **Characteristics:** Deep, ruby. Delicate flavors nose. Raspberry and blackcurrant flavor, touch of vanilla. Velvety, supple, mellow tannins. **Serving temperature:** 17°. **Served with:** Grilled meat, poultry, game, roasts, cheese. **Vintages available in 89/90:** 1983, 1985.

Characteristics of vintages

1986: Gold Medal, Bordeaux. Flowery nose, fruity, vanilla and red berry flavors. **1985:** Gold medal, Concours de Paris – fruity nose, vanilla, raspberry and blackcurrant flavor. **1983:** Intense ruby color, good structure, mellow tannins, good development for ageing. Price range (pre-tax, ex-warehouse): Between 20 F.F. and 50 F.F.

Sales volume:
– Wholesale: 48%. – Retail: 50%. – Restaurants: 2%.
Sales in France: 52%.
Export sales: 48%.
Main trading partners : Belgium, Netherlands, Denmark, USA, Germany.

• *Classification of the great Bordeaux wines in 1988. The ratings of Châteaux Lascombes (Margaux), Mazeris-Bellevue (Canon-Fronsac) and Haut-Maco (Côtes-de-Bourg) are improving, as well as those of certain other surprising crus (Châteaux Trocard, Melin, Gazin, Chantegriue, Gloria, La Croix-Saint-André, Fombrauge...). See the 1988 Classification in the Chapter on Bordeaux wines.*

PAUILLAC

CHÂTEAU FONBADET

Pierre Peyronie
33250 Pauillac
56 59 02 11

Type of vineyard: Family-owned. **Established:** 1750. **Vine stocks:** 60% Cabernet Sauvignon, 15% Cabernet Franc, 20% Merlot. **Soil:** Gravel. **Exposure:** North South. **Average annual production in hectoliters:** 530. **Appellation:** Pauillac. **Type:** Red. **Technique:** In the old style. **Maturing:** Oak casks. **Alcohol content:** 12%. **Characteristics:** Very full bodied, beautiful structure, for keeping. **Serving temperature:** Room temperature. **Served with:** All meats and cheeses. **Vintages available in 89/90:** From 1966 to 1987.

Characteristics of vintages

1988: Not yet tasted. **1987:** Deep color, velvety, well bred wine, tasty, surprising Pauillac in a much criticized year. **1986:** Deep red color, velvety, rich red fruit fragrance, dense, with a beautiful mature tannin finish, long. **1985:** Very rich aromas, robust, heady wine, round, full and very long. Very promising wine to be kept. **Other:** 1982: Smooth, rich in extract, full, long aromatic persistance. The Château oenologist, Mr. Perez says "It is a magnificent masterpiece with the characteristics of a great wine". To keep 30 to 50 years. Price range (pre-tax, ex-warehouse): between 50 and 80 F.F.

Sales volume:
– Wholesale: 80%. – Retail: 15%. – Restaurants: 5%.

Sales in France: 30%.

Export sales: 70%.

Main trading partners : Benelux Countries, Switzerland, United States, Japan.

References in France

Restaurants: Le Taillevent, Jamain (Paris), Château Eza (06360 Éze Village).

Abroad

Germany

Bacchus & Minensa, Salzstrasse 22, 7800 Fribourg.

Comments

In 1817, the château was purchased by Pierre de Géres de Loupes, Lord of Camarsac. The various parts of the domain are far from being contiguous; the sixteen hectares cultivated by the Peyronie family are the result of the addition of a number of parcels spread out over the Pauillac appellation.

Château Fonbadet

Wine selected by the Association for the Fiftieth Anniversary of the A.O.C. and the I.N.A.O. at Paris

Château Fonbadet
MISE EN BOUTEILLES AU CHÂTEAU
PAUILLAC
APPELLATION PAUILLAC CONTROLÉE

PIERRE PEYRONIE
PROPRIÉTAIRE
A PAUILLAC MÉDOC (GIRONDE)
75 cl
MODÈLE DÉPOSÉ
PRODUCE OF FRANCE

Vin sélectionné par l'Association du Cinquantenaire des A.O.C. et de l'I.N.A.O. à Paris

Château Padarnac — Château Montgrand-Miion
Château Tour du Roch-Milon
Château Haut-Pauillac — Château Pauillac

CHÂTEAU BATAILLEY

Émile Casteja
33250 Pauillac
56 59 01 13

Type of vineyard: Family-owned. **Number of employees:** 35. **Vine stocks:** 75% Merlot. **Soil:** Gravel. **Exposure:** Hillcrest. **Average annual production in hectoliters:** 2,250.
Appellation: Grand Cru Classé, Pauillac. **Type:** Red. **Technique:** Classic. **Maturing:** In barrels. **Alcohol content:** 12.5%. **Characteristics:** Beautiful aroma, red fruit flavor. Tannic, vigorous, full-bodied, fleshy, soft and rich, well structured, woody, round and long not astringent. **Serving temperature:** 15° to 18°. **Served with:** All meats and cheeses. **Vintages available in 89/90:** 1984, 1985, 1986.

Characteristics of vintages

1986: Not yet tasted. **1985:** Remarkable, full and supple wine, good color, will age well. **1984:** A successful year.

CHÂTEAU PONTET-CANET

Guy and Alfred Tesseron
Château Pontet-Canet – 33250 Pauillac
56 59 00 79/56 59 04 04
Bordeaux office: 56 52 15 71 – Telex: 541 479 F

Established: 18th Century. **Vine stocks:** 70% Cabernet Sauvignon, 20% Merlot, 10% Cabernet franc. **Soil:** Gravel. **Exposure:** Full South. **Average annual production in hectoliters:** 35hl per hectare.
Appellation: Pauillac, Grand Cru Classé in 1855. **Type:** Red. **Technique:** Stainless steel tanks, permitting complete temperature control. **Maturing:** Traditional, 30% new barrels each year. **Characteristics:** Complex and rich wines. Red fruit, flower, spice and vanilla fragrance. Beautiful balance of tannins, alcohol and acidity. Flattering wines, distinguished and well-bred. **Serving temperature:** 18°. **Served with:** Red meat, white meat, poultry, all vegetables, cheese, desserts with red fruit, pears or peaches or fruit in red wine. **Vintages available in 89/90:** 1978, 1981, 1982, 1983, 1984, 1985.

Characteristics of vintages

1986: Still maturing, intense color. Red fruit fragrance. Beautiful balance. Superb. **1985:** Deep color. Rich, very fruity fragrance. Rich, balanced and harmonious structure. A great wine. **1984:** Cherry color. Elegant bouquet. Beautiful constitution. Pleasant aftertaste. Lovely wine. **1983:** Intense color. Preserved (red) fruit fragrance. Supple attack. Delightful aftertaste. Beautiful wine. **1982:** Beautiful purple color. Soft spice and vanilla fragrance. Rich and complex flavor. Great wine. **Other:** 1981: Natural red. Aromatic. Heady attack. Long. Beautiful wine. 1978: Beautiful color. Soft, complex nose. Fleshy attack. Long. Beautiful wine.

• Blending – a method consisting of mixing different wines from different lots or different vintages in order to obtain a more homogeneous product.

• The naturally sweet wines of the Loire region, such as Quarts-de-Chaume or Coteau-du-Layon, offer the possibility of some very lovely wine tastings. Very fruity, full, supple and harmonious, they will keep well. (See the Chapter on the Loire Valley).

SAINT-ESTÈPHE

CALON SEGUR

Philippe Capbern Gasqueton
33250 Saint-Estèphe

Type of vineyard: Agricultural Association. **Soil:** Gravelly. **Exposure:** East, West. **Average annual production in hectoliters:** 3,000.

Appellation: Saint-Estèphe. **Type:** Red. **Technique:** Traditional. **Maturing:** 30% in new casks, 70% in 2-3 year old casks. **Alcohol content:** 12.5%. **Characteristics:** Delicate, slightly woody, class and distinction, fine color, result of rigorous selection. **Serving temperature:** 17°. **Served with:** Red meat. **Vintages available in 89/90:** 1979, 1982, 1983, 1985, 1986.

Characteristics of vintages

1988: Soft and full, rich and well balanced, harmonious, great wine, very promising. **1987:** Finesse and breed, perfectly controlled vintage. **1986:** Character, marked by Cabernet, dense, good keeping. **1985:** Finesse and breed, predominance of Merlot, fine development.
Sales volume:
- Wholesale: 100%.

Sales in France: 25%.
Export sales: 75%.
Main trading partners : European countries, Japan.

Comments

Since the Roman era, Calon which means "rowboat" has continued to play an important role in the winemaking world and has had the right to the title of Premier Cru as early as 1775. (See "Classification 89").

CHÂTEAU COS D'ESTOURNEL

Domaines Prats S.A. (Director: Bruno Prats)
Saint-Estèphe - 33250 Pauillac
56 44 11 37 - Telex: 540 966 - Fax: 56 44 51 92

Type of vineyard: Family-owned. **Established:** 1917. **Number of employees:** 50. **Vine stocks:** Cabernet 60%, Merlot 40%. **Soil:** Günzian gravel on a limestone base. **Exposure:** Hilltop exposed to the South and the East. **Average annual production in hectoliters:** 1,800. **Appellation:** Saint-Estèphe. **Type:** Red. **Technique:** Traditional vinification of the Grands Crus Classés of the Médoc. **Maturing:** In oak barrels. **Alcohol content:** 12.5%. **Characteristics:** Deep color, aroma combining a touch of wood with the fragrance of red fruit, leading to a slight animal and truffle scent. Very long, very rich and full-bodied, deep, lasting after-taste. Ages very well thanks to the richness of its mellow tannins. **Serving temperature:** 16° to 18° depending upon the room temperature. **Served with:** Simple meat dishes to allow the wine to express its finesse and complexity. Leg of lamb, for example. **Vintages available in 89/90:** Most vintages.

Characteristics of vintages

1988: Very intense and complex aromas great concentration. Long and full bodied with great ageing potential. **1987:** Scent of raspberries dense, with a touch of liquorice. **1986:** Not yet tasted. **1985:** Not yet tasted. **1983:** Very round and seductive with beautiful, well ripened tannins, lovely aroma with spicy overtones. **1982:** A concentrated vintage, excellent for ageing, very supple tannins and full-bodied structure. Price range (pre-tax, ex-warehouse): Over 160 F.F.

Sales volume: - Wholesale: 98%. - Retail: 2%.

Main trading partners : USA, UK, Switzerland, Belgium, Netherlands, Germany, Denmark, Japan, Canada, Sweden.

CHÂTEAU BEAU-SITE

Émile Casteja
86, cours Balguerie-Stuttenberg
33300 Bordeaux
56 48 57 57 - Telex: 550 766

Vine stocks: 70% Cabernet Sauvignon, 30% Merlot. **Appellation:** Saint-Estèphe. **Type:** Red. **Technique:** Traditional (under the supervision of Professor Ribereau-Gayon). **Maturing:** Oak barrels. **Characteristics:** Very typical St. Estèphe, full-bodied, long, ripe fruit aroma, tannin, round, very strong aroma, rich in alcohol, well-balanced, soft and full. **Serving temperature:** 19° to 20°. **Served with:** Cheese and meat in general. **Vintages available in 89/90:** 1985 and 1986.

Characteristics of vintages

1986: Excellent fruity, tonic, a wine with good potential. **1985:** Rich full bodied, a great wine.

Sales volume:
- Wholesale: 100% Borie Manoux. Wine merchants.

References in France

Restaurants: Mainly restaurants with Michelin Stars.
Shops: Hédiard, Fauchon, Fine Grocers, etc.

CHÂTEAU COS LABORY

Bernard Audoy
33250 Saint-Estèphe
56 59 30 22

Type of vineyard: Agricultural Association. **Established:** 1800. **Number of employees:** 12. **Vine stocks:** 30% Merlot, 40% Cabernet Sauvignon, 25% Cabernet Franc, 5% Petit Verdot. **Soil:** Gravel on chalky marl sub-soil. **Exposure:** South. **Average annual production in hectoliters:** 600.

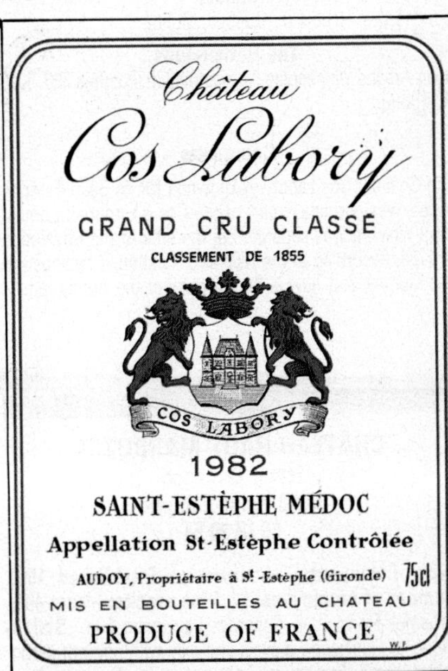

Appellation: Saint-Estèphe, Médoc. **Type:** Red. **Technique:** Traditional. **Maturing:** In oak casks, one third next each year. **Alcohol content:** 12.5%. **Characteristics:** Lovely ruby color, vanilla nose, elegant, round full, good tannic harmony and fruit. **Serving temperature:** 18°. **Served with:** Meat and cheese. **Vintages available in 89/90:** 1986, 1987, 1988.

Characteristics of vintages

1988: Beautiful color, very aromatic nose, round, full. **1987:** A good success for the vintage. **1986:** The vintage of the century, to be left to age. Price range (pre-tax, ex-warehouse): between 30 and 50 F.F.
Sales volume:
– Wholesale: 60%. – Retail: 20%. – Restaurants: 20%.
Sales in France: 40%.
Export sales: 60%.
Main trading partners : Belgium, Germany, United Kingdom, Netherlands, Denmark, Switzerland.

References in France

Restaurants: Chiberta, Trois Marches, Georges Blanc.
Shops: Caves de Passy, Caves de l'Avenue des Ternes, Bordeaux Magnums, Legrand Fils.

Abroad

Germany
Hawesko, Raiffeisenstrasse 14, 2082 Tornesch.

Switzerland
Fritz Lanz, Lerzerstrasse 24, 8953 Dietikon.

Belgium
Frui S.A., Kapoenstraat 8, 8130 Zarren.

Canada
Société des Alcools du Québec, Montréal.

The Netherlands
Jean Arnaud Wijnkopers, Orionstraat 30, Postbus 350, 5000 AJ Tilburg.

Comments

The Château Cos-Labory, reknowned for its Saint-Estèphe wines, was origninally part of the Cos d'Estournel domain from which it was separated at the time of the Revolution of 1789. According to the 1855 classification, it belonged to Mr. Martyns and now is the property of the Audoy family.

CHÂTEAU HAUT-MARBUZET

Henri Duboscq
33250 Saint-Estèphe
56 59 30 54

Type of vineyard: Civil Corporation. **Established:** 1952. **Number of employees:** 32. **Vine stocks:** Merlot 40%, Cabernet Franc 10%, Cabernet Sauvignon 50%. **Soil:** A hilltop of Gunzienne gravels and clay with calcium carbonate sub-soil. **Exposure:** East, facing the Gironde. **Average annual production in hectoliters:** 1,800.
Appellation: Saint-Estèphe. **Type:** Red. **Technique:** Manually harvested grapes, with on maturing possibilities research; total destemming. **Maturing:** Very long maceration with daily pumping over maturing 18 months in new oak barrels for each vintage. **Characteristics:** A charmer, exuberant in its youth: ageing spells out the subtleties derived from the soil. **Serving temperature:** 16 to 18°. **Served with:** All kinds of beef, red meat and game. **Vintages available in 89/90:** 1985, 1986.

Characteristics of vintages

1986: Rich and promising. Its consistant body delights now, but has great possibility too. **1985:** Perfect harmony between the fruit (blackcurrent, cherry), exotic touche (vanilla, cinnamon) and noble tannins. Price range (pre-tax, ex-warehouse): Between 80 and 120 F.F.
Sales volume:
– Wholesale: 5%. – Retail: 75%. – Restaurants: 20%.
Sales in France: 80%.
Export sales: 20%.
Main trading partners : England, Switzerland, Belgium, Holland, Austria, USA.

References in France

Restaurants: Taillevent, Bristol, Maxim's, Robuchon, Les 3 Marches, Paris. La Belle Époque, L'Huîtrière in Lille, The Miramar Hotel in Biarritz.
Shops: Stevent Spurier, Caveau de Bacchus, Hédiard.

Abroad

United States
Kermit Lynch, Berkeley, California. Tel: 524. 1524. Silenus Wines in Waltham, Mass. 02154. Tel: 617 890 0876. Direct Import Wines in des Plaines, Illinois.

United Kingdom
G & J Greeenall Ltd, Narrington. Tel: 925 50111.

Germany
Wienimport Rutshauser in 8750 Aschaffenburg. Tel: 6021/ 42097. Champa Vins Français – 5190 St. Olberg. Tel: 242/ 20064.

Canada
SAQ CP, 1058 Place d'Armes, Montréal, Québec.

The Netherlands
Wijnkoperij HFA, Okhuysen B.V. Gierstraat 34/38 in Harrlem 2011. Tel: 23 31 22 40.

Switzerland
Manoiral SA, Lentschacker 919 – 4614 Hagendorf. Tel: 62 46 14 50.

Austria
Alois Morandell & Sohn, 6300 Worgl/Tirol. Tel: 5334 33550.

Belgium
Van Geyseghem – Leopoldvest 36, 3300 Tienen.

Comments

The nature of the soil and the faithfulness of its participants permit the Château Haut-Marbuzet to perfectly reflect the Family oath, "Quality is my truth".

Château Laffitte Carcasset - Saint-Estèphe en Médoc

CHÂTEAU LAFFITTE-CARCASSET

Viscount de Padirac Saint-Estèphe
56 59 32 29 – Telex: 571 675 F

Type of vineyard: Agricultural Association. **Established:** 1976. **Vine stocks:** 60% Cabernet, 40% Merlot. **Soil:** Gravelly plateau. **Exposure:** Heart of the Saint-Estèphe Commune. **Average annual production in hectoliters:** 150 barrels.
Appellation: AOC Saint-Estèphe. **Type:** Red. **Technique:** Total destemming, pumping over. **Maturing:** Temperature control. Fermentation on skins for 2 to 3 weeks. **Alcohol content:** 12.1%. **Characteristics:** Fragrant, soft wines, very rich in taste. Conforms to the traditional quality of the great Saint-Estèphe wines. **Serving temperature:** 17 to 19°. **Served with:** Red meat, cheese. **Vintages available in 89/90:** 1985, 1986.

Characteristics of vintages

Price range (pre-tax, ex-warehouse): between 30 and 50 F.F.
Sales volume:
– Wholesale: 85%. – Retail: 15%.
Sales in France: 70%.
Export sales: 30%
Main trading partners : USA, Belgium.

Comments

The Foulhiac de Padirac family, originally from Bort in the Limousin, has been established at Gramat in Quercy since the end of the 15th century. In 1956, Viscount Pierre de Padirac invested in the purchase of the Château Laffitte-Carcasset in the parish of Saint-Estèphe, which goes back to the 18th century. Pierre de Padirac was a strong character who had his own ideas on the art of making good wine. Unfortunately, he was called to his maker in 1961. In 1978, his son Philippe married Constance de Quelen, descended from an old family from Brittany. With more the 35 hectares at his disposal, Viscount Philippe immediately set out to reestablish the excellent reputation enjoyed by the Château Laffitte-Carcasset in the past.

• Would you like to know to recognize the caracteristic fragrances of certains wines, their woodland, fruity, flowery or leather aromas, the evaluate the level of acidity or the presence of tannins, to ascertain the mellowness or the color of a wine...? See the Chapter entitled "The Art and Manner of Wine Tasting".

CHÂTEAU MONTROSE

J.-L. Charmolue
Saint-Estèphe, 33250 Pauillac
56 59 30 12

Type of vineyard: Family-owned. **Established:** 1815. **Number of employees:** 32. **Vine stocks:** Cabernet Sauvignon 65%, Cabernet Franc 10%, Merlot 25%. **Soil:** Coarse gravel, 3 to 4 meters deep, on clay and marl subsoil. **Exposure:** Very sunny, mild micro-climate due to the nearby Gironde. **Average annual production in hectoliters:** 2,900.

Appellation: Saint-Estèphe. **Type:** Red. **Technique:** Traditional in wooden vats with maceration (25 to 28 days). **Maturing:** In casks (30 to 40% new each year) for 21 months. **Alcohol content:** 12.5%. **Characteristics:** Beautiful red-brown color, rich and full, round, high tannin content, great finesse, delicate and complex bouquet which develops with ageing – long keeping. **Serving temperature:** 18-19°. **Served with:** Young lamb, small game.

Characteristics of vintages

1988: A bit early for comments – but most certainly a remarkable year. **1987:** Good fruity bouquet, finesse and elegance, good tannic structure – a perfectly successful vintage. **1986:** Great vintage – rich and full, tannic, very long. **1985:** Fruity, elegant, round and fleshy, excellent vintage, supple and harmonious, full, very good development. Price range (pre-tax, ex-warehouse): 120 to 160.

Sales volume:
– Wholesale: 99%. – Retail: 1%.
Sales in France: 15%.
Export sales: 85%.
Main trading partners : USA, United Kingdom, Switzerland, Belgium, Germany.

References in France

Restaurants: All of the great restaurants.
Shops: All important shops.

Comments

The grounds of the Château Montrose were bought on March 6, 1778 by E.T. Dumoulin. His son built the château and planted the vineyard, starting in 1815. Sold by the Dumoulin family in 1866 to Mathieu Dollfus, the domain passed, in 1889, to Jules Hostein who bequeathed it to his son-in-law, Louis Charmolue, in 1896. Since, it has remained the property of this family, represented today by J.L. Charmolue. Montrose is a superb wine (see "Classification 89"), remarkably vinified, at the forefront of the great Bordeaux wines. Special attention is paid to structure, softness, aromatic concentration and elegance. Great art, long evolution.

• *Want to know more about wine, its vinification, its nature and its vocabulary? See Chapter "The Chemistry of Wine".*

CHÂTEAU SÉGUR DE CABANAC

Guy Delon
33250 St. Estephe
56 59 70 10

Type of vineyard: Family-owned. **Established:** 1985. **Number of employees:** 2. **Vine stocks:** Merlots 30%, Cabernets Sauvignons 60%, Petits Verdots 10%. **Soil:** Gravelly hillcrests on a chalky clay sub-soil. **Exposure:** Facing the Gironde. **Average annual production in hectoliters:** 40.

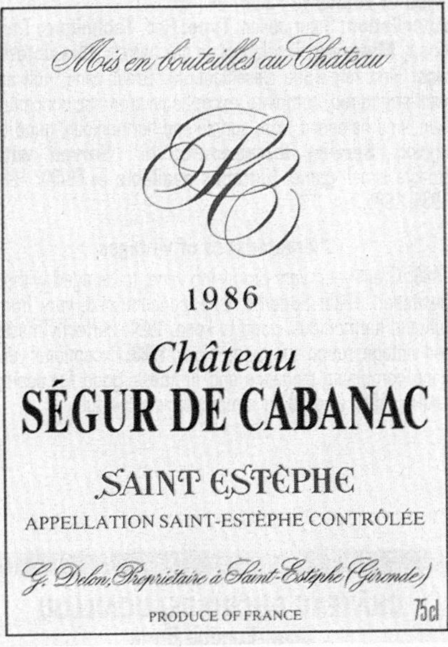

Mis en bouteilles au Château
1986
Château
SÉGUR DE CABANAC
SAINT ESTÈPHE
APPELLATION SAINT-ESTÈPHE CONTRÔLÉE
G. Delon, Propriétaire à Saint-Estèphe (Gironde)
PRODUCE OF FRANCE
75cl

Appellation: St.-Estephe Contrôlée. **Type:** Red. **Technique:** Fermentation for 15 to 20 days in stainless steel tanks. **Maturing:** Oak casks, 25% new. **Alcohol content:** 12 to 12.5% according to the year. **Characteristics:** The product of old vines, the wines are tannic, full bodied, with a certain suppleness, lots of fragrance and exceptional robustness. **Serving temperature:** Room temperature,17 to 18°. **Served with:** Meat, game, cheese. **Vintages available in 89/90:** 1986.

Characteristics of vintages

1988: Lots of body, very long keeping. **1987:** Very agreeable, supple, to be drunk in less than 10 years. **1986:** Full bodied, tannic, for very long keeping. Price range (pre-tax, ex-warehouse): between 30 an 50 F.F.
Sales volume:
– Wholesale: 20%. – Retail: 80%.
Sales in France: 90%.
Export sales: 10%.
Main trading partners : Belgium, Netherlands (retail).

Comments

Ségur de Cabanac, acquired in 1985, is the result of the deep attachment of its proprietor, Guy Delon, to the St-Estephe appellation. The 6.25 hectares which make up this exploitation are located on beautiful gravelly hillcrests, overlooking the Gironde, contiguous with the greatest crus of the appellation. Its old Merlot, Cabernet Sauvignon, Cabernet Franc and Petit Verdot vinestocks are already synonymous with quality. Production varies according to the vintages from 30 to 35,000 bottles, sold for the most part to individual clients. The wines are full bodied, tannic without loss of suppleness, fragrant and have great distinction.

CHÂTEAU DOMEYNE

Mmes. Franchini (Managers)
Saint-Estèphe 33250 Pauillac
56 59 30 21

Type of vineyard: Agricultural Association. **Established:** 1978. **Vine stocks:** Cabernet 65%, Merlot 35%. **Soil:** Gravel. **Exposure:** Plateau. **Average annual production in hectoliters:** 50 hl/ha.
Appellation: Saint-Estèphe. **Type:** Red. **Technique:** Total destemming, long fermentation on skins, hand harvesting. **Maturing:** In oak casks for 22 months. **Alcohol content:** 12%. **Characteristics:** Clean and natural, vigorous, good body. **Serving temperature:** 16 to 18°. **Served with:** Red meat, cheese. **Vintages available in 89/90:** 1986, 1987, 1988.

Characteristics of vintages

1988: Good keeping, promising. **1987:** Drink soon. **1986:** Good keeping, rich in color, concentrated, dense. Price range (pre-tax, ex-warehouse): 30 to 50 F.F.
Sales volume: – Wholesale: 45%. – Retail: 35%. – Restaurants: 20%.
Sales in France: 75%.
Export sales: 25%.
Main trading partners : Belgium, Switzerland, Germany.

References in France

Shops: Vignobles de France, (Paris).

Abroad

United Kingdom

Windrushwines, Cecily Hill Cirencester, Gloucestershire GL 7 2 EF.

Germany

A. Rohrl, Asamstrasse 32-8420 Kelheim.

Switzerland

Schererherer S.A. 11-13, rue Vautier, Case Postale, 127 Carouge, Geneva.

Belgium

Delmas-Nony SARL 755, Domaine de la Vigne, 59910 Bondues.

Others

Sidvs 25, bd. Jubelin, BP 912, 87338 Cayenne Cedex.

Comments

The property is located in the heart of the Commune of Saint-Estèphe. It was acquired in 1978 by the Franchini ladies, who renovated the fermenting vats and the storehouses, and is presently being extended.

CHÂTEAU LES ORMES DE PEZ

A. et J.-M. Cazes
17, rue Jean-Jaurès – 33250 Pauillac
56 59 19 19 – Telex: 550 468 F

Type of vineyard: Family-owned. **Established:** 17th Century. **Number of employees:** 15. **Vine stocks:** Cabernet Sauvignon 55% – Cabernet Franc 10% – Merlot 35%. **Soil:** Silica-clay and gravel on chalky sub-soil. **Exposure:** The plateau of Saint-Estèphe. **Average annual production in hectoliters:** 1,400.
Appellation: Saint-Estèphe. **Type:** Red. **Technique:** Fermentation about 2 weeks in temperature regulated steel tanks. **Maturing:** In oak barrels. **Alcohol content:** 12.5% **Characteristics:** Supple and full-bodied, rich and well-balanced, well made, suitable for ageing. **Serving temperature:** 16° to 18°. **Served with:** Red meat and dishes served with sauce go perfectly with these Saint-Estèphe wines which have lots of body.

Characteristics of vintages

1986: Tannic and powerful, for long conservation. **1985:** Supple, elegant, lots of body and complexity. **1984:** Light and well-balanced year, to be drunk as of 1987-1988. **1983:** Very balanced and well made, a very successful vintage. **1982:** Great vintage round, lots of body and power.

SAINT-JULIEN

CHÂTEAU LÉOVILLE-LAS-CASES

Michel Delon
Saint-Julien-Beychevelle – 33250 Pauillac
56 59 25 26

Type of vineyard: Family-owned.
Appellation: Saint-Julien. **Type:** Red. **Technique:** Traditional. **Maturing:** Traditional, in oak barrels. **Characteristics:** First rate (See classification). Great wine, rich and well-structured, complete, exceptional aromatic concentration, well-balanced, soft, supple and harmonious, good for ageing. **Serving temperature:** 16°. **Served with:** Roasts, small game. **Vintages available in 89/90:** 1983, 1984, 1985.

Characteristics of vintages

1986: Great year, very promising wine, to be aged without hesitation. **1985:** Superbe wine, concentrated, very fruity, full and harmonious, good to keep. **1984:** Perfectly mastered vintage, round and harmonious. **1983:** Exceptional year, wine combining elegance and firmness, good for ageing. **Other: 1980 and 1979:** remarkably successful.

CHÂTEAU DUCRU-BEAUCAILLOU

Jean-Eugène Borie
Saint-Julien-Beychevelle – 33250 Pauillac
56 59 05 20

Type of vineyard: Family-owned. **Vine stocks:** (50 hectares): Cabernet-Sauvignon 65%, Merlot 25%, Cabernet Franc 5%, Petit Verdot 5%. **Soil:** Gravel.
Appellation: Saint-Julien. **Type:** Red. **Technique:** Traditional – Hand harvesting. **Maturing:** In oak barrels. **Characteristics:** Great Saint-Julien. (See classification.) Deep color, rich and complex nose, fine woody aroma, vanilla taste, well-balanced, good for ageing. **Serving temperature:** 16°. **Served with:** Roasts, lamb, small game. **Vintages available in 89/90:** 1983 and 1985.

Characteristics of vintages

1986: Promising year. To be aged. **1985:** Superb wine, combining suppleness and strength, very fragrant, good for ageing. **1983:** Exceptional year, structured wine, aroma of fully ripe grapes, full bodied, vigorous, very elegant, good to age. **Othter:** 1979: exceptional vintage, soft, supple and harmonious, velvety, very well-balanced.

SOCIÉTÉ FERMIÈRE DES CHATEAUX LANGOA
ET LÉOVILLE-BARTON
SAINT-JULIEN-BEYCHEVELLE 33250 PAUILLAC - TÉL. : 56 59 06 05

CHÂTEAU LEOVILLE BARTON

Anthony Barton
St-Julien Beychevelle, 33250 Pauillac
56 59 06 05 – Telex: 570 241

Type of vineyard: Agricultural Association. **Established:** 1983. **Number of employees:** 40. **Vine stocks:** Cabernet Sauvignon 70%, Merlot 20%, Cabernet Franc 8%, Petit Verdot 2%. **Soil:** Gravelly soil on clay sub-soil. **Exposure:** North South, for the most part. **Average annual production in hectoliters:** 2000.
Appellation: Saint Julien. **Type:** Red. **Technique:** Fermentation in wooden vats. **Maturing:** Casks, 50 to 60% new. **Alcohol content:** 12.5%. **Characteristics:** Well balanced, fruity with elegance and a good ageing potential. **Serving temperature:** 17°. **Served with:** Red meat, game. **Vintages available in 89/90:** 1984, 1985, 1986, 1987.

Characteristics of vintages

1988: Deep color, harmonious tannins, alcohols and acids, good keeping. **1987:** Supple and fruity wine, well balanced, very successful. **1986:** Very deep color, tannic wine, but round and fruity. **1985:** Less tannic than the '86, but exceptional finesse. Price range (pre-tax, ex-warehouse): between 80 and 120 F.F.

Sales volume:
– Wholesale: 100%.

Comments

A very great vineyard which has belonged to the Barton "dynasty" for generations. A sublime wine, rich and well balanced, full of grace and distinction, among the greatest of the Bordeaux wines. (see "Classification 89").

SOCIÉTÉ CIVILE DU CHÂTEAU BEYCHEVELLE

Maurice Ruelle and Yves Fourault
Saint-Julien – 33250 Pauillac
56 59 23 00

Type of vineyard: Corporation. **Number of employees:** 49. **Vine stocks:** Cabernet-Sauvignon 62%, Cabernet Franc 8%, Merlot 28%, Petit Verdot 2%. **Average annual production in hectoliters:** 6,000.
Appellation: Saint-Julien. **Type:** Red. **Technique:** Fermentation with skins (20-25 days), temperature control (about 30°). **Maturing:** In new barrels for 20 months. **Alcohol content:** 11.5°-11.9%. **Characteristics:** Rich aromas, fruity, concentrated, deep color, tannic, firm and

full-bodied, very long finish, very well-balanced. **Serving temperature:** About 16°. **Served with:** Red meat and game. **Vintages available in 89/90:** 1970, 1975, 1978, 1979, 1980, 1981, 1982, 1983, and 1984.

CHÂTEAU MOULIN DE LA ROSE

Guy Delon
33250 St-Julien-Beychevelle
56 59 08 45

Type of vineyard: Family-owned. **Established:** Acquired in 1971. **Number of employees:** 2. **Vine stocks:** Merlots 30%, Cabernet Sauvignons 60%, Petits Verdots 10%. **Soil:** Gravelly hillcrest on clay, iron pan and gravel subsoil. **Exposure:** Mostly facing the river. **Average annual production in hectoliters:** 40.

Appellation: St-Julien Contrôlée. **Type:** Red. **Technique:** Fermentation for 15 to 20 days in stainless steel tanks. **Maturing:** Entirely in casks, 25% new. **Alcohol content:** 12%. **Characteristics:** Full bodied, tannic but supple, very fragrant, considerable grace and distinction. **Serving temperature:** 17 to 18°. **Served with:** Meat, game, cheese. **Vintages available in 89/90:** 1984, 1985, 1986.

Characteristics of vintages

1988: Full bodied, long keeping. **1987:** Supple, very agreeable, to be drunk in the next 10 years. **1986:** Tannic, lots of body, for very long keeping. **1985:** Supple, tannic, to be drunk in the next 15 years. Price range (pre-tax, ex-warehouse): between 30 and 50 F.F.

Sales volume:
– Wholesale: 20%. – Retail: 80%.
Sales in France: 80%. **Export sales:** 20%.
Main trading partners: Belgium, Netherlands, Germany.

Comments

The 4.6 hectares of the Château are divided among the greatest classified Crus (Léoville Las-Cases, Ducru, Beaucaillou, Beychevelle, etc.). Vinestocks of 30% Merlots, 55% Cabernet Sauvignons and the rest in Cabernets Francs and Petit Verdots are used to produce full bodied, tannic though supple wines, that are very fragrant, have considerable grace and dignity, and are worthy of the best of tables. The wine is entirely aged in oak casks, some of which are new. Bottling follows 20 months of attentive care (racking 7 times and fining with egg whites).

CHÂTEAU LÉOVILLE POYFERRE

Didier Cuvelier
St-Julien Beychevelle – 33250 Pauillac
56 59 08 30

Established: 1968. **Number of employees:** 35. **Vine stocks:** Merlot 25%, Cabernet Franc 2%, Cabernet Sauvignon 65%, Petit Verdot 8%. **Soil:** Gravel from the Garonne Basin.
Type: Red. **Technique:** Traditional. **Maturing:** 65% new barrels. **Alcohol content:** 12%. **Characteristics:** Very aromatic. Violet bouquet. Great finesse, vigorous, very well-balanced, lingering color. **Serving temperature:** 17°. **Served with:** All meats. **Vintages available in 89/90:** From 1978 to 1986.

Characteristics of vintages

1988: Great vintage. Very good structure with very soft tannins. Very good keeping. **1987:** Good year thanks to a careful selection. Well-balanced, fine vanilla aroma. Perfect to drink in 4 years. Very good quality/price ratio. **1986:** Very great year, rich in tannins. **1985:** Good year, very fruity, full-taste, structured, good flavor wine for ageing. **1984:** Quite successful with a difficult vintage. **1983:** Great year, very rich and well-balanced, good tannins, good from wine for ageing. **1982:** Exceptional year, very ripe grapes. For the cellar. Price range (pre-tax, ex-warehouse): 100-200 F.F.

CHÂTEAU LALANDE-BORIE

Borie
Saint-Julien-Beychevelle – 33250 Pauillac
56 59 05 20

Type of vineyard: Family-owned. **Vine stocks:** (18 hectares): Cabernet 75%, Merlot 25%. **Soil:** Gravel.
Appellation: Saint-Julien. **Type:** Red. **Technique:** Tradi-

tional. **Maturing:** In barrels. **Characteristics:** Excellent wine, rich color, vegetal and red berry nose, supple and dense at the same time, harmonious, good for ageing (See Classification). **Serving temperature:** 16°. **Served with:** Roasts. **Vintages available in 89/90:** 1985 and 1986.

Characteristics of vintages

1986: Promising year. **1985:** Good year, fine woody aroma, deep red color, full and fruity, good for ageing.

CHÂTEAU TERREY GROS CAILLOUX

A. Fort & H. Pradère
Saint-Julien
- Beychevelle 33250 Pauillac
56 59 06 27

Type of vineyard: Agricultural Association. **Number of employees:** 10. **Vine stocks:** Merlot 25%, Cabernet 70%, Petit Verdot 5%. **Soil:** Poor gravelly soil. **Exposure:** Sunny. **Average annual production in hectoliters:** 900.

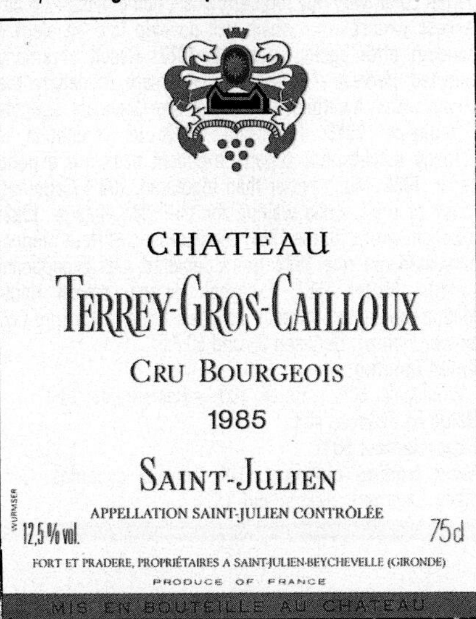

CHATEAU
TERREY-GROS-CAILLOUX
CRU BOURGEOIS
1985
SAINT-JULIEN
APPELLATION SAINT-JULIEN CONTRÔLÉE
12,5 % vol.
75cl
FORT ET PRADERE, PROPRIÉTAIRES A SAINT-JULIEN-BEYCHEVELLE (GIRONDE)
PRODUCE OF FRANCE
MIS EN BOUTEILLE AU CHATEAU

Appellation: Saint-Julien. **Type:** Red. **Technique:** Traditional. **Maturing:** In casks. **Alcohol content:** 12.5%. **Characteristics:** Fine, fragrant, tannic. **Serving temperature:** 17%. **Served with:** Meat, cheese. **Vintages available in 89/90:** 1985-1986.

Characteristics of vintages

1988: Still in casks, promising. **1987:** Not yet tasted. **1986:** great, tannic, beautiful color, full-bodied, to be kept. Price range (pre-tax, ex-warehouse): 50 to 80 F.F.
Sales volume:
- Wholesale: 70%. - Retail: 20% - Restaurants: 10%.
Main trading partners : Belgium, Switzerland, USA.

HAUT-MÉDOC

CHÂTEAU DILLON

Lycée agricole
33290 Blanquefort
56 35 02 27

Vine stocks: Merlot, Cabernet Sauvignon, Petit Verdot, Carmenère. **Soil:** Clay with calcium carbonate and gravel. **Exposure:** South. **Average annual production in hectoliters:** 1, 500.
Appellation: Haut-Médoc. **Type:** Red. **Technique:** Fermentation with thermo-regulation. **Maturing:** In oak casks. **Alcohol content:** 12%-12.5%. **Characteristics:** Well-balanced, supple, beautiful ruby color. May be aged from 5 to 12 years, according to the vintage. **Serving temperature:** 16°-17°. **Served with:** Meat, game, cheese. **Vintages available in 89/90:** 1984, 1985.

Characteristics of vintages

1985: Very good color, strong aroma, good balance, lingering flavor. **1984:** Cherry color, quite nature, successful vintage, not to be missed. Price range (pre-tax, ex-warehouse): 20 F.F.-50 F.F.
Sales volume:
- Wholesale: 35%. - Retail: 60%. - Restaurants: 5%.
Sales in France: 60%.
Export sales: 40%.
Main trading partners : Belgium, Netherlands, USA, Germany, UK, Spain, Switzerland, Australia, Japan, Canada.

CHÂTEAU DE CAMENSAC

M. Forner
33112 Saint-Laurent-du-Médoc
56 59 41 72

Type of vineyard: Family corporation. **Established:** 16th century. **Vine stocks:** Cabernet Sauvignon 60%, Cabernet Franc 20%, Merlot 20%. **Soil:** Gravel.
Appellation: Haut-Médoc. **Type:** Red. **Technique:** Traditional (See "Classification 89"). **Serving temperature:** 17%.

Characteristics of vintages

1988: Great wine, rich, promising. **1987:** Rather successful vintage. **1986:** Very good vintage, tannic, firm and supple. **1985:** Great vintage, good keeping. **Other:** **1983:** Deep color, a great vintage.

CHÂTEAU BEL-ORME TRONQUOY DE LALANDE

Heirs of Paul Quie
33250 St-Seurin-de-Cadourne (Pauillac)
Téléphone à la propriété: 56 59 31 09
Office: 135, rue de Paris - 94220 Charenton
Téléfax Office: (1) 43 68 92 99 - Office: (1) 43 68 08 41

Type of vineyard: Family-owned. **Established:** 1936. **Number of employees:** About 1 to 12. **Vine stocks:** 40% Merlot, 30% Cabernet Sauvignon, 30% Cabernet franc. **Soil:** Deep gravel - 1/4 gravel and 3/4 clay. **Exposure:** Plateau and hilltop. **Average annual production in hectoliters:** 1,100 to 1,200 hl.
Appellation: Cru Grand Bourgeois A.O.C., Haut-Médoc. **Type:** Red. **Technique:** Destemming, fermentation with skins for 12 to 15 days. **Maturing:** In oak barrels for about 14 to 18 months. **Alcohol content:** 12%. **Characteristics:** Supple and tannic, good structure, long. **Serving temperature:** 18° to 20° maximum. **Served with:** All meats, even those in sauce, game. **Vintages available in 89/90:** 1985.

Characteristics of vintages

1985: Excellent wine, supple, rich and well-balanced with fine tannins. Price range (pre-tax, ex-warehouse): Between 20 F.F. and 50 F.F.
Main trading partners : UK, Belgium.

Abroad

United Kingdom
Importers: J.T. Davies, Croydon.

Canada
Importers: Sté des Alcools du Québec, Montréal.

Others
Importers: Monsieur Jean-Pierre Hertig, 1, avenue du Belvedère, 2025 Chez-le-Bart, Switzerland.

CHÂTEAU LAMOTHE CISSAC

Messrs. Fabre
Cissac - 33250 Pauillac
56 59 58 16 - Télécopie: 56 59 57 97

Type of vineyard: Family-owned. **Established:** 1964. **Vine stocks:** Cabernet Sauvignon 70%, Merlot Noir 26%, Cabernet Franc 2%, Petit Verdot 2%. **Soil:** Half deep gravel and half clay with calcium carbonate. **Exposure:** Excellent. **Average annual production in hectoliters:** 1,500. **Appellation:** A.O.C. Haut-Médoc. **Type:** Red. **Technique:** Total destemming, followed by long fermentation with skins. **Maturing:** Entirely in barrels, 1/5 renewed every year. **Alcohol content:** 12.4%. **Characteristics:** Bright color, fine, elegant bouquet, supple and full-bodied. Develops rapidly, but holds up well with ageing. **Serving temperature:** 16° to 18°. **Served with:** Red and white meat, cheese. **Vintages available in 89/90:** 1984, 1985, 1986, 1987.

Characteristics of vintages

1988: Reminiscent of the 1983, 1985 and 1986 wines. Deep garnet color, very ripe red berry nose, rich tannins - no bitterness whatsover - which will develop into an elegant bouquet after ageing in casks. **1987:** Result of strictly selected harvest - everything necessary to satisfy the connoisseur. Awarded a medal at the Concours agricole d'Aquitaine. **1986:** Promising. **1985:** Its reputation is 'already established; superb, excellent basic for a good cellar. **1984:** Much better than reputated, 100% Cabernet, ready to drink while waiting for the 1985 vintage. **1983:** Excellent similar to the 1981, characteristic of Haut-Médoc, harvested very ripe. **1982:** Stock depleted, alas. Exceptional vintage. **Note:** 1981: Excellent vintage, typical Haut-Médoc, beginning to reach its peak. Price range (pre-tax, ex-warehouse): Between 30 and 50 F.F.
Sales volume:
- Wholesale: 80%. - Retail: 10%. - Restaurants: 10%.
Sales in France: 40%.
Export sales: 60%.
Main trading partners : UK, Benelux countries, Germany, Denmark, Switzerland, USA.

CHÂTEAU LAROSE TRINTAUDON

33112 Saint-Laurent-du-Médoc
56 59 41 72

Type of vineyard: Corporation owned. **Established:** 19th century. **Vine stocks:** Cabernet Sauvignon 60%, Cabernet Franc 20%, Merlot 20%. **Soil:** Gravel on iron pan. **Appellation:** Haut-Médoc Cru Bourgeois. **Type:** Red. **Technique:** Traditional. **Maturing:** Supple, rich bouquet (See "Classification 89"). **Serving temperature:** 17-18°.

Characteristics of vintages

1986: Good vintage. **1985:** Very great vintage, approaching the 1961 and 1975, deep ruby color.

CHÂTEAU DE LAMARQUE

Pierre-Gilles Gromand d'Evry
Lamarque 33460 Margaux
56 58 90 03
FAX 56 58 93 43

Type of vineyard: Agricultural Association. **Established:** 1841. **Number of employees:** 17. **Vine stocks:** Cabernet 70%, Merlot 25%, Petit Verdot 5%. **Soil:** Garonne gravel. **Exposure:** South-East.
Appellation: Haut-Médoc, Cru Grand Bourgeois. **Type:** Red. **Technique:** Traditional. **Characteristics:** Beautiful

wine, complex, very aromatic, rich, well balanced and distinguished, combining firmness and elegance. Good keeping (See classification). **Serving temperature:** 17°.

Characteristics of vintages

1988: Remarkable wine, rich dense, beautiful color, combining finesse richness and balance, good keeping. **1987:** Very successful, well colored, fragrant, strict selection. **1986:** Excellent year, well colored, rich and firm, good keeping (Gold medal in Paris). **1985:** Deep ruby color, note of wild fruit, well constituted wine.

CHÂTEAU LIEUJEAN

Fournier-Karsenty Family
Saint-Sauveur 33250 Paulliac
56 59 57 23

Agricultural association. Number of employees: 6. **Vine stocks:** Merlot 40%, Cabernet Sauvignon 50%, Cabernet Franc 10%. **Soil:** Sand and gravel, rocky sub-soil. **Exposure:** South - South-West. **Average annual production in hectoliters:** 720.

GRAND VIN DE BORDEAUX
1986
Château Lieujean
CRU BOURGEOIS
HAUT-MÉDOC
APPELLATION HAUT-MÉDOC CONTRÔLÉE
12%Vol
MIS EN BOUTEILLE AU CHATEAU
750ml
S.C.E.V. Château Lieujan Saint-Sauveur de Médoc 33250 Pauillac France
PRODUCT OF FRANCE
MÉDAILLE D'OR 1988
CONCOURS GÉNÉRAL AGRICOLE DE PARIS

Appellation: Haut-Médoc. **Type:** Red. **Maturing:** In oak vats (100 new). **Alcohol content:** 11.5 - 12.5%. **Served with:** Meat, cheese. **Vintages available in 89/90:** 1987, 1988.

Characteristics of vintages

1988: Intense deep color, ripe fruit nose, rich and very well-balanced, very long ageing potential. **1987:** Bright cherry color, very developed nose, already pleasant – to be consumed rather young. Price range (pre-tax, ex-warehouse): 20 to 30 F.F.

Sales volume:
- Wholesale: 15%. – Retail: 80%. – Restaurants: 5%.

Main trading partners : Germany, UK, USA, Switzerland.

References in France

Restaurants: Relais ST. Jacques (Deols 36). Domaine d'Auriac, (Carcassonne 11), La Regalido, (Fontvielle 13), Le Fer à Cheval, (Gemenos 13), Château Layauga, (Lesparre 33), Villa Borghese, (Greoux 04).
Shops: L'Amour du Vin.

Comments

The creation of the Château Lieujean goes back to 1868, although some of the buildings and part of the residential section were built towards 1750 and the vineyard existed even before. Some say that Lieujean was once part of the great Lynch estate From 1870 to the present, the size of the vineyard and its production have evolved as a function of the economy and the health of the vines. The vineyard now covers 19.5 hectares.
Vinification is in typical Médoc style with pumping over and fermentation on skins at 30° assuring good extraction. Excellent quality is assured by very careful maturing. Entirely in casks. Château Lieujean is similar to the Pauillac wines, but somewhat less robust and more fruity.

CHÂTEAU LE MEYNIEU

Jacques Pedro
Vertheuil, 33250 Pauillac
56 41 98 17

Type of vineyard: Family-owned. **Established:** 1961. **Number of employees:** 12.**Vine stocks:** 70% Cabernet Sauvignon, 30% Merlot. **Soil:** Chalky clay plateau. **Exposure:** West. **Average annual production in hectoliters:** 350 to 400.

1978
Château le Meynieu
CRU BOURGEOIS
HAUT-MÉDOC
APPELLATION HAUT-MEDOC CONTROLEE
Jacques PEDRO Propriétaire à Vertheuil-Médoc (Gironde) France
MIS EN BOUTEILLE AU CHATEAU
12 % Vol
Produce of France
75cl

Appellation: Haut-Médoc. Grand Cru Bourgeois. **Type:** Red. **Technique:** Traditional, long fermentation on skins 4

to 5 weeks. **Maturing:** 3 months in vats then 16 to 22 months in oak casks. **Alcohol content:** 12%. **Characteristics:** Beautiful color, elegant bouquet, high quality tannic structure, well balanced, soft and full. Classic Haut-Médoc wines. **Serving temperature:** 16 to 18°. **Served with:** Red meat and cheese. **Vintages available in 89/90:** 1975, 1977,1978, 1979, 1980, 1981, 1982, 1983, 1985, 1986.

Characteristics of vintages

1988: Solid thanks to a tannic character where the fruit is still dominant. **1987:** Fresh fragrance, good constitution. Seductive vintage which has pleasant surprises in store. **1986:** Deep, very marked color. Great aromatic richness. Exceptionally rich and well balanced, full bodied. **1985:** Fragrant, rich, well balanced, soft and full. Tannic flavor which confers remarkable length and fullness of taste. Price range (pre-tax, ex-warehouse): between 30 and 80 F.F.
Sales volume:
– Other: Specialized retailers, winecellars, hotels, restaurants, foreign distributors.
Sales in France: 40%. **Export sales:** 60%.
Main trading partners : Belgium, Switzerland, Germany, Luxemburg, Netherlands, United Kingdom, United States, Japan.

Comments

One of the oldest vineyards in Vertheuil, located in the heart of Médoc, whose château dates from the 19th century, tucked in among the greenery and surrounded by its well exposed 15 hectare vineyard under a single owner. The present proprietor, who is also mayor of the commune, has, by meticulous care over more than 25 years, restored the château and the warehouses, improved and renewed the vineyard to restore it to its former importance and spread its reknown.

CHÂTEAU PEYRABON

Jacques Babeau
Saint-Sauveur du Médoc – 33250 Pauillac
56 59 57 10 – Telex: 540 127 Public Bordx, Attn. Château Peyrabon

Type of vineyard: Agricultural Association. **Established:** 1976. **Number of employees:** 19. **Vine stocks:** Cabernet Sauvignon 50%, Merlot 27%, Cabernet Franc 23%. **Soil:** Sand and gravel on iron pan. **Average annual production in hectoliters:** 2300.
Appellation: Haut Médoc. **Type:** Red. **Technique:** Traditional fermentation on skins 21 to 28 days. **Maturing:** Everything in oak casks for 18 months. **Alcohol content:** 12%. **Characteristics:** Traditional wine for keeping, good tannic structure, fine and elegant fragrance dominated by vanilla, liquorice, red fruit and spices. **Serving temperature:** 16 to 18° according to the year. **Served with:** Red roasted or grilled meat, cheese, chocolate desserts. **Vintages available in 89/90:** 1985, 1986, 1987.

Characteristics of vintages

1988: Beautiful color, fragrant, rich in extract, ripe grapes, fleshy, soft and full, rich, aristocratic. **1987:** Fruity, supple and round, an agreeable and elegant wine, quite successful in a difficult year. **1986:** Rich and well balanced, lots of color and aroma, to be kept. **1985:** Rich tannins, forthcoming and heady, for long keeping, a classical wine. Price range (pre-tax, ex-warehouse): between 30 and 50 F.F.
Sales volume:
– Wholesale: 7%. – Retail: 7%. – Restaurants: 12%.
– Other: 74% foreign distributors.
Sales in France: 40%.
Export sales: 60%.
Main trading partners: Belgium, Germany, Switzerland, Netherlands, United States.

References in France

Restaurants: Robuchon, La Chiberta, Le Cochon d'Or, Le Laurent, Le Camelia.

Abroad

United States

Misselis, 27, allées de Chartres – 33000 Bordeaux.

Germany

Domaine Shenk, Baden-Baden.

Switzerland

Shenk Rolle.

Belgium

Renglet S.A., Brussels.

Comments

Built in the 18th century, the Château Peyrabon was, under Napoléon, the home of the assistant military administrator of Bordeaux, JA. Varre, and, afterwards, the seat of the family of the Counts of Courcelle. The "Cru Grand Bourgeois" of the Haut-Médoc is located in the commune of Saint-Sauveur, in the vicinity of the illustrious Châteaux of Latour, Lafite and Mouton Rothschild. Its poor soil yields an average of 45 hectoliters per hectare. These poor yields are the source of the richness (by concentration) of the wines, and demonstrated by the 85 and 86 vintages (see "Classification of Bordeaux Wines 89").

CHÂTEAU PONTOISE-CABARRUS

François Tereygeol
rue Georges Mandel, St-Seurin de Cadourne
33250 Pauillac
56 59 34 92

Type of vineyard: Family-owned. **Established:** 1959. **Number of employees:** 8. **Vine stocks:** 60% Cabernet Sauvignon, 30% Merlot, 5% Petit Verdot, 5% Cabernet Franc. **Soil:** Gravel. **Exposure:** Gravelly hilltops overlooking the Gironde estuary. **Average annual production in hectoliters:** 1,500.

Appellation: Haut-Médoc. **Type:** Red. **Technique:** Traditional, with the addition of modern chemicals, temperature regulation. **Maturing:** In new wooden casks for 1/8 of the harvest. **Alcohol content:** 12%. **Characteristics:** Wine for keeping. **Serving temperature:** 18°. **Served with:** Red meat and cheese. **Vintages available in 89/90:** 1984, 1986, 1987, 1988.

Characteristics of vintages

1988: Great year, very similar to the 86 (rich, well balanced, beautiful bigarreau cherry color). **1987:** Lighter than the 86 but fruity and well colored. Very successful, well vinified. **1986:** Rich and well balanced, robust but with the roundness of ripe fruit, excellent evolution. Price range (pre-tax, ex-warehouse): between 30 and 50 F.F.

Sales in France: 50%. **Export sales:** 50%.

Main trading partners : Belgium.

References in France

Shops: Eurovial (Caves Royales, Versailles), Caves St. Georges (Paris), L'Amour du Vin (Paris).

Abroad

United Kingdom

Brusina Brandler (dealer in France).

Germany

Potthof Heinz (Boksee).

Switzerland

Schenk (Rolle).

Belgium

Cooreman (Dendermonde), Cooreman (Dilbek), Mempae (Brussels).

Canada

Descas (dealer in France).

The Netherlands

Fischer and Velingsheide.

Others

Denmark: Erik Sorensen.

Comments

Property which, until 1859, belonged to the family of Thérésa Cabarrus. A cask warehouse, constructed in 1988, alongside of the present fermenting room, allows ageing in casks of one sixth of the harvest. This use of new wood started with the 86 vintage (1/8 of the harvest) and has led to an improvement in the quality of the product.

• *Read labels carefully – An indication to watch out for: "Bottled in the 'region' of production", which often refers to a blend of wines from several producers and not just one.*

RAMAGE LA BÂTISSE

Sci Ramage I.B.
Saint-Sauveur - 33250 Pauillac
56 59 57 24

Established: 1962. **Number of employees:** 23. **Vine stocks:** 30% Merlot, 55% Cabernet Sauvignon, 15% Cabernet Franc and Petit Verdot. **Soil:** Gravel, clay subsoil. **Exposure:** Plateau. **Average annual production in hectoliters:** 2,300.
Appellation: Haut-Médoc contrôlée. **Type:** Red. **Technique:** Traditional. **Maturing:** In oak casks, 50% new each year. **Alcohol content:** 12%. **Characteristics:** Elegant, lots of finesse, subtile vanilla fragrance, lots of fruit. Perfectly controlled vinification. **Serving temperature:** 18° to 20°, open the day before tasting, at least 2 hours before a meal. **Served with:** Red meat, poultry or game. **Vintages available in 89/90:** 1983, 1985, 1986, 1987.

Characteristics of vintages

1988: Exceptional, very fruity, very rich and tannic, supple. **1987:** Very rich wine, tannic, beautiful color. Gold Medal. **1986:** Exceptional structure, very promising. **1985:** Complete, rich and well-balanced, lots of fruit, Gold Medal at the Concours Général (Principal Competition) de Paris. **1984:** A success for this vintage, supple and fruity, beautiful color. **1983:** Gold Medal at the Concours Général Agricole de Paris, light vanilla fragrance, a balanced and harmonious wine. Do not hesitate.
Sales volume:
- Wholesale: 30%. - Retail: 50%. - Restaurants: 20%. - Particulars: 17,5%. - C.H.R.: 12,5%. - Export: 70%.
Sales in France: 85%.
Export sales: 15%.

References in France

Restaurants: Le Drapeau National, Chez Max, L'Escargot Montorgueil, La Diligence, Club Vénétien, Le Coupe-Chou, Le Cochon d'Or, Hôtel Ritz, La Ferme St-Simon, Maxime, Le George V.
Shops: L'Amour du Vin, 94, Rue Saint-Dominique, 75007 Paris. Tel: 45 56 12 94.

CHÂTEAU PUY CASTERA

Bertrand de Rozières
Cissac Médoc, 33250 Pauillac
56 59 58 80

Type of vineyard: Corporation. **Established:** 1973. **Number of employees:** 9. **Vine stocks:** Cabernet Sauvignon 58%, Cabernet Franc 10%, Merlot 30%, Malbec 2%. **Soil:** Chalky clay. **Exposure:** Hillcrest, facing in all directions. **Average annual production in hectoliters:** 1,400. **Appellation:** Haut-Médoc. **Type:** Red. **Technique:** Long with temperature control. **Maturing:** In vats and tanks. **Alcohol content:** 12.5%. **Characteristics:** Typical Médoc, grown on chalky clay - very pronounced red berry aroma. **Serving temperature:** 17 to 18°. **Served with:** Meat in sauce, typical dishes of the Bordeaux region, cheese. **Vintages available in 89/90:** 1984, 1985, 1986.

Characteristics of vintages

1988: Very typical Médoc - ripe harvesting, good color, rich and well balanced. **1987:** Well made, quickly developing wine. **1986:** In keeping with an excellent vintage. **1985:** Very ripe harvesting. **Other:** 1984: as with almost all Médoc wines, much better than its media coverage. Price range (pre-tax, ex-warehouse): 30 to 50 F.F.
Sales volume:
- Wholesale: 50%. - Retail: 20%. - Other: 30% cellars and agents.
Sales in France: 60%. **Export sales:** 40%.
Main trading partners: Netherlands, Belgium, United Kingdom.

References in France

Shops: Entre 2 Verres (48, rue St Anne, 75002 Paris), Cave du Moulin Vieux (rue de la Butte-aux-Cailles, Paris).

Abroad

United Kingdom
Windrush Wines Ltd., Cecily Hill, Cirencester.

Switzerland
O. Frey and Co, 22 Guterstrasse, 3000 Bern, (Tel: 031252661).

Belgium
Wilfrid lems Karel Soctelaan 26, 2210 Borsbeck 03/3219668.

The Netherlands
Intercaves BV postbus 517, 8000 AM Zwolle.

Comments

"Puy" comes from the old French word meaning hill or knoll, and "Castera" from "castum" in latin, which means camp or fortress. From the hillcrest which dominates the property at its center, can still be seen a disruption of the terrain which clearly indicates the location of an ancient fortified camp. Château Puy-Castera was classified as Cru Bourgeois in 1978 at the time of its second vinification in appellation contrôlée.

ageing potential. Price range (pre-taxe, ex-warehouse): 30 to 50 F.F.

Sales volume:
– Wholesale: 90%. – Retail: 10%.

Main trading partners : USA.

Abroad

United States

Importers: Frederick Wildman and Sons Ltd, 21 East 69th Street, New York, N.Y. 10021 (Tel: (212) 288 80 00).

CHÂTEAU SÉNÉJAC

Comte Charles de Guigne
33290 Le Pian-Médoc
56 72 00 11

Vine stocks: Cabernet Sauvignon 60%, Cabernet Franc 14%, Merlot 25%, Petit Verdot 1%, Sémillon 100%. **Soil:** Gravel and silica on a clay and gravel base. **Exposure:** East, West. **Average annual production in hectoliters:** Red: 1,200. White: 22.

Appellation: Haut-Médoc, Bordeaux Blanc. **Type:** Red, White. **Technique:** White: fermented in 50% new oak barrels. Red: traditional in stainless steel, temperature controlled vats, maceration 2 to 3 weeks. **Maturing:** White: in oak barrels (50% new). Red: in oak barrels (25% new) for 12 to 18 months. **Characteristics:** White: rich aromatic bouquet with hints of oak and vanilla, complex, full bodied, lingering flavor. Ages well. Red: a wine with much finesse and elegance. Rich in red fruit flavours with hints of spice and vanilla. Fine tannins long finish, harmonious. **Serving temperature:** White: 12°. Red: 18°. **Served with:** White: fish, cheese soufflé. Red: veal chops marinated in olive oil and fresh herbs cooked on the grill over vine prunings. **Vintages available in 89/90:** White: 1988. Red: 1984, 1985, 1986, 1987, 1988.

Characteristics of vintages

1988: Classic Haut-Médoc. Deep color, elegant with firm tannic structure. Will age well. **1987:** Delicious blend of wood, fruit and spice flavor. To be drunk young. **1986:** Deep color, intense and complex nose, well structured, tannic but full-bodied. To be aged. **1985:** Rich, concentrated and fruity. Combines finesse and richness, good

CHÂTEAU SOCIANDO MALLET

Jean Gautreau
Saint-Seurin-de-Cadourne – 33250 Pauillac
56 59 36 57 – Telex: 540 386

Type of vineyard: Family-owned. **Number of employees:** 18. **Vine stocks:** Cabernet Sauvignon 60%, Cabernet Franc 10%, Merlot 25%, Petit Verdot 5%. **Soil:** Gravel, with clay and calcium, carbonate. **Exposure:** Near the Gironde.

Appellation: Haut-Médoc. **Type:** Red. **Technique:** Traditional, long. **Maturing:** Barrels according 60% to 90% new according to the quality of the vintage. **Characteristics:** Rich and well-balanced, good color, with long life. **Serving temperature:** 16 to 17°. **Serving with:** Red meat, game. **Vintages available in 89/90:** 1983, 1984, 1985.

Characteristics of vintages

1986: Very promising vintage. **1985:** Beautiful color, round, supple tannins, tenace. **1984:** Surprising color, rich and well-balanced for the vintage, very fine and fragrant. **1983:** Concentrated, rich tannins, no agressivity, remarkable vinification, long keeping, insuring long life. Alls well structured with a complex nose. No hesitation; good investment. Price range (pre-tax, ex-warehouse): Between 50 and 90 F.F.

Sales volume:
– Wholesale: 60%. – Retail: 25%. – Restaurants: 15%.

Sales in France: 50%.

Export sales: 50%.

Main trading partners : Throughout the USA, Europe, Japan, Canada, Australia.

References in France

Restaurants: Taillevent, Robuchon, Tour d'Argent, Georges Blanc, Amat, Ramet.
Shops: Legrand, Hédiard, Caves de la Madeleine.

Abroad

United States

Well diffused by Bordeaux salesmen.

United Kingdom

Richards-Walford Lincs.

Germany

Segnitz, Brême.

Canada

SAQ, Montréal.

The Netherlands

Kerstens, Tilburg.

Far East

Same than USA.

Others

Palais du Vin, Bruxelles. Reichmuth, Zurich. Gottardi, Innsbruck.

TOUR DU ROC
Philippe Robert
Arcins 33460 Margaux
56 58 90 25

Type of vineyard: Family-owned. **Established:** 19th century. **Number of employees:** 2. **Vine stocks:** 50% Cabernet Sauvignon, 45% Merlot, 5% Petit Verdot. **Soil:** Sand and gravel. **Average annual production in hectoliters:** 450.

MÉDAILLE D'ARGENT CONCOURS BORDEAUX 1987
CRU BOURGEOIS
1986
CHATEAU
Tour-du-Roc
HAUT-MÉDOC
Appellation Haut-Médoc contrôlée
MISE EN BOUTEILLE AU CHATEAU
12%Vol. PRODUCE OF FRANCE 75 cl
Philippe ROBERT, propriétaire à ARCINS (33460) France
WETTERWALD, BORDEAUX

Appellation: Haut-Médoc. **Type:** Red. **Technique:** Traditional. **Maturing:** 18 months in casks, 1/4 new. **Alcohol content:** 12%. **Characteristics:** Supple, fruity and robust. **Served with:** Meat, cheese. **Vintages available in 89/90:** 1986, 1987, 1988.

Characteristics of vintages

1988: Tannic, beautiful color, complete, round. **1987:** Supple and fruity. **1986:** Full, supple, balanced. **1985:** Fruity, round and supple. Price range (pre-tax, ex-warehouse): between 20 and 30 F.F.

Sales volume:
– Wholesale: 30%. – Retail: 30%.
Sales in France: 60%.
Export sales: 40%.
Main trading partners: Germany, Belgium, Denmark, United Kingdom.

Abroad

United States

Victory, New York.

Belgium

Mr. Lignier, Ligny B 6338 (Tel: 071 888019). De Grauw, Wilsels (Tel: 016 45 328).

The Netherlands

Vermeulen, Bergen of Zoom.

Others

Denmark: United Wine Import, Copenhagen (Tel: 02 91 33 22).

SOCIÉTÉ COOPÉRATIVE AGRICOLE LES VITICULTEURS DU FORT MÉDOC
Denis Fedieu (President)
Dominique Billa (Cellar man)
Les Caperans – Cussac Fort Médoc
33640 Margaux
56 58 92 85

Type of vineyard: Vine growers grouped in to an Agricultural Association. **Established:** 1973. **Vine stocks:** Cabernet Sauvignon 50%, Merlot 40%, Cabernet Franc 10%. **Soil:** Sand and gravel on a gravel sub-soil. **Exposure:** Hilltops with gravel near the river (Gironde). **Average annual production in hectoliters:** 3,500.
Appellation: Haut-Médoc. **Type:** Red. **Technique:** Traditional vinification of Médoc/long fermentation on skins. **Maturing:** Stainless steel tanks, many rackings, bottling 18 to 24 months after with skins. **Alcohol content:** 12°. **Characteristics:** Fruity wines, good color, well-balanced, long, rich and very fine tannins. **Serving temperature:** 18°. **Served with:** Red meat, cheese. **Vintages available in 89/90:** 1982, 1984, 1985, 1986.

Characteristics of vintages

1988: Very good year due to very ripe harvesting – rich and well-balanced wines, a must in the cellar. **1987:** Pleasant, to be drunk young while waiting for other vintages which should be aged. **1986:** Good year, promising vintage. **1985:** Excellent year, very rich, promising to a great vintage. **1984:** Cabernet dominant, must age. **1982:** Exceptional year, very rich and well-balanced, exceptional aromas, may still be aged. Price range (pre-tax, ex-warehouse): Between 30 and 40 F.F.
Sales volume:
– Wholesale: 10%. – Retail: 80%. – Other: 10%.

Sales in France: 80%.
Export sales: 20%.
Main trading partners : Belgium, Holland, England.

Comments

The Association is made up of a group of 20 winemakers from the commune "Cussac". They work together to make the best product from their harvested grapes; their products are the Chevaliers du Roi Soleil: Château Le Neurin. Numerous Medals for the quality of their wines.

CHÂTEAU TOUR DU HAUT MOULIN

Béatrice & Lionel Poitou
Cussac Fort Médoc, 33460 Margaux
56 58 91 10

Type of vineyard: Family-owned. **Established:** 1986. **Number of employees:** 13. **Vine stocks:** Cabernet 50%, Sauvignon 45%, Merlot 5%, Petit Verdot. **Soil:** Gravel of the Garonne basin 20 to 22 m. **Average annual production in hectoliters:** 1500.

HAUT-MÉDOC
APPELLATION HAUT MÉDOC CONTROLÉE
CHATEAU
TOUR DU HAUT-MOULIN
CRU BOURGEOIS
1985
L. Poitou
PROPRIÉTAIRE A CUSSAC - GIRONDE FRANCE
MISE EN BOUTEILLES AU CHATEAU
Alc. 12 % Vol.
PRODUCT OF FRANCE
750 ml

Appellation: Haut Medoc. **Type:** Red. **Technique:** All grape varieties. **Maturing:** 3 to 4 weeks in wooden casks, 1/3 new. **Alcohol content:** 12.5%. **Characteristics:** Soft and full, round, slightly fruity, rich and long. **Serving temperature:** 17°. **Served with:** Game, red meat, and cheese. **Vintages available in 89/90:** 1981, 1983, 1984, 1985, 1986, 1987.

Characteristics of vintages

1988: Very deep color, very concentrated fruit flavor (blackcurrant), similar to the 1986 vintage. **1987:** Very woody aroma, sharp attack, supple, good balance. **1986:** Very intense color, well balanced, rich, full bodied, dense, soft and full, remarkable finish. Great wine. **1985:** Fruity (cherry, raspberry, peony), well balanced, harmonious, beautiful round tannins, clean attack, full, very good keeping.

Sales volume:
- Wholesale: 25%. - Retail: 50%. - Restaurants: 5%.
- Other: 15% (Paris cellars).

Sales in France: 50%.
Export sales: 50%.
Main trading partners : European Economic Community.

References in France

Shops: Fauchon, Caves de la Madeleine, Repère de Bacchus, Chez Nicolas.

Abroad

United Kingdom
Charles Taylor Wines (Surrey).

Germany
Wienhandelshaus Im Lehel (Munich). Médoc Wein Import (Bremen).

Switzerland
Wyss Pierre, Onnens – Maison du Champagne, Cologny.

Belgium
Aux Côteaux Vinalmont – Provino (Brussels) – Benevins (Brussels) – Nivaille (Verdrion) – Catule (Brussels) – Groupvin (Gembloux).

The Netherlands
Winsjtransport, Le Vigneron Manqué (Amsterdam), Brawkenimport.

Others
Denmark: Vinicole-Vinimport.

Comments

The château and the vineyard are located just a few steps from the historic Fort Médoc, reknowned for its wine for centuries. Following five generations, Lionel Poitou took over the Château Tour du Haut Moulin two years ago, at the age of nineteen. He manages the entire vineyard with his sister Béatrice. The 1987 and 1988 vintages have been vinified by Lionel.

• Classification of the great Bordeaux wines in 1988. The ratings of Châteaux Lascombes (Margaux), Mazeris-Bellevue (Canon-Fronsac) and Haut-Maco (Côtes-de-Bourg) are improving, as well as those of certain other surprising crus (Châteaux Trocard, Melin, Gazin, Chantegriue, Gloria, La Croix-Saint-André, Fombrauge...). See the 1988 Classification in the Chapter on Bordeaux wines.

CHÂTEAU VERDUS

Mr. & Mrs. Jacques Dailledouze,
Mr. Alain Dailledouze
Saint-Seurin-de-Cadourne 33250 Pauillac
56 59 31 59

Type of vineyard: Family-owned. **Vine stocks:** Cabernet 65%, Merlot 35%. **Soil:** Chalky clay. **Exposure:** South-East, facing the Gironde. **Average annual production in hectoliters:** 375.

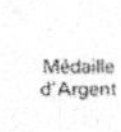

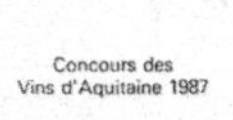

1986

CHÂTEAU VERDUS

CRU BOURGEOIS

HAUT-MÉDOC

Appellation Haut-Médoc contrôlée

12,5%Vol. 75 cl

G.A.E.C. DAILLEDOUZE PÈRE ET FILS

33250 SAINT-SEURIN-DE-CADOURNE (FRANCE)

Produce of France

MIS EN BOUTEILLES AU CHATEAU

Appellation: Haut-Médoc. **Type:** Red. **Technique:** Long maceration. **Maturing:** Oak vats and casks. **Alcohol content:** Around 12.5%. **Characteristics:** Very tannic, long keeping. **Serving temperature:** Around 17°. **Served with:** Red meat, game, lamprey cooked Bordeaux style, eel stew, quail with grapes. **Vintages available in 89/90:** 1979 and 1981 (in very small quantity), 1984, 1985, 1986.

Characteristics of vintages

1986: Still young, worth waiting for. **1985:** Almost ready, agreeable. **Other:** 1979, 1981: Has aged well, very pleasant. 1984: Supple, pleasant, a little light. Price range (pre-tax, ex-warehouse): 30 to 70 F.F.

Sales volume:
- Wholesale: 10%. - Retail: 70%. - Restaurants: 10%. - Other: 10% (export).

Sales in France: 90%.
Export sales: 10%.

References in France

Restaurants: La Forge d'Antant, Pen Al Valannec, 28118 Clohars-Fouesnant. (Tel: 98 54 84 00). Dhenain Drouard, 3, rue du Château, 80300 Aveluy (Tel: 22 75 13 35). Arapagous, 134, rue Saint-Urcisse, 46000 Cahors. Restaurant du Midi, Saint-Seurin-de-Cadourne, Pauillac, etc.
Shops: Maison Guy de Florent, Davy, Saint-Pierre-du-Regard, Condé-sur-Noirot.

Abroad

United Kingdom

Mr. Hourlier, 390 Burton Road, Derby DE3 AD, Tel, Derby: 41 46 6.

Belgium

Caves Le Pré Clos, Chaussée de Charleroi 03, 6220 Fleurus.

Comments

The property has been in the same family, by direct succession, since 1656. An old pigeon house remains where one can see various winegrowing and winemaking tools.

VILLEGEORGE

Lucien Lurton
33420 Avensan
56 88 70 20 - Telex: 572 861

Type of vineyard: Family-owned. **Established:** 1973. **Vine stocks:** Cabernet Sauvignon 30%, Cabernet Franc 10%, Merlot 60%. **Soil:** Deep Pyrenean gravel. **Appellation:** Haut-Médoc. **Type:** Red. **Technique:** In the Bordeaux tradition. **Maturing:** 20 months in oak barrels (1/3 renewed each year). **Characteristics:** Full-bodied, round, aromatic, good structure. **Serving temperature:** 18° to 20°. **Served with:** Red meat.

Characteristics of vintages

1988: Good structure, fruity, complex. **1987:** Delicate, light structure to be drunk in the next three years. **1986:** Complex, full bodied, a good vintage for ageing. **1985:** Good classic year. Fragrant, good color, structured, to be aged. **1984:** Finesse, rich aroma, round, a success. **1983:** Very balanced and complex, typical vintage, full and velvety, good for ageing. Price range (pre-tax, ex-warehouse): Between 50 to 80 F.F.

Sales volume:
- Wholesale: 90%. - Retail: 10%.

References in France

Shops: Hédiard, Good Parisian wine cellars.

• *The 1980 vintage is badly understood. In Bordeaux the wines are already quite surprising and will do quite well while waiting for the development of the other vintages. See "The last five vintages" in the Chapter on Bordeaux wines.*

MÉDOC

CHÂTEAU DES BROUSTERAS

Renouil Frères
33340 Saint-Yzans-de-Médoc
56 09 05 44

Type of vineyard: Agricultural Association. **Established:** 1977. **Number of employees:** 4. **Vine stocks:** 1/3 Merlot, 1/3 Cabernet Franc, 1/3 Cabernet Sauvignon. **Soil:** Silica-clay with calcium carbonate. **Average annual production in hectoliters:** 900.
Appellation: Médoc Cru Bourgeois. **Type:** Red. **Technique:** Traditional. **Maturing:** Barrel and vat. **Alcohol content:** 12%. **Characteristics:** Robust, good color, bouquet, to be aged. **Serving temperature:** About 16° to 18°. **Served with:** Game, red meat, poultry, cheese. **Vintages available in 89/90:** 1985, 1986.

Characteristics of vintages

1988: Soft and full, rich, beautiful ruby color, wonderful aromas, great success. A superb vintage for several decades. **1987:** Good wine for an undervalued year, fresh, good aromas, pleasant, to be consumed rather rapidly. Will be available as of end of 1989. **1986:** Good, deep color, with promise, well-balanced. Gold Medal (Macon 1987) and Silver Medal (Paris 1988). **1985:** Deep color, well-developed aroma a very good year. Silver Medal (Bordeaux 1986 and Paris 1987). Price range (pre-tax, ex-warehouse): Between 30 and 50 F.F.
Sales volume:
– Wholesale: 30%. – Retail: 50%. – Restaurants: 20%.
Sales in France: 50%. **Export sales:** 50%.
Main trading partners : UK, Germany, Netherlands, Belgium, Suisse.

CHÂTEAU LA FRANCE

Michel Querre
33340 Blaignan
57 51 00 40 – Telex: 571 895 F

Type of vineyard: Corporation. **Established:** 1986. **Vine stocks:** 23 hectares planted; Merlot 50%, Cabernet-Sauvignon: 50%. **Soil:** Clay with calcium carbonate. **Average annual production in hectoliters:** 1,000.
Appellation: Médoc Cru Bourgeois. **Type:** Red. **Technique:** Casks. **Maturing:** Oak barrels (30% new). **Alcohol content:** 12.5%. **Characteristics:** Round and tannic. **Serving temperature:** 18°. **Served with:** Meat, game, cheese. **Vintages available in 89/90:** 1986 available in the Spring of 1988.

CHÂTEAU HAUT-GARIN

Gilles Hue
Prignac en Médoc, 33340 Lesparre
56 09 00 02

Type of vineyard: Family-owned. **Established:** For about one century. **Number of employees:** 1. **Vine stocks:** Cabernet Sauvignon 65%, Merlot 5%, Petit Verdot and Cabernet Franc. **Soil:** Chalky clay. **Exposure:** Small hillsides to the South and North-East. **Average annual production in hectoliters:** 350.

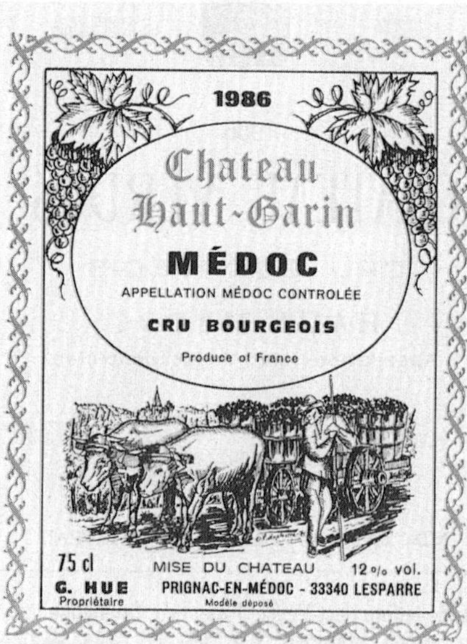

Appellation: Médoc Contrôlée. **Type:** Red. **Technique:** Traditional with destemming and long fermentation. **Maturing:** In oak casks. **Alcohol content:** 12%. **Characteristics:** Supple, pleasant, full bouquet. **Serving temperature:** 15 to 18°. **Served with:** Grilled meat, roasts, poultry, game, cheese. **Vintages available in 89/90:** 1985, 1986, 1987, 1988.

Characteristics of vintages

1988: Very promising, should be a great year. **1987:** Pleasant. To be drunk rather young. **1986:** Great year, more supple than the 1985 vintage. **1985:** Great year, full-bodied, tannic, to be kept. Price range (pre-tax, ex-warehouse): 20 to 30 F.F.
Sales volume:
– Wholesale: 70%. – Retail: 30%.

Comments

Family enterprise for five generations.

CHÂTEAU GREYSAC

Begadan 33340 Lesparre-Médoc
56 41 50 29 - Telex: 571 209

Established: 1960. **Number of employees:** 20. **Vine stocks:** Cabernet Sauvignon 50%, Cabernet Franc 10%, Merlot 38%, Petit Verdot 2%. **Soil:** gravel, sand and chalky clay. **Average annual production in hectoliters:** 3, 500 to 4, 000.
Appellation: Cru Grand Bourgeois A.C. Médoc. **Type:** Red. **Technique:** Modern, in stainless steel tanks with temperature control. Maceration for 15 days. **Maturing:** In oak casks – 20% new each year. **Alcohol content:** 12.5%. **Characteristics:** Deep color, supple, tannic silky texture, delicate wood fragrance, sometimes slightly reminiscent of tobacco after 3-4 years in the bottle. **Serving temperature:** 19 to 21°. **Vintage available in 89/90:** 1983, 1984, 1985, 1986.

Characteristics of vintages

1988: Deep color, fruity aroma, tannic structure much like the 1985 and 1986 vintages. **1986:** Beautiful garnet color, ripe fruit aroma, full bodied, magnificent. **1985:** Ruby color, flowery and very complex nose, perfectly balanced, great elegance. **Other:** 1984: Bright color, nose suggesting Cabernet, slight vanilla aroma, full. 1983: Bright red color, nose suggesting tobacco, tannic structure, but not overly agressive, good balance. Price range (pre-tax, ex-warehouse): 30 to 50 F.F.
Sales volume:
– Retail: 5%. – Restaurants: 70%. – Other: 20% (specialized shops).
Sales in France: 20%.
Export sales: 80%.
Main trading partners : USA, UK, Belgium, Germany, Switzerland, Netherlands.

References in France

Restaurants: Taillevent, Lasserre, La Marée, Chez André.
Shops: Fauchon.

Abroad

United States
Importers: Seagram Chateau & Estate Wines CO. 375 Park Avenue, New York NY 10152. Tel: (212) 572 76 50 – Telex: 236574.

United Kingdom
International Distillers & Vintners, Fourth Ave. Harlow Essex CM20 10X. Tel: (0279) 26801 – Telex: 81232.

Germany
Schlumberger Buschstrasse 20, D – 5309 Meckerheim. Tel: 022 25 88 09 0. Telex: 8 869 940.

Switzerland
Berthaudin, 11, rue Fernier, 1202, Geneva. Tel: 022 32 06 26 – Telex: 28 337 MBSA.

Belgium
Mampaey, Gossetlaan 21 B 1720, Groot Bijgaarden. Tel: 02 466 58 58 – Telex: 24795.

Canada

Seagram Quebec Vins et Spiritueux, Roland W. Theroux, 2101 route Transcanadienne, Dorval H9P, 151 Québec.

The Netherlands

Vannieuland, Baronielaan 159 4818 PO Breda. Tel: 076 - 226360.

ROLLAN DE BY

Ph. Malcor
33340 By Begadan
56 41 57 21

Type of vineyard: Family-owned. **Established:** 1983. **Vine stocks:** 60% Cabernet Sauvignon, 39% Merlot, 1% Petit Verdot. **Soil:** Garonnaise gravel. **Exposure:** South. **Average annual production in hectoliters:** 110. **Appellation:** Médoc. **Type:** Red. **Technique:** Traditional, floating cap. **Maturing:** 1/2 barrels, 1/2 tanks. **Alcohol content:** 12%. **Serving temperature:** 16° to 18°. **Served with:** Red, meat, cheese. **Vintages available in 89/90:** 1983, 1984, 1985 (1986 in 1988).

Characteristics of vintages

1985: Supple and structured, good tannins, to be aged. Price range (pre-tax, ex-warehouse): Between 20 F.F. and 30 F.F., 27 F.F.
Sales volume:
- Retail: 50%.
- Other: 50% (Prisunic department stores - Paris).
Sales in France: 100%.

CHÂTEAU SAINT-SATURNIN

Adrien Tramier
33340 Bégadan
56 41 50 82

Type of vineyard: Family-owned. **Vine stocks:** Merlot, Cabernet.
Appellation: Médoc. **Type:** Red. **Technique:** Traditional. Destemming. Long fermentation with skins. **Maturing:** In stainless steel and wooden vats and tanks. **Characteristics:** Concentration of color and aromas, rich, fragrant wines, good for ageing. **Serving temperature:** 16° - 17°. **Served with:** All meats. **Vintages available in 89/90:** 83, 84, 85.

Characteristics of vintages

1986: Very promising. **1985:** Excellent year. Age in the cellar.

CHÂTEAU LA CLARE

Paul de Rozières
Bégadan - 33340 Lesparre Médoc
56 41 50 61

Type of vineyard: Family-owned. **Established:** 1.11.1969. **Vine stocks:** Cabernet Sauvignon 57%, Merlot 36%, Cabernet Franc 7%. **Average annual production in hectoliters:** 1,000 to 1,200.
Type: Red. **Technique:** Traditional. **Maturing:** Wood. **Alcohol content:** 12.5°. **Serving temperature:** Room temperature, but no more than 18°.

Characteristics of vintages

1986: Best wine produced at the La Clare since 1970 (Bottling in sept. 88). **1985:** Very brilliant primary aromas very brilliant. **1984:** Agreeable, good to drink now. **1983:** Classic Medoc, to be held. **1982:** Very good wine, the same standart than '70, '75, '82, '86. **1981:** Wait. **1979:** Starting to open. **1970:** Must wait. **1976:** Should be good. **1971 and 1973:** Fully developed. **1975:** Wait.
Sales volume:
- Wholesale: 50%. - Retail: 50%.
Sales in France: 50%.
Export sales: 50%.
Main trading partners : USA, UK, Belgium.

Abroad

United States

Wine Connoisseurs of America: National Marketting & Sales Office 420.
Restaurants: Washington Street, 102 Braintree. MA 02124 USA.

United Kingdom

K.F. Butler & Co Ltd. Cockburn & Co Ltd. Michael Druitt. Shops: Wines Ltd. The Hilbre Wine Co Ltd. Martinez & Co Ltd.
Restaurants: Sheperd Neam LTD.

Canada

Liquor Control Board of Alberta. Société des Alcools du Québec. Montréal.

MAISON YVON MAU

Jean-François Mau
33190 Gironde-sur-Dropt
56 71 11 11

Type of vineyard: Family-owned. **Established:** For three generations. **Vine stocks:** Bordeaux vine stocks.
Appellation: Bordeaux, Graves, Médoc. **Type:** Red, White. **Technique:** First rate (white: cold fermentation, temperature control, cryœxtraction. Red: desteming maceration). **Characteristics:** Excellent selections, most rigorous wine making technique. **Vintages available in 89/90:** 1983, 1984, 1985, 1986, 1987, 1988.

CHÂTEAU LESTRUELLE
Jean-Claude Ladra
Saint Yzans de Médoc 33340 Lesparre
56 09 05 01

Type of vineyard: Agricultural association. **Established:** 1980. **Number of employees:** 3. **Vine stocks:** Merlot 65%, Cabernet 30%, Cabernet Franc 5%. **Soil:** Chalky clay. **Exposure:** North-South. **Average annual production in hectoliters:** 1,200.
Appellation: A.O.C. Médoc. **Type:** Red. **Technique:** Temperature control (modern equipment). **Maturing:** In casks (1/4 new). **Alcohol content:** 12.3%. **Characteristics:** Very round, vanilla flavor, ruby color. **Serving temperature:** 17°. **Served with:** Roasted chicken, red meat. **Vintages available in 89/90:** 1986.

Characteristics of vintages

1988: Tannic, long, fruity flavor. **1987:** Depleted. **1986:** Very good wine with a pleasant woody flavor. **1985:** Out of stock. Price range (pre-tax, ex-warehouse): 30 to 50 F.F.
Sales volume:
- Wholesale: 65%. – Retail: 35%. – Restaurants: 5%.

Sales in France: 80%. **Export sales:** 20%.
Main trading partners : Belgium, Switzerland, Denmark, UK.

CHÂTEAU DES GRANDS-CHÊNES
Mme Jacqueline Gauzy-Darricade
Saint-Christoly-de-Médoc – 33340 Lesparre
56 41 53 12

Type of vineyard: Family-owned. **Vine stocks:** Cabernets and Merlot. **Soil:** Clay with calcium carbonate.
Appellation: Médoc. **Type:** Red. **Technique:** Traditional. **Maturing:** In barrels. **Characteristics:** Excellent Médoc, fruity taste and aroma, rich, well-balanced and supple. Keeps well. **Serving temperature:** 16°. **Served with:** Roast. **Vintages available in 89/90:** 1985 and 1986.

Characteristics of vintages

1988: Beautiful vintage, rich aromatic structure, beautiful concentration which will yield a well bred, rich and well-balanced wine, for long keeping. Now still in oak casks. **1987:** Strictly selected harvest, only 50% of which will be bottled. Great success, Silver Medal at the Concours agricole de Paris (March 1989). **1986:** Excellent year. Fragrant wine, rich in alcohol and color. Good keeping. **1985:** Beautiful wine, very strong bouquet, reminiscent of red berries and undergrowth, full bodied and well structured, keeps well. Price range (pre-tax, ex-warehouse): 30 to 50 F.F.

References in France

Shops: L'Amour du Vin, 94, rue Saint-Dominique, 75007 Paris.

CHÂTEAU PATACHE D'AUX

Claude Lapalu
Begadan 33340 Lesparre Médoc
56 41 50 18 - Telex: 571 361

Type of vineyard: Family-owned. **Vine stocks:** Cabernet Sauvignon 70%, Merlot 20%, Cabernet Franc 8%, Petit Verdot 2%. **Soil:** Chalky clay. **Average annual production in hectoliters:** 1,900.
Apellation: Médoc. **Type:** Red. **Technique:** Fermentation for about 3 weeks, pumping over several times. **Maturing:** Oak casks and vast – bottling after 20 months of ageing. **Alcohol content:** 12%. **Characteristics:** Wines market by the Cabernet Sauvignon, basic vinestock of Médoc, which yields wines for keeping, characterized by their delicacy, richness and balance. **Serving temperature:** 18°. **Served with:** Meat, roasted or in sauce. **Vintages available in 89/90:** 1984, 1986, 1987, 1988.

Characteristics of vintages

1988: Very balanced and harmonious wine, beautiful color, quality tannins. To be kept. **1987:** Made from a selection of harvests, the wine is less rich than the 1986, but well balanced, graceful and delicate with all of its characteristics harmoniously combined. **1986:** Very great year, no doubt superior to the 1985, with lots of grace and delicacy. To be kept. **1985:** Great wine, harmonious, perfect taste balance, supple and rich at the same time. To be kept. **Other: 1984:** Made from a selection of harvests mostly from Cabernet Sauvignon. Good quality tannins, beautiful color, very successful vintage. Price range (pre-tax, ex-warehouse): between 20 and 50 F.F.
Sales volume:
- Wholesale: 40%. - Retail: 30%. - Restaurants: 20%.
- Other: 10% various.

Sales in France: 55%. **Export sales:** 45%.
Main trading partners: United Kingdom, Belgium, Luxemburg, Netherlands, Denmark, Switzerland, Germany, United States, Canada, Japan.

References in France

Restaurants: Michel Guerard, Les 3 Marchés, La Fermette Marbeuf, Potager du Roy, Joel Robuchon, La Grande Cascade, Lucas Carton, Nandron, La Devinière, L'Aubergade, Larivoire.
Shops: Bordeaux – Magnum, Legrand, Le Repaire de Bacchus, Centre de Distribution des Vins des Propriétés, Etc. Sabatier, Aux Vignes Pasquier, Caves de Becon.

Abroad

United States
Paramount – Jean Claude Boisset.

United Kingdom
Hayward Brothers – Thorman Hunt.

Germany
Champa Vins – Friedrich Krote – Curt E. Geibel.

Switzerland
Fritz Lanz A.G. – Stampfli A.G. – Hugi – Gloggner Frères.

Belgium

Velu Vins, Rue Bollinckx, 1070 Brussels, tel: 2520 6068.

Canada

Saq – LCBO.

The Netherlands

Van Der Linden, Postbus 31041, 3003 HA Rotterdam. Tel: (010) 141977.

Far East

Japan: Izumi Trading, Tel: (03) 964-8255 & 2272.

Comments

Of ancient origin, the Château Patache d'Aux belonged to the Aux family, descendents of the Counts of Armagnac, until the Revolution. It was also a coach station and this is why tradition associates the name Patache (French for a run-down stagecoach) with Aux.
In the year 4 of the Revolution (1796), the château was sold as national property for 52,569 pounds.
The recent vintages are remarkable (particularly 86). Rich and concentrated, fragrant, combining grace, delicacy and character (see "Classification 89").

CHÂTEAU SESTIGNAN

Bertrand de Rozières
Jan - Dignac et Loivac
33590 St-Vivient-de-Médoc
56 09 43 06

Type of vineyard: Family-owned. **Established:** 1973. **Number of employees:** 3, **Vine stocks:** Cabernet Sauvignon 74%, Merlot 25%, Cabernet Franc, Malbec, Petit Verdot 1%. **Soil:** Gravel on iron pan and clay. **Exposure:** All directions. **Average annual production in hectoliters:** 700.
Appellation: Médoc. **Type:** Red. **Technique:** Temperature control, long fermentation on skins. **Maturing:** In vats and casks. **Alcohol content:** 12%. **Characteristics:** Fine and complex. **Serving temperature:** 17 to 18°. **Served with:** Game, meat in sauce, special dishes of the Bordeaux region. **Vintages available in 89/90:** 1984, 1985, 1986.

Characteristics of vintages

1988: Typical Médoc, promising. **1987:** Very successful for this year, supple, well colored. **1986:** Beautiful vintage, rich lingering taste, good keeping. **1985:** Very ripe fruit fragrance. **Other:** 1984: prizes at the 4 great French competitions. Price range (pre-tax, ex-warehouse): 30 to 50 F.F.
Sales volume:
– Retail: 40%. – Other: 60% agents and winecellars.
Sales in France: 60%.
Export sales: 40%.
Main trading partners : Switzerland, Belgium.

References in France

Shops: Entre 2 Verres (48, rue Ste Anne, 70002, Paris).

Abroad

United Kingdom

Sante Wines 21 Coventry road Warwich (0926) 49218.

Switzerland

Philippe Wehrle Obsgartenweg 15, 8136 Gattikon – Tel: 01/7206817.

Belgium

Wilfrid Lems Karel Sootelaan 26 Borsbeek 2210 03/3219668.

The Netherlands

Jacobus Boelem B.V. Donanweg 12, 10H3 AJ Amsterdam 020/114701.

CHÂTEAU
SESTIGNAN
1983
CRU BOURGEOIS
MÉDOC
APPELLATION MÉDOC CONTRÔLÉE
Bertrand de ROZIÈRES, JAU-DIGNAC ET LOIRAC 33590
MIS EN BOUTEILLE AU CHÂTEAU
12 % Vol
PRODUIT DE FRANCE
75 cl

Comments

Sestignan, from "Sextinus" in Latin, is the name given to the place by the Roman colonist who first exploited the soil. During the 1660's, when Colbert ordered the Dutch to clean up the marshlands of the Gironde, the commune was an island, called at the time "Insula Jovis". The Roman galleys brought the vine to these hillsides and exported the wines. "Sestignan" is found right in the center of a winegrowing region on a map of the Médoc dated 1783. The TRAITÉ SUR LES VINS DU MÉDOC (trading in the Médoc wines) of 1845 refers to the property as Cru Bourgeois. It is mentioned in BORDEAUX ET SES VINS (Bordeaux and its wines) up to the 1949 edition, after which the entire commune is no longer to be found, for lack of winegrowers. Awarded many medals (gold and silver) since 1979 at Paris and Mâcon.

1981
Médoc
Château Sigognac
CRU BOURGEOIS
APPELLATION MÉDOC CONTROLÉE
MIS EN BOUTEILLE AU CHATEAU
Bonny-Grasset
PROPRIÉTAIRE A SAINT-YZANS-DU-MÉDOC (GIRONDE)
PRODUCE OF FRANCE

CHÂTEAU SIGOGNAC

Colette Bonny
33340 Saint Yzans-de-Médoc
56 09 05 04 – ITAG 540 495 F CODE B 35
Fax: 56 09 00 65

Type of vineyard: Agricultural Association. **Number of employees:** 15. **Vine stocks:** 33% Merlot, 33% Cabernet Franc, 33% Cabernet Sauvignon. **Soil:** Chalky clay on clay subsoil. **Average annual production in hectoliters:** 40 hl/ha.
Appellation: AOC Médoc Cru Grand Bourgeois. **Type:** Red. **Technique:** Complete destemming, then in vats (3-4 weeks). **Maturing:** In wooden casks and vats for a year and a half, drawing off, fining with egg whites. **Characteristics:** Supple, elegant, fruity, great finesse and vinosity, full maturity after 5 to 10 years (See "Classification 89"). **Serving temperature:** 18°. **Served with:** Roasts, cheese. **Vintages available in 89/90:** 1983, 1984, 1986, 1987, 1988.

Characteristics of vintages

1988: Deep color, beautiful tannins, ripe red berry aroma. **1987:** Limpid color, light tannins, very well balanced. **1986:** Fruity and flowery, elegant tannins, deep color. **Other: 1983:** Very typical Cabernet vintage. **1984:** Beautiful limpid color, subtle aromas.
Sales in France: 35%.
Export sales: 65%.
Main trading partners : USA, UK, Denmark, Switzerland, Belgium, Germany.

References in France

Restaurants: Auberge du Beau Rivage (Villeneuve-le-Roi), La Clef du Périgord (Paris), Le Rouzic (Bordeaux), Hostellerie du Cerf (Marlenheim), etc.
Shops: L'Amour du Vin (Paris), Soperco SA, Lajarrige (Paris).

Abroad

United States

Importers: Brand Promotion Corporation, 57th Avenue, Tualatin, Oregon 97062. Tel: (503) 692 61 63.

United Kingdom

Goujon et Fils Ltd 1 Monza Street, London. Tel: 01 488 4971/2/3/4. Teltschers Brothers Ltd, Lutomer House Prestons Road, London.

Germany

Domaines et Châteaux D.C. Frances Lessingrasse 42D, 6230 Hofheim.

Switzerland

Obrist S.A. 26, avenue Reller, 1800 Vevey.

Belgium

The Continental Bogeda Company, rue des Quatre Vents 1080 Brussels.

Others

Denmark: Vinicole Vinimport, Strandlodsvej 15, 23000 Copenhagen. Dawinco International Hornebyvej 62 E Hornbaek.

Comments

Perfectly controlled vinification, well colored wines, combining richness and finesse, regularly successful, excellent evolution (the 83 vintage is already superb).

CHÂTEAU TOUR HAUT CAUSSAN

Philippe Courrian
33340 Blaignan Médoc
56 09 00 77

Type of vineyard: Family-owned. **Established:** 1877. **Number of employees:** 4. **Vine stocks:** 50% Merlot, 50% Cabernet Sauvignon. **Soil:** 50% Gravel, 50% clay with calcium carbonate. **Exposure:** On one of the aighest plateau 36 meters of the Medoc. **Average annual production in hectoliters:** 900/17 ha.
Appellation: Médoc. **Type:** Red. **Technique:** Long fermentation with skins, 100% destemming. **Maturing:** Barrels 100%: 1/4 new. 12 months, then 6 months tanks. **Characteristics:** To be aged. **Serving temperature:** 17°. **Served with:** Poultry, mushrooms, giblets, cheese, guinea-hen-«Martons». **Vintages available in 89/90:** 1984, 1985, 1986.

Characteristics of vintages

1986: Very structured, great analytic balance. To be aged, a bit severe and young. **1985:** Elegant, nice woody, too in its youth, long nevertheless. **1984:** Successful vintage. First taste not so fine, a bit short. Price range (pre-tax, ex-warehouse): Between 30 F.F. and 50 F.F.
Sales volume:
– Retail: 66 %. – Restaurants: 4%.
Sales in France: 30%.
Main trading partners : Belgium, Netherlands, Switzerland.

CHÂTEAU VIEUX ROBIN

F. Dufau – M. Roba
Begadan – 33340 Lesparre
56 41 50 64

Type of vineyard: Family-owned. **Established:** 1840. **Vine stocks:** 60% Cabernet Sauvignon, 38% Merlot, 5% Cabernet franc, 5% Petit Verdot. **Soil:** Clay with calcium carbonate. **Exposure:** Plateau. **Average annual production in hectoliters:** 850.
Appellation: Médoc. **Type:** Red. **Technique:** Total destemming, vinification in a pressurized tank, long fermentation with skins. **Maturing:** Ageing one year in Oak barrels, racking every 3 months, fining with egg whites. **Alcohon**

content: 12%. **Characteristics:** Typical Cabernet Sauvignon, tannic with a great capacity for ageing. **Serving temperature:** 16 to 17°. **Served with:** Grilled red meat or roasts for the robust years; Roasted white roast meat for light vintages. **Vintages available in 89/90:** 1981, 1982, 1983, 1984, 1985.

Characteristics of vintages

1986: Dark garnet color, excellent depth, full, no monolithic tannin, ending without hardness. **1985:** Dark ruby, cherry reflections, red fruit close to balckberry, slow to mature. **1984:** Woody, light, raspberry taste, very harmonious, aromatic very present. **1983:** Well-balanced, aromatic expression, fine woody, full and forthcoming. **1982:** Very present tannic structure, supple soft and full, round, agreeable taste. **1981:** Rich and well-balanced, meaty, starting to develop. Price range (pre-tax, ex-warehouse): Between 20 F.F. and 30 F.F.

Sales volume:
- Wholesale: 39.5%. - Retail: 60%. - Restaurants: 0.5%.

Sales in France: 60%.
Export sales: 40%.

References in France

Restaurants: Medoc Restaurants.
Shops: Bordeaux Magnum, Bordeaux.

CHÂTEAU LA TOUR DE BY

Marc Pages
Bégadan 33340 Lesparre Médoc
54 41 50 03 - FAX 56 41 36 10

Type of vineyard: Corporation. **Established:** 1976. **Number of employees:** 25. **Vine stocks:** 70% Cabernet Sauvignon, 28% Merlot, 2% Cabernet Franc. **Soil:** Gravel on iron pan sub-soil. **Exposure:** On a gravel hillcrest bordering the Gironde. **Average annual production in hectoliters:** 4,500.
Appellational: A.O.C. Médoc. **Type:** Red. **Technique:** Floating cap under carbonic gas. **Maturing:** In oak casks (20% new each year). **Alcohol content:** 12.5%. **Characteristics:** Typical Médoc, tannic, supple, aromatic, fruity, very rich and well balanced. **Serving temperature:** 15 to 18°.
Served with: Grilled meats, roast, game, cheese. **Vintages available in 89/90:** 1984, 1985, 1986, 1987 (in May 1989) and 1988 (next wine).

Characteristics of vintages

1988: Very well balanced wine, round, very fine, it can be drunk as of 1992 and can be kept a long time. It is very rich - a compromise between the 1985 and the 1986. **1987:** Made from very ripe grapes, the wine is very well balanced and harmonious, round, supple and fine. **1986:** Extremely rich and well balanced wine, round and firm with very rich tannins, supple with an excellent fruitiness. **1985:** Very great year, well developed bouquet and fruity flavor.

Other: 1984: Vintage made entirely from Cabernet. Price range (pre-tax, ex-warehouse): between 30 and 60 F.F.

Sales volume:
- Retail: 40%. - Restaurants: 10%.

Sales in France: 50%.
Export sales: 50%.
Main trading partners : Belgium, Switzerland, Germany, Netherlands, Canada, United States, Japan, United Kingdom, Denmark, Austria.

References in France

Restaurants: La Tour d'Argent, Le Ritz, Chez Maxim's, La Tour Rose (Lyon), L'Archestrade, le Grand Véfour, Le Taillevent.
Shops: Caves de la Madeleine, Hédiard, Fauchon.

Abroad

United Kingdom

Direct sale.

Germany

Franz Keller. Jacques' Wein Depot.

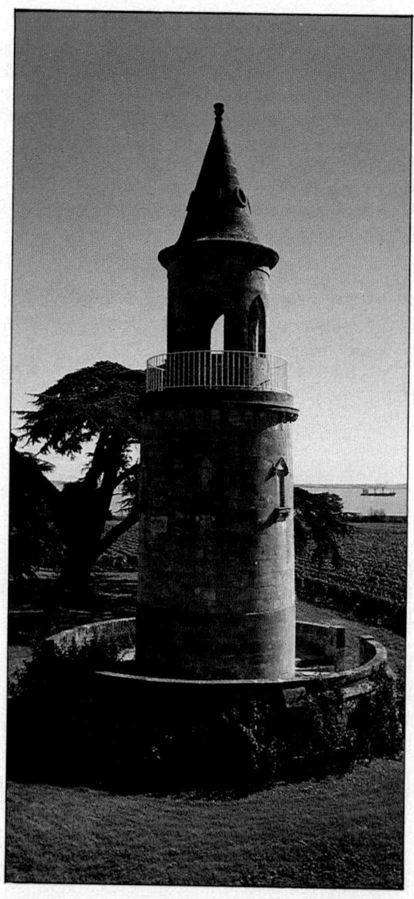

The Netherlands

Oud Wijnkopers & Hustinx BV. Maison Leon Colaris BV.

Comments

The Château La Tour de By owes its name to the Tower which is an ancient lighthouse, built in 1825 on the ruins of a flour mill. The tower overlooks the entire vineyard. The vines have been cultivated for several centuries. The first Château built on the property, called Château La Roque de By, goes back to 1730. The Château La Tour de By, overlooking the Gironde, was built in 1876.
The 71 hectare vineyard is planted in noble vinestocks (Cabernet Sauvignon, Merlot and Cabernet Franc). The vinification is the object of the most meticulous care and respects the techniques and tradition indispensable for the production of these great wines. The warehouse, half underground, allows the wines to age slowly in oak casks, bringing out the grace, delicacy and suppleness which, by their distinction, classify them among the very first crus of the Médoc appellation (see "Classification 89").

GRAVES

GRANDS CRUS DE PESSAC-LÉOGNAN

CHÂTEAU BARET

Société Civile du Château Baret
Villenave d'Ornon - Administrateur Philippe Casteja
86, cours Balguerie-Stuttenberg
33300 Bordeaux
56 48 57 57 - Telex: 550 766

Vine stocks: Red: 75% Cabernet Sauvignon, 25% Merlot. White: 52% Sauvignon, 45% Sémillon, 3% Muscadelle. **Average annual production in hectoliters:** 40 to 50. **Appellation:** Pessac Léognan. **Type:** Red, white. **Technique:** White: 30% fermentation in new cask, keeping wine on yeart during 2 to 3 months. 70 % fermentation low temperature in vat. Classic and traditional for the reds, low temperature for the whites. **Maturing:** In oak barrels. **Alcohol content:** 12.5%. **Characteristics:** Tannic, good color and a certain finesse. **Serving temperature:** Red: 19° - White: 8 to 9°. **Served with:** Red: Meat and cheese. White: Fish and shellfish and as an aperitif. **Vintages available in 89/90:** Reds: 1985/1986. Whites: 1987/1988.

Characteristics of vintages

1986: Promising. **1985:** Very good vintage. Good white; successful red, flowery and round.
Sales volume: - Wholesale: 100% (Borie-Manoux).

References in France

Restaurants: Mainly restaurants with Michelin Stars.
Shops: Hédiard, Fauchon, Boutiques etc.

BOUSCAUT

Lucien Lurton
33140 Cadaujac
56 30 72 40

Type of vineyard: Corporation. **Established:** 1980. **Vine stocks:** Reds: 35% Cabernet Sauvignon, 5% Cabernet Franc, 60% Merlot. Whites: 70% Semillon, 30% Sauvignon. **Soil:** Gravel and clay with calcium carbonate. Classified Growth.
Appellation: Pessac-Léognan. **Technique:** Bordeaux tradition. **Serving temperature:** 20°. **Served with:** Red: red meat, fish in sauce. White: scallops, prawns, cheese. **Vintages available in 89/90:** 1985, 1986, 1987.

Characteristics of vintages

1987: Red: very pleasant and a fine balance. White: very elegant and lively, with flesh and nerve. **1986:** Red: very tannic, rich and well-balanced. Whites: Very aromatic, fleshy. Hold. **1985:** Red very successful, rich and seductive at the same time, flowery, full, keeps well. Excellent white.

References in France

Restaurants: Le Beauvilliers – Closerie des Lilas – Le Divellec – Le Méridien – Plaza-Athénée – Jean Ramet – Michel Guérard – André Daguin.
Shops: Hédiard – Caves de Nîmes – Cave Clémente – Caves de la Madeleine – Pétrissans.

Abroad

United States

Importers: Château & Estate Wine C° 375 Park Ave. New York, N.Y. 10015.

Japan

Million Trading Co Ltd. 15-2,1 Chome, Shinkawa, Chuo-Ku, Tokyo.

CHÂTEAU COUHINS-LURTON

Cru classé
André Lurton
Administrative office at Grezillac 33420
57 84 52 07 – Telex: 570 215

Type of vineyard: Agricultural Association. **Established:** 18th Century. **Vine stocks:** Sauvignon. **Soil:** Deep gravel, slightly sandy. **Exposure:** Southwest. **Average annual production in hectoliters:** 200.
Appellation: Pessac Léognan. **Type:** White. **Technique:** In new barrels. **Maturing:** 6 months. **Characteristics:** Very lovely color, slightly golden, richness with prononced oak aromas. Touch of vanilla, soft and supple, associated with the aroma of very ripe grapes. Remarkable impression of richness, body and balance, an elegant woody touch which adds to its great finesse. **Serving temperature:** 12°. **Served with:** fish and white meat.

Characteristics of vintages

Price range (pre-tax, ex-warehouse): between 30 F.F. and 50 F.F.
Sales in France: 80%. **Export sales:** 20%.

References in France

Restaurants: Not in many restaurants.

CHÂTEAU DE CRUZEAU

André Lurton
Administrative office at Grezillac 33420
57 84 52 07 – Telex: 570 215

Type of vineyard: Agricultural Association. **Established:** In the 18th Century. **Number of employees:** 10. **Vine stocks:** Reds: Cabernet Sauvignon, Merlot. Whites: Sauvignon, Sémillon. **Soil:** Deep gravel. **Exposure:** South. **Average annual production in hectoliters:** 2,000.
Appellation: Pessac Léognan. **Type:** Red, white. **Technique:** Temperature controlled stainless steel tanks. **Maturing:** One year in barrels (1/3 new each year for the reds). **Characteristics:** White: beautiful straw color, distinctly Sauvignon aroma with a flowery touch suggesting lime, light structure, very fresh, vinous, body, flavor. Red: deep, intense color. Fragrance reminiscent of prunes and grilled almonds. Very complex. Remarkable balance of rich and mellow tannins, hint of wood. Successful combination of Merlot and very ripe Cabernet Sauvignon. May be age for many years. **Serving temperature:** White: 10° – Red: 18°. **Served with:** White: fish and white meat. Red: red meat. **Vintages available in 89/90:** Red: 1980, 1984, 1985. White: 1986.

Characteristics of vintages

1986: Excellent year, a big success. **1985:** 95% of the harvest destroyed by hail. **1984:** Very good year, very successful, full of charm. **1983:** Excellent year, supple, fragrant wine. **1982:** Exceptional year. **Other: 1981:** Excellent year, very promising. Price range (pre-tax, ex-warehouse): between 20 F.F. and 30 F.F.
Sales in France: 40%. **Export sales:** 60%.

CHÂTEAU DE ROCHEMORIN

André Lurton
Administrative office at Grezillac 33420
57 84 52 97 – Telex: 570 215

Type of vineyard: Agricultural Association since 1973. **Established:** 1072; remained in the Secondat Family for 9 Centuries. **Number of employees:** 10. **Vine stocks:** Red: 40% Merlot, 60% Cabernet Sauvignon. White: 85% Sauvignon, 15% Sémillon. **Soil:** Deep gravel, slightly sandy. **Exposure:** South. **Average annual production in hectoliters:** 2,000.
Appellation: Pessac Léognan. **Type:** Red, white. **Technique:** Traditional. **Maturing:** White: in new barrels. Red: in one year old barrels plus 1/3 new barrels.**Characteristics:** White: agreeable aroma, fine and light, discretely Sauvignon, slightly musky. Dry, light and supple, light and pleasant at the same time, with an excellent taste of good wood. Red: beautiful deep color, perfect aroma, reminiscent of vanilla and toast. Lovely balance of strong tannins, round, rich and well-balanced, round, rich and well-balanced, supple, strong tannins, round, rich and well-balanced, velvety. **Serving temperature:** White: 12°; Red: 18°. **Served with:** White: fish and white meat. Red: red meat, game, cheese. **Vintages available in 89/90:** Red: 1984, White: 1986.

Characteristics of vintages

1986: Excellent year, very promising. **1985:** Exceptional year. Price range (pre-tax, ex-warehouse): between 20 F.F. and 30 F.F.

CHÂTEAU CARBONNIEUX

Anthony Perrin
33850 Leognan
56 87 08 28
Telex: 550 370 Telefax: 56 87 52 18

Type of vineyard: Agricultural Association. **Established:** in the 14th century. **Vine stocks:** White: Sauvignon 60%. Sémillon 40% – Red: Cabernet Sauvignon 60%, Merlot 30%, Cabernet Franc 7%, Malbec 3%. **Soil:** silica and gravel. **Exposure:** gentle slopes – North-West. **Average annual production in hectoliters:** 4,000.

Appellation: Pessac Leognan. **Type:** Red, White. **Technique:** in vats. **Maturing:** in casks. **Alcohol content:** 12%. **Characteristics:** White: dry – Red: long. **Serving temperature:** White: 9-10°. Red: 18°. **Vintages available in 89/90:** 88, 87, 86, 84, 82, 79.

Characteristics of vintages

1988: White: soft and full, long – Red: deep color, supple tannins. **1987:** White: fruity, vigorous – Red: fruity (blackcurrant flavor), round, supple. **1986:** White: full, round, peach aroma – Red: tannic, lingering taste. **1985:** Red: typical of the soil, liquorice, mellow tannins. Price range (pre-tax, ex-warehouse): 50 F.F. to 80 F.F.

Sales volume:
– Wholesale: 95%. – Retail: 5%.

Sales in France: 33%.
Export sales: 67%.
Main trading partners: EEC countries, USA, Japan, Canada, Switzerland.

Comments

The Château Carbonnieux vineyard is located 12 kilometers to the South of Bordeaux in the magnificent Graves region, cradle of Bordeaux winegrowing. The domain, covering 172 hectares, 80 of which are planted in noble vinestocks, belonged to the Benedictines of the Ste-Croix Abbey before the Revolution. It is said that the monks sold the famous white wine to the Court of the Sultan of Turkey under the name of Carbonnieux Mineral Water, despite the Koranic insistence on abstinence. It now belongs to the Société Civile des Grandes Graves and is administered by the Perrin family, winemakers for several generations. Continuing the traditions of quality, they are surrounded by the highest œnological authorities of the South-West. Their universally known wines are a source of joy to those who taste them and are distributed world-wide. The dry and vigorous whites are unique. They are recommended for the beginning of meals, particularly with shellfish, and should be served at 6 to 8°. The reds, related to the Médoc wines, have a great deal of character and can be kept for many years. They should be served at room temperature, preferably between 16 and 18°. Bottling is done exclusively at the château, after meticulous selection.

Château Carbonnieux - Grand Cru Classé de Graves

CHÂTEAU DE FIEUZAL

Gérard Gribelin
Leognan 33850
56 21 77 86
Telefax: 56 21 18 88 Telex: Sodicru 541 434

Type of vineyard: Corporation. **Established:** 1974. **Number of employees:** 20. **Vine stocks:** white gravel. **Exposure:** North-South. **Average annual production in hectoliters:** 1600.
Type: Red, White. **Technique:** Red: in lined tanks. White: in casks. **Maturing:** in wooden casks. **Alcohol content:** 12-12.5%. **Characteristics:** rich in color, very concentraded, good keeping, complex, perfect balance sought between alcohol content, acidity and tannins. **Serving temperature:** White: 10-12°. Red: 16-18°. **Vintages available in 89/90:** Red: 1984 and 1986 (in bottles) 1988 (Primeur).

Characteristics of vintages

1988: very great year, very rich, marvelous balance. **1987:** lesser year, but charming and delicate wine (magnificent success for the vintage). **1986:** very great year, rich and well-balanced, concentrated wines. Wait at least of 10 years. **1985:** very great year, long, more harmonious tannins than the 1986, marvelous balance. Price range (pretax, ex-warehouse): 50 F.F. to 80 F.F. (dealers). 80 F.F. to 120 F.F. (retail).
Sales volume:
– Wholesale: 90%. – Retail: 10%.
Sales in France:
Export sales: sold through Bordeaux dealers.
Main trading partners:

References in France

Restaurants: Lucas Carton, Tour d'Argent, Taillevent, Lasserre, Drouant, Pre Catelan, Auberge de l'Ill, Le Crocodile etc.
Shops: Bordeaux, Magnum, L'Amour du Vin, Nicolas.

Comments

The Château de Fieuzal is located at Leognan, 15 kilometers South of Bordeaux, in the Graves region which was the cradle of the Gironde vineyard about 2000 years ago. Its name comes from the locality on which the vineyard is situated. It enjoys an exceptional location on one of the best hillcrests of the region, particularly well exposed, with a characteristic gravelly soil (white pebbles). Under the monarchy, the vineyard belonged to the La Rochefoucauld family. The family author wrote in one of his maxims: "To my mind, sobriety is a sort of impotence". The vineyard, abandoned during the Revolution, made great strides at the end of the First Empire and, ever since the crown-corks have been decorated with a bee, one of the enblems of the Napoleonic Empire. At the time, the property belonged to Alfred De Griffon, when it was sold in 1892 to the Jean Ricard distributors, very important dealers, established at Leognan since 1855 and owners of a number of Leognan vineyards, notably the Château Malartic-Lagravière and the Domaine De Chevalier. Fieuzal is also proud, in 1893, an exceptional year, to have been a supplier to the Vatican winecellars, those of the very great Pope Léon XIII. Today, the vineyard belongs to the S.A. Château De Fieuzal, whose President and Director General is Gérard Gribelin. Since the official classification of 1959, the red wines of the Château De Fieuzal are considered as a Grand Cru Classé. The production of white wine at the time was only three barrels. Considereing the quantity, Fieuzal white, as well as several illustrious neighbors such as Haut-Brion, Smith Haut-Lafitte And Pape Clement did not ask to be classified in white. The vineyard extends over about 40 hectares, of which 33 are in full production (29 hectares in red and 4 hectares in white).

CHÂTEAU SMITH HAUT LAFITTE

(Maison Louis Eschenauer)
Martillac 33650 La Brede
56 30 72 30

Vine stocks: 52 hectares of which 45 for red wines and 7 for white wine. Red: Cabernets 74%, Merlot 26%. White: Sauvignon 100%. **Soil:** Gravel of the Garonne on hillcrest. **Appellation:** Pessac Leognan. **Type:** Red, White. **Technique:** Traditional. **Maturing:** In barrels for both red and white. **Characteristics:** White: superb wines, full and structured, very fine, fragrant. Red: great elegance, soft, supple wines with long persistence (see classification). **Serving temperature:** White: 12°. Red: 16°. **Served with:** White: fish and white meat in cream. Red: roasts, poultry, cheese. **Vintages available in 1989** (Red): 1982, 1984, 1985 and 1986. **Vintages available in 1990** (Red): 1984, 1985, 1986 and 1987.

Characteristics of vintages

1987: White: intense aromatic nose. Well-balanced in mouth. Red: very fine, with a nice bouquet. A great success for this vintage. **1986:** Great vintage for the exceptional whites as well as the reds, very promising. **1985:** Beautiful red wine, good colour, very fine, complex aromas, full, good keeping. **1984:** Perfectly mastered vintage.

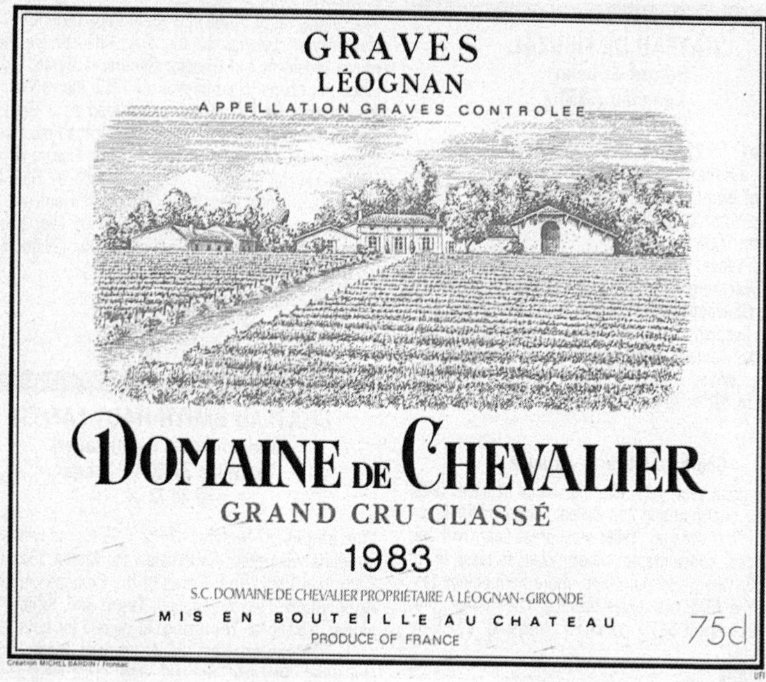

DOMAINE DE CHEVALIER

Claude Ricard and Olivier Bernard
33850 Léognan
56 21 75 27

Type of vineyard: Family-owned. **Established:** 1865. **Number of employees:** 12. **Vine stocks:** Cabernet-Sauvignon, Merlot, Cabernet Franc, Sauvignon, Sémillon. **Soil:** Clay and sandy gravel on subsoil of sand and gravel, sometimes clay and sand, or limestone. **Exposure:** Hilltop. **Average annual production in hectoliters:** 630. **Type:** Red, white. **Technique:** Traditional, fermentation with skins at high temperature. **Maturing:** In barrels (1/2 new for reds – 1/4 new for whites). **Alcohol content:** Red: 12% – White 12.5 %. **Characteristics:** Finesse and elegance. Keeps an exceptionally long time – red as well as white. **Serving temperature:** Red: 18° – White: 10°-12°. **Served with:** Red: Red and white meat, poultry. White: Fish, shellfish. **Vintages available in 89/90:** Red 1975 – 1985.

Characteristics of vintages

1986: Fine, complex and full. Strong, yet mellow tannic structure. **1985:** Substantial, soft and full, fleshy, very long. Strong and flavorful tannins. **1984:** Astonishing richness, balance and concentration. Abundant tannins, robust but full of flavor. **1983:** Remarkable harmony, finesse, race, elegance. First prize at the Olympiades du Vin (Gault et Millau – Feb. '87) – Elected Wine of the Year by the Belgian Section of the Académie internationale du Vin (Jan. '87). Graded 19 out of 20 by Cive Coates, MW (The Vine – Jan. 1987). **1982:** Rich and abundant tannins. Firm and vigorous, lingering, long. **Note:** White '83: Fine peach aroma. Firm, robust. Beautiful aromatic finish. Price range (pre-tax, ex-warehouse): 120 F.F. – 160F.F. (over 160 F.F for whites and for reds in great years).

Sales volume:
– Wholesale: 100%.

Main trading partners: Belgium, UK, Switzerland, Netherlands.

References in France

Restaurants: Taillevent – Dutournier – Guy Savoy – Faugeron – Michel Rostang – Lucas Carton: Paris. L'Aubergade (Puymirol) – Comme chez soi (Bruxelles).

Comments

Rigorous selection of grapes ensures the production of wines of exceptional uniformity. The "Chevalier" is often referred to as the "Champion" of the minor vintages.

• *Read labels carefully – An indication to watch out for: "Bottled in the 'region' of production", which often refers to a blend of wines from several producers and not just one.*

CHÂTEAU GAZIN

Michotte/Foures
Route de Cestas - 33850 Léognan
56 23 31 29 - Telex: 540 744 F

Type of vineyard: Family-owned. **Established:** 1974. **Vine stocks:** Merlot 10% - Cabernet Franc 40% - Cabernet Sauvignon 50%. **Soil:** Sandy gravel. **Average annual production in hectoliters:** 400.
Appellation: Graves Léognan. **Type:** Red. **Technique:** Classic - maceration for 10 days. **Maturing:** Oak casks. **Characteristics:** Typical of the commune of Leognan. Rich wines, pleasant, young - can be aged for half a century. **Serving temperature:** 18°. **Vintages available in 89/90:** 1984, 1985, 1986.

Characteristics of vintages

1986: Typical Léognan, very successful. **1985:** Very mature year - wine soft and full. **1984:** Exceptionally successful vintage due to the specific character of the soil. Price range (pre-tax, ex-warehouse): between 50 F.F. and 80 F.F.

CHÂTEAU LARRIVET-HAUT-BRION

Philippe Gervoson
Chemin du Haut-Brion 33850 Leognan
56 21 75 51

Established: in the 19th century. **Vine stocks:** White: Sémillon 50%, Sauvignon 50%. Red: Merlot 45%, Cabernet Sauvignon 55%. **Soil:** gravelly. **Average annual production in hectoliters:** 700.

Appellation: Pessac Leognan. **Type:** Red, White. **Technique:** Red: concrete tanks, temperature control. White: fermentation and maturing in new casks. **Maturing:** Red: new barrels (40%) for 12 months. **Alcohol content:** 12.5%. **Serving temperature:** Red: 20°. White: 6-8°. **Served with:** Red: red meat, cheese. White: as an aperitif and with white meat and fish. **Vintages available in 89/90:** 86-87-88.

Characteristics of vintages

1988: Red: rich and well-balanced, full of character, very long keeping - White: white fruit aroma, lingering taste. Wait 10 years. **1987:** Red: harmonious, very delicate, mellow. To be drunk within 2 to 5 years. White: full, fruity, lingering taste. **1986:** Red: very well-balanced, developing tannins, to be drunk in 10 years or so. White: very well-balanced, well developed aromas. Wait another 5 years. **1985:** Red: tannic, rich and well-balanced, very long keeping. Price range (pre-tax, ex-warehouse): 50 F.F. to 80 F.F.
Sales volume:
- Wholesales: 90%. - Retail: 5%. - Restaurants: 5%.
Sales in France: 30%. **Export sales:** 70%.
Main trading partners: UK, Switzerland, Germany, Benelux, countries.

CHÂTEAU LA LOUVIÈRE

André Lurton
33850 Léognan
56 21 75 87 - 57 84 52 07 - Telex: 570 215

Type of vineyard: Agricultural Association. **Established:**

Very old - 15th Century at least. **Number of employees:** 25. **Vine stocks:** Cabernet Sauvignon, Merlot, Cabernet Franc for reds, Sauvignon and Sémillon for whites. **Soil:** Deep gravel with clay in the sub-soil. **Exposure:** Southwest. **Average annual production in hectoliters:** 2,000.
Appellation: Pessac Léognan. **Type:** Red, white. **Technique:** In temperature controlled stainless steel tanks for the reds. Barrels for the whites. **Maturing:** New barrels for the whites. 50% new barrels every year for the reds. **Characteristics:** Reds: very beautiful color, very ripe aroma a soft note of vanilla and grilled almonds. Rich, well-balanced, full and long, soothing, but at the same time serious. Whites: lovely color slightly golden, rich aromas with a touch of oak. A note of vanilla, the soft and supple aroma of ripe grapes. Excellent impression of richness, balances and body. Finesse. **Serving temperature:** Whites: 12°. Reds: 18°. **Served with:** Whites: fish and white meat. Reds: red meat, game cheese. **Vintages available in 89/90:** 1981, 1983, 1984, 1985 (reds), 1982, 1984, 1986 (whites).

Characteristics of vintages

1986: Excellent year. **1985:** Exceptional year. Superb white and structured red, dense, to be aged. **1984:** Very successful vintage. **1983:** Excellent year. **1982:** Excellent year, to be kept. Price range (pre-tax, ew-warehouse): Between 40 F.F. and 50 F.F.
Sales volume: - Wholesale: 100%.
Sales in France: 25%. **Export sales:** 75%.

References in France

Restaurants: Everywhere.
Shops: Many.

CHÂTEAU HAUT-BAILLY

Jean Sanders
33850 Léognan
56 21 75 11 or 56 27 16 07 – TELEFAX 56 27 16 02

Type of vineyard: Family-owned Agricultural Association. **Established:** 1987. **Number of employees:** 11. **Vine stocks:** Cabernet Sauvignon 65%, Cabernet Franc 10%, Merlot 25%. **Soil:** Typical of the region – sand and gravel of the Tertiary era. **Average annual production in hectoliters:** 1,500.

CRU EXCEPTIONNEL

CHATEAU HAUT-BAILLY
GRAND CRU CLASSÉ
APPELLATION GRAVES CONTRÔLÉE

S.C.I.A. SANDERS, PROPRIETAIRE à LEOGNAN (Gironde)

MIS EN BOUTEILLES AU CHATEAU 750 ml

Appellation: Pessac, Léognan. **Type:** Red. **Technique:** Traditional, temperature control. **Maturing:** In casks. **Alcohol content:** 12.5%. **Characteristics:** Very supple, low acidity, charming and feminine. **Serving temperature:** 18°. **Vintages available in 89/90:** 1984, 1986, 1987.

Characteristics of vintages

1988: Rich in ripe tannins, beautiful color, great wine for long keeping. **1987:** Supple, fruity, very pleasant. **1986:** 100% Cabernet, firm, good keeping, very successful. **1985:** Full and pleasant. Price range (pre-tax, ex-warehouse): 80 to 120 F.F.
Sales volume: – Wholesale: 80%. – Retail: 20%.
Main trading partners : Belgium, Switzerland, Germany, UK and USA.

References in France

Restaurants: Many.
Shops: Vignes, Pasquiers, Fauchon.

Abroad

United States

Stacole Co. 819 South Federal Highway Deerfield Beach, 33441 (Florida).

United Kingdom

Laurence Webber, Pommery Distribution.

CHÂTEAU MALARTIC-LAGRAVIÈRE

Jacques Marly
33850 Léognan
56 21 75 08

Type of vineyard: Agricultural Association. **Established:** Domain about 1850. **Number of employees:** 10. **Vine stocks:** Red: Cabernet Sauvignon 50%, Cabernet Franc 25%, Merlot 25%. White: Sauvignon 100%. **Soil:** Chalky clay and gravel. **Exposure:** South-West. **Average annual production in hectoliters:** 680.
Appellation: Pessac-Léognan. **Typel** Red, white. **Technique:** Traditional. **Maturing:** In casks (50 to 60% new) for 22 months. **Alcohol content:** 12.5%. **Characteristics:** Rich and well balanced, tannic. **Serving temperature:** Red: 17 to 18°. White: 12 to 13°. **Served with:** Red: game. White: fish cooked in sauce. **Vintages available in 89/90:** Red: 1966,1969, 1972, 1973, 1980, 1981, 1982, 1986. White: 1986, 1987.

Characteristics of vintages

1988: Tasted in the cask, very promising. **1987:** Excellent white, flowery and dense – successful red, well made, good development. **1986:** Great year – red: well colored, dense, rich in fragrance and structure, good keeping. Price range (pre-tax, ex-warehouse): 50 to 80 F.F.
Sales volume:
– Wholesale: 100%.

References in France

Restaurants: All great restaurants in Paris and elsewhere in France.
Shops: Chez Nicolas.

• Blending – a method consisting of mixing different wines from different lots or different vintages in order to obtain a more homogeneous product.

• The naturally sweet wines of the Loire region, such as Quarts-de-Chaume or Coteau-du-Layon, offer the possibility of some very lovely wine tastings. Very fruity, full, supple and harmonious, they will keep well. (See the Chapter on the Loire Valley).

• Paulée – traditional meal which brings winelovers and winegrowers together after the harvest, particularly in Burgundy.

Avec Malartic-Lagravière
Graves prennent le large.....
h Château Malartic-Lagravière
Graves take to horizons new.
MARIE ELISABETEH
CHATEAU
MALARTIC-LAGRA
1985
GRAND CRU CLAS
GRAVES
LEOGNAN
PRODUCE OF FRANCE
CHATEAU
MALARTIC-LAGRA
1985
GRAND CRU CLA

CHÂTEAU PAPE CLÉMENT

Léo Montagne - Director: Bernard Pujol
33600 Pessac
56 07 04 11

Type of vineyard: Family-owned. **Established:** In the XIIth century. **Number of employees:** 15. **Vine stocks:** Cabernet Sauvignon 60%, Merlot 40%. **Soil:** Sandy gravel, alluvial terraces with a sub-soil of Miocene shell marl on a chalky layer of Stampian asteriated opal. **Exposure:** Long gravelly hillcrest. **Average annual production in hectoliters:** 1,300.
Appellation: Pessac-Léognan. **Type:** Red. **Technique:** Traditional, fermentation in small capacity stainless steel tanks, temperature control. **Maturing:** In new casks. **Alcohol content:** 12.5%. **Characteristics:** Very deep color, tannic, long keeping. **Serving temperature:** 17 to 18°. **Served with:** Meat, leg of lamb. **Vintages available in 89/90:** 1982, 1983, 1985, 1986, 1987.

Characteristics of vintages

1987: Beautiful lively color, delicate bouquet, smoky character, typical Graves. Beautiful structure, harmonious, mellow and round tannins. A great success. **1986:** Remarkable deep garnet color. Rich and complex bouquet, very personalized, smoky, animal, woodland notes. Substantial, rich and well-balanced. Mellow, dense, well-bred, harmonious wine of great distinction. A very great bottle. Price range (pre-tax, ex-warehouse): 120 to 160 F.F.

Sales volume: – Wholesale: 80%. – Retail: 20%.
Sales in France: 60%. **Export sales:** 40%.
Main trading partners : UK, Belgium, Switzerland, Germany, USA.

References in France

Restaurants: La Tour d'Argent, Le Carré des Feuillants, Le Ritz.
Shops: Hédiard, Fauchon, Cave de la Madeleine.

Abroad

United States

Importers: Sherry Lehman, Zacchys, Morell (New York). La Caravelle (New York). Le Cirque (New York). Le Pavillon (Washington).

Comments

In 1299, Bertrand de Goth, youngest son in a rich and noble family whose possessions extended over the Bordeaux and Bazas regions, was named Archibishop of Bordeaux by Pope Boniface VIII. His brother Béraud, honored, as was the entire family by this nomination, offered him his Pessac property. On June 20, 1305, with the influence of Philippe le Bel, Bertrand de Goth was elected Pope and chose the name Clément V. The one and only Gascon Pope, he left his imprint on the history of France as well as on the Bordeaux region. To celebrate his memory, Pessac named his estate the "Pape Clément". The Château Pape Clément has belonged to the Montagne family since 1939. The present manager is Mr. Léo Montagne.

GRAND VIN DE BORDEAUX
CHATEAU PAPE CLÉMENT
GRAND CRU CLASSE DE GRAVES
APPELLATION PESSAC-LEOGNAN CONTROLEE
PESSAC - LEOGNAN
1986
Ste MONTAGNE & Cie PROPRIETAIRE A PESSAC-GIRONDE
MIS EN BOUTEILLE AU CHATEAU
12,5% vol.
75cl
PRODUCT OF FRANCE

GRAVES

CHÂTEAU D'ARCHAMBEAU

Jean-Philippe Dubourdieu
33720 Illats
56 62 51 46

Type of vineyard: Family-owned. **Established:** In the family since the beginning of the Century. **Vine stocks:** White: Sémillon 55%, Muscadelle 10%, Sauvignon 35%. Red: Merlot, Cabernet. **Soil:** Gravel and clay. **Exposure:** Hilltop. **Average annual production in hectoliters:** Red: 600, White: 730.
Appellation: Graves. **Type:** Red, white. **Technique:** Manual harvesting. Low temperature, Carbonic maceration. **Maturing:** Directly in casks. **Characteristics:** Red: wine a bit herbaceous due to the soil and the youth of the vines (about 10 years). White: 60 year old vines. Taste and fragrance go together. **Serving temperature:** Cool but not cold for the whites. **Served with:** White with all seafood.

Characteristics of vintages

Price range (pre-tax, ex-warehouse): between 30 F.F. and 50 F.F.
Sales volume:
– Wholesale: 50%. – Restaurants: 50% (and winecellars).
Sales in France: 80%. **Export sales:** 20%.
Main trading partners : USA, Germany, Belgium.

CHÂTEAU D'ARDENNES

François Dubrey
Illats – 33720 Podensac
56 62 53 80

Type of vineyard: Corporation. **Established:** 1968. **Number of employees:** 4. **Vine stocks:** Red: 40% Merlot, 60% Cabernet Sauvignon. White: 80% Sémillon, 20% Sauvignon. **Soil:** Gravels, clay with calcium carbonate. **Exposure:** Southeast. **Average annual production in hectoliters:** 500 for white Graves, 1,000 for red Graves.
Appellation: Graves. **Type:** Red, white. **Technique:** Red: traditional (long fermentation wirh skins for 21 days). **Maturing:** Stainless seel tanks and new Oak casks for 1/3. **Alcohol content:** 12%.
Characteristics: White: vinification with temperature control (16° to 17°). Red: rich, good color, a little tannic. White: lindent-tea aroma, pale yellow. **Serving temperature:** Red: 17°. White: 10° to 12°. **Vintages available in 89/90:** Red: 1981, 1982, 1983, 1984, 1985 (+ 1986). White: 1982, 1985, 1986.

Characteristics of vintages

1986: Very good, above all white. **1985:** Exceptionnal red wine, full and fine, beautiful white: **1984:** Good, Gold Medal in Paris, Agriculture Salon. Price range (pre-tax, ex-warehouse): Red: between 20 F.F and 30 F.F. White: 30 F.F. and 50 F.F.
Sales volume:
– Wholesale: 20%. – Retail: 70%. – Restaurants: 10%.
Sales in France: 90%. **Export sales:** 10%.
Main trading partners : UK, USA.

BARRE – GENTILLOT

Cazenave, Mahé
Arveyres 33500 Libourne
57 24 80 26

Type of vineyard: Family-owned since 1918. **Established:** Agricultural association since 1981. **Vine stocks:** Merlot Rouge, Cabernet Franc, Cabernet Sauvignon, Pressac. **Soil:** Chalky clay. **Exposure:** Plateau. **Average annual production in hectoliters:** 350.

Appellation: Graves de Vayres. **Types:** Red. **Technique:** Traditional. **Maturing:** In vats. **Alcohol content:** 12.3%. **Characteristics:** Young: rich, fresh and with the fruity taste of merlot, becoming rounder with age, with an intense bouquet. **Serving temperature:** 16 to 18°. **Served with:** Young: with white meat and poultry. Older: with red meat and cheese. **Vintages available in 89/90:** 1983, 1985, 1986, 1987, 1988.

Characteristics of vintages

1988: Rich and promising. **1987:** Will age well. **1986:** Tannic, good for keeping. **1985:** Excellent red, supple and fruity. Good keeping. **Other:** This vineyard also produces, under the appellation "Château de Barre", a red Bordeaux Supérieur and a white Bordeaux. Price range (pre-tax, ex-warehouse): between 20 and 30 F.F.
Sales volume: – Retail 100%.
Sales in France: 100%.

CHÂTEAU DE CHANTEGRIVE

Henri Lévêque
33720 Podensac
56 27 17 38 - Telex: 570 650 LEVECVIN

Type of vineyard: Family-owned. **Established:** 1966. **Number of employees:** 30. **Vine stocks:** White: Sémillon, Sauvignon and Muscadelle. Red: Cabernet Sauvignon, Merlot, Cabernet Blanc. **Soil:** Round quartz gravel and sand on chalky clay. **Exposure:** Full South. **Average annual production in hectoliters:** 3,500.

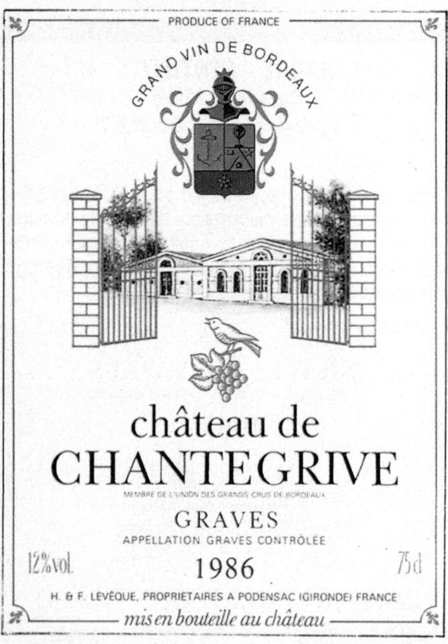

PRODUCE OF FRANCE
GRAND VIN DE BORDEAUX
château de
CHANTEGRIVE
GRAVES
APPELLATION GRAVES CONTRÔLÉE
12%vol.
1986
75cl
H. & F. LEVÊQUE, PROPRIETAIRES A PODENSAC (GIRONDE) FRANCE
mis en bouteille au château

Appellation: Graves Rouge, Graves Blanc. **Type:** Red, white. **Technique:** Traditional. **Maturing:** In oak casks (red). **Alcohol content:** 12%. **Characteristics:** Red: wild fruit, leather and vanilla aromas, touch of wood and spice, very fine. White: fine aromas, fresh, flowery and fruity. **Serving temperature:** White: 10°. Red: 17°. **Served with:** White: fish, shellfish. Red: grilled meat, game, roasts, poultry. **Vintages available in 89/90:** White: 1987 and 1988. Red: 1984, 1985, 1986, 1987, 1988.

Characteristics of vintages

1988: Red: exceptional year. **1987:** Red: very successful for a minor year. Wines matured in new casks have a beautiful color, a superb nose and a vanilla and fruity flavor. White: pitted fruit and Sauvignon fragrance, excellent evolution, explosive finish. **1986:** Fruity, soft and full, tannic, supple and well balanced. **1985:** Finesse, deep red color, complex bouquet (mulberry, spices and vanilla) very well balanced, good keeping. Price range (pre-tax, ex-warehouse): 30 to 60 F.F.

Sales volume:
– Wholesale: 80%. – Retail: 10%. – Restaurants: 10%.
Sales in France: 30%.
Export sales: 70%.
Main trading partners : Japan, Belgium, USA, Germany.

Characteristics of vintages

Restaurants: Maxim's, Le Ritz, Pavillon Élysée, Le Ciel de Paris, Paris Hilton, Trianon Palace.
Shops: Caves Estève (10, rue de la Cerisaie, Paris 4th), L'Amour du Vin (94, rue Saint-Dominique, Paris 7th).

Abroad

United States
Seagram Château Estate Wines, New York 375 Park Avenue.

Germany
Firme d.c., lessingstr 42 d 6238 Hoffeim – Tel: (06192) 22726.

Switzerland
Shenk S.A. 1180 Rolle – Tel: 021/825 1714.

Belgium
Sprl Vermeiren 8, Place du Chat Botté, Brussels – Tel: 02/3749033.

Comments

The Château de Chantegrive, one of the largest wine-making establishments in the Graves region, owes its name to a sparrow well known in Bordeaux: the "grive musicienne" (song thrush). This bird, which by instinct and gluttony, invades the vineyard at harvest time to enjoy the seeds of the sundrenched grapes, is particularly well known on the well exposed hillsides of the property, and is responsible for the name Chantegrive (song of the thrush). The domain covers 80 hectares in the communes of Podensac, Illats and Virelade, on gravelly terraces formed by the Garonne during the Quatenary era. Thanks to the patient re-allocation of the terrain undertaken, for the last 20 years, by Mr. and Mrs. Henri Lévêque, Chantegrive has become one of the best equipped enterprises in the region, making use of the most modern vinification techniques without losing sight of tradition (methods of cultivation and production of wines).

CHÂTEAU BOYREIN

Jean Medeville & Fils
Roaillan 33410 Cadillac
56 62 65 80

Type of vineyard: Family-owned. **Number of employees:** 3. **Vine stocks:** Red: Cabernet Sauvignon 40%, Cabernet Franc 20%, Merlot 40% – White: Sauvignon 50%, Muscadelle 20%, Semillon 30%. **Soil:** Pebbles, gravel of various colors and coarse sand. **Average annual production in hectoliters:** 1,500.
Appellation: Red: Château Boyrein. White: Château Boy-

rein. **Type:** Red, white. **Technique:** Traditional, temperature control and destemming (for white). **Maturing:** In stainless steel tanks. **Alcohol content:** 12.4%. **Characteristics:** Red: rich, very well balanced and supple. White: hand harvested, very dry and fragrant. **Serving temperature:** Red: 17°. White: 7 to 8°. **Served with:** Red: red meat, game, cheese. White: fish, shellfish. **Vintages available in 89/90:** Red: 1985, 1986, 1987. White: 1988.

Characteristics of vintages

1988: White: exceptionally fragrant, vinified at very low temperature. **1987:** Red: clean, well made, beautiful bright and lively color. **1986:** Delicate, very good right now. **1985:** Very beautiful color, fruity aromas, very promising tannins. Price range (pre-tax, ex-warehouse): 20 to 30 F.F.
Sales volume:
– Wholesale: 80%. – Retail: 15%. – Restaurants: 5%.
Sales in France: 60%.
Export sales: 40%.
Main trading partners: USA, Belgium, Netherlands, Germany.

References in France

Restaurants: Oustau de Beaumanière (Baux-de-Provence), Bas-Bréau (Barbizon), Castiglionne & Concorde La Fayette (Paris).
Shops: Nicolas.

Abroad

United States
Direct Import Wine, Des Plaines (Illinois).

Germany
Ets Weigand Mainzer Strass 54, Bingen, Les Crus d'Origine, Kehl.

Belgium
Le Palais du Vin, Brussels. Huis Clerckx Tessenderlo.

The Netherlands
Ets Boomsma, Leeuwarden.

Far East
Japan: Hatta Shoten Ltd.

Others
Ets N & Paul Plum, Denmark. Patrick Callaghan, Dublin, Ireland. United Wine Import, Copenhagen, Denmark.

Comments

The Château Borein, former castle of the Lords of Gourgues and the Barons of Roaillan, is located on top of a gravelly hill. This privately owned 75 hectare domain, 40 of which are planted with grapevines, straddles two communes. While the Roaillan vineyard produces a very fragrant red Graves and a quality dry Graves, the Fargues vineyard turns out a dozen barrels of "Château Barbier" Sauternes. In the same winegrowing region, Jean Medeville's sons manage a vineyard of about 10 hectares, the Château Pessan, in the commune of Portes, as well as the château Fayau in the Premières Côtes region.

CLOS FLORIDÈNE

Denis & Florence Dubourdieu
Château Reynon, Béguey 33410 Cadillac
56 62 96 51 – Telex: REYNON 573 023

Type of vineyard: Family-owned. **Established:** 1982. **Vine stocks:** Sauvignon 20%., Sémillon 80%. **Soil:** Chalky clay. **Average annual production in hectoliters:** 225.

Appellation: Graves Blanc Sec. **Type:** White. **Technique:** Fermentation in barrels. **Maturing:** In barrels, on lees. **Alcohol content:** 12.6%. **Characteristics:** Fruity, rich and well balanced, good keeping. **Serving temperature:** 16°. **Served with:** Fish. **Vintages available in 89/90:** 1988.

Characteristics of vintages

1988: Intense fruity aroma, smoky touch, very tasty. **1987:** Depleted. **1986:** Depleted. **1985:** Depleted. Price range (pre-tax, ex-warehouse): 30 to 50 F.F.
Sales volume:
– Wholesale: 15%. – Retail: 15%. – Restaurants: 10%. – Other: 60% (export).
Sales in France: 40%.
Export sales: 60%.
Main trading partners: Belgium, Netherlands.

Abroad

Germany
Spezialitaten Kontor – Mr. Schiechel, Berlin.

Switzerland
Sordet, Gevena.

Belgium
Ets Velu Vins, Brussels.

Canada
Reserve & Selection, Montreal (Mr. Parent).

The Netherlands
Kerstens, Tilburg.

Others

Denmark: Hansen, Postbox 927, Odense.

Comments

The Clos Floridène is a small 6 hectare estate, located at Pujols-sur-Ciron, near Barsac in the Graves appellation. On a single parcel, surrounded by a wall, with its old residence and its winecellar, the vineyard was recently reconstituted, starting in 1982, by Denis and Florence Dubourdieu, who are also proprietors of the Château Reynon at Béguey.

CHÂTEAU MAGENCE

Dominique Guillot de Suduiraut
Saint-Pierre-de-Mons 33210 Langon
56 63 19 34 – Telex: 541 298 F Sicalan

Type of vineyard: Agricultural Association. **Established:** 1780 – Association since 1978. **Vine stocks:** White: Sauvignon 50%, Sémillon 50%, Red: Cabernet Sauvignon 40%, Cabernet Franc 30%, Merlot 30%. **Soil:** deep siliceous gravel. **Exposure:** plateau.

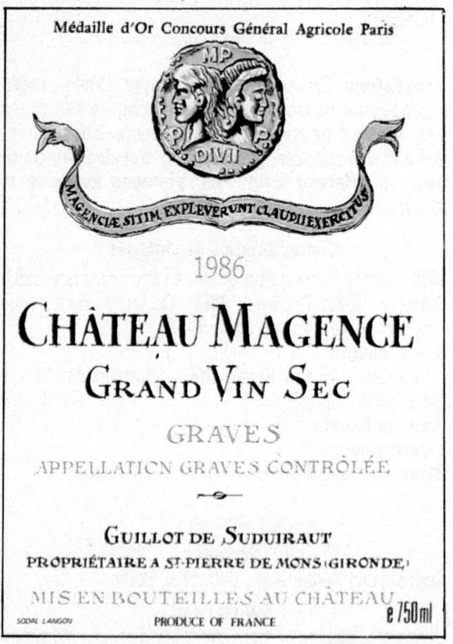

Type: Red, White. **Technique:** a good combination of tradition and modern techniques. **Maturing:** in stainless steel tanks. **Characteristics:** The winemaker tries to maintain the natural qualities of the grapes at their best in order to obtain wines which well represent the region. **Serving temperature:** White: 10°, Red: 17-18°. **Served with:** White Graves: smoked salmon. **Vintages available in 89/90:** White: 1984-1985-1986, Red: 1984-1985-1986.

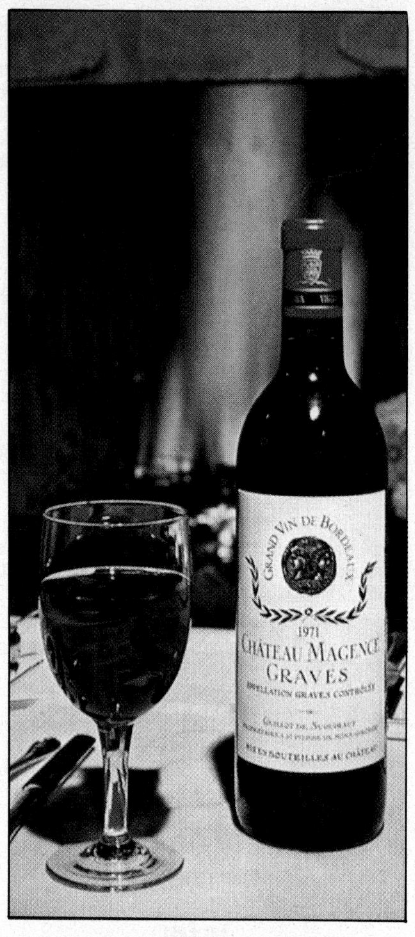

Characteristics of vintages

1986: White: dry, firm and full, rich ripe fruit bouquet, Red: comparable in quality to the 1985, with richer tannins. **1985:** Red: vigorous and fleshy, intense fruity tannins, to be aged. White: good, aromatic intensity, full and lond. **Other: 1984:** Red: fine, pleasant bouquet, very supple, balanced, vigorous and delicate. White: the aroma of fine Sauvignon, firm and vigorous but not green, good length.
Sales volume: – Wholesale: 50%. – Retail: 20%. – Restaurants: 15%. – Other: 15% (winecellars).
Sales in France: 50%.
Export sales: 50%.
Main trading partners : Japan, USA, Netherlands.

References in France

Restaurants: Lucas Carton, Taillevent, Jean Bardet, Jacques Cagna, Olympe, Guy Savoy, Saint James, Les Pyrénées, Pavillon de l'Élysée, Claude Darroze, Beauvilliers, Jean Ramet, Le Centenaire, La Chamade, Tan Dinh, La Maison Blanche etc.

Shops: Ste Millesimes, Œntoheque, Caves de La Madeleine, Ets. Lenotre, Maison de la Truffe, Caves Royales.

Abroad

United States

World Wide Wines, 155 School House Road, Cheshire Ct, 06410 Tel: (203) 272 2980.

The Netherlands

Gedistelleerd en Wijngroep, Nederland B.V. 2700 AE Zoetermeer.

Far East

Japan: Meidi-Ya Company LTD., 2-8 Kyobashi, 2 Chome, Chuo-Kiu, Tokyo 104 – Tel: 271 1111.

Comments

Creation of an association by D. Guillot de Suduiraut together with other winegrowers of the Langon region (Graves) for wines distribution.
Address: SICA Les Vignobles de Bordeaux, BP 114, St-Pierre-de-Mons - 33212 Langon Cedex. Tél: 56 63 19 34. Telex: 541 298 F.

CHÂTEAU DE MAUVES

Bernard Bouche
25, rue François Mauriac
33720 Podensac
56 27 17 05

Type of vineyard: Family-owned. **Established:** 1859. **Vine stocks:** Red: Cabernet Sauvignon 70%, Merlot 30%, White: Sémillon. **Soil:** Gravel on miocene sub-soil. **Exposure:** South, South-West. **Average annual production in hectoliters:** 45 hl/ha.
Appellation: Graves. **Type:** Red, White. **Technique:** traditional, temperature control. **Maturing:** In vats. **Alcohol content:** 12% on the average. **Characteristics:** Red: complex bouquet, tannic structure, full, well balanced. White: light color, very flowery, fruity, firm and vigorous. **Serving temperature:** Red: 17°. White: 8 to 10°. **Served with:** Red: practically with the entire meal and in particular with red meat. White: fish and shellfish and as an aperitif. **Vintages available in 89/90:** Red: 1985,1986,1987. White: 1988.

Characteristics of vintages

1988: White: light color, very flowery, fruity, firm and vigorous. **1987:** Red: rather well structured wine. To be drunk within 5-6 years. **1986:** Red: ruby color, complex bouquet, tannic structure, full-bodied, well balanced. Price range (pre-tax, ex-warehouse): 20 to 30 F.F.
Sales volume:
– Retail: 90%. – Restaurants: 10%.
Sales in France: 95%.
Export sales: 5%.
Main trading partners : Switzerland, Belgium.

References in France

Restaurants: Le Grand Écuyer (Cordes 81170), La Tanière (Bayonne 64100), Les 2 Platanes (Grenoble 38000), Le Colvert (Nantes 44000), La Taquetière (Thun 59158), Le Cheval Blanc (Changé 72560).

Abroad

Switzerland

Ets Darmon & Cie, Chemin de la Tour Champel, 1206 Geneva.

Comments

The Château de Mauves vineyard, one of the oldest in the region, is located at the center ot the Podensac territory, on particulary well exposed gravelly hillsides. Operated by the Moreau family since 1859, it was acquired in 1965 by Bernard Bouche, winemaker from the Oran region.

CHÂTEAU GRAVA-LACOSTE

Anne Marie Leglise
33210 Bommes
56 63 63 58

Type of vineyard: Family-owned. **Vine stocks:** Merlot 95%. **Soil:** Gravelly. **Average annual production in hectoliters:** 50.
Appellation: AOC Graves. **Type:** Red. **Technique:** Destemming, temperature control. **Maturing:** In stainless steel tanks. **Characteristics:** Supple, ripe fruit aroma, ele-

gant. **Serving temperature:** 17°. **Served with:** Meat, cheese. **Vintages available in 89/90:** 1986-1988.

Characteristics of vintages

1988: Very promising – rich and tannic. **1986:** Very successful.

CHÂTEAU PICHON BELLEVUE

Daniel Reclus
33870 Vayres
57 74 84 08

Type of vineyard: Family-owned. **Established:** 1873. **Number of employees:** 5. **Vine stocks:** Sémillon 55%, Sauvignon 25%, Muscadelle 20%, Merlot Rouge 60%, Cabernet Franc 20%, Cabernet Sauvignon 20%... **Soil:** Gravelly and silica. **Exposure:** Plateau (slightly hilly). **Average annual production in hectoliters:** Red 700. White 500.

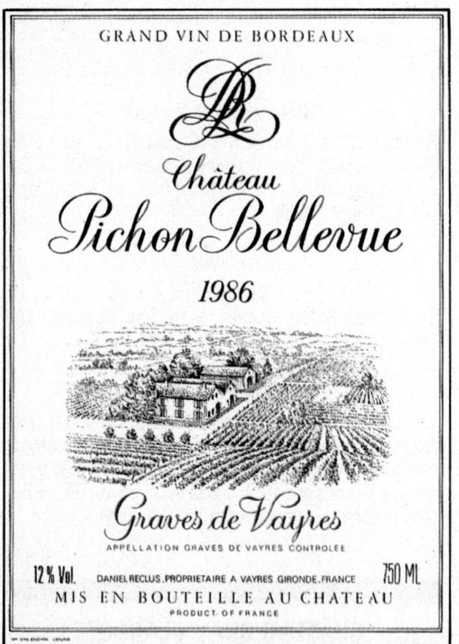

Appellation: Graves de Vayres. **Type:** Red, white. **Technique:** Red: traditional. White: low temperature. **Maturing:** white (6 months). Red (18 months). **Alcohol content:** 12%. **Characteristics:** White: fresh and fruity, dry, very typical. Red: well colored, pronouced bouquet combining finesse and balance. **Serving temperature:** White: 6 to 8°. Red: 16-18°. **Vintages available in 89/90:** White: 1988, 1989. Red: 1986-87-88.

Characteristics of vintages

1988: White: very fresh, aromatic, supple and round. **1987** Red: well balanced, supple. **1986:** Red: rich and well balanced, pronounced bouquet. Price range (pre-tax, ex-warehouse): 10 to 20 F.F. Red and White.

Sales volume:
– Wholesale: 30%. – Retail: 62%. – Restaurants: 5%. – Other: 3% (cellars).

Sales in France: White: 30%. Red: 85%.
Export sales: White: 70%. Red: 15%.
Main trading partners: Germany, UK, USA, Belgium, Canada.

Comments

Continuing a tradition as a stopover on the Imperial Bordeaux-Lyon road, the Château de Vayres (historical monument of the 15th century) has today becom a gastronomic al shrine. This former property of Henry IV, which was one of the principal fortresses of the Aquitaine, with its French gardens extending to the Dordogne, should not he missed.

For any suggestions or criticisms, please don't hesitate to write to us at:

THE BEST FRENCH WINES

Gilles Temime
14, rue Rennéquin - 75017 Paris
Tél. (1) 46 22 22 18

CHATEAU PIRON

Mr. Paul Boyreau
Piron - Saint-Emilion
33650 Labrède
56 20 25 61

Vine stocks: 1/2 Sauvignon, 1/2 Sémillon. **Soil:** Chalky and gravelly. **Average annual production in hectoliters:** 900.

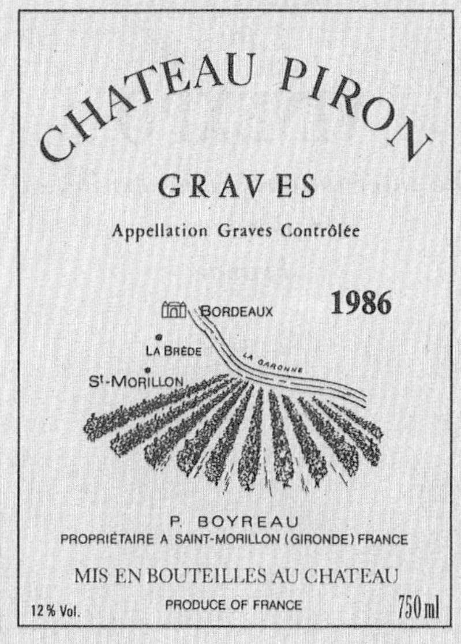

Appellation: Graves. **Type:** Red, white. **Technique:** Traditional. **Maturing:** Traditional. **Alcohol contents:** 12%. **Characteristics:** White: fruity and long. Red: Delicate and fragrant. **Served with:** White: fish, delicatessen. **Vintages available in 89/90:** 1987, 1988.

Comments

Highly reputed for the quality its whites, the Château de Piron vineyard has belonged, for almost three centuries, to the same family which has looked after it with utmost care. Located on the gravelly and chalky slopes of the commune of St. Morillon, the domain extends over 20 hectares, 13 of which are which are devoted to the production of white wine. The superior quality vinestocks (1/2 Sémillon, 1/2 Sauvignon) and the attention paid to the vinification technique combine to produce top quality, dry, light and fruity Graves. The reds, which should not go unnoticed, are appreciated for their great finesse. This rather old vineyard yields wines, both white and red, with a remarkable ageing potential. The Château Piron wines which are mostly consumed abroad have greatly contributed to the high reputation of all Graves wines.

CHATEAU RESPIDE MEDEVILLE

Mr. Christian Medeville
33210 Preignac
(16) 56 63 27 59 and 56 63 37 11

Vine stocks: White: Sémillon 38%, Sauvignon 50%, Muscadelle 12% – Red: Merlot 48%, Cabernet Sauvignon 46%, Cabernet Franc 6%. **Soil:** Gravelly clay. **Exposure:** Very sunny – hill-crest.

Appellation: Graves. **Type:** Red, white. **Characteristics:** Wines of uniform quality due to excellent sun exposure (hill-crest). Red: beautiful deep color, full-bodied, well-balanced. Whites: much appreciated for their finesse and bouquet.

Comments

If Christian Medeville gave his name to this very old estate immortalized by François Mauriac, it is because, much before acquiring it, he had already brought his influence to bear. This 10 hectare vineyard yields wines of uniform quality, due mostly to its ideal location on a beautifully exposed gravelly clay hill-crest. Important drainage works have recently been undertaken to facilitate the evacuation of ground water. The wines, very marked by the vinestocks, will win you over, by their character and complexity. Mr. Medeville pays great attention to the vinification and ageing of his wines which have received a number of awards at the Salon agricole de Paris and are much appreciated in France as well as overseas.

DOMAINE DE SANSARIC

Abadie
33640 Castres - Gironde
56 67 03 17

Type of vineyard: Family-owned. **Established:** 1640. **Vine stocks:** Merlot 2/3, Cabernet, Cabernet-Sauvignon 1/3. **Soil:** Gravelly, chalky clay. **Exposure:** South-West, North. **Average annual production in hectoliters:** 200.

Appellation: Graves Rouge. **Type:** Red. **Technique:** In stainless steel tanks – destemming. **Maturing:** Aged for 18 months in new oak casks. **Alcohol content:** 12%. **Characteristics:** Rich, good keeping, dense flowery aromas, supple, seductive. **Serving temperature:** 14 to 16°. **Vintage available in 89/90:** 1983, 1985, 1986.

Characteristics of vintages

Price range (pre-tax, ex-warehouse): 20 to 30 F.F.
Sales volume:
– Wholesale: 75%. – Retail: 25%.
Sales in France: 99%.
Export sales: 1%.
Main trading partners : Belgium.

Comments

Small estate, reconstituted since 1958. The vines and the wines are well cared for and production is more for pleasure than profit, with due respect to traditional value.

LE LIBOURNAIS

FRONSAC

CLOS DU ROY

Philippe Hermouet
33141 Saillans
57 74 38 88

Type of vineyard: Family-owned. **Vine stocks:** Merlot 90%, Cabernet Franc 10%. **Soil:** Chalky clay on chalk. **Average annual production in hectoliters:** 250. **Appellation:** Fronsac. **Type:** Red. **Technique:** Hand harvesting, partial destemming, long fermentation on skins. **Maturing:** In vats, bottled after 30 months. **Characteristics:** Rich and well balanced, roundness thanks to the Merlot, tannic due to vinification and maturing techniques – great classical Bordeaux. **Serving temperature:** 17°. **Served with:** Red and white meat. **Vintages available in 89/90:** 1983, 1985, 1986, 1987.

1988: Very beautiful year, perfect maturity, complex wines. **1987:** Successful year thanks to the Merlot vinestocks, which mature earlier than the Cabernet and can thus be harvested at its best. **1986:** Supple and well balanced thanks to the Merlot, very long keeping. **1985:** Full-bodied and firm, a wine that must be aged. **Other:** 1983: tile-red color, complex bouquet for the vintage, typical, rich and very well balanced. Price range (pre-tax, ex-warehouse): 30 to 50 F.F.

Sales volumes:
– Retail: 75%. – Restaurants: 10%. – Other: 15 % industrial gifts.
Sales in France: 60%.
Export sales: 40%.
Main trading partners : Belgium, Luxemburg.

References in France

Restaurants: A number of restaurants in Paris and elsewhere in France.

Comments

The quality of these wines depends not only on the vinification but also on the rigorous care of the wines and the soil, no use of chemical herbicides, very limited fertilization, relatively unproductive grafting stocks and severe pruning to limit yields.

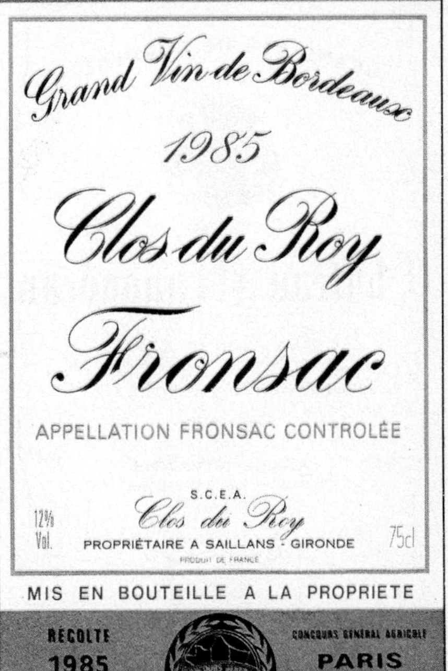

• *Glycerine – wine component responsible for its unctuosity. It appears in the course of the alcoholic fermentation but, in the case of mellow and naturally sweet wines, can also come from the favorable action of noble rot on the grapes. See Sauternes.*

CHÂTEAU MAGONDEAU
CHÂTEAU MAGONDEAU BEAU SITE

Mr & Mrs. André Goujon
Saillans 33141
57 84 32 02

Type of vineyard: Family-owned. **Number of employees:** 7. **Vine stocks:** Merlot, Cabernet, Bouchet. **Soil:** Chalky clay. **Average annual production in hectoliters:** 900.

Appellation: Fronsac. **Type:** Red. **Technique:** Magondeau: aged in bulk. **Maturing:** Magondeau Beau Site: aged in new oak casks. **Alcohol content:** 12,5%. **Characteristics:** Typical, full-bodied, fruity and tannic. **Serving temperature:** 16 to 17°. **Served with:** Red meat, game, cheese. **Vintages available in 89/90:** Beau Site: 1985, 1986, 1987.

Characteristics of vintages

1987: Silver and Bronze Medal at the Concours Agricole de Paris, 1989. Very pleasant, easy to drink, goes down well. **1986:** Very fruity, already very pleasant, will be ready for drinking soon. Beau Site: excellent wine, velvety texture, deserves to be aged long enough to bring out all of the value acquired during its stay in the cask. **1985:** Beau Site: maturing in new oak casks gives this wine, made from sun drenched grapes, its noble character and tannins. It will age very well. Price range (pre-tax, ex-warehouse): 30 to 40 F.F.

Sales in France: 70%.
Export sales: 30%.
Main trading partners : Belgium, Germany.

References in France

Restaurants: Astier, (Paris), Taverne Basque, Le Limons, Au cochon d'or des Halles.
Shops: Le Marché du Vin.

Others

Cellars.

CHATEAU PUY GUILHEM

Mrs Janine Mothes
33141 Saillans
57 84 32 08

Type of vineyard: Family-owned. **Established:** 18th century. **Vine stocks:** Merlot, Cabernet, Malbec. **Soil:** Chalky clay. **Exposure:** Sunny – slopes and terraces.

Appellation: Fronsac. **Technique:** Natural – hand harvesting, long fermentation on skins, destemming (80%). **Maturing:** In vats and casks. **Characteristics:** Forthcoming and well bred. Vinification carried out with care and total respect for the soil. This Fronsac cru is a wine of tradition as well as a winemaker's wine. It acquires, with age, a delicate and distinguised bouquet. The numerous rewards obtained in various national competitions testify to its quality.

Characteristics of vintages

1986: Harmonious, promising. **1985:** Rich and fortcoming, beautiful tannins, red fruit flavor, long ageing potential – Paris Gold medal. **Other:** 1981: Bronze medal (Blaye) - 1983, 1982, 1979: Silver medal (Paris) - 1978: Gold medal (Paris).

Comments

The Château Puy Guilhem is located in the heart of the Bordeaux vineyard. Family estate since the 18th century, it overlooks the right bank of the l'Isle valley, 7 kms from Libourne, offering the visitor a breathtaking panorama.

CHÂTEAU VILLARS

Jean-Claude & Brigitte Gaudrie & Sons.
33141 Saillans
57 84 32 17

Established: 6th generation. **Number of employees:** 8. **Vine stocks:** 70% Merlots Noirs, 20% Cabernets Francs, 10% Cabernets Sauvignons. **Soil:** Chalky clay on chalk with asteriated opal. **Exposure:** Hillsides South-West. **Average annual production in hectoliters:** 6, 000 to 8, 000 cases of 12 bottles.

Appellation: Fronsac. **Type:** Red. **Technique:** In closed vats, temperature control, frequent pumping over. **Maturing:** Oak casks, chosen and renewed from the 3 best coopers. **Alcohol content:** 12.5%. **Characteristics:** Round, full bodied, beautiful balance, great complexity. To be kept 15 to 30 years. **Serving temperature:** 17 to 18°. **Served with:** Game, roast beef. **Vintages available in 89/90:** 1984, 1986, 1987.

Characteristics of vintages

1988: Elegant, majestic, very fine tannins, for keeping. **1987:** More supple, quite long, raspberry aroma, vanilla after taste. **1986:** Superb maturity of the Cabernets Francs and Sauvignons, wines for long keeping. **1985:** Graceful and distinctive balance between the oak and mature tannins. Price range (pre-tax, ex-warehouse): between 30 and 80 F.F.

Sales volume:
– Wholesale: 35%. – Retail: 50%. – Restaurants: 5%.
– Other: 10% winecellars.
Sales in France: 75%.
Export sale: 25%.
Main trading partners : United States, United Kingdom, Belgium, Netherlands, Luxemburg, Germany, Iceland, Japan, Switzerland.

References in France

Restaurants: Tour d'Argent, Taillevent, Vedel, Le Vivarois (Paris), Au Vieux Couvent (Rhinau), La Briqueterie (Épernay).
Shops: The cellars of Taillevent, Legrand, Estève, Galéries Gourmandes, Fief de Vignes, Caves Beffroi and Caves Tissandier.

Comments

For six generations, the same family has devoted itself to winemaking at the Château Villars.
– 1958: first bottling – 1978: first maturing in new casks
– 1907: Gold Medal at Anvers (proprietor, grandfather Octave Trocard).
Since, 18 medals, 8 of which were gold, have testified to the quality of the wines.

CHÂTEAU DE LA RIVIÈRE

J. Borie
B.P. 2 – 33126 St-Michel-de-Fronsac
57 24 98 01 – Telex: 560 761

Type of vineyard: Family-owned/Association since 1962. **Established:** In 769, by Charlemagne. **Number of employees:** 23. **Vine stocks:** 60% Merlot, 30% Cabernet Sauvignon, 5% Cabernet Franc Pressac. **Soil:** Clay with limestone (44 ha). **Exposure:** Full South. **Average annual production in hectoliters:** 2,000 to 2,500. **Appellation:** Fronsac. **Type:** Red. **Technique:** Traditional, thermo-processing and concentration. **Maturing:** Barrels. **Alcohol content:** 12.5° to 13°. **Vintages available in 89/90:** 1979, 1980, 1981, 1982, 1983, 1984, 1985, 1986.

Characteristics of vintages

1986: Promising vintage. **1985:** Beautiful wine, solid and rich color and aroma, ages well. **1984:** No savor. **1983:** Excellent, full, elegant, a combination of rich and well-balanced, with beautiful, fine subtle tannis, to be aged. Prices available upon request.
Sales volume:
– Wholesale: 2% for french restauration. – Retail: 10%.
– Other: 88% (export).
Sales in France: 12%.
Export sales: 88%.
Main trading partners : Switzerland, Denmark, Belgium, Holland, UK, Ivory Coast, Cameroun, USA.

CANON-FRONSAC

CHÂTEAU MAZERIS BELLEVUE

Jacques Bussier
St-Michel de Fronsac, 33126 Fronsac
57 24 98 19

Type of vineyard: Family-owned. **Established:** 1848. **Number of employees:** 2. **Vine stocks:** Cabernet Sauvignon 50%, Merlot Rouge 40%, Malbec 10%. **Soil:** Chalky clay on chalk banks with asteriated opal. **Exposure:** Hillsides, hard to work. **Average annual production in hectoliters:** 450.
Appellation: Canon Fronsac. **Type:** Red. **Technique:** In concrete tanks, temperature control by heat exchanger. **Maturing:** In vats, racking, every second month. **Alcohol content:** 12%. **Characteristics:** Full-bodied and tannic – astringent when young developing great finesse and bouquet with ageing and acquiring rather quickly a topaz glint. **Serving temperature:** 15° to 18° depending on the season. **Served with:** Red meat, game, cheese. **Vintages available in 89/90:** 1983, 1984, 1985, 1986, 1987, 1988.

Characteristics of vintages

1988: Very tannic, will be long in developing, to be kept. **1987:** Rich in bouquet and fruit, perfectly controlled vintage. **1986:** Typical, firm and full-bodied, to be kept. **1985:** Tannic and elegant. Should be kept. **Other:** 1984: seductive, successful, ready now 1983: tannic, full-bodied, elegant, ready. Price range (pre-tax, ex-warehouse): 20 to 30 F.F.
Sales volume:
– Wholesale: 50%. – Retail: 40%. – Restaurants: 10%.
Sales in France: 60%.
Export sales: 35%.
Main trading partners : Belgium, UK, USA, Germany, Netherlands, Denmark, Switzerland.

References in France

Restaurants: Taillevent (Paris).
Shops: L'Amour du Vin, Caves des Vignerons (Bougival), Centre de Distribution de Vins de Propriétés (75018 Paris), Caves Taillevent (Paris).

Abroad

United States

Cellar Masters, San Francisco California 94107 – Lema Wine Company 120 Se Market Street, Portland, Oregon 97214 – Prestige Wine 25 West 39th St, Suite 808, New York 10018 – Consolidated Distilled Products Inc. Chicago etc.

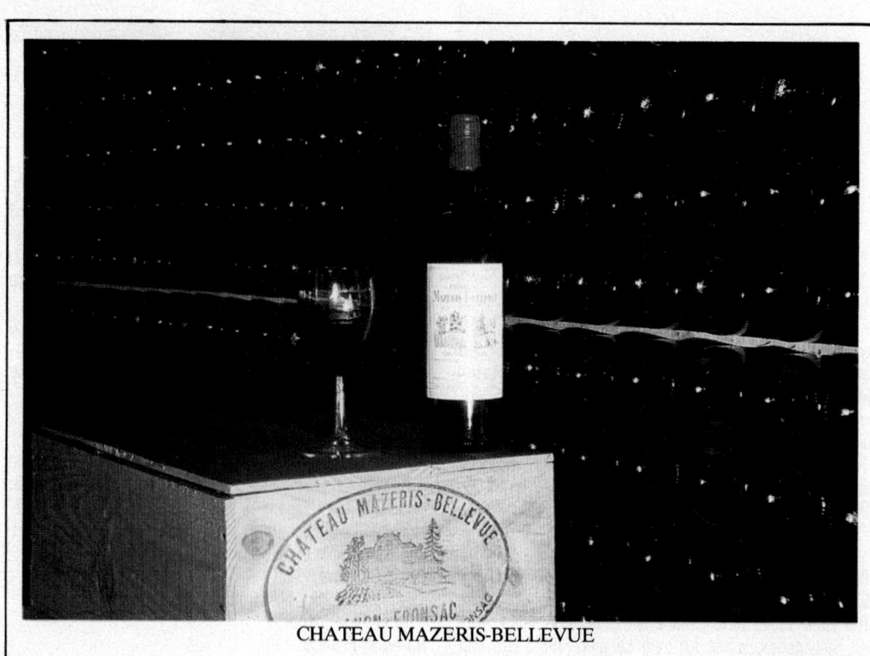

CHATEAU MAZERIS-BELLEVUE

Saint-Michel-de-Fronsac

33126 FRONSAC – Téléphone : 57 24 98 19

United Kingdom

Bon Wine Vaults LTD, London Eca M 9 DO – Hourlier Quality Wines 390 Burton Road Derby de 3 6AD etc.

Germany

Les Crus d'Origine Wein Import West Strasse D 7640 Kehl Am Rhein – Hotel Landhaus Hopen 3043 Schneverdingen.

Switzerland

Les Crus d'Origine 25 av. Juste Olivier Lausanne.

Belgium

Chais et Entreposts du Nord St Franciscustraat 3840 Oostende – Monard Pro-Vino rue a Lavallee 14 1080 Brussels.

The Netherlands

Rijkmans Lex Helling 16 9202 TR Drachten – Verkruijsen de Lagne Barkenessergracht 25 20 2000 Al Haarlem.

Others

Denmark: DZ Wine Milleparken 34 DK 2730 Herley-Vinlager Egegardesvej 43 DK 8900 Renders – Guildbrandt Avangen 67 5750 Ringe.

Comments

The Domaine de Mazeris-Bellevue was created by combining various parts of the old Mazeris landholding, famous for as long as one can remember for the production of delicate wines. It has become a model vineyard where all of the winegrowing and winemaking progress has been put to use. In 1986 it was awarded the Gold Medal of the Ministry of Agriculture rewarding the best cultivated vineyards in the Libourne region. Child of the region, wine grower by birth and Vice-President of the Agricultural Association of the Libourne region, J. Bussier, great grandfather of the present proprietor, reconstituted and replanted the vineyard with discernment and made his wine under the best of conditions. Jacques Bussier continues in the family tradition with such success that his wines are excellent and sought after. Here one enjoys the view of one of the most beautiful panoramas to be found anywhere along the picturesque banks of the Dordogne.

• In 1985, the wines of the following regions received the A.O.C. (Appellation d'Origine Contrôlée) classification: Minervois, Coteaux-des-Baux, Coteaux-d'Aix-en-Provence, Coteaux-du-Lyonnais and Coteaux-du-Languedoc.

• Watch out for wines that lose their authenticity, most often because of carbonic maceration (see Roussillon, Southwest, Périgord...).

• Scandal in Saint-Émilion. To find out all about his appellation and the real quality of its wines, from the least pretentious to the greatest, see "Open Letter" in the Chapter on Bordeaux wines.

CHÂTEAU LA CHAPELLE LARIVEAU

Serge Ravat

57 24 97 27

Type of vineyard: Family-owned. **Vine stocks:** Merlot Rouge. **Soil:** Chalky clay. **Exposure:** Hillsides. **Average annual production in hectoliters:** 200.

Appellation: Canon Fronsac. **Type:** Red. **Technique:** Traditional. **Alcohol content:** 12.5%. **Characteristics:** Well made, elegant and fragrant – good keeping. **Serving temperature:** 15 to 18°. **Served with:** Red meat, cheese. **Vintages available in 89/90:** 1985.

Characteristics of vintages

1985: Excellent, good keeping. Price range (pre-tax, ex-warehouse): 30 to 50 F.F.

Sales volume:

– Wholesale: 50%. – Retail: 40%. – Restaurants: 10%.

Sales in France: 100%.

References in France

Restaurants: Les Platanes (Etambiers), Le Chanteclair (13 rue du Versoix, Ferney Voltaire 01210), Les Chaumes (route de Monclar, 82000 Montauban).

Comments

Traditional enterprise, passed down from father to son. The grapes are harvested by hand, then vinified with care and aged in oak casks.

CHÂTEAU CASSAGNE HAUT CANON

Jean Jacques Dubois
33126 St Michel de Fronsac
57 51 63 98

Type of vineyard: Family-owned. **Established:** 1956. **Number of employees:** 3. **Vine stocks:** Merlot, Cabernet Franc, and Sauvignon. **Soil:** Pebbly and shallow on a base of fossil-bearing chalk and sandstone. **Exposure:** All directions. **Average annual production in hectoliters:** 400.

Appellation: Canon Fronsac. **Type:** Red. **Technique:** Control of fermentation, long maceration. **Maturing:** In oak vats (15 to 18 months). **Alcohol content:** 12%. **Characteristics:** Character, personality and elegance, typical product of the exceptionnal Canon Fronsac soil. Beautiful ruby color, very fruity, long keeping. **Serving temperature:** 16 to 18°. **Served with:** Red meat, game, cheese. **Vintages available in 89/90:** 1984, 1985, 1986, 1987 (in 1990).

Characteristics of vintages

1987: Beautiful color, very fine, very fruity. **1986:** Robust, fruity, well balanced, with the vigor of long keeping wines (Paris Silver Medal). **1985:** Beautiful tannins, very fine, fruity nose, combining richness with finesse and elegance. Price range (pre-tax, ex-warehouse): 20 to 30 F.F. – 30 to 50 F.F.

Sales volume:
– Wholesale: 15%. – Retail: 75%. – Restaurants: 10%.
Sales in France: 85%.
Export sales: 15%.
Main trading partners: Belgium, Netherlands, Switzerland.

References in France

Restaurants: Le Delphin (Nantes), Le Lion d'Or (Gramat), Le Lion d'Or (Port Marly), Le Chêne Vert (St Pourçain), Le Plaisance and l'Otelin (St Emilion).
Shops: Vins Guillot (St. Etienne), Maison André Perrin (Vouvray).

Abroad

Switzerland

Le Parc Eaux Vives, Geneva – Maison Scherer, Geneva.

Belgium

Rodrigues, Zele.

The Netherlands

Idee 10 (Wijnen), Teteringen.

Comments

The estate was a hunting lodge of the Duc de Richelieu. Here, there is a strong attachment to traditional methods of cultivation and maturing in oak casks, taking advantage nevertheless of the progress in winemaking techniques, in particular with respect to the control of the fermentation process (fining with egg whites before bottling). This leads to the production of good keeping, typical wines, with enough character to be drunk young.

POMEROL

CHÂTEAU CERTAN DE MAY DE CERTAN

Mrs. Barreau-Badar
Pomerol 33500 Libourne
57 51 41 53

Type of vineyard: Family-owned. **Vine stocks:** Merlot 65%, Cabernet Franc 25%. Cabernet Sauvignon 5%, Malbec 5%. **Soil:** gravelly clay. **Exposure:** South-East (Pomerol plateau). **Average annual production in hectoliters:** 180.
Appellation: Pomerol. **Type:** Red. **Technique:** Tradition in small stainless steel tanks. **Maturing:** in casks. **Characteristics:** Aromatic, velvety texture, long, round, complex, pronounced bouquet. **Serving temperature:** 16 to 17°. **Served with:** Red meat, game, sauces. **Vintages available in 89/90 :** 1983, 1984, 1986.

Characteristics of vintages

1987: Very round, very pleasant, grape flavor, to be consumed in 2-3 years. **1986:** Elegant, supple, rich tannins, full bodied. **Other:** 1984: Grape aroma, very round, and very pleasant, ready now but be kept very long. **1983:** Atypical, very ripe harvesting, full-bodied and forthcoming. Price range (pre-tax, ex-warehouse): over 160 F.F.
Sales volume:
– Wholesale: 60%. – Retail: 35%. – Restaurants: 5%.
Sales in France: 30%.
Export sales: 70%.
Main trading partners : USA, Belgium, UK, Germany.

Abroad

Belgium
De Brabandère - 8781 Wielsbeke. Seagram Chateau & Estate New York.

- *Paulée – traditional meal which brings winelovers and winegrowers together after the harvest, particularly in Burgundy.*

- *To better understand the evolution and adherence to type of the various vintages, consult our "Vintage Code" chart.*

Château Certan de May de Certan - Pomerol

VIEUX CHÂTEAU CERTAN

Alexandre Thienpont
Pomerol 33500 Libourne
57 51 17 33

Type of vineyard: Family Association. **Established:** 1957. **Number of employees:** 5. **Vine stocks:** 50% Merlot, 25% Cabernet Franc, 20% Cabernet Sauvignon, 5% Malbecs. **Soil:** Gravelly clay on a sub-soil of iron clay. **Average annual production in hectoliters:** 450.
Appellation: Pomerol. **Technique:** Traditional, wooden vats and casks. **Maturing:** In casks. **Alcohol content:** 12.3%. **Characteristics:** Well-colored, rich, complete (see "Classification 89"). **Serving temperature:** 18°. **Vintages available in 89/90:** Exclusively sold as "primeur" in the Bordeaux market.

Characteristics of vintages

1988: Not yet tasted. **1986:** Superb wine, well-colored, full, will age beautifully. **1985:** Very great year, well-structured, for keeping.
Sales volume:
- Wholesale: 100%.

Sales in France: 60%.
Export sales: 40%.
Main trading partners : Belgium, United Kingdom, United States.

L'ÉGLISE CLINET

Denis Durantou
Pomerol - 33500 Libourne
57 51 79 83

Type of vineyard: Family Association Property. **Number of employees:** 3. **Vine stocks:** 70% Merlot, 20% Cabernet Franc, 10% Cot. **Soil:** Gravels and clay. **Average annual production in hectoliters:** 180.
Appellation: A.O.C. **Type:** Red. **Technique:** Long maceration during 3 weeks average, in tanks, cement, material of cooling. **Maturing:** In barrels (some 1/3 new) from 12 to 18 months. **Characteristics:** Red deep color, young year, fruity (even grapes); chocolate notes; tannic structure, dense, very present; complex nose after 12 months maturing in barrels. **Serving temperature:** Room temperature (16° to 18°). **Served with:** Poultry (pigeons, guinea-fowl), game (pheasant, hare, rabbit, not very high game), red meat.

Characteristics of vintages

1988: Perhaps a bit hard to describe. Harmonious, classical, presence of tannins, firm and aromatic (marked by the Pomerol Merlot). **1987:** Harmonious, easy to drink, yet dense with a pronounced liquorice and crystallized fruit aroma. This unjustly maligned vintage should age well. **1986:** Rich and complex tannins, fleshy, overripe harvest (low temperature vinification), more woody than other vi

tages but noticeable presence of ripe grape aromas. **1985:** Beautiful wine marked by the Merlot, full and good flavor.
Sales volume:
– Wholesale: 100%.
Sales in France: 15%.
Export sales: 85%.
Main trading partners: USA, Belgium, Great Britain, Switzerland.

CLOS DU PÈLERIN

Egreteau
Pomerol – 33500 Libourne
57 74 03 66

Type of vineyard: Family-owned. **Vine stocks:** 75% Merlot, 25% Cabernet Franc. **Soil:** Sandy with fine gravel. **Average annual production in hectoliters:** 120. **Appellation:** Pomerol. **Type:** Red. **Technique:** Traditional. **Maturing:** Oak casks. **Alcohol content:** 12°. **Characteristics:** Supple, meaty, sustained color, good capacity for ageing. **Serving temperature:** 16°. **Served with:** Red meat and cheese. **Vintages available in 89/90:** 1981, 1982, 1983, 1985 and 1986.

Characteristics of vintages

1986: A little like the standart '85, less dense, promising. **1985:** Very rich, robust and tannic, excellent vintage to be aged. **1984:** Very light. **1983:** Good year, still a little hard, must age more. **1982:** Excellent vintage, very rich and well-balanced, to be age. **1981:** Very good vintage. Price range (pre-tax, ex-warehouse): Between 50 F.F. and 80 F.F.
Sales volume:
– Retail: 100%.
Sales in France: 95%.
Export sales: 5%.

CLOS RENÉ

Pierre Lasserre & Jean-Marie Garde
33500 Pomerol
57 51 10 41

Type of vineyard: Family-owned 12 hectares. **Established:** Mid - 19th century. **Number of employees:** 8. **Vine stocks:** Merlot 60%, Cabernet Franc 30%, Malbec 10%. **Soil:** Sand and gravel on iron pan. **Average annual production in hectoliters:** 500. **Appellation:** AOC Pomerol. **Type:** Red. **Technique:** Traditional, in oak casks (25% new each year), fining with egg whites, bottled at the Château 2 years later. **Alcohol content:** 12.5%. **Characteristics:** Very pronounced bouquet (truffle) – elegant and subtle, generally full-bodied (depending on the year), but always supple – as a Pomerol should be. **Serving temperature:** 17 to 18° maximum. **Served with:** Grilled meat or roasts, cheese. Full-bodied vintages with red meat and game – lighter vintages with white meat. After a few years ageing, all of them with any type of cheese. **Vintages available in 89/90:** 1985, 1986, 1987.

Characteristics of vintages

1987: La maturité des Merlot a permis des vendanges précoces. Unis de qualité, aimables à boire, plaisants et souples. **1986:** Elegance and breed. Very classical year, well structured, rich and well balanced. **1985:** Very typical, a great year for Pomerol, richness and fullness derived from Merlot. Price range (pre-tax, ex-warehouse): autour de 85 F.F.
Sales volume:
– Wholesale: 90%. – Retail: 10%.
Main trading partners: Belgium, USA, UK, Netherlands, Switzerland, Germany.

Comments

The neighbouring estate of Château Moulinet-Lasserre (5 ha) is under the same ownership and management and produces wines of a similar character and quality.

• *The quality of the 1987 vintage, particularly in Bordeaux, is questionable. Much of the Merlot suffered from coulure and a good bit of the harvesting was done in the rain. Only a few vineyards will produce a good vintage (see the Chapter on Bordeaux wines and the "Vintage Code").*

CHÂTEAU LA "CROIX DE GAY" POMEROL

Noël Raynaud
33500 Libourne
57 51 19 05

Type of vineyard: Family-owned Association. **Number of employees:** 5. **Vine stocks:** Merlot 80%, Cabernet Franc and Sauvignon 20%. **Soil:** Clay and sandy gravel. **Exposure:** South, South-West. **Average annual production in hectoliters:** 500.

Appellation: Pomerol. **Type:** Red. **Technique:** In closed tanks with temperature control and maceration (1 month). **Maturing:** In casks. **Alcohol content:** 12 to 12.5%. **Serving temperature:** 16 to 18°. **Served with:** Meat, game and cheese. **Vintages available in 89/90:** 1984, 1985, 1986, 1987, 1988.

Characteristics of vintages

1988: Very great vintage, very promising. **1987:** Rather successful, well colored wines, fruity, supple. **1986:** Excellent wine, rich, well colored, dense and lingering. **1985:** Still a beautiful year – rich, structured, typical, very good development. Price range (pre-tax, ex-warehouse): 70 à 100 F.F.

Abroad

Others

Scandinavia (Sweden, Norway, Denmark). Belgium, U.S.A., Canada, Suisse.

Comments

For more than five generations, the vineyard of "La Croix de Gray" has been the property of the Raynaud family which has been linked to the beautiful area of Pomerol since time immemorial. We find reference to the "La Barrauderie" estate belonging to the Barraud brothers, ancestors of the Raynaud family as long ago as 1477. Mr. Barraud was one of the founding members of the Vinegrowers' Improvement Society in 1901. His grandson, Mr. Raynaud, the present owner, has actively participated in the creation of the brotherhood of "Les Hospitaliers de Pomerol". (See Classification 89).

CHÂTEAU L'ENCLOS

Mme Marc
Pomerol - 33500 Libourne
57 51 04 62

Type of vineyard: Creation in the last Century. **Vine stocks:** 80% Merlot, 19% Cabernet, 1% Malbec. **Soil:** Gravel, silica with gravel. **Average annual production in hectoliters:** 40 hectoliters/ha.
Appellation: Pomerol. **Type:** Red. **Technique:** Traditional. **Maturing:** Barrels. **Alcohol content:** 12%. **Characteristics:** Supple, fragrant. **Serving temperature:** Room temperature. **Served with:** Meat, poultry, "cepes" French mushrooms, cheese. **Vintages available in 89/90/** 1983, 1984, 1986.

Characteristics of vintages

1988: Forthcoming wine, round and supple, lovely bouquet. **1987:** Very successful, beautiful color and bouquet. **1985:** Rich and supple at the same time, fine tannins, ripe.

• *If you find that there are one or more elements missing, so that you are unable to contact a particular proprietor or importer, please write to us at the following address for additional information:*

Gilles Temime, Éditions Vintage,
14, rue Rennéquin - 75017 Paris.

CHÂTEAU L'ÉVANGILE
Mrs. Louis Ducasse
Pomerol 33500 Libourne
57 51 15 30

Type of vineyard: Agricultural Association. **Number of employees:** 8. **Vine stocks:** Merlot 65%, Cabernet Franc 35%. **Soil:** Sandy clay and gravel. **Exposure:** Pomerol high plateau. **Average annual production in hectoliters:** 450 to 500.

Appellation: Pomerol. **Type:** Red. **Technique:** Traditional. **Maturing:** In casks. **Characteristics:** Rich and well balanced, fruity and elegant. **Serving temperature:** Room temperature. **Served with:** Red meat, game, foie gras. **Vintages available in 89/90:** 1982, 1983, 1984, 1985, 1986.

Characteristics of vintages

1988: Maturing. **1987:** Well controlled vintage. **1986:** Deep color, distinguished, velvety texture, very long. **1985:**Exceptional, rich and well balanced, distinguished, ripe fruit fragrance. Price range (pre-tax, ex-warehouse): over 160 F.F.
Sales volume:
– Wholesale: 100%.
Main trading partners : USA, Germany, UK, Switzerland, Austria, Norway, Sweden.

Comments

In 1862, the property belonged to Mr. and Mrs. Paul Chaperon, who bequeathed it to their daughter Mrs. Louis Ducasse, great-grandmother of the present proprietors.

CHÂTEAU MOULINET
Mr. Armand Moueix
Pomerol – 33500 Libourne
57 51 50 63 – Telex: 541 635 AMOUEIX
Telefax: 57 25 22 14

Type of vineyard: Family-owned. **Established:** Since the 17th Century. **Vine stocks:** 60% Merlot, 30% Cabernet Sauvignon, 10% Cabernet Franc. **Soil:** Gravel and old sand. **Exposure:** Nothern slope of the Pomerol plateau. **Average annual production:** 7,500 cases.
Appellation: Pomerol. **Type:** Red. **Technique:** Destemming 90% to 95%. Vinification in concrete vats (2 to 3 weeks). **Maturing:** In Oak barrels, (one third new) for 18 months, fining with fresh egg whites. **Characteristics:** Deep color, combines the finess of flowery Cabernet with the elegance of the ripe fruit aromas of the Merlot, a vanilla touch. Harmonious, full and forthcoming, soft and velvety tannins. Delicate, should be left to mature, subtle, spicy and smoky overtones. **Serving temperature:** Room temperature 19° to 20°. **Vintages available in 89/90:** 1985, 1986, 1987.

Characteristics of vintages

1988: To summarize 1988's grape harvest, we can say that Merlots have produced very harmonious wines, intensely coloured, with very aromas, of exceptional body and very rich in excellent tannins. As regards Cabernets, harvested ten days or so after Merlots, a bright colour with shades of purple and a very well developed fragrance of blackcurrant. They have produced well-balanced and full-bodied wines. **1987:** Soft, well-balanced and full-bodied wines, with fruity aromas and an average tannic power. The wines can keep well, but will soon come to maturity. **1986:** Very deep color, rich in alcohol and well-balanced, very long, pleasant nose of ripe fruit. **1985:** Still young aromas, flowery and fruity, vanilla overtone, harmonious, full-bodied, balanced. **1983:** Deep ruby color, woody, soft and full. **1982:** Deep and bright color, very aromatic, fruity, smoky overtone, round, harmonious.

CHÂTEAU GOMBAUDE-GUILLOT

Laval
33500 Pomerol
57 51 17 40

Type of vineyard: Family Agricultural Association. **Established:** 1981 (creation of the association) – family estate for four generations. **Vine stocks:** Merlot 60%, Cabernet Franc 42%, Malbec 8%. **Soil:** Gravel on clay. **Exposure:** South-West. **Average annual production in hectoliters:** 230 hl/ha.

Appellation: Pomerol. **Type:** Red. **Technique:** Traditional in concrete tanks – long fermentation on skins (3/4 weeks). **Maturing:** In stainless steel tanks. **Alcohol content:** 12.5%. **Characteristics:** Rich and well balanced, tannic, developing with age a complex, rich and elegant bouquet. **Serving temperature:** 16 to 18° according to the vintage. **Served with:** Game, red meat, aged wines go very well with the finest dishes. **Vintages available in 89/90:** 1984, 1985, 1986, 1987.

Characteristics of vintages

1987: Clean careful harvesting of ripe grapes. A little light, a pleasant sweet wine from a minor year. **1986:** Charm and elegance, beautiful balance, round tannins and promising aromas. **1985:** Rich and full, full bodied, balanced, long and concentrated. **Other:** 1984 – quite successful for a minor year, rich and well balanced, very aromatic. Price range (pre-tax, ex-warehouse): 50 to 95 F.F.

Sales volume:
– Wholesale: 50%. – Retail: 40%. – Restaurants: 5%.
– Other: 5% (cellars).

Sales in France: 60%.
Export sales: 40%.
Main trading partners: USA, Switzerland, Belgium, Denmark, Germany.

References in France

Restaurants: Faugeron, L'Avant-Scène, la Giberne, Le Pain et le Vin (Paris), Dubern, St-James (Bordeaux), Le Grand Cœur (Meribel).
Shops: L'Impériale (Rueil-Malmaison), Le Jardin des Vignes, l'Amour du Vin (Paris), La Vinothèque (Bordeaux).

Abroad

United States
Robert Chadderson Selections. 30 Rockefeller Plaza Suite, 1920, 10020 New York City.

Germany
Weinimport Andresen und Jauch.

Switzerland
Jean-Pierre Mathieu, Trey Blanc, 6 1006 Lausanne.

Belgium
Maison Leroy Prevost – Roger Drapier.

Others
Denmark: New wine per Wilhem Pedersen Jeppe, Aakjaersvej 18, 3460 Birkerd.

Comments

A family estate for at least four generations, the Château Gombaude-Guillot belonged to Mme. S. Laval Darbeau up to 1981. At that time, a family agricultural association, which she manages, was created. Her daughter Claire is responsible for directing the vineyard. The Château Gombaude-Guillot is located right in the center of the appellation, facing the Pomerol Church, that is to say, on one of the best soils of the appellation. The average age of the vines (more than 35 years) as well as constant efforts to maintain quality explain the progress of the Château Gombaude-Guillot wines towards the heights of tasting pleasure. Remarkable, very successful 83 and 88 vintages.

CHÂTEAU DU DOMAINE DE L'ÉGLISE

Philippe Casteja – Madame Preben Hansen
86, Cours Balguerie-Stuttenberg
33300 Bordeaux
56 48 57 57 – Telex: 550 766

Vine stocks: 90% Merlot, 10% Cabernet Franc. **Soil:** Deep gravel of great quality surrounding the old Church. **Exposure:** In the heart of Pomerol – one of the best exposures. **Average annual production in hectoliters:** 250 to 300.
Appellation: Pomerol. **Type:** Red. **Technique:** Classic, long fermentation with skins followed by Prof. Ribereau-Gayon. **Maturing:** Oak casks. **Alcohol content:** 12% to 13%. **Characteristics:** Typical Pomerol, a great classic

with character, long, good bouquet, rich and abundant tannins, not hard, very velvety, but fragrant and aromatic, rich, ripe fruit. **Serving temperature:** 19° to 20°. **Served with:** Cheese and meat, in general, particularly game. **Vintages available in 89/90:** 1986 only.

Characteristics of vintages

Sales volume:
Wholesale: 100% Borie-Manoux. Wine Merchants.

CHÂTEAU HAUT TROPCHAUD

Michel Coudroy
Maison Neuve 33570 Montagne
57 74 62 23

Type of vineyard: Family-owned. **Established:** Bought in 1987. **Vine stocks:** Merlot Rouge. **Soil:** Gravel and clay. **Exposure:** Plateau (Pomerol). **Average annual production in hectoliters:** 80.
Appellation: Pomerol. **Type:** Red. **Technique:** Traditional, long fermentation on skins. **Maturing:** In oak casks (new). **Characteristics:** Fragrant, velvety texture, inimitable blackcurrant flavor, reminiscent of Trotanoy, Certan, Pétrus. **Serving temperature:** 18°. **Served with:** Grilled meat, poultry, soft cheese. **Vintages available in 89/90:** 1987, 1988.

Characteristics of vintages

1988: Exceptional year – intense, beautiful tannic balance. **1987:** In new casks for 14 months and still far from its peak, should develop fully in 4 to 6 years. Price range (pre-tax, ex-warehouse): 50 to 80 F.F.

Comments

Acquired by Michel Coudroy in 1987, the vineyard is located in the heart of the Pomerol appellation, between the Château Trotanoy and the Vieux Château Certan, in the neighbourhood of the Château Pétrus.

• *To help us improve our next edition, please send in your suggestions and answer our questionnaire.*

• *The 1980 vintage is badly understood. In Bordeaux the wines are already quite surprising and will do quite well while waiting for the development of the other vintages. See "The last five vintages" in the Chapter on Bordeaux wines.*

• *Please note that all temperatures in this book are expressed in degrees Centigrade.*

CHÂTEAU "LA GANNE"

Michel Dubois
224 avenue Foch – 33500 Libourne
57 51 18 24

Type of vineyard: Family-owned. **Established:** 1925. **Number of employees:** 2. **Vine stocks:** Merlot, Cabernet Franc and Sauvignon. **Soil:** Gravel, iron clay. **Exposure:** South, South-West. **Average annual production in hectoliters:** 120.
Appellation: Pomerol. **Type:** Red. **Technique:** Fermentation control, long maceration. **Maturing:** In oak casks (15 to 18 months). **Alcohol content:** 12%. **Characteristics:** Great character, forthcoming, velvety texture, very elegant, deep ruby color. **Serving temperature:** 16 to 18°. **Served with:** Foie gras, white meat, cheese. **Vintages available in 89/90:** 1986, 1987 (in 1990).

Characteristics of vintages

1987: Well balanced, very fine, beautiful topaz color. **1986:** Robust, forthcoming, fruity, deep color (Paris Gold Medal). Price range (pre-tax, ex-warehouse): 30 to 50 F.F.
Sales volume:
– Wholesale: 15%. – Retail: 75%. – Restaurants: 10%.
Sales in France: 85%.
Export sales: 15%.
Main trading partners : Belgium, Netherlands, Switzerland.

References in France

Restaurants: Le Lion d'Or (Gramat), Le Plaisance and L'Otelin (Saint-Emilion), Le Chêne Vert (St Pourçain), Le Lion d'Or (Port Marly).
Shops: Vins Guillot (St Etienne), Vignerons de France (Strasbourg), Le Pressoir (Dinard).

Abroad

Switzerland

Maison Scherer, Geneva – Carouge (Tel: 41 22 43 67 12).

Belgium

Rodriguez, Zele.

The Netherlands

Idee 10 (Wijnen), Teteringen, Tel: 31 76 71 00 43.

Comments

In the family for several generations.

CHÂTEAU DE SALES

Bruno de Lambert
Château de Sales – Pomerol – 33500 Libourne
57 51 04 92

Type of vineyard: Agricultural Association (Family-owned). **Established:** In the same family for 5 and a half Centuries. **Number of employees:** 18. **Vine stocks:**

Merlot 70%, Cabernet Franc 15%, Cabernet-Sauvignon 15%. **Soil:** Sand and gravel – gravel with iron oxide. **Exposure:** terraces. **Average annual production in hectoliters:** 2,000.
Appellation: Pomerol. **Type:** Red. **Technique:** Traditional – fermentation with temperature control – fermentation with skins for 3 weeks. **Maturing:** Racking every three months withs rotation between barrels and vats. (2 to 7 years old barrels). **Alcohol content:** 12.5%. **Characteristics:** Pleasant, supple, round with good balance thanks to the Merlot and the sandy soil. Fruity aroma, scent of undergrowth and truffles with ageing. Pleasant when young, they reach full development after 5 to 15 years, depending on the vintages. Second-rank wines like Château Chantalouette and Château du Delias develop more quickly. **Serving temperature:** 18°. **Served with:** red meat, game, cheese.

Characteristics of vintages

1986: Fleshy, full soft and rich. Willage well. **1985:** Well-balanced, soft and rich. Must be aged. **1984:** Superior to the year's reputation. Will be pleasant in 2 years. **1983:** Distinguished, very good balance. To be kept. **1982:** Seductive, fleshy, already pleasant but full of promises. Price range (pre-tax, ex-warehouse): 80 F.F.-120 F.F.

CHÂTEAU MAZEYRES

Mrs. M. Boutet & M. Querre
56, av. Georges Pompidou, 33500 Libourne
57 24 65 15 - Telex: 571 895 F

Type of vineyard: Agricultural Association. **Established:** 1972. **Number of employees:** 6. **Vine stocks:** Merlot 66%, Cabernet Franc 33%. **Soil:** Sand and gravel. **Exposure:** Terraces, West of the Pomerol plateau. **Average annual production in hectoliters:** 450.

Appellation: Pomerol. **Type:** Red. **Technique:** In lined steel tanks. **Maturing:** In casks (50% new). **Alcohol content:** 12.5%. **Characteristics:** Very supple, finesse and elegance. **Serving temperature:** 17°. **Served with:** Red meat and game. **Vintages available in 89/90:** 1986, 1987.

Characteristics of vintages

1987: Good quality/price ratio. **1986:** Good development – already pleasant. Price range (pre-tax, ex-warehouse): 50 to 80 F.F.
Sales volume:
– Wholesale: 24%. – Retail: 10%. – Restaurants: 66%.
Sales in France: 75%.
Export sales: 25%.
Main trading partners : Belgium, Germany, Switzerland, Netherlands, UK, Denmark, USA.

References in France

Restaurants: In 80% of the great restaurants with Michelin stars.

Abroad

United States
Celliers de France, Los Angeles.

United Kingdom
Field Wine Merchant, London.

Germany
France Vinicole, Kiehl.

Switzerland
Société des Planteurs Réunis, Vevey.

Belgium
Velu Vins, Brussels.

CHÂTEAU TAILLEFER

Bernard & Jean-Michel Moueix
Pomerol – 33500 Libourne
57 51 50 63 – Telex: 541 635 AMOUEIX
Telefax: 57 25 22 14

Type of vineyard: Family-owned. **Established:** Bought by the Moueix family in 1923. **Vine stocks:** 55% Merlot, 30% Cabernet Franc, 15% Cabernet Sauvignon, 5% Malbec. **Soil:** Gravel and old sand over a thick layer of iron pan. **Exposure:** On the southern slope of the Pomerol plateau. **Average annual production in hectoliters:** 7,500 cases.
Appellation: Pomerol. **Type:** Red. **Technique:** Destemming (90 to 95%). Vinification in concrete vats (2 to 3 weeks). **Maturing** In Oak barrels (one third new) for 18 months, fining with fresh egg whites. **Characteristics:** Richness of color is their first characteristic. Balanced, rich in alcohol, aroma will develop after several years in the bottle, full-bodied, complex fragrances with animal, vegetal and balsamic overtones. Full flavor, very well-balanced, remains firm for a long time. **Serving temperature:** Room temperature 19° to 20°. **Vintages available in 89/90:** 1985, 1986, 1987.

Characteristics of vintages

1985: Subtle and delicate, good keeping. **1983:** Very soft, full, round, forthcoming, lots of body, pleasantly woody. **1982:** Deep and persistent aromas, very harmonious, forthcoming, smooth tannins, full.

CHÂTEAU BOURGNEUF-VAYRON

Charles & Xavier Vayron
"Bourgneuf" – 33500 Pomerol
57 51 42 03

Type of vineyard: Family-owned. **Established:** 1821. **Vine stocks:** Merlot 80%, Bouchet Franc 20%. **Soil:** Clay and chalky clay. **Exposure:** Hillsides – setting sun. **Average annual production in hectoliters:** 380.
Appellation: AOC Pomerol. **Type:** Red. **Technique:** Long fermentation on skins, temperature control. **Maturing:** In vats and casks. **Alcohol content:** 12.5%. **Characteristics:** Rich and well balanced, round, fruity, pronounced bouquet. **Serving temperature:** 17 to 18°. **Served with:** Red meat, game. **Vintages available in 89/90:** 1981, 1982, 1983, 1985, 1986 – later 1987 and 1988 not yet bottled.

Characteristics of vintages

1988: Excellent year, round fruity, beautiful color. **1987:** Quite full, pleasant, will develop rather rapidly. **1986:** Round, supple, full, beautiful color. **1985:** Full-bodied, lingering flavor, rich and well balanced, very aromatic, very beautiful color. **Other: 1982:** Great finesse, supple, lingering flavor, fruity, beautiful color. Price range (pre-tax, ex-warehouse): 50 to 80 F.F.
Sales volume:
– Wholesale: 70%. – Retail: 20%. – Restaurants: 10%.
Sales in France: 30%.
Export sales: 70%.
Main trading partners: USA, UK, Belgium, Germany.

References in France

Restaurants: "Les 3 Marches", (Versailles), Joël Robuchon, (Paris), La Côte St. Jacques, (Joigny), Le Coq Hardy, (Bougival), Beauvilliers, (Paris), Potager des Halles, (Paris), Relais Louis XIII, (Paris), Le Zinc, (Cergy-Pontoise), Guy Savoy, (Paris), etc.

Abroad

United States

Ets. Jean-Pierre Moueix, Libourne.

Comments

The 9 hectare vineyard, in a single parcel, has been the property of the Vayron family since 1821. Located in the center of the commune of Pomerol, on the hillside, facing the setting sun, it receives an optimum amount of sunshine. Charles and Xavier Vayron personally direct the vinification.

LALANDE DE POMEROL

CHÂTEAU LA-CROIX-SAINT-ANDRÉ

Francis Carayon
Néac – 33500 Libourne
57 51 08 36

Type of vineyard: Family-owned. **Established:** Bought by the Carayon Family in 1965. **Vine stocks:** Merlot 80%, Cabernet Franc and Sauvignon 20%. It is, without doubt, the oldest of the appellation's vineyards. **Soil:** A great diversity over the 15 hectares of the vineyard. Clay and gravel, sandy loam on a subsoil of iron pan. **Exposure:** In the commune of Néac on the famous Néac-Pomerol-Saint-Émilion plateau.
Average annual production in hectoliters: 570. **Yield:** 38 hectoliters per hectare, on the average. The low yield allows the extraction of all the minerals, in a never ending search for quality.
Appellation: Lalande de Pomerol. **Type:** Red. **Cultivation:** "Special management of the individual lots", which consists of dividing the vineyard into lots according to the nature of the soil and the vinestocks. **Technique:** The vinification by lot, which goes on for 6 to 8 weeks, is, of course, accompanied by temperature and fermentation control and particularly late devatting (in order to extract all the tannins). Only the best lots, after fermentation, are used for La-Croix-Saint-André. **Maturing:** The entire production is matured in Oak casks (1/3 new) and is fined with fresh egg whites. The management by lot doesn't stop with the production or the vinification: the yield of each lot is matured in its own set of casks, the blending being reserved for the last step, during bottling. **Characteristics:** Elegant wines, well-bred, very concentrated, with very deep color and aroma of truffles. Full and complex flavor, long persistence, rich and well-balanced. **Serving temperature:** 17°.

Characteristics of vintages

1986: Fermentation with skins is pushed to the limit, up to the month of November, in order to extract the maximum of tannins and aroma. This harvest, which was already that of a great year, has yielded rich, well-balanced, concentrated wines. **1985:** Intense aroma with a touch of pepper, rose, lightly mentholated. Very supple attack, great harmony between wood and fruit with a very spicy and complex after-taste. The wine for a winelover who likes to take the time to analyze his wines in all their complexity. **1983:** Exceptional sunshine has yielded "cooked" wines with an alcohol content never before attained from the oldest Merlot Vines. **1982:** Rich, dense, with rich woody aromas, but with lots of nuance. Full attack, very rich and well-balanced, ending on a note of conserves and spices. A collector's wine. **1981:** Beautiful rich color, rich-flavor, balance, well-bred aroma combining vegetable and musky animal fragrances. Vigorous and full-bodied, a real mouthful. Average pre-tax, ex-warehouse price: 59 F.F. to 95 F.F. (until December, 1988).

Comments

Sale of each vintage only begins after 4 years of ageing at the Château. Over 7000 clients, among whom are several hundred personalities of the world in arts, science, medecine, politics and business, as well as diplomats, appreciate and are faithful to La-Croix-Saint-André. The Château La-Croix-Saint-André decided, with Mrs. Aniela Rubinstein and her children, to dedicate its great 1982 vintage to Arthur Rubinstein, thus associating the name of the great musician with his favorite wine.

CHÂTEAU HAUT-CHÂTAIN

Mr. Philippe Junquas or Mr. André Rivière
Néac 33500 Libourne
57 74 02 79 or 57 51 51 02

Type of vineyard: Family-owned since 1912. **Established:** 1912. **Vine stocks:** Merlot 70%, Cabernet Franc 15%, Cabernet Sauvignon 15%. **Soil:** Extremely variable, clay and gravel with traces of iron. **Exposure:** Gentle slopes, part of the Pomerol plateau. **Average annual production in hectoliters:** 550.

Appellation: Lalande-de-Pomerol. **Type:** Red. **Technique:** Harvested at optimum maturity, daily pumping over, permanent temperature control and frequent testing in order to obtain concentrated and full bodied wines. Maceration for a month. **Maturing:** Around 18 months, some in vats some in new oak casks, the proportion depending on the vintage. **Alcohol content:** 12%. **Characteristics:** Powerful, intense aromas, well structured (see below). **Serving temperature:** 17 to 18°. **Served with:** Meat, cheese. **Vintages available in 89/90:** 1983, 1984, 1985, 1986, 1987, 1988.

Characteristics of vintages

1988: Very promising, similar to 1983 and 1985. Deep red color (ink), complex crystallized fruit aromas, soft and full, opulent, very great vintage. **1987:** Natural, clear color, round, very well balanced, supple, can be drunk fairly young. Not unlike 1984 vintage. **1986:** Intensely aromatic, ripe fuit fragrance, spicy touch* supple, rich and generous, excellent tannins, rich and harmonious. **1985:** Beautiful cherry color with violet glints, intense vegetal (roasted coffee) and animal (venison) fragrance, supple, harmonious and with a richness that sets off the aromas rather than concealing them. **Other:** 1984 – Brilliant ruby color, intense ripe fruit aromas fine wood note. Supple, round, ripe and well developed tannins. 1983: Great year, cask wood aroma (leather touch), rich tannins. Price range (pre-tax, ex-warehouse): 30 to 50 F.F.

Sales volume:
– Wholesale: 75%. – Retail: 25%.
Sales in France: 90%.
Export sales: 10%.
Main trading partners : Belgium, Denmark.

CHÂTEAU DES MOINES

Henri Darnajou
Lalande de Pomerol – 33500 Libourne
57 51 40 41

Type of vineyard: Family-owned. **Established:** From father to son. **Vine stocks:** 75% Merlot, 25% Cabernet. **Soil:** Gravel and iron. **Average annual production in hectoliters:** 600.
Appellation: Lalande de Pomerol. **Type:** Red. **Technique:** Traditional vinification. **Maturing:** Vats and casks. **Alcohol content:** About 12%. **Characteristics:** Supple, fruity, rather rapid ageing, long conversation. **Serving temperature:** About 15°. **Served with:** Poultry, game, cheese. **Vintages available in 89/90:** 1984, 1986, 1987 in 1988. 1988 as of May 1990.

Characteristics of vintages

1988: Very good year, concentrated wine, promising. **1987:** Vintage quite well in hand, somewhat lighter, more rapid evolution. **1986:** Good year. Well colored, fragrant wine. Good keeping. Price range (pre-tax, ex-warehouse): between 20 and 30 F.F

Sales volume:
– Wholesale: 20%. – Retail: 65%. – Restaurants: 10%.
– Other: 5% shops and certain enterprises.
Sales in France: 90%.

CHATEAU DES MOINES
LALANDE·DE·POMEROL
APPELLATION LALANDE·DE·POMEROL CONTRÔLÉE
H. DARNAJOU & FRERES
PROPRIETAIRES A LALANDE DE POMEROL (GIRONDE)
PRODUCE OF FRANCE
75 cl
MIS EN BOUTEILLE AU CHATEAU

Export sales: 10%.
Main trading partners: Switzerland, Belgium.

References in France

Restaurants: Michel Guérard (Les Sources d'Eugénie 40), Thermes de Gréoux les Bains (04), Relais du Bois St Georges (Saintes 17), Grand Hôtel Pelisson (Nontron 24).

Comments

This family property covers about 15 hectares. Classical procedures are followed (plowing, no herbicides used), manual harvesting. The vinification is carefully controlled. Ageing takes place in vats and casks. All this care has assured the regular success of the recent vintages, which have all of the characteristics of the good wines of this appellation.

• The quality of the 1987 vintage, particularly in Bordeaux, is questionable. Much of the Merlot suffered from coulure and a good bit of the harvesting was done in the rain. Only a few vineyards will produce a good vintage (see the Chapter on Bordeaux wines and the "Vintage Code").

CHÂTEAU MONCETS de JERPHANION

Néac 33500 Libourne
57 51 19 33

Type of vineyard: Family-owned. **Established:** 1872. **Number of employees:** 5. **Vine stocks:** 60% Merlot, 30% Cabernet Franc, 10% Cabernet Sauvignon. **Soil:** Sand and sandy clay. **Exposure:** East, South-East. **Average annual production in hectoliters:** 700.
Appellation: Lalande de Pomérol. **Type:** Red. **Technique:** Traditional. **Maturing:** Half in casks, half in vats. **Characteristics:** Supple and fine. **Serving temperature:** 18°. **Served with:** Meat, cheese. **Vintages available in 89/90:** 1980, 1984, 1985, 1986, 1988.

Characteristics of vintages

1988: Rich, dense, well balanced. **1986:** Fine, fruity, lovely supple wine. **1985:** Excellent year, very well balanced. **Other:** 1980: The aromas of aged wine are starting to appear. Price range (pre-tax, ex-warehouse): between 30 and 50 F.F.
Sales volume:
– Wholesale: 1/3. – Retail: 1/3. – Other: 1/3 various agents.
Sales in France: 30%.
Export sales: 70%.
Main trading partners: United Kingdom, Belgium, Netherlands, Luxemburg, Denmark.

Château Moncets
LALANDE-DE-POMEROL
MISE EN BOUTEILLE AU CHATEAU
1985
PROPRIÉTAIRES BARON L. G. ET E. DE JERPHANION
à NÉAC (Gironde) France
75cl
APPELLATION LALANDE-DE-POMEROL CONTROLÉE
PRODUCE OF FRANCE

Comments

In 1789 the vineyard prospered as a result of improvements introduced by the previous owner over a period of 10 years. An ancestor of the present proprietor was president of the Bordeaux parliament where he managed to abolish torture on the wheel.
Continuity, which makes it possible for dedication to arrive at its goal, has put the Château Moncets among the "greats" of its appellation.

CHÂTEAU LE ROQUEBRUNE

Claude Guinjard
Les Galvesses Cidex 6 B10 Lalande de Pomerol
57 51 44 54

Type of vineyard: Family-owned. **Established:** Very old. **Vine stocks:** Merlot Noir (1/3), Cabernet Sauvignon (2/3). **Soil:** Sandy. **Exposure:** South. **Average annual production in hectoliters:** 80 to 100 hl on 3 hectares.
Appellation: Lalande de Pomerol. **Type:** Red. **Technique:** In the old style. **Maturing:** By the proprietor himself. **Alcohol content:** 12.8 to 13.2%. **Characteristics:** Forthcoming, well-colored, very digestible. **Serving temperature:** 18 to 20°. **Served with:** Red meat, game, cheese. **Vintages available in 89/90:** 1971, 1981, 1986.

Characteristics of vintages

1988: Beautiful color, body, good future. **1987:** Not bottled. Vintage considered unworthy of the Château (very rare). **1986:** Very beautiful color, fruity and subtle bouquet, good balance. Price range (pre-tax, ex-warehouse): 86: between 30 and 50 F.F. 81: between 50 and 80 F.F. 71: between 120 and 160 F.F.
Sales volume:
-Wholesale: 50%. – Retail: 50%.
Sales in France: 100%.

References in France

Shops: Vinothèque (Bordeaux).

Comments

On a 3 hectares family property, Mr. Guinjard cultivates his vineyard himself without the use of chemical herbicides. The grapes are harvested by hand and close attention is paid to the evolution of the harvest in the winecellars.

CHÂTEAU TOURNEFEUILLE

Néac – 33500 Libourne
57 51 18 61

Type of vineyard: Family Corporation. **Number of employees:** 8. **Vine stocks:** Merlot 70%, Cabernet Franc 15%, Cabernet Sauvignon 15%. **Soil:** Clay gravels. **Exposure:** Full South hillsides. **Average annual production in hectoliters:** 900.
Appellation: Lalande de Pomerol. **Type:** Red. **Technique:** Pressing, partial destemming, temperature control, long cuvaison. **Maturing:** 2 years in oak casks partial annual renewal. **Alcohol content:** 11.5%. **Characteristics:** Very typical of gravelly hillsides, round and meaty, truffle aromas and vanilla with age. **Serving temperature:** 17°. **Served with:** Red and white meat, small game, all dense cheeses; braised calf's hazel nut, poultry fricassée, entrecôte Maitre de Chai, roe-deer fillet. **Vintages available in 89/90:** 1981, 1983, 1985, 1986.

Characteristics of vintages

1988: Rich, well-balanced and vigorous, firm tannins, long ageing potential. **1987:** Rather poor quality, not bottled. **1986:** Delicate, supple, mellow tannins, already seductive. **1985:** Rich and well-balanced: supple; a great lively wine. **1984:** Bad quality, no bottling. **1983:** Rich and well-balanced; very great wine for ageing. **1981:** Perfect structure harmony, the accuracy of the proportions slow developing. Price range (pre-tax, ex-warehouse): Between 40 and 55 F.F.
Sales volume:
– Retail: 50%. – Restaurants: 20%. – Other: 30% small and average foreign importers.
Sales in France: 70%.
Export sales: 30%.
Main trading partners : Belgium, Switzerland, Germany, Denmark, USA.

References in France

Restaurants: Les Prés et les Sources de Michel Guérard, La Tour d'Argent, Les Trois Marches à Versailles.
Shops: Les Caves de la Madeleine, Les Caves Royales, L'Œnothèque in Paris.

CHÂTEAU DES TOURELLES LALANDE-DE-POMEROL

François Janoueix
20, quai du Priourat – B.P. 135 –
33502 Libourne Cedex
57 51 55 44 – Telex: F. 571 962 JAFRANC

Type of vineyard: Family-owned. **Established:** Winegrowers for 3 generations. **Vine stocks:** Merlot 60%, Cabernet Sauvignon 20%, Cabernet Franc 20%. **Average annual production in hectoliters:** 800.
Appellation: Lalande-de-Pomerol. **Type:** Red. **Technique:** Traditional, manual harvesting, ageing in oak casks. **Maturing:** In vats with temperature regulation, then oak barrels. **Alcohol content:** 12%. **Characteristics:** "Black" color, sumptuous Merlot texture, an energetic wine with firm tannins. **Serving temperature:** Room temperature; 18° to 19°. **Served with:** Full-bodied wine for red meat, recommended, for example, for entrocôte à la Bordelaise grilled steak with shallots. **Vintages available in 89/90:** 1985, 1983, 1982.

Characteristics of vintages

1986: Not for sale yet. **1985:** Certainly the year of the Merlot; rich and well-balanced, body equivalent to 1970. **1983:** Truffle aroma; Gold Medal at the Concours Agricole, Paris 1985. **1982:** Tile-red color beginning to show, to be traditionally aged. Price range (pre-tax, ex-warehouse): between 30 and 50 F.F.
Sales volume:
– Wholesale: 5%. – Retail: 75%. – Restaurants: 20%.
Sales in France: 70%.
Export sales: 30%.
Main trading partners : Germany, Belgium, Switzerland.

References in France

Restaurants: Café de la Paix in Paris – Aux Armes de France at Ammerschwir and L'Hostellerie at Merlenheim.

Comments

The Association of Former Winegrowers (from Normandy) comes to help regularly, ever since the Thirties, and organizes a great banquet every year in honor of those who have been hired since the last harvest. An audio-visual presentation entitled "Knowledge of Wine", dealing with winegrowing and wine making, is offered free to each visitor.

CHÂTEAU VIEUX CHEVROL

Jean-Pierre Champseix
Néac – 33500 Libourne
57 51 09 80

Type of vineyard: Corporation. **Established:** 1985. **Number of employees:** 10. **Vineyard Area:** 20 hectares. **Vine stocks:** Merlot 70%, Cabernet Franc 15%, Cabernet Sauvignon 15%. **Soil:** Gravel, clay with calcium carbonate, grey ferruginous soil, type Alios. **Exposure:** Plateau. **Average annual production in hectoliters:** 1,200.

Appellation: Lalande-de-Pomerol. **Type:** Red. **Technique:** Submerged "marc", slow and prolonged maceration, 4 to 5 weeks. **Maturing:** Wood. **Alcohol content:** 12°. **Characteristics:** Great long, elegant, small fruit aroma (bouquet wine, of raspberry, blackcurrant). **Serving temperature:** 18°. **Served with:** Traditional Bourgeois and cuisine. **Vintages available in 89/90:** 1985.

Characteristics of vintages

1985: Will age for a long time, hold , Fragrant, fine and long. Price range (pre-tax, ex-warehouse): between 30 and 50 F.F.

Sales volume:
– Wholesale: 50%. – Retail: 25%. – Restaurants: 5%. – Other: 20% small salers (cellars, fine shops).

Sales in France: 70%.

Export sales: 30%.

Main trading partners : Belgium, Netherlands, Switzerland, Germany, USA.

• *If you find that there are one or more elements missing, so that you are unable to contact a particular proprietor or importer, please write to us at the following address for additional information:*

Gilles Temime, Éditions Vintage,
14, rue Rennéquin - 75017 Paris.

SAINT-ÉMILION

GRAND PONTET

Gérard Bécot
33330 Saint-Émilion
57 74 46 88

Appellation: Saint-Émilion Grand Cru. **Type:** Red. **Technique:** In stainless steel tanks, electronic temperature control. **Maturing:** In casks, 80% new for the 1988 vintage. **Alcohol content:** 12.7%. **Served with:** Red meat, game, cheese. **Vintages available in 89/90:** 1982, 1983, 1986, 1987.

Characteristics of vintages

1988: Excellent year – rich and well balanced, beautiful tannins. **1987:** Beautiful wine, cited amongst the best St. Emilions by Michel Bettane. **1986:** Magnificent wine, round, rich and well balanced. **1985:** Beautiful ruby color, round, supple and yet tannic and full-bodied. **Other:** 1982, 1983: Beautiful. Price range (pre-tax, ex-warehouse): 50 to 80 F.F. – 80 to 120 F.F.

Sales volume:
– Wholesale: 90%.
Sales in France: 10%. **Export sales:** 90%.

Abroad

United States

Barton & Guestier.

Comments

On this famous plateau, west of Saint Émilion, Grand-Pontet spreads out over 14 chalky hectares, 900 meters from the Collégiale and 500 meters from the old Church of Saint-Martin de Mazerat. For several years, it was the property of the wholesalers Barton & Guestier. In 1980, the Pourquet, Bécot (Beau-Séjour Bécot) families pooled their resources to acquire the property. The wines are both substantial and firm. The large proportion of Merlot contributes roundness but the soil imposes its vigor.

BEAU SÉJOUR-BÉCOT

Gérard Bécot
33330 Saint-Émilion
57 74 46 87

Type of vineyard: Family Association and Corporation. **Vine stocks:** Merlot 60-70%, Cabernet Sauvignon, Cabernet Franc 30-40%. **Soil:** Chalky clay. **Exposure:** High plateau (78 meters) – the advantage of being on a high plateau is that one does not need air anymore. **Average annual production in hectoliters:** 600.
Appellation: Saint Émilion Grand Cru. **Type:** Red. **Technique:** Stainless steel tanks, electronic temperature control. **Maturing:** In casks (80% new), in one year old casks (20%) for the 1988 vintage. **Alcohol content:** 12.8%. **Characteristics:** Rich and well balanced. **Served with:** Meat, cheese, game. **Vintages available in 89/90:** 1981, 1982, 1983, 1984, 1985, 1986, 1987.

Characteristics of vintages

1988: Charming, rich and harmonious tannins which improve in the cask. **1987:** Very good vintage. **1986:** Deep red color, supple, forthcoming, beautiful and aromatic tannins, elegant. **1985:** Beautiful color, delicate nose (cinnamon, spices) very harmonious. Price range (pre-tax, ex-warehouse): 120 to 160 F.F.

Sales volume:
– Wholesale: 80%. – Retail: 20%.

References in France

Restaurants: Bocuse, Tour d'Argent, Guérard, etc.

Comments

Three members of the Bécot family direct Château Beau Séjour-Bécot: Michel, the father, Gérard and Dominique his two sons. One of the 12 best wines produced by the prestigious soil of Saint-Émilion (B. Ginestet). At Beau Séjour-Bécot, the bottles age under the cemetery. Some say that is there that the wine develops its "spirit". And Francis Blanche added: "I prefer drinking the wine now, or else only in the beyond, rather than the water from here." "One can make good wines only in beautiful places."

VIGNOBLES BASSILIEAUX

J.C. Bassilieaux
33350 St-Magne-de-Castillon
57 40 06 71

Type of vineyard: Family Corporation. **Established:** For 5 generations. **Number of employees:** 10. **Vine stocks:** Merlot 65%, Cabernet Franc 25%, Cabernet Sauvignon 10%. **Soil:** Clay with calcium carbonate. **Average annual production in hectoliters:** 2,500.
Appellation: Bourg Clairet, Bourg Supérieur, Grand Cru Côtes-de-Castillon, Saint-Émilion Grand Cru. **Type:** Red. **Technique:** Traditional. **Maturing:** TanKs and new barrels cycled for 3 years. **Alcohol content:** 12%. **Characteristics:** Fruity, robust and supple. **Served temperature:** 16 to 18°. **Serving with:** Clairet: shellfish, and pork. Bordeaux Supérieur & Côtes-de-Castillon: meat. St-Émilion Grand Cru: game and cheese. **Vintages available in 89/90:** 1986.

Characteristics of vintages

Price range (pre-tax, ex-warehouse): Between 20 and 30 F.F.

Sales volume:
– Wholesale: 40%. – Retail: 40%. – Restaurants: 10% Firms – committees and groups. – Other: 10%.
Sales in France: 3/4.
Export sales: 1/4.
Main trading partners : Belgium, Germany, Switzerland, Holland, England.

Abroad

Belgium

Van Leor Liege.
Shops: André Charleroi.

United Kingdom

Henri James London.

Germany

Shmidt Buende.

Denmark

Jacobsen's, Copenhague.

The Netherlands

Kelders Bussum.

Austria

Polacek Gerasdorf.

Switzerland

Shops: Bolsiger, Bern. Riotton, Geneva. 97133: Iles St-Barthélemy, Ets Courtois.

CHÂTEAU VIEUX CHAIGNEAU (Lalande de Pomerol) CHÂTEAU LA CROIX JURA (Montagne St-Émilion)

Berlureau Père & Fils
"Moulin du Jura", Montagne, 33570 Lussac
57 51 27 98

Type of vineyard: Agricultural Association. **Established:** 1885 – Agricultural association since 1983. **Number of employees:** 2. **Vine stocks:** Merlot 75%, Cabernet Franc 15%, Cabernet Sauvignon 10%. **Soil:** Ordinary and sandy soil on clay sub-soil. **Exposure:** Plateau and hillsides. **Average annual production in hectoliters:** 650 to 700. **Appellation:** Montagne-St.-Emilion and Lalande-de-Pomerol. **Technique:** Traditional Bordeaux style. **Maturing:** In vats (1 year) and in oak casks (1 year). **Alcohol content:** 12.5%. **Serving temperature:** 18%. **Served with:** Meat and cheese. **Vintages available in 89/90:** 1986 and 1987 (as from September 1989).

Characteristics of vintages

1987: Successful, fruity, pleasant wines. **1986:** Excellent year, structured, well colored, good keeping.
Sales volume: – Wholesale: 30%. – Retail: 70%.
Sales in France: 90-95%. **Export sales:** 5-10%.
Main trading partners : Belgium.

CHÂTEAU CANTENAC

Jean-Baptiste Brunot
F – 33330 St-Émilion
57 51 35 22

Type of vineyard: Real estate company. **Established:** 1970. **Vine stocks:** Merlot noir 75%, Cabernet Franc 15%, Cabernet Sauvignon 10%. **Soil:** Sand and gravel on clay subsoil. **Exposure:** On the plain. **Average annual production in hectoliters:** 580.

Appellation: St-Emilion Grand Cru. **Type:** Red. **Technique:** Fermentation on skins 21 days with temperature control. **Maturing:** Mostly in vats, a part in casks. **Alcohol content:** 12.5%. **Characteristics:** Supple, fragrant, good keeping, little acidity. **Serving temperature:** 17 to 18°. **Served with:** Red meat and cheese for the more tannic vintages, hors d'œuvres and white meat for the more supple vintages. **Vintages available in 89/90:** 80, 81, 83, 84, 85, 86, 87 (in September 89) , 88 (in September 90).

Characteristics of vintages

1988: Very tannic wine, for long keeping, ripe fruit taste. **1987:** Very supple wine, vanilla fragrance, will age more rapidly. **1986:** Very fine wine, very fragrant with soft tannins, supple, successful. **1985:** Very fine, supple with soft tannins, excellent ageing. Price range (pre-tax, ex-warehouse): between 30 and 50 F.F.

Sales volume:
– Wholesale: 25%. – Retail: 65%. – Restaurants: 10%.

Sales in France: 60%.

Export sales: 40%.

Main trading partners: Netherlands, Switzerland, Belgium, Germany, United Kingdom.

References in France

Restaurants: Restaurant Le Saint-Pierre (La Bouille), Restaurant le Président (St Quentin), Grand Hôtel de Valenciennes, Rest. Bourillot Le Célestin (Lyon), Restaurant Castel-Régis (29 Brignogan), Restaurant Au Petit Maxim (Strasbourg).
Shops: Bordeaux Magnum (Bordeaux), Sodicru (33 Léognan).

Abroad

United Kingdom

Kimble Trading, 33 Highfields Road – Hall Green, Birmingham B28 0HH. Tel: 021–7772011.

Germany

Collong, D6227 Oestrich, Winkel. Tel: 06723/3433. Bûhler, Köln. Tel: 0221/635014–15.

Switzerland

Gstaad Palace, Lausanne Palace, Hôtel des 3 Rois, Basel. Old Swiss House, Luzern.

Begium

Les Terroirs, Ivoz-Ramet, Neyrinck 8130 Werken-Kortemark. Au Tastevin, 2100 Deurne.

The Netherlands

Robbers en vanden Hoogen Velperweg, 23 6824, BC Arnhem.

Comments

Property of the Brunot family since 1937. A vineyard expanded by the purchase of neighboring parcels where no effort is spared to produce a classical wine, marked by its soil and appropriate vinification techniques.

CORBIN-MICHOTTE

J.N. Boidron
33330 Saint-Émilion
56 96 28 57

Type of vineyard: Family-owned. **Vine stocks:** Merlot 65%, Cabernet Franc 30%, Cabernet-Sauvignon 5%. **Soil:** Gravel and sand on a sandy-iron-clay subsoil. **Average annual production in hectoliters:** 250.
Appellation: Saint-Émilion Grand Cru, Grand Cru Classé. **Type:** Red. **Technique:** Long maceration – harvest and selection of bunches done by hand – temperature control. **Maturing:** New barrels and tanks. **Alcohol content:** 12,5%. **Characteristics:** Supple, robust. Fruity, vanilla fragrance, musky, pepery. **Serving temperature:** 17°. **Served with:** Red meat. **Vintages available in 89/90:** 1986, 1983, 1982, 1980, 1977.

Characteristics of vintages

1986: Well-structured wine, very tannic, typical, full and rich. **1983:** Fruity, very tannic, full, blackcurrant and sandalwood fragrance, long. **1982:** Very rich and supple, silky texture, unctuous, very long, cherry and musky aroma. **Note:**

1980: one of the best St-Émilion, well developed, good structure and balance. 1977: a great success, fine, elegant, well-balanced. 1973: typical aged St-Émilion. Well-balanced, amber color, spicy. Price range (pre-tax, ex-warehouse): 50 F.F. – 80 F.F.
Sales volume:
– Wholesale: 65%. – Retail: 30%. – Restaurants: 5%.
Sales in France: 40%.
Export sales: 60%.
Main trading partners : Belgium, Switzerland, Germany, Denmark.

CHÂTEAU CARTEAU CÔTES DAUGAY

Jacques Bertrand
33330 Saint-Émilion
57 24 73 94

Type of vineyard: Family-owned. **Established:** For three generations. **Number of employees:** 4. **Vine stocks:** Merlot 70%, Cabernet Franc 22%, Cabernet Sauvignon 8%. **Soil:** Chalky clay, foothills. **Exposure:** South, South-West (Côte Daugay).
Appellation: Saint-Émilion Grand Cru. **Type:** Red. **Technique:** Long maceration, temperature control. **Maturing:** 8 to 10 months in new casks or barrels (renewed every third year). **Alcohol content:** 12.5%. **Characteristics:** Very tannic, rich aromas, intense, woodland note, rich and well
balanced, long finish. **Serving temperature:** 15 to 18°. **Served with:** Red meat, grilled or roasted, steak grilled on vine cuttings. **Vintages available in 89/90:** 1986, 1987.

Characteristics of vintages

1988: Not yet available. **1987:** Will be on the market as of June 89. **1986:** Similar to the 1985 vintage. Very rich, substantial good ageing potential. **1985:** Depleted stock. Price range (pre-tax, ex-warehouse): 30 to 50 F.F.
Sales volume:
– Wholesale: 50%. – Retail: 30%. – Restaurants: 10%.
– Other: 10%.
Sales in France: 70%.
Export sales: 30%.
Main trading partners : Belgium, Netherlands, UK.

Abroad

United Kingdom
John Armit Wines Ltd, 190 Kensington Park Rd, London W 11 2ES.

Belgium
Sté Frui, Kapoenstraat 8, 8130 Zarren.

The Netherlands
Ets Colaris, 6000 Weert.

Comments

Château Carteau Côtes Daugay is a winegrowing enterprise typical of the region, based on an infrastructure dating from the 19th century. The wines of the Château are prepared using modern techniques while never losing track of tradition. To produce a quality wine, the vines must be treated with respect, that is, without chemical herbicides. The grapes must be cared for and harvested manually then carefully selected. The vinification is long (21 to 28 days) and is followed by ageing in oak casks, one third renewed each year. At the moment, the 1986 is at its best and will go marvelously well with a steak Bordeaux style.

Jacques BERTRAND
Château Carteau Côtes Daugay
33330 SAINT-ÉMILION

• *Paulée – traditional meal which brings winelovers and winegrowers together after the harvest, particularly in Burgundy.*

CHÂTEAU COUTET

Jean David-Beaulieu
Coutet 33330 Saint Émilion
57 24 72 27

Type of vineyard: Family-owned. **Established:** 1968. **Vine stocks:** Merlot, Cabernet, Bouchet, Pressac, Malbec. **Soil:** chalky clay. **Exposure:** South – South-West. **Average annual production in hectoliters:** 450.

CHATEAU COUTET

J. DAVID-BEAULIEU

33330 SAINT-EMILION
(France)

✆ 57 24 72 27

CHATEAU COUTET
SAINT-EMILION
GRAND CRU CLASSÉ
Appellation St-Emilion Grand Crû Classé Contrôlée
1983
DAVID BEAULIEU
PROPRIÉTAIRE A SAINT-EMILION (GIRONDE)
MIS EN BOUTEILLE AU CHATEAU
75cl

Beautiful 83
Robust, full

•

84 : Light and agreeable

Appellation: Saint Émilion Grand Cru. **Type:** Red. **Technique:** traditional, in stainless steel tanks. **Maturing:** in vats and casks. **Alcohol content:** 12.5%. **Characteristics:** supple, fruity, full-bodied. **Serving temperature:** 15° – 18°. **Served with:** red meat, game. **Vintages available in 89/90:** 1986.

Characteristics of vintages

1986: beautiful color, delicate nose, fruity and woody, good tannic structure. **1985:** beautiful color, supple and full--bodied, ripe tannins. Price range (pre-tax, ex-warehouse): 50 to 80 F.
Sales volume: – Wholesale: 80%. – Retail: 20%.
Sales in France: 40%. **Export sales:** 60%.
Main trading partners : Switzerland, Belgium, Germany, USA.

Abroad

United Sates

Transat Trade – Inglewood – Tel: (213) 672 1930.

Germany

Poullig KG – Dusseldorf – (2011) 7334807.

Switzerland

Koch – Reinach – 064713838 – Chanton, Visp – 02846153 De Montmollin – Auvernier – Bauermeister – Corcelle – 038246464 – Claus – Carouge Genève. Bruegger Von Tobel, Bern – Hahn-Rickli, Bale – 061 6928940.

Belgium

The Continental Bodega, Brussels – 02/523 43 22.

CHÂTEAU DESTIEUX

Dauriac
33330 Saint-Émilion
57 40 25 05

Type of vineyard: Family corporation. **Established:** 1971. **Number of employees:** 5. **Vine stocks:** 2/3 Merlot, 1/3 Cabernet. **Soil:** Clay with calcium carbonate. **Exposure:** Full South.
Appellation: Saint-Émilion Grand Cru. **Type:** Red. **Technique:** Alcoholic fermentation and thermovinification in stainless steel tanks. **Maturing:** Entirely in wood, half new barrels each year. **Alcohol content:** 12.5° to 13°. **Characteristics:** Very tannic wines, very rich and well-balanced, wines for ageing, above an. **Serving temperature:** Room temperature. **Served with:** Red meat, game and cheese. **Vintages available in 89/90:** 1975, 1977, 1978, 1979, 1980, 1982, 1983, 1984, 1985, 1986, 1987, 1988.

Characteristics of vintages

1988: Very deep color, very tanic and full-bodied, all the ingredient of a very great vintage. Variable according to its reaction to wood. **1987:** Very deep coor, delicate, very round, made from Merlot harvested before the rains, reminiscent of the 1981 vintage. **1985:** A very great vintage because '85 is the year of the Merlot and, in fact, the St-Émilion and Pomerol as well. **1983:** Very fine wine, very successfull. **1982:** A great vintage; Gold Medal in the Foire de Paris 1985. Price range (pre-tax, ex-warehouse): between 50 and 80 F.F.
Sales volume:
– Wholesale: 90% abroad. – Retail: 9% – Restaurants: 1%.
Sales in France: 10%. **Export sales:** 90%.
Main trading partners : USA, Great Britain, RFA, Netherlands, Belgium, Switzerland, Austria, Luxemburg, Canada, Mexique, Danemark.

CHÂTEAU FIGEAC

Thierry Manoncourt
33330 Saint-Émilion
57 24 72 26

Established: 2nd century A.D. **Vine stocks:** Cabernet 70% (1/2 Cabernet Sauvignon, 1/2 Cabernet Franc), Merlot 30%. **Soil:** Gravel, sand, clay, sandstone, iron pan. **Exposure:** Three hillcrests. **Average annual production in hectoliters:** 30-35 hl/ha.
Appellation: Saint-Émilion Premier Grand Cru Classé. **Type:** Red. **Technique:** Submerged cap. **Maturing:** In casks (100% new each year). **Alcohol content:** 11.5-13%. **Characteristics:** Finesse and distinction, due to Cabernet Sauvignon and Cabernet Franc (70%). **Serving temperature:** 18°. **Served with:** Red meat, game and cheese.

Characteristics of vintages

1987: "One of the best of the vintage I tasted." Ron Fonte, Firends of Wine, Summer 88. **1986:** Already acclaimed as one of the greatest 1986 Bordeaux. **1985:** "The best St-Emilion of this vintage, with the intense flavor, finesse and subtlety to outperform the two St. Emilion premiers "A", The Wine Spectator, Dec. 31, 88. **Other: 1983:** "Intense cherry and berry aromas with overlays of cedar, mint, vanilla, nutmeg and jasmine. Some slight vegetal aroma, complex and intense layers of flavor. Gobs of fruit balanced by plenty of new wood. Very generous flavors of young currants and berries. Softish finish, but great! Should continue to ascend for many years." International Wine Review. Platinum Medal with Château Margaux 83 topping the list of Bordeaux Premiers Crus for this vintage. Price range (pre-tax, ex-warehouse): 120 to 160 F.F. and 160 F.F. and over.
Sales volume: – Wholesale: 100%.
Sales in France: 20%. **Export sales:** 80%.
Main trading partners: UK, Belgium, USA, Germany, Switzerland, Canada, Denmark, Netherlands, Sweden, Norway, Japan, Singapore, Hong Kong, Austria.

References in France

Restaurants: All the great restaurants.
Shops: In fine food shops.

Comments

Figeac dates back to Gallo-Roman times when, under the name of Figeacus, its founder, it was already a large estate. In the Middle Ages it became a vast feudal manor and so it remained until the French Revolution. Afterwards, in the 19th century, the "Château de Figeac" was split up; various parts were sold to landowners who developed their own vinestocks the best known of which is Cheval Blanc. The wines of Figeac enjoyed an outstanding reputation in the 18th century, and until the last years of the 19th century remained unquestionably the best known of all the St-Emilion Graves. Wine specialists writing today about Figeac's old or recent vintages acknowledge the constant and sustained high quality of the wines. Their assessments explain the brilliant revival of Figeac's reputation today (See "Classification 89").

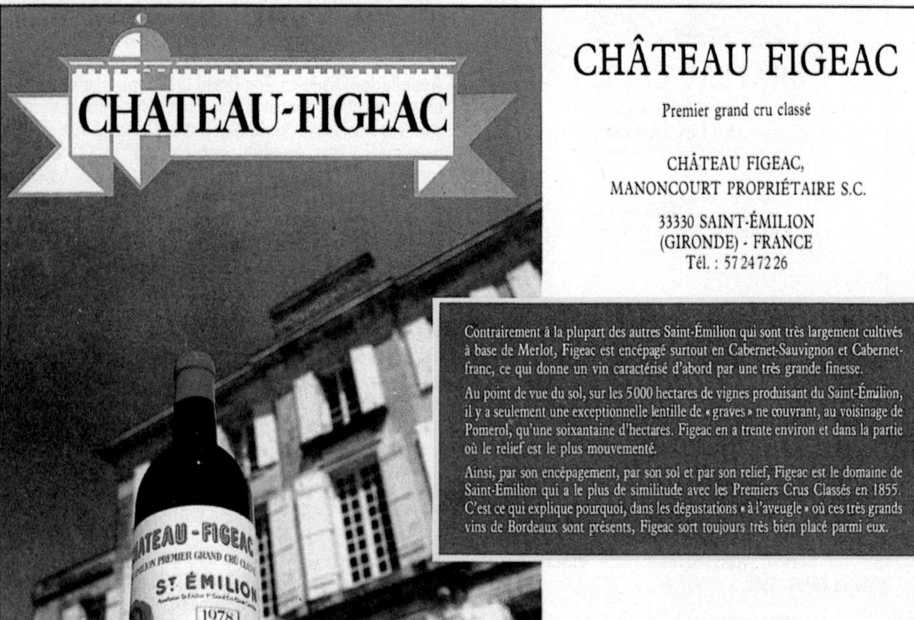

CHÂTEAU FOMBRAUGE

Saint-Christophe-des-Bardes
33330 Saint-Émilion
57 24 77 12 - Telex: 541 627

Type of vineyard: Company. **Number of employees:** Approx. 18. **Vine stocks:** Merlot 60%, Cabernet Franc 30%, Cabernet Sauvignon 10%. **Soil:** Mostly clay with calcium carbonate. **Exposure:** Plateau Northern and Southern slopes. **Average annual production in hectoliters:** 2,200.
Appellation: Saint-Émilion Grand Cru. **Type:** Red. **Technique:** Traditional, long maceration. **Maturing:** In oak casks, about 30% new. **Alcohol content:** 12.5%. **Characteristics:** Rich, well-balanced, full-bodied, harmonious, well-bred, soft and full, elegant, very sustained purple color. **Serving temperature:** 17°. **Served with:** Red meat, game, goose and duck preserves, lamprey. **Vintages available in 89/90:** 1981 (magnums), 1984, 1985, 1986, 1987, 1988.

Characteristics of vintages

1988: Exceptional year, full-bodied and rich. A very promising wine. **1987:** A very elegant wine, supple with great finesse. **1986:** A very great year, full-bodied very complex with great finesse developing slowly. **1985:** Great year, harmonious and full-bodied wine. **1984:** Very successful wine for considering vintage.
Sales in France: 40%.
Export sales: 60%.
Main trading partners : France, Netherlands, Belgium: Ste Marnier-Lapostolle - Denmark: Hans just A/S - U.S.A.: Kobrand Corporation - U.K.: Mr James Burgis.

CHÂTEAU FOURNEY

Jean-Pierre Rollet
St-Pey-d'Armens
3330 St-Émilion
57 47 15 13 - Telex: 570 598 CCI Libo/Rollet

Type of vineyard: Family-owned. **Vine stocks:** Merlot 64%, Cabernet Franc 30%, Cabernet Sauvignon 6% on 18 hectares. **Soil:** Silica-clay on ferruginous subsoil. **Average annual production in hectoliters:** 100,000 bottles. **Appellation:** Saint-Émilion Grand Cru. **Type:** Red. **Technique:** Traditional, destemming and thermo-regulation at 27 to 29°C. **Characteristics:** Good color, fragrant, lots of finesse. **Serving temperature:** 17°. **Served with:** Meat and roasts. **Vintages available in 89/90:** 1986 and 1985.

Characteristics of vintages

1985: Fine wine, combining richness, balance and roundness, good keeping. **1986:** Promising vintage.

CHÂTEAU FONPLEGADE

Armand Moueix
33330 Saint-Émilion
57 51 50 63 - Telex: 541 635 AMOUEIX
Telecopieur: 57 25 22 14

Type of vineyard: Family-owned. **Established:** One of the oldest St-Émilion vineyards, dates form the Roman Era. **Vine stocks:** Merlot 60%, Cabernet Franc 35%, Carbenet Sauvignon 5%. **Soil:** The plateau: mostly chalk. The slopes: clay with calcim carbonate. The foothills: silica with calcium carbonate. **Exposure:** Sunny, sheltered from the wind. **Average annual production in hectoliters:** 675.
Appellation: Grand Cru Saint-Émilion (classified Grand Cru Classé). **Type:** Red. **Technique:** Destemming (90 to 95%). Vinification in concrete vats 15 days to 3 weeks. **Maturing:** In oak barrels for 18 months, 1/3 new wood. Fined with fresh egg whites. **Serving temperature:** 19 to 20° room temperature. **Vintages available in 89/90:** 1981, 1982, 1983, 1985, 1986, 1987.

Characteristics of vintages

1986: Beautiful, dense, purple color. Lots of finesse, rich. Fresh well-balanced and aromatic. **1985:** Deep purple color, fresh, lively, with body, very long. Ages well. **1983:** Dense, purple color, vanilla aroma, fine, rich, well-balanced, woody and very long. **1982:** Intense color. Complex, developed aroma. Well-balanced, round, rich, elegant.

DOMAINE DU HAUT-PATARABET

Pierre Ouzoulias BP 93
17, rue du Colonel Picot - 33500 Libourne
57 51 07 55

Type of vineyard: Family owned. **Vine stocks:** 90% Merlot, 10% Cabernet Franc. **Average annual production in hectoliters:** 13 000 bottles.
Appellation: Saint-Émilion Grand Cru. **Type:** Red. **Technique:** Traditional. **Muturing:** Traditional. **Characteristics:** Well-colored, fragrant, combining finesse and suppleness. **Serving temperature:** 16°. **Served with:** Meat, roasts, poultry. **Vintages available in 89/90:** 1986, 1985.

Characteristics of vintages

1988: Great vintage. Well-colored wines, rich, beautiful future. **1986:** Remarkable success. Rich, supple wine, long, for keeping. **1985:** Beautiful wine combining finesse and fullness, for keeping.

Comments

Patarabet means "stock of the vine". The Château is contiguous with its neighbor, La Gaffelière, at the foot of the Château Pavie hillside.

CHÂTEAU "LA GRACE DIEU LES MENUTS"

Max Pilotte
"La Grace Dieu" 33330 Saint-Emilion
57 24 73 10

Type of vineyard: Agricultural Association. **Established:** 1865. **Number of employees:** 6. **Vine stocks:** Merlot 65%, Cabernet Franc 30%, Cabernet Sauvignon 5%. **Soil:** chalky clay – silica clay. **Exposure:** Plateau and foothills. **Average annual production in hectoliters:** 550. **Appellation:** Saint Emilion Grand Cru. **Type:** Red. **Technique:** Traditional, marc immersed 20 to 30 days. **Maturing:** In oak casks 1/3 new. **Alcohol content:** 12.7%. **Characteristics:** Ruby color, rich, balanced tannins, rich and robust, red berry nose (bigarreau cherry), woody finish (vanilla), very good balance. **Serving temperature:** 18-19°. **Served with:** Sauces, game, meat and soft cheese. **Vintages available in 89/90:** 1984, 1985, 1986, 1987, 1988.

Characteristics of vintages

1988: Still a bit early to judge but quite promising, most certainly a great year. **1987:** Beautiful ruby color, fruity nose (raspberry, wild strawberry) mellow tannins, well balanced. **1986:** Deep color, crystallized fruit fragrance (touch of prune and apricot), fleshy, woody, rich and well balanced tannins. **1985:** Deep red cherry (bigarreau) color, blackcurrant aroma, woody finish, young and soft tannins, round, lingering aftertaste. Silver Medal (Concours Général Agricole de Paris). Price range (pre-tax, ex-warehouse): 30 to 50 F.F.

Sales volume:
– Wholesale: 65%. – Retail: 30%. – Restaurants: 5%.
Sales in France: 60%.
Export sales: 40%.
Main trading partners : Belgium, Switzerland, Netherlands, Germany.

Abroad

United Kingdom

Château Somerset.

Germany

Mr. Heintz Pottoff, Booksee.

Switzerland

Maison Besancon, Yverdon – Maison Wyss, Onnens – Maison Henchoz, Prilly.

Belgium

Ets de Moor, Aalst – Ronald Deryck, Dendebleenw.

The Netherlands

Maison Colaris, Weert.

Comments

Family enterprise since 1865. The 6th generation is currently working the vineyards where excellent, regularly successful wines can be tasted (see "Classification 89").

CHÂTEAU HAUT ROCHER

Jean de Monteil
33330 Saint Emilion
57 40 18 09 - Telex: 572 093 F Montei CP

Type of vineyard: Family-owned. **Vine stocks:** Merlot 65%, Cabernet Franc 20%, Cabernet Sauvignon 15%. **Soil:** Brown chalky soil, alluvial clay. **Exposure:** South-East. **Average annual production in hectoliters:** 320.

PRODUCE OF FRANCE
CHATEAU
HAUT-ROCHER
1986
MIS EN BOUTEILLE AU CHATEAU
SAINT-ÉMILION GRAND CRU
APPELLATION SAINT-ÉMILION GRAND CRU CONTROLÉE
J. de Monteil
Saint-Étienne de Lisse (Gironde)
France
12,5% vol.
75cl

Appellation: Saint-Emilion Grand Cru. **Type:** Red. **Technique:** Traditional, long fermenting on skins. **Maturing:** In vats and casks, 1/3 renewed each year. **Alcohol content:** 12.5%. **Characteristics:** Strutured wines with a good tannic support, full and forthcoming, should be aged. **Serving temperature:** Aged wines: 18°. Young wines: 15°. **Served with:** Red and white meat, cheese. Goes very well with lamb. **Vintages available in 89/90:** 1987, 1986, 1985, 1984, 1983, 1981, 1980.

Characteristics of vintages

1988: Not available in 1989. **1987:** Supple wine, fruity, full-bodied, will be ready to drink in 3 years. **1986:** Fine woody flavor, elegant, well-bred, well-balanced, can be aged. **1985:** Rich and well-balanced wine, full-bodied, substantial tannic support, to be aged. **Other:** 1984: Supple, full-bodied. 1983: Rich and well-balanced, supple bouquet, meaty. 1981: Élegant, fine, wellbred wine, ready but can still be kept. 1980: Supple, delicate wine to be drunk now. Price range (pre-tax, ex-warehouse): between 30 and 50 F.F.

Sales volume:
- Wholesale: 30%. - Retail: 30%. - Other: 30%.

Sales in France: 90%. **Export sales:** 10%.

Main trading partners: Belgium, Germany, Denmark, U.K.

References in France

Shops: L'Amour du Vin, Les Toques Gourmandes.

Comments

Property in the family since the beginning of the 16th century. The proprietor does his best to perpetuate tradition so as to maintain the typical character of his wines and to assure their ageing for up to twenty years. No effort is spared to attain quality.

CHÂTEAU LA DOMINIQUE

Clément Fayat
Lieu dit "Château La Dominique"
33330 Saint-Émilion
57 51 44 60 - Telex: 540 298 F

Type of vineyard: Family Association. **Established:** 1969. **Number of employees:** 10. **Vine stocks:** Merlot 70%, Cabernet Franc et Cabernet Sauvignon 25%, Malbec 5%. **Soil:** Clay, gravel. **Exposure:** Southeast. **Average annual production in hectoliters:** 600.
Appellation: Saint-Émilion Grand Cru Classé. Type: Red. **Technique:** Long fermentation with skins, 3 weeks in stainless steel tanks. **Maturing:** Barrels. **Alcohol content:** 12°. **Characteristics:** Deep color, very complex nose, long, intense. **Serving temperature** 16° to 18°. **Vintages available in 89/90:** 1982, 1983, 1985, 1986, 1987.

Characteristics of vintages

1988: Very well colored, aromas still a bit undeveloped. Forthcoming fragance of black currant, vanilla and licorice. Superb tannic presence for long keeping. Excellent secondary aromas while drinking. **1987:** Surprising intensity for the vintage. Forthcoming fragrance with a suggestion of ripe fruit. Harmonious taste with the presence of round tannins. **1986:** Rich wine, good concentration, beautiful future. **1985:** Deep red color, full flavor, to be aged, 10 year average. **1983:** Beautiful, rich and well-balanced. **1982:** Exceptional year, intense color, fruity aroma (red fruits) richness, balance, length surprizing. **Others:** 1978: Rich, structured year, already evolving, ready drink. Price range (pre-tax, ex-warehouse): between 100 and 150 F.F.

Sales volume:
- Wholesale: 70%. - Retail: 30%.

Sales in France: 40%.
Export sales: 60%.
Main trading partners: Europe, United States, Canada, Japan.

• *Please note that all temperatures in this book are expressed in degrees Centigrade.*

CHÂTEAU LARCIS-DUCASSE

Mrs. H. Gratiot Alphandery
33330 Saint-Émilion
57 24 70 84

Type of vineyard: Family-owned. **Established:** 1893. **Vine stocks:** Merlot 65%, Cabernet Franc and Sauvignon 35%. **Soil:** Chalky clay – sandy at foothills. **Exposure:** Facing full South. **Average annual production in hectoliters:** 500.

Appellation: Grand Cru Classé Saint-Émilion. **Type:** Red. **Technique:** Long maturing. **Maturing:** In wooden barrels and casks. **Alcohol content:** 12%. **Characteristics:** The much sought after qualities of the wines can be attributed to the very special soil. Elegant, rich and well balanced. **Serving temperature:** 16°. **Served with:** Regional cuisine. **Vintages available in 89/90:** 1985, 1986, 1987, 1988.

Characteristics of vintages

1988: Exceptional structure. A great among greats. **1987:** Surprisingly delicate, very successful for the vintage. **1986:** Concentrated enough to be compared to the 1985. **1985:** Perfect harmony – typical of the estate. Price range (pre-tax, ex-warehouse): 80 to 120 F.F.
Sales in France: 40%.
Export sales: 60%.
Main trading partners : Belgium, UK, Switzerland, Germany, Netherlands, USA, Japan, Denmark.

References in France

Restaurants: Lucas Carton and others.
Shops: Nicolas.

Abroad

United Stades

Importers: Bordeaux, Millésime, Bordeaux.

United Kingdom

C.V.C.B. (Joanne), Tresses.

Switzerland

Ricard & Doutreloux, Bordeaux.

Belgium

Barrière Frères, Bordeaux.

Far East

Ponty, Fronsac.

Comments

The Château Larcis-Ducasse, producing a Saint-Émilion classified "Grand Cru", was acquired about a hundred years ago by Mr. Henry Raba, descendant of an old Bordeaux family. It now belongs to his great-grand children. The vineyard, all in one block, is entirely located to the South on one of the hillsides that crowns Saint-Émilion. The Château Larcis-Ducasse is an associate member of the Académie du Vin de Bordeaux and a member of the Union des Grands Crus of Bordeaux.

CHÂTEAU LARMANDE

Sté des Vignobles Méneret
33330 Saint-Émilion
57 24 71 41

Type of vineyard: Family-owned. **Number of employees:** 8. **Vine stocks:** Merlot 65%, Bouchet 30%, C.S. 5%. **Soil:** A bit of clay, coarse sand and iron with fine sand. **Exposure:** North. **Average annual production in hectoliters:** 800.
Appellation: Saint-Émilion Grand Cru Classé. **Type: Red. Technique:** In stainless steel tanks. **Maturing:** 1/3 new barrels – 1/3 b. first wine – 1/3 b. second wine. **Characteristics:** Deep color, round, well-balanced and fine. **Serving temperature:** 16-18°. **Served with:** White and red meat, game, cheese. **Vintages available in 89/90:** At the estate – 1984, 1986, 1987, 1988 (Primeurs).

Characteristics of vintages

1988: Very aromatic, remarkable density of color and rich tannins due to Merlot and Cabernet Franc. Should, in all likelihood develop a rich and delicate bouquet with ageing. **1987:** Mellow tannins, slightly more supple than the two preceding vintages. Charming, well-developed aromas, very good color. **1986:** Excellent – very concentrated. Combination of roundness, finesse and balance. **1985:** Excellent – very concentrated. Very aromatic. Full. **1984:** Good. Fine, elegant. Price range (pre-tax, ex-warehouse): 75 F.F. – 115 F.F.
Sales volume:
– Wholesale: 90%. – Retail: 5%. – Restaurants: 5%.
Sales in France: 35%.
Export sales: 65%.

Main trading partners : Belgium, Switzerland, Germany, UK, Netherlands, USA.

References in France

Restaurants: Taillevent, Troisgros, Guérard, Chapel, Le Crillon, Le Doyen, etc.

Abroad

Germany

Reidemeister & Ulrichs.

Canada

Import Board of Alberta.

Switzerland

Berthaudin, Hertig, Wymann.

Belgium

Raes, Provino, Mouliez, Werco, Beral, Palais du Vin, Deldaele.

CHÂTEAU LA GAFFELIÈRE

Comte de Malet Roquefort
33330 Saint-Émilion
57 24 72 15

Type of vineyard: Corporation. **Established:** 1/1/82. **Number of employees:** 8. **Vine stocks:** Merlot 65%, Cabernet Franc 25%, Cabernet Sauvignon 10%. **Soil:** Clay with calcium carbonate. **Exposure:** Slope and downhill slope. **Average annual production in hectoliters:** 750. **Appellation:** Saint-Émilion 1er Grand Cru Classé. **Type:** Red. **Technique:** Stainless steel tanks, long fermentation. **Maturing:** 100% new casks in Merrain Oak. **Alcohol content:** 12.6°. **Characteristics:** Ruby, brilliant, agreeable nose with aromas truffle and blackcurrant dominant aromas, supple and well-balanced, long, needs a when aged long agein, to develope its qualities completely. **Serving temperature:** 16° to 17°. **Served with:** Red meat grilled with "sarments" Vine clippings, game, cheese. **Vintages available in 89/90:** 1982, 1983, 1986, 1988.

Characteristics of vintages

1988: Deep purple color, rich and complex nose, well-balanced, tannic, soft and full, lingering taste. Long keeping, with the 1970 and 1985 one of the best vintages since 1961. **1987:** Ruby color, delicate fragrances, elegant, initially undervalued, but many professionals are now changing their minds. Very pleasant and well-balanced, very good quality/price ratio. **1986:** Deep ruby, rich and well-balanced, but supple, long, hold. **1983:** Aromatic, very agreeable, a great wine. **1982:** Purple, well-balanced, long and supple. Price range (pre-tax, ex-warehouse): between 85 and 170 F.F.
Sales volume: – Wholesale: 95%. – Retail 5%.
Sales in France: 15%. **Export sales:** 85%.
Main trading partners : USA, England, Benelux, Switzerland, Japan, Germany.

ETS OUZOULIAS

Pierre Ouzoulias
17, rue du Colonel Picot
BP93 – 33503 Libourne
57 51 07 55

Type of vineyard: Family-owned. **Established:** 1898. **Vine stocks:** 75% Merlot, 25% Cabernet (Château Franc Pourret). **Soil:** Chalky clay. **Exposure:** Hillside South-West.

Appellation: Saint-Emilion Grand Cru. **Type:** Red. **Technique:** Temperature regulation and maceration. **Maturing:** 24 months, of which 12 are in oak casks. **Alcohol content:** 12%. **Characteristics:** Tannic, good keeping. **Serving temperature:** 18°. **Served with:** Meats and cheeses. **Vintages available in 89/90:** 1978 to 1986.

Characteristics of vintages

1986: Beautiful color, complex, nose, mostly red fruit and woodland, long, full and firm. Possibility of a long and good evolution. (Manual harvesting, selection at full maturity). Price range (pre-tax, ex-warehouse): between 30 and 50 F.F
Sales volume:
– Wholesale: 5% (winecellars). – Retail: 80%. – Restaurants: 5%.
Sales in France: 90%.
Export sales: 10%.

References in France

Restaurants: Great restaurants in departments: 08, 59, 62, 74.
Shops: Winecellars.

Comments

Four generations of effort consecrated to the great Bordeaux wines. Art combined with enthousiasm. Wines with character, typical Saint-Emilion, Fronsac, Lalande de Pomerol, Graves, Haut Médoc, Pauillac, St-Estephe and Bordeaux Superieur.
Note: All of these wines are aged in oak casks. Several are the result of biological cultivation. None of these wines is sold in super markets. What is of paramount importance

here is the seriousness and dedication to his wines of Pierre Ouzoulias who watches ofer them like a mother hen in order to produce the great crus as we like them.

CHÂTEAU PATRIS

Michel Querre
33330 Saint-Émilion
57 24 65 15 – Telex: 571 895 F

Type of vineyard: Family-owned. **Established:** 1967. **Number of employees:** 6. **Vine stocks:** Merlot 85%, Cabernet Sauvignon 15%. **Soil:** Sandy on clay. **Exposure:** Southern slope of St-Émilion. **Average annual production in hectoliters:** 600.

Appellation: St-Émilion Grand Cru. **Type:** Red. **Technique:** Stainless steel tanks. **Maturing:** Casks (25% new each year). **Alcohol content:** 12.5%. **Serving temperature:** 17°. **Served with:** Red meat. **Vintages available in 89/90:** 1985, 1986, 1987.

Characteristics of vintages

1987: Light and elegant, rapid development. **1986:** Already developed, fruity and delicate. **1985:** Rich and well balanced but as yet undeveloped – long keeping. Price range (pre-tax, ex-warehouse): 50 to 80 F.F.

Sales volume:
– Wholesale: 24%. – Retail: 10%. – Restaurants: 66%.
Sales in France: 75%.
Export sales: 25%.
Main trading partners: Belgium, Germany, Denmark, Switzerland, Netherlands, UK, USA.

Abroad

United States
Celliers de France, Los Angeles.

United Kingdom
Waverley Wintness.

Germany
France Vinicole, Kehl/Rhein 7640.

Switzerland
Planteurs Réunis (1800) – Vevey P.P. Box 180.

Belgium
Velus Vins, Brussels.

CHÂTEAU DE PRESSAC

Jacques Pouey
Saint-Étienne-de-Lisse 33330 Saint-Émilion
56 81 45 00 – Telex: 530 955 F

Type of vineyard: Agricultural Association. **Number of employees:** 20. **Vine stocks:** Merlot 67%, Cabernet Franc 26%, Cabernet Sauvignon 5%, Pressac Noir and others 2%. **Soil:** Chalky clay veins in red soil. **Average annual production in hectoliters:** 1,500 to 1,700. **Appellation:** Saint-Émilion Grand Cru. **Type:** Red. **Technique:** In stainless steel and concrete tanks. **Maturing:** In oak casks. **Alcohol content:** 12%. **Characteristics:** Rather full-bodied, pronounced bouquet, rich, harmonious, and well balanced. **Serving temperature:** 18% (room temperature). **Served with:** Game, grilled meat, cheese, chocolate cake. **Vintages available in 89/90:** 1975 to 1985 (except for 1977 and 1984 which have not been bottled).

Characteristics of vintages

1988: Similar to 1982 – intense color, ripe fruit aroma. **1986:** Beautiful structure, pronounced bouquet, rather complex aromas, good keeping. **1985:** Full bodied but not too much so, well balanced, harmonious. Price range (pre-tax, ex-warehouse): 50 to 80 F.F. (1978-1981-1982-1983-1985).

Sales volume:
– Wholesale: 50 %. – Retail: 20 %. – Restaurants: 5 %.
– Other: 25% (export).
Sales in France: 70%.
Export sales: 30%.
Main trading partners: Belgium, Germany, Netherlands, Switzerland.

References in France

Restaurants: Caviar Kaspia, (Paris), Pavillon des Boulevards and Le Vieux Bordeaux, (Bordeaux), Le Rouzic, (Blanquefort), Les Criquets.

Comments

It was at the Château de Pressac, after the Battle of Castillon, that was signed the Peace Treaty which put an end to the Hundred Years War. Vassal de Montviel, proprietor from 1737 to 1747, imported the Auxerrois, a noble vinestock from Quercy, and planted it in his vineyards. Others followed suit and the vinestock took on the name of "Noir de Pressac". This same vinestock was later planted by Lord Malbec in his Médoc vineyards.

SANSONNET
Robin
33330 Saint-Émilion
57 51 03 65

Type of vineyard: Family-owned. **Established:** Family heritage for several generations. **Number of employees:** 3. **Vine stocks:** 60% Merlot, 20% Cabernet Franc, 20% Cabernet Sauvignon. **Soil:** Clay with calcium carbonate. **Exposure:** East of the town of St-Émilion. **Average annual production in hectoliters:** 300.

Appellation: Saint-Émilion Grand Cru Classé. **Type:** Red. **Technique:** Traditional. **Maturing:** In OAK casks. **Alcohol content:** 12%. **Characteristics:** Full bodied, a beautiful color, an agreable sap, forthcoming; a wine for long keeping. **Serving temperature:** 17 to 18°. **Served with:** All meat and cheese. **Vintages available in 89/90:** 1986.

Characteristics of vintages

1986: Must wait, vintage unavailable for tasting. Price range (pre-tax, ex-warehouse): Between 30 and 50 F.F.

Sales in France: 60%.
Export sales: 40%.
Main trading partners : Belgium, Denmark, Germany, Great Britain, Switzerland

References in France

Shops: Direct sales to private individuals.

Comments

The Château Sansonnet, classified a St. Émilion – Great Cru has won top prizes in International Fairs in Paris, Lille, Bordeaux, Liège, Anvers...

CHÂTEAU SAINT-GEORGES CÔTE PAVIE
Jacques Masson
33330 Saint-Émilion
57 74 44 23

Type of vineyard: Family-owned. **Established:** Belongs the family since 1873. **Vine stocks:** Merlot, Bouchet, Cabernet Franc. **Soil:** Clay with calcium carbonate. **Exposure:** South, West. **Average annual production in hectoliters:** 200.
Appellation: Saint-Émilion. **Type:** Red. **Technique:** Traditional. **Maturing:** 18 months to 2 years, at first in vats; then in barrels. **Characteristics:** Forthcoming, full of color and fragrance; charming and elegant; excellent lifetime in bottles; very good for ageing. **Vintages available in 89/90:** 1983, 1984, 1985, 1986 marketed it in May 88.

Characteristics of vintages

1988: Promising but much too early to tell – Wait a few months for a more accurate evaluation. **1987:** Pleasant but not good enough to be considered as a "Grand Cru Classé" – total production downgraded into the Saint-Emilion general appellation. **1986:** Very good vintage, rather close to the '85. **1985:** Exceptional vintage, will be excellent for ageing. **1984:** Light but elegant; very agreeable to taste. **1983:** Robust, very rich and well-balanced; may still be aged, hold. Price range (pre-tax, ex-warehouse): between 50 and 80 F.F.
Sales volume:
– Wholesale: Variable proportion.
Sales in France: Variable.
Main trading partners : Switzerland, England, Belgium.

References in France

Hédiard, Place de La Madeleine, Paris, end 1986 of 1981; Nicolas, 85 and 86 of 1982.

• *Blending – a method consisting of mixing different wines from different lots or different vintages in order to obtain a more homogeneous product.*

CHÂTEAU SOUTARD

Jacques et François des Ligneris
33330 Saint-Émilion
57 24 72 23

Type of vineyard: Family-owned. **Established:** 1782. **Number of employees:** 11. **Vine stocks:** 60% Merlot, 40% Cabernet Franc (Bonschet). **Soil:** Silica clay (20%); clay with calcium carbonate (80%) Silica clay covered. **Average annual production in hectoliters:** 900 to 1,000.

Appellation: Saint-Émilion Grand Cru Classé. **Type:** Red. **Technique:** Traditional, with maceration at the end of the fermentation. **Maturing:** In OAK casks 1/2 new each year. **Vintages available in 89/90:** 1985.

Characteristics of vintages

1985: Beautiful wine, full and distinguished, very successfull, to be aged. Price range (pre-tax, ex-warehouse): Between 50 and 80 F.F.

Sales volume:
– Wholesale: Direct export only. – Retail: France only.
Sales in France: 30%.
Export sales: 70%.
Main trading partners : UK, Belgium, Switzerland, Germany, USA, Holland, Denmark.

References in France

Restaurants: All the great restaurants; ex: Guerard Haeberlin Blanc.

Comments

Continual search for better balance for better as well as better quality and longer life. Visitors welcomed.

• *Would you like to know to recognize the caracteristic fragrances of certains wines, their woodland, fruity, flowery or leather aromas, the evaluate the level of acidity or the presence of tannins, to ascertain the mellowness or the color of a wine...? See the Chapter entitled "The Art and Manner of Wine Tasting".*

CHÂTEAU TERTRE DAUGAY

Comte de Malet Roquefort
33330 Saint-Émilion
57 24 72 15

Type of vineyard: Family-owned. **Established:** 5. **Number of employees:** 7. **Vine stocks:** Merlot 60%, Cabernet Franc 40%. **Soil:** Clay with calcium carbonate, silica, rocky. **Exposure:** Plateau and Southern hillsides and southwest. **Average annual production in hectoliters:** 500.

Appellation: Saint-Émilion Grand Cru Classé. **Type:** Red. **Technique:** Stainless steel tanks, long fermentation. **Maturing:** Merrain oak barrels; new 50%. **Alcohol content:** 12.6°. **Characteristics:** Full body and color; rich and well-balanced, deep color, complex bouquet due to the variety of the soil; tannic and long; typical of the wines of the Cotes in Saint-Émilion. **Serving temperature:** 16° to 17°. **Served with:** Game, fine cheese, red meat. **Vintages available in 89/90:** 1982, 1983, 1986, 1987, 1988.

Characteristics of vintages

1988: Purple color, complex nose, rich aromas (as yet difficult to distinguish), very rich, well-balanced, yet soft and full. A great bottle – for long keeping. One of the best vintages for this Cru. **1987:** Deep ruby color, very flowery nose. Pleasant, much better than expected at harvesting time. Excellent quality/price ratio. **1986:** Deep ruby very rich in tannins, rich and well-balanced. **1985:** Well-balanced, round and long. **1984:** No production. **1983:** Purple: very fruity and lively, well-balanced; great vintage. **1982:** Rich, fortified nose, full of complex aromas, supple, soft and full. Price range (pre-tax, ex-warehouse): 40 to 70 F.F.

Sales volume:
– Wholesale: 90%. – Retail: 10%.
Sales in France: 20%.
Export sales: 80%.
Main trading partners : Switzerland, Germany, Belgium, England, USA.

CHÂTEAU LA TOUR DU PIN FIGEAC MOUEIX

Bernard & Jean-Michel Moueix
33330 Saint-Émilion
57 51 50 63 – Telex: 541 635 AMOUEIX

Type of vineyard: Family-owned. **Established:** 1947. **Vine stocks:** Merlot 60%, Cabernet Franc 30%, Malbec & Cabernet Sauvignon 10%. **Soil:** Old sand and gravel over a layer of blue clay. **Exposure:** Stuated on a hilltop – favorable sunshine. **Average annual production in hectoliters:** 4,000 cases (x12).

Appellation: Grand Cru Saint-Émilion. **Type:** Red. **Technique:** Destemming (90 to 95%). Vinification in concrete vats (2 to 3 weeks). **Maturing:** In oak barrels, for 18 months. Fining with fresh egg whites. **Serving temperature:** Room temperature 19° to 20°. **Vintages available in 89/90:** 1985, 1986, 1987.

Characteristics of vintages

1988: To summarize 1988's grape harvest, we can say that Merlots have produced very harmonious wines, intensely coloured, with very fruity aromas, of exceptional body and very rich in excellent tannins. As regards Cabernets, harvested ten days or so after Merlots, a bright colour with shades of purple and a very well developed fragrance of blackcurrant. They have produced well-balanced and full-bodied wines. **1987:** Soft, well-balanced and full-bodied wines, with fruity aromas and an average tannic power. The wines can keep well, but will soon come to maturity. **1986:** Deep color, very pleasant attack, very round soft and full, rich in alcohol and well-balanced. **1985:** Fresh color, strong, very firm and young, forth coming, rich in alcohol and well-balanced, still very hard and closed. **1983:** Woody, resinous, strong vanilla aroma, very round, soft and full, strong color. **1982:** Strong color, powerful aroma, forthcoming, harmonious, woody, long.

CHÂTEAU TOUR SAINT-CHRISTOPHE

Mr. Guiter
St-Christophe-des-Bardes – 33330 Saint-Émilion
57 24 77 15

Established: 1942. **Vine stocks:** 2/3 Merlot, 1/3 Bouchet. **Soil:** Clay with calcium carbonate.

Appellation: Château Tour Musset. **Type:** Red. **Technique:** Traditional. **Maturing:** In oak casks – 2 years. **Alcohol content:** 12° to 12.5°. **Serving temperature:** 15° to 18°. **Served with:** Red meat. **Vintages available in 89/90:** 1981, 1982, 1983, 1985.

Characteristics of vintages

1985: Well-balanced, very rich. **1983:** Supple, light. **1982:** Very robust, very rich and well-balanced. **1981:** Robust without excess. Price range (pre tax, ex-warehouse): between 30 and 50 F.F.

References in France

Restaurants: Hôtel Pullman (French chain).

CHÂTEAU TROPLONG MONDOT

Christine Fabre-Valette
33330 Saint-Émilion
57 24 70 72

Type of vineyard: Family-owned. **Established:** 18th Century. Belongs to the Family since the beginning of the 20th Century. **Number of employees:** 12. **Vine stocks:** Merlot 65%.. **Average annual production in hectoliters:** 1,000.

Appellation: Grand Cru Classé Saint-Émilion. **Typel** Red. **Technique:** Traditional. **Served with:** Meat and cheese. **Vintages available in 89/90:** 1985, 1983.

Characteristics of vintages

1985: Good vintage, promising, hold. Price range (pre-tax, ex-warehouse): Between 80 and 100 F.F.
Sales volume:
– Wholesale: 95%. – Retail: 5%.
Sales in France: 20%.
Export sales: 80%.
Main trading partners : Belgium, England.

References in France

Restaurants: Maxim's (Paris).

CHÂTEAU DU VIEUX GUINOT

Jean-Pierre Rollet
St-Étienne-de-Lisse
33330 St-Émilion
57 47 15 13 – Telex: 570 598 Libo/Rollet

Type of vineyard: Family-owned since 1729. **Vine stocks:** Merlot 55%, Cabernet Franc 25%, Cabernet Sauvignon 20% on 13 hectares. **Soil:** Clay with calcium carbonate. **Average annual production in hectoliters:** 80,000 bottles.
Appellation: Saint-Émilion Grand Cru. **Type:** Red. **Technique:** Traditional, destemming and thermoregulation at 27 to 29°C. **Characteristics:** Good color and aroma, fine and rich, good keeping. **Serving temperature:** 17°. **Served with:** Roasts, meat, game. **Vintages available in 89/90:** 1986, 1985.

Characteristics of vintages

1986: Promising vintage. **1985:** Good year. Structured, full and fragrant wine, for keeping.

CHÂTEAU TROTTEVIEILLE

Mr. Casteja
86, Cours Blaguerie-Stuttenberg
33300 Bordeaux
56 48 57 57 – Telex: 550 766

Type of vineyard: Family-owned. **Vine stocks:** Cabernet Franc 45%, Carbenet Sauvignon 10%, Merlot 45%. **Soil:** Chalky. **Exposure:** South. **Average annual production in hectoliters:** 400.
Appellation: Saint-Émilion 1er Grand Cru Classé. Type: Red. **Technique:** Traditional – under the supervision of Prof. Ribereau-Gayon. **Maturing:** In new barrels. **Alcohol content:** 12% to 13%. **Characteristics:** Full-bodied wine with a combination of vigor, firm body and aroma, abundant but smooth tannin, racy, distinguished, vanilla overtones, fruity, balanced, always a success thanks to a remarkable soil composition. **Serving temperature:** Cellar temperature 19° to 20° (seems preferable). **Vintages available in 89/90:** 1986.

Characteristics of vintages

1986: Great wine, in keeping with the 1985 vintage, very promising. **1985:** Stocks practically depleted. **1984:** Stocks practically depleted. **1983:** Stocks practically depleted. **1982:** Stocks depleted.
Sales volume:
– Wholesale: 100% to Borie-Manoux. Wine Merchants.

References in France

Restaurants: Mainly restaurants with Michelin Stars.
Shops: Hédiard, Fauchon, Fine Grocers, etc.

CHÂTEAU VILLEMAURINE GRAND CRU CLASSÉ SAINT-ÉMILION

Robert Giraud
33330 Saint-Émilion
57 43 01 44 – Telex: 540 798 F

Type of vineyard: Family Corporation. **Vine stocks:** Merlot 70%, Cabernet Sauvignon 30%.
Appellation: Saint-Émilion. **Alcohol content:** 12%. **Characteristics:** Forthcoming, very colored, rich and well-balanced, tannic. **Serving temperature:** Around 16° to 18°. **Served with:** All red meat or game. **Vintages available in 89/90:** 1985, 1983, 1982.

Characteristics of vintages

Price range (pre-tax, ex-warehouse): between 50 and 80 F.F.
Sales volume: 55,000 bottles.
– Wholesale: Exclusive marketing by the maison Robert Giraud S.A. – Retail: 10%. – Restaurants: 60%. – Other: 30% fine shops, specialized shops.
Sales in France: 35%.
Export sales: 65%.
Main trading partners : Canada, USA.

LUSSAC-SAINT-ÉMILION

CHÂTEAU DE TABUTEAU

Mr Bessou
Château Durand – La Plagne – 33570 Puisseguin
57 74 63 07

Type of vineyard: Family-owned. **Established:** 1982. **Vine stocks:** Merlot 70%, Cabernet Franc 15%, Cabernet Sauvignon 15%. **Soil:** Silica and clay on an iron-clay club-soil. **Average annual production in hectoliters:** 720. **Appellation:** Lussac-St-Émilion. **Type:** Red. **Technique:** Traditional, very long maceration. **Maturing:** Concrete and stainless steel tanks. **Alcohol content:** 12.6%. **Characteristics:** Fine, robust, typical Merlot stock. **Serving temperature:** 16° – 18°. **Served with:** Meat and cheese. **Vintages available in 89/90:** 1978, 1979, 1981, 1983, 1985.

Characteristics of vintages

1985: Good quality/price ratio. Order now. Do not hesitate. **1983:** Gold Medal, at the Agricultural Competition in Paris. **1982:** Out of stock. Price range (pre-tax, ex-warehouse): between 20 and 50 F.F.

VIGNOBLES TROCARD

Jean-Louis Trocard
Les Artiques de Lussac
57 24 31 16

Type of vineyard: Family Corporation (father and son). **Established:** Time immemorial... **Number of employees:** 17. **Vine stocks:** Merlot 70%, Cabernet Franc 15%, Cabernet Sauvignon 15%. **Soil:** Clay with calcium carbonate for the St Émilion; gravel for the Bordeaux and Lalande Pomerol. **Average annual production in hectoliters:** 2,500.
Appellation: Lussac-Saint-Émilion, Lalande de Pomerol, Bordeaux Supérieur. **Typel** Red. **Technique:** Traditional. **Maturing:** In casks for the Château de la Croix des Moines; in vats for others. **Alcohol content:** 12.5%. **Characteristics:** Château Trocard, Bordeaux Supérieur: fruity, body. Château La Croix des Moines Lalande de Pomerol: ruby color, onctuous. Château Croix de Rambeau, Lussac-Saint-Émilion. **Serving temperature:** 17°. **Vintages available in 89/90:** 1975, 1978, 1979, 1981, 1982, 1983, 1984, 1985, 1986.

Characteristics of vintages

1986: To be aged, very well-balanced, tannic. **1985:** This vintage of great renown gives supple tannins, soft, full wines. **1984:** Light, agreeable; to be drunk in 2 to 3 years. **1983:** With body, very rich and well-balanced, persistant final. **1982:** Good promise, fruity, aromatic, very round. **1975:** Agreeable wine: to be drunk now, very good quality. Price range(pre-tax, ex-warehouse): between 10 F.F. and 20 F.F., 20 F.F. and 30 F.F., 30 F.F. and 50 F.F.
Sales volume:
– Wholesale: 30%. – Retail: 50%. – Restaurants: 10%. – Other: 10% caves.
Sales in France: 70%.
Export sales: 30%.
Main trading partners : Belgium, Luxemburg, Denmark, Germany.

MONTAGNE-SAINT-ÉMILION

CHÂTEAU CALON

Jean-Noël Boidron
33570 Montagne
56 96 28 57

Type of vineyard: Family-owned. **Vine stocks:** Merlot 70%, Bouchet 15%, Cabernet Sauvignon 12%, Malbec 32%. **Soil:** Clay with calcium carbonate; Sub-soil of asteriated opal in limestone. **Exposure:** East/Southeast. **Average annual production in hectoliters:** 1,200.
Appellation: Montagne-Saint-Émilion. **Type:** Red. **Technique:** Harvesting and grape selection done by hand – Long maceration – temperature control. **Maturing:** Casks and barrels. **Alcohol content:** 12.2%. **Characteristics:** Fruity, fresh, robust, long finish. Concentrated but not heavy. Rich in natural extracts. **Serving temperature:** 17°. **Vintages availables in 89/90:** 1985, 1983, 1982, 1981, 1979, 1974.

Characteristics of vintages

1985: Very fruity, raspberry, sloe and violet aromas. Full and well-balanced. **1983:** Amber color, fruity, spicy. Beautiful balance, robust, long finish. **1982:** Vanilla, mulberry, liquorice flavor. Intense and rich. Soft and full, well-balanced. **Note:** 1981: Amber color, rich, concentrated, sloe, leather, tobacco, spicy fragrance. 1979: Rich, fresh, firm. Very fruity and robust. Fully developed. 1974: amber color, ages remarkably well tannic, firm. Tobacco, leather fragrances. Price range (pre-tax, ex-warehouse): 30 – 50 F.F.
Sales volume:
– Wholesale: 80%. – Retail: 15%. – Restaurants: 5%.
Sales in France: 60%.
Export sales: 40%.
Main trading partners : Belgium, Luxemburg, Denmark, USA.

CHÂTEAU BELLEVUE

Robert Gaury
33870 Montagne
57 74 62 24

Established: For several generations. **Vine stocks:** Merlot 80%, Cabernet 10%, Bouchet 10%. **Soil:** Clay with calcium carbonate, rocky. **Exposure:** Hillsides - to the South. **Average annual production in hectoliters:** 800.

Appellation: Montagne-Saint-Émilion. **Type:** Red. **Technique:** Traditional. **Alcohol content:** 12.5%. **Characteristics:** Finesse, beautiful ruby color, good structure, aromatic with ageing. **Served with:** Roasts, cheese. **Vintages available in 89/90:** 1962, 1972, 1977, 1981, 1982, 1983, 1985 Primeur through September 1987 and 1986 Primeur.

Characteristics of vintages

1986: Very promising. Hold. **1985:** Excellent wine. rich and fine, good for ageing. do not hesitate. **1984:** Not suitable for bottling. **1983:** Good for ageing. **1982:** Good. **Note:** Try to get hold a few old vintages (superb 1962 &1972). **Sales volume:**
- Wholesale: 50%.
- Retail: 50 %.

Main trading partners : Belgium, Switzerland, Germany.

Comments

Traditional wine production and vinification techniques.

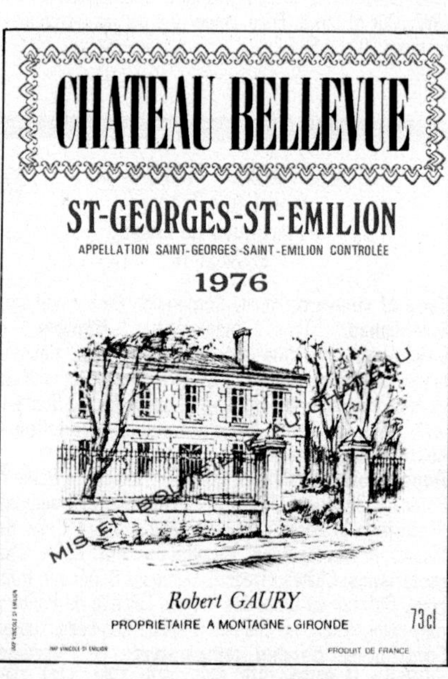

• *Read labels carefully – An indication to watch out for: "Bottled in the 'region' of production", which often refers to a blend of wines from several producers and not just one.*

CHÂTEAU LA BERGÈRE

Pierre & Geneviève Yerles
33570 MONTAGNE
57 74 65 53

Type of vineyard: Family-owned. **Established:** 1980. **Number of employees:** 1. **Vine stocks:** Merlot en 1,3%, Cabernet Sauvignon en 2,3%. **Soil:** Chalky clay. **Exposure:** South facing the northern boundary of St-Émilion. **Average annual production in hectoliters:** 360.

PRODUIT DE FRANCE
1983
MIS EN BOUTEILLE AU CHATEAU
CHÂTEAU LA BERGÈRE
MONTAGNE - SAINT-EMILION
APPELLATION MONTAGNE-SAINT-EMILION CONTRÔLÉE
750ml
PIERRE & GENEVIEVE YERLES, PROPRIETAIRES A MONTAGNE - GIRONDE - FRANCE

Appellation: Montagne-Saint-Émilion. **Type:** Red. **Technique:** Traditional. **Maturing:** Stainless steel tanks. **Alcohol content:** 11 to 12%. **Characteristics:** Firm and lively, full-bodied, beautiful color, well balanced, fine bouquet. **Serving temperature:** 18°. **Served with:** Red meat and cheese. **Vintages available in 89/90:** 1985, 1986, 1988.

Characteristics of vintages

1985: Very great wine, solid, structured, fine, tannic. Price range (pre-tax, ex-warehouse): 20 to 30 F.F.

Sales volume:
– Wholesale: 50%. – Retail: 50%.

Main trading partners : Germany, USA, Belgium, Netherlands, Switzerland.

CHÂTEAU PETIT CLOS DU ROY MONTAGNE SAINT-ÉMILION

François Janoueix
20, quai du Priourat – B.P. 135
33502 Libourne Cedex
57 51 55 44 – Telex: F 571 962 JAFRANC

Type of vineyard: Family-owned. **Established:** Winemakers for 3 generations. **Vine stocks:** Merlot 80%, Cabernet Franc 20%. **Soil:** Clay – heavy and deep. **Exposure:** Jonction of St-Émilion, Pomerol, Neac, Montagne. **Average annual production in hectoliters:** 700. **Appellation:** Montagne-Saint-Émilion. **Type:** Red. **Technique:** Traditional, manually harvest, long fermentation on skins – 20 days. **Maturing:** In vats with temperature regulation, then ageing in oak barrels. **Alcohol content:** 11.5%. **Characteristics:** Lighter but more fruity, beautiful color. **Serving temperature:** Room temperature, 18° to 19°. **Served with:** All meats, perfect with certain fish dishes such as "Lamprey à la Bordelaise". A fish specialty. **Vintages available in 89/90:** 1985, 1983.

Characteristics of vintages

1985: Harmonious, very well-balanced, very fragrant, look for rapid development. **1983:** Beautiful deep color, delicate aroma of ripe red fruit, slightly woody. Price range (pre-tax, ex-warehouse): between 30 and 50 F.F.

CHÂTEAU LACOSTE CHÂTAIN

Philippe Junquas, Mrs. Martine Junquas
Châtain Néac 33500 Libourne
57 74 02 79

Type of vineyard: Family-owned. **Established:** 1985. **Vine stocks:** Merlot 65%, Cabernet Franc 20%, Cabernet Sauvignon 15%. **Soil:** Acid, extremely variable, alluvial eclay, gravel and iron clay. **Exposure:** Slight slope, part of the Pomerol and St.Emilion plateau. **Average annual production in hectoliters:** 150.

Appellation: Montagne-Saint Emilion. **Type:** Red. **Technique:** Harvested at optimal maturity – daily pumping over, permanent temperature control, frequent testing. **Maturing:** Stainless steel tanks, pumping over and aeration every 40 days. **Alcohol content:** 12%. **Characteristics:** Powerful aromas, noted for their structure (see below). **Serving temperature:** 17-18°. **Served with:** meat, cheese. **Vintages avaitable in 89/90:** 1986, 1987, 1988.

Characteristics of vintages

1988: Rich aroma, intense color, round, exceptional vintage. **1987:** Fresh and flowery bouquet, rich and long finish, crystallized fruit aroma. **1986:** Intense aromas coming from very ripe harvesting, round and well balanced, soft and rich tannins. Beautiful finish, very rich for this perfectly balanced wine. Price range (pre-tax, ex-warehouse): 20 to 30 F.F.

Sales volume:
– Wholesale: 50%. – Retail: 50%.

Sales in France: 95%. **Export sales:** 5%.

Main trading partners : Belgium.

Comments

Philippe Junquas is an agronomist engineer. Martine is a oenologue. They created this winemaking establishment in 1985, bringing to it all of their technical know-how and the results of their research in order to obtain an optimum product. They also produce wine under the appellation Lalande-de-Pomerol (Château Haut-Châtain) and Bordeaux-Supérieur (Domaine du Châtain).

CHÂTEAU MAISON NEUVE

Michel Coudroy
33570 Montagne
57 74 62 23

Type of vineyard: Family-owned. **Established:** 16th century. **Number of employees:** 9. **Vine stocks:** Merlot Rouge 80%, Cabernet Sauvignon 20%. **Soil:** Chalky clay. **Average annual production in hectoliters:** 2,000.

Appellation: Montagne – St.-Émilion. **Type:** Red. **Technique:** Traditional, long fermentation on skins. **Maturing:** Stainless steel and concrete tanks. **Serving temperature:** 18°. **Served with:** Grilled meat, poultry, soft cheese. **Vintages available in 89/90:** 1978, 1979, 1981, 1983, 1985, 1986, 1987, 1988.

Characteristics of vintages

1988: Full-bodied, ripe fruit aroma, rich and well balanced substantial. **1987:** Fresh and long. **1986:** Rich and well balanced, touch of grilled meat and spices. **1985:** Full, sharp tannins, elegant. Price range (pre-tax, ex-warehouse): 10 to 20 F.F.

Sales volume:
– Wholesale: 50%. – Retail: 50%.

Sales in France: 50%.

Export sales: 50%.

Main trading partners : USA, Belgium, UK.

Abroad

United States

Air lines.

United Kingdom

Viticulteur 16 Anson road, London NW2 3UT.

Germany

Welog Wein und logistik Breitwieser ohg – In Dun Veingaerten – 6504 Oppenhein/Rhein.

Belgium

Bollaert – Remue Wijnen Import T Wijnhuis – Mundelgemsesteenweg 286 – 9220 Melelbeke – Verhelle Ter Merenlaan 51 B 1930 Zaventem.

Comments

Winemakers at the Château Maison-Neuve, from father to son, since the 16th century. Many awards from various competitions testify to the efforts of the proprietor who personally vinifies and matures all of his harvests.

VIEUX CHÂTEAU SAINT-ANDRÉ

Jean-Claude Berrouet
Montagne – 33570 Lussac
57 51 01 14

Type of vineyard: Family-owned. **Established:** 1979. **Vine stocks:** Merlot 75%, Cabernet Franc 20%, Cabernet Sauvignon 5%. **Soil:** Clay with calcium carbonate. **Exposure:** South and south-west. **Average annual production in hectoliters:** 250.

Appellation: Montagne Saint-Émilion. **Type:** Red. **Technique:** Traditional (3 weeks). **Maturing:** Barrels. **Alcohol content:** 12.3°. **Characteristics:** Lively vermilion color, lively nose vith flowery notes, tannic structure, classic but always harmonious, aromatic with finesse at the end. **Serving temperature:** 18°. **Served with:** Red and white meat, roasts or grilled fouds. **Vintages available in 89/90:** 1986.

Characteristics of vintages

1988: Deep color, rich and complex aromas. Good tannic balance, beautiful constitution. Classic wines for long keeping. **1987:** Supple wine, fruity, developing rapidly, unpretentious but full of charm. **1986:** Light and supple year, quicker evolution; great distinction. **1985:** Very successfull, combines finesse and constitution; good, aromatic with harmony. **1984:** Out of stock. price range (pre-tax, ex-warehouse): between 20 and 30 F.F.

Sales volume:
– Wholesale: 90% Bordeaux Vintage in France. – Retail: 9%. – Restaurants: 1%.

Sales in France: 60%.

Export sales: 40%.

Main trading partners : England, Canada, Luxemburg, Japan, Belgium.

Abroad

United Kingdom

Bordeaux Direct (The Wine Club).

Luxemburg

Resuma S.A.

Canada

S.A.Q.

Japan

Japan Barclay and Company Inc.

Australia

Smith & Son PTY Ltd.

Comments

Œnologist of Etz, consulting J.-P. Moueix, winemaker of Petrus since 1964.

PUISSEGUIN-SAINT-ÉMILION

CHÂTEAU DURAND LAPLAGNE

Mr. Bessou
33570 Puisseguin
57 74 63 07

Type of vineyard: Family Corporation. **Established:** 1982. **Number of employees:** 4. **Vine stocks:** Merlot 70%, Cabernet Franc 15%, Cabernet Sauvignon 15%. **Soil:** Hillsides and plateau of Puisseguin. **Average annual production in hectoliters:** 585.
Appellation: Puisseguin St-Émilion. **Type:** Red. **Technique:** Traditional, very long maceration. **Maturing:** Concrete and stainless steel tanks. **Alcohol content:** 12.6%. **Characteristics:** Robust, beautiful ruby color, body and breed. **Serving temperature:** 16° - 18°. **Served with:** Meat and cheese. **Vintage available in 89/90:** 1979, 1980, 1981, 1985.

Characteristics of vintages

1985: Gold Medal, Concours Agricole de Paris (Agricultural Competition) Very successful, full-bodied and structured, good for ageing. **1984, 1983, 1982:** Out of stock. Price range (pre-tax, ex-warehouse): between 20 an 50F.F.
Sales volume:
- Wholesale: 30%. - Retail: 20%. - Other: 50% (export).
Sales in France: 50%.
Export sales: 50%.
Main trading partners : Belgium, Netherlands, Switzerland, UK, Germany.

• *Please note that all temperatures in this book are expressed in degrees Centigrade.*

CHÂTEAU SOLEIL

Jean Soleil, Mlle D. Soleil, Mme D. Garcie.
Puisseguin, Saint-Émilion, 33570 Lussac
57 74 63 46

Type of vineyard: Family-owned. **Established:** 1799. **Number of employees:** 6. **Vine stocks:** Merlot 70%, Cabernet Sauvignon 15%, Cabernet Franc 15%. **Soil:** Chalky clay on rocky sub-soil. **Exposure:** Plateau and hillsides South, South-West. **Average annual production in hectoliters:** 900 maximum.
Appellation: Puisseguin-St. Émillion. **Type:** Red. **Technique:** Long and traditional, almost total destemming, careful temperature control since 1975. **Maturing:** 3 years in oak casks and vats. **Alcohol content:** 12.7%. **Characteristics:** Full bodied, tannic without being aggressive, fruity, typical of a great St. Émillion. **Serving temperature:** 17 to 19°. **Serving with:** Red meat, game, poultry, cheese, etc. **Vintages available in 89/90:** 1983, 1985, 1986, 1987.

Characteristics of vintages

1988: Will not be available before 1991. **1987:** Very beautiful success for the year, light and fruity. **1986:** Very beautiful wines, tannic, full bodied, these 3 vintages are first rate. Price range (pre-tax, ex-warehouse): between 20 and 50 F.F.
Sales volume:
– Retail: 75%. – Restaurants: 5%. – Other: 20% export, wholesale.
Sales in France: 80%.
Export sales: 20%.
Main trading partners : United Kingdom, Belgium, Germany, Netherlands, Denmark, Switzerland.

References in France

Restaurants: Restaurant Marc Demund (Bordeaux), Restaurant Le Croque Note (Bordeaux), Auberge des Criquets (Bordeaux Blanquefort).
Shops: L'Amour du Vin (Rue St. Dominique, Paris) and several smaller shops.

Abroad

Switzerland

Promovias S.A., Mr. Scarbonc, 2103 Noiraigue/N.E. Tel: 02 673 45 98.

The Netherlands

Inter-Caves B.V., Mr. J.W. Kampman, 8000 AM Zwolle. Tel: 038 69 69 69.

Belgique

Ets. Vinalgros Mr. Dewulf, 1160 Bruwelles. Tel: 02 673 45 98.

Denmark

Ets. Hoyer Vinimport, Mr. & Mrs. Hoyer, 2660 Bronby-Strand. Tel: 02 73 17 11.

Comments

Today, Jean Soleil, the present proprietor of the Château Soleil, aided by his daughter Dominique and a group of highly competent assistants and well known œnologists (in the tradition of Émile Peynaud, one of the world's best known œnologists), produces a « Very Great Wine which is a product of nature, associated with advanced technology and know-how, in the service of the purest Bordeaux traditions ». (Spread the word!). It has received a number of gold, silver and bronze medals at various competitions in Paris, Bordeaux and Mâcon. It has also received awards such as the Prix d'Excellence and the Grand Prix d'Excellence from the Union National des Œnologues of Bordeaux, Colmar and Narbonne.

ST-GEORGES-ST-ÉMILION

CHÂTEAU CALON

Jean-Noël Boidron
33570 Montagne
56 96 28 57

Type of vineyard: Family-owned. **Vine stocks:** Merlot 80%, Bouchet 10%, Cabernet Sauvignon 10%. **Soil:** Hillsides, clay with calcium carbonate on asteriated opal in limestone. **Exposure:** South. **Average annual production in hectoliters:** 280.
Appellation: Saint-Georges, Saint-Émilion. **Type:** Red. **Technique:** Hand harvest with selection of bunches. Long maceration, temperature control. Fermentation with natural grape leavening agents. **Maturing:** In barrels and casks. **Alcohol content:** 12.2%. **Characteristics:** Rich color, robust, well-balanced, high tannic content, very soft and full. Fruity and spicy. Vanilla aroma, amber color, musky with ageing – very long finish. **Serving temperature:** 17°. **Served with:** Meat. **Vintages available in 89/90:** 1985, 1983, 1982, 1980, 1976, 1973.

Characteristics of vintages

1985: Very fruity, intense, slight vanilla aroma, robust, exceptional. Rich and well-balanced. Very great wine. **1983:** Deep color. Strawberry, mint, spicy, slightly woody aroma. Intense tannin, silky texture. **1982:** Vanilla, mulberry, sloe, strawberry fragrance. Soft tannin. Rich, well-balanced and long. **Note:** 1980: delicate woody fragrance, fruity. Remarkable balance. Good concentration. 1976: bouquet of aged wine, soft and full, robust concentrated wine. 1973: amber color, fine and firm. At its peak. Price range (pre-tax, ex-warehouse): 30 F.F. – 50 F.F.
Sales volume: – Wholesale: 50%. – Retail: 50%.
Sales in France: 60%. **Export sales:** 40%.
Main trading partners : Switzerland, Denmark, Luxemburg.

CHÂTEAU ST GEORGES

Petrus Desbois
Montagne, 33570 Lussac
57 74 62 11

Type of vineyard: Family Association. **Established:** 1974. **Number of employees:** 30. **Vine stocks:** Merlot 60%, Cabernet Sauvignon 20%, Cabernet Franc 20%. **Soil:** Chalky clay. **Exposure:** South, South-West. **Average annual production in hectoliters:** 1,900.
Appellation: Saint Georges, St-Emilion. **Type:** Red. **Technique:** Stainless steel tanks and wooden casks. **Maturing:** In oak vats 1/2 new each year. **Alcohol content:** 11.5%. **Characteristics:** Supple, fruity and long. Good ageing potential. **Vintages available in 89/90:** 1983, 1985, 1986, 1987.

Characteristics of vintages

1986: Superb, bright color, truffle and red berry bouquet.
1985: Great year, very deep color, fine and delicate nose, forthcoming, round and supple. Price range (pre-tax, ex-warehouse): 50 to 80 F.F.
Sales volume:
– Retail: 100%.
Sales in France: 70%.
Export sales: 30%.
Main trading partners: Canada, USA, European countries, Japan.

Abroad

United Kingdom

Friarwood London.

Germany

Movenpick Kellereien.

Switzerland

Ets Reichemuth.

Belgium

Ets de Conink.

Canada

LCBO – SAQ.

The Netherlands

Hustinx.

Far East

Japan Seiwa, Tokyo.

Comments

As a result of a traditional devotion to vine and wine, these marvellous "Mises du Château" possess the qualities which make the fame of the great Bordeaux wines; suppleness, taste, balance and elegance.

> • *Watch out for wines that lose their authenticity, most often because of carbonic maceration (see Roussillon, South-west, Périgord...).*

VINS DE CÔTES

PREMIÈRES CÔTES-DE-BLAYE

CHÂTEAU BERTINERIE

Daniel Bantegnies
Cubnezais 33620 Cavignac
57 68 70 74

Type of vineyard: Family-owned.
Appellation: Premieres cotes de Blaye. **Type:** Red, White. **Technique:** traditional. **Maturing:** Red: in casks. **Characteristics:** White: delicate, intense bouquet, flowery, rich and well balanced – Red: excellent, marked by the soil, well colored, supple. **Serving temperature:** White: 12°, Red: 16°. **Vintages available in 89/90:** 88-87-86-83.

Characteristics of vintages

1988: beautiful white, perfectly controlled vinification. **1987:** good year, fruity wines, good development. **1986:** remarkable, red, classical, very aromatic, combining balance, richness and finesse, excellent keeping.

Comments

Like the Grands Crus Classés, the Premières Côtes-de-Blaye rouge are matured in new oak casks, which accounts for their delicate woody aroma. Wine from grapes grown on lyre-supported vines.

CHÂTEAU CHANTE ALOUETTE

Georges Lorteaud
Plassac – 33390 Blaye
57 42 16 38

Type of vineyard: Family-owned. **Established:** Beginning of this Century. **Number of employees:** 3. **Vine stocks:** Merlot 60%, Cabernet 25%, Malbec 15%. **Soil:** Clay with calcium carbonate. **Exposure:** South and southeast. **Average annual production in hectoliters:** 900 to 1,000.
Appellation: Premières Côtes-de-Blaye. **Type:** Red. **Technique:** Traditional. **Maturing:** Tanks and new barrels. **Alcohol content:** 12%. **Characteristics:** Brillant, elegant ruby, well-bred, well-balanced, harmonious. **Serving temperature:** 16°. **Served with:** Game (white meat), roast lamb, grilled or roast duck, mild cheese, Bordeaux lamprey (fish). **Vintages available in 89/90:** 1981, 1982, 1983, 1985.

Characteristics of vintages

1985: Great year, ruby, rich and well-balanced, well-bred, good evolution. **1983:** Limpid, pleasant, supple, clear, ready now. **1982:** Great year, brillant, elegant, round, harmonious. **1981:** Limpid, fruity, supple, ready now. Price range (pre-tax, ex-warehouse): between 20 and 30 F.F.
Sales volume:
– Wholesale: 15%. – Retail: 60%. – Restaurants: 5%. – Other: 20% (big shops).
Sales in France: 80%.
Export sales: 20%.
Main trading partners : Belgium, Switzerland.

CHÂTEAU L'ESCADRE

SCEV Georges Carreau & Fils
Cars – 33390 Blaye
57 42 36 57

Type of vineyard: Agricultural Corporation. **Established:** 1982. **Number of employees:** 10 plus the Château Les Petits Arnauds. **Vine stocks:** Merlot 75%, Cabernet Sauvignon 15%, Malbec 10%. **Soil:** Clay with calcium carbonate, clay sub-soil. **Exposure:** South, and northeast. **Average annual production in hectoliters:** 1,650.
Appellation: Premières Côtes-de-Blaye (red), Blayais (white). **Type:** Red, white. **Technique:** Traditional. **Maturing:** 1 year in wooden-casks and cement vats, 6 months in barrels. **Alcohol content:** 12°. **Characteristics:** Not too robust, great finesse when young, supple, fruity, ruby color. May be drunk after 5 years and up until 15 years, on the average. **Serving temperature:** 16°. **Served with:** Red meat, white meat, sauces. **Vintages available in 89/90:** 1977, 1979, 1981, 1983, 1984, 1985 (86 aptitude may 88).

Characteristics of vintages

1986: Very young, good constitution, but less tannic than the '85 apparent alcohol, good color, hold. **1985:** Good color very tannic, excellent bouquet; good for ageing. **1984:** Light, agreeable to drink, for all occasions. **1983:** Vintage quite fruity and fragrant juices. **1982:** Tannic, beautiful color, great year. **1979:** Supple and very agreeable, to be drunk. **Note:** 1977: Light and fruity. Price range (pre-tax, ex-warehouse): between 20 and 30 F.F.
Sales volume:
– Wholesale: 40%. – Retail: 40%.
Sales in France: 50%.
Export sales: 50%.
Main trading partners : Belgium, UK, USA, Gabon.

References in France

Restaurants: La Tupina, Bordeaux. La Citadelle, Blaye.
Shops: Vinothèque Bordeaux, Ets Lagrue.

Comments

Also exploit "Château Les Petits Arnauds", 23 ha in high Côtes-de-Blaye: Very characteristic wine for the appellation "Château L'Escadre". Family vineyard since 1850. Named L'Escadre, because the first owner was a naval officer. He had given it the name: "His Escadre".

CHÂTEAU LES CHAUMES
Robert Parmentier
Fours 33390 Blaye
57 42 18 44

Type of vineyard: Agricultural Association. **Established:** 18th century. **Number of employees:** 5. **Vine stocks:** 10% Malbec, 40% Merlot, 50% Cabernet. **Soil:** Chalky clay. **Exposure:** North and South. **Average annual production in hectoliters:** 1,000.
Appellation: Premières Côtes de Blaye. **Type:** Red. **Technique:** Long fermentation on stems and maceration. **Maturing:** In oak casks for 15 months. **Alcohol contents:** 11.7%. **Characteristics:** Lightly tannic, red fruit taste, excellent conservation. **Serving temperature:** 18° in winter, 16° in summer. **Served with:** All meats, grilled or in sauce; first courses, pies and pastries. **Vintages available in 89/90:** 1986, 1987, 1988.

Characteristics of vintages

1988: Well colored, rich and well balanced, for keeping. **1987:** Agreeable, fresh and supple. **1986:** Good wine, dominated by the structure of the soft tannins, can be drunk but can also be kept. Price range (pre-tax, ex-warehouse): between 10 and 20 F.F.
Sales volume:
– Wholesale: 10%. – Retail: 50%. – Restaurants: 10%. – Other: 30% export.
Sales in France: 70%. **Export sales:** 30%.
Main trading partners : Belgium, Netherlands, United Kingdom.

GRAND VIN DE BORDEAUX
CHATEAU
LES CHAUMES
PREMIÈRES COTES DE BLAYE
APPELLATION PREMIERES COTES DE BLAYE CONTROLEE
1985
12% Vol.
75cl
ROBERT PARMENTIER
PROPRIETAIRE A FOURS - GIRONDE - FRANCE
MIS EN BOUTEILLE AU CHATEAU
FRANCE

Comments

Excellent, charming proprietor, enthousiastic, very much attached to tradition.

CHÂTEAU GASSIES
Jean
Route de Brun 33360 Lataline
56 86 14 27 – 56 44 60 10

Type of vineyard: Agricultural association. **Established:** 1985. **Vine stocks:** Merlot 70%, (8 hectares). **Exposure:** chalky clay.
Appellation: Premieres Cotes de Bordeaux. **Type:** Red. **Technique:** traditional. **Maturing:** casks – 1/3 new each year. **Characteristics:** well colored, fragrant, woodland aromas, dense, rich and well balanced. **Serving temperature:** 16°. **Served with:** meat, roasts. **Vintages available in 89/90:** 87, 86, 85.

Characteristics of vintages

1988: still in casks. **1987:** rather well controlled, supple, rich bouquet. **1986:** excellent wine, well colored, dense, full, long, good development. Price range (pre-tax, ex-warehouse): 30 to 50 F.F.

References in France

Shops: L'Amour du Vin, 94, rue St. Dominique, 75007 – Paris.

CHÂTEAU DU GRAND BARRAIL

Denis Lafon
Cars 33390 Blaye
57 42 33 04

Type of vineyard: Family-owned. **Established:** 1967. **Number of employees:** 4. **Vine stocks:** Merlot 70%, Malbec 10%, Cabernet 20%. **Soil:** Chalky clay **Exposure:** Hillsides. **Average annual production in hectoliters:** 400.

Appellation: Premières côtes-de-Blaye. **Type:** Red, white. **Technique:** Traditional. **Maturing:** In wooden casks (partly new). **Alcohol content:** 12%. **Characteristics:** Fruity, tannic, rich in color, ripe fruit aroma thanks to the Merlot. **Serving temperature:** 16°. **Served with:** Red meat, cheese. **Vintages available in 89/90:** 1986, 1987, 1988.

Characteristics of vintages

1988: Very great year, full, round, rich in color, tannic. **1987:** Sometimes judged too soon and too harshly – supple, and fruity, very pleasant when drunk young. **1986:** Well-balanced, tannic, aromatic, very good year. Price range (pre-tax, ex-warehouse): 15.50 F.F.
Sales in France: 40%.
Export sales: 60%.
Main trading partners : Belgium, Netherlands, Germany, Denmark.

Abroad

United Kingdom

Agent: Corcalinebtal Overseas Wines Cheshire WA14 5QJ Tel. 061-976 3696.

Germany

Poullig Ambermeshous Dusseldorf 0211 733 4807.

Belgium

Qualivino – Liers – 03.4890223 – Mirouin-Liège. 041435992 – De Comink Brussels 02 6731722.

The Netherlands

De Druivemtros Uggelen 055334449 – Jean Berger Roemond 0475032966.

CHÂTEAU LES GRAVES

R. Pauvif
"St-Vivien" – 33920 St-Savin
57 58 90 88 or 57 42 47 37

Type of vineyard: Family-owned. **Established:** 1885. **Vine stocks:** Merlot Noir, Cabernet Franc and Sauvignon. **Soil:** Gravelly clay. **Exposure:** Hillsides South and Southwest. **Average annual production in hectoliters:** 800. **Appellation:** 1st Côtes-de-Blaye-Bordeaux. **Type:** Red, rosé. **Technique:** Traditional for the fermentation, with complete destemming. **Maturing:** In vats. **Alcohol content:** 12% to 12.5%. **Characteristics:** Raised on gravelly terrain, wine very aromatic (good nose), not very tannic with finesse. After ageing, a touch of raspberry and a bouquet of ripe fruit. **Serving temperature:** 18° to 19°. **Served with:** All meats (white and red). I recommend my wine for the entire meal. **Vintages available in 89/90:** 1985, 1986, 1987, 1988.

Characteristics of vintages

1988: Balanced and harmonious, rich, tannic, to be kept. **1987:** Supple, fruity and round. Ready. **1986:** Hold. **1985:** Great vintage, roundness, tannins and aromas in perfect harmony, to be aged. Average pre-tax, ex-warehouse price: 23 F.F. for the 1985.
Sales volume: – Retail: 100%. **Sales in France:** 100%.

CHÂTEAU LES JONQUEYRES

Pascal Montaut
Courgeau – 33390 St-Paul-de-Blaye
57 42 34 88

Type of vineyard: Family-owned. **Established:** 1977. **Vine stocks:** Merlot 90%, Cabernet Franc 5%, Malbec 5%. **Soil:** Deep clay on limestone. **Average annual production in hectoliters:** 100.
Appellation: Premières Côtes-de-Blaye. **Type:** Red. **Technique:** Fermentation with skins 20 to 30 days in cement vats. **Maturing:** Oak barrels: 50% new, plus 50% on year old. **Alcohol content:** 13%. **Characteristics:** Richness of the Merlot. **Serving temperature:** 17° to 18°. **Served with:** Game, red meat, cheese with character. **Vintages available in 89/90:** 1985 and 1986 with reservation from Sept. 87. **Vintages available in 89/90:** 1986, 1987.

Characteristics of vintages

1988: This vintage was vinified under the motto: to acquire finesse without losing richness, and it was a success. Fantastic body with a lingering aftertaste of black fruit. Tannins of wine matured in new oak casks (2 monts). Interesting results of maturing in heated casks. **1987:** Red fruit, fine taste of the wood (short stay). Good balance and body, good finish due to grape tannins. Deserves better than the reception given to the 87 vintage a year ago.

Sales volume:
– Wholesale: 15%. – Retail: 80%. Restaurants: 5%.
Sales in France: 90%. **Export sales:** 10%.
Main trading partners : Belgium, Netherlands, Germany, Switzerland.

Comments

The only wine the Blayais which almost only Merlot. Produced from vines 30 to 80 years old in very dense plantation.

CHÂTEAU LARDIÈRE

René Bernard
33860 Marcillac
57 32 41 38

Type of vineyard: Family-owned. **Established:** Several generations. **Vine stocks:** Red: merlot 50%, Cabernet Sauvignon 50%. White: Sauvignon, Sémillon, Colombard. **Soil:** Gravelly clay. **Exposure:** Hillsides to the South. **Average annual production in hectoliters:** 450.

VIN DE BORDEAUX
1986
1986
Médaille d'Or Concours International en Blayais-Bourgeais 1987
CHATEAU
LARDIÈRE
Premières Côtes de Blaye
APPELLATION PREMIÈRES CÔTES DE BLAYE CONTRÔLÉE
VIEILLI EN FÛTS DE CHÊNE
René BERNARD
Propriétaire-Viticulteur à Marcillac 33 France
Tél. 57.32.41.38
12%vol.
MIS EN BOUTEILLES AU CHATEAU
75cl

Appellation: Côtes-de-Blaye Blanc, 1ᵉˢ Côtes-de-Blaye Rouge, Bordeaux Supérieur Blanc Moelleux, Bordeaux Méthode Champenoise. **Type:** Red, White. **Technique:** Continuous pressing, separation of juice, temperature control. **Maturing:** In stainless steel tanks – ageing in oak casks. **Alcohol content:** 12%. **Characteristics:** White (dry): beautiful pale yellow color, intense fragrance, very typical. To be drunk young with oysters and all seafood. Red: deep color, ripe fruit aroma, round, charming, rich and well balanced, harmonious, good keeping. **Serving temperature:** Red: 18°. White: 10°. **Served with:** Red: red and white meat, cheese. White (dry): seafood and hors d'œuvre. **Vintages available in 89/90:** Red: 1987, 1986. White (dry): 1988.

Characteristics of vintages

1988: Dry white: very aromatic and firm. Excellent red. **1987:** Red: developing well. **1986:** Red: balanced and harmonious, good ageing potential, Gold Medal (Bourg sur Gde. 1987) – also available in 150 cl. Price range (pre-tax, ex-warehouse): 10 to 20 F.F. Blanc sec 1988 – 20 to 30 F.F. Rouge 1986.
Sales volume: – Wholesale: Red 20% – White 60%. – Retail: Red 80% – White 30%. – Restaurants: White 5%. – Other: (cellars) White 5%.
Sales in France: 60%. **Export sales:** 40%.
Main trading partners : Germany, Belgium, USA.

References in France

Restaurants: Hôtel des 3 Canards (17350 Arvert).
Shops: Caves Vauban (33370 Blaye), Nicolas (29, avenue Jean-Jaurès 92140 Clamart), Bouquet (13, bd Pasteur 17390 La Tremblade), Giraudet "Huchegrolle" (85580 Triaize).

Abroad

United States

Mr. Yves Fedrigault 8917 Mangum Pl. Alex Va 22308, Baltimore.

Germany

Acco Communication Gmbh Never Wall, 54200 Hambourg 36 – Promt Handelgeselbschaft MBH Import, 2201 Bevern Union Rheinbraun Gmbh, Köiner Strasse 38 D 5047 Wesseling.

Belgium

Mr. Euler Antwerpsedreef 105, 2153 Zoersel.

GFA DE LAGARCIE

Philippe De Lagancie
Le Crusquet Cars – 33390 Blaye
57 42 15 21

Type of vineyard: Family Corporation. **Established:** Became a Corporation in 1975. **Number of employees:** 12. **Vine stocks:** Merlot 60%, Cabernet Sauvignon 35%, Malbec 5%. **Soil:** Clay with calcium carbonate. **Average annual production in hectoliters:** 1,800.
Appellation: 1ᵉʳ Côtes de Blaye. **Type:** Red. **Technique:** Cement vats and oak casks long fermentation with skins (20 days). **Maturing:** In barrels, regularly renewed. **Alcohol content:** 12°. **Characteristics:** Ruby color, finesse owing to the Cabernet Sauvignon ages well, long tannin. **Serving temperature:**16°. **Served with:** Red meat and game, cheese. **Vintages available in 89/90:** 1986, 1987, [1988, in June 1990].

Characteristics of vintages

1988: Rich and well-balanced, deep color, tannic, good keeping. **1987:** Supple, harmonious, should develop rapidly. **1986:** Round, supple, quickly developed. **1985:** Dark color, long tannin, long, ripe fruit. Price range (pre-tax, ex-warehouse): between 23 and 30 F.F.
Sales volumes: – Retail: 95%. – Restaurants: 5%.
Sales in France: 98%. **Export sales:** 2%.
Main trading partners : England, Nederland.

CHÂTEAU LA RIVALERIE

Joël Pauvif
BP 3 - 33390 Saint-Paul de Blaye
57 42 18 84 - Telex: 571 765 - Telefax: 57 42 12 39

Type of vineyard: Corporation. **Established:** 1972. **Number of employees:** 7. **Vine stocks:** Cabernets 57%, Merlot 40%, Cot 3%. **Soil:** Clay with calcium carbonate, clay sub-soil. **Exposure:** Plateau. **Average annual production in hectoliters:** 50.
Appellation: Premières Côtes-de-Blaye. **Type:** Red. **Technique:** Traditional with rigorous temperature control during vinification. **Maturing:** Stainless steel tanks and oak casks for 2 to 3 months. **Alcohol content:** 12.2°. **Characteristics:** Important percentage of Cabernet. Exceptional for the appellation; the wines are very objective, and agreeable to be drunk young. Good capacity for ageing. **Serving temperature:** 15° to 16° (recommended oxygenation). **Served with:** Fish: jugged burbot. Meat: wild boar, venison. **Vintages available in 89/90:** 1986, 1987, 1988.

Characteristics of vintages

1988: Intense color, complex aromas, round, excellent structure, no aggressivity. **1987:** Lovely color, very elegant, very delicate aromas. Very pleasant, to be drunk young. **1986:** Very typical Cabernet. Delicate aromas, good structure, long finish. To be kept. **1986:** Promising. **1985:** Exceptional vintage, long life, full and good flavor, fragrant, full, to be aged. Price range (pre-tax, ex-warehouse): between 17 and 18 F.F.
Sales volume:
– Retail: 40%. – Restaurants: 30%. – Other: 30%.
Sales in France: 60%.
Export sales: 40%.
Main trading partners : Belgium, England, Denmark, Germany, Switzerland, Holland, Australia, Luxemburg.

References in France

Restaurants: L'Oustau de Baumanière, Troisgros, Lameloise Julien, Le Vaudeville, L'Auberge Bretonne, Bœuf sur le Toit.
Shops: The "Flo Prestige". Chain of restaurants and caterers.

Comments

The Château La Rivalerie introduced to this initiative, plus exceptional cultivation techniques, won the great Departemental Gold Medal for the Château in 1870.

CHÂTEAU MAGDELEINE BOUHOU

Mr. Rousseau, Père et fils
Cars 33390 Blaye
57 42 19 13

Type of vineyard: Family-owned. **Established:** 1895. **Number of employees:** 4. **Vine stocks:** Merlot 55%, Cabernet 40%, Malbec 5%, Sauvignon, Sémillon, Muscadelle. **Soil:** Chalky clay. **Exposure:** Plateau, South-West. **Average annual production in hectoliters:** Red: 1,500 – White: 150.

GRAND VIN DE BORDEAUX
Chateau
Magdeleine Bouhou
PREMIÈRES COTES DE BLAYE
Appellation Premières Côtes de Blaye Contrôlée
1985
G.A.E.C. DES VIGNOBLES ROUSSEAU Père et Fils
Récoltants à Cars (Gironde) France
12%Vol. MIS EN BOUTEILLE AU CHATEAU 75 cl

Appellation: 1ᵉʳ Côtes-de-Blaye AOC, Bordeaux & AOC. **Type:** Red, White, Rosé. **Technique:** Traditional. **Maturing:** In oak casks. **Alcohol content:** 12%. **Characteristics:** Supple, robust, fruity, very good ageing potential. **Serving temperature:** 18°. **Served with:** Red meat, game. **Vintages available in 89/90:** 1988, 1986, 1985.

Characteristics of vintages

1988: White (dry). **1987:** Red. **1986:** Red: deep color, tannic, long, very good vintage. **1985:** Red: harmonious, supple, fruity, can be aged 15 to 20 years. Price range (pre-tax, ex-warehouse): 10 to 20 F.F.
Sales volume:
– Wholesale: 15%. – Retail: 80%. – Restaurants: 5%.
Main trading partners : Belgium, Germany, USA.

CHÂTEAU SOCIONDO

Michel Elie
33390 Blaye
57 42 12 49 – Telex: 571 765 – TELEFAX 57 42 12 39

Type of vineyard: Family-owned. **Established:** 1902. **Number of employees:** 1. **Vine stocks:** Merlot 63%, Cabernet Sauvignon 27%, Cabernet Franc 10%. **Soil:** Chalky clay with stones on chalk sub-soil. **Exposure:** Beautiful, well exposed hillcrest. **Average annual production in hectoliters:** 55 hl/ha.

Appellation: Premières Côtes de Blaye. **Type:** Red. **Technique:** Traditional in stainless steel tanks, temperature control. **Maturing:** In oak casks for 2 to 3 months, then in stainless steel tanks. **Alcohol content:** 12.2%. **Characteristics:** Beautiful ruby color, round and soft tannins, very good structure, supple and long. **Serving temperature:** 14 to 15°. **Served with:** Grilled meat, mutton chops. **Vintages available in 89/90:** 1986, 1987, 1988.

Characteristics of vintages

1988: Beautiful deep color, harmonious, rich, soft and full. **1987:** Light in color and structure, drink in 5 years or so. **1986:** Marked by Cabernet, good keeping, tannin presence, firm, soft and full. Price range (pre-tax, warehouse): 10 to 20 F.F.

Sales volume:
– Retail: 70%. – Restaurants: 15%. – Other: 15% (cellars).
Sales in France: 85%.
Export sales: 15%.
Main trading partners : Denmark, Belgium, Netherlands, Switzerland, Germany.

References in France

Restaurants: Paris: Chez les Anges, Bauman, la Tour d'Argent. Strasbourg: Le Crocodile. Mulhouse: le Moulin de Kaegy.
Shops: Petrissans, Caves des Gobelins, Jacques Mélac.

Abroad

Germany

Le Vigneron Français, Hanauer Strasse 12, D 6360 Friedberg (Tel: 49 0603112888).

Switzerland

Sordet Dominique, 9, rue de St-Jean, CH 1211, Geneva (Tel: 41 22 45 92 92). Cave du Léman, Avenue du Léman 34, CH 1005 Lausanne (Tel: 41 21 28 68 68).

Belgium

Cedimar, 122, rue de la Glacerie, 6180 Courcelles (Tel: 32/71455991).

The Netherlands

Beckers et Timmers, Wilhelminastraat 38, 6131 KR Sittard (Tel: 44 9025810).

Others

Denmark: Fransk Vinimport, Mr Moeller, Periknovej 10 Seys, Dr. Silkeborg (Tel: 68 45 188).

Comments

Since 1979, Michel Elie has been making wines produced on the family estate. Beautifully situated, the buildings of the enterprise are harmoniously distributed around an imposing central courtyard. Very limited quantities are produced on this rather small vineyard of less than 10 hectares.

CHÂTEAU PEYBONHOMME-LES-TOURS

S.C.E.A. des Vignobles Bossuet Hubert
Ltd. Château Peybonhomme – Cars
33390 Blaye
57 42 11 95

Type of vineyard: Agricultural Association (family-owned). **Established:** 1883. **Number of employees:** 13. **Vine stocks:** Merlot, Cabernet Sauvignon, Cabernet Franc, Malbec. **Soil:** Clay and calcium carbonate on limestone. **Exposure:** Hillsides – West-East and slopes North-south. **Average annual production in hectoliters:** Around, 3,500.

Appellation: Premières Côtes-de-Blaye. **Technique:** Long fermentation with temperature control (30°). **Maturing:** In vats for 18 months, fining, filtration, racking under pressurized air (several times). **Alcohol content:** 12%. **Characteristics:** Supple but tannic wines, good keeping. Ripe fruit taste when young, reach full maturity in 8 to 15 years, depending upon the vintage. **Serving temperature:** 1986: 15°. 1985: 18°. **Served with:** Red meat and game. **Vintages available in 89/90:** 1986, 1987 until the end of 1989, 1988 as of September 1989.

Characteristics of vintages

1986: Harmonious, good body, supple, fleshy, raspberry flavor, pronounced Cabernet character.
Sales in France: 60%.
Export sales: 40% (April 1987).
Main trading partners : Belgium, Germany, Luxemburg, Switzerland, UK, Netherlands, Denmark, Ivory Coast, Japan.

PREMIÈRES CÔTES-DE-BORDEAUX

CHÂTEAU ANNICHE

Michel Pion
Vignobles Michel Pion - Langoiran - 33550 Haux
56 23 05 15 - Telex: PION 572 083 F

Type of vineyard: Family-owned. **Established:** 1971. **Number of employees:** 7. **Vine stocks:** Cabernet Sauvignon and Franc 60%, Merlot 30%, Malbec 10%. **Soil:** Plateau – silica-clay, slopes – silica-clay and gravel. **Exposure:** South and East. **Average annual production in hectoliters:** 3,000.
Appellation: Premières Côtes-de-Bordeaux. **Type:** Red. **Technique:** Traditional. **Maturing:** Stainless steel tanks for a year, then bottling. **Alcohol content:** 12%. **Characteristics:** Ruby color, pleasant bouquet, fine and fruity. **Serving temperature:** Between 16° and 18°. **Served with:** Red meat. **Vintages available in 89/90:** 1985 and 1986.

Characteristics of vintages

1985: Ruby color, powerful fragrance, tannins still a bit rough, taste of ripe fruit. Price range (pre-tax, ex-warehouse): between 10 F.F. and 20 F.F.
Sales volume:
- Wholesale: 10%. - Retail: 40%. - Restaurants: 5%.
- Other: 45% (staff associations).

Sales in France: 30%.
Export sales: 70%.
Main trading partners : European Common Market, Switzerland, Japan, Canada, USA.

• To help us improve our next edition, please send in your suggestions and answer our questionnaire.

CHÂTEAU BARREYRE

Lucien Viollet
33550 Langoiran
56 67 20 52

Type of vineyard: Family-owned. **Established:** Very old, renovated 1962. **Number of employees:** 4. **Vine stocks:** 50% Merlot, 25% Cabernet Sauvignon, 25% Cabernet Franc. **Soil:** Silica clay on chalky subsoil. **Exposure:** South-West. **Average annual production in hectoliters:** 450.

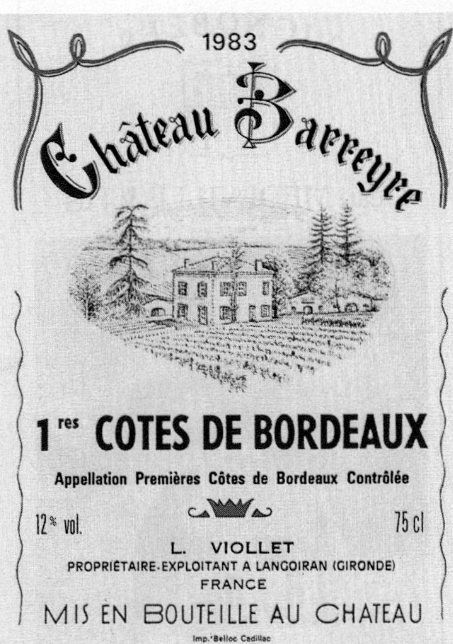

1983
Château Barreyre
1res COTES DE BORDEAUX
Appellation Premières Côtes de Bordeaux Contrôlée
12% vol.
75 cl
L. VIOLLET
PROPRIÉTAIRE-EXPLOITANT A LANGOIRAN (GIRONDE)
FRANCE
MIS EN BOUTEILLE AU CHATEAU
Imp. Belloc Cadillac

Appellation: Premières Côtes de Bordeaux. **Type:** Red. **Technique:** Traditional. **Maturing:** Alternating between vats and casks. **Alcohol content:** 12%. **Characteristics:** Wines to be kept. Full bodied, long, beautiful sustained color. **Serving temperature:** 17 to 18°. **Vintages available in 89/90:** 1982, 1983, 1985, 1986, 1987, 1988.

Characteristics of vintages

1988: Very good wine. Great year. **1987:** Good wine for average keeping, quite successful, beautiful color. **1986:** Full bodied and fruity. Very good wine for keeping. **1985:** Very great year, superb wine to drink now or to keep. Price range (pre-tax, ex-warehouse): between 20 ant 30 F.F.
Sales volume:
- Wholesale: 20%. - Retail: 80%.

Sales in France: 75%.
Export sales: 25%.
Main trading partners : Belgium, Germany, Luxemburg, Switzerland.

CHÂTEAU FAYAU

Jean Medeville and sons
Château Fayau, 33410 Cadillac
56 62 65 80

Type of vineyard: Family-owned. **Established:** 1896. **Number of employees:** 9. **Vine stocks:** Merlot, Cabernet, Sémillon, Sauvignon. **Soil:** Chalky and silica clay. **Average annual production in hectoliters:** 1,800.

Appellation: Red: Premières Côtes de Bordeaux, Bordeaux Supérieur. White: Cadillac, Bordeaux Blanc. **Type:** Red, white. **Technique:** Traditional with temperature control. Destemming for the reds. **Maturing:** In stainless steel tanks. **Alcohol content:** 12%. **Characteristics:** Red: supple and full bodied. Naturally Sweet Wines: Round with the fragrance of overripe grapes. Dry: fruity. **Serving temperature:** Red: 17°. White: 7 to 8°. **Served with:** Red meat. Dry: Fish and shellfish. Naturally Sweet: as an aperitif or with foie gras and poultry. **Vintages available in 89/90:** Red: 1985, 1986, 1987. Dry: 1988. Naturally Sweet: 1986, 1987.

Characteristics of vintages

1987: Very supple wines with red berry aromas. **1986:** Fresh aromas, delicate. **1985:** Beautiful color, rich, well balanced, very ripe grapes, quite tannic. Price range (pre-tax, ex-warehouse): between 20 and 30 F.F.
Sales volume:
- Wholesale: 80%. - Retail: 15%. - Restaurants: 5%.
Sales in France: 60%. **Export sales:** 40%.
Main trading partners : Benelux Countries, United Kingdom, Germany, United States, Switzerland;

References in France

Restaurants: Hôtel Oustau de Baumanière (Baux-de-Provence), Hôtel Bas Bréau (Barbizon), Hôtel Castiglionne (Paris), Hôtel Concorde La Fayette (Paris).
Shops: Nicolas.

Abroad

United States
Direct Import Wines, Des Plaines, Illinois. Wine Imports of Poughkeepsie, New York.

United Kingdom
Morris and Verdin, 28 Churton Street, London. MM F & E May ltd, London.

Germany
Ets Weigand, Mainzer Strasse 54, Bingen.

Belgium
Ets Cedimar SA., Courcelles 6180.

The Netherlands
Ets Boomsma, leewarden.

Switzerland
Scherrer Carouge.

Others
Denmark, Ets N. & Paul Plum, Mecobenzo.

Comments

The domain, located on the right bank of the Garonne, has been operated by the Medeville family since 1826. The famous hilltops of the Premières Côtes de Bordeaux produce red and white wines for which the region is reknowned. (See also Château Boyrein/Graves).

CHÂTEAU DU BIAC

Nicole Ducatez
33550 Langoiran
56 67 19 98

Type of vineyard: Family-owned. **Established:** 1977. **Vine stocks:** Sémillon, Sauvignon, Merlot, Cabernet Sauvignon. **Soil:** Gravel, clay with calcium carbonate. **Expo-**

sure: South. **Average annual production in hectoliters:** 500.

Appellation: 1er Côtes-de-Bordeaux, Rouge, Blanc et Blanc Sec (red, white and dry white). **Type:** Red, white. **Technique:** Traditional red and white; with temperature control. **Maturing:** Barrels, red and sweet white. **Alcohol content:** 12.5° red and dry white, 13.5° sweet white. **Characteristics:** Brilliant color, finesse, bouquet, good ending, great capacity with ageing. **Serving temperature:** Red: 18°. White: 8° to 10°. **Served with:** Red: meat, game, cheese. White (sweet): as an aperitif. Dry white: seafood, fish. **Vintages available in 89/90:** 1979, 1981, 1982.

Characteristics of vintages

1985: Excellent, full, round, well-balanced, sustained color, very fruity. **1983:** Already good developement, beautiful, brillant color, very ripe fruit aromas. **1982:** Great finesse of aromas, excellent ending. **1979:** Light, great finesse of aromas. Price range (pre-tax, ex-warehouse): between 10 and 20 F.F. 20 and 30 F.F. for red, white.

Sales volume:
– Retail: 75%. – Restaurants: 5%. – Other: 20% (fine caves, specialized shops).
Sales in France: 60%.
Export sales: 40%.
Main trading partners: Germany, Belgium, England, USA.

References in France

Restaurants: Relais et Châteaux, Chain.
Shops: Very fine wine cellars Paris & Province.

CHÂTEAU BRETHOUS

François and Denise Verdier
33360 Camblanes
56 20 77 76

Type of vineyard: Family-owned. **Established:** 1760: owned by the Verdier family since 1963. **Number of employees:** 4. **Vine stocks:** Merlot 45%, Cabernet Franc 25%, Cabernet Sauvignon 20%, Malbec 10%. **Soil:** Pebbly gravel over red clay and limestone. **Exposure:** South and West. **Average annual production in hectoliters:** 650. **Appellation:** Premières Côtes de Bordeaux and Bordeaux Clairet. **Type:** Red. **Other:** Clairet. **Technique:** Fermentation in pressure tanks for 15 days at 28° – 30°C, pumping over twice a day, then draining, followed, as quickly as possible, by malo-lactic fermentation. **Maturing:** In casks (18 months) then bottles. Part is matured in barrels. **Alcohol content:** 12%. **Characteristics:** Very typical, well-balanced, elegant tannin and very good ageing potential. Red berry flavor, then later prune, with ageing. **Serving temperature:** 16° – 18° depending on the vintage. **Served with:** Red or white meat, particularly good with leg of lamb or steak. Soft cheese: Camember, Brie, Reblochon. Almost everything except salads and asparagus. **Vintages available in 89/90:** 1985, 1986.

Characteristics of vintages

1986: Very young, but quite promising. **1985:** Beautiful vintage, Gold Medal at the Concours Régional de Bordeaux, 1986 Regional Competition in Bordeaux. Rich tannin, red currant and blackcurrant fragrance, great elegance. **Note:** Be sure to taste the Clairet, a beautiful rosé, seductive, lively and robust at the same time. Price range (pre-tax, ex-warehouse): 20 F.F. – 30 F.F.

Sales volume:
– Wholesale: 10%. – Retail: 80%. – Restaurants: 10%.
Sales in France: 85%.
Export sales: 15%.
Main trading partners: Ireland, Germany, Belgium, Netherlands.

Abroad

United Kingdom
Quinnworth, Dublin (Ireland).

Germany
Stéphane de Castelbajac, Muhlstrasse 66, 69 Heidelberg.

The Netherlands
Heisterkamp, 7630 AB Ootmarsum, Oostwal 5.

Belgium
De Landtshher, Mandekenstraat 209, 9360 Buggenhout – P.V.B.A. Pigeon d'Or, Meerstraat 80, 8790 Waregen.

Comments

The Château Brethous probably dates back to the Roman Settlement in Aquitaine. The present Estate was built by Mr. Brethous, a Bordeaux Magistrate, in the 18th Century. It was taken over by Mr. et Mrs. Verdier in 1963.

• *Read labels carefully – An indication to watch out for: "Bottled in the 'region' of production", which often refers to a blend of wines from several producers and not just one.*

• *To help us improve our next edition, please send in your suggestions and answer our questionnaire.*

• *The 1980 vintage is badly understood. In Bordeaux the wines are already quite surprising and will do quite well while waiting for the development of the other vintages. See "The last five vintages" in the Chapter on Bordeaux wines.*

• *Please note that all temperatures in this book are expressed in degrees Centigrade.*

CHÂTEAU LAMOTHE

Fabrice Neel
Haux - 33550 Langoiran
56 23 05 07 - Telex: 571 383 F

Type of vineyard: Agricultural Association. **Established:** 1976. **Number of employees:** 8. **Vine stocks:** 60% Merlot, 50% Cabernet Sauvignon, 10% Cabernet Franc. **Soil:** Chalky clay. **Exposure:** South, South-West. **Average annual production in hectoliters:** 2,500.
Appellation: Premières Côtes de Bordeaux. **Type:** Red, white. **Technique:** Fermentation with temperature control, long maceration, checked daily. **Maturing:** In casks. **Alcohol content:** 12°. **Charateristics:** Many references and Gold Medals for these first rate wines of the region. Number 1 in the Decanter Panel - Tasting of January 1988. **Serving temperature:** 19°. **Vintages available in 89/90:** 1986, 1987.

Characteristics of vintages

1988: White: a very fruity white wine, supple, round, with a long and fresh finish. **1987:** Red: ageing in new oak casks gives this vintage a fine woody touch. **1986:** Red: deep color, fine woody nose, rich, well balanced and full bodied, will age well. Price range (pre-tax, ex-warehouse): between 18 and 26 F.F.
Sales in France: 30%.
Export sales: 70%.

Main trading partners: United States, Germany, Belgium, Switzerland, United Kingdom, Spain, Denmark, Netherlands, Japan, Singapore.

References in France

Restaurants: Amat, Saint-James.
Shops: Fauchon (Paris), Manuel and Lasseur (Switzerland), Harrods (London).

Abroad

United States
Vintners International, New York.

United Kingdom
Rodney Densen Wines, Nantwich CW5 7JW.

Germany
Marwede (Hamburg), Brueder-Buchner (Passau), Wein 0 Glas (Berlin).

Switzerland
Manuel and Lassuer (Cuisier).

Belgium
Justin Monard (Zonhoven), Vossen (Lennik), Saute (Charneux).

The Netherlands
Van Vissen (Maastricht).

Far East
Budohtei Wine Cellar, Tokyo, Japan. Franchetau (Singapore).

Others

Denmark: Jorgensens (Hellerup). Spain: Covifra (Barcelona).

Comments

A 46 hectare vineyard, planted on hillsides, most of which, oriented South South-West, benefits from a maximum of sunshine. Château Lamothe is a family property managed by Fabrice, oenological would suggest, adding. Château engineer and his wife Anne, who make it a point of honor to produce their wines and commercialize them, without outside help, for a clientele with whom they they have a very special relationship. Note: maturing in casks is now on the way to being very well controlled.

CHÂTEAU GRAND MOUEYS

Aimé Icard, Managers
33550 Capian
56 72 31 01

Type of vineyard: Agricultural Association. **Established:** very old (Knights Templars of the middle ages). **Number of employees:** 6. **Vine stocks:** Red: Merlot, Cabernet Franc, Cabernet, Sauvignon. White: Sauvignon and Sémillon. **Soil:** Chalky clay and gravel. **Exposure:** Mostly South, a bit West. **Average annual production in hectoliters:** Red: 1400. White: 400.

Appellation: Premières Côtes de Bordeaux Rouge and Bordeaux Blanc. **Type:** Red, white. **Technique:** Red: traditional. White: low temperature fermentation and maceration. **Maturing:** Red: in vats. White: on lees. **Alcohol content:** Red: 12.5%. White: 12%. **Characteristics:** White: elegant, fruity, very rich and well-balanced, aromatic. Red: ruby color, tannic and agreeable. To be drunk very young or after a few years ageing. **Served with:** Red: leg of lamb, meat. White: fish and shellfish. **Vintages available in 89/90:** 86, 87, 88.

Characteristics of vintages

1988: Rich and very well-balanced, can age a long time. **1987:** Fine, agreeable wine, very fragrant, will be at its best in 2 years. **1986:** Red: Gold Medal, Concours Général Agricole, Paris 1988. Price range (pre-tax, ex-warehouse): between 20 F.F. and 30 F.F.
Sales volume:
– Wholesale: 80%. – Retail: 10%. – Restaurants: 5%. – Other: 5% (industrial works committees).
Main trading partners : UK.

References in France

Shops: Drugstore (Champs Elysées, Paris).

Abroad

United Kingdom

Paul Boutinot, Stockport.

CHÂTEAU LA CLYDE

G.A.E.C. Cathala
Tabanac – 33550 Langoiran

Type of vineyard: Family vineyard. **Established:** 1939. **Number of employees:** 4. **Vine stocks:** Merlot 55%, Cabernet 40%, Cot 5% (Malbec). **Soil:** Clay with calcium carbonate and gravel. **Exposure:** South, Southwest. **Average annual production in hectoliters:** 800.
Appellation: Premières Côtes-de-Bordeaux. **Type:** Red, white (dry or sweet), rosé. **Maturing** Merrain oak casks for the red only. **Alcohol content:** 12.5%. **Characteristics:** Red: rich and well-balanced, to be aged. White dry: supple and easily digestible. Rosé: fruity. **Served with:** Red: all meats. White dry: fish. **Vintages available in 89/90:** 1985, 1986.

Characteristics of vintages

1986: Promising vintage. **1985:** Very good year, notably for the reds, round and fragrant. Price range (pre-tax, ex-warehouse): between 12 and 20 F.F.
Sales volume:
– Wholesale: 20%. – Retail: 80%.
Sales in France: 70%. **Export sales:** 30%.
Main trading partners : United Kingdom, Germany, Belgium, Netherlands, Ivory Coast.

Abroad

United Kingdom

Cristopher Lynas, 12 Fairfield Road, Ayr Scotland. Allo: 203.267461.
Wine Import – Edinburgh – T. 031 553 4601.

Germany
Klippel, 6464 Linsengericht. Allo: 069 843 142.
Gastronomie Pütter, 2000 Hamburg 13. Allo: 44 45 30.

The Netherlands + Belgium
Particular Clientele.

Africa
Exclusive Sales in Ivory Coast: Sté Tastevin, Abidjan. Allo: 225 35 58 30.

CHÂTEAU LA ROCHE

Julien and Martine Palau
33880 Baurech
56 21 31 03 - Telex: PALFORD 541 665

Type of vineyard: Corporation. **Established:** 1976. **Number of employees:** 7. **Vine stocks:** Merlot 60%, Cabernet-Sauvignon 20%, Cabernet Franc 15%, Malbec 5%. **Soil:** Gravel and clay with calcium carbonate. **Exposure:** North-South. **Average annual production in hectoliters:** 1,000.

PRODUCE OF FRANCE
GRAND VIN DE BORDEAUX
CHATEAU LAROCHE
PREMIERES COTES DE BORDEAUX
Appellation premières Côtes de Bordeaux contrôlée
MIS EN BOUTEILLE AU CHATEAU
1986
12% vol.
75cl. e
JULIEN ET MARTINE PALAU, PROPRIÉTAIRES A BAURECH 33880 FRANCE

Appellation: 1res Côtes de Bordeaux Rouge and Bordeaux Blanc. **Type:** Red, white. **Technique:** In concrete and stainless steel tanks (15 to 21 days) - pre-fermentation maceration for whites. Cuvée Spéciale in tanks. **Maturing:** In "Laroche Bel Air" barrels. **Alcohol content:** Approx. 12%. **Characteristics:** Young wines - red berry aroma, full-bodied later developing an elegant and complex bouquet of spices and undergrowth. **Serving temperature:** 15-16°. **Served with:** Roasts and grilled meat. **Vintages available in 89/90:** 1981 - 1983 - 1985 - 1986.

Characteristics of vintages

1986: Rich color and full-bodied – intense aroma of ripe fruit, soft tannins, lovely finish – promising. **1985:** Typical of the year. **1983:** Not yet developed. Very elegant, subtle bouquet with ageing. **Note:** 1981: Try it right now. Strong scent of undergrowth, distinguished, harmonious. Average pre-tax, ex-warehouse price: 18 F.F.-20 F.F.

Sales volume:
- Wholesale: 3%. - Retail: 90%. - Restaurants: 2%.
- Others: 1% (cellars).

Sales in France: 90%.
Export sales: 10%.
Main trading partners: UK, Netherlands, Germany, Switzerland.

References in France

Restaurants: Several small parisian and regional restaurants.

Abroad

United Kingdom
Borg Castel Wine Merchants – Samlesbury Bottoms, Preston PR 5 ORN.

Germany
Gourment Galerie and Enno Folkert Weinagentur (München).
Restaurants: Hotel vier Jahreszeiten (München).

The Netherlands
Verkruijsen and De Lange.

Switzerland
Restaurants: Hotel Richmond (Geneva).

CHÂTEAU MELIN

Claude Modet
33880 Baurech
56 21 34 71

Type of vineyard: Family-owned. **Number of employees:** 7. **Vine stocks:** Red: Merlot, Cabernet Sauvignon – White: Sémillon, Sauvignon. **Soil:** Sandy clay on gravel or chalk. **Exposure:** South. **Average annual production in hectoliters:** 500.
Appellation: Premières Côtes de Bordeaux. **Type:** Red, White, Rosé. **Maturing:** 12 months in oak casky *Alcohol cintent:* 12.5%. **Characteristics:** Red: well colored, woodland aroma, rich and well-balanced, soft and full. White: fruity and fresh. **Serving temperature:** Red: 17°, White: 6-8°. **Served with:** Red: red meat, game – White: shellfish. **Vintages available in 89/90:** Red: 1986, White: 1988.

Characteristics of vintages

1986: Beautiful ruby color, very fruity, ripe fruit aroma, full bodied, woodland fragrance. Price range (pre-tax, ex-warehouse): 20 F.F. to 30 F.F.
Sales volume:
- Retail: 60%. - Restaurants: 15%. - Other: 25% (export).

Sales in France: 75%.
Export sales: 25%.
Main trading partners: Switzerland, Belgium, Netherlands, Denmark.

Comments

In 1850, a family of laborers workerd in the communes of Baurech and Tabanac for the Bourgeois, well known mem-

bers of the Bordeaux nobility who owned winegrowing estates in the region; this was the Modet family. Thanks to their strenuous efforts, they were able to put a little aside, bit by bit, with which, to acquire parcels, owner-operated or share-cropped farms, that luxury, high living and waste obliged their owners to sell. It was in this way that Maurice Modet, grandfather of the present owner (on the cart in the photo on the "Château Constantin" label) became, in 1908, the owner of a part of Melin. His father, Louis, had, several years earlier, bought part of Constantin. Successions and partitions interfered with the rapid reconstruction of the two domains, in spite of additional purchases. But everything always went forward in the framework of a cordial family relationship. It was André Modet, father of the present owner, who reconstituted the Melin domain and leased a part of Constantin. This latter was partly acquired in 1972 from the Dubourg family and the rest, in 1979, from the Barbe heirs. Thus, after 70 years of work, the two domains were finally restructured. On top of the hills skirting the right bank of the Garonne (altitude 95 m), an sandy clay soil over gravel or chalk, excellent wines are produced, both red and white.

CHATEAU MELIN
PREMIÈRES-COTES-DE-BORDEAUX
APPELLATION PREMIERES COTES DE BORDEAUX CONTROLEE
1986
Nº 10049
12,5% vol.
Claude MODET
75cl
PROPRIÉTAIRE A BAURECH - GIRONDE - FRANCE
MIS EN BOUTEILLE AU CHATEAU
PRODUIT DE FRANCE

CHÂTEAU PUY BARDENS

Yves Lamiable
33880 Cambes
56 21 31 14 – Telefax: 56 21 86 40

Type of vineyard: Family Agricultural Association. **Number of employees:** 2 (1 permanent – 1 temporary). **Vine stocks:** Cabernet Sauvignon 50%, Cabernet Frac 10%, Merlot 40%. **Soil:** Chalky clay and gravel. **Exposure:** Plateau and hillsides – facing full South. **Average annual production in hectoliters:** 550.
Appellation: Premières côtes de Bordeaux, Bordeaux Rosé. **Type:** Red, rosé. **Technique:** In stainless steel tanks – temperature control, maceration (15 to 20 days). **Maturing:** In oak casks (30% new). **Alcohol content:** 12.5%. **Characteristics:** Rich and well-balanced, tannic, ruby color, good keeping (10 to 12 years) – Bordeaux (rosé): a favorite for the summer. **Serving temperature:** Red: 16-17° – Bordeaux (rosé): 8-10°. **Served with:** Red and white meat. **Vintages available in 89/90:** 1984, 1985, 1986. Rosé: 1988.

GRAND VIN DE BORDEAUX
CHATEAU
Puy Bardens
1986
APPELLATION PREMIERES COTES DE BORDEAUX CONTROLEE
MIS EN BOUTEILLE AU CHATEAU
12,6% vol
G.F.A LAMIABLE - A 33880 CAMBES (GIRONDE)
750 ml
PRODUCE OF FRANCE

Characteristics of vintages

1988: Very promising (still in casks and vats). **1987:** To be drunk while waiting for the preceding vintages. **1986:** Excellent, well-balanced, dark fruit fragrance, tannic, will age well. **1985:** Exceptional success on the property selected by the Syndicat des premières Côtes de Borbeaux in 1987. Price range (pre-tax, ex-warehouse): 20 to 30 F.F.
Sales volume:
- Wholesale: 10%. – Retail 85%. – Restaurants: 5%.
Sales in France: 90%.
Export sales: 10%.
Main trading partners : UK, Germany.

References in France

Restaurants: Regional restaurants, Lacaussade, Auberge André and a number of the smaller Parisian restaurants.

CHÂTEAU DE PIC

François Masson Regnault
Le Tourne 33550 Langoiran
56 67 07 51 - 56 72 50 08

Type of vineyard: Agricultural Association. **Established:** 1975. **Number of employees:** 3. **Vine stocks:** Merlot, Cabernet Sauvignon. **Soil:** gravelly clay and chalky rock. **Exposure:** hillsides facing South & South-East. **Average annual production in hectoliters:** 1 000.
Appellation: Premières Côtes de Bordeaux Rouge. **Type:** Red. **Technique:** traditional Bordeaux style (long fermentation on skins) at high temperature. **Maturing:** 18 to 24 months prior to bottling at the Château. **Alcohol content:** 12%. **Characteristics:** Well colored wines, rich nose, red berry overtones, slightly spicy, full-bodied and well structured, good keeping, excellent quality-price ratio. **Serving temperature:** 16-18°. **Served with:** delicatessen, red meat (cooked on the grill), white meat, poultry, game, cheese. **Vintages available in 89/90:** 79-80-81-84-86-87.

Characteristics of vintages

1988: rich in color, quite promising, available in June 1990. **1987:** less structured, an ideal wine for those who just can't wait, and never seem to forget the bottles that are waiting in the cellar... **1986:** out of stock – the best test of quality! **Other:** 1984: an often forgotten but quite rewarding year, taste it now. 1980-1981: have reached full maturity. 1979: keep a few bottles if you can. Price range (pre-tax, ex-warehouse): 10 F.F. to 20 F.F.

Sales volume:
- Wholesale: 60%. - Retail: 30%. - Restaurants: 5%.
- Other: 15% (dealers).

Sales in France: 70%.
Export sales: 30%.
Main trading partners : USA, UK, Belgium, Middle East, Danemark.

GRAND VIN DE BORDEAUX
CHATEAU DE PIC
PREMIERES COTES DE BORDEAUX
Appellation Premières Côtes de Bordeaux Contrôlée
MIS EN BOUTEILLES AU CHATEAU
12%vol.
1986
75cl. e
SEPIC PROPRIETAIRE - LE TOURNE - 33350 LANGOIRAN GIRONDE
PRODUCE OF FRANCE

Abroad

Crus et domaines de France, 33000 Bordeaux.

United States

Barton & Guestier.

United Kingdom

Nigel Baring & Co Ltd, 11 Stanhope Place London W2 2HH.

Belgium

Bernard Marchal, rue du Patch 16 16 B 1330 Rixensart.

Danemark

Alsace Vinimport, M. Matthes, Ellingvej 18, DK 8600 Silkebork, Danemark.

Comments

According to legend, this manor house was built by the family of the famous Pic de la Mirandole who came to settle in Guyenne, and whose heiress, Isabeau, lived at the time when the Epernonists and the residents of Bordeaux were at war in the commune... It is in fact much older, since one of its towers dates from the 14th century, and it is known from documents dated 1561, that it belonged to the Peyrat family, one of whom, Guillaume, Counselor of Parliament, was Lord of the "Maison noble du Pic". Then, for almost three centuries it remained in the family of d'Abbadie de Pic, through family alliances with de Brassier, Baron de Guyenne, and de Beauvoir, Marquis de Las-Cases. The Château de Pic was then sold several times until 1975, when its new owners undertook a complete restoration of the vineyard and buildings.

CHÂTEAU RENON

Jacques Boucherie
Tabanac - 33550 Langoiran
56 67 13 59

Type of vineyard: Family-owned. **Established:** 1950. **Vine stocks:** Red: 60% Merlot, 40% Cabernet Sauvignon. White: 50% Sauvignon, 50% Sémillion. **Soil:** Gravelly clay on chalky subsoil. **Exposure:** South, South-West. **Average annual production in hectoliters:** 450.
Appellation: Red: Premières Côtes de Bordeaux. White: Bordeaux blanc sec. **Type:** Red, white. **Technique:** Fermentation for 15 days followed by malolactic fermentation. **Maturing:** In oak casks. **Alcohol content:** 12%. **Characteristics:** Red: Typical, well balanced, fine tannins, excellent aptitude for ageing. **Serving temperature:** 17°. **Served with:** All meats and cheeses. **Vintages available in 89/90:** 1986 and 1987.

Characteristics of vintages

1987: A fine and delicate wine from ripe grapes, promising, will age well. **1986:** Very good year, complex fine woody bouquet, silky tannins, rich and well balanced, excellent finish. Silver Medal, Concours Agricole, Bordeaux. **Other:** Blanc sec "Sauvignon". **1988:** Fragrant, grapes bursting with sunshine, good balance, long. 1987 Floral aromas, well balanced. Very agreeable finish. Price range (pre-tax, ex-warehouse): White: between 10 and 20 F.F. Red: between 20 and 30 F.F.
Sales volume:
– Retail: 80%. – Restaurants: 5%. – Other: 15% C.E.
Sales in France: 90%.
Export sales: 10%.
Main trading partners: Netherlands, Belgium, People's Republic of the Congo.

References in France

Restaurants: Many in the Bordeaux region.

Abroad

Belgium

Renavins, rue du Cerf 20 B 7400, Soignies. Tel: 67 33 45 12.

The Netherlands

Importer: Oud. Wijnkopers and Hustinx, Spaarndamseweg 120 – 2021 Ka Haarlem. Tel: 23 25 92 01.

Others

Congo: Importer: S.A.M. Daron, Pointe Noire.

Comments

The property can be traced back to the 11th century. In 1583, the proprietor, Jean De Renon, gave it his name. A well-known name among the winegrowing fraternity, the De Lur Saluces family (Château Yquem, Sauternes) were proprietors in the 18th century of the Château Renon. The wine-producing buildings date from the 17th century. The domain has been awarded a number of Gold and Silver Medals at the Concours Générales Agricole of Paris and Bordeaux which confirm the regular quality of the recent vintages. Very successful, full and fragrant.

CHÂTEAU REYNON

Denis & Florence Dubourdieu
56 62 96 51 – Telex: Reynon 573 026

Type of vineyard: Family-owned. **Established:** 1976. **Vine stocks:** White: Sauvignon 50%, Sémillon 50%. Red: Merlot 40%, Cabernet Sauvignon 60%. **Soil:** Gravel and chalky clay. **Exposure:** South. **Average annual production in hectoliters:** Red 600. White: 600.

PRODUCE OF FRANCE
Château Reynon
PREMIERES COTES DE BORDEAUX
APPELLATION PREMIERES CÔTES DE BORDEAUX CONTROLEE
DENIS et FLORENCE DUBOURDIEU DAVID
PROPRIETAIRES A BEGUEY GIRONDE
1986
12 % VOL. MIS EN BOUTEILLE AU CHATEAU 750 ml

Appellation: Premières Côtes de Bordeaux Rouge and Bordeaux Blanc. **Type:** Red, White. **Technique:** Traditional Bordeaux style. **Maturing:** In casks (12 to 18 months). **Alcohol content:** 12.3%. **Characteristics:** Fruity, full-bodied, elegant tannins. **Serving temperature:** 16 to 18°. **Served with:** Meat, cheese. **Vintages available in 89/90:** 1986, 1987.

Characteristics of vintages

1988: Not yet tasted. **1987:** Fruity, elegant, to be drunk young. **1986:** Delicate, silky tannins, complex bouquet. Price range (pre-tax, ex-warehouse): 30 to 50 F.F.

Sales volume:
- Wholesale: 20%. – Retail: 30%. – Restaurants: 10%.
- Other: 40% (export).

Sales in France: 60%. **Export sales:** 40%.
Main trading partners : Belgium, Netherlands, Switzerland, Germany, Luxemburg.

References in France

Restaurants: Le Saint James (Bordeaux), La Tupina (Bordeaux), Michel Guérard (Eugénie-les-Bains), Joël Robuchon & Ambroisie (Paris).
Shops: Le Tastevin (Saint-Nazaire).

Abroad

Germany
Spezialitaten Kontor, Berlin.

Switzerland
Domaines et Châteaux, Lausanne – Grands Châteaux S.A. Lausanne.

Belgium
Ets. Velu – Vins, Brussels.

Canada
Jean Parent – Réserve et Sélection, Montreal.

The Netherlands
Brand Wijimport, Leiden Colaris, Weert.

Others
Luxemburg: Abi Duhr, 73 route de Treves – Grevenmacher.

Comments

The origins of the property go back to the 15th century, at which time it was known as Château de Begey. At the end of the 16th century, the domain was still a nobleman's manor, belonging to Jean de la Roque, who was also a proprietor at Barsac. In the 18th century the vineyard was owned by the Carles de Trajet family who emigrated at the time of the Revolution. It was then sold by the State to Mr. Laspeyrère. In 1848, his son demolished the old château and replaced it with the present building, constructed in the classic style. Shortly before 1900, the property was bought by Emile Pollet, a Parisian wine dealer, then in 1958 by Jacques David, who completely replanted the vineyard. In 1976, his daughter Florence and his son-in-law Denis Dubourdieu, agricultural engineer and oenologist succeeded him.

CHÂTEAU ROQUEBERT

Christian and Philippe Neys
Quinsac 33360 Latresne
56 97 01 21 – Telex: 550 417 F

Type of vineyard: Family-owned. **Established:** 19th century. **Vine stocks:** 40%. Cabernet Sauvignon, 15% Cabernet Franc, 40% Merlot. **Soil:** Chalky clay. **Exposure:** Quinsac hillsides, overlooking the Garonne river, on the right bank, facing the sun.
Appellation: AOC Premières Côtes de Bordeaux Rouge, AOC Bordeaux Clairet. **Type:** Red, Clairet. **Technique:** Vinification with temperature regulation, controlled by an oenologist. **Maturing:** Vats. **Alcohol content:** Red: 12.5%. Clairet: 12%. **Characteristics:** Red: supple, vigorous, well-colored. Clairet: original, fleshy, fruity. **Serving temperature:** Red: room temperature. Clairet: 8°. **Served with:** Red: red meat, game, roasts. Clairet: seafood, shellfish, white meat. **Vintages available in 89/90/** Premières Côtes de Bordeaux: 1987. Bordeaux Clairet: 1988.

Characteristics of vintages

1988: Bordeaux Clairet: exceptional quality, fruity, fleshy, very full, subtle perfume. **1987:** Premières Côtes de Bordeaux: Gold Medal, Concours des Vins d'Aquitaine, superb color, agreeable fragrance, very rich and well-balanced, a perfect "Côtes de Bordeaux". Price range (pre-tax, ex-warehouse): Bordeaux Clairet: between 10 F.F. and 20 F.F. Premières Côtes de Bordeaux: between 20 F.F. and 30 F.F.

Sales volume:
– Wholesale: 20%. – Retail: 50%. – Restaurants: 30%.
Sales in France: 60%. **Export sales:** 40%.
Main trading partners : Belgium, UK.

References in France

Restaurants: Various restaurants in and around Bordeaux, Chez Philippe, Bordeaux, Les Viviers, Gujan (Bayonne region), Hôtel du Palais, Biarritz, Hôtel Pas de Rolland, Cambo, Le Royal Capucines, Paris.

Abroad

United Kingdom

Mr. Alan Mayne, Lindfiedkd, 62 Bromley Common, Bromley Kent BR2 – 9 PF. Edward Dillon and Co., Ltd., 25 Moutjoy Square, East Dublin 1, Ireland.

Belgium

The Continental Bodega Company, Pierre Van Humbeek Straat 5, Brussels 1080. Tel: 02 521 54 55.

Comments

The vines, in this vineyard created in the 19th century have an average age of 20 years. The Château Roquebert is located on the Quinsac hillsides, overlooking the marvelous Garonne River and benifits form what Virgil referred as the "open hills", inundated with sunshine. The sunlight striking the hillsides is the true magician of quality. The fifteen hectare estate, planted with Cabernet Sauvignon, Merlot and a bit of Malbec, yields excellent red wines, vigorous and well-colored, each vintage having its own personality: full-bodied like the 75 and 85, light and delicate like the 78, 82 and 86. Cultivation and tilling are traditional. No herbicides are used. All of the grapes are hand picked. The wines are matured in oak barrels and stainless steel tanks. All this care has resulted in the following awards: Gold Medal, Concours Agricole, Paris 1973; Bronze Medal, Concours Agricole, Paris 1980; Gold Medal, Concours Agricole, Paris 1985; Silver Medal, Concours Agricole, Paris 1988; Gold Medal, Concours Régional, Bordeaux 1988.

CHÂTEAU SUAU

Monique Aldebert
Capian F. – 33550 Langoiran
56 72 19 06 – Telex: 530 584 – FAX: 63 61 46 33

Type of vineyard: Agricultural Association. **Established:** 1981. **Number of employees:** 9. **Vine stocks:** Red: Merlot 32%, Cabernet Sauvignon 33%, Cabernet Franc 35%. White: Sémillon 60%, Muscadelle 30%, Sauvignon 10%. **Soil:** Gravelly clay. **Exposure:** Hillsides and plateau. **Average annual production in hectoliters:** Red: 1,600. White: 300.

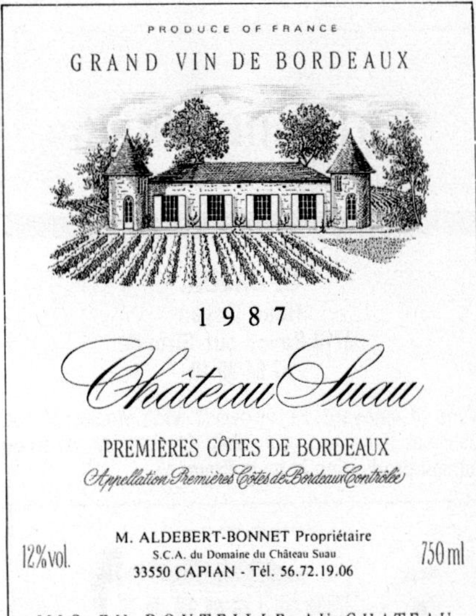

Appellation: Premières Côtes de Bordeaux (Rouge) – Bordeaux (Blanc Sec). **Type:** Red, Dry white. **Technique:** Red: temperature controlled fermentation on skins (14 to 18 days). Dry white: pre-fermentation maceration (12 hours), stabilization at 7 to 8° before fermentation – temperature controlled fermentation with yeast inoculation, maturing in new oak barrels on fine lees for 2 months, beating of the lees for part of the wine. **Maturing:** Red: in vats and new oak casks. **Alcohol content:** Red: 12°. Dry white: 11.5%. **Characteristics:** Red: full-bodied, average keeping. Dry white: fruity, fresh, flowery, soft and full, lingering taste. **Serving temperature:** Red: 17 to 18°. Dry white: 7 to 8°. **Served with:** Red: grilled meat, leg of lamb roasts, cheese. Dry white: as an aperitif and with shellfish, seafood, and fish cooked in sauce. **Vintages available in 89/90:** Red: 1986-1987 (in April 1989), 1988 (June 1990). Dry white: 1987. 1988-1989 (January 1990).

Characteristics of vintages

1988: Red: tannic, well structured, ripe fruit aroma, good keeping. Dry white: very flowery, complex citrus fruit

aroma, firm and fresh. **1987:** Red: supple, very pleasant. Dry white: pear, lime-blossom and almond aroma, soft and full. **1986:** Red: beautiful color, rich and well balanced, vanilla and liquorice aroma, good keeping. Dry white: fruity. Price range (pre-taxe, ex-warehouse): 10 to 20 F.F.
Sales volume:
– Wholesale: 20%.

Comments

Very old residence, going back to 1400, which has belonged to the Guénant family for 5 centuries.

CÔTES-DE-BOURG

LE BREUIL
Henri Doyen
33710 Bayon-sur-Gironde
57 64 80 10

Type of vineyard: Family-owned. **Vine stocks:** Merlot, Cabernet Sauvignon, Cot. **Soil:** Chalky clay. **Average annual production in hectoliters:** 45.

GRAND VIN DE BORDEAUX
1986
CHATEAU LE BREUIL
CÔTES DE BOURG
APPELLATION CÔTES DE BOURG CONTRÔLEE
HENRI DOYEN / BAYON-SUR-GIRONDE
Mis en bouteilles au château
ALC. 12% BY VOL.
750ml
PRODUCT OF FRANCE

Appellation: Côtes de Bourg. **Type:** Red. **Technique:** Traditional with temperature control. **Maturing:** Vats. **Alcohol content:** 12 to 12.5%. **Characteristics:** Tannic but not agressive, rich, well structured. **Serving temperature:** 16 to 17°. **Served with:** Red and white meats, soft cheeses. **Vintages available in 89/90:** 1986.

Characteristics of vintages

1986: Well structured, rich color, delicate tannins, can age a long time. Price range (pre-tax, ex-warehouse): between 10 and 20 F.F.
Sales volume:
– Wholesale: 50%. – Retail: 20%. – Restaurants: 20%. – Other: 10%.
Sales in France: 70%.
Export sales: 30%.
Main trading partners : Belgium, United Kingdom, Germany.

References in France

Restaurants: Bretagne.

Abroad

United States
Importers: Stanmor Liquor Co., PO Box 878, Rochester, NY 14603.

United Kingdom
Enotria Wine Ltd, 48 Chandos Park Estate, Chandos Road, London NW10 6NF.

Germany
Dieter Franze, Schultheisenweg 109, 6000 Frankfurt/Main 90.

Belgium
Heylen NV, Wouwerstraat 4, 3100 Heist. OP. Den. Berg. Verpoorte, Vivier 1024, 5730 Malonne.

The Netherlands
Dommelsche Biersbrouwerij, Brouwerijplein 4, 5551 AE Dommelen.

CHÂTEAU BRULESECAILLE
Jacques Rodet
Tauriac – 33170 Bourg-sur-Gironde
57 68 40 31

Type of vineyard: Family-owned. **Established:** 3 generations. **Number of employees:** 4. **Vine stocks:** Merlot 60%, Cabernet Franc 30%, Cabernet Sauvignon 15%, Malbec 5%. **Soil:** Clay with calcium carbonate. **Exposure:** South and southwest and southeast. **Average annual production in hectoliters:** 750.
Appellation: Côtes-de-Bourg. **Type:** Red. **Technique:** Long, total destemming, temperature control, stainless steel tanks. **Maturing:** Barrels. **Alcohol content:** 12%. **Characteristics:** Typical of its soil, well-balanced, may age 10 to 20 years according to the vintage, elegant, well-bred at their apogee. **Serving temperature:** 16°. **Served with:** Roasts, grills, for the usual vintages. Game with sauce, for the great vintages. **Vintages available in 89/90:** 1986, 1987.

Characteristics of vintages

1988: Exceptionally rich, matured in new casks, should develop complex aromas. Full-bodied, rich and well balanced, will be a great vintage wine. To be kept. Available as of September 1990. **1987:** Fruity, harmonious, no bitter-

ness, a very successful year. **1986:** Rich in aroma, full, rich and well-balanced, fine structure. **1982:** On the average, still lively, starting to develop. Price range (pre-tax, ex-warehouse): 30 F.F. – 18 F.F. – 25 F.F.
Sales volume:
– Retail: 50%. – Restaurants: 10%. – Other: 40% (wholesalers, half-wholesalers).
Sales in France: 60%.
Export sales: 40%.
Main trading partners : Belgium, Netherlands, Germany, UK, Switzerland.

CHÂTEAU DE LIDONNE

Roger Audoire
33790 Bourg-sur-Gironde
57 68 47 52

Type of vineyard: Family-owned. **Average annual production in hectoliters:** 900.
Appellation: Côtes-de-Bourg. **Type:** Red. **Technique:** Traditional with modern œnology adaptations. **Characteristics:** Robust and aromatic. **Served temperature:** 17 to 18°. **Serving with:** Lamprey, jugged hare, red meat, cheese. **Vintages available in 89/90:** 1983, 1984, 1985, 1986, 1987.

Characteristics of vintages

1988: Balanced and harmonious, will be a remarkable year. Fruity and full-bodied, will be a very great wine. To be kept. **1987:** Harvested before the rains, aromatic, very successful. Awarded a Gold Medal at the Concours des Grands Vins de France Blayais-Bourgeais in 1988 and a Silver Medal at the Concours Général de Paris, in 1989. **1985:** Flowery flavor, supple, rich and balanced, good for ageing. Price range (pre-tax, ex-warehouse): between 20 and 30 F.F.
Sales volume:
– Wholesale: 5%. – Retail: 45%. – Restaurants: 15%. – Other: 35% (export).
Sales in France 65%.
Export sales: 35%.
Main trading partners : Belgium, England.

CHÂTEAU DE MENDOCE

Philippe Darricarrère
Villeneuve – 33710 Bourg
57 42 25 95

Type of vineyard: Family-owned. **Established:** 1660. **Number of employees:** 5. **Vine stocks:** 16 hectares planted; Merlot 60%, Cabernet Sauvignon 40%. **Soil:** Clay with calcium carbonate on limestone base. **Exposure:** Hillsides facing West and South, separated by a stream. 6 hectare plateau on top. **Average annual production in hectoliters:** 734.
Appellation: Côtes de Bourg (Vignoble de Bordeaux). **Type:** Red. **Technique:** Bordeaux style: total destemming – fermentation in stainless steel vats. **Maturing:** In stainless steel vats for 20 months, then in bottles, except for 100 hl matured in new casks, sold at a special price, with a corresponding label. **Alcohol content:** 12%. **Characteristics:** In general wines with rather soft tannin, not overly aggressive. Supple, fruity, long finish. **Serving temperature:** 20°. **Served with:** Red meat (grilled) cheese and almost everything excep salads in oil and vinegar dressing. **Vintages available in 89/90:** At the estate, 1989: 1986, 1987. 1990: 1986, 1987, 1988. With dealers: 1982, 1983, 1985.

Characteristics of vintages

1988: Deep purple color, tannic, full-bodied, good keeping. **1987:** Bright ruby color, good concentration – will become rounder after a few years ageing. **1986:** Supple and fruity – mellow tannins, lingering taste, – well developed aromas, ready. **1986:** Same as 1985 but less concentrated. **1985:** Soft and full, rich color, soft tannin, long finish. **1984:** Average richness and balance. Fruity and fragrant. Pleasant. To be drunk now. **1983:** Out of stock (at the estate). **1982:** Out of stock (at the estate).
Sales volume:
– Retail: 20%. – Other: 80% (direct export).
Sales in France: 20%.
Export sales: 80%.
Main trading partners : Belgium, Netherlands, UK, Denmark, Germany.

Comments

The name Mendoce is derived from Mendoza, Spanish nobility who emigrated to the court of François I and then established a family in the Bordeaux region during the 16th Century, on their estate at Villeneuve-de-Bourg. Villeneuve is derived from Villa Nova, the new villa, which was built during the 4th century by a Gallic Roman at the edge of the river.

CHÂTEAU GUIONNE

Lansac – 33170 Bourg-sur-Gironde
57 68 42 17

Type of vineyard: Family-owned. **Established:** 1970. **Vine stocks:** Merlots 45%, Cabernets 50%, Malbecs 5%. **Soil:** Clay with calcium carbonate rocky sub-soil. **Exposure:** Hillsides parallel to the Gironde River facing South. **Appellation:** Côtes-de-Bourg. **Type:** Red. **Technique:** Traditional, fermentation with skins 10 to 20 days in stainless steel tanks. **Maturing:** Primeurs: in new barrels. Others in concrete. **Alcohol content:** 12.3% to 13% according to the year. **Characteristics:** Rich, and typical wines, good for ageing, matured with rigor and passion. **Vintages available in 89/90:** 1985, 1984, 1978, 1977.

Characteristics of vintages

1986: Promising vintage. Hold. **1985:** Excellent wine, typical, good aroma and flavor, combines richness, balance and distinction, to be aged. **1984:** Successful vintage, order now, without any hesitation. Price range (pre-tax, ex-warehouse): between 15 and 30 F.F.
Sales volume:
– Retail: 20 to 30%. – Others: 70 to 80% (export).
Sales in France: 20 to 30%. **Export sales:** 70 to 80%.
Main trading partners : Belgium, Netherlands, Germany, UK, USA.

Abroad

United Kingdom

Parrot, London.Tel: 01 480 6312.

CHÂTEAU HAUT ROUSSET

Joël Grellier
Les Arnauds – St-Ciers-de-Ganesse
33710 Bourg
57 64 92 45

Type of vineyard: Family-owned. **Established:** 1970. **Number of employees:** 9. **Vine stocks:** Merlot, Malbec, Cabernet. **Soil:** Clay with calcium carbonate. **Exposure:** South.
Appellation: Côtes-de-Bourg. **Type:** White, red. **Technique:** oak casks. **Maturing:** Traditional. **Alcohol content:** 12%. **Characteristics:** Red: fine, full of the vine, rich color. **Served temperature:** 14° to 15°. **Serving with:** Red: red meat and game. White: shellfish and fish. **Vintages available in 89/90:** 1983, 1985, 1986.

Characteristics of vintages

1985: Good vintage, full, fine, good color. Price range (pre-tax, ex-warehouse): between 16 F.F. and 18 F.F. per 75 cl.
Sales volume:
– Wholesale: 10%. – Retail: 80%. – Restaurants: 10%.
Sales in France: 80%. **Export sales:** 20%.
Main trading partners: Belgium, Germany, USA, England.

References in France

Restaurants: Les Sans Culottes (Paris).

CHÂTEAU LE CLOS DU NOTAIRE

R. Charbonnier
33170 Bourg-sur-Gironde
57 68 44 36

Type of vineyard: Family-owned. **Number of employees:** 3. **Vine stocks:** Merlot 50%, Cabernet Sauvignon 35%, Malbec, Cabernet Franc. **Soil:** Clay with calcium carbonate. **Exposure:** South and hillsides to the south and southeast. **Average annual production in hectoliters:** Near 1,000.
Appellation: Côtes-de-Bourg. **Type:** Red. **Technique:** Maceration 20 days after destemming, temperature control. **Maturing:** Barrels and tanks (all new). **Alcohol content:** 12° to 12.5°. **Characteristics:** Well-balanced, elegant, with fine tannins, good capacity when good years are aged; often prized and avoided. Soil on cliff facing Margaux gives easy, tannic wines with truly great quality. **Serving temperature:** 14 to 17°. **Vintages available 89/90:** 1981, 1982, 1984, 1985, 1986.

Characteristics of vintages

1986: Surprizingly aromatic, well-balanced with good tannins. **1985:** Already well evolved; may be drunk quite now and keeps well. **1984:** Very good today, light and agreeable wine. **1982:** The most complete of all; a bit firm now, but to have also. Fine for the cellar in cave. **1981:** Start to open; should be kept a little while longer. Price range (pre-tax, ex-warehouse): 15 F.F. by 100 ml, 12 ml, 750 ml between 10 and 20 F.F.; 20 an 30 F.F.
Sales volume: – Retail: 30%. – Restaurants: 5%. – Other: 5% (small distributers).
Sales in France: 40%. **Export sales:** 50%.
Main trading partners : Belgium, Holland, Switzerland, Germany, Canada, England.

References in France

Restaurants: Dubern in Bordeaux, Bistrot de Paris.
Shops: Caves de la Madeleine, Paris.

CHÂTEAU HAUT-MACO

Bernard and Jean Mallet
Tauriac, 33710 Bourg-sur-Gironde
57 68 81 26

Type of vineyard: Agricultural Association. **Established:** 1970. **Number of employees:** 6. **Vine stocks:** Cabernet Sauvignon & Cabernet Franc 60%, Merlot 40%. **Soil:** Chalky clay, alluvial gravel. **Exposure:** South – South-West. **Average annual production in hectoliters:** 2,000.
Appellation: Côtes-de-Bourg. **Type:** Red. **Technique:** Destemming, temperature control (28°), pumping over, maceration (15 – 25 days). **Maturing:** In vats and new casks. **Alcohol content:** 12 to 12.5%. **Characteristics:** Full-bodied yet not fleshy, lively but not acid, fine without pretention. **Serving temperature:** 17 to 18°. **Served with:** White meat, red meat, duck steaks, lamprey. **Vintages available in 89/90:** 1986 and 1987.

Characteristics of vintages

1988: Very rich, promising, good keeping. **1987:** Well balanced, fruity, supple and pleasant tannins. **1986:** Superb density, rich, good keeping, complex and seductive nose. Price range (pre-tax, ex-warehouse): 10 to 20 F.F.
Sales volume:

GRAND VIN DE BORDEAUX

CHATEAU

Haut Macô

COTES DE BOURG

MALLET FRÈRES 33710 TAURIAC

– Wholesale: 10 % – Retail: 85%. – Restaurants: 5%.
Sales in France: 90%.
Export sales: 10%.
Main trading partners : Belgium, Japan, Netherlands, Switzerland, Germany.

References in France

Restaurants: Hôtel George V (Paris), La Rose des Vins (Lyon), Dubern (Bordeaux).
Shops: L'Amour du Vin, Paris.

Abroad

Switzerland

Boutique Christevin, 63, rue des Eaux Vives, 1207 Geneva.

Belgium

Unimport Berol Wijnimport, Roesellaarsestraat 132 BP, Tzegem Agnesti Gaetan Agresti, 974 Chaussée de Waterloo, Brussels 1180.

The Netherlands

P.L.I. Wijnen Herrikaard 3, 4847 Er Tetringen.

Far East

Japan: Odex Japan 89, Takanawa 4 Chome Minato, Tokyo.

Comments

One of the very first vineyards in the Côtes de Bourg (see "Classification 89") where one can taste superb wines. The wines, which age well are rich, well-colored, full and have a lingering flavor.

CHÂTEAU MONTAIGUT

François de Pardieu
Nodeau – St-Ciers-de-Canesse
33170 Bourg-en-Gironde
57 64 92 49

Type of vineyard: Family-owned. **Established:** 1975. **Number of employees:** 5. **Vine stocks:** Merlot 65%, Cabernet Franc 15%, Cabernet Sauvignon 15%, Malbec 5%. **Soil:** Acid soil on hillsides, clay with calcium carbonate on the slopes. **Exposure:** South/Southwest. **Average annual production in hectoliters:** 1,200.
Appellation: Côtes-de-Bourg. **Type:** Red, white. **Technique:** Traditional, complete destemming, temperature control. **Maturing:** In new barrels (4 months) for part of the production (160 hl). **Alcohol content:** 12.5%. **Characteristics:** Very well-balanced and harmonious wines. **Vintages available in 89/90:** 1985, 1986 – red and white.

Characteristics of vintages

1986: Still a bit young, very high quality, very good keeping. **1985:** Young wine but already mature and aged – very good for ageing. Average pre-tax, ex-warehouse price: 18.50 F.F. – 24 F.F. Price range (pre-tax, exwarehouse): 20 F.F. – 30 F.F.
Sales volume:
– Wholesale: 40%. – Retail: 20%. – Restaurants: 10%. – Other: 30% (works councils & associations).
Sales in France: 70%. **Export sales:** 30%.
Main trading partners : Belgium, Netherlands, UK, Germany.

CHÂTEAU MERCIER

Philippe and Martine Chety
St-Trojan – 33710 Bourg-sur-Gironde
54 64 92 34

Type of vineyard: Family-owned. **Established:** 1970. **Number of employees:** 3. **Vine stocks:** Merlot Noir 45%, Cabernet Sauvignon 35%, Carbenet Franc 15%, Malbec 5%. **Soil:** Silica-clay with gravel on hillside. **Average annual production in hectoliters:** 700.
Appellation: Côtes-de-Bourg. **Type:** Red, dry white. **Technique:** Traditional maceration for 2 to 4 weeks.

Maturing: In vats and new Oak casks. **Alcohol content:** 12%. **Characteristics:** Heady red wine with a delicate finesse that characterises a supple wine like gravel that crunches under the feet of the passerby, cascades down the throat of the drinker like the song of a bird. White wine, supple with Sauvignon fruitiness, non-astringent, which leaves the head light and the tongue agile. **Serving temperature:** Red: 14° to 16° according to the vintage. Dry white: 8°. **Served with:** Red: steak or lamprey fish. Dry white: seafood, grilled shad, or an eel fricassee. **Vintages available in 89/90:** 1981, 1983, 1984, 1985, 1986.

Characteristics of vintages

1986: Great year, well-structured, rich in color and tannins. **1985:** Deep purple color, fragrance of ripe fruit, truffles, unctuous and tannic, long lifetime. **1984:** Beautiful success, rich color, harmonious, fresh nose, very fragrant. **1983:** Round, supple woodland and violet aromas, will reach its peak in 6 to 10 years. Price range (pre-tax, ex-warehouse): between 10 and 20 F.F.

Sales volume:
– Retail: 85%. – Restaurants: 5%. – Other: 10% (export wholesalers).

Sales in France: 80%.

Export sales: 20%.

Main trading partners : Belgium, Denmark, Netherlands, Luxemburg.

CHÂTEAU MOULIN DES GRAVES

Jean Bost
Teullac – 33710 Bourg-sur-Gironde
57 64 30 58 ou 57 64 39 41

Type of vineyard: Family-owned. **Established:** Beginning of the Century. **Vine stocks:** Red: Merlot, Cabernet Sauvignon, Malbec. White: Sauvignon. **Soil:** Clay with calcium carbonate and gravel. **Exposure:** Southern slopes or plateau. **Average annual production in hectoliters:** 400.

Appellation: Côtes-de-Bourg. **Type:** Red, white. **Technique:** Red: destemming, temperature control. **Maturing:** In vats. **Characteristics:** Red: fragrant, fruity, balanced and tannic. White: typical Sauvignon aroma, round and balanced. Gold Medal in the General Competition in Paris, 1987. **Serving temperature:** White: 8° to 10°. Red: 16° to 18°. **Served with:** White: especially seafood. Red: red or white meat according the age of the wine. **Vintages available in 89/90:** Red: 1986. White: 1988 (for 1989).

Characteristics of vintages

Price range (pre-tax, ex-warehouse): between 10 and 20 F.F.

Sales volume:
– Retail: 90%. – Restaurants: 10%.

Sales in France: 90%.

Export sales: 10%.

CHÂTEAU DU MOULIN VIEUX

J.-Pierre Gorphe
33710 Tauriac
57 68 26 21

Type of vineyard: Family-owned. **Vine stocks:** Merlot 40%, Cabernet 40%, Malbec 20%. **Soil:** Chalky clay. **Exposure:** Plateau – slope to the south. **Average annual production in hectoliters:** ~~700~~.

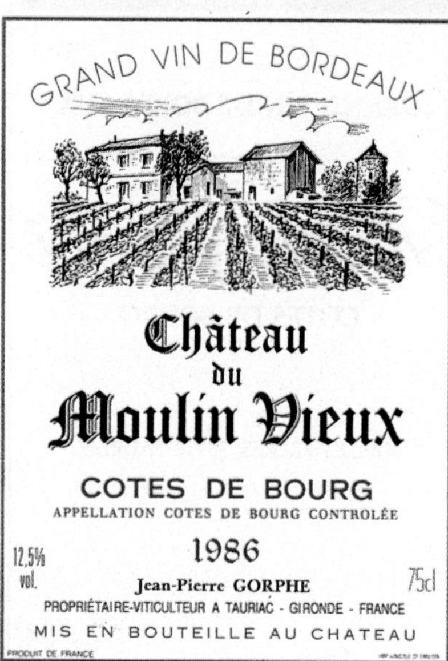

GRAND VIN DE BORDEAUX
Château du Moulin Vieux
COTES DE BOURG
APPELLATION COTES DE BOURG CONTROLÉE
1986
12,5% vol.
75cl
Jean-Pierre GORPHE
PROPRIÉTAIRE-VITICULTEUR A TAURIAC - GIRONDE - FRANCE
MIS EN BOUTEILLE AU CHATEAU
PRODUIT DE FRANCE

La récolte 1986 du Château Moulin Vieux a produit 64 400 bouteilles.
Cette bouteille porte le **№ 02142**

Appellation: Côtes-de-Bourg. **Type:** Red. **Technique:** Traditional. **Maturing:** Stainless steel tanks, later in casks. **Alcohol content:** 12.5%. **Characteristics:** Charming, beautiful color, rich and well balanced, tannic and long. **Serving temperature:** 16 to 18°. **Vintages available in 89/90:** 1986, 1986 Prestige, 1987.

Characteristics of vintages

1988: Rich and well balanced, long development, to be kept. **1987:** Light, quite seductive, drink when young, successful vintage. **1986:** Rich and well balanced, long, beautiful structure. **1985:** Beautiful vintage, rich, well balanced and full at the same time, good keeping. Price range (pre-tax, ex-warehouse): 1986-1987: 10 to 20 F.F. – 1986 Prestige, 1988 20 to 30 F.F.

Sales volume:
– Retail: 85%. – Restaurants: 5 %. – Other: 10% (cellars).

Sales in France: 85%.

Export sales: 15%.

Main trading partners : Belgium, RFA, USA.

References in France

Restaurants: La Cariole (Paris), l'Entracte (La Rochelle), etc.
Shops: L'Amour du Vin.

Comments

The exact number of generations of the Gorphe family associated with the Moulin Vieux is of little importance. There were certainly quite a few. For the last twenty years, this vineyard, which has been entirely dedicated to white wines, has been converted to red, then little by little, reconverted. Rural lodgings have been set up on the property to receive visitors on Summer holiday from the north of France. The first to arrive in 1968 was from the region of Paris. He developed a taste for the wine, bought some for his own wine cellar, spread the word about the Moulin Vieux production. Il was the beginning of an individual clientele. Later they came from Brest, Rouen and various other regions. They spent their vacations at the Moulin Vieux, learned about the touristic richness of the Bourges region and became convinced ambassadors of the Côtes du Bourg and of the Moulin Vieux wines.

CHÂTEAU HAUT-GUIRAUD

Jean Bonnet
Saint-Ciers-de-Canesse
33710 Bourg-sur-Gironde
57 64 91 39

Type of vineyard: Family-owned. **Established:** 1630. **Number of employees:** 5. **Vine stocks:** Merlot rouge 65%, Cabernet Franc and Cabernet Sauvignon 35%. **Soil:** Clay and calcium carbonate, gravel. **Exposure:** Hillsides. **Average annual production in hectoliters:** 1,300. **Appellation:** Côtes-de-Bourg. **Type:** Red. **Technique:** Traditional. **Maturing:** Stainless steel tanks and barrels. **Alcohol content:** 12°. **Characteristics:** Supple, pleasant tannins, good wines for ageing. **Serving temperature:** 15°. **Served with:** Grilled steak, roast. **Vintages available in 89/90:** 1981, 1982, 1983, 1984, 1985.

CHÂTEAU LES HEAUMES

Max & Jean-Michel Robin
Saint-Ciers-de-Canesse
33710 Bourg-sur-Gironde
57 64 92 11

Type of vineyard: Family-owned. **Established:** 1660. **Number of employees:** 3. **Vine stocks:** Merlot 75%, Cabernet Franc 20%, Malbec 5%. **Soil:** Clay with calcium carbonate. **Exposure:** North. **Average annual production in hectoliters:** 500. **Appellation:** Côtes-de-Bourg. **Type:** Red. **Technique:** Traditional. **Maturing:** 18 months in casks. **Alcohol content:** 12%. **Characteristics:** Supple, woody flavor, ages well. **Serving temperature:** 16°. **Served with:** Grilled meat and poultry. **Vintages available in 89/90:** 1985.

Characteristics of vintages

1985: Excellent year, combining structure and elegance, good for ageing. Price range (pre-tax, ex-warehouse): 20-30 F.F.
Sales volume: – Wholesale: 25%. – Retail: 75%.
Sales in France: 90%. **Export sales:** 10%.
Main trading partners : Belgium, Netherlands.

Comments

Estate run by the Robin Family since 1660. Vineyard entirely cultivated. Grapes are picked by hand and the ageing of selected harvests is done in barrels.

CÔTES-DE-CASTILLON

CHÂTEAU LA TOUR D'HORABLE

J.-Albert Faytout
Horable – 33350 Castillon-La-Bataille
57 40 04 98

Type of vineyard: Family-owned. **Established:** 3 generations. **Vine stocks:** 2/3 Merlot, 1/3 Cabernet. **Soil:** Clay with calcium carbonate sometimes with gravel. **Exposure:** South. **Average annual production in hectoliters:** 700. **Appellation:** Côtes-de-Castillon. **Type:** Red. **Technique:** Traditional. **Maturing:** Concrete or stainless steel tanks. **Alcohol content:** 12%. **Characteristics:** Fragrant, robust, good capacity with ageing. **Serving temperature:** 16°. **Vintages available in 89/90:** 1983, 1985.

Characteristics of vintages

1985: Good color, fragrant, round, rich and well-balanced, made well, keeps well. Price range (pre-tax, ex-warehouse): between 12 F.F. and 22 F.F.
Sales volume: – Retail: 45%. – Restaurants: 5%. – Other: 50% (Caves or shops).

References in France

Restaurants: Les petits Parcyluies, Hôtel de la Poste, Rest. Dufour, Auberge du Vieux Puits, Auberge Milane.
Shops: Cave Bretagne, St. Nouvelles des Vignerons, Caves Georges, Caves Matton.

CHÂTEAU BLANZAC

Bernard Depons
33350 St Magne-de-Castillon
57 40 11 89

Type of vineyard: Family-owned. **Number of employees:** 2. **Vine stocks:** Merlot 65%, Cabernet Franc 35%. **Soil:** Chalky clay - plateau. **Exposure:** South - South-West. **Average annual production in hectoliters:** 800.

CHATEAU BLANZAC
1985
BORDEAUX SUPÉRIEUR CÔTES DE CASTILLON
APPELLATION BORDEAUX SUPÉRIEUR CÔTES DE CASTILLON CONTRÔLÉ
12,5%vol
MIS EN BOUTEILLE AU CHATEAU
75cl
B. DEPONS, PROPRIÉTAIRE A St-MAGNE-DE-CASTILLON
MARQUE DÉPOSÉE
(GIRONDE, FRANCE)
PRODUCE OF FRANCE

Appellation: Côtes de Castillon. **Type:** Red. **Technique:** Traditional, rather long. **Maturing:** In vats. **Alcohol content:** 12.5%. **Characteristics:** Rich and well balanced, full-bodied, good ageing potential. **Serving temperature:** 18°. **Served with:** Red meat, game, cheese. **Vintages available in 89/90:** 1981, 1983, 1985, 1986.

Characteristics of vintages

1986: Full-bodied, aromatic made from very ripe grapes. **1985:** Rich and well balanced, tannic, good keeping. **Other:** 1983: pronounced bouquet, round, ripe and developed tannins. **1981:** Fully developed wines. Price range (pre-tax, ex-warehouse): 20 to 30 F.F.
Sales volume: - Wholesale: 60%. - Retail: 40%.
Sales in France: 50%. **Export sales:** 50%.
Main trading partners : UK.

Comments

Family enterprise for three generations, whose principal concern is to offer a product with an excellent quality/price ratio, by combing modern techniques with time-tested traditional methods.

BEYNAT

Daniel Borliachon
St-Magne-de-Castillon 33350
57 40 01 14

Type of vineyard: Family-owned + 1 worker. **Established:** 1916. **Number of employees:** 2 plus my sister. **Vine stocks:** Merlot 65%, Cabernet Franc 25%, Cabernet Sauvignon 8%. **Soil:** Clay with calcium carbonate plus 2% silica clay on the hillsides. **Exposure:** East and South. **Average annual production in hectoliters:** 38 to 45 (except 86).
Appellation: Côtes-de-Castillon, Bordeaux Supérieur. **Type:** Red. **Technique:** Old or traditional + gully erosion. **Maturing:** 18 months in vats + 8 to 10 in bottles. **Alcohol content:** 11.8°. **Characteristics:** Beautiful color, various bouquets, typical, opening after 4 to 5 years in the bottles; rich and well-balanced on the robust; all great for ageing; 10 years average. **Serving temperature:** 17° in summer, 18° to 19° in winter. **Served with:** 1980 white meat, fine and delicate cuisine. 1981: grilled meat and cheese (except goat cheese and Maroilles). 1982: all red meat and game. 1983: same as 1982, but need ageing. 1985: red meat and game to be kept. **Vintages available in 89/90:** 1980, 1981, 1983, 1985.

Characteristics of vintages

1985: Intense color, fruity, flowery and stones, meaty, robust, rich and well-balanced, very good ripe tannins. **1983:** Cristallin, leathery, aromas; firm, promising tannins with ageing. **1982:** Deep garnet, intense bouquet, prune, vanilla, stones, very rich and well-balanced. **1981:** Brillant, complex bouquet, little fruit, leather and stones, very robust, firm tannins. Price range (pre-tax, ex-warehouse): Between 20 and 30 F.F.
Sales volume:
- Wholesale: 98%. - Retail: 12%.
Sales in France: 99%.
Export sales: 1%.
Main trading partners : Belgium.

References in France

Restaurants: Moulin de Vernegues, Mallemort 13370.
Shops: Caves des Envierges, rue des Envierges, Paris. 20. Caves de Longchamp, 72 rue G. Lafont, Nantes 44300.

VINS LIQUOREUX

SAUTERNES

CHÂTEAU CLIMENS

Lucien Lurton
33270 Barsac
56 27 15 33 - Telex: 572 861

Type of vineyard: Agricultural Association. **Established:** Proprietor since 1971. **Vine stocks:** Semillon 98%, Sauvignon 2%. **Soil:** Red sand and gravel on cracked limestone base. **Average annual production in hectoliters:** 30,000 cases.
Appellation: Sauternes. **Type:** Sweet white. **Technique:** Harvested in 3 or 4 successive pickings of the botrytised bunches. Fermentation in barrels. **Maturing:** Maturing for 20 months in barrels. **Alcohol content:** 14% (sweet 18%). **Characteristics:** Very balanced and delicate, extreme refinement, superb aromatic complexity. **Serving temperature:** 6° to 8°. **Served with:** Alone at any time of day, as an aperitif or with cooked shellfish, poultry (duck with turnips, for example), cheese (blue, goat, Roblochon, Vacherin). **Vintages available in 89/90:** 1982, 1983.

Characteristics of vintages

1986: Great vintage. **1985:** Rich, balanced year. Not for sale yet. **1984:** Delicate and refined. Sold entirely under the name "Les Cyprès de Climens". **1983:** Rich, soft, full-bodied, fleshy, complex. An exceptional vintage. Superb, concentrated aroma, long. **1982:** Delicatel, long, soft, supple and harmonious. Price range (pre-tax, ex-warehouse): between 120 F.F. and 160 F.F.
Sales volume:
– Wholesale: 100% through Bordeaux wholesalers.

References in France

Restaurants: Michel Gurérard – Jean Ramet – Le Carré des Feuillants – Taillevent – Lucas-Carton.
Caves: Hédiard, Nicolas.

CHÂTEAU LAMOURETTE

Anne Marie Leglise
Bommes 33210
56 63 63 58

Type of vineyard: family-owned. **Established:** in the family since 1860. **Number of employees:** 2. **Vine stocks:** Sémillon 85%, Muscadelle 10%, Sauvignon 5%. **Soil:** mostly sand on rock. **Average annual production in hectoliters:** 180.

Appellation: Sauternes. **Type:** White. **Technique:** Harvesting with 3 or 4 selections of grapes. **Maturing:** in stainless steel tanks. **Characteristics:** delicate, fruity, soft and rich, well-balanced. **Serving temperature:** 8-10°. **Served with:** foie gras, fish cooked in sauce, white meat, and cheese. Pleasant as an aperitif, it will be appreciated on all festive ocaccasions. **Vintages available in 89/90:** 1986-1988.

Characteristics of vintages

1988: very promising. **1986:** very good year.

Château Filhot-Sauternes

Grand cru classé en 1855

Comte Henri de Vaucelles
33210 SAUTERNES
Tél. : 56636109

CHÂTEAU FILHOT

H. de Vaucelles
33210 Sauternes
56 63 61 09

Type of vineyard: Family-owned Agricultural Association. **Established:** 1709, Association in 1973. **Number of employees:** 20. **Vine stocks:** Semillon, 50%, Sauvignon 45%, Muscadelle 5%. **Soil:** Gravel and sand on cracked chalk. **Exposure:** West and South-West. **Average annual production in hectoliters:** 1,250.
Appellation: Sauternes. **Type:** Gold, naturally sweet white. **Technique:** Successive selection of grapes attacked by noble rot. **Maturing:** In vats and casks. **Alcohol content:** 13.5%. **Characteristics:** Naturally sweet wine: complex, good ageing potential. **Serving temperature:** Young: 10°. Aged 18°. **Served with:** White meat, poultry (foie gras), fish cooked in cream sauce. **Vintages available in 89/90:** 1983 to 1986, plus a few bottles from 1967 to 1982 for special occasions.

Characteristics of vintages

1988: Great year for naturally sweet wines. Make sure to reserve a few bottles with your wine merchant. **1987:** Minor year, soft, rich and fruity. **1986:** Good year, rich, well colored, to be aged. **1985:** Drier, flinty due to maturing in casks. **Other:** 1984: Soft and rich, lighter, marked by Sauvignon. 1983: rich and complex, amber color – great year.

Price range (pre-tax, ex-warehouse): 80 to 120 F.F. – 120 to 160 F.F. – 160 F.F. and over.
Sales volume:
– Wholesale: 90% (in Bordeaux). – Retail: 5%. – Restaurants: 5%.
Sales in France: 99% (but 75% exported via Bordeaux).
Main trading partners: European countries, Japan, USA.

References in France

Restaurants: Throughout the country.

Comments

The Château Filhot is one of the oldest and most extensive domains in the Gironde with vineyards covering 60 hectares, 20,000 square meters of buildings, all on 350 hectares. Its convenient use for receptions of all kinds has been the source of lots of publicity for the Sauternes of the 18th and 19th centuries but has accelerated the inflation of the use of this communal appellation. Very great Sauternes, at the head of the appellation (see Classification 89 – Sauternes), characterized by elegance and a great potential for evolution.

• *To better understand the evolution and adherence to type of the various vintages, consult our "Vintage Code" chart.*

CHÂTEAU SAINT-AMAND

Louis Ricard
33210 Preignac
56 63 27 28

Vine stocks: Sémillon and Sauvignon. **Soil:** Very varied: chalky clay, gravel, sand and rocks. **Average annual production in hectoliters:** 20.
Appellation: Sauternes. **Type:** White. **Technique:** Traditional. **Maturing:** Vats and casks. **Characteristics:** Very good wine, fruity, soft and full, long, ripe fruit aroma. **Serving temperature:** About 6°. **Served with:** As an aperitif and with fish in cream sauce, foie gras, cheese (Roquefort, in particular), white meat, etc. **Vintages available in 89/90:** 1986 and 1987.

Characteristics of vintages

1988: Very promising, Grande Année. **1987:** Very good success for the vintage, does not dishonor its predecessors. **1986:** Wine made from a very ripe harvest, lots of noble rot, long future. **1985:** Very good balance, unctuous, fruity. Price range (pre-tax, ex-warehouse): between 50 and 80 F.F.
Sales volume: – Wholesale: 80%. – Retail: 19%, – Restaurants: 1%. **Sales in France:** 50%. **Export sales:** 50%.

References in France

Restaurants: Bistrot de Paris (Oliver), Restaurant Benoit (Paris), La Rivaldière (Paris), Dame Tartine (Beaune), Darroze (Langon), Relais de Roane, etc.
Shops: Badie (Bordeaux).

Abroad

United States

No direct sales. Distribution handled by Cheval Quancard, Coste Exportation in Langon and by Sichel Frères, Quai de Bacalan, Bordeaux.

United Kingdom

Same as for US.

Germany

Same as for US.

Switzerland

Same as for US.

Belgium

Ets Velu, Brussels and Maison Lanhar, Harelbeke.

Canada

Same as for US.

The Netherlands

Same as for US.

Far East

Same as for US.

Others

Denmark: La Maison du Vin, Birkerod 30, Carinaparken.

Comments

Tradition and written texts agree that the property, which

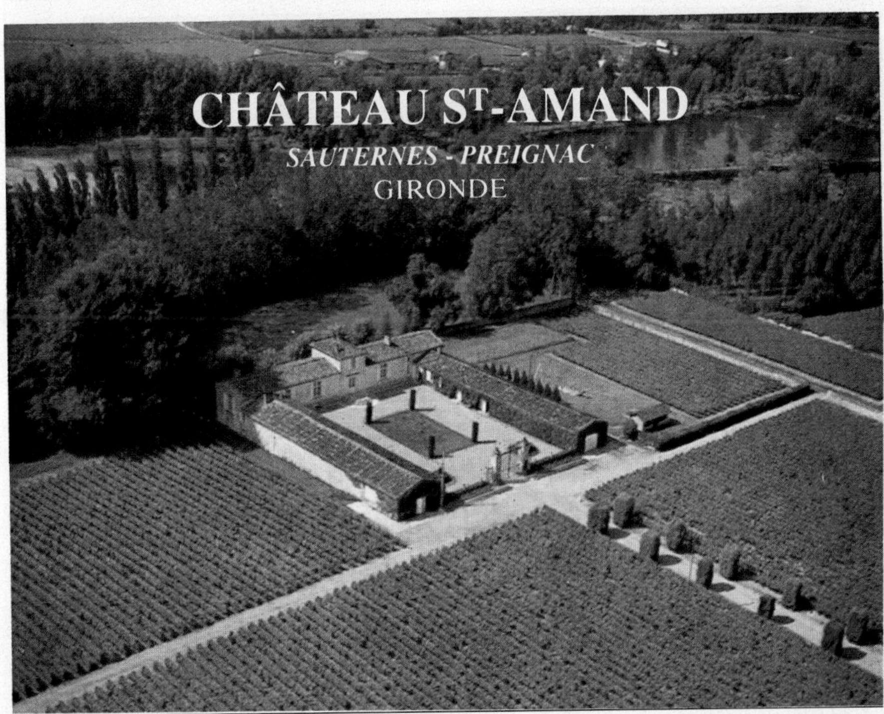

has been in the same family for more than a century, goes back to early antiquity. According to archives of the diocese, it is thought to have been the home of Saint-Amand, Archbishop of Bordeaux in 414, whose name it bears. On the grounds of the estate is a fountain in which, "since time immemorial" (according to family archives dated 1691), the inhabitants of Preignac used to come to bathe to cure certain deseases. Finally a chapel, of which no trace remains, was built and dedicated to the protection of the inhabitants. Note that this very old property is one of the rare winegrowing localities figuring on a map made at the time of Louis XVI by M. de Belleyme, engineer and surveyor to the King.

CHÂTEAU RAYMOND-LAFON

Francine & Pierre Meslier
Sauternes 33210 Langon
56 63 21 02

Established: 1850. **Vine stocks:** Sémillon 80%, Sauvignon Blanc 20%. **Soil:** chalky clay and gravel. **Average annual production in hectoliters:** 9 hl/ha.
Appellation: Sauternes. **Type:** White. **Technique:** traditional – ageing in casks (3 years). **Maturing:** 3 years in new casks. **Characteristics:** naturally sweet white wine. **Serving temperature:** 12°. **Served with:** foie gras, Roquefort cheese, white meat, fish in cream sauce, oysters. **Vintages available in 89/90:** 1985.

Characteristics of vintages

1985: brilliant gold color, very long, good acidity, bitterness and "roti" due to the botrytis (noble rot), honey, prune, apricot cyrstallized citrus, vanilla aromas. Average pre-tax, ex-cellar price: 170 F.F.
Sales in France: 30%.
Export sales: 70%.
Main trading partners : USA, Japan, Switzerland, Belgium, Italy, Spain, Germany, Canada, UK, Denmark, Hong Kong, Singapore, etc. Vente directe à la propriété.

References in France

Restaurants: Tour d'Argent, Alain Chapel, Lucas Carton, St. James, Pavillon Elysée, Cannes Festival etc.
Shops: Fauchon, Legrand, Caves Six, Aux Vignes Pasquier, Malleval (Lyon), Caves de la Madeleine etc.

Comments

Not yet classified in 1855 because it was created just before. Rare wine. Yields are only 9 hl per hectare, which corresponds to one glass of wine per vine! Sought after the world over. Motto of the estate: "Prestige through quality". As of the 1985 vintage, a maximum of 60 numbered bottles of the Collection d'Impériales are produced annually. A different label every year, reproduced by Yan de Siber, painter of the Bordeaux châteaux. Certificate of authenticity. Sold all over the world with great success.

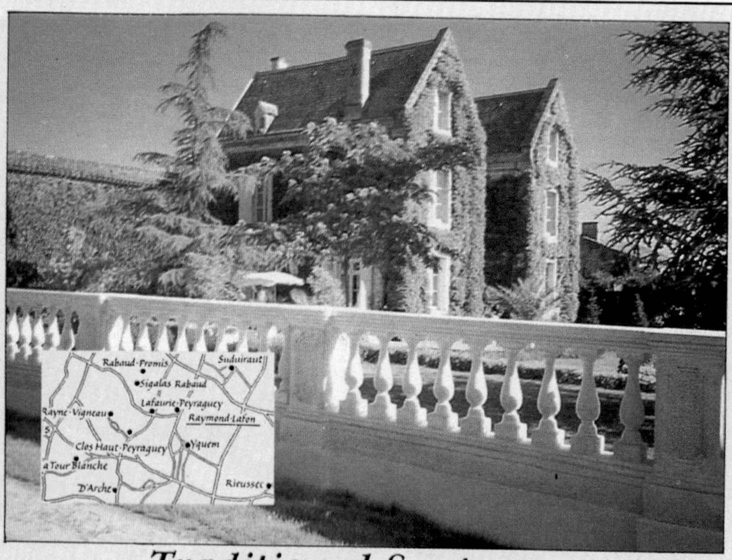

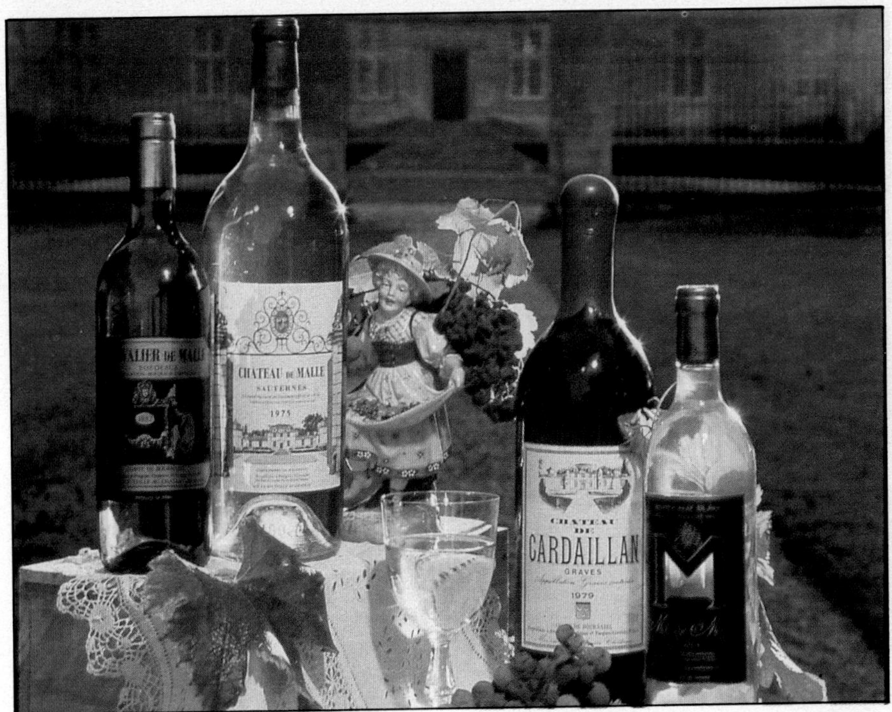

CHÂTEAU DE MALLE

Comtesse Pierre de Bournazel
33210 Preignac
56 63 28 67

Type of vineyard: Family-owned for over more than 500 years. **Vine stocks:** Graves: Cabernet Sauvignon 80%, Merlot 20%. Sauternes: Semillon 70%, Sauvignon 28%, Muscadelle 2%. **Soil:** clay – gravel and silica. **Exposure:** Very sunny. **Average annual production in hectoliters:** 50,000 bottles.
Appellation: Cru Classe de Sauternes en 1855 – AOC Graves Rouge, AOC Graves Blanc. **Type:** Red, white. **Technique:** Traditional. **Maturing:** In oak casks. **Characteristics:** Le Château de Malle, more fruity than liquorous, takes after the Barsac in its vigor and the Sauternes in its distinction. **Served with:** Duck foie gras, duck cooked with peaches.

Characteristics of vintages

1987: Very exceptional for this vintage – golden color, crystallized apricot flavor, lingering taste. **1986:** Magnificent wine for ageing, will be bottled in 1989, very long keeping. **1985:** Very small harvest after hail storm, crystallized apricot and lime-blossom aroma. **Other: 1983:** Very high class wine, well balanced, to be kept. Golden yellow color, woody nose, fresh, apple, grapefruit, a touch of anis. Price range (pre-tax, ex-warehouse): 80 to 120 F.F.
Sales volume:
– Wholesale: 30%. – Retail: 20%. – Restaurants: 5%.
– Other: 45%.
Main trading partners : Scandinavian countries, Benelux countries, Italy, Switzerland, UK.

References in France

Restaurants: L'Aquitaine (Paris 15[e]), Les Glenan (Paris 7[e]), Le Sully d'Auteuil (Paris 16[e]), La Vieille Fontaine (Maison Laffitte).
Shops: Caves Bailly, Caves St. Antoine.

Comments

Château de Malle and its "Italian style" gardens are classified as "historical monuments". Its construction by Jacques de Malle, direct ancestor of the present proprietor, goes back to the beginning of the 17th century. The gardens, arranged in terraces, shelter a number of sculptured stone groups, the works of Italian artists brought to Guienne in the 17th century. The château and the gardens are open to the public from March to mid November. The Malle vineyard, under a single proprietor, has the unique advantage of extending over the noble regions of Sauternes and Graves, and produces very beautiful wines (superb 83 and 86 vintages). See "Classification of Sauternes".

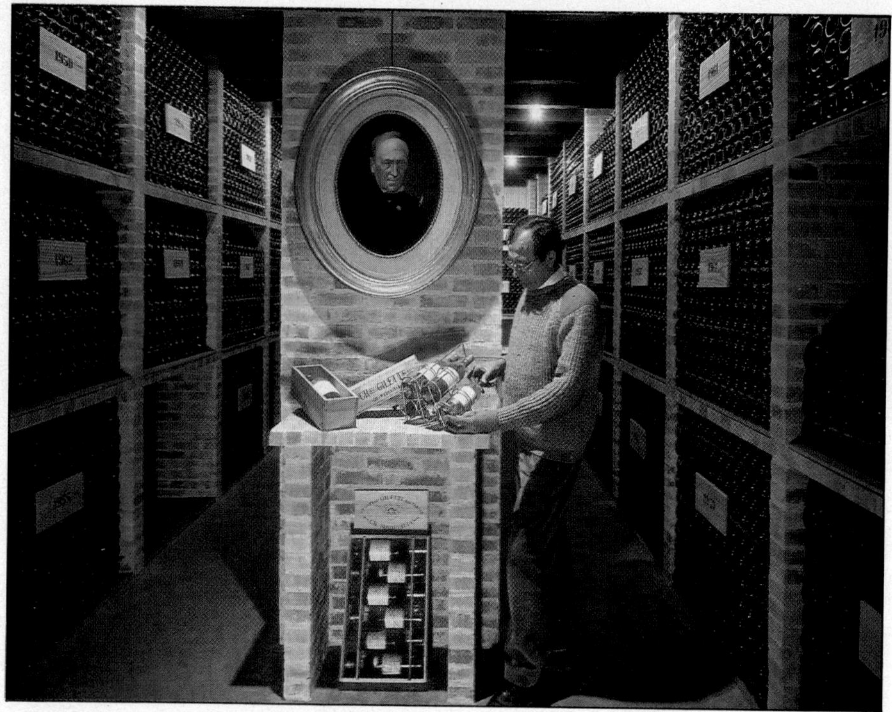

CHÂTEAU GILETTE

Christian Medeville
"Sauternes Antique Dealer"– 33210 Preignac
56 63 27 59 – Telex: 57 10 09 Gilette

Type of vineyard: Family-owned. **Established:** In the family since the 18th century. **Vine stocks:** Sémillon 85%, Sauvignon 10%, Muscadelle 5%. **Soil:** Sand and gravel. **Average annual production in hectoliters:** 40 to 50. **Appellation:** Sauternes. **Types:** White. **Technique:** Vinification in stainless steel tanks with temperature control. **Maturing:** In large vats (12 to 15 years before bottling). **Alcohol content:** 14 to 15%. **Characteristics:** With a soft and supple texture, these are very complex wines, that can be aged a long time. The yongest wine presently offered for sale is a 1962. A unique phenomenon in Bordeaux – the Gilette wines are only sold there after 20 years of ageing, which explains the epithet "Antique Dealer". **Serving temperature:** 8°. **Served with:** Excellent as an aperitif, it is at its best with cooked fish, foie gras, white meat and fruit desserts. **Vintages available in 89/90:** 1956 1/2 Sec, 1961 Crème de Tête, 1962 Doux.

Characteristics of vintages

Other: 1961: Crème de Tête: Very beautiful topaz color, very concentrated fragrance of thick acacia honey and apricots, great pineapple flavor, long, unimaginable grace, distinction and breed. **1962:** Doux: Golden color, mango, melon, banana, hazel nut fragrance, perfectly balanced sumptuous wine. Price range (pre-tax, ex-warehouse): more than 160 F.F.

Sales volume:
- Wholesale: 50%. - Retail: 30%. - Restaurants: 10%.
- Other: 10% wine cellars.

Sales in France: 60%.
Export sales: 40%.
Main trading partners: United States, Canada, Australia, United Kingdom, Switzerland, Belgium, Netherlands, Denmark, Italy.

References in France

Restaurants: Taillevent, Tour d'Argent, Bardet, Carré des Feuillants, Bocuse, Blanc, Chapel, Point, La Marée, Michel Rostang, Orsi, Saint James, Ramet, Trois Gros, Restaurant Le Moulin de Mougin.
Shops: Chedeville, Club Amical du Vin, Dubœuf, Legrand, Pétrissans, Taillevent.

Abroad

United States

Associated Wine Distributors, 2650 Shop Road, Columbia – Tindall Family: Colorado. Noir Import: Washington – Direct Import: Boston.

United kingdom

TW Wine, Norfolk.

Switzerland

Elie Gazzar, Chemin du Dévent Ecublens.

Belgium

Velghe, Izegheim.

Canada

Saq, Montreal, Quebec, Vancouver.

Far East

Hong Kong: Le Regent. Japan: Simtory, Tokyo.

Others

Italy: Amadeo Sarzi, Milan. Instituto, Verona. Denmark: Vinopol, Copenhagen.

Comments

The Château Gilette has been in the Medeville family for more than 200 years. Today, the Medevilles (Christian and his wife) remain profoundly attached to the Sauternes region where they also produce other excellent varieties (Château de Respide-Medeville in particular). Unique in Bordeaux, the Medeville wines are aged for twenty years before bieng offered for sale.

CHÂTEAU DE FARGUES

A. De Lur Saluces
33210 Fargues-de-Langon
56 44 07 45

Type of vineyard: Family-owned. **Established:** 1472. **Number of employees:** 6. **Vine stocks:** 80% Sémillon, 20% Sauvignon. **Average annual production in hectoliters:** 8,000 to 9,000 bottles.
Appellation: Sauternes. **Type:** White. **Maturing:** 3 years. **Serving temperature:** 12%. **Served with:** As an aperitif, with foie gras rich cooking. **Vintages available in 89/90:** 1983, 1982, 1981.

Characteristics of vintages

1983: Exceptional wine, very fragrant, full-flavor, typical a successful wine. Price range (pre-tax, ex-warehouse): 1981: 190 F.F. 1982: 250 F.F.
Sales volume:
- Wholesale: 90%. - Retail: 10%.

References in France

Restaurants: Hédiard. Boutiques.

Abroad

United States

Châteaux & Estates.

Comments

The management of The vinification is under the responsability of the same owner.

CHÂTEAU LA TOUR BLANCHE

Mr. Jean-Pierre Jausserand
Bommes 33210 Langon
56 63 61 55 - Telex: 540 127 PUBLI BORDEAUX

Number of employees: 9. **Vine stocks:** Semillon 77,80%, Sauvignon 19,50%, Muscadelle 2,7%. **Soil:** Gravel. **Appellation:** Sauternes. **Type:** White. **Technique:** Temperature regulated tanks. **Maturing:** In Oak barrels (from Nièvre, Limousin, Châteauroux). **Serving temperature:** 10 to 12°. **Served with:** The young Sauternes (4 to 5 years old) as an apéritif, with foie gras, poultry and white meats. For the mature Sauternes (12 to 15 years old) at the end of the meal with Roquefort cheese or sherbet.

Characteristics of vintages

1986: Very promising. **1985:** Balanced, deep color, aroma of stewed and exotic fruit. **1984:** To be drunk within the next 10 years, vanilla fragrance. **1983:** Balanced, great finesse. Price range (pre-tax, ex-warehouse): between 80 F.F. and 120 F.F.
Sales volume:
- Wholesale: 50%. - Retail: 10%. - Restaurants: 10%.
- Other: 30%.
Sales in France: 60%.
Export sales: 40%.
Main trading partners : USA, Canada, UK, Belgium, Germany, Denmark, Netherlands, Italy, Sweden, Japan.

BARSAC

CHÂTEAU GRAVAS

Pierre Bernard
33720 Barsac
56 27 15 20

Type of vineyard: Family-owned. **Number of employees:** 2. **Vine stocks:** 80% Sémillon, 10% Sauvignon, 10% Muscadelle. **Soil:** Chalky clay. **Exposure:** Haut Barsac Plateau. **Average annual production in hectoliters:** 245.
Appellation: Barsac. **Type:** White. **Technique:** Traditional. **Maturing:** Casks and vats. **Characteristics:** Remarkable naturally sweet wine, balanced and harmonious, regularly successful, with an excellent quality/price ratio (see "Classification of the Sauternes"). **Serving temperature:** 6°. **Served with:** Foie gras, as an aperitif, fish in cream sauce, cheese. **Vintages available in 89/90:** 1986, 1987.

Characteristics of vintages

1988: Good year, fruity, full, soft and supple, for keeping. **1987:** Balanced wine, perfectly controlled vinification. **1986:** Great year, rich, floral, persistant wine which will evolve well, dominated by honey and white flower aromas. Price range (pre-tax, ex-warehouse): between 50 and 120 F.F.
Sales volume:
– Wholesale: 20%. – Retail: 20%. – Restaurants: 20%.
Sales in France: 60%. **Export sales:** 40%.
Main trading partners: Belgium, Netherlands, Spain, Canada, Germany.

References in France

Restaurants: Auberge de l'Ill, La Tupina, etc.
Shops: Bordeaux Magnums, Lagrue, Amour du Vin.

Abroad

Germany

Französische Weindepot.

Belgium

Werco.

The Netherlands

Okhysen.

Comments

Château Gravas has long been reknowned, along with other fine Sauternes, since the time of Richard the Lion-hearted, going back to the 12th century. The name of "Gravas" comes from the "graves" or fine, well-drained soil, ideally suited to wines of quality. After many different

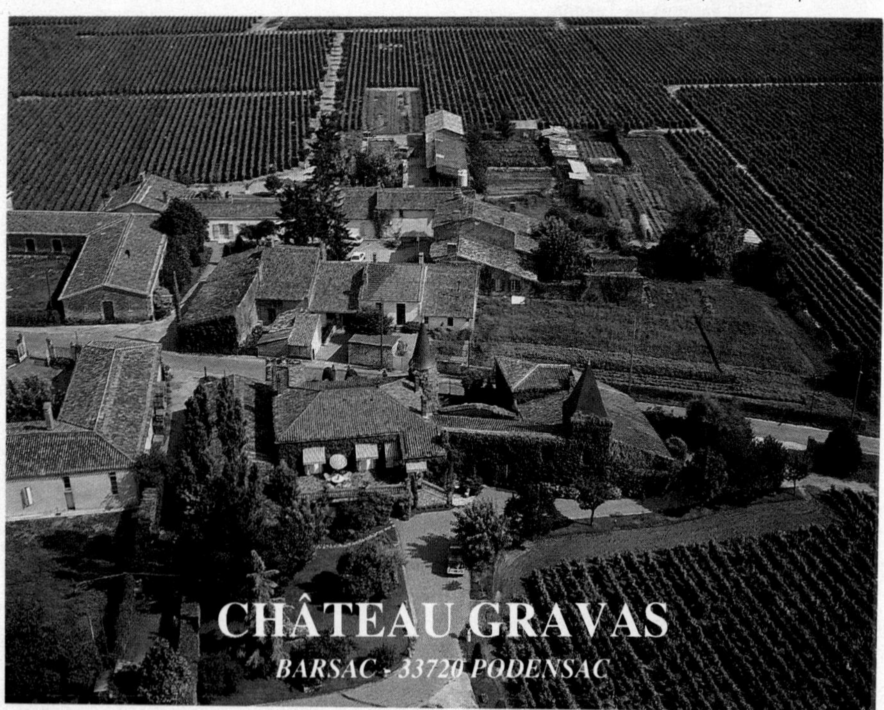

owners throughout the years, Château Gravas was purchased by the Bernard family in 1850, and they have since come to be considered among the most respected winegrowers in the region. Only about 2,500 cases a year. By the very nature of the production, Sauternes in general, and Château Gravas in particular, must remain a rare wine of limited availability that will continue to be sought out by connoisseurs.

CHÂTEAU PIADA BARSAC

Jean Lalande
33720 Barsac
56 27 16 13

Type of vineyard: Family-owned. **Vine stocks:** Sémillon 90%, Sauvignon 10%. **Soil:** Chalky red clay and silica plateau. **Average annual production in hectoliters:** 200.

Appellation: Barsac Sauternes, Bordeaux Blanc Sec and Bordeaux Rouge. **Type:** Red, White. **Technique:** Traditional. **Maturing:** In oak casks. **Serving temperature:** 10 to 12°. **Served with:** As an aperitif and with foie gras, delicate fish, white meat, poultry.

Characteristics of vintages

1988: Extremely rich. **1987:** Firm, vigourous and fragrant. **1986:** Well balanced and elegant, exceptional finish. **1985:** soft and full, lively, very delicate aromas. **Other:** 1967: a great Sauternes, spicy aromas. 1971: delicate nose, elegant, complex.

Sales volume:
- Wholesale: 60%. - Retail: 35%. - Restaurants: 5%.

Sales in France: 50%. **Export sales:** 50%.

References in France

Restaurants: Le Taillevent, Paris.

Abroad

United States

Importers: Walker, Massachussetts, Direct Import II, 60106, Bauer & Foss, Ohio.

United Kingdom

J. Goedhuis & Co. - London 2NU.

Germany

Schuller GMBH Kanalstr. 15, D 7107 Neckarsulm.

Switzerland

Schuller & Cie, Franzosenstrasse 14, 6423 Seewen Schwyz - Tel: 043 24 31 31.

Belgium

Ets Baugnees, rue Hamel 2, 6180 Courcelles.

Canada

SAQ Montreal H2Y 3J8.

The Netherlands

De Wijnkamer Postbus 2218, 5202 Ce Hertogenbosch - Tel: 073 21 02 49.

Others

Australia: Cellarcraft, Mona Vale NSW 2103 / Nicks Wine Victoria - The de Burgh Day Wine Company, Victoria.

Comments

The Château Piada domain is mentioned as early as 1274 in a deep preserve in the archives of the Tower of London, referring to the Aquitaine & Barsac tribute. (See "Classification of Sauternes").

LOUPIAC

CHÂTEAU DU CROS

Michel Boyer
Loupiac - 33410 Cadillac
56 62 99 31

Type of vineyard: Family-owned. **Number of employees:** 28. **Vine stocks:** Sauvignon, Semillon, Muscadelle. **Soil:** Clay with calcium carbonate on limestone banks. **Average annual production in hectoliters:** 2,000.

Appellation: A.C. Bordeaux and A.C. Loupiac. **Type:** Dry white and liqueur-like. **Technique:** Dry white Sauvignon: fermented at low temperature. **Maturing:** Cros-Sec (dry): aged in barrels. Liqueur-like: aged 2 years in barrels, some new. **Characteristics:** Sauvignon: fresh without being green, aromatic with a certain roundness, to be drunk young. Cros-Sec: a wine that ages marvelously, rich and well-balanced, body. Cros (liqueur-like): the characteristics of the great liqueur-like wines of the region cannot be described in two lines. Too complex, can age more than 30 years. **Served with:** Sauvignon: fish, shell-fish, hors-d'œuvre or chilled as an aperitif. Cros sec: goes with everything. To be drunk cool but not cold. Cros liqueur-like: as an aperitif, but also with white meat, poultry, Croustades and, of course, foie gras. **Vintages available in 89/90:** Sauvignon: 1988. Cros sec: 1983. Cros liqueur-like: 1970, 1973, 1985.

Characteristics of vintages

Average pre-tax, ex-warehouse price: Sauvignon: 25 F.F. V.A.T. Included, Cros sec: 32 F.F. V.A.T. included, Cros liqueur-like: 39 F.F. in the 1985, all tax included.
Sales volume: – Wholesale: 60%. – Retail: 20%. – Other: 20% in bulk for wine of quality not considered representative of the Château.
Sales in France: 40%. **Export sales:** 60%.
Main trading partners: USA, Belgium, Germany, Netherlands, Denmark, Sweden, UK, Switzerland.

CHÂTEAU LOUPIAC GAUDIET

Marc Ducau
56 62 99 88

Established: For four generations. **Vine stocks:** Sémillon 80%, Sauvignon 20%. **Soil:** Chalky clay. **Exposure:** South. **Average annual production in hectoliters:** 800.
Appellation: Loupiac. **Type:** White. **Technique:** Tradition, with temperature control. **Maturing:** In stainless steel and enamelled tanks (about 3 years). **Alcohol content:** 13%. **Characteristics:** Typical Sauternes. **Serving temperature:** 7-8°. **Served with:** Foie gras, white meat, cheese, and as an aperitif. **Vintages available in 89/90:** 1983-1985.

PRODUIT DE FRANCE
CHATEAU
Loupiac-Gaudiet
LOUPIAC
APPELLATION LOUPIAC CONTROLÉE
1985
75 cl
MARC DUCAU, PROPRIÉTAIRE A LOUPIAC (GIRONDE)
MISE EN BOUTEILLE AU CHATEAU

Characteristics of vintages

1985: Beautiful golden color, full-bodied and very fruity. Price range (pre-tax, ex-warehouse): 20 to 30 F.F.
Sales volume: – Wholesale: 60%. – Retail: 40%.
Sales in France: 50%. **Export sales:** 50%.
Main trading partners: Belgium, Germany, Switzerland, Denmark, UK, USA.

Comments

The Château Loupiac Gaudiet was once the property of Michel Montaigne.

SAINTE-CROIX-DU-MONT

CHÂTEAU LA RAME

Armand Yves
Sainte Croix du Mont 33410 Cadillac
56 62 01 50

Type of vineyard: Agricultural Association. **Established:** 1973. **Vine stocks:** Sémillon, Sauvignon. **Soil:** Chalky clay. **Exposure:** South. **Average annual production in hectoliters:** 700.
Appellation: Sainte-Croix-du-Mont. **Type:** White. **Technique:** traditional. **Maturing:** in new casks. **Alcohol content:** 14%. **Serving temperature:** 7°. **Vintages available in 89/90:** 83, 86, 87, 88.

Comments

Located to the South East of Bordeaux on hillsides overlooking the Garonne, facing full South, the 30 hectares of the Château de la Rame descend towards the river. During the revolution La Rame (The Rock in old French) belonged to the Baron de Vertheuil, govenor of the Island of Oléron, and Lord of a Rame. At the beginning of the century, the Château la Rame was classified 1er Cru Classe by the Bordeaux wine dealers.

CERONS

CHÂTEAU DE CERONS

Mr. Perromat
33720 Cerons
56 27 01 12

Type of vineyard: Family-owned. **Vine stocks:** Sémillon, Sauvignon, Muscadelle, Cabernet, Merlot.
Appellation: Cerons, Sauternes, Graves. **Type:** Red. **Technique:** Traditional. **Characteristics:** Liquorous, robust wines, for ageing. Graves & Bordeaux Supérieur Rouge: rich color and bouquet. **Vintages available in 89/90:** 1983, 1984, 1985 and 1986.

Characteristics of vintages

1986: Good year. Liquorous, very fruity wines. **1985:** Excellent year for reds and whites alike.

BORDEAUX SUPÉRIEUR

CHÂTEAU BAUDUC

David Thomas
33670 Créon
56 23 23 58

Established: 1981. **Number of employees:** 3. **Vine stocks:** Merlot 60%, Cabernet Sauvignon 25%, Malbec 5%, Cabernet Franc 20%. **Soil:** Sandy, clay and gravel. **Exposure:** Hillsides and plateau. **Average annual production in hectoliters:** 580.
Appellation: Bordeaux Supérieur. **Type:** Red. **Technique:** Traditional. **Maturing:** Barrels tanks. **Alcohol content:** 12%. **Characteristics:** Rich and well-balanced, dense color. **Serving temperature:** 17°. **Served with:** Red meat in sauce. **Vintages available in 89/90:** 1988, 1987, 1986.

Characteristics of vintages

1988: Very mature wine, note of chocolate and prune. For keeping. **1987:** Fine and aromatic, fruity. **1986:** Heavy, to be aged. Price range (pre-tax, ex-warehouse): 18 F.F.
Sales volume:
– Wholesale: 5%. – Retail: 5%. – Restaurants: 5%. – Other: 85% (export).
Sales in France: 10%.
Export sales: 90%.
Main trading partners : Belgium, Holland, UK, USA.

CHÂTEAU DE BELCIER

33350 Les Salles de Castillon
(Paris) 47 04 38 85

Type of vineyard: Corporation. **Vine stocks:** (35 hectares): Merlot (50%) and Cabernets. **Soil:** Clay with calcium carbonate.
Appellation: Bordeaux Supérieur – Côtes-de-Castillon. **Type:** Red. **Technique:** Traditional (long). **Maturing:** In barrels. **Characteristics:** Good wines, fine woody nose, light and supple, well-balanced, very seductive, Good for ageing. **Serving temperature:** 16°. **Vintages available in 89/90:** 1985, 1986 and 1987.

Characteristics of vintages

1988: Black color, slightly crystallized ripe red fruit flavor, very dense with rich, ripe tannins, for keeping. **1987:** Very beautiful color, good fragrance, the fruit and wood are beginning to harmonize. Good lingering taste. Very successful for the vintage. **1986:** Very promising. **1985:** Fragrant and supple, fine tannins, good for ageing.

References in France

Shops: L'Amour du Vin, 94, rue Saint-Dominique 75007 Paris. Tél. 45 56 12 94.

CHÂTEAU CAP DE MERLE

Mr. Bessou
Château Durand – La Plagne – 33570 Puisseguin
57 74 63 07

Type of vineyard: Family Corporation. **Established:** 1982. **Number of employees:** 4. **Vine stocks:** Merlot 70%, Cabernet Franc 15%, Cabernet Sauvignon 15%. **Soil:** Flat, sweet soil, sandy clay and gravel. **Average annual production in hectoliters:** 360.
Appellation: Bordeaux Supérieur. **Type:** Red. **Technique:** Traditional, very long maceration. **Maturing:** Produced in concrete vats, aged in stainless steel tanks. **Alcohol content:** 12.5%. **Characteristics:** Fine, light, fruity, wines, good vinification technique, frequent prizes in competitions. **Serving temperature:** 16°-18°. **Served**

with: Meat and cheese. **Vintages available in 89/90:** 1978, 1983, 1985.

Characteristics of vintages

1985: Silver Medal at the Agricultural Competition in Paris, fine and supple vintage, good for ageing. Price range (pre-tax, ex-warehouse): Between 20 F.F. and 30 F.F.
Sales volume:
– Wholesale: 30%. – Retail: 20%. – Other: 50% (export).
Sales in France: 50%.
Export sales: 50%.
Main trading partners : Belgium, Netherlands, Switzerland, UK, Germany.

DOMAINE DU CHÂTAIN

Philippe & Martine Junquas
Châtain Néac 33500 Libourne
57 74 02 79

Type of vineyard: Family-owned. **Established:** 1985. **Vine stocks:** Merlot 30%, Cabernet Franc 40%, Cabernet Sauvignon 30%. **Soil:** Acid, sandy clay. **Exposure:** Slight slope. **Average annual production in hectoliters:** 120. **Appellation:** Bordeaux Supérieur. **Type:** Red. **Technique:** Harvested at optimum maturity – daily pumping over, permanent temperature control and frequent testing. **Maturing:** Stainless steel tanks – pumping over and aeration every 40 days. **Alcohol content:** 12%. **Characteristics:** Rich aromas, well structured (see below). **Serving temperature:** 17 to 18°. **Servet with:** Meat, cheese. **Vintages available in 89/90:** 1986, 1987, 1988.

Characteristics of vintages

1988: Deep color, subtle aromas, very promising. **1987:** Ripe red berry aromas, supple, soft and full. **1986:** Rich and complex aromas, round and concentrated, beautiful soft tannins. Price range (pre-tax, ex-warehouse): 10 to 20 F.F.
Sales volume:
– Wholesale: 10%. – Retail: 90%.
Sales in France: 100%.

CHÂTEAU GRAND TERTRE

Jean-Pierre Rollet
Gardegan – 33350 Castillon
57 47 15 13 – Telex: 70 598 CCI Libo/Rollet

Type of vineyard: Family-owned. **Vine stocks:** Merlot (78%) Cabernets franc (14%), Cabernet Sauvignon (8%) on 8 hectares. **Soil:** Clay with calcium carbonate on slopes. **Average annual production in hectoliters:** 60,000 bottles.
Appellation: Bordeaux Superieur, Côtes-de-Castillon. **Type:** Red. **Technique:** Traditional, destemming and thermo-regulation at 27 to 29°C. **Characteristics:** Good color and structure, well made, combining suppleness, richness and balance. **Serving temperature:** 16°. **Served with:** Meat and cheeses. **Vintages available in 89/90:** 1986 and 1985.

Characteristics of vintages

1986: Very successful vintage. **1985:** Excellent vintage.

CHÂTEAU GRAND MONTEIL

Jean Techenet
33370 Sallebœuf
56 21 29 70

Type of vineyard: Family Agricultural Association. **Established:** 20 years ago. **Number of employees:** Near 14. **Vine stocks:** Merlot, Cabernet Franc, Cabernet-Sauvignon, Malbec for red, Sauvignon 50% for white with Sémillon 50%. **Soil:** Clay and sand. **Average annual production in hectoliters:** 4,000/500,000 bottles by year. **Appellation:** Bordeaux Supérieur Entre-Deux-Mers. **Type:** Red, white, rosé. **Maturing:** Oak casks. **Alcohol content:** 12°. **Characteristics:** Very fruity, red with tannin, white with a balance of alcohol and acidity. **Vintages available in 89/90:** 1985, 1986.

Characteristics of vintages

1985: Fruity, light tannins. Price range (pre-tax, ex-warehouse): Between 20 F.F. and 30 F.F.
Sales volume:
– Wholesale: 5%. – Retail: 50%. – Other: 5%.
Sales in France: 60%.
Export sales: 40%.
Main trading partners : Belgium, Holland, Denmark, Germany, Austria.

References in France

Restaurants: Flora Danica Paris, L'Étoile Paris, St-James 33 Bouliac.

Abroad

Belgium

Louis Delhaize Group.

Comments

Cellars built by Gustave Eiffel.

• *Glycerine – wine component responsible for its unctuosity. It appears in the course of the alcoholic fermentation but, in the case of mellow and naturally sweet wines, can also come from the favorable action of noble rot on the grapes. See Sauternes.*

CHÂTEAU DE LUGAGNAC

Mylène and Maurice Bon
33790 Pellegrue
56 61 30 60

Type of vineyard: Family-owned. **Established:** 1969. **Number of employees:** 4. **Vine stocks:** Cabernet Sauvignon 43.5%, Cabernet Franc 13.5%., Merlot Noir 43.5%. **Soil:** Chalky sea-shells 35%, iron-clay 66%. **Exposure:** Plateau 50%, slope to the South 15%, slight slope to the North 20%, slope to the West 15%. **Average annual production in hectoliters:** 2,000.
Appellation: Bordeaux Supérieur. **Type:** Red, rosé. **Technique:** Traditional in stainless steel tanks. **Maturing:** In stainless steel tanks and barrels. **Alcohol content:** 12%. **Characteristics:** Balanced and harmonious, very well colored, rich and full, balanced, to be aged a few years in bottles in order to attain peak quality. **Serving temperature:** 16 to 20°. **Served with:** Traditional cuisine. **Vintages available in 89/90:** 1983, 1985, 1986, 1987, 1988.

Characteristics of vintages

1988: Beautiful wine, good keeping, which can only be properly judged after bottling in 1990. **1987:** Less concentrated and more supple, the 1987 vintage can be consumed right now. **1986:** Very successful like the 1985 vintage, top quality. **1985:** Exceptional year, a concentrated wine which needs a few more years to reach its peak. **Other:** 1983 – balanced, reaching maturity after five years ageing. Price range (pre-tax, ex-warehouse): 20 to 30 F.F.
Sales volume:
– Wholesale: 50%. – Retail: 40%. – Restaurants: 10%.
Sales in France: 90%.
Export sales: 10%.
Main trading partners : United Kingdom.

References in France

Restaurants: Royal Monceau, Miramar, Biarritz, Le Mathusalem, Le Jeroboam, Pasquet, Circus Line.
Shops: Amour du Vin – Caves Estève – Maison d'Aquitaine.

Comments

Consecrated to the vine over the centuries, the Château de Lugagnac has always been one of the major wines of its appellation, as indicated by the ancient maps of the region. Much neglected before and after the war, the vineyard has been entirely rebuilt since 1970 by the present proprietors and now covers more than 42 hectares. Very balanced, the Lugagnac wines are treated exclusively by classical methods with sulfur dioxide, to the exclusion of bisulfite and other chemical additives. In particular, they don't receive an antitarter treatment and sometimes have, as a result a light sediment in the bottle, proof of their integrity.

Château de LUGAGNAC

CHÂTEAU LA FOURQUERIE

Jean-Pierre Rollet
Gardegan - 33350 Castillon
57 47 15 13 - Telex: 570 598 CCI Libo/Rollet

Type of vineyard: Family-owned. **Vine stocks:** Merlot (70%) Cabernet franc (14%), Cabernet-Sauvignon (8%) on 6 hectares. **Soil:** Clay with calcium carbonate on slopes. **Average annual production in hectoliters:** 45,000 bottles.
Appellation: Bordeaux Superior, Côtes-de-Castillon. **Type:** Red. **Technique:** Traditional, destemming and thermo-regulation at 27 to 29°C. **Characteristics:** Good color, rich and well-balanced, supple and fruity. **Serving temperature:** 16°. **Served with:** Meat and cheeses. **Vintages available in 89/90:** 1986 and 1985.

Characteristics of vintages

1986: Good year. **1985:** Excellent vintage.

DOMAINE DES RAIGNEAUX

Jean Bustarret
Madirac - 33670 Créon
56 30 64 48

Type of vineyard: Family-owned. **Established:** 1835. **Number of employees:** 3. **Vine stocks:** Merlot, Cabernet Sauvignon, Cabernet Franc, Malbec. **Soil:** Gravel with clay - gravelly subsoil. **Exposure:** South, Southeast. **Average annual production in hectoliters:** Around 500.

Appellation: Bordeaux Supérieur, Bordeaux Clairet. **Type:** Red. **Other:** Clairet. **Technique:** Traditional, topping up twice a day - fermentation with skins for 3 weeks. **Maturing:** Stainless steel and Oak casks. **Characteristics:** Dense, rich, well-balanced, round, red wines. Fine bouquet. Needs considerable ageing. **Served with:** Depending upon age and the vintage with red meat, grilled steaks, poultry, white meat, cheese, according to age and vintages. **Vintages available in 89/90:** 1982, 1983, 1984 (in magnum only).

Characteristics of vintages

1984: Distinguished and fine. Should be aged. Very successful vintage. **1983:** All the qualities of this region area. Should be aged but quite good already. Price range (pre-tax, ex-warehouse): Between 20 and 30 F.F.
Sales volume:
- Wholesale: 1%. - Retail: 98%.
- Restaurants: 1%.

Main trading partners : Belgium, Netherlands, Germany, Japan.

Abroad

Germany

Importers: Vin et Vino - Weinspezialtitaten - Mullerstrasse 40 8000 - Munchen 5. Tel: (089) 260 79 63.

The Netherlands

Importers: Jam Herbrink - Gebr - Heisterkam, Kljnkopers - 07630 Ootmarsum Oostwal 5 7631 Egootmarsum. Tel: 05419 2222.

CHÂTEAU TERRASSON

Christophe Lavau
Succession of Jean Boutin
Le Faure Monbadon - 33570 Puisseguin
57 40 60 55

Type of vineyard: Family-owned. **Established:** November 1983. **Vine stocks:** 70% Merlot, 30% Cabernet Sauvignon. **Soil:** Clay with calcium carbonate, rocky. Covered with silica and clay. **Exposure:** Plateau. **Average annual production in hectoliters:** 50 to 55/ha 85 and 86: 65/ha. **Appellation:** Bordeaux Supérieur, Côtes-de-Castillon. **Type:** Red. **Technique:** Classic vinification. **Maturing:** Traditional. **Alcohol content:** 12.5% to 13%. **Characteristics:** 17° to 18°. **Served with:** Red meat and cheese. **Vintages available in 89/90:** 1986, 1987.

Characteristics of vintages

1986: Gold Medal at the Agricultural Competition in Paris. **1984:** Silver Medal at the Blayais Bourgeais Competition in 1985. Price range (pre-tax, ex-warehouse): between 20 F.F. and 30 F.F.
Sales volume:
- Retail: 15%. - Other: 85% Work's council.

Sales in France: 100%.

• *Scandal in Saint-Émilion. To find out all about his appellation and the real quality of its wines, from the least pretentious to the greatest, see "Open Letter" in the Chapter on Bordeaux wines.*

CHÂTEAU LA TREILLE DES GIRONDINS

Alain Goumaud
"Mézières", 33350 St-Magne-de-Castillon
57 40 05 38

Type of vineyard: Family-owned. **Established:** 1926. **Number of employees:** 4. **Vine stocks:** Merlot Noir 60%, Cabernet Franc 25%, Cabernet Sauvignon15%. **Soil:** Sand and clay on iron pan. **Exposure:** Plain and foothills – to the south. **Average annual production in hectoliters:** 750.
Appellation: Bordeaux Supérieur, Côtes de Castillon. **Type:** Red. **Technique:** Long maceration, destemming 80%, pumping over (first five days). **Maturing:** In stainless steel and concrete tanks, and oak casks. **Alcohol content:** 12%. **Characteristics:** Young wines: Fruity, raspberry or blackcurrant flavor, developing with age a complex bouquet – touch of vanilla or spices. **Serving temperature:** 1 to 3 years old: 16°. 3 years and over: 17 to 18°. **Served with:** Red meat, game, conserves (goose, etc.), mushroom (cèpes), lamprey cooked à la Bordelaise. **Vintages available in 89/90:** 1981, 1983, 1985, 1987, 1988 (as of Jan. 1990).

Characteristics of vintages

1988: Still too young. Very rich wine, with exceptional ageing potential. **1987:** Bordeaux Bronze Medal – Great success for a difficult year. **1985:** Good balance, getting rounder, deep color, character developing with ageing. **Other:** 1983 – prune fragrance, slight amber color, developed bouquet, spicy taste. **1981:** Amber color, bouquet now reaching full maturity, ready to drink. Price range (pre-tax, ex-warehouse): 10 to 20 F.F.
Sales volume:
– Wholesale: 25%. – Retail: 75%.
Sales in France: 80%. **Export sales:** 20%.
Main trading partners : Belgium, UK, Luxemburg.

References in France

Shops: L'Amour du Vin (Paris), L'Allée des Vins (Lyon).

Abroad

United Kingdom

Cachet Wines, 61-65 Heworth Road, York (Tel: (0904) 425853).

Belgium

Ets Six. Les Caves du Vieux Tournay 80-90 Chaussée de Douai 7500 Tournai (Tel: 069/223751).

Comments

Castillon and its region, rich in history and tradition, prides itself on being the symbol of the end of the Hundred Years War. This famous battle in which, on July 17, 1453 the English General John Talbot was killed, was the event that allowed the Guienne to rejoin the Kingdom of France. For the soil of the Treille des Girondins, plot of ground in the Castillon countryside, the image remains associated with those terrible moments of the French Revolution when, banished and pursued under the Reign of Terror, the three last deputies of the Gironde ended their days in the shade of the mulberry tree that sheltered them, thus indelibly marking this nevertheless so generous soil. You will notice, on the labels, this emblem representing the Statue of Liberty, this liberty which was the dream of the Girondins. It reminds us of the statue erected on top of the magnificent monument dedicated to their glory in Quinconces Square in Bordeaux. The family property dates back to 1926.

• *The quality of the 1987 vintage, particularly in Bordeaux, is questionable. Much of the Merlot suffered from coulure and a good bit of the harvesting was done in the rain. Only a few vineyards will produce a good vintage (see the Chapter on Bordeaux wines and the "Vintage Code").*

CHÂTEAU LE GRAND VERDUS

Ph. and A. le Grix de la Salle
33670 Sadirac
56 30 64 22 – Telex: 540 127 Bordeaux

Type of vineyard: Agricultural Association. **Vine stocks:** Merlot noir 40%, Cabernet Sauvignon 40%, Cabernet Franc 20%. **Soil:** Chalky clay and gravel. **Exposure:** Full South. **Average annual production in hectoliters:** 3,500.

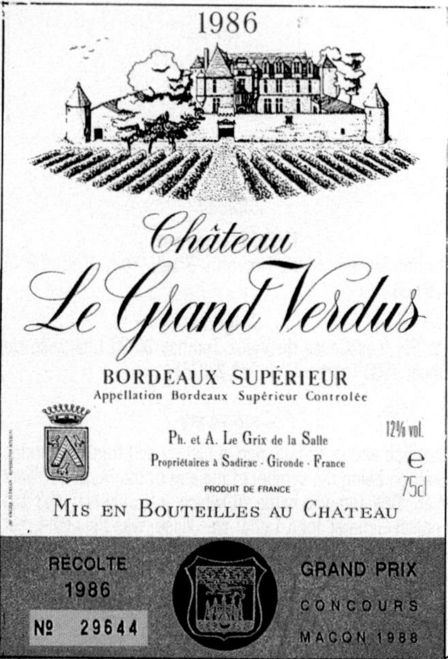

Appellation: Bordeaux Supérieur. **Type:** Red. **Technique:** Stainless steel tanks which allow good control of the fermentation. **Alcohol content:** 12 to 12.5%. **Characteristics:** Rich and well balanced with small red berry aromas, ruby-garnet color, tannic but supple. **Serving temperature:** 17°. **Served with:** Game, red meats. **Vintages available in 89/90:** 85 and 86.

Characteristics of vintages

1986: Grand Prix at Mâcon, gold medal. Ruby-garnet color, rich and well balanced, supple. Small red berry aromas.
1985: Deep ruby color, rich prune aroma. Supple attack, round, soft, full bodied and fleshy, 2 stars in the Hachette Guide. Medals at the Paris, Macon and Vinexpo competitions. Price range (pre-tax, ex-warehouse): between 30 and 50 F.F.
Sales volume: – Wholesale: 60% export. – Retail: 10%. – Restaurants: 30%.
Sales in France: 60%. **Export sales:** 40%.
Main trading partners: Luxembourg, Belgium, Germany, Switzerland, Denmark, United Kingdom.

References in France

Restaurants: The very great restaurants cannot put a Bordeaux Supérieur on their wine lists! Sold in prestigious restaurants in and outside of Paris.
Shops: Amour du Vin and numerous winecellars.

Abroad

United Kingdom
The Wine Schoppen, Sheffield.

Germany
Horstkotte, Norden.

Switzerland
Scherer, Geneva. Schuler, Schwyz.

Belgium
Soced (Pommery-Lanson).

Canada
Vins Ph. Dandurand.

The Netherlands
"Trouvailles", Jutphaas.

Others
Denmark: Jorgensed, Hellerup. Luxemburg: Resuma.

Comments

Château Le Grand Verdus is a beautiful fortified manor house of the 16th century. Its 75 hectare vineyard extends over the communes of Sadirac and Lignan, 15 km from Bordeaux. Chalky clay and gravelly soil on slopes exposed to the South favor the ripening of the Merlots (40%), the Cabernets Sauvignons (40%) and the Cabernets Francs (20%). Le Grand Verdus has received numerous awards since the 1975 vintage at all of the wine competitions in France as well as the Internatinal Vinexpo competitions and the Concours Européen at Blaye-Bourges.

CHÂTEAU TRINCAUD

Isabelle Lacaze
Bonzac 33910 St-Denis-De-Pile
57 74 25 71

Type of vineyard: Family-owned. **Vine stocks:** Merlot 55%, Cabernet 45% (13 hectares). **Soil:** chalky clay. **Appellation:** Bordeaux-Superieur. **Technique:** very traditional (destemming, long fermentation on skins). **Maturing:** traditional. **Characteristics:** well colored wines, pronounced bouquet, delicate and supple, very pleasant. **Serving temperature:** 16°. **Served with:** meat, poultry. **Vintages available in 89/90:** 87-86.

Characteristics of vintages

1988: not yet tasted. **1987:** well controlled vintage, lighter, well-made wines. **1986:** excellent wine, fragrant, red fruit dominance, clean, lingering, good development.

References in France

Shops: L'Amour du Vin, 94, rue St. Dominique, Paris 75007.

CHÂTEAU ROC MEYNARD

Philippe Hermouet
33141 Villegouge
57 74 38 88

Type of vineyard: Family company. **Vine stocks:** Merlot 90%, Cabernet Sauvignon 10%. **Soil:** Chalky clay on chalk. **Exposure:** Foothills and hillsides. **Average annual production in hectoliters:** 400.
Appellation: Bordeaux Supérieur. **Type:** Red. **Technique:** Hand harvesting, partial destemming, long fermentation on skins. **Maturing:** In vats – bottled after 24 months. **Characteristics:** Rich and well balanced, roundness thanks to the Merlot, tannic due to vinification and maturing technique – very classical Bordeaux. **Serving temperature:** 17°. **Served with:** White and red meat. **Vintages available in 89/90:** 1985, 1986, 1987.

Characteristics of vintages

1986: Round and well balanced for a wine that can be drunk young, fruity aromas. **1985:** Well balanced, will be better after a few years ageing. Price range (pre-tax, ex-warehouse): 20 to 30 F.F.
Sales volume:
– Retail: 75%. – Restaurants: 10%. – Other: 15% industrial gifts.
Sales in France: 60%. **Export sales:** 40%.
Main trading partners : Belgium, Luxemburg.

BORDEAUX ENTRE-DEUX-MERS

CHÂTEAU BONNET

André Lurton
Château Bonnet – 33420 Grezillac
57 84 52 07 – Telex: 570 215

Type of vineyard: Family-owned. **Established:** 15th Century. **Number of employees:** 50. **Vine stocks:** Reds: Cabernet Sauvignon, Merlot. Whites: Muscadelle, Sémillon and Sauvignon. **Soil:** Clay with calcium carbonate. **Average annual production in hectoliters:** 10,000.
Appellation: Entre-Deux-Mers, Bordeaux Rouge, Bordeaux Rosé. **Technique:** Temperature controlled stainless steel tanks. **Maturing:** One year in barrels for the reds. **Characteristics:** White: beautiful pale color, lively aroma characteristics of well-ripened Sauvignonn liquorice and acacia fragrance. Dry, soft, supple and easy to drink, very fruity and elegant. Red: beautiful deep color, rich aroma of ripe fruity and vanilla. Complex slightly "cooked" flavor, soft and round, very full and velvety, long because of very good tannins. **Serving temperature:** White and rosé: 8°. Red: 16° to 18°. **Served with:** White and rosé: oysters, shellfish, grilled fish. Red: grilled meat, cheese, poultry and venison. **Vintages available in 89/90:** White 1986. Rosé 1986. Red 1984 and 1985.

Characteristics of vintages

1985: Exceptional quality, good color, very rich and well balanced. Hold. Price range (pre-tax, ex-warehouse): Between 17 F.F. to 20 F.F.
Sales in France: 40%.
Export sales: 60%.
Main trading partners : Germany, Canada, UK, Denmark, Switzerland, Belgium, Netherlands.

References in France

Restaurants: St-James (Bordeaux), Prunier (Paris), Crillon (Paris).
Shops: Vinothèque (Bordeaux), Caves de la Madeleine (Paris) plus other cellars.

Abroad

United States

Grand Domaine de Bordeaux.

United Kingdom

Damis Agencies. Shops: Marks and Spencer. Restaurants: Ebury – Wine – Bar.

Germany

Shops: Jacques Wein Depot.

Canada

Shops: S.A.Q.

The Netherlands

Jean Arnaud. Shops: Gastrovino.

CHÂTEAU LES ARROMANS

Jean Duffau
Moulon - 33420 Branne
57 84 50 87

Type of vineyard: Family-owned. **Established:** 1966. **Number of employees:** 2 full time, 5 temporary. **Vine stocks:** 50% Sauvignon, 50% Sémillon. Rouge: 65% Merlot, 35% Cabernet Franc et Cabernet Sauvignon. **Soil:** Clay with calcium carbonate: one part gravel. **Exposure:** East and West. **Average annual production in hectoliters:** 1,600.

Appellation: Bordeaux, Entre-deux-Mers, Bordeaux Sec. **Type:** Red, white, rosé. **Technique:** Red: traditional. White: at low temperatures after destemming. **Maturing:** Tanks. **Alcohol content:** 12.3%. **Characteristics:** Bordeaux red: beautiful ruby color, blanckcurrant fragrance. Bordeaux rosé: from Cabernet, meaty rich and well-balanced, velvety ending. Sauvignon: very fruity, lively, agreeable. Entre-deux-Mers dry white: very typical, agreeable Sauvignon, no agressive acidity, very flowery fragrance. **Served with:** Bordeaux, red: meat and cheese. Bordeaux, rosé hors-d'œuvre, pork, a wine for summer holidays. Entre-deux-Mers: fish, oysters and seafood. **Vintages available in 89/90:** 1987: Bordeaux. Red. 1986: Bordeaux. Rosé and White Entre-deux-Mers.

Characteristics of vintages

1988: Beautiful wine, deep ruby color, red berry nose (mainly blackcurrant). Right now aggressive, tannic, rich and well-balanced, a bit hard, its roundness and fullness still masked by a relatively high level of acidity. Should be a very fine vintage for long keeping. **1987:** Red: deep color, ripe and mellow tannins, bouquet starting to develop, round, easy to drink, pleasant finish – can be consumed now. **1986:** Good white, lively rosé. Price range (pre-tax, ex-warehouse): Between 10 F.F. and 20 F.F. 15 F.F. Bordeaux Red 86, 16 F.F. Bordeaux Red 87, 15 F.F. White and Rosé, 12.50 F.F.

CHÂTEAU DUCLA

Michel Mau
33190 Gironde-sur-Dropt
56 71 11 11 - Telex: 570 629

Type of vineyard: Family-owned. **Established:** Long ago. **Vine stocks:** Red: 60% Cabernet, 40% Merlot. White: 50% Sémillon, 25% Muscadelle, 25% Sauvignon. **Soil:** Clay with calcium carbonate. **Exposure:** Hillside; full South. **Average annual production in hectoliters:** Red: 4,000 hl. White: 1,700 hl.

Appellation: Red: Bordeaux. White: Entre-Deux-Mers. **Technique:** Red: traditional. White: fermentation at low temperatures. **Maturing:** Red: ageing in stainless steel tanks for 18 months. White: rapid bottling. **Alcohol content:** 11.8%. **Characteristics:** Red: harmonious, rich and well-balanced, tannic, to be aged. White: very dry, fruity, elegant, balanced. **Serving temperature:** Red: 16° to 18°. White: 7° to 10°. **Served with:** Red: red meat, cheese. White: fish, seafood. **Vintages available in 89/90:** Red: 1983, 1984, 1985, 1986, 1987, 1988. White: 1986, 1987, 1988, 1989.

Characteristics of vintages

1988: Red: fullbodied wine. White: full of delicate flower aromas. **1987:** Red: not yet ready to drink. White: very aromatic, fruity wine. Cryœxtraction. **1986:** Red: mature, ready to drink. White: beautiful success. **1985:** Excellent year, finesse, tannins prominent. **1984:** Well-balanced, very pleasant, to be drunk young a successful vintage. **1983:** Still tannic, firm and vigorous, full of promise. **1982:** Fully mature. Average pre-tax, ex-warehouse price: Red: 20 F.F. White: 15 F.F. **Sales volume:** Distribution varies from country to country.
Sales in France: 40%.
Export sales: 60%.
Main trading partners : Belgium, UK, USA, Japan, Sweden, Canada, Switzerland.

References in France

Restaurants: Very varied. Ex: Darroze (Langon).
Shops: Very varied. Ex: Hédiard, Place de la Madeleine, Paris.

Abroad

United States

Importers: Yvon Mau Wines, Inc. 1301 Madison Ave. New York, N.Y. 10128. Tel: (212) 860 0756. Telex: 425 399 Yvon.

United Kingdom

Importers: London office: Tony Stebbings, 17 Church Street Esher, Surrey K.T. 10 8QS. Tel: (372) 68 571. Telex: 929 988.

Germany

Importers: Yvon Mau, Mrs. Véronique Lagahuzere, Im Lochseif 63 6458 Rodenbach. Tel: 061 84 555 93. Telex: 410 2487.

Canada

Importers: Present in all provinces.

Far East

Importers: The Daimaru Inc., 44 Higashishimizu, Machi, Minami Ku Osaka, Japan. Tel: 06 245 1231. Telex: 633 79.

Others

Sweden.

Comments

The label represents an impressionist painting of part of the domaine built in the 13th Century by English shipbuilders. The word Ducla comes from MacDouglas, a Scotch family who were the proprietors of the estate a long time ago.

CHÂTEAU LESPARRE

Michel Gonet
Cailleau, 33750 St-Germain-du-Puch
57 24 51 23 – Telex: 830 159

Type of vineyard: Family-owned. **Established:** At least since 1850. **Vine stocks:** Merlot, Cabernet Franc, Cabernet Sauvignon, Semillon, Muscadelle, Sauvignon. **Soil:** Sand and gravel. **Exposure:** East. **Average annual production in hectoliters:** 30.

Appellation: Graves-de-Vayres, Entre-deux-Mers. **Type:** Red, white. **Technique:** Maceration in stainless steel tanks. **Alcohol content:** 11.5%. **Serving temperature:** 15 to 18°. **Vintages available in 89/90:** 1986, 1987.

Characteristics of vintages

1988: Excellent year. **1987:** Red: very fruity, supple and well colored. White: excellent. Price range (pre-tax, ex-warehouse): 20 to 30 F.F.
Sales in France: 80%.
Export sales: 20%.

Comments

Property taken over by Michel Gonet in 1986.

MILLESIMES

LA BIBLE INTERNATIONALE DES VINS

BOURGOGNE
La balade des grands crus

BORDEAUX
L'irrésistible ascension des rouges

Les classements 1989

PATRIMOINE
Les 100 vins de l'année

LES GRANDES DÉGUSTATIONS
Champagne, Grands Vins du Rhône, du Beaujolais, de Sauternes, du Languedoc...

EXCLUSIF : LE MYTHE PETRUS

BURGUNDY

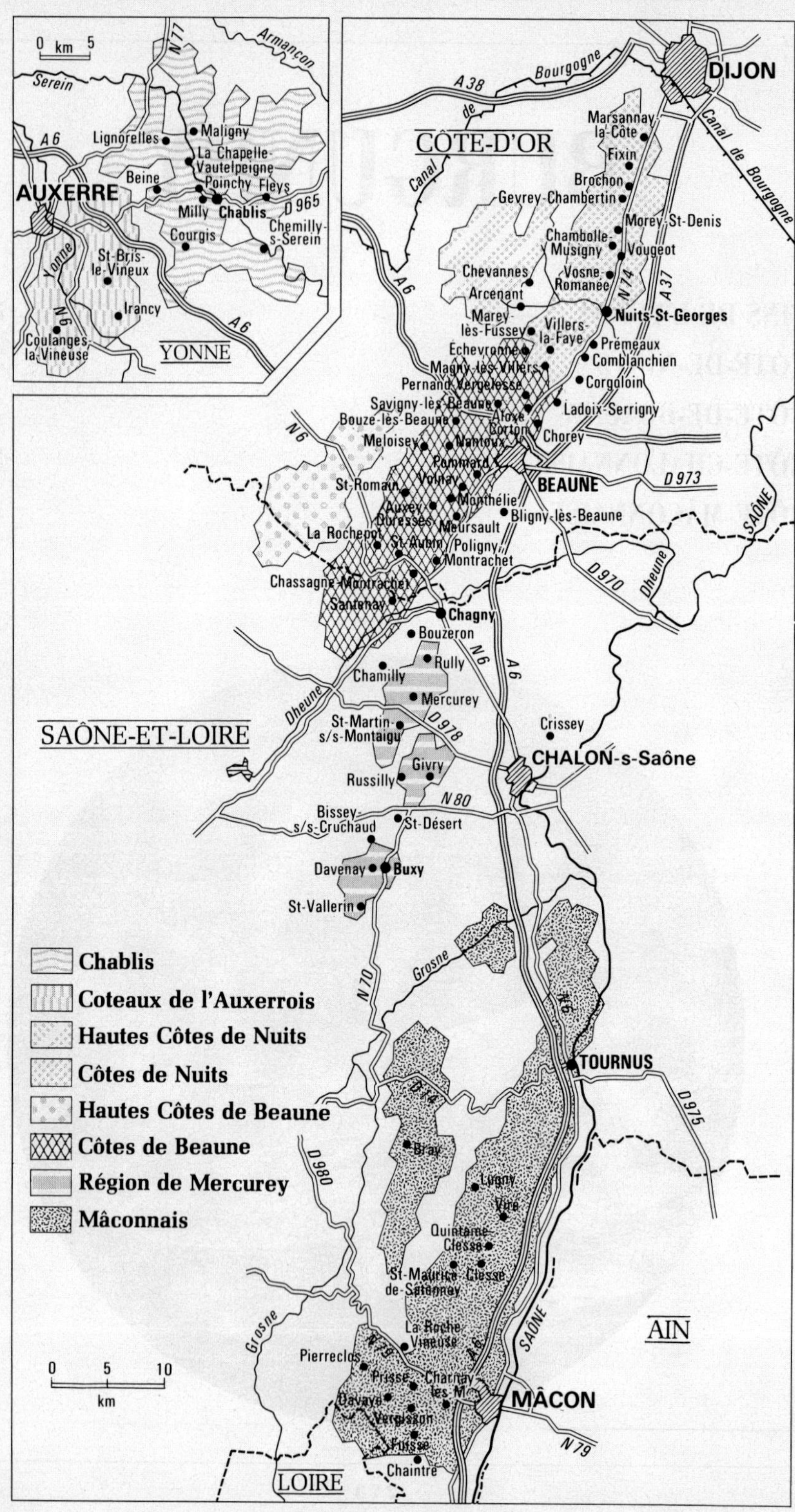

0 km 5
Serein
Armançon
N 77
A 6
Lignorelles
Maligny
La Chapelle-Vautelpeigne
Poinchy
Fleys
Beine
AUXERRE
Milly
Chablis
D 965
Chemilly-s-Serein
Courgis
Yonne
St-Bris-le-Vineux
Irancy
N 6
Coulanges-la-Vineuse
YONNE
DIJON
Bourgogne
A 38
Canal de Bourgogne
CÔTE-D'OR
Marsannay-la-Côte
Fixin
Brochon
Gevrey-Chambertin
Morey-St-Denis
Chambolle-Musigny
Vougeot
Vosne-Romanée
Chevannes
Arcenant
N 74
A 37
Nuits-St-Georges
Marey-lès-Fussey
Villers-la-Faye
Échevronne
Prémeaux
Comblanchien
Magny-lès-Villers
Pernand-Vergelesse
Corgoloin
Savigny-lès-Beaune
Ladoix-Serrigny
Bouze-lès-Beaune
Aloxe-Corton
Chorey
Meloisey
Nantoux
Pommard
Volnay
St-Romain
BEAUNE
D 973
Monthélie
Auxey-Duresses
Meursault
Bligny-lès-Beaune
La Rochepot
St-Aubin
Poligny
Montrachet
Chassagne-Montrachet
Santenay
D 970
Dheune
Saône
Chagny
Bouzeron
Rully
Chamilly
Mercurey
N 6
A 6
St-Martin-s/s-Montaigu
D 978
Crissey
SAÔNE-ET-LOIRE
Givry
CHALON-s-Saône
Russilly
N 80
Bissey-s/s-Cruchaud
St-Désert
Davenay
Buxy
St-Vallerin
Grosne
N 70
TOURNUS
D 975
D 14
Bray
D 980
Lugny
Viré
Quintaine-Clessé
St-Maurice-de-Satonnay
Clessé
La Roche-Vineuse
AIN
Pierreclos
Prissé
Charnay-lès-M.
Davayé
MÂCON
Vergisson
Fuissé
N 79
Chaintré
LOIRE
Chablis
Coteaux de l'Auxerrois
Hautes Côtes de Nuits
Côtes de Nuits
Hautes Côtes de Beaune
Côtes de Beaune
Région de Mercurey
Mâconnais
0 5 10
km

A new begining

Burgundy is the Kingdom of the soil, of aromas, of harmonious, dense wines. Last year, I was the first to dare to declare that the entire Burgundy region, from the greatest crus to the most "modest" (from the South), was undergoing an exceptional qualitative resurgence. And this is now being confirmed beyond any doubt. The great whites (Montrachet, Meursault, Chablis and their "satellites") are still, and probably always will be, among the greatest dry white wines in the world. With all due deference to the others, they deserve the prices that they command because, as a result of meticulous production practices, they remain so typical of their soil. The reds are also coming along although there are those who feel that additional efforts to improve the vinification are justified. The 85, 86 and 88 vintages are excellent. It seems to be the producers (and the soil) that count, rather than the reputations of the countless appellations whose complexity is getting a bit out of hand.

"With a pen in one hand, I sing of their bouquet . . .
But with a glass in the other, I write a sonnet."

HISTORICAL BACKGROUND

This region owes its name to the Burgundians, a Germanic people who invaded Gaul in 406 A.D. and founded the first kingdom of Burgundy in 411 under the leadership of their chief, Gundicar.

Clovis, the famous king of the Franks, married a Burgundian princess and their son expelled King Gondemar II, thus bringing Burgundy into the Frank Empire. Charlemagne made it a duchy and from 884 to 1002 the Duchy of Burgundy belonged to princes, including Richard the Justiciary, Count of Autun. The duchy was then brought under the crown from 1002 to 1032, giving birth to a new ducal house of Burgundy, which was the first "House of the Capetian."

The second house of the Capetian, "The House of Valois," was headed by Philip the Bold, Duke of Burgundy, who had a special interest in winegrowing. He banned the growing of grapes for Gamay and insisted that wine from Beaune be served at official meals.

The reputation of Burgundy wines dates back to the Middle Ages; monks were the first to cultivate the vine. In 587, King Gontran turned over lands containing vines to monks at the Abbey of Saint Bénigne. In 630, Duke Amalgaire of Lower Burgundy founded Bèze Abbey and had its monks work vineyards in Chenôve, Marsanna, Conchey, Gevrey, Vosne and Beaune. In 910, Benedictine monks founded Cluny Abbey, which acquired a great deal of land in Côtes de Nuits and owned all the vineyards surrounding Gevrey.

Wine is a sign of wealth, and some monks forgot their monastic vow and lived "the good life." The ascetic Bernard de Clairvaux denounced that life of luxuriousness and went to the Benedictine Abbey of the monks of Cîteaux, located across from Vougeot. The Benedictine monks were charmed by the hard-working Bernard de Clairvaux. They adopted as their motto, "by the cross and by the swing plough" and became the Cistercian monastic order. They cleared the woods, cultivated vast areas of moors and planted vineyards. We owe them Clos Vougeot vineyard, which today is owned by the Chevaliers du Tastevin. Huge wine presses cut from large oak trees dating back to the year 1000 can still be seen in the chateau.

The monks had noticed the differences between wines from the lower slope and wines from the upper slope. They therefore respected the rank and circumstance of their time by establishing three *cuvées* or vintages: the vintage of the popes, which was the best because it came from the upper slope; the vintage of kings, which came from the middle slope; and the vintage of monks, which came from the lower slope.

In 1147, Chablis was made for the first time at the Pontigny Monastery. It was also made by the Cistercian monks who were the first to grow Chardonnay Blanc.

One bit of trivia: Clos Vougeot had such an excellent reputation that during the French Revolution, a certain Colonel Bisson began the tradition of having French troops present arms when marching by Clos Vougeot.

Burgundy wines were among the favorites of the kings of France, but in the late 18th century when the French Republic was founded all vineyards belonging to the Church were brought under the public domain and land areas in Burgundy were split up.

The French theologian and writer Jacques Bossuet, a native of Burgundy, said: "Wine has the power to use the soul, in all its truth, knowledge, and philosophy."

THE WINES

CHABLIS (Yonne)

GRANDS CRUS. They are seven in number (Blanchots, Bougros, Clos, Grenouilles, Preuses, Valmur and Vaudésir). Dry and fragrant, these wines are of a beautiful golden color.

The "Premiers Crus." About thirty winegrowing areas have been classified by a 1967 decree. The wines are of astonishing quality, though they tend to be less rich than those of earlier years. Among the best: Montée de Tonnerre, Fauchourme, Vaulorent, Montmain and Vaucopins.

- **Simple CHABLIS:** The most common wine, for the most part produced mainly by blending of commercial wines.

COTE DE NUITS (Côte d'or)

- **FIXIN.** Full-bodied red wines, deep color, bouquet developing with age. Good keeping.
- **GEVREY-CHAMBERTIN.** Nine great Crus of rich, firm, forthcoming and delicate wines.
- **MOREY-SAINT-DENIS.** Supple wines, deep color, generally well structured and aromatic.
- **CHAMBOLLE-MUSIGNY.** Musigny and Bonnes-Mares are among the finest and best-structured red wines of the region and those with the strongest bouquet.
- **VOUGEOT.** The reds are full-bodied and generally well made. The whites are dry and fruity.
- **VOSNE-ROMANEE.** Very typical, soft and full reds with deep color.
- **NUITS-SAINT-GEORGES.** Fine and powerful wines, deep color, for keeping.

COTE DE BEAUNE (Côte d'or)

- **LADOIX-SERRIGNY.** Light and rather tannic red wines, good bouquet.
- **ALOXE-CORTON.** Rich and fine reds. Full and remarkable whites (Corton and Corton-Charlemagne), for keeping.
- **PERNAND-VERGELESSES.** Dry, supple vigorous whites. Light and fragrant reds.
- **SAVIGNY-LES-BEAUNE and BEAUNE.** Light and supple reds, with finesse and pronounced bouquet.
- **POMMARD.** Full, rich and velvety, firm and round.
- **VOLNAY.** Fine, elegant wines, supple with pronounced bouquet.
- **MONTHELIE.** Fragrant, light and supple reds.
- **AUXEY-DURESSES.** Rather rich whites, plenty of bouquet.

- **SAINT-ROMAIN and SAINT-AUBIN.** Charming and rather fruity white and red wines.
- **MEURSAULT.** Soft and rich whites, powerful but subtle bouquet.
- **PULIGNY-MONTRACHET and CHASSAGNE-MONTRACHET.** As for the Grands Crus produced under these two appellations, they are all superb. The Premiers Crus (Pucelles, Caillerets, Demoiselles, Ruchettes and Boudriotte) are quite seductive due to their vigor and flowery bouquet. The Chassagne reds are somewhat better balanced than the Puligny.
- **SANTENAY.** Fruity, quite powerful and well-balanced reds.
- **HAUTES COTES DE NUITS and HAUTES COTES DE BEAUNE.** Red wines made from Pinot, pleasant to drink, plenty of bouquet.

COTE CHALONNAISE

- **GIVRY.** Good red wines, well-balanced and fruity. Dry and fruity whites.
- **MERCUREY.** Fine and elegant reds, with plenty of bouquet. Fragrant whites.
- **MONTAGNY.** Pleasant whites.
- **RULLY.** Reds and whites combine body, fullness and bouquet.

LE MACONNAIS

Wine area producing mainly white wines. The best is the Pouilly-Fuissé, which is light with a marked bouquet. Saint-Véran also produces a delicate and flowery white.

THE CHARACTERISTICS OF THE VINEYARD

In the heart of Burgundy lies the beautiful Côte d'Or with its sub-regions of Dijon to the north; the very narrow Côte de Nuits extending from Marsannay to Cargoloin; and the Côte de Beaune, a 1.6-mile long plateau (1-2 km). The northern part of the prestigious Côte d'Or produces vintage reds. The southern part specializes in vintage whites.
There are, of course, hundreds of smaller vineyards in Burgundy. Many have an acreage of less than a hectare.

Soil

The soil of Burgundy is very diverse. In the areas where red wine is grown, there is a high limestone content. Marl, a mixture of clay and limestone, is common in the white wine growing areas.

Climate

Because of Burgundy's continental to semi-continental climate, winters are extremely cold and summers are relatively hot. The sun shines ?? days a year. The average temperature is 50°F (10°C). Summer storms, accompanied by hail, are the biggest threat to the vines and sometimes destroy entire vineyards. The amount of rainfall is excellent, especially in autumm.

BURGUNDY

A STROLL AMOND THE GRANDS CRUS

When one speaks of the terrain of a great wine, of its typical nature, its complexity, its particular character which distinguishes it from the others – grown only a few meters away on e neighboring property – one can't help applauding the Burgundy region. Where else, with a single vinestock, can one pride oneself on so great a variety of grands crus, all different one from the other, each remarkably marked by its sub-soil, its exposure, its microclimate and that incredible symbiosis between the earth and the vine, between man and the wine. To prove it, let's wander through this kingdom of grands crus and take a look at the best winemakers among them who, through the meticulous care accorded to their vines have become the greatest winegrowers in the world on these "doll-sized" plots. A delightful excursion, magic and tasty.

Chambertin

The Grand Cru Chambertin-Clos-de-Bèze (on 28 hectares), along with seven other grands crus, should not be confused with the Gevrey-Chambertin appellation which, like most of the great Burgundy appellations, includes a good twenty or so "Premiers Crus".

The Chambertin is one of the most beautiful crus of the region, very characteristic of a gently sloping terrain with chalky soil enriched with red ferruginous marl. A magnificent wine, which absolutely requires ageing for a number of years before it can be tasted in all its splendor, it is very full-bodied, vigorous, rich but extremely supplle, combining an exceptional aromatic complexity, dominated in its youth by notes of blackcurrant, liquorice and roasted coffee. It attains its peak in vintages like the 69 or the 78...

So you will need patience before uncorking the 86 and 85 vintages of the Domaines Jacques Prieur (21190 Meursault. Tel: 80 21 23 85), of Henri Rebourseau (21220 Gevrey-Chambertin. Tel: 80 34 30 46), of Louis Jadot (21200 Beaune. Tel: 80 22 10 57) or of Charles Quillardet (21220 Gevrey-Chambertin. Tel: 80 34 10 26), as well as for the extremely rich and concentrated, extraordinary 83 vintage of Louis Trapet (21220 Gevrey-Chambertin. Tel: 80 34 30 40) or of the Domaines Thomas-Moillard, in Chambertin-Clos-de-Bèze.

Next door to Chambertin, three "cousins" are qualitatively very close, standing at the head ot the other great wines ot the commune. For example, in MAZIS AND LATRICIERES-CHAMBERTIN (12.5 and 7 hectares), there are the 83, 85 and 86 vintages of the Chanson (21200 Beaune. Tel: 80 22 33 00) and the Faiveley (21700 Nuits-Saint-Georges. Tel: 80 61 04 55) estates, balanced, harmonious and dense which are excellent successors to the 78 and 76 vintages. The same goes for Latriècres, especially the 85 vintage, matured by Louis Latour

(21200 Beaune. Tel: 80 22 31 20) or by the Domaines Tortochot (21220 Gevrey-Chambertin. Tel: 80 34 30 68). In CHARMES-CHAMBERTIN (31 hectares), great bottles were tasted at the estate of Henri Rebourseau, who has been completely successful with his 86 vintage as well as at the Drouhin estate (21200 Beaune. Tel: 80 24 66 88) with their 83 and 85 vintages (superb Griottes, also), the Domaines Pierre Ponnelle in Beaune (Tel: 80 22 28 25) or Camus in Gevrey (Tel: 80 34 30 64) for the 83 and 86 vintages, which are typical, velvety and evolving extremely well.

A few kilometers from Gevrey-Chambertin, the CLOS-DE-LA-ROCHE (16 hectares), the CLOS SAINT-DENIS (6.5 hectares) and the CLOS-DE-TART (7 hectares) form, with the Bonnes-Mares, the 4 grands crus of the Morey-Saint-Denis commune.

The Clos-de-la-Roche has a style quite similar to that of the great Chambertin wines. Like the Chambertins, they are rich and well-balanced, with considerable aromatic concentration, slightly more supple, like the 86 and 85 vintages of the Domaine Pierre Amiot in Morey-Saint-Denis (21220 Gevrey-Chambertin. Tel: 80 34 34 28), which are very balanced wines, with a beautiful color and should be drunk towards 1995.

For the Clos-Saint-Denis, two proprietors have been entirely successful with their 86 vintage: the Domaines Dujac, in Mory (Tel: 80 34 32 58), where a great aromatic sublety combines with substantial body, and Georges Lignier et fils (Tél. : 80 34 32 55).

As for the unique (and fortunate) proprietor of the Clos-de-Tart, the Monmessin estate in Mâcon (Tel: 85 34 47 74), he carefully vinifies and matures a great wine, a bit lighter and more supple, with suggestions of kirsch and humus, somewhat woody like the 83 and 85 vintages, very balanced and evolving beautifully.

Bonnes-Mares

(15 hectares) Part of this Grand Cru is located in the More-Saint-Denis commune but most of it is in Chambolle-Musigny. The wines are well-colored, dense, balanced, harmonious and vigorous, dominated by a slightly "wild" touche of wood-land fragrances, of spices and sandalwood. Chanson Père et Fils and the Domaines Pierre Ponnelle regularly succeed in the vinification of very beautiful wines (the 81 and 86 vintages), like the Domaine Seguin-Manuel (21420 Savigny-les-Beaune. Tel: 80 21 50 42) whose 83, 85 and 86 vintages are rich in flavor, substantial, unctuous, soft and full. Add the exceptional Bonnes-Mares of the Domaine Comte Georges de Vogüe in Chambolle-Musigny (21220 Gevrey-Chambertin. Tel: 80 62 86 25), whose 86 vintages is religiously appreciated, well-structured and with a great future.

Musigny

This is the other (10 hectares) Grand Cru appellation of the Chambolle-Musigny commune which goes back at least as far as the 11th century. Entirely different-,where delicacy combines with finesse and an enchanting aromatic subtlety, dominated by mulberry and wild rose, vanilla and raspberry, it is a wine that evolves beautifully. You will be carried away at the Domaine Comte Georges de Vogüe, by their extraordinary "Cuvée Vieilles Vignes", vintage 85, one of the most beautiful successes in Musigny, marked by wood-land and sweet-briar fragrances. Continue on your way with the 82 and 86 vintages of Drouhin (remarkable 84 and 85) and Faiveley, of the Domaines Jacques Prieur and of the Domaine Jacques-Frédéric Mugnier (Chambolle-Musigny – 21220 – Gevrey-Chambertin. Tel: 80 62 85 39), the latter notably for a splendid 85 vintage, well-bred, dense, very rich and well-balanced, for keeping.

Clos-de-Vougeot

A single Grand Cru (50 hectares) in the Vougeot commune shared by about 70 proprietors. The wines are deliciously perfumed with fragrances of truffles, overripe berries, rich and flavorful, for long keeping, but often quite irregular, depending on whether they come from the upper or the lowerpart of the Clos. In the 85 and 86 vintages, the Château de la Tour (21640 Vougeot. Tel: 80 62 86 13), the Pierre André (see Corton) and Thomas-Moillard estates reach the heights with very firm wines, rich, well-balanced and flavorful, followed by the Domaines François Gerbet (Vosne-Romanée – 21700 – Nuits-Saint-Georges. Tel: 80 61 07 85), and a superb 83 vintage Lamarche (Vosne-Romanée. Tel: 80 61 07 94), Jacques Prieur, Henri Rebourseau, René Engel in Vosne-Romanée (Tel: 80 61 10 54) or Paul Misset in Gevrey (Tel: 80 34 30 30).

Grands-Echezeaux and Echezeaux

To the South of the Clos-de-Vougeot are the two Grands Crus (9 and 30 hectares) of the Flagey-Echezeaux commune, planted on the hillsides, above the Vosne-Romanée appellation. The Grands Echezeaux wines, more prestigious, are marked by a terrain adjacent to the best part of the Clos-de-Vougeot which yields a special vigor and richness, both in flavor and fragrance. The Chanson estate produces some remarkable examples. The Echezeaux are more supple, certainly solid now, but easier to wait for. The best that we have tasted in the 85 and, especially, in the 86 vintages, come from the Drouhin and Moillard estates and from the Lamarche and Mongeard-Mugneret domains (Vosne-Romanée 21700 Nuits-Saint-Georges. Tel: 80 61 11 95).

Romanée-Conti

This is the most prestigious Grand Cru in all of Burgundy (1.80 hectare), cultivated exclusively by Madame Bize-Leroy and Monsieur de Villaine in Vosne-Romanée (Tel: 80 61 04 57). A myth more than a wine, produced from perfect late-maturing grapes, severely selected, vinified by long fermentations (3 to 4 weeks according to the vintage!), matured in new casks, marked by exotic, oriental fragrances – it's the soil – and dominated by a wild, vegetal flavor, dense, soft, supple and harmonious, it is a wine for very long keeping. A ridiculously small production (between 3600 and 6500 bottles, according to the quality of the vintage), its rarety, its reknown and its price result in a wine – you will certainly understand – that is not easily tasted. Among the "old" vintages, there are three great memories, the 59 (fabulous), 62 and 69 and, for the more recent, tasted by the dealer and one of our great Belgian friends, the 81, 84 and 85 vintages which, each with its own specific character, is right at the top of the heap... Nothing wrong with dreaming.

Also in the Vosne-Romanée commune, RICHEBOURG (8 hectares), produces very elegant wines, dominated by woodland and musk nuances, soft, supple and harmonious, with a silky texture and a beautiful finish. In the 85 vintage, make sure to try those of the Domaine de la Romanée-Conti and of the Albert Bichot (Beaune. Tel: 80 22 17 99) and Charles Viénot (Nuits-Saint-Georges. Tel: 80 62 31 05) estates. Somewhat softer, the wine of LA ROMANEE, made exclusively by the Comte Liger-Belair (0.85 hectare), comes from the smallest vineyard in France. A very great wine of incomparable character, it is sublime in vintages such as the 78, 80 (very successful in that "delicate" year) or 83 and evolves exceptionaly well (Maison Bouchard Père et Fils in Beaune. Tel: 80 22 14 41).

More solid, richer, extremely well-bred, the ROMANEE-SAINT-VIVANT (9.5 hectares) is a balanced and harmonious wine which combines richness with elegance, that only arrives at its proper expression with time, like this fabulous 69 vintage which we shared with Denis Thomas (Maison Moillard-Grivot). In the 76, 78, 80 and particularly 85 or 86, it is a wine to wait for, heady and full of flavor, like the wine from Moillard, of course, but also from Charles Noëllat in Vosne-Romanée (21700 Nuits-Saint-Georges. Tel: 80 61 10 82) and Alain Hudelot-Noëllat in Chambolle-Musigny (21220 Gevrey-Chambertin. Tel: 80 62 85 47), whose 83 and 85 vintages are astounding.

CÔTE-DE-BEAUNE

Soil: silica and chalky clay for the red wines, chalky marl or marly chalk for the whites.

All of the wines considered here are white (fermentation and maturing in casks, new or not new), with the exception of the Corton.

Corton

The most extensively planted of the Burgundy grands crus (160 hectares) where it is quite difficult to find homogeneous quality even though, in general, the Corton wines are intrinsically superior to those of Aloxe-Corton. To be precise, it is certainly the hilltop vines, with the exception, perhaps, of Corton-Bressandes, that yield the richest, most colorful wines, dominated by musk, blackcurrant and conserved fruit, full-bodied but more delicate and "mellow" than the grands crus of the Côte-de-Nuits, but evolving well. In the 83, 85 and 86 vintages, Pierre André, particularly in Corton Clos du Roi, Louis Latour or Louis Jadot (superb

Corton Pougets 85), the Domaines Bonneau-Du-Martray (very great 82 and 83, see below), Chandon de Brialles (magnificent Clos du Roi), the Caves de la Reine Pédauque (21400 Aloxe-Corton. Tel: 80 26 44 00), and Bouchard Père et Fils regularly produce great wines.
Along side, there are Daniel Senard (21420 Aloxe-Corton. Tel: 80 26 41 65), Maurice Chapuis (21240 Aloxe-Corton. Tel: 80 26 40 99), for the 86 and, especially, the 85 vintages, very fragrant and round, the domaines Louis Prin Père et Fils (21550 Ladoix-Serigny. Tel: 80 26 40 63) and André Nudant et Fils (21550 Ladoix-Serigny. Tel: 80 26 40 82) who have been entirely successful with their Corton-Bressandes 85, like Adrien Belland, for his superb Corton-Grèves vintage 86, very typical, firm and velvety, good keeping (21590 Santenay. Tel: 80 20 61 90).
In white, produced from Chardonnay, of course, there is the CORTON-CHARLEMAGNE (71.88 hectares), a complex and subtle grand cru that only reveals itself after several years. At present, the 70, 71, 76, 78 and the superb 79 vintages are at their best, dominated by soft perfumes mixed with intense spicy and floral fragrances, with suggestions of cinnamon, acacia flower and pineapple. The best wines of recent years, in particular the 86, 83 and 82 vintages, are to be found at the Domaine Bonneau-du-Martray which produced one of the greatest whites ever in 86 (Pernand-Vergelesses 21420 Savigny-les-Beaune. Tel: 80 21 50 64), at the Domaine Chandon-de-Briailles and on the estates of Louis Latour and Faiveley and at the Caves de la Reine Pédauque.

Montrachet

We continue here into an extraordinary region where the symbiosis between the Chardonnay and each type of soil, half way up the hillside (8 hectares) becomes perfect, tenacious and guarantees a longevity and a complexity, both in fragrance and structure, which result in the greatest white wines in the world.
The Montrachet is a sensual, well-bred wine, dry and vigorous at the same time, extremely elegant, combining finesse and firmness, long aromatic persistence where notes of almond, rose and hawthorn, toast and fern are intermixed. In "old" vintages (see those of Corton-Charlemagne) as in more recent vintages, from 86 to 82, the most beautiful regular successes in this unusual appellation are found on the Drouhin estate, in Beaune, which markets the extraordinary Montrachet du Marquis de Laguiche, on the Bouchard Père et Fils and Louis Latour estates (sublime Chevalier-Montrachet, in particular) and on the domaines Jacques Prieur and Joseph Belland (21590 Santenay. Tel: 80 20 61 13) which produces a remarkable Criots-Bâtard-Montrachet, splendid in the 83 and 86 vintages, destined for a great evolution.
In BÂTARD-MONTRACHET, finally (11.86 hectares), equally high-flying wines, in the style of the great Montrachet, are to be found at the Domaine Etienne Sauzet (Puligny-Montrachet 21190 Meursault. Tel: 80 21 32 10), very successful in the 85 and 86 vintages and, also in the Chassagne commune, on the estates of Marc Morey (Tel: 80 21 30 11) or Jean-Noël Gagnard (Tel: 80 21 31 68).

Hervé Cassar and Patrick Dussert-Gerber

LE NOM DES CRUS

I. — CÔTE-DE-NUITS

Communes et Appellations	Liste des climats classés en « premier cru »	Grands crus
FIXIN : Fixin Côte-de-Nuits-Villages	Aux Cheusots, La Perrière, Le Clos-du-Chapitre, Les Arvelets, Les Hervelets, Les Meix-Bas.	
GEVREY-CHAMBERTIN : Gevrey-Chambertin	Au Closeau, Aux Combottes, Bel-Air, Cazetiers, Champeaux, Champitennois dite « Petite Chapelle », Champonnets, Cherbaudes, Clos-Prieur, Clos-du-Chapitre, Combe-aux-Moines, Craipillot, Ergots, Estournelles, Issarts, La Perrière, Lavaut, Le Fonteny, Le Clos-Saint-Jacques, Les Corbeaux, Les Goulots, Les Gemeaux, Les Varoilles, Poissenot.	Chambertin Chambertin-Clos-de-Bèze Latricières-Chambertin Mazoyères-Chambertin Charmes-Chambertin Mazis-Chambertin Griottes-Chambertin Ruchottes-Chambertin Chapelle-Chambertin
MOREY-SAINT-DENIS : Morey-Saint-Denis	Aux Charmes, Calouères, Chabiots, Clos-Bussière, Côte-Rôtie, La Riotte, Le Clos-Baulet, Le Clos-des-Ormes, Le Clos-Sorbès, Les Bouchots, Les Chaffots, Les Charrières, Les Chénevery, Les Faconnières, Les Fermières, Les Froichots, Les Genevrières, Les Gruenchers, Les Larrets ou Clos-des-Lambrays, Les Mauchamps, Les Millandes, Les Ruchots, Les Sorbès, Maison-Brûlée, Meix-Rentiers, Monts-Luisants.	Clos-de-Tart Clos-Saint-Denis Clos-de-la-Roche Bonnes-Mares (une partie)
CHAMBOLLE-MUSIGNY : Chambolle-Musigny	Aux Beaux-Bruns, Aux Combottes, Derrière-la-Grange, Les Amoureuses, Les Baudes, Les Borniques, Les Chatelots, Les Charmes, Les Combottes, Les Fuées, Les Fousselottes, Les Gras, Les Groseilles, Les Gruenchers, Les Hauts-Doix, Les Lavrottes, Les Noirots, Les Plantes, Les Sentiers.	Musigny Les Bonnes-Mares

Communes et Appellations	Liste des climats classés en « premier cru »	Grands crus
VOUGEOT : Vougeot	Clos-de-la-Perrière, Le Clos-Blanc, Les Gras, Les Petits-Vougeot.	Clos-de-Vougeot
FLAGEY-ÉCHEZEAUX : Vosne-Romanée		Grands-Échezeaux Échezeaux
VOSNE-ROMANÉE : Vosne-Romanée	Aux Brûlées, Aux Malconsorts, La Grand'Rue, Le Clos-la-Perrière, Le Clos-des-Réas, Les Beaux-Monts, Les Chaumes, Les Gaudichots, Les Petits-Monts, Les Suchots, Les Reignots	Romanée-Saint-Vivant Richebourg La Romanée La Tâche La Romanée-Conti
NUITS-SAINT-GEORGES : Nuits-Saint-Georges	Aux Argillats, Aux Boudots, Aux Bousselots, Aux Chaignots, Aux Champs-Perdrix, Aux Cras, Aux Crots, Aux Damodes, Aux Murgets, Aux Thorey, Aux Vignes-Rondes, En La Chaîne-Carteau, La Perrière, La Richemone, La Roncière, Les Cailles, Les Chabœufs, Les Hauts-Pruliers, Les Poulettes, Les Procès, Les Pruliers, Les Saint-Georges, Les Vallerots, Les Vaucrains, Rue-de-Chaux, Perrière-Noblet.	
PRÉMEAUX : Nuits-Saint-Georges	Aux Perdrix, Clos-Arlots, Clos-de-la-Maréchale, Clos-des-Argillières, Clos-des-Corvées, Clos-des-Forêts, Le Clos-Saint-Marc, Les Corvées-Paget, Les Didiers.	
COMBLANCHIEN, BROCHON, CORGOLOIN, PRISSEY : Côte-de-Nuits-Villages		

II. - CÔTE-DE-BEAUNE

Communes et appellations	Liste des climats classés en « premier cru »	Grands crus
LADOIX-SERRIGNY : Ladoix (surtout vins rouges)		

Communes et Appellations	Liste des climats classés en « premier cru »	Grands crus
ALOXE-CORTON : Aloxe-Corton (surtout vins rouges)	Basses-Mourettes, En Pauland, La Coutière, La Maréchaude, La Toppe-au-Vert, Les Chaillots, Les Grandes-Lolières, Les Guérets, Les Fournières, Les Maréchaudes, Les Meix, Les Petites-Lolières, Les Valozières, Les Vercots.	Corton (R et B) Corton-Charlemagne (B)
CHOREY-LES-BEAUNE : Chorey ou Chorey-Côtes-de-Beaune		
PERNAND-VERGELESSES : Pernand-Vergelesses (R et B)	En Caradeux, Creux-de-la Net, Ile-des-Vergelesses, Les Basses-Vergelesses, Les Fichots.	
SAVIGNY-LÈS-BEAUNE : Savigny-lès-Beaune Savigny-Côte-de-Beaune (surtout vins rouges)	Aux Cloux, Aux Fourneaux, Aux Gravains, Aux Grands-Liards, Aux Guettes, Aux Petits-Liards, Aux Serpentières, Aux Vergelesses, Aux Vergelesses dit Bataillière, Basses-Vergelesses, La Dominode, Les Charnières, Les Jarrons, Les Hauts-Jarrons, Les Hauts-Marconnets, Les Lavières, Les Marconnets, Les Narbantons, Les Peuillets, Les Rouvrettes, Les Talmettes, Petits-Godeaux, Redrescuts.	
BEAUNE : Beaune (surtout vins rouges)	A L'Écu, Aux Coucherias, Aux Cras, Champs-Pimont Clos-du-Roi, En Genêt, En l'Orme, La Mignotte, Le Bas-des-Theurons, Le Clos-de-la-Mousse, Le Clos-des-Mouches, Les Aigrots, Les Avaux, Les Blanches-Fleurs, Les Boucherottes, Les Bressandes, Les Cent-Vignes, Les Chouacheux, Les Épenottes, Les Fèves, Les Grèves, Les Marconnets, Les Montrevenots, Les Perrières, Les Reversées, Les Sisies, Les Teirons, Les Toussaints, Les Vignes-Franches, Montée-Rouge, Per-Tuisots, Sur-les-Grèves, Tiélandry ou Clos-Landry.	

Communes et Appellations	Liste des climats classés en « premier cru »	Grands crus
POMMARD : Pommard (R)	Clos-Blanc, Clos-de-la-Commaraine, Clos-du-Verger, Es-Charmots, Derrière-Saint-Jean, La Chanière, La Platière, La Refène, Le Clos, Micot, Les Argilières, Les Argelets, Les Bertins, Les Boucherottes, Les Chaponnières, Les Chanlins-Bas, Les Combes-Dessus, Les Croix-Noires, Les Épenots, Les Fremiers, Les Garollières, Les Petits-Épenots, Les Pézerolles, Les Poutures, Les Rugiens-Bas, Les Rugiens-Hauts, Les Sausilles.	
VOLNAY : Volnay (R)	Brousse-d'Or, Caillerets-Dessus, Carelles-Dessous, Carelles-sous-la-Chapelle, Chanlin, En Caillerets, En Champans, En Chevret, En l'Ormeau, En Verseuil, Fremiets, La Barre ou Clos-de-la-Barre, Le Clos-des-Chênes, Le Clos-des-Ducs, Les Angles, Les Aussy, Les Brouillards, Les Lurets, Les Milans, Les Petures, Les Petures-Dessus, Les Santenots, Pointe-d'Angles, Ronceret, Taille-Pieds, Robardelle, Village-de-Volnay.	
MONTHÉLIE : Monthélie (R)	Duresse, La Taupine, Le Cas-Rougeot, Le Château-Gaillard, Le Clos-Gauthey, Le Meix-Bataille, Les Champs-Fulliot, Les Riottes, Les Vignes-Rondes, Sur Lavelle.	
AUXEY-DURESSES : Auxey-Duresses (R et B)	Climat-du-Val dit Clos-du-Val, Les Bas-des-Duresses, Les Bretterins, Les Bretterins dits La Chapelle, Les Duresses, Les Écusseaux, Les Grands-Champs, Reugne, Reugne dit La Chapelle.	
SAINT-ROMAIN : Saint-Romain (B et R) SAINT-AUBIN : Saint-Aubin (B et R)	Champlot, En Remilly, La Chatenière, Les Castets, Les Combes, Les Créots, Les Frionnes, Les Murgers-des-Dents-de-Chien, Sur Gamay, Sur-le-Sentier-du-Clou.	

Communes et Appellations	Liste des climats classés en «premier cru»	Grands crus
MEURSAULT : Meursault vins blancs, un peu de vins rouges Blagny (rouges)	Aux Perrières, La Goutte-d'Or, Le Poruzot, Les Poruzot-Dessus, Les Bouchères, Les Caillerets, Les Charmes-Dessous, Les Charmes-Dessus, Les Cras-Dessus, Les Genevrières-Dessous, Les Genevrières-Dessus, Les Perrières-Dessous, Les Perrières-Dessus, Les Petures, Les Santenots-Blancs, Les Santenots-du-Milieu.	
PULIGNY-MONTRACHET : Puligny-Montrachet Côte-de-Beaune	Clavoillons, Hameau-de-Blagny, La Garenne, Le Cailleret, Le Champ-Canet, Les Chalumeaux, Les Combettes, Les Folatières, Les Pucelles, Les Referts, Sous-le-Puits.	Chevalier-Montrachet Bâtard-Montrachet Bienvenues-Bâtard-Montrachet Montrachet
CHASSAGNE-MONTRACHET : Chassagne-Montrachet Côte-de-Beaune vins blancs et rouges	Clos-Saint-Jean, Chassagne ou Cailleret, En Caillerets, Grandes-Ruchottes, La Boudriotte, La Maltroie, La Romanée, Les Brussolles, Les Champs-Gain, Les Chevenottes, Les Macherelles, Les Vergers, Morgeot, Morgeot dit Abbaye-de-Morgeot	Montrachet Bâtard-Montrachet Criots-Bâtard-Montrachet
SANTENAY : Santenay Santenay-Côte-de-Beaune (rouges et quelques blancs)	Beauregard, Beaurepaire, Clos-de-Tavannes, La Comme, La Maladière, Le Passe-Temps, Les Gravières.	
CHEILLY-LÈS-MARANGES : Cheilly-lès-Maranges **SAMPIGNY-LÈS-MARANGES :** Sampigny-lès-Maranges **DEZIZE-LÈS-MARANGES** Dezize-lès-Maranges (vins rouges)	La Boutière, Le Clos-des-Rois, Les Maranges, Les Plantes-de-Maranges.	

The Vintages and how they rate

1970

Extraordinary year for whites, the best of all. One finds the breeding and subtlety of the great wines. The reds are very good and quite fragrant.

1971

Exceptional year for reds as well as whites. For the reds, it is the best vintage for drinking now, like the 1979. The whites are one step down.

1972

Astonishing vintage. No qualitative potential based on intrinsic value, but red wines which are excellent now, very aromatic. The great whites hold their own.

1973, 1974, 1975

Forget them.

1976

Great year, a bit below the 1978. The reds have not yet opened up; wait a bit. The whites are good but somewhat disappointing.

1977

Some reds are quite pleasant, but forget the whites.

1978

For reds, the best year of the decade. Solid wines, subtle, a whole spectrum of aromas. Wait a bit.
The whites are exquisite, but are not yet ready for drinking. They have not yet reached their qualitative potential.
The Beaujolais crus are ready to drink and stand up well.

1979

Good year for reds, quite pleasant at the moment, full, supple and fragrant, quite rich and well-balanced.
Exceptional year for whites, the best since 1970. The wines are vigorous

with lots of body and present a superb aromatic complexity. Still good for keeping.
The Beaujolais is ready to drink, but without much breadth.

1980

If the whites are on their way down, the reds, consistently disparaged, make relatively good drinking, with surprising, soft aromas. Not much worth waiting for, however. Avoid the Beaujolais.

1981

Irregular year. Insipid white wines, but fresh and fruity, ready to drink. The reds are thin, without structure, overestimated and should be forgotten, except for the very great crus which are worth drinking. Good year for Beaujolais.

1982

Uneven year, a bit better than average for reds. Wines rich in alcohol, lacking in finesse and balance, not to be kept long, but quite pleasant right now. Excellent year, on the other hand, for the whites which are fragrant and full, just beginning to open up.
The Beaujolais is quite good.

1983

Good year for reds but quite inferior to the 78 and 76. In spite of the frost, the vines flowered well, healthy grapes produced dark, concentrated, fleshy wines which seem to have a real potential for ageing.
This analysis will only be confirmed in the course of time. Most of these crus are not good to drink now, being neither rich nor really fragrant. Some of the wines have little breadth, are rather flat but come across rather well nevertheless, despite being a bit disappointing. If they close up and start to age, it might be a great year. Once more, because of high temperatures at the time of fermentation, many of the wines were rather hard to control. The whites, in intrinsic value, have more of a future than the reds. Very rich in alcohol (some Montrachet Crus at 14%!), rich in sugar, quite aromatic. An exceptional year for the Beaujolais, one of the best of the last fifteen. Robust, forthcoming like the 76, finer and more fruity, well-bred, good keeping. A surprise in the region which confirms that great Beaujolais can also be thoroughly beautiful wines.

1984

A vintage to be reckoned with. Inclement weather, lots of rain. Some healthy grapes, but a general tendency towards diluted wines without structure, richness or balance. A typical year to wreak havoc in Burgundy; only the best winemakers will make an acceptable wine.
Average year for the whites. The wines are fruity but have little body and probably won't keep very long. To be watched.

1985

Reds: Very good year, fine tannins, deeply colored, rich and well-balanced wines, quite supple with complex aromas, good keeping.
Whites: Good year, fine and fragrant wines, average keeping.

1986

Reds: Excellent vintage. Rich and structured wines, full of aromatic nuance, beautifully balanced, combining firmness and elegance, good keeping.
Whites: Beautiful vintage, almost up to the 1982 and 1983. Wines that will stand up well, very fruity, soft, supple and distinguished, long, good keeping.

1987

Reds: Average but correct year. Relatively supple wines, quite fruity. Successful if the grapes were not harvested in the rain.
Whites: Quite good year. Fragrant, light and supple wines. The Grands Crus are quite rich and well-balanced.

1988

Reds: Beautiful year. Deeply-colored wines combining finesse and richness, to be kept.
Whites: More "delicate" year, sometimes very successful, very fruity, evolving well and sometimes lacking acidity.

VINS DE L'YONNE

CHABLIS

DOMAINE JEAN-MARC BROCARD

Jean-Marc Brocard
Prehy
86 41 42 11 – Telex: 351 734

Type of vineyard: Agricultural Association. **Established:** 1973. **Number of employees:** 12. **Vine stocks:** Chardonnay, Pinot Noir. **Soil:** Chalky clay. **Exposure:** 80% South. **Average annual production in hectoliters:** 2,000.

Appellation: Chablis 1er Cru, Chablis, Bourgogne (Chardonnay & Pinot Noir). **Type:** Red, white, rosé. **Technique:** White: temperature control (18°), red: temperature control (30°) – pressing. **Maturing:** 90% in stainless steel tanks and 10% in oak casks. **Alcohol content:** 12.5%. **Characteristics:** Typical, personal character. **Serving temperature:** 12°. **Served with:** Delicate fish, white meat in sauce, poultry. **Vintages available in 89/90:** 1988.

Characteristics of vintages

1988: Pronounced bouquet, seductive, commercial. **1987:** Typical, natural, marked tannins. **1986:** Full-bodied, forthcoming. Price range (pre-tax, ex-warehouse): 20 to 30 F.F. (Aligoté, Bourgogne Blanc & Rouge) 30 to 50 F.F. (Chablis 1er Cru).

Sales volume:
– Retail: 15%. – Restaurants: 20%. – Other: 65% export.
Sales in France: 20%.
Export sales: 80%.
Main trading partners : UK, Netherlands, Demark, Belgium.

References in France

Restaurants: Marc Meneau (Vézelay), Côte St-Jacques (Joigny), La Petite Auberge (Vaux), La Bonne Auberge (Clisson), Le Mas d'Artigny (St-Paul de Vence), Le Château de Gilly-les-Citeaux (Vougeot), etc.
Shops: Les Caves de la Madeleine, etc.

Abroad

United States
Baron François, NJ.

United Kingdom
Bacchus, London. JB 114 Upton Lane Forest Hill, London 07 GP 5.

Germany
Starosky Hanover – Geibel Eulgem.

Belgium
Naud Rullens Brussels.

Far East
Japan, Foodliner.

Others
Denmark, K.B. Vinimport.

Comments

In 1973 Jean-Marc Brocard inherited a small vineyard (2 hectares) from his father-in-law in nearby Saint-Bris-le-Vineux. Mr. Brocard quickly purchased small parcels of land in the Chablis appellation in and around the village of Prehy, situated high above Chablis near the Paris-Lyon motorway. In 1980 the business moved from Saint-Bris-le-Vineux to the modern cellars which were expressly built in the center of the vineyard, near Prehy's fortified church.

• Blending – a method consisting of mixing different wines from different lots or different vintages in order to obtain a more homogeneous product.

JEAN DURUP
DOMAINE DE L'ÉGLANTIÈRE
DOMAINE DU CHÂTEAU DE MALIGNY

Jean Durup
4, Grande Rue, Maligny 89800 Chablis
86 47 44 49

Type of vineyard: Family-owned. **Established:** Several centuries ago. **Vine stocks:** Chardonnay. **Soil:** Clay with calcium carbonate. **Exposure:** South, Southeast. **Average annual production in hectoliters:** 5,000.

Appellation: Petit Chablis, Chablis, Chablis 1er Cru, Fourchaume, Chablis 1er Cru Vau de Vey, Chablis 1er Cru Montée de Tonerre, Chablis 1er Cru Montmain. **Type:** White. **Technique:** Traditional. **Maturing:** In vats. **Characteristics:** Fine and delicate, fragrant, entirely characteristic of the appellation, beautiful golden green color. **Serving temperature:** About 12°. **Served with:** Seafood, shellfish, fish, delicatessen products, white meat, cheese. **Vintages available in 89/90:** 1987, 1988 (still a few bottles).

Characteristics of vintages

1988: Excellent year, body, length, finesse, typical of the appellation. **1987:** Very good year, lingering taste. **1986:** Excellent vintage, balanced, with body and finesse, soft, supple and long.

DOMAINES ÉTIENNE & DANIEL DEFAIX

Daniel Defaix
23, rue de Champlain – 89800 Milly-Chablis
86 42 42 05 and 86 42 14 44
Telex: 800 997 CHAMCOM AUXERRE
Fax: (33) 86 42 48 56

Type of vineyard: 2 vineyards, father and son team. **Established:** Several Centuries. **Number of employees:** 9. **Vine stocks:** Chardonnay. **Soil:** Kimmeridgian (upper Jurassic). **Exposure:** South and Southeast. **Average annual production in hectoliters:** 1 300 hl on 22 hectares.

Appellation: Chablis 1er Cru (Les Lys, Les Vaillons, Côte de Lechet, Beugnons, Sechets), Chablis and soon a replanted Grand Cru (Blanchots). **Technique:** Top of the vat, centrifuging, very low temperature (16°). **Maturing:** On fine lees (autolysis of yeasts) for 1 year. **Alcohol content:** 12.7% average. **Characteristics:** Concentrate on the Chablis for considerable ageing (collector's items). Very discreet when young, blossoms out with age. Ages well and will satisfy the buyer for about 25 years. Conserves its glycerol and flowery fragrance. **Serving temperature:** Young: 12° to 13°. Old: 14° to 16°. **Served with:** Chablis: oysters, shellfish, first courses. 1er Cru and Grand Cru (Lys, Côte de Lechet and Blanchot): fine fish, bass, turbot. Beugnons, Vaillons, Sechets: with salmon, red mullet, sole, trout. **Vintages available in 89/90:** (1981), 1983, 1984, 1985, 1986.

Characteristics of vintages

1986: Have the patience to wait discover this proud, yet timid, wine. **1985:** Very round, forthcoming, knows how to please and to inspire love. **1984:** Reference year for the wise collector who knows the wines from the North, finesse (flowery), soft, full and long. **1983:** Excellent, but already rare. **Other:** 1981: Overflowing with finesse and length. By 1988 only the great restaurants will still have some. Price range (pre-tax, ex-warehouse): Between 35 and 65 F.F.

Sales volume:
– Wholesale: 9%. – Retail: 18%. – Restaurants: 43%.
– Other: 30% (fine wine shops).
Sales in France: 50%. **Export sales:** 50%.
Main trading partners: Germany, Netherlands, Denmark, Sweden, Japan, UK, Belgium, Canada, Italy, Luxemburg, Switzerland, USA.

References in France

Restaurants: From average to First Class restaurants, mostly in Lyon and Paris. *Shops:* Mostly in Paris, for example: Caves de la Madeleine, Willi's, Les Deux Magots.

Comments

The domain also possesses a small retail cellar – Le Monde du Vin – 14, rue Auxerroise, 89800 Chablis – which specializes in the sale of Chablis Premier Cru and old Chablis to Restaurants, wine bars and other quality distribution channels.

DOMAINE ALAIN GEOFFROY

Alain Geoffroy
4, rue de l'Equerre, Beines 89800 Chablis
86 42 43 76 – Telex: 351 877 F

Type of vineyard: Family-owned. **Number of employees:** 8. **Vine stocks:** Chardonnay. **Soil:** Kimmeridgian chalky-clay marl. **Exposure:** South. **Average annual production in hectoliters:** 1, 350.
Appellation: Chablis, Chablis 1er Cru. **Type:** White. **Technique:** Traditional, in vats. **Maturing:** In vats and casks. **Alcohol content:** 12%. **Characteristics:** Dry, pronounced bouquet, reputed for its finesse, lingering taste and yellow green color. **Serving temperature:** 10 to 12°. **Served with:** Fish and shellfish. **Vintages available in 89/90:** 1988.

Characteristics of vintages

1988: Balanced and harmonious, very good aromatic development. Price range (pre-tax, ex-warehouse): 30 to 50 F.F.
Sales volume:
– Retail: 5%. – Restaurants: 10%.
Sales in France: 25%.
Export sales: 75%.
Main trading partners : Germany, UK.

References in France

Restaurants: Le Bal du Moulin Rouge, Cabaret Le Lido, Le Fouquet's (Paris).

Abroad

United States
Baron François Ltd. – Suite 3E 315 W 57TH Street, New York, NY 10019. Tel: 212 307 19 44.

United Kingdom
Enotria, 4-6 Chandos Park Estate, Chandos Road, London NW 106NF – Tel: 1961 4411.

Germany
Weinland J.S. Keiler, Nacht Dortmund – Tel: 231 65 388.

Canada
Soc. des Alcools du Québec, 905, av. De Lorimier, Montreal QC H2K 3V9.

Far East
Japan: Unexpa Japan Co Ltd, 3-6-24 Jingumae Shibuya-Ku, Tokyo 150.

Comments

The domain, created towards 1850 by Honoré Geoffroy, great - grandfather of the philosopher Alain, is located in the communes of Beines and la Chapelle-Vaupelteigne, in the heart of the Chablis vineyard. The principal concern of four generations of winemakers has been to conserve the traditional family character of the enterprise.

JEAN-PAUL DROIN

Jean-Paul Droin
14 bis, rue Jean-Jaurès - 89800 Chablis
86 42 16 78

Type of vineyard: Privaftely owned. **Established:** 1982. (original vineyard established in 1698). **Vine stocks:** Pinot Chardonnay 100%. **Soil:** Clay with calcium carbonate, Kimmeridgian marl. **Exposure:** South, Southeast, Southwest. **Average annual production in hectoliters:** 50 to 55.
Appellation: Chablis. **Type:** White. **Technique:** Slow pressing, destemming, temperature regulation in tanks. **Maturing:** Fermentation in new casks for the Grands Crus. Maturing in new casks for the 1er Crus, 1/3 new casks each year for the others, bottling after 9 months. **Characteristics:** Chablis: fresh and light. 1er Cru: long, seductive. Grands Crus: vinous, soft and full, very long. **Serving temperature:** 8 to 12° according to the Cru and vintage. **Served with:** Chablis: oysters, trout, snails, dry goat cheese. 1er Cru: seafood in pastry, pike, perch, white meat (veal, poultry). Grands Crus: crayfish, scallops, lobster, poullard. **Vintages available in 89/90:** 1985, 1986.

Characteristics of vintages

1986: Excellent, fine, more vigorous than the 1985. Typical Chablis, harmonious, balanced, to be aged. **1985:** Very aromatic, soft and full, rich, long. Price range (pre-tax, ex-warehouse): Chablis: between 30 and 50 F.F., 1er Crus: between 50 and 80 F.F., Grands Crus: between 80 and 120 F.F.
Sales volume:
- Wholesale: 35%. - Retail: 16%. - Restaurants: 16%. - Other: 33% (export).
Sales in France: 67%.
Export sales: 33%.
Main trading partners : UK, Japan, Belgium, Germany, USA, Denmark, Netherlands, Finland, Sweden.

DOMAINE DES ILES

Gérard Tremblay
12, rue de Poinchy - 89800 Chablis
86 42 40 98

Established: For several generations. **Vine stocks:** Chardonnay. **Soil:** Clay with calcium carbonate. **Average annual production in hectoliters:** 1 200 to 1 500. **Appellation:** Petit Chablis, Chablis, Chablis 1er Cru, Chablis Grand Cru. **Technique:** Traditional. **Characteristics:** Petit Chablis: dry, fruity, to be drunk very young (primeur). Chablis: fruity, much softer. Chablis 1er Cru: finesse, length. Chablis Grand Cru: finesse, length, needs several years of ageing. **Serving temperature:** 10° to 12°. **Vintages available in 89/90:** 1985, 1986.

Characteristics of vintages

1986: Good vintage, fragant, soft and supple, full and structured, remarkably well made. Price range (pre-tex, ex-warehouse): Between 20 and 80 F.F.
Sales volume:
- Wholesale: 10%. - Retail: 20%. - Restaurants: 10%. - Other: 60%.
Sales in France: 40%.
Export sales: 60%.
Main trading partners : UK, Germany, Belgium, Netherlands, Japan, etc.

References in France

Restaurants: Lasserre (Paris), Côte 108 (Reims), Flambard (Lille).
Shops: Hédiard, le Boepatre de Bacchus.

Abroad

United States
Greenhall - Eldridge Pope etc.
Germany
De Crigni'she Kellerei Wein Schulz, Nehrbass.
The Netherlands
Turkenburg.
Belgium
Young Charly.

DOMAINE D'ELISE

Frédéric Prain
Milly - 86800 Chablis
86 42 40 82

Type of vineyard: Family-owned. **Established:** 1970. **Number of employees:** 3. **Vine stocks:** Chardonnay. **Soil:** Portlandian oolite and Kimmeridgian. **Exposure:** South. **Average annual production in hectoliters:** 500. **Appellation:** Chablis. **Type:** White. **Technique:** Low temperature (thermoregulation). **Maturing:** Glasslined tanks. **Alcohol content:** 13%. **Characteristics:** Dry and fruity. Roundness and finesse increasing with age. **Serving temperature:** 12°. **Served with:** Oysters, shellfish, fine fish in sauce, Chitterlling Sausage. **Vintages available in 89/90:** 1987 and 1988.

Characteristics of vintages

1988: Excellent year, to be drunk now or to be kept, the choice is yours... **1987:** Excellent year. To be drunk as soon as possible. **1984:** Excellent Premier Cru "Côte-de-Lechet". Average pre-tax, ex-warehouse price: 35 F.F.
Sales volumes:
- Wholesale: 40%.
- Retail: 10%.
- Restaurants: 20%
- Other: 30% (export).

Sales in France: 30%. **Export sales:** 70%.
Main trading partners : USA, Germany, Singapore.

References in France

Restaurants: Morot-Gaudry, Dutournier, Faugeron, etc.
Shops: Toques Gourmandes, Marly.

Abroad

Great Britain
Windrush wines Cirencester, Gloucestershire. Tel: (0285) 67121.

DOMAINE LAROCHE
Michel Laroche
L'Obédiencerie - 89800 Chablis
86 42 14 30 - Telex: 800 029

Type of vineyard: Corporation. **Established:** 1850. **Number of employees:** 70. **Vine stocks:** Chardonnay. **Soil:** Clay with calcium carbonate. **Exposure:** Southeast, Southwest. **Average annual production in hectoliters:** 50 hl/ha.
Appellation: Chablis, Chablis 1er Cru, Chablis Grand Cru. **Type:** White. **Technique:** Temperature controlled. **Maturing:** Casks for the 1er Cru and the Grand Cru. **Alcohol content:** 12 to 12.5%. **Characteristics:** Fine, structured, austere at the beginning, long keeping. **Serving temperature:** 10 to 13°. **Served with:** Shellfish, fish. **Vintages available in 89/90:** 1987, 1986, 1985.

Characteristics of vintages

1988: Good year for whites. **1987:** Excellent vintage. Price range (pre-tax, ex-warehouse): Between 40 and 150 F.F.
Sales volume:
- Retail: 10%. - Restaurants: 70%. - Other: 20% (airlines).

Sales in France: 20%. **Export sales:** 80%.
Main trading partners : UK, Germany, USA, Japan, Canada.

References in France

Restaurants: 200 restaurants with Michelin stars.
Shops: Fauchon, etc.

Abroad

United States
Henri Laroche Inc., 321 Millburn Ave., Millburn, N.J. Tel: (201) 379 9494.

United Kingdom
Mentzendorff 31 Great Peter St. London SW1. Tel: 01 222 2522.

Germany
Hawesko, Doormansweg 43, 2000 Hamburg 19. Tel: 40 431 70 20.

Canada
Vins Philippe Dandurand Inc, Mr. Philippe Dandurand 355 Est, rue St Paul Montréal, Québec. Tel: 514 866 69 66.

The Netherlands
Jacobus Boelen B.V, Mr. Roland Van Bommel Donauweg 12, 1043 AJ Amsterdam. Tel. 20/11 47 01.

Far East
Jardine Wines and Spirits, 33F World Trade Centre, P.O. Box 30748, Causeway Bay, Hong Kong. Tel: 5/837 38 88.

DOMAINE DES MALANDES
Lyne and Jean-Bernard Marchive
63, rue Auxerroise - 89800 Chablis
86 42 41 37 - Telex: 800 977 CHAMCOM

Type of vineyard: Family-owned. **Established:** 1972. **Number of employees:** 5. **Vine stocks:** Chardonnay. **Soil:** Clay and chalk marl of the Kimmeridgian. **Exposure:** Variable, mostly Southeast. **Average annual production in hectoliters:** 1,000.
Appellation: Chablis. Chablis 1er Crus (Montmains-Vau de Vey - Côte de Lechet - Fourchaume). Chablis Grand Cru (Vaudesir). **Type:** White. **Technique:** Alcoholic fermentation at low temperature - malo-lactic fermentation at 18°C maximum. **Maturing:** In stainless steel tanks. **Alcohol content:** Chablis: 12% - 1er Crus: 12.5% - Grand Cru: 13%. **Characteristics:** Chablis 86: Fresh and rich, good aromatic balance, excellent for keeping. Grang Cru 86: fine, long, very promising (try after 5 years). **Serving temperature:** 12°. **Served with:** Hors-d'œuvre in pastry, bay scallops, quenelles, crayfish and fish cooked in sauce. **Vintages available in 89/90:** 1986 and 1987.

Characteristics of vintages

1986: Very successful year: high quality vintage, balanced, typical and firm wines.
Sales volume: - Wholesale: 10%. - Retail: 5%. - Restaurants: 5%. - Other: 10% (mass distribution). 70% (export).
Sales in France: 30%.
Export sales: 70%.
Main trading partners : Canada, UK, Belgium, Switzerland, Germany, South-East Asia.

DOMAINE SERVIN

Mr. Servin
20, avenue d'Oberwesel - 89800 Chablis
86 42 12 94

Established: Four generations. **Vine stocks:** Chardonnay. **Exposure:** Slopes (sheltered from the winds). **Appellation:** Chablis. **Type:** White. **Technique:** Traditional. **Serving temperature:** 12°. **Served with:** Cold first courses, fish, shelfish, snails. **Vintages available in 89/90:** 1987 - 1986.

Characteristics of vintages

1986: Excellent year - Grand Cru: rich, very aromatic, full and long. Premiers Crus: more supple, fruity, seductive.

MOSNIER SYLVAIN

Sylvain Mosnier
4, rue Derrière-les-Murs - 89800 Chablis
86 42 43 96

Type of vineyard: Family-owned. **Established:** 1978 (took over 50 years old family vineyard). **Vine stocks:** Chardonnay. **Soil:** Clay with calcium carbonate. **Exposure:** South, Southeast. **Average annual production in hectoliters:** 500.
Appellation: Chablis, Chablis 1er Cru. **Type:** White. **Technique:** Traditional plus lactic precipitation and refrigeration. **Maturing:** Enamelled tanks. **Alcohol content:** 12.5%. **Characteristics:** Pale color with green glints. Persistent flavor, well-balanced, will keep a long time. **Serving temperature:** 10 to 12°. **Served vith:** Seafood, hors-d'œuvre shellfish, fish. **Vintages available in 89/90:** 1986, 1985.

Characteristics of vintages

1986: Well-balanced wines, to be aged, full, soft, supple and harmonious. **1985:** Very delicate, light and supple, fruity.
Sales volume:
- Wholesale: 50%. - Retail: 25%.
Sales in France: 75%.
Export sales: 25%.
Main trading partners : UK, Belgium, Germany.

SIMONNET FEBVRE & FILS

Jean-Pierre Simonnet
9, Avenue d'Oberwesel 89800 Chablis
86 42 11 73 - Telex: 351 816 F

Type of vineyard: Corporation. **Established:** 1840. **Vine stocks:** Chardonnay. **Soil:** Kimmeridgian. **Exposure:** South. **Average annual production in hectoliters:** 60. **Appellation:** Chablis premier Cru "Mont de Milieu". **Type:** White. **Technique:** In stainless steel tanks. **Maturing:** In stainless steel tanks. **Alcool content:** 12.8%. **Characteristics:** Dry. **Served with:** Fish, shellfish, white meat. **Vintages available in 89/90:** 1987, 1988.

Characteristics of vintages

1988: Supple, elegant, fragrant. **1987:** Soft and full, lingering flavor, rich and well balanced. Price range (pre-tax, exwarehouse): 50 to 80 F.F.
Sales volume:
- Retail: 10%. - Restaurants: 30%. - Other: 60% (export).
Sales in France: 40%.
Export sales: 60%.
Main trading partners : UK, Netherlands, Belgium, Germany, Japan.

References in France

Restaurants: Fouquet's, Grand Café des Capucines, Chez

Guilio-Hameau d'Auteuil, Isard, Luce de Passy, La Méditerranée, etc.
Shops: Comestibles Vignon, rue Marbeuf, (Paris).

Abroad

United States

21 Brands Inc., 155 East 44th Street, New York NY (Tel: (212) 573 02 00).

United kingdom

Waverly vintners, PO Box 22, Crieff road, Perth PH1 2SL 73829621. G Belloni 128-132 Albert St Regents Park, London NW1 12 67 11 21. Jackson Nugent Vintners 60 Hight st, Wimbledon Village, London SW19 5EE 19441048.

Germany

Karl Weber, Umbachstrasse 20, 5000 Köln 80 (Tel: 22 16 84 500).

Switzerland

Jacques Vins, case Postale 29, 1211 Geneva 6 (Tel: 22 52 17 48).

Belgium

Raes – Chaussée de Jette, 559 Brussels (Tel: (02) 427 27 38).

Canada

Carrington Imports, 36 Butterick road, Toronto, Ontario M8W 3Z8.

The Netherlands

Heeren Van Heusden Wijnkoopers, Nieustraat 4-6, Postbus 66, 5256 BB Heusden (Tel: 41 62 30 25).

Far East

Japan: Fuji Hakko Kogyo Co Ltd, 31-6 Motoyoyogi – Shibuya-Ku, Tokyo 03460 20 51.

Comments

Simonnet-Febvre is also building up quite a reputation for its selection of wines other than Chablis, the wine of the Yonne most particularly. Here they boast such great red appellations as Irancy, Palotte, Coulanges and Épineuil and such great white appellations as Bourgogne Aligoté and Sauvignon de Saint-Bris.

AUXERROIS

DOMAINE FRANÇOIS COLLIN

François Collin
Les Mulots – 89700 Tonnerre
86 75 93 84

Type of vineyard: Family-owned. **Established:** 1977. **Number of employees:** 1. **Vine stocks:** Pinot Noir. **Soil:** Clay with calcium carbonate on Kimmeridgian. **Exposure:** Southeast and Southwest. **Average annual production in hectoliters:** 45.
Appellation: Burgundy Epineuil. **Type:** Red, rosé. **Technique:** Alcoholic fermentation and conversion of malic to lactic acid in enamelled steel tanks. **Maturing:** In Oak casks, 25% new each year, for 6 to 18 months, according to the vintage and type of wine desired. **Alcohol content:** 12.5%. **Characteristics:** Typical Pinot, woody and vanilla fragrance with a touch of red fruit (strawberry, red currant, cherry), often with a woodland base. **Serving temperature:** Red: 14°, Rosé: 10°. **Served with:** Red: Particularly with red meat grilled or roasted (beef). For the older vintages, game and even foie gras. Rosé: Chicken, rabbit, pork, veal, delicatessen products, fish, shellfish. **Vintages available in 89/90:** Red: some 1988 and 1987, 1986, 1985, Rosé: 1988.

Characteristics of vintages

1988, 1987, 1986: Two good years, supple and fruity, will age well. Price range (pre-tax, ex-warehouse): Rosé: between 10 and 20 F.F. Red: between 20 and 30 F.F.
Sales volume:
– Retail: 80%. – Restaurants: 10%. –Others: 10% (shops).
Sales in France: 90%.
Export sales: 10%.
Main trading partners: Germany, Belgium, England, Suisse, Pays Bas.

Abroad

England

Villandry. 89, Marilebone High Street, London W1M de Belgium – J.P. Duyck. Le cellier des Moines, 109, av. du Centenaire, 6080 Montignies-sur-Sambre.

• The price scandal, botched up vintages and compromised reputations: the truth and nothing but the truth (see Bordeaux, Provence and Châteauneuf-du-Pape Classifications).

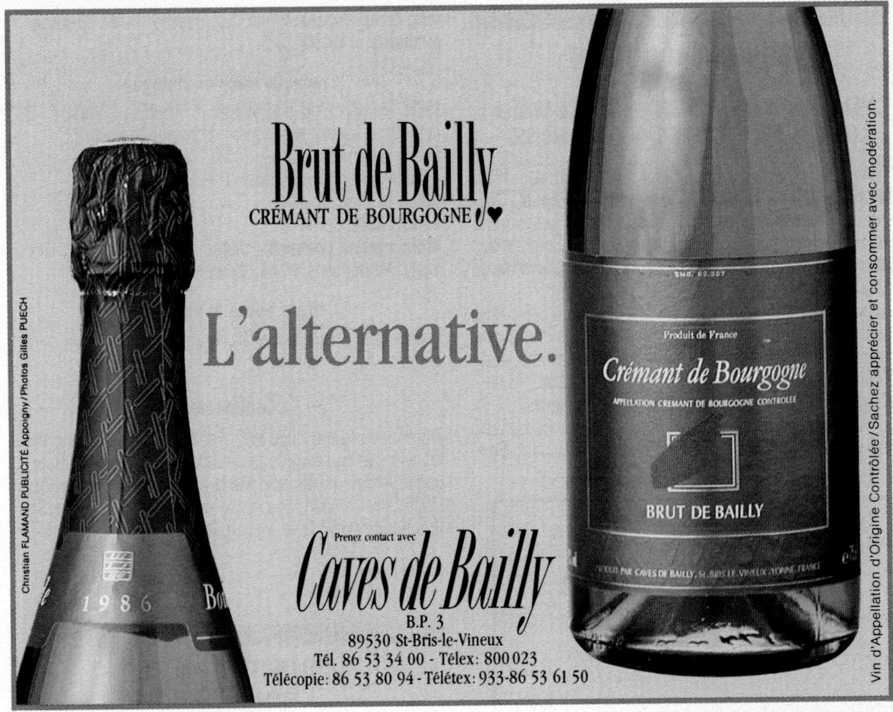

Brut de Bailly
CRÉMANT DE BOURGOGNE
L'alternative.
Prenez contact avec
Caves de Bailly
B.P. 3
89530 St-Bris-le-Vineux
Tél. 86 53 34 00 - Télex: 800 023
Télécopie: 86 53 80 94 - Télétex: 933-86 53 61 50
Produit de France
Crémant de Bourgogne
BRUT DE BAILLY
Christian FLAMAND PUBLICITÉ Appoigny/Photos Gilles PUECH
Vin d'Appellation d'Origine Contrôlée/Sachez apprécier et consommer avec modération.

CAVES DE BAILLY

Alain Cornelissens
Sica du Vignoble Auxerrois, BP 3
89530 Saint-Bris-Le-Vineux
86 53 34 00 – Telex: 800 023 FAX: 86 53 80 94

Type of vineyard: Agricultural Association. **Established:** 1972. **Number of employees:** 8. **Vine stocks:** Pinot Noir, Aligoté, Chardonnay, Sacy, Gamay. **Average annual production in hectoliters:** 12,000 (on 280 ha). **Appellation:** Crémant de Bourgogne. **Type:** White, rosé. **Technique:** Champagne method. **Alcohol content:** 12%. **Characteristics:** Excellent wines, delicate and light foam, fruity, lively. **Serving temperature:** 6-8°.

Characteristics of vintages

1987: White and rosé. **1986:** White and rosé. **1985:** White. **Other:** 1982 and reserves. Price range (pre-tax, ex-warehouse): 20 to 30 F.F.
Sales volume:
- Wholesale: 34%. – Retail: 28%. – Other: 38% (export).

Sales in France: 62%.
Export sales: 38%.
Main trading partners : UK, Germany, USA, Switzerland, Japan, Belgium, Netherlands.

References in France

Restaurants: L'Espérance, St-Père, Côte St-Jacques, Les Clos, Chablis, etc.
Shops: Legrand, Paris.

Abroad

Germany

Schumberger Medienhein, Jacques Wein Dedot Dusseldorf Wein Wolf Bonn.

Switzerland

Divo Case Postale 145 1003 Lausanne 9.

Belgium

Wijntransit 2508 Kessel – A.F. Nampaey, B 1720 Groot Bijgaarden.

The Netherlands

Wijnimport J. Bart Purmerend.

Far East

Japan: Toyo Menka Kaisha LTD Tokyo.

Comments

Established in the heart of the Auxerre vineyard, 15 kilometers form Auxerre and Chablis, the Caves de Bailly have an exceptional infrastructure. A 22,000 hl capacity fermenting room has been set up in an old 3.5 hectare 12th century quarry. In addition, there is high quality equipment for cold treatment, bottling and shaking.

DOMAINE LUC SORIN

M. Sorin
13 bis, rue de Paris, 89530 St-Bris-Le-Vineux
86 53 36 87 or 86 53 86 97 - Telex: 800 953

Type of vineyard: Corporation. **Established:** 1969. **Number of employees:** 9. **Vine stocks:** Aligoté, Sauvignon, Chardonnay, Pinot Noir, César. **Soil:** Jurassic era, Kimmeridgian chald. **Exposure:** South, South-West, West. **Average annual production in hectoliters:** 1,600-1,700.

Appellation: Bourgogne Aligoté, Sauvignon de Saint-Bris, Bourgogne Rouge, Bourgogne Chardonnay, Bourgogne Passetoutgrain, Bourgogne Irancy. **Type:** Red, white, rosé. **Technique:** Temperature controlled vinification. **Maturing:** White: vats. Red: casks. **Alcohol contents:** 12 to 13%. **Characteristics:** White: "Chablis" type. Red: made from a blend of Pinot and César, original, individual. **Serving temperature:** White: 12°. Red: 17 to 18°. **Vintages available in 89/90:** 1988.

Characteristics of vintages

1988: Fruity, round and supple in all three colors. Price range (pre-tax, ex-warehouse): between 20 an 30 F.F.

Sales volumes:
- Retail: 10%. - Restaurants: 10%.

Sales in France: 20%.
Export sales: 80%.
Main trading partners: United Kingdom, Belgium, Germany, Netherlands, Nordic Countries, Japan.

References in France

Restaurants: L'Espérance, St. Père, Vézelay.
Shops: L'Amour du Vin.

Comments

From father to son since 1577. Ten Gold medals among the many prizes and awards for excellence. Specialities: Bourgogne Aligoté (1986 Gold Medal), Bourgogne Chardonnay (1986 Silver medal), Sauvignon de St-Bris, Bourgogne St-Bris Rouge (1987 Gold Medal), Bourgogne Irancy.

COLINOT Père et Fils

Robert Colinot
Irancy - 89290 Champs-sur-Yonne
86 42 20 76

Type of vineyard: Family-owned. **Established:** Several centuries. **Vine stocks:** Pinot Noir, César, Gamay (white juice). **Soil:** Kimmeridgian clay with calcium carbonate. **Exposure:** South and Southwest. **Average annual production in hectoliters:** 200.

Appellation: Burgundy Irany, Burgundy Palotte, Burgundy (rosé), Passetougrains (red and rosé). **Type:** Red, rosé. **Technique:** Traditional, no destemming, fermentation with skins for about 10 days, Oaks vats, filtration. Manual harvesting. **Maturing:** In Oak casks. **Alcohol content:** 12% to 13% according to the year and the sun. **Characteristics:** Initially tannic, they become more round with ageing. Average ageing weather years. Certain great vintages period be kept for 20 years. **Serving temperature:** 15° maximum. **Served with:** Passetougrain: delicatessen products. Burgundy (Irancy and Palotte): rabbit or duck stew, leg of lamb. **Vintages available in 89/90:** 1987, 1988.

Characteristics of vintages

Price range (pre-tax, ex-warehouse): between 20 and 38 F.F.

Sales volumes:
- Retail: 90%. - Restaurants: 10%.

Sales in France: 80%.
Export sales: 20%.
Main trading partners: Germany, Luxembourg, Belgium, Netherlands, UK.

CÔTES DE NUIT

FIXIN

DOMAINE PIERRE GELIN

2, rue du Chapitre-Fixin
21220 Gevrey-Chambertin
80 52 45 24

Type of vineyard: Family-owned 12 hectares. **Established:** 1930. **Number of employees:** 7. **Vine stocks:** Pinot Noir. **Soil:** Mostly chalky clay. **Average annual production in hectoliters:** 450.

Mis en bouteilles
au Domaine
N
FIXIN 1ER CRU
CLOS NAPOLÉON
APPELLATION FIXIN CONTROLÉE
13 % vol.
DOMAINE PIERRE GELIN
75 cl
VITICULTEUR A FIXIN (COTE-D'OR) - FRANCE
PRODUCT OF FRANCE

Appellation: Fixin Clos Napoléon. **Type:** Red. **Technique:** Traditional, long fermentation on skins – in wooden vats. **Maturing:** In oak casks. **Alcohol content:** 13°. **Characteristics:** Somewhat untamed character, pronounced woody bouquet, rich and well balanced, should be aged for about 10 years. **Serving temperature:** 15°. **Served with:** Red meat, game. **Vintages available in 89/90:** 1984, 1986, 1987.

Characteristics of vintages

1988: Great year for keeping. **1987:** Elegance, harmony, structure – good ageing potential. **1986:** Fruity, elegant. **1985:** Great year – good keeping. Price range (pre-tax, ex-warehouse): 50 to 80 F.F.
Sales volume:
– Retail: 70%. – Restaurants: 20%. – Other: 10% wine dealers.
Sales in France: 40%.
Export sales: 60%.
Main trading partners: USA, Japan, UK, Switzerland, Benelux countries.

References in France

Restaurants: Tour d'Argent (Paris).

Abroad

United States

Importers: Château and Estate Wines Co. New York.

DOMAINE MARION - FIXIN

Doctor Marion – distribution exclusive
Bouchard Ainé et Fils
21203 Beaune
80 22 07 67 – Telex: 350 163 F

Vine stocks: Pinot Noir. **Soil:** Clay Limestone and silica. **Exposure:** Southeast. **Average annual production in hectoliters:** 34.
Appellation: Fixin "La Mazière" Domaine Marion. **Type:** Red. **Technique:** Traditional. **Maturing:** Oak barrels. **Alcohol content:** 13%. **Characteristics:** Deep color, solid perfume, full, round, good keeping wine for ageing. **Serving temperature:** 17°. **Served with:** Roast beef, beef stews with wine sauces and cheese. **Vintages available in 89/90:** 1979, 1983, 1984, 1985.

Characteristics of vintages

1985: Medium tannin, deep color, full-bodied. **1984:** Fine and subtle. **1983:** Very good wine to age, solid and well balanced. **Other:** 1979 – fine robe, delicate and perfumed. Price range (pre-tax, ex-warehouse): 50-80 F.F.
Main trading partners: Canada, England, USA, Switzerland, Denmark, Germany.

• *A dish for each wine. According to the age of your wines, their style, their typical nature, their color, adapt your menu without sticking to stereotypes (see "Wine and Foods".*

GEVREY-CHAMBERTIN

DOMAINE ALAIN BURGUET

Alain Burguet
B.P. 29 – 18, rue de l'Église
21220 Gevrey-Chambertin
80 34 36 35

Type of vineyard: Family-owned. **Established:** 1974. **Vine stocks:** Pinot. **Soil:** Clay with calcium carbonate. **Exposure:** Rising sun. **Average annual production in hectoliters:** 100 to 150.
Appellation: Gevrey-Chambertin. **Type:** Red. **Technique:** Traditional. **Maturing:** In casks. **Alcohol content:** 13%. **Characteristics:** Quite long traditional vinification brings out the color and an interesting aromatic richness (blackcurrant, mulberry, raspberry, coffee...). Grapes from old vines produce a full-bodied wine. Guaranteed good for ageing. **Serving temperature:** 14°. **Served with:** Charolais steak, game. **Vintages available in 89/90:** 1984, 1985, 1986.

Characteristics of vintages

1986: Well sustained color, abondant fruit fragrance (blakcurrant, raspberry), for long keeping. Very good year. **1985:** Very beautiful red ochre color, very full-bodied, long life, great year. **1984:** More limpid color (cherry), more savage character, good for agein, good year. Price range (pre-tax, ex-warehouse): Between 50 and 80 F.F.
Sales volume:
– Wholesale: 1/3. – Retail: 2/3.
Sales in France: 50%.
Export sales: 50%.
Main trading partners : UK, USA, Australia, Japan, Belgium, Switzerland, Netherlands, Germany.

References in France

Restaurants: Troisgros, Georges Blanc, Les Millésimes at Gevrey, Taillevent, L'Hostellerie du Vieux Moulin at Bouilland (21).

Comments

Alain Burguet comes from an old Gevrey-Chambertin family (he was born in Gevrey). He spent his entire youth among the wines and in the winecellars, talking with the old winemakers of the village and tasting many different wines. At the age of 19, he had a passion for the winemaking business. He wanted to make wine in the old, traditional way and put his name on the bottles.

DOMAINE CAMUS PÈRE & FILS

Hubert Camus
21, rue Maréchal de Lattre de Tassigny,
21220 Gevrey-Chambertin
80 34 30 64 – 80 34 31 70

Type of vineyard: Agricultural Association. **Established:** Association since 1956, family-owned since 1860. **Number of employees:** 8. **Vine stocks:** Pinot Noir. **Soil:** Chalky clay. **Exposure:** East, South-East. **Average annual production in hectoliters:** 500 to 600.

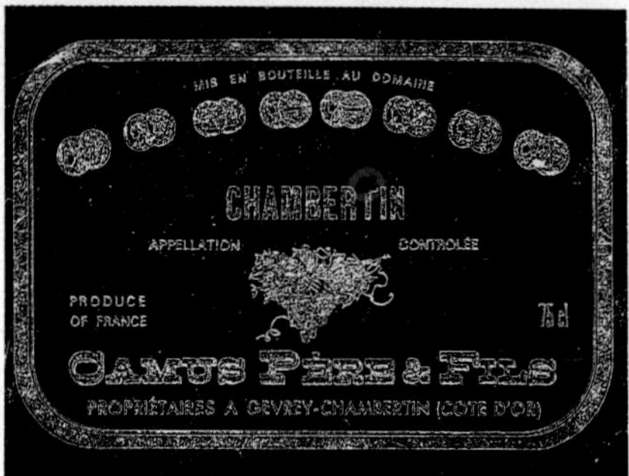

Appellation: Chambertin, Latricières-Chin, Charmes-Chin, Mazis-Chin, Mazoyères-Chin, Gevrey-Chin. **Type:** Red. **Technique:** Long vinification (3 weeks). **Maturing:** 30 months in oak casks. **Alcohol content:** 13%. **Characteristics:** Delicate bouquet, deep color. **Serving temperature:** 16 to 18°. **Served with:** Game, red meat, cheese and nuts. **Vintages available in 89/90:** 1980, 1981, 1982, 1983, 1984, 1985 and 1986 (as of September).

Characteristics of vintages

1988: Not yet bottled. **1987:** Not yet bottled. **1986:** Full-bodied, deep color, delicate, for average keeping. **1985:** Full-bodied, deep color, pronounced bouquet, very delicate, long keeping. Price range (pre-tax, ex-warehouse): 40 to 180 F.F.
Sales volume:
– Wholesale: 10%. – Retail: 90%.
Sales in France: 30%.
Export sales: 60%.
Main trading partners : Japan, Canada, Germany, Switzerland, Belgium, Luxemburg, Denmark, UK, USA.

DUPONT TISSERANDOT

Dupont-Tisserandot
21220 Gevrey-Chambertin
80 34 10 50

Type of vineyard: Family-owned. **Established:** For three generations. **Number of employees:** 8. **Vine stocks:** Pinot, Aligoté. **Exposure:** Hillsides. **Average annual production in hectoliters:** 35 to 40 hl/ha.

Appellation: Gevrey-Chambertin, Marssanay-la-Côte. **Type:** Red, White, Rosé. **Technique:** Traditional. **Maturing:** In casks. **Alcohol content:** 12.5%. **Characteristics:** Aged in oak casks (1 1/2 to 2 years). **Serving temperature:** 12°. **Served with:** Meat, cheese. **Vintages available in 89/90:** 1986, 1987.

Characteristics of vintages

1988: Very good but astringent. **1987:** Good, fruity. **1986:** Very good, especially the Côtes de Nuits. **1985:** Very good, but out of stock. Price range (pre-tax, ex-warehouse): 10 to 20 F.F. – 20 to 30 F.F. – 30 to 50 F.F. – 50 to 80 F.F. – 80 to 120 F.F.
Sales volume:
– Wholesale: 80%. – Retail: 10%. – Restaurants: 1%. – Other: Wine bars.
Sales in France: 50%.
Export sales: 50%.
Main trading partners : Switzerland, Germany, Belgium, UK, USA.

References in France

Shops: Unico, Annecy.

Comments

Family enterprise, from father to daughter, for three generations.

JEAN-CLAUDE FOURRIER

7, route de Dijon, 21220 Gevrey-Chambertin
80 34 33 99

Type of vineyard: Family-owned. **Established:** 1967. **Vine stocks:** Pinot Noir. **Soil:** Chalky clay. **Exposure:** East. **Average annual production in hectoliters:** 25 to 30 hl/ha.
Appellation: Vougeot 1er Cru, Chambolle Musigny, Morey Saint Denis, Gevrey Chambertin, Gevrey Chambertin 1er Cru, Gevrey Chambertin Combe-aux-Moines, Gevrey Chambertin Clos-Saint-Jacques, Griottes Chambertin. **Type:** Red. **Technique:** Long fermentation on skines. **Maturing:** In casks. **Alcohol content:** 12.8 to 13.5%.
Characteristics: Fine, elegant, silky texture, fruity, pronounced bouquet. **Serving temperature:** 13° to 14°. **Served with:** Soft wines: white meat. Harder wines: meat in sauce. **Vintages available in 89/90:** 1986, 1987.

Characteristics of vintages

1988: Will not be bottled before August 1990. **1987:** Slighly deeper in color than the 1986 and fruity. **1986:** Delicate, elegant, pronounced bouquet. Price range (pre-tax, ex-warehouse): 50 to 80 F.F. – 80 to 120 F.F. over 160 F.F.
Sales volume:
– Wholesale: 10%. – Retail: 10%. – Restaurants: 20%. – Other: 60% (retailers).
Sales in France: 25%.
Export sales: 75%.
Main trading partners : Switzerland, Germany, Luxemburg, Belgium, UK, Netherlands.

References in France

Restaurants: Lameloise, Alain Chapel, Georges Blanc, La Côte St-Jacques, Auberge des Templiers, Léon de Lyon, Le Toit de Passy, Chez Pauline, etc.

Abroad

Germany

Kellervin Moëvenpick Moerikestrasse 67 – D 7000 Stuttgart 1.

Switzerland

Entrepôts Vins et Spiritueux Moëvenpick CH 118 Vinzel.

Belgium

Les Courtiers Vinicoles PVBA 3500 Hasselt.

The Netherlands

Alliane Vinicole 2400 AS Alpen aan den Ryn.

Comments

The wines should be aged in a absolutely dark cellar at a temperature between 10° and 12° C, and protected against vibration. They should not be served at too high a temperature and require rather little time to warm up. It is no longer necessary, as in the past, to place the wine near the fireplace overnight for it to arrive at the proper drinking temperature.

SCE GOILLOT-BERNOLLIN

Laurent Goillot
29, route de Dijon
21220 Gevrey-Chambertin
80 34 36 12

Established: 1900. **Number of employees:** 1. **Vine stocks:** Pinot Noir. **Exposure:** East. **Average annual production in hectoliters:** 200.

Appellation: Gevrey-Chambertin. **Type:** Red. **Technique:** Traditional. **Maturing:** 14 to 18 monts in oak casks. **Alcohol content:** 13%. **Characteristics:** Supple and fragrant thanks to a short vinification (about 7 days) at temperatures not exceeding 30°. **Serving temperature:** 17°. **Served with:** Game, meat in sauce, cheese. **Vintages available in 89/90:** 1987 and 1988.

Characteristics of vintages

1988: Lots of body and fragrance already developed, to be kept. **1987:** Lighter than the 1988, but with very subtle perfumes, will evolve well. Price range (pre-tax, ex-warehouse): between 50 and 80 F.F.
Sales volume:
– Wholesale: 50%. – Retail: 30%. – Restaurants: 20%.
Sales in France: 90%.
Export sales: 10%.
Main trading partners: Switzerland, Germany, Belgium, United Kingdom.

References in France

Restaurants: Bernard Loiseau (Saulieu), Michel Bras (Laguiole), Bernard Lebrun (Villeneuve/Lot), "Les Jardins de l'Opéra" (Toulouse), Jean-Pierre Silva (Bouilland), "Les Millésimes" (Gevrey-Chambertin).

Comments

Good classical wines in their appellation, very successful in vintages such as 86 or 83. Open every day for tasting.

PHILIPPE LECLERC

Philippe Leclerc
13, avenue des Halles
21220 Gevrey-Chambertin
80 34 30 72

Type of vineyard: Family-owned. **Established:** 1974. **Vine stocks:** Pinot Noir. **Soil:** Chalky clay. **Exposure:** Hillsides facing East. **Average annual production in hectoliters:** 40 hl/ha.
Appellation: Gevrey – Chambertin. **Type:** Red. **Technique:** Long fermentation on skins. **Maturing:** 1er Cru: in new casks for more than 2 years. Alcohol content: 13%. **Characteristics:** Rich and well balanced, velvet texture, full-bodied, long keeping (between 10 to 20 years). **Serving temperature:** 15 to 16°. **Served with:** Meat, game, cheese. **Vintages available in 89/90:** 1986, 1985.

Characteristics of vintages

1986: Very soft tannins, very delicate wines. **1985:** Typical, a great wine, to be aged. Price range (pre-tax, ex-warehouse): 30 to 50 F.F. – 120 to 160 F.F.
Sales in France: 30%.
Export sales: 70%.
Main trading partners : USA, UK, Germany, Italy.

References in France

Restaurants: The Ritz (15, place Vendôme, 75041 Paris), Divo France (30 bis, avenue de la Baltique, 91940 Les Ullis), etc.

Abroad

United Stades
Robert Chadderdon, New York. Wine Import, 75 Broadway, San Francisco.

United Kingdom
Market Vintners & Co. London. Bishopsmead, London.

Germany
Le Canard, Hamburg.

DOMAINE JEAN PHILLIPPE MARCHAND

Jean Phillippe Marchand
1, place du Monument, 21220 Gevrey-Chambertin
80 34 33 60

Type of vineyard: Individual. **Established:** 1984. **Number of employees:** 1. **Vine stocks:** Pinot Noir 16149 and SO4. **Soil:** Chalky clay. **Average annual production in hectoliters:** 200.

Produce
of France
CHARMES-CHAMBERTIN
APPELLATION CONTROLÉE
GRAND CRU
1986
mis en bouteilles à la propriété par
Jean-Philippe MARCHAND
Viticulteur à GEVREY-CHAMBERTIN 21220 (COTE-D'OR) FRANCE
13% Vol.
75 cl

Appellation: Morey Saint Denis, Gevrey Chambertin, Chambolle Musigny. **Type:** Red. **Technique:** Traditional vinification for 3 weeks. **Maturing:** 100% in casks, 15% new. **Alcohol content:** 13%. **Characteristics:** Tannic, quite hard when young, to be aged a minimum of 5 years. **Serving temperature:** 15°. **Served with:** Game in sauce, fine cheeses. **Vintages available in 89/90:** 1987.

Characteristics of vintages

1988: Beautiful color, tannic, very soft and full, rich and well balanced wine. **1987:** Quite fine wine, but with rather sustained tannins. **1986:** Very agreeable wines, quite round, maturity in 6 years. Price range (pre-tax, ex-warehouse): Info Missing.
Sales in France: 50%.
Export sales: 50%.
Main trading partners : United States, Switzerland, Belgium, Netherlands, Japan, Spain.

References in France

Restaurants: Le Rempart (Tournus), La Renaissance (42800), Auberge de Fond Rose (69300), Trois Gros (Roanne).

Abroad

United States
Select Vineyards Ltd, Neal Rosenthal, New York 10021.

United Kingdom
George Barbier of London, SE12 London. Friarwood Ltd, SW6 4ST London. Andrew Gordon Wines, Dorking RH4 3YZ. Bishopsmead Wine, Dorking RH4 2EZ.

Switzerland
Vins Précieux, H.J. Senn, 8703 Erlenbach. Hans Muller Weihandlung, 9630 Wattwil.

Belgium
Aux Coteaux S.P.R.L., Vinalmont.

The Netherlands
Beeren Wijnimport, Overveen 2051.

Others
Spain: Alcyon Alto Consulting, 28013 Madrid.

Comments

An old 16th century exploitation, recently restored in 1984. The only 16th century wheel press remaining in the village is worth seeing.

CHARLES QUILLARDET VIGNERON

18, route de Dijon
21220 Gevrey-Chambertin
80 34 10 26 – Telex 283 155F

Type of vineyard: Family-owned. **Established:** 1679. **Number of employees:** 6. **Vine stocks:** Pinot noir 75%, Chardonnay 20%, Aligoté 5%. **Soil:** Bajocian chalky clay. **Exposure:** South-East. **Average annual production in hectoliters:** 700.

QUILLARDET
QUALITÉ
№ 01722
CHARLES QUILLARDET
VIGNERON à GEVREY-CHAMBERTIN
1986
Gevrey-Chambertin
APPELLATION GEVREY-CHAMBERTIN CONTROLÉE
12,5% vol.
750 ml
Produit de France

Appellation: Chambertin, Ruchottes Chambertin, Gevrey Chambertin 1er cru, Gevrey Chambertin, Côte de Nuits, Fixin, Marsannay White, Rosé and Red. **Type:** Red, white, rosé. **Technique:** Traditional with temperature control. **Maturing:** In oak casks. **Characteristics:** Typical of the Côte de Nuits with all of the red fruit aromas, wine to be kept except for the Marsanny Rosé which is fresh and goes down well. **Serving temperature:** Rosé and white: 8°. Red: 12 to 15°. **Served with:** Marsannay Rosé: delicatessen. Aligoté: fish, shellfish, white meats, Kir. Marsanny White: fish. Red: red meat and cheese. **Vintages available in 89/90:** 1986, 1987.

Characteristics of vintages

1988: Very beautiful wine, great future. **1987:** Delicate tannins, beautiful color, red fruit aroma. **1986:** Just beginning to open up, very solid, spicy aroma. Beautiful future. **1985:** For perfect harmony, wait a little. Splendor is just down the road. Full bodied wines, balanced and harmonious aromas, marked fragrance, subtle tannins.
Sales volume:
– Retail: 40%. – Restaurants: 20%. – Other: 40% agents.
Sale in France: 60%.
Export sales: 40%.
Main trading partners: Switzerland, Belgium, United Kingdom, Germany, United States, Italy, Japan.

References in France

Restaurants: Hostellerie de Levernois (M. Crotet), Belle Epoque (Chateaufort), Rotisserie de la Paix (Beaune).
Shops: Chedeville (Orly South and West), Master Wines (Paris 17).

Comments

A remarkable winemaker, from father to son (or daughter) since 1679 in the purest Burgundy tradition, whose principal concern is the quality of the wine. The vineyard is called Montre Cul is used to commemorate the bicentenary of the Revolution. Some very great wines, really superb, perfectly vinified, like his Gevrey-Chambertin, vintages 83 to 88 or his Marsannay wines which are uniformly successful.

NOUVELLE SOCIÉTÉ D'EXPLOITATION DU DOMAINE HENRI REBOURSEAU

Jean de Surel
B.P. N° 39-10, place du Monument
21220 Gevrey-Chambertin
80 51 88 94

Type of vineyard: Corporation. **Established:** 1949-1981. **Number of employees:** 6. **Vine stocks:** Pinot. **Soil:** Chalky clay. **Exposure:** North-West, South-East. **Average annual production in hectoliters:** 33 hl per hectare.

Appellation: Gevrey-Chambertin, Gevrey-Chambertin 1er cru, Charmes-Chambertin, Mazis-Chambertin, Clos de Vougeot, Chambertin, Chambertin Clos de Beze. **Type:** Red. **Technique:** Traditional, open vat, floating cap. **Maturing:** 17 months. **Alcohol content:** 13%. **Characteristics:** Grace, delicacy and distinction. **Serving temperature:** 16 to 18° according to the vintage. **Served with:** Meat and cheese. **Vintages available in 89/90:** 1984, 1986, 1987, 1988 (new wine).

Characteristics of vintages

1988: Excellent, harmonious wines, rich and concentrated, to be kept. **1987:** Good average year, should be quite aromatic. **1986:** Good year, quite tannic, to keep and enjoy in 5 years.
Other: 1984: Average year, wine evolving quite rapidly, can be drunk at present or you might wait 3 to 4 years.
Price range (pre-tax, ex-warehouse): between 80 and 160 F.F.
Sales volume:
– Wholesale: 50%. – Retail: 50%.
Sales in France: 50%.
Export sales: 50%.
Main trading partners: Switzerland.

References in France

Restaurants: La Mère Blanc.

Abroad

Germany
Vinum, Gutenbergstrasse 5, 7600 Karlsruhe 1. Wahnschaffe Weinimport, Konigsallee 173, 4190 Kleve.

Switzerland
Raphael Clerc, 1751 Cottens. Tel: 3737 1139.

Belgium
Simon Delvigne Vins, 85 Romeinse Kassei, 3700 Tongeren. Tel: 012 23 21 70.

Far East
Japan: Daiei Sangyo Kaisha Ltd, 18-4 Chome Honjindori Nakamura nagoya 453.

Comments

A serious and dedicated proprietor who regrets that the wines are consumed too young (except for certain years). He is right because his wines deserve to be tasted when fully mature, after 5 to 10 years or more.

DOMAINE ARMAND ROUSSEAU S.A.

Mr. Charles Rousseau
21220 Gevrey-Chambertin
80 34 30 55

Vine stocks: Pinot Noir. **Soil:** Chalky clay. **Exposure:** East, South-East. **Average annual production in hectoliters:** 30 to 36 hl/ha.
Appellation: AOC Gevrey Chambertin 1er Cru, Mazy Chambertin, Charmes-Chambertin Clos de la Roche/ Ruchottes, Clos St.Jacques, Chambertin, Chambertin Clos

de Beze. **Type:** Red. **Technique:** Traditional. **Maturing:** Grands Crus: 2 years in new oak casks. **Characteristics:** Various according to the appellations. **Serving temperature:** 15°. **Served with:** Game, meat in sauce, roasts, cheese. **Vintages available in 89/90:** None available.

Characteristics of vintages

1988: Rich, colored, concentrated wines, very promising. **1987:** More supple, good color, bouquet. **1986:** Great vintage, fruity and well balanced, good keeping.
Sales in France: 20%.
Export sales: 80%.
Main trading partners : United Kingdom, Switzerland, Germany, U.S.A., Australia, Japan, Belgium, Denmark, Austria, Luxemburg, Canada, Sweden, Italy.

References in France

Restaurants: Most 2 and 3 star restaurants (Guide Michelin).
Shops: Hediard, Vins Rares & de Collection – etc. (S/Paris). – Legrand (Caves).

Abroad

United States
Frederick Wildman, New York.

United Kingdom
Adnams – Atkinson Baldwin – Loeb, Heyman Brothers, Lay 1 Wheeler – I.E.C.W.S. etc.

Germany
Grandu Cru Select (Bonn) – Académie du vin – Fegers & Uterberg – etc.

Switzerland
Caves Fischer – Divo – Baur-au-Lac – St. Gotthard – Reichmuth.

Belgium
Pirard.

Canada
Saq. Montreal.

The Netherlands
Prinses Juliana – Wijnkoperij Prosper van Nieulande BV.

Far East
Ross Duke (Australia) Toyo Menka (Japan).

Others
Gottardi (Austria) L'Esprit du Vin (Denmark).

DOMAINE TORTOCHOT

Gabriel Tortochot and family
12, rue de l'Église, 21220 Gevrey-Chambertin
80 34 30 68

Type of vineyard: Agricultural Association. **Established:** Domain (1880), Association (1986). **Number of employees:** 2 (monthly), 2 (by the hour). **Vine stocks:** Pinot. **Soil:** Chalky clay – marl and stones on hillsides, sand in the plains. **Exposure:** East. **Average annual production in hectoliters:** 40 hl/ha.

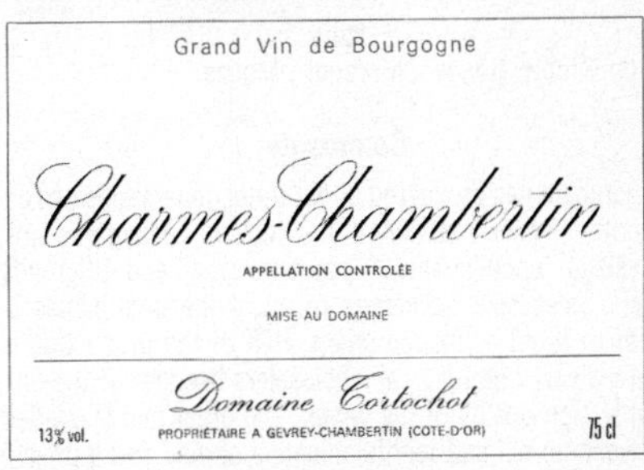

Appellation: Gevrey-Chambertin and 2 1[er] Crus: Lavaux St. Jacques & Les Champeaux. Morey St Denis and 4 Grands Crus: Chambertin, Charmes Chambertin, Mazio Chambertin, Clos de Vougeot. **Type:** Red. **Technique:** Open vats (12 to 14 days). **Maturing:** In oak casks (18 months). **Alcohol content:** 13-13.5%. **Characteristics:** Substantial, tannic in 76-78-85. More supple in average years 82-84-86. **Serving temperature:** 16°. **Served with:** Great vintages with game and ripe cheese Average vintages: all meats, and softer cheese. **Vintages available in 89/90:** 1986, 1987, 1988.

Characteristics of vintages

1988: Great year, beautiful color, long – similar to the 1978 or 1985 vintages. **1987:** Well balanced, pleasant, very fragrant. **1985:** Stock depleted, small harvest (18 hl/ha). Price range (pre-tax, ex-warehouse): 50 to 80 F.F. (AOC "Villages"), 80 to 120 F.F. (AOC "Premiers Crus"), 120 to 160 (AOC "Grands Crus").
Sales volume:
– Wholesale: 50%. – Retail: 40%. – Restaurants: 10%.
Sales in France: 75%.
Export sales: 25%.
Main trading partners : Switzerland, Belgium.

References in France

Restaurants: "Les Millésimes" (Gevrey-Chambertin), La Mère Blanc (Vonnas), Les Trois Marches et Le Potager du Roy (Versailles), L'Aubergrade (Pontchartrain), Château de la Chèvre d'Or, Eze, Moulins de Mougins, L'Avant-Scène, Boulogne.

Abroad

United Kingdom
Lay & Wheeler Ltd. Colchester – Essex.

Germany

Weinimport Rutishauser, D7750 Konsgtag/Weincontor – 6940 Weinheim, Merus 4005 Merbusch.

Switzerland

Sté E.G. Bürgdorf, Ets Thiébaut, Bole – Les "Vins Précieux", Erlenbach – Pierre Belet, Le Mont, Lausanne – Véric, Zurich.

Belgium

Collot, Falmignoul – Choisy, Anvers – Willy Gordon Huizingen.

The Netherlands

Léon Colaris – 6000 Weert.

Italy

Moon Import, Gênes – Meregalli, Monza.

Comments

The domain has prospered under three generations of Tortochots for over a century. It now covers 12 hectares with 2 "village" appellations, 2 "premiers crus" and 4 "grands crus". Sales take advantage of all of the possibilities in order to avoid economic crises. Half of the production is sold via very faithful local wholesalers because of the uniformly high quality of the wines. The other half is divided between an old and faithful clientèle abroad and a private clientèle in France.

DOMAINE LOUIS TRAPET

Louis Trapet
53, route de Beaune – 21220 Gevrey Chambertin
80 34 30 40

Vine stocks: Pinot Noir.
Appellation: Chambertin, Gevrey Chambertin. **Type:** Red. **Technique:** Open cap vats, fermentation on skins 12 to 15 days. **Maturing:** In oak casks for 15 to 18 months. **Characteristics:** Remarkable wines, well-colored, well-bred, characteristics of the great Burgundies, typical of the region, full and distinguished, to be kept. **Vintages available in 89/90:** 1986, 1985, 1984.

CHAMBERTIN
GRAND CRU
APPELLATION CONTROLÉE
DOMAINE
LOUIS TRAPET PÈRE & FILS
PROPRIÉTAIRE A GEVREY-CHAMBERTIN (COTE-D'OR)
FRANCE
MIS EN BOUTEILLE AU DOMAINE
75 cl
13,5% vol.
PRODUCE OF FRANCE

Characteristics of vintages

1985: Very great wine for long keeping, rich, with complex aromas, superb. **1984:** Very successful vintage where the "hand" of man has made the difference. At the peak. No hesitation.

VACHET ROUSSEAU

Gérard & Georges Vachet
15, rue de Paris, 21220 Gevrey-Chambertin
80 34 32 03

Type of vineyard: Corporation. **Established:** For four generations. **Number of employees:** 1. **Vine stocks:** Pinot Noir. **Soil:** Chalky clay. **Exposure:** East. **Average annual production in hectoliters:** 250 to 300.

1986 1986

Gevrey-Chambertin

APPELLATION GEVREY-CHAMBERTIN CONTROLEE

MISE EN BOUTEILLES A LA PROPRIÉTÉ

G. VACHET-ROUSSEAU Père et Fils
Propriétaires-Récoltants à GEVREY-CHAMBERTIN (Côte-d'Or)

75 cl PRODUCE OF FRANCE 13% vol.

Appellation: Gevrey-Chambertin, Lavaux, St. Jacques 1er Cru, Mazis, Chambertin Grands Crus. **Type:** Red. **Technique:** Traditional, self-crushing. **Maturing:** In casks. **Alcohol content:** 13%. **Characteristics:** Graceful and delicate, very aromatic (red berries) – more robust in the 1[er] Crus and Grands Crus. **Serving temperature:** 15°. **Served with:** Red meat, game. **Vintages available in 89/90:** 1987, 1988.

Characteristics of vintages

1988: Rich and well balanced, beautiful color, soft and full. **1987:** Lighter, aromatic. Price range (pre-tax, ex-warehouse): 50 to 80 F.F.

Sales volume:
– Wholesale: 1-2%. – Retail: 60%. – Restaurants: 4-5%.
Sales in France: 70%.
Export sales: 30%.
Main trading partners: United Kingdom, Switzerland, Belgium.

References in France

Restaurants: Le Bacchus Gourmand (Paris), L'Estourelle (Paris), Troisgros (Roanne).
Shops: L'Arbre à vin, 75012 Paris.

Abroad

United States

Neal Rosenthal, 976 Lexington Ave. New York 10002 – Tel: (212) 249 66 50.

United Kingdom

Georges Barbier, 267 Lee High Road, London – Tel: 44 01 852 5801.

Switzerland

Albert Reichmuth, Stauffacherstrasse 15a, Zurich – Tel: 01 241 56 38 39.

Belgium

Maison José François , 4 les Petites Rues, Florenville – Tel: 61 31 11 26.

Canada

Office des Grands Vins, 1455, rue Bourgeoys, Longueuil, Québec – Tel: (514) 647 5377.

The Netherlands

Wynkopers & Hustinx, Spaarndamseweg, 120 Haarlem – Tel: 023 25 92 01.

Comments

Winemakers for four generations at Gevrey-Chambertin. Father Georges has been increasing the size of the domain for forty years.

VIGNOBLE DU VAL DE VERGY

Yves Chaley

Curtil-Vergy 21220 Gevrey-Chambertin

Average annual production in hectoliters: 70 000 bottles.
Appellation: Bourgogne-aligoté, Hautes-côtes-de-Nuits. **Type:** Red, white. **Other:** Crémant. **Technique:** Traditional. **Maturing:** Traditional (in vats and casks). **Characteristics:** Regularly well-made wine typical of their appellation. **Serving temperature:** White: 11°. Red: 15°. **Served with:** The entire meal. **Vintages available in 89/90:** 1987, 1986, 1985.

Characteristics of vintages

1987: Lovely white, fresh and fruity. **1986:** Excellent year for white and red, well colored, fragrant, dense and lingering, good keeping.
Sales in France: 40%.
Export sales: 60%.
Main trading partners : UK, Belgium, Japan, Netherlands.

• *Scandal in Saint-Émilion. To find out all about his appellation and the real quality of its wines, from the least pretentious to the greatest, see "Open Letter" in the Chapter on Bordeaux wines.*

MOREY-SAINT-DENIS

DOMAINE PIERRE AMIOT ET FILS

Pierre & Jean Louis Amiot

27 Grande rue 21220 Morey Saint Denis

80 34 34 28

Type of vineyard: Agricultural Association. **Established:** 1979. **Number of employees:** 2. **Vine stocks:** Pinot Noir 95%. **Soil:** Chalky clay. **Exposure:** Hillsides. **Average annual production in hectoliters:** Variable.

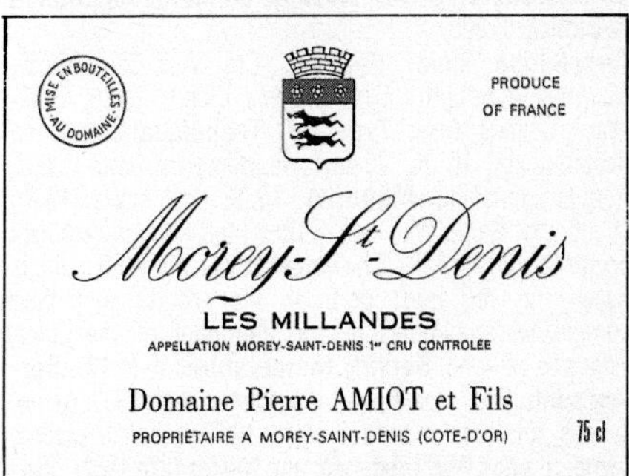

MISE EN BOUTEILLES AU DOMAINE
PRODUCE OF FRANCE
Morey-St-Denis
LES MILLANDES
APPELLATION MOREY-SAINT-DENIS 1er CRU CONTROLÉE
Domaine Pierre AMIOT et Fils
PROPRIÉTAIRE A MOREY-SAINT-DENIS (COTE-D'OR)
75 cl

Appellation: Morey St Denis, Morey Saint Denis 1er Cru Clos de la Roche. **Type:** Red. **Technique:** In open vats, floating cap. **Maturing:** In casks (16 to 18 months). **Alcohol content:** 12-13%. **Characteristics:** Supple, light and supple, delicate, good keeping depending on the year. **Serving temperature:** 3° less than room temperature. **Served with:** Grand cru: game and cheese. 1[er] cru: red meat. **Vintages available in 89/90:** 1986-1987.

Characteristics of vintages

1988: Still in casks, tannic, well colored, great keeping wine. **1987:** Very fragrant, light and supple, full-bodied, rich and well balanced. **1986:** Very well colored, tannic, fragrant, good keeping. Price range (pre-tax, ex-warehouse): 10-20 F.F. – 20-30 F.F. – 50-80 F.F. – 80-120 F.F.
Sales in France: 27%. **Export sales:** 63%.
Main trading partners : Belgium, Luxemburg, Denmark, Norway.

References in France

Restaurants: Loiseay (Saulieu), Georges Blanc (Vorras), Jacques Gourmand (Paris), Côte St-Jacques (Joigny).

Abroad

United States

Importers: World Shippers, Philadelphia – Martine's Wines, San Rafael.

Switzerland
Philippine Wehile, Gattehon – Hessvverne, Berne.

Comments

Pierre Amiot's family have been winemakers for 5 generations. Singular or plural.

DOMAINE DUJAC

Jacques Seysses
7, rue de la Bussière – Morey-Saint-Denis
21220 Gevrey-Chambertin
80 34 32 58

Type of vineyard: Family-owned. **Established:** 1967. **Vine stocks:** Pinot Noir. **Average annual production in hectoliters:** 300.
Appellation: Morey, Gevrey 1er Cru "Aux Combottes", Charmes Chambertin, Clos St-Denis, Clos la Roche, Échézeaux, Bonnes Mares. **Type:** Red. **Technique:** Classic, no destemming, 15 to 20 days fermentation with skins, frequent crushing. **Maturing:** 100% new casks, 12 to 16 months, fining with egg whites, non-filtered. **Alcohol content:** 12% to 13%. **Characteristics:** The vinification is based, for the most part, on the aromas and their complexity, sometimes to the detriment of the color. Wines to be aged. **Serving temperature:** 15 to 17°. **Served with:** 1984: roast poultry or white meat. 1983: game, sauces, foie gras or truffles, duck. 1982: red wine sauces, game, terrines. 1985: red meat and sauces (like 1982). **Vintages available in 89/90:** 1986, 1987.

Characteristics of vintages

1986: Very good year, falls somewhere between 1982 and 1985. **1985:** Exceptional year for ageing: ideal between 1995 and 2005. **1984:** Light, fruity year: ideal between 1988 and 1992. **1983:** Excellent but hard: hold until 1993, ideal between 1998 and 2000. **1982:** Good vintage, begin to drink; ideal between 1988 and 1992. Price range (pre-tax, ex-warehouse): Between 80 F.F. and 220 F.F.
Sales volume:
– Retail: 10%. – Restaurants: 10%. – Other: 80% (export).
Sales in France: 20%. **Export sales:** 80%.
Main trading partners : UK, USA, Switzerland, Germany, Japan, Denmark, Canada.

References in France

Restaurants: Restaurant Greuze (Tournus), Bocuse (Lyon), Gagnaire (Saint-Étienne), Père Bise (Talloires), Vivarois (Paris), etc.
Shops: Les Caves de la Madeleine.

Abroad

United States
Chambers & Chambers, San Francisco. Tel: 626-2121 – Frederick Wildman, New York, N.Y. Tel: 288 - 8000.
Shops: Mac-Arthur Beverages, 4877 Mac-Arthur Blvd., Washington, D.C. 20007. Tel: FE8 1433.

Canada
Vintages, Ontario Liquor Board.

The Netherlands
Winjnkoperij Okhuysen, Gierstraat 34-38, Haarlem. Tel: 02402/20064.
Shops: Henri Bloem, Zuidsingel 62, Amerafoort. De-Geus Breitnerlaan, 243-245 Den Haag. Tel: 070 241226.

Japan
Mr. Taguchi, Mitsumi Co. Ltd., 8-7, 6 Chome Ginza, Chuo-Ku, Tokyo 104. Tel: 571 4228.

CLOS DE TART

Société Mommessin - La Grange St-Pierre
BP 504 - 71009 Mâcon
Morey-St-Denis - 21220 Gevrey-Chambertin
85 34 47 74 - Telex: 800 886

Vine stocks: Pinot Noir. **Exposure:** East. **Average annual production in hectoliters:** 135.

Appellation: Clos de Tart. **Type:** Red. **Technique:** Traditional (Burgundy). **Maturing:** In Oak casks for 16 to 18 months - all new casks. **Characteristics:** Wines characterized by the distinction of their aroma and fine tannins. **Serving temperature:** 16°. **Vintages available in 89/90:** 1982, 1984, 1985.

Characteristics of vintages

1985: Vanilla and violet aromas, fine and elegant tannins, no astringency. **1982:** Fine, elegant vintage, to be consumed within the next 5 years. Price range (pre-tax, ex-warehouse): Over 160 F.F. **Sales volume:**
- Retail: 40%.
- Restaurants: 60%.
Sales in France: 40%. **Export sales:** 60%.
Main trading partners : Germany, USA, Canada, UK, Switzerland.

References in France

Restaurants: In all the better French Restaurants with Michelin, or Gault & Millau stars.
Shops: Fauchon - Paris, plus other quality wine cellars.

CHAMBOLLE-MUSIGNY

JACQUES FREDERIC MUGNIER

Frédéric Mugnier
Château de Chambolle-Musigny
21220 Chambolle-Musigny
80 62 85 39

Type of vineyard: Family-owned. **Established:** 1870. **Vine stocks:** 100% Pinot Noir. **Average annual production in hectoliters:** 120.

Appellation: Musigny (Grand Cru), Bonnes Mares (Grand Cru), Chambolle-Musigny 1er Cru, Les Amoureuses, Les Fuées, Les Plantes. **Type:** Red. **Technique:** Traditional. **Maturing:** In oak casks. **Alcohol content:** 13%. **Characteristics:** Vinification which tries to preserve the characteristic delicacy of the Chambolle wines without losing the depth and richness expected of a great Burgundy. **Serving temperature:** 16 to 17°. **Vintages available in 89/90:** 1986 and 1987.

Characteristics of vintages

1987: Fine and fruity, very successful. **1986:** Dense, long keeping. Exceptional red grands crus.
Sales in France: 25%.
Export sales: 75%.
Main trading partners : USA, UK, Switzerland.

References in France

Restaurants: Troisgros.

Abroad

United Kingdom
Haynes, Hanson & Clark, 17 Lettice Street, London.

Comments

Excellent winemaker attached to the great Burgundy tradition. Superb wines, typical, rich and fragrant.

HUDELOT NOELLAT

Alain Hudelot
21640 Vougeot
80 62 85 17

Type of vineyard: family-owned. **Established:** 1960. **Number of employees:** 4. **Vine stocks:** Exclusively Pinot Noir. **Soil:** Chalky clay. **Exposure:** Hillsides facing East. **Average annual production in hectoliters:** 30 to 35 hl/hectare.

Appellation: Richebourg, Romanée St. Vivant, Clos Vougeot, Vosne Romanée Suchots, Vosne Romanée Malconsorts, Vosne Romanée Beaumonts, Nuits St. Georges Murgers, Chambolle Musigny, Charmes, Bourgogne. **Type:** Red. **Technique:** Traditional, fermentation on skins 15 to 18 days, 30% destemming. **Maturing:** 228 liter Oak casks. **Characteristics:** Fine, fruity wines, lots of fragrance, very long. Can be kept from 15 to 30 years, according to the vintage. **Served with:** Game, red meat. **Vintages available in 89/90:** 87,88.

Characteristics of vintages

1988: Well-colored, fragrant, full, tannic wines with a future. Can be kept a long time. **1987:** A vintage with a beautiful color, very fruity. Will be ready to drink in 5 to 15 years. Average pre-tax, ex-warehouse price: Bougogne between 30 F.F. and 50 F.F.; Chambolle Musigny and Vosne Romanée between 50 F.F. and 80 F.F.; Premier Cru – Suchots, Murgers, Charmes, Beaumonts, Malconsorts between 80 F.F. and 120 F.F.; Grands Crus – Richebourg, Romanée St. Vivant, Clos Vougeot more than 160 F.F.
Sales volume:
– Retail: 30%. – Restaurants: 10%.
Export sales: 60%.
Main trading partners : Switzerland, UK, USA, Netherlands, Belgium, Germany.

References in France

Restaurants: Crotet-Levernois.

Comments

The vineyard was founded in 1960, starting with several hectares inherited from the owner's father and enlarged over the years by additional purchases. In 1978, grands crus from the Domaine Charles Noellat (grandfather of Mrs. Alain Hudelot) were added. Today, the estate consists of a dozen hectares of vineyards in the communes of Chambolle, Musigny, Vougeot, Vosne Romanée and Nuits St. Georges.

Canada

Société des Alcools du Québec.

Comments

Excellent family enterprise (for 100 years), very much attached to tradition. The Chambolle-Musigny wines are typical and well bred.

SIGAUT MAURICE

Chambolle Musigny 21220 Gevrey-Chambertin
80 62 85 47

Established: Very old. **Vine stocks:** Pinot. **Soil:** Chalky. **Exposure:** East.

Appellation: Chambolle Musigny 1er Cru, Morey St Denis 1er Cru. **Type:** Red. **Maturing:** oak casks. **Alcohol content:** 13%. **Serving temperature:** Cooler in summer than in winter. **Vintages available in 89/90:** 1986, 1987, 1988.

Characteristics of vintages

1988: Very well balanced, a good year, well colored, full, to be kept. **1987:** Agreeable, supple, a bit light, very pleasant to drink now. Price range (pre-tax, ex-warehouse): between 50 and 80 F.F.

Sales volume:

- Wholesale: 40%. - Retail: 20%. - Restaurants: 5%.
- Other: 35% French and foreign dealers.

Main trading partners: Switzerland, Belgium, United Kingdom, United States, Canada.

References in France

Restaurants: Sommellerie (Gevrey 21), Villa des Fleurs (Talloires 74), Chez Henri (Romainville 93230).
Shops: Conseillerie des Tonneliers (Beaune).

Abroad

United Kingdom

Friarwood, 26 New Kings, London. Pierre Hourlier, 390 Burton Road, Derby.

Switzerland

Loew et Cie. (Neuchâtel). Yenny (Bevaix).

J. SERVELLE-TACHOT

J. Servelle-Tachot
21220 Chambolle-Musigny
80 62 86 91

Type of vineyard: Family-owned. **Vine stocks:** Pinot Noir. **Soil:** Shallow iron bearing red clay soil. **Exposure:** East, South-East. **Average annual production in hectoliters:** 35 to 40 hl/ha.
Appellation: Chambolle Musigny, Chambolle Les Charmes, Clos Vougeot, Bourgogne Aligote. **Type:** Red, White. **Technique:** Traditional, in open tanks. **Maturing:** In oak vats (2.28 hl). **Characteristics:** Very harmonious, fruity, fragrant, high tannic content. **Serving temperature:** 16°. **Vintages available in 89/90:** 1986, 1987, 1988.

Characteristics of vintages

1988: Great vintage. Red: very well structured, lots of fruit, very promising. **1987:** Red: less structured, but breed and elegance. **1986:** Red: rich bouquet and very high tannic content.
Sales in France: 50%.
Export sales: 50%.
Main trading partners: Switzerland, Belgium, Germany, Netherlands.

References in France

Restaurants: In a number of great restaurants in France and abroad.

Comments

Successful vineyard, noted for its Chambolle-Musigny wines, well-made, typical of this great appellation.

MUSIGNY
APPELLATION MUSIGNY CONTROLÉE
CUVÉE VIEILLES VIGNES
Domaine Comte Georges de VOGÜÉ
CHAMBOLLE-MUSIGNY (CÔTE D'OR)

Réserve numérotée Nº 07688 750 ml — 1985 PRODUCE OF FRANCE — *Mis en bouteilles au domaine SCE du Domaine Comte Georges de Vogüé*

Sté d'Exploitation du Domaine
Comte Georges de Vogüé
21220 CHAMBOLLE MUSIGNY

MUSIGNY: Grand cru - is considered one of the most distinguished wines in all of Burgundy wine with a perfect combination of balance, elegance and finesse. It has a vigor, a firmness of body and aroma, in which the bouquet of blackcurrant, sweet-brier and raspberry is set off by a little touch of pepper. It is a wine that is balanced and harmonious yet supple. It is often said that it is the foremost of the Côte de Nuits wines.
BONNES MARES: Grand cru - is a more substantial wine, rich and well-balanced while remaining fine and distinguished.
CHAMBOLLE MUSIGNY LES AMOUREUSES: 1st cru - is more feminine, and seductive. It is known as a supple wine with the silky texture of fine lace.
CHAMBOLLE MUSIGNY: The "village" appellation is one of the finest of the Côte de Nuits wines. It is full, round and the most elegant of all the Burgundies.

DOMAINE COMTE GEORGES DE VOGUE

Baronne Bertrand de Ladoucette
21220 Chambolle-Musigny
80 62 86 25

Type of vineyard: Family-owned. **Established:** 1450. **Vine stocks:** Red: Pinot Noir. White: Chardonnay. **Soil:** Chalky clay. **Exposure:** South-East. **Average annual production in hectoliters:** 250 to 300.
Appellation: Musigny, Bonnes Mares, Amoureuses, Chambolle-Musigny, Musigny Blanc. **Type** Red, White. **Technique:** Oak vats. **Maturing:** Oak casks. **Characteristics:** Musigny: elegant and full. Bonnes Mares: more solid, rich and well balanced. Amoureuses: delicate. Chambolle-Musigny: typical. Côtes de Nuits: fine and elegant. Musigny Blanc: exclusive. **Serving temperature:** Red: around 15°. White: cool. **Served with:** Musigny: red meat, poultry. Bonnes Mares: game, meat in sauce. Amoureuses: light meat. Chambolle-Musigny: first course, meat. Musigny (white): fish, shellfish. **Vintages available in 89/90:** 1982, 1984, 1985, 1986, 1987.

Characteristics of vintages

1987: Still in casks, good structure, very promising. **1986:** Round, delicate, fruity – a remarkable Musigny blanc. **1985:** Well structured, elegant. **Other:** 1984: Balanced, should be aged for 5 years. 1983: full-bodied, quite masculine but very delicate. 1982: Goes down well, fruity, to be drunk in 2 to 3 years. Note: a few bottles of older vintages are available: Superb Chambolle-Musigny, Bonnes Mares and Musigny. Price range (pre-tax, ex-warehouse): 95 to 280 F.F.
Sales in France: 20%.
Export sales: 80%.
Main trading partners : Germany, UK, Belgium, Canada, USA, Netherlands, Italy, Japan, Switzerland.

• Classification of the great Bordeaux wines in 1988. The ratings of Châteaux Lascombes (Margaux), Mazeris-Bellevue (Canon-Fronsac) and Haut-Maco (Côtes-de-Bourg) are improving, as well as those of certain other surprising crus (Châteaux Trocard, Melin, Gazin, Chantegriue, Gloria, La Croix-Saint-André, Fombrauge...). See the 1988 Classification in the Chapter on Bordeaux wines.

HERVÉ SIGAUT

Hervé Sigaut
Chambolle-Musigny – 21220 Gevrey-Chambertin
80 62 80 28

Type of vineyard: Family-owned. **Established:** 3 generations. **Vine stocks:** Pinot Noir and some Aligoté. **Soil:** Chalky. **Exposure:** Southeast. **Average annual production in hectoliters:** 30 to 40 hl/hectare.
Appellation: Chambolle, Chambolle 1er Cru, Pommard. **Type:** Red, Burgundy Aligoté. **Technique:** Traditional, in wooden wats. **Maturing:** Oak casks. **Characteristics:** Fine, round and vinous. A beautiful color and rich in fragrance. They are typical and represent the village well. **Served with:** The Chambolle is a delicate wine. Many dishes go with it, provided that they are very, very fine. This wine can't stand heavy cooking. **Vintages available in 89/90:** 1985, 1986.

Characteristics of vintages

1986: Fine and fragrant. Excellent 1er Cru. **1985:** Excellent. It has all the qualities necessary to make a very good wine in 2 or 3 years. Remarkable Chambolle 1er Cru, dense and full.

VOSNE-ROMANÉE

DOMAINE FRANÇOIS GERBET

Marie Andrée & Chantal Gerbet
Vosne Romanée
80 61 07 85

Type of vineyard: Family-owned Agricultural Association. **Established:** 1908. **Vine stocks:** Pinot. **Soil:** Chalky. **Average annual production in hectoliters:** 600.

GRAND VIN de BOURGOGNE
MIS EN BOUTEILLE A LA PROPRIÉTÉ
Vosne-Romanée 1er Cru
Les Petits Monts
APPELLATION CONTROLÉE
Domaine François Gerbet
75 cl
Marie-Andrée et Chantal Gerbet
12,8% vol.
PROPRIÉTAIRES-RÉCOLTANTS A VOSNE-ROMANÉE (COTE-D'OR)

Appellation: Vosne Romanée "Aux Reas". **Type:** Red. **Technique:** Traditional, temperature control. **Maturing:** in casks. **Characteristics:** fragrant, fine, supple. **Serving temperature:** 16 to 18°. **Served with:** Poultry, white meat, roasts. **Vintages available in 89/90:** 1986, 1987.

Characteristics of vintages

1987: Small fruit fragrance, lingering flavor. **1986:** Cherry color, strong red berry flavor. Price range (pre-tax, ex-warehouse): 50 to 80 F.F.

Sales volume:
- Retail: 80%.

Sales in France: 90%.
Export sales: 10%.
Main trading partners : Belgium, United Kingdom, Switzerland, Germany.

Comments

The domain was created in 1947 by François Gerbet, who had married a daughter of the winemaker Sirugue. It includes 15 hectares... Clos Vougeot. The property was taken over by François Gerbet's two daughters – who themselves produce, with considerable care, high quality wines.

DOMAINE RENÉ ENGEL

Michèle ou Philippe Engel (Mother and son)
Vosne-Romanée – 21700 Nuits-Saint-Georges
80 61 10 54

Type of vineyard: Agricultural Association. **Established:** 1982. **Number of employees:** 4. **Vine stocks:** Pinot. **Exposure:** East – West. **Average annual production in hectoliters:** 300.
Appellation: Clos-Vougeot. **Technique:** Wooden fermentation. **Maturing:** In casks (1/3 renewed). **Characteristics:** Deep color, soft and full, presence of tannins ensuring good ageing. Fruit aroma (blackcurrant, raspberry), rich and unctuous, superb wine. **Serving temperature:** 18°. **Served with:** Red meat, perfect with cheese. **Vintages available in 89/90:** 1987, 1988.

Characteristics of vintages

1988: Still a bit to early to tell, but already possesses all the requisites of a good bootle: lots of aromas, a lovely color, good structure. **1987:** Well-balanced, fruity aroma, very typical Pinot Noir, depth of color, sound, lingering taste. **1986:** Good year. Wines for keeping. Supple, firm, pronounced bouquet. **1985:** Excellent year, good keeping. Rich and structured.
Sales volume:
- Wholesale: 20%. – Retail: 40%. – Restaurants: 10%.
- Other: 30% (export).

Sales in France: 50%. **Export sales:** 50%.
Main trading partners : Germany, UK, Switzerland, Netherlands, USA, Japan, Australia.

References in France

Restaurants: Alain Chapel (Mionnay), Hôtel de la Côte d'Or (Nuits-St-Georges), Hôtel Marchal (Les 3 Épis), The Ritz Hôtel, place Vendôme (Paris), Carlton (Cannes).

Abroad

United States
Prestige wine corp. New York, Grape Expectations, 4097 Harlan Street, Emeryville, California 94608. Binday Imports, Pearson's wine Washington, 7826 Eastern Avenue, N.W. 410 Washington. Direct Import Wine, 535 E. Oakton, Des Plaines, Ill. 60015.

United Kingdom
Heyman Brothers Ltd., 130 Ebury Street, London SW1W 900.

Germany
Van Riesen, Falkenstr. 21, Ascencio, 7813 Staufen-Grunern, 8 Munich 90.

The Netherlands
Erman, Westraat, 6 4571 Axel.

Far East
Takenouchi Tokyo, Hatta Shoten Ota-Ku Tokyo 143.

Australia
Murray D., Tyrrell Tyrell's Vineyards Ptd Ltd, Pokoblin, N.S.W. 2321.

Switzerland

Haun-Rickli, Haltingerstrasse 101, 4021 Basel. Hirchengraben Vins, Zurich.

DOMAINE LAMARCHE

François Lamarche
Vosne Romanée, 21700 Nuits-Saint-Georges
80 61 07 94

Type of vineyard: Family-owned. **Established:** Last century (4th generation). **Number of employees:** 5. **Vine stocks:** Pinot Noir 100%. **Soil:** Chalky clay. **Exposure:** East. **Average annual production in hectoliters:** 250. **Appellation:** Vosne-Romanée La Grande Rue, Clos-de-Vougeot, Grands-Échezeaux, Échezeaux, Vosne-Romanée Malconsorts, Vosne-Romanée-Chaumes, Vosne-Romanée-Suchots. **Type:** Red. **Technique:** Traditional, under the supervision of an œnologist. **Maturing:** In oak casks (2 years) about 40% new. **Alcohol content:** 12 to 13.5 depending on the year. **Characteristics:** Feminine, elegant, soft and rich, wait minimum of 5 to 6 years before drinking. **Serving temperature:** 15°. **Served with:** White meat, fine game, or light cheese (Citeaux). **Vintages available in 89/90:** 1984 an 1986. 1987 in September 1989.

Characteristics of vintages

1988: Not available until September 1990. **1987:** Very small harvest – excellent year. **1986:** Good quality harvest, similar to, but better than 1982. Wait till 1992-93 for tasting. **1985:** Exceptional vintage – unfortunately depleted. **Other:** 1984 – excellent quality price ratio for this Burgundy vintage. Price range (pre-tax, ex-warehouse): 25 to 220 F.F. according to vintage and appellation.

Sales volume:
– Wholesale: 5 to 10%. – Retail: 95 to 90%.

Sales in France: 50%.

Export sales: 50%.

References in France

Restaurants: Le Pré Catelan (Paris 16th), Aux Armes de Bretagne (Paris 14th), Lenôtre, Pavillon Élysée (Paris 8th). *Shops:* L'Arbre à Vin (Paris 12th), Grandes Caves (Clichy), Caves Nôtre-Dame (Montpellier), La Cave (Lorient).

Abroad

United Kingdom

Heyman Brothers, London. Lay and Wheeler, Colchester. F. and E. May, London.

Germany

Fegers und Unterberg, Köln. Wahnschaffe, Kleve.

Belgium

Young Charly, Merksem (Antwerpen).

Canada

LCBO for Ontario. SAQ for Quebec.

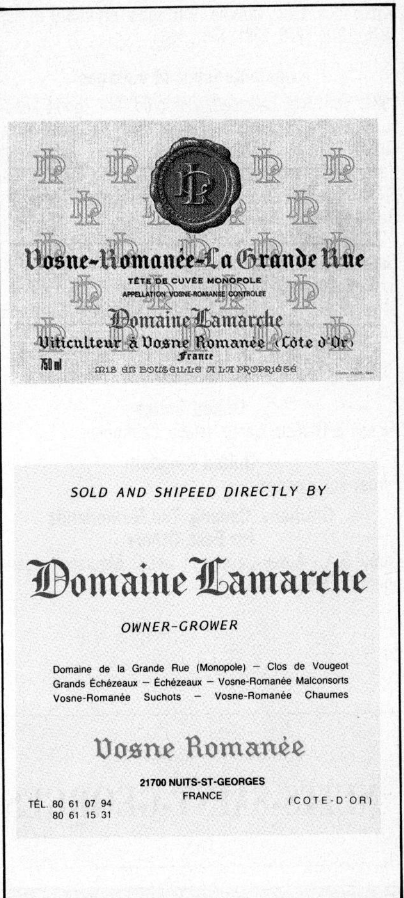

Vosne-Romanée-La Grande Rue
TÊTE DE CUVÉE MONOPOLE
APPELLATION VOSNE-ROMANÉE CONTROLÉE
Domaine Lamarche
Viticulteur à Vosne Romanée (Côte d'Or)
France
750 ml
SOLD AND SHIPEED DIRECTLY BY
Domaine Lamarche
OWNER-GROWER
Domaine de la Grande Rue (Monopole) – Clos de Vougeot
Grands Échézeaux – Échézeaux – Vosne-Romanée Malconsorts
Vosne-Romanée Suchots – Vosne-Romanée Chaumes
Vosne Romanée
21700 NUITS-ST-GEORGES
FRANCE
TÉL. 80 61 07 94
80 61 15 31
(COTE-D'OR)

SOCIÉTÉ CIVILE DU DOMAINE DE LA ROMANÉE CONTI

Mme Bize-Leroy and M. de Villaine, managers
21670 Vosne-Romanée
80 61 04 57 – Telex: 350 176

Established: 1942. **Vine stocks:** Pinot Noir and Chardonnay. **Soil:** Clay with calcium carbonate. **Exposure:** East. **Average annual production in hectoliters:** 700. **Appellation:** Red: Romanée-Conti, La Tache, Richebourg, Grands Échézeaux, Romanée St-Vivant. White: Montrachet. **Technique:** Traditional. **Maturing:** In new oak casks. **Alcohol content:** 13%. **Characteristics:** The most highly regarded wines on this planet... they merit their reputation, combining structure, fullness, elegance and balance. **Serving temperature:** 14° to 15°. **Served**

with: Rich, fancy cuisine. **Vintages available in 89/90:** 1975, 1978, 1979, 1981, 1982, 1984.

Characteristics of vintages

1984: Very well-balanced, well-bred, fine, good keeping, successful vintage. **1982:** Elegant, fine. Seductive vintage. **Other:** 1978 and 1979: really great vintages, superb, rich in flavor. 1981: still tannic, a beautiful wine for the future. Price range (pre-taxe, ex-warehouse): Over 160 F.F.
Sales volume:
– Wholesale: 100%.
Sales in France: 30%.
Export sales: 70%.
Main trading partners : USA, UK, Japan, Switzerland, Germany.

Abroad

United States
Wilson & Daniels, Santa Helena, California.

United Kingdom
Percey-Fox, London,

Germany, Canada, The Netherlands
Far East, Others
Leroy S.A., Auxey-Davens – 21190 Meursault (general agent for France also).

NUITS-SAINT-GEORGES

ROBERT DUBOIS ET FILS

Régis Dubois
Prémeaux-Prissey 21700 Nuits-Saint-Georges
80 62 30 61

Type of vineyard: Family Agricultural Association. **Established:** 1969. **Number of employees:** 4. **Vine stocks:** Pinot Noir de Bourgogne. **Soil:** Chalky clay. **Exposure:** South and South-East. **Average annual production in hectoliters:** 800.
Appellation: Nuits 1er Cru "Clos des Argillières", Nuits 1er Cru "Les Porêts", Nuits-Saint-Georges, Chambolle-Musigny, Vosne-Romanée, Côtes de Nuits-Villages, Savigny-lès-Beaune, Beaune, Bourgogne Rouge, Bourgogne Rosé, Bourgogne Passetoutgrain, Bourgogne Aligoté, Bourgogne Hautes Côtes de Beaune Blanc. **Type:** Red, White, Rosé. **Technique:** Traditional with temperature control. **Maturing:** 6 months in new oak casks, 12 months in vats. **Alcohol content:** 13%. **Characteristics:** Red: good color, rich and well-balanced, with character, fragrance of red fruit, to be aged. White and Rosé: fruity, agreeable, youthful. **Serving temperature:** White and Rosé: 5 to 6°. Red: 15 to 17° depending on age and appellation. **Served with:** White and Rosé: delicatessen and fish. Red: poultry, game and red meat as well as low fat cheese.

Characteristics of vintages

1988: Great wines, well colored and very well balanced, to be kept. **1987:** Very fragrant, well constructed, lovely color. **1986:** Similar to last year.
Sales volume:
– Retail: 70%. – Restaurants: 5%. – Other: 25% (agents and distributors).
Sales in France: 50%.
Export sales: 50%.
Main trading partners : United States, United Kingdom, Germany, Belgium, Switzerland, Luxemburg, Netherlands.

References in France

Restaurants: Hostellerie de Levernois (Beaune), Hôtel-Restaurant de la Côte d'Or (Nuits-Saint-Georges) and, soon, the Relais Châteaux-Hôtels de France.

Abroad

United States
Château and Estate Wines Company, Joseph Seagram, New York.

United Kingdom
Fields Wine and John Gwen, Chelsea.

Germany
J. Buhler, Cologne. Maison Sichel, Mayence.
Shops: Ernst Simon, Schwerte.

Switzerland
La Vinothèque de Bourg, 17, Chéneau de Bourg, 1003 Lausanne.

Belgium
Le Vignoble M. Cardjmann, avenue de Port 104, B1210 Brussels.

Canada
Vin Sélect International, M. Gilles Duclos, 3765 Maricourt, Trois Rivières Ouest, Québec.

The Netherlands
Wijnkoperij de Oude Warande, Berkel-Enschot.

Comments

The Domaine R. Dubois et Fils has developed over three generations, since the end of the last century. It covers 432 ouvrées (an ancient land measure), on excellent parcels in the Côte de Nuits and Côte de Beaune regions, corresponding to 18 hectares in a varied choice of appellations that complement each other well.

• *Read labels carefully – An indication to watch out for: "Bottled in the 'region' of production", which often refers to a blend of wines from several producers and not just one.*

R. DUBOIS & SONS *Winemakers*

Three generations…
and a domain

Combination of
technique and tradition
FOR A TOP QUALITY HARVEST

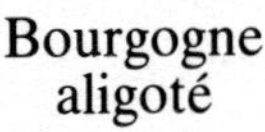

Bourgogne
passetoutgrain

Bourgogne
rosé

Côte de nuits
village

Bourgogne
Haute-Côte
de beaune blanc

Beaune

Vosne-
romanée

Chambolle-
musigny

Nuits-
saint-georges

Nuits-
saint-georges
1er cru

Savigny-
les-beaune

R. DUBOIS & SONS

Premeaux-Prissey

Tél. 80.62.30.61

JEAN-CLAUDE BOISSET

Jean-Claude Boisset
rue des Frères Montgolfier
21700 Nuits-Saint-Georges
80 61 00 06 – Telex: 350 814

Type of vineyard: Corporation. **Established:** 1961. **Vine stocks:** Bourgogne Rouge: Pinot Noir 100%; Bourgogne Blanc: Chardonnay 100%; Beaujolais: Gamay 100%. **Average annual production in hectoliters:** 110,000. **Appellation:** All Beaujolais appellations and 100 Bourgogne appellations. **Type:** Red, white, rosé. **Maturing:** ageing in oak casks (Bourgogne wines). **Vintages available in 89/90:** 1935 to 1988.

Characteristics of vintages

1988: Very promising. Well balanced wines, for keeping.
1987: White: very successful. Red: more supple, fruity.
1986: Great year for red and white. Fine evolution.
Price range (pre-tax, ex-warehouse): 20 to 30 F.F. – 30 to 50 F.F. – 80 to 120 F.F.
Sales volume:
– Wholesale: 40%. – Retail: 10%. – Restaurants: 20%. – Other: 30 %.
Sales in France: 60%.
Export sales: 40%.
Main trading partners: United Kingdom, Switzerland, USA, Germany, Belgium.

References in France

Restaurants: Le Jules Verne, Cazaudehore, Le Grand Véfour, Pavillon Montsouris, Drouant.

Abroad

United States
Jean-Claude Boisset Wines Inc. – Lion Imports – 1520 Custer Avenue, San Francisco CA. 94124 (USA).

United Kingdom
Jean-Claude Boisset UK LTD – 18 Mulfords Hill – Tadley – Basingstoke, Hampshire RG 26 6 JEB.B. Tel: 44 73 56 33 58.

Switzerland
Jean-Claude Boisset S.A. – 134, rue des Prés – 2503 Bienne.

Belgium
Martini & Rossi, rue Van Den Boogaerde 108 – 1020 Brussels Tel: 32 24 27 43 70.

Comments

The Jean-Claude Boisset company was created in 1961 by its present director. Despite its relatively recent origin, it stands today among the first Burgundy houses, combining the Burgundy tradition with technical innovations. It is the exclusive distributor for the wines of the Domaine Claudine Deschamps, a 20 hectare vineyard producing prestigious wines, among which are Corton, Charmes Chambertin, Bonnes Mares, Nuits Saint Georges 1er Cru Les Damodes, Gevrey-Chambertin 1er Cru Bel Air.

• *The price scandal, botched up vintages and compromised reputations: the truth and nothing but the truth (see Bordeaux, Provence and Châteauneuf-du-Pape Classifications).*

MAISON FAIVELEY

BP 9 - 21702 Nuits-Saint-Georges Cedex
80 61 04 55 - Telex: FAIWINE 350 542 F

Vine stocks: Chardonnay, Pinot Noir.
Appellation: Musigny, Echezeaux, Nuits-St-Georges Chambertin, Rully. **Type:** Red, white. **Technique:** Traditional - long fermentation. **Maturing:** 12 - 18 months in oak casks (1/2 renewed each year). **Serving temperature:** White: 12°-14° - Red: 16°-18°. **Served with:** The entire meal - rich food. **Vintages available in 89/90:** 1983, 1984, 1985, 1986.

Characteristics of vintages

1986: Good year for reds, and very promising for whites. **1985:** Excellent reds, especially Chambolle, Musigny, Nuits-St-Georges. Rich color, fragrant, firm and well-balanced Corton and Gevrey-Chambertin - good for ageing.
Main trading partners: Germany, UK, Australia, Belgium, Canada, Denmark, Netherlands, Ireland, Japan, Luxemburg, Singapore, Switzerland, USA, Venezuela.

P. DE MARCILLY FRÈRES

Olivier de Marcilly
Rue des Frères Montgolfier
21700 Nuits-Saint-Georges
80 61 14 26 - Telex: 351 304 F

Established: 1849.

Appellation: Bourgogne Marcilly Première. **Type:** Red. **Technique:** Long fermentation on skins. **Maturing:** In oak casks. **Alcohol content:** 13%. **Characteristics:** Very good development potential. Full bodied, silky texture, natural and clean, rich and complex. **Serving temperature:** 17-18°. **Served with:** Red meat, game, cheese. **Vintages available in 89/90:** 1983-1985.

Characteristics of vintages

1985: Excellent year - Colored, well made, good keeping.
Other: 1983: Red berry fragrance, clean, rich attack, fine balance. Price range (pre-tax, ex-warehouse): 30 to 50 F.F.
Sales volume:
- Retail: 25%. - Restaurants: 75%. - Other: 5% (fine delicatessen and cellars, etc.).
Sales in France: 30%.
Export sales: 70%.
Main trading partners: Scandinavia, United Kingdom, Netherlands, Switzerland.

References in France

Restaurants: Loiseau (Saulieu), Pic (Valence), Lameloise (Chagny), Lasserre (Paris).

Abroad

England
Churton Cousins - Rossett, 0244 571333.
Switzerland
Bindella - Zurich - 1027 66060.
Canada
Saq - Montreal - 514 8735719.
The Netherlands
Huinck - Amsterdam - 020 260297.
Others
South Africa; Tayler-Westville - 031 82 11 28.

Comments

Founded in 1849, P. de Marcilly Frères has never stopped improving the reputation of its Burgundy wines. Since 1915 the Bourgogne Marcilly Premiere have been extensively exported to grace the best tables of the world.

MAISON MOILLARD-GRIVOT

Denis Thomas
2, rue François-Mignotte
B.P. 6 - 21700 Nuits-Saint-Georges
80 61 03 34

Type of vineyard: Family-owned. **Vine stocks:** Pinot Noir and Chardonnay.
Appellation: Vosne-Romanée, Nuits-Saint-Georges, Corton, Romanée. **Type:** White. **Technique:** Traditional. **Maturing:** In casks. **Characteristics:** Remarkable House which offers exceptionnal Burgundy Grands Crus, in white (splendid Corton-Charlemagne) as well as red (Vosne-Romanée "Les Malconsoris") vinified with a master's hand, for very long keeping, dense and complete. **Serving temperature:** White: 12° - Red: 15°. **Served with:** Rich cuisine, fish cooked in sauce, meat, game. **Vintages available in 89/90:** 1982, 1983, 1984, 1985 and 1986.

Characteristics of vintages

1986: Exceptional whites, soft, supple and harmonious. Very promising reds. **1985:** Reds that keep well, rich color, very aromatic. Must be aged. **1984:** Remarkably well mastered vintage. **1983:** Extraordinary reds, much like the 78, rich and structured, complex bouquet, good for ageing. Do not hesitate. To invest.

References in France

Shops: L'Amour du Vin, 94, rue Saint-Dominique 75007 Paris. Tél: 45 56 12 94.

PIERRE PONNELLE

Michel Gabaut
5, rue du Moulin, B.P. 19
21700 Nuits-Saint-Georges
Tel: 80 61 22 41 – Telex: 351617 F ECVNUIT

Type of vineyard: Corporation. **Established:** 1875. **Vine stocks:** Pinot Noir, Chardonnay. **Soil:** Chalky clay. **Exposure:** East, South-East. **Average annual production in hectoliters:** 35 to 40 hl/ha.
Type: Red, white. **Technique:** Temperature control. **Maturing:** In casks. **Alcohol content:** 12.5%. **Serving temperature:** White: 8°. Red: 12-14°. **Served with:** White: shellfish, fish. Red: meat in sauce. **Vintages available in 89/90:** 1981 to 1987.

PRODUCE OF FRANCE
TRADE MARK
MUSIGNY
GRAND CRU
Appellation Contrôlée
DOMAINE PONNELLE
75cl
mis en bouteille par
13%Vol.
Maison Pierre Ponnelle, Négociant à Nuits-Saint-Georges, Côte-d'Or, France.

Characteristics of vintages

1988: Exceptional year. **1987:** Limited but interesting production. **1986:** Elegant wines, fruity aromas, forthcoming. **1985:** Deep color, rich aromas, tannic, a great year.

Sales in France: 5%.
Export sales: 95%.
Main trading partners : United Kingdom, Switzerland, Benelux countries, Germany, Italy, USA, Canada, Japan, Denmark, Netherlands, Australia.

References in France

Restaurants: Restaurants with Michelin Stars.
Shops: Shops specializing in fine products.

Abroad

United Kingdom

Hayward Bros. Wines Ltd., 40 Crimscott St. London SE1. Tel: 1237 0576. Bucktrout P.O. Box 27, Waterloo House, St. Peter Port Guernsey. Tel: 481 24 44.

Germany

Gerwig Import Solitudeallee 123 D-7014 Kornwestheim.

Canada

Saq, LCBO, BCLSDB, Le Marchand de Vin, 1538 Ouest, rue Sherbrooke – Suite 510, Montreal, Québec H36 IL5 – Allan Marketing Group, 13020 Delf Place Richmond, British Columbia.

The Netherlands

Wijnimport Rijkmans b.v. Helling 16, NL 9202 Drachten. Tel: 5120 30 730.

Comments

Established in 1875, the company owns the Abbaye St. Martin in Beaune and property in the communes of: Clos de Vougeot, Bonnes Mares, Charmes Chambertin, Chambolle Musigny les Argillières, Musigny, Corton Clos du Roi, Beaune Grèves, Beaune Clos du Roi and Vougeot le Prieuré.

REMORIQUET HENRI ET GILLES

Henri Remoriquet
25, rue de Charmois – 21700 Nuits-St-Georges
80 61 08 17

Type of vineyard: Family-owned. **Established:** 1890. **Number of employees:** 1. **Vine stocks:** Aligoté (Burgundy Aligoté), Gamay and Pinot (Passetoutgrain), Pinot Noir. **Soil:** Clay with calcium carbonate on Bathonian limestone. **Exposure:** Southeast. **Average annual production in hectoliters:** 350.
Appellation: Burgundy, Haute Côtes de Nuits, Nuits-St-Georges, Nuits St-Georges 1er Cru. **Type:** Red. **Technique:** Long fermentation with skins (14 to 18 days), grapes partly destemmed. **Maturing:** In Oak casks, 1/4 to 1/3 renewed each year. **Alcohol content:** 12.5% to 13.5% according to the appellation and vintage. **Characteristics:** Quite tannic, to be aged, need several years to develop fully. **Serving temperature:** 16° to 17°. **Served with:** Red meat, game, cheese. **Vintages available in 89/90:** 1984, 1985.

Characteristics of vintages

1986: Good year, comparable to 1979. **1985:** Great year, but to be aged. Must wait 4 to 5 years (10 years for the 1st cru). **1984:** Average year, can be appreciated as of 1988 while waiting for the 1985. Price range (pre-tax, ex-warehouse): Between 20 F.F. and 80 F.F.
Sales volume:
– Wholesale: 40%. – Retail: 27%. – Restaurants: 3%. – Other: 30% (export).
Sales in France: 70%.
Export sales: 30%.
Main trading partners : Benelux countries, UK, Germany, Switzerland, USA.

MAISON CHARLES VIENOT

Georges Legrand - General Manager
Jean-François Curie - Export Manager
5, quai Dumorey, B.P. 19
21700 Nuits St-Georges
80 62 31 05 – Telex: ECVNUIT 351 617 F
Fax: (33) 80 61 30 46

Type of vineyard: Corporation. **Established:** 1735. **Number of employees:** 44. **Vine stocks:** Pinot Noir. **Soil:** Conglomerate, chalk and clay **Exposure:** East.

Appellation: Nuits Saint-Georges, Corvées Pagets. **Type:** Red. **Technique:** Traditional. **Maturing:** Oak casks, 25% new. **Characteristics:** Deep color, well-balanced, great potential for evolution. **Serving temperature:** 14° to 15°. **Served with:** Burgundy specialties: Morvan Ham on lees, Nuitonne Style Ham, fish in red wine, fish stew, roasted red meat, poultry in sauce, Guinea Hen ragout, Coq au Vin, game, wild boar, venison, cheese. **Vintages available in 89/90:** 1982, 1983, 1984, 1986.

Characteristics of vintages

1986: Very deep purple-violet color, almost inky, very promising vintage. **1984:** Brilliant and limpid ruby color, successful vintage. **1983:** Intense ruby color, still firm, to be aged. **1982:** Brilliant ruby color. Price range (pre-tax, ex-warehouse): Between 80 and 120 F.F.

Sales volume:
– Wholesale: 3%. – Retail: 15%. – Restaurants: 27%.
– Other: Airlines, export.

Sales in France: 45%. **Export sales:** 55%.
Main trading partners: UK, Belgium, Japan, Switzerland, Denmark.

References in France

Restaurants: 150 restaurants with Michelin Stars.

Abroad

United States

Lion Imports, 1520 Custer Avenue, San Francisco, CA. Tel. (415) 957 9716.

United Kingdom

Harvey John & Sons ltd., Whitchurch Lane, Bristol BS99 7JE. Tel. 0272 836161.

Germany

La Petite France, M. Sindezingue, Florentiusgraben 29, 5300 Bonn 1. Tel. 228 691388. Weltenburger Vinothek, Klostergut Buchhof, 8423 Abensberg. Tel. 9441 12361.

The Netherlands

Amsterdamse Wijnkoperij, Browersgraacht 222-234, 1013 HE Amsterdam. Tel. 26 56 52. Peters Wijnagenturen, Drommedarisstraat 46, 6531 Nijmegen.

Japan

Nikka Whisky Co. Ltd., 4-31 Minami Aoyoama 5 Chome, Minato Ku, Tokyo 107, Japan. Tel. 03 498 0331.

Denmark

Importers: Kjaer & Sommerfeldt, Ole Larsen, GL Mont 4, 1117 Copenhagen. Tel. (01) 11 13 05. St Gertruds.

Comments

Charles Vienot is the originator of the most beautiful wine list contest for French restaurants.

CÔTES DE BEAUNE

LADOIX-SERRIGNY

DOMAINE PRIN PÈRE ET FILS

Louis Prin
Rue de Serrigny, 21550 Ladoix Serrigny
80 26 40 63

Type of vineyard: Family-owned. **Established:** 3 generations. **Number of employees:** 2 part time. **Vine stocks:** Pinot Noir. **Average annual production in hectoliters:** between 200 and 250.
Appellation: Bourgogne Aligoté, Bourgogne Rouge, Ladoix Côte de Beaune, Savigny-lès-Beaune, Aloxe Corton, Corton Bressaudes. **Technique:** Traditional (fining with egg whites...). **Maturing:** In oak casks. **Alcohol content:** 12 to 13%. **Characteristics:** Lingering taste, fruity. **Serving temperature:** 12 to 13°. **Served with:** Red meat and cheese.

Characteristics of vintages

1987: Ladoix: very fruity. Bourgogne and Savigny: supple and fruity. **1986:** Aloxe Corton and Corton Bressaudes: long, persistant aromas, to be kept. Price range (pre-tax, ex-warehouse): between 30 and 120 F.F.
Sales volume:
– Wholesale: 5%. – Retail: 75%. – Restaurants: 20%.
Sales in France: 70%. **Export sales:** 30%.
Main trading partners : Belgium, Luxemburg, Switzerland, Netherlands.

ALOXE-CORTON

PIERRE ANDRE

Château de Corton-André
Christian Ciamos
80 26 44 25 – Telex: 351 383 F Vinovin
Fax: 80 26 42 00

Type of vineyard: Agricultural Association **Established:** 1923. **Vine stocks:** Bourgogne: Pinot Noir, Chardonnay. Beaujolais: Gamay. Côtes du Rhône: Grenache, Syrah, Mourvèdre, Cinsault. **Soil:** chalky clay. **Exposure:** South, South-East. **Average annual production in hectoliters:** 9,000.

Appellation: Bourgogne, Beaujolais, Côtes du Rhône. **Type:** Red, White, Rosé, Other: Crémant (traditional method). **Technique:** Fermentation with temperature control (submerged cap). **Maturing:** In oak casks. **Characteristics:** Deep respect for the character of the soil not only between villages, but within the same village between different vineyard sites. **Serving temperature:** White: 12°. Bourgogne (red): 18°. Cooler for the Beaujolais and Côtes du Rhône wines. **Served with:** Fish, grilled meat, meat in sauce, game and cheese – depending on the wine.

Characteristics of vintages

1988: Only Beaujolais and Côtes du Rhône wines. **1987:** Bourgogne, Beaujolais and Côtes du Rhône. **1986:** Bour-

gogne, Beaujolais and Côtes du Rhône. **1985:** Bourgogne, Côtes du Rhône (Northern region). **Other:** Aged wines available. Exceptional list of old burgundies.
Sales volume:
- Wholesale: 30% (export). - Retail: 40% (France). - Restaurants: 30% (France).
Sales in France: 70%.
Export sales: 30%.

References in France

Several prestigious restaurants among others: Chez Pétrus (Paris), Maxim's (Paris), Hôtel Grillon (Paris), La Closerie des Lilas (Paris), Carré Cartal (Firminy), Auberge de Mougins (Mougins), Louis XV - Hôtel de Paris (Monte-Carlo), etc.
Large support of the french wine professionals including the French Sommeliers Association.

Abroad

Several Agents and Distributors over the 5 continents application for new agencies possible.

Comments

Enterprise founded in 1923 by Mr. Pierre André. Since, the Château de Corton-André has concentrated on the traditional sector of direct sales to individuals and quality restaurants. Though incorportated, the establishment maintains its family spirit. The exceptional 55 hectares Côte d'Or domain is planted in both Côtes de Nuits and Côtes de Beaune other prestigious and exclusive domaines in both Beaujolais and Côtes du Rhône featuring the family Andre's own cellars. Family's slogan: the search for perfection family's logo: roof of Château de Corton-André.

DOMAINE MAURICE CHAPUIS

Maurice Chapuis
21420 Aloxe-Corton
80 26 40 99

Type of vineyard: Family-owned. **Established:** End of the last Century. **Vine stocks:** Pinot Noir and Chardonnay. **Soil:** Clay with calcium carbonate. **Exposure:** East and South. **Average annual production in hectoliters:** 300. **Type:** Red, white. **Technique:** Traditional. **Maturing:** Oak casks. **Characteristics:** Quite supple wines (because of total destemming) but long keeping (open only after 5 years). **Serving temperature:** Red: 16 to 17°. White: 12°. **Served with:** Red: red meat and cheese. White: first courses and fish. **Vintages available in 89/90:** 1986, 1987, 1988.

Characteristics of vintages

1988: Very good year, full and rich, reminiscent of the 1985 - a great wine. **1987:** Pleasant, well-balanced, but reds a little lighter in color. **1986:** Fruity, but with a rather pronounced tannic character. **1985:** Round, full, rich and well-balanced. Great class. **1984:** Elegant, despite a slight acid overtone. **1983:** Excellent wine for keeping. Price range (pre-tax, ex-warehouse): between 50 and 120 F.F.
Sales volumes:
- Wholesale: 50%.- Retail: 25%. - Other: 25% (export).
Sales in France: 50%.
Export sales: 50%.
Main trading partners : Switzerland, Germany, UK, USA.

REINE PÉDAUQUE

D. Santiard
Aloxe Corton B.P. 10 - 21420 Savigny-les-Beaune
80 26 40 00 - Telex: 350 634 - FAX: 80 26 42 00

Type of vineyard: Private company. **Established:** 1923. **Number of employees:** 125. **Vine stocks:** Burgundy and Chardonnay: Pinot Noir. Côtes du Rhône: Grenache, Syrah, Cinsault, Mourvèdre, Carignan. Whites: Grenache Blanc, Ugni Blanc, Clairette.
Technique: Traditional, in open vats, submerged cap method. **Maturing:** In oak casks, 1/3 new each year. Great vintages 100% in casks - Premiers Crus in one year old casks - Villages in two year old casks. **Vintages available in 89/90:** There are still some 1984 and 1985. The 1986 is beginning to be available and, after bottling, the 1987 will be available as of March 1989.

Characteristics of vintages

1987: Burgundy: a very good vintage. Pleasant fragrance, deep purple color. Wines are quite tannic and have good body. Whites are very aromatic and elegant. Côtes du Rhône: excellent structure with very good fruit. Easy drinking. **1986:** Burgundy: Nice velvety color with subtle aromas. Wines with more elegance than richness. The whites are fragrant, tender and easy to drink. **1985:** Burgundy: great vintage, rich, good color, full-bodied, well balanced, for ageing. In Côtes du Rhône the first year since 1981 in which the Grenache has flowered well. A wine which remains aromatic while having more richness and body than the preceding vintages. **Other:** 1984: Burgundy: very elegant, it is slightly acid guaranteeing sustained freshness. 1983: Great vintage, very rich, full-bodied, highly tannic - unfortunately very little stock available. Price range (pre-tax, ex-warehouse): 30 to 200 F.F. and over.

Sales volume:
– Wholesale: 55%. – Retail: 5%. – Restaurants: 10%. – Other: 30% (GMS)*.
Main trading partners : Europe, North America, Far East.

Comments

Sales of the estate's wines and those of the estates managed under contract are considerable in value and prestige but are only a small portion of total sales of wines from these regions: Burgundy, Beaujolais, Côtes du Rhône. The vineyards have received numerous medals each year at the Paris Concours Général Agricole. Awards received in 1988: – a Gold Medal for: Corton 1985, Corton-Pougets 1985, Gevrey-Chambertin 1985. – a Silver Medal for: Corton-Renardes 1985, Clos Vougeot 1985.

DOMAINE DU COMTE DANIEL SENARD

Philippe Senard
21420 Aloxe Corton
80 26 41 65 – Tefefax: 80 26 45 99

Type of vineyard: Agricultural Association. **Vine stocks:** Pinot Noir 95%, Pinot Gris 5%. **Soil:** Chalky clay. **Exposure:** East, South. **Average annual production in hectoliters:** 280.

PRODUCE OF FRANCE
ESTATE BOTTLED
Mis en bouteilles au Domaine
CORTON
CLOS DU ROI
APPELLATION CONTROLÉE
75 cl
SCE DU DOMAINE
DANIEL SENARD
PROPRIÉTAIRE A ALOXE-CORTON, COTE-D'OR

Appellation: Corton clos du Roi, Bressandes, Clos de Meix, Aloxe Corton 1er Cru, Aloxe Corton. **Type:** Red, White. **Technique:** Long (1 month), low temperature. **Maturing:** 18 months in oak casks (12% new). **Alcohol content:** 13°. **Characteristics:** Long keeping, delicate, rich and well balanced – low temperature vinification (22° maximum) brings out the fruit fragrance. **Serving temperature:** 15 to 16°. **Served with:** Corton: meat in sauce. Aloxe: cheese and grilled meat. **Vintages available in 89/90:** 1980, 1981, 1982, 1983, 1984, 1985, 1986, 1987.

Characteristics of vintages

1987: Very good vintage. **1986:** Should be kept in the cellar for another 2 years, very successful. **1985:** Best year of the two last decades. Price range (pre-tax, ex-warehouse): 50 to 80 F.F. Aloxe Corton. 120 to 160 F.F. Corton.
Sales volume: – Wholesale: 10%. – Retail: 25%. – Restaurants: 10%. – Other: 55% (export).
Sales in France: 45%.
Export sales: 55%.
Main trading partners : UK, USA, Japan, Belgium, Switzerland, etc.

References in France

Restaurants: Tour d'Argent, Méridien, La Marée.

Abroad

United States

Importers: Frederick Wildman & Sons, New York.

United Kingdom

Ingletons Wines, Maldon, Essex.

Belgium

Cooremann, Zellik.

Canada

S.A.Q. Québec.

The Netherlands

Verlinden, AG's Hertogenbosch.

Far East

Japan: D.S.K. Tokyo.

DOMAINE LATOUR

Mr. Louis Latour
Aloxe-Corton – 21420 Savigny-les-Beaune
80 22 31 20 – Telex: 350 826

Type of vineyard: Agricultural Association. **Number of employees:** 20. **Vine stocks:** Chardonnay, Pinot Noir. **Soil:** Clay with calcium carbonate. **Exposure:** Southeast. **Average annual production in hectoliters:** 1,500. **Appellation:** Aloxe-Corton, Pernand-Vergelesses, Beaune, Volnay, Pommard, Corton, Chambertin, Romanee-St-Vivant, Corton-Charlemagne. **Type:** Red, white. **Technique:** Traditional in vats/Oak casks. **Maturing:** 12 months for the whites, 15 month for the reds. **Alcohol content:** 13%. **Characteristics:** Reds: full, robust, great qualities for ageing. Whites: perfumed and full-bodied. **Serving temperatures:** Red: 18°. White: 12°. **Served with:** Red: game, red meat. White: fish, seafood. **Vintages available in 89/90:** 1979, 1982, 1983, 1985, 1986, 1987.

Characteristics of vintages

1988: Great year (reds). Well-balanced, concentrated. To be aged. **1987:** Good year, elegant, to be drink young. **1986:** Good year, promising. **1985:** Great year, Romanée-St-Vivant very durable, to be aged. **1984:** Fresh and perfumed. **1983:** To be aged, balanced. **1982:** Good year, ready to drink. **Other:** 1979 vintage combining finesse with richness and balance, aromatic. Price range (pre-tax, ex-warehouse): Between 80 F.F. and 120 F.F.
Sales volume: – Wholesale: 100%.
Sales in France: 10%. **Export sales:** 90%.
Main trading partners : USA, UK, Japan, Canada.

References in France

Restaurants: La Tour d'Argent, Lucas-Carton, L'Oasis, Troisgros, etc.

PERNAND-VERGELESSE

DOMAINE P. DUBREUIL-FONTAINE PÈRE ET FILS

Bernard Dubreuil
Pernand-Vergelesses 21420 Savigny-lès-Beaune
80 21 51 67

Type of vineyard: Corporation. **Vine stocks:** Aligoté 5%, Chardonnay 20%, Pinot Noir 75%. **Soil:** Chalky clay. **Exposure:** East, South-East. **Average annual production in hectoliters:** 20-45 according to the vintage.

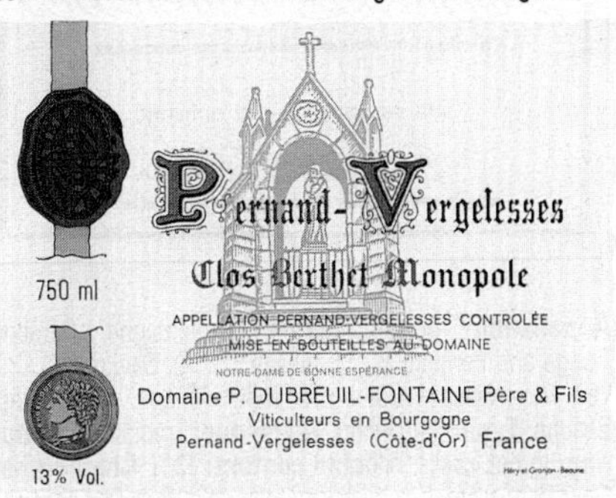

Pernand-Vergelesses
Clos Berthet Monopole
750 ml
APPELLATION PERNAND-VERGELESSES CONTROLÉE
MISE EN BOUTEILLES AU DOMAINE
NOTRE-DAME DE BONNE ESPÉRANCE
Domaine P. DUBREUIL-FONTAINE Père & Fils
Viticulteurs en Bourgogne
Pernand-Vergelesses (Côte-d'Or) France
13% Vol.

Appellation: Village, 1er Crus – Grands Crus. **Type:** Red, white. **Technique:** White: in casks – Red: in wooden vats. **Maturing:** In oak casks. **Characteristics:** White, dry and fruity Red: full-Bodied and tannic. **Serving temperature:** White: 10-12°. Red 15-16°. **Served with:** White: fish, Red: meat.

Characteristics of vintages

1987: Red: to be aged – White: Firm and fruity. **1986:** Red: light and supple – White: balanced and fragrant, very successful, soft and supple, fine development.
Sales volume:
– Wholesale: 50 % export. – Retail: 40 %. –Restaurants: 10%.
Sales in France: 50%.
Export sales: 50%.
Main trading partners : United Kingdom, USA, Japan, Netherlands.

References in France

Restaurants: Troisgros, Marc Meneau, Lameloise, Villa Lorraine, Jacques Cagna, Georges Blanc, Laurent Taillevent.

Abroad

United States
Robert Chadderdon, New York – Matine's Wines, California.

United Kingdom
Russel Mc Iver – Berkmann wine cellars London.

Switzerland
Fischer Rihs – Bienne.

The Netherlands
Noordman Bros., Leiden.

Far East
Toyo-Menka, Yokohama.

Comments

A family enterprise, founded in 1879 by Pierre Arbinet and enlarged by Pierre Dubreuil-Fontaine. It is presently managed by Bernard Dubreuil. The wines are regularly successful, in particular, since 83.

DOMAINE BONNEAU DU MARTRAY

Jean Le Bault de la Morinière
Hea office: 89, rue de l'Université, 75007 Paris
(1) 42 25 71 22
Vineyard: Pernand-Vergelesses,
21420 Savigny-les-Beaune

Type of vineyard: Corporation. **Established:** Company 1978. (Vineyard existed before that.) **Number of employees:** 4 winemakers, 1 administrator. **Vine stocks:** Chardonnay for the Corton Charlemagne (white), Pinot Noir for the Corton (red). **Exposure:** Half way up Corton Mountain. **Average annual production in hectoliters:** About 375.
Appellation: Corton, Corton Charlemagne. **Type:** Red, white. **Technique:** White (Corton Charlemagne): traditional with rigorous temperature control, not exceeding 20° during fermentation. Red (Corton): traditional with temperature control – open Oak vats. **Maturing:** New Oak casks. **Alcohol content:** White: 13%. Red: 13.5%. **Vintages available in 89/90:** Corton Charlemagne: 1985, 1986. Corton: 1982, 1984, 1986.

Characteristics of vintages

1988: Corton Charlemagne – rich and well-balanced, very aromatic. **1987:** Corton Charlemagne – delicate, elegant, good acid/alcohol/aroma balance. **1986:** Promising yar. **1985:** Quite exceptional for Corton Charlemagne, rich, vigorous, firm body and aroma. Price range (pre-tax, ex-warehouse): Over 160 F.F.
Sales in France: 7%.
Export sales: 93%.
Main trading partners : USA, UK, Switzerlands, Germany, Belgium, Netherlands, Canada, Japan, Australia, Hong Kong, Sweden, Denmark, etc.

References in France

Restaurants: Most of the restaurants with Michelin Stars.
Shops: Hédiard, Caves de la Madeleine, for example, in Paris.

ROGER JAFFELIN ET FILS

Jaffelin & Sons
21420 Pernand Vergelesses
80 21 52 43

Type of vineyard: Agricultural Association. **Established:** 1951. **Vine stocks:** Pinot Noir, Chardonnay, Aligoté. **Soil:** Chalky and chalky clay. **Exposure:** South, South-East. **Average annual production in hectoliters:** 420-450. **Appellation:** Pernand Vergelesses Blanc & Rouge, Corton Charlemagne, Savigny les Beaune. **Type:** Red, white. **Technique:** Fermentation on skins 10 to 15 days. **Maturing:** Oak casks. **Alcohol content:** 13%. **Serving temperature:** White, 12° Red: 18°. **Served with:** White: fish, raw vegetables. Red: red meat, game, cheese. **Vintages available in 89/90:** 1986, 1987, 1988.

Characteristics of vintages

1988: Blackcurrant and raspberry aroma, great vintage. **1987:** Bright color, to be aged a few years. **1986:** Beautiful color, fruity and pleasant. Price range (pre-tax, ex-warehouse): 20 to 30 F.F. & 120 to 160 F.F.

Sales volume:
- Wholesale: 60%. - Retail: 25%. - Restaurants: 5%.
- Other: 10% (export).

Sales in France: 85%. **Export sales:** 15%.
Main trading partners : Switzerland, Belgium, Germany etc.

References in France

Restaurants: Didier Denis (Chalon) sur Saone, Hatton 62150 (Gauchin le Gal), Chez Henri (21 Arnay Le Duc), La Bonne Auberge (21 Bouilland).

Abroad

United States
Robert Kächer Selection - Washington D.C.20018.

Belgium
L'Art et la Mer, Avenue L. Gillard 3 Zellik.

Comments

10 hectare estate, established for several generations. Constant improvement of technical know how and considerable extension of vineyard since 1950.

DOMAINE LALEURE PIOT PÈRE ET FILS

Mr. Laleure
Pernand-Vergeglesses,
21420 Savigny-lès-Beaune
80 21 52 37

Type of vineyard: Agricultural Association. **Number of employees:** 3. **Vine stocks:** Chardonnay, Pinot Noir. **Soil:** Chalky marl. **Average annual production in hectoliters:** 400.

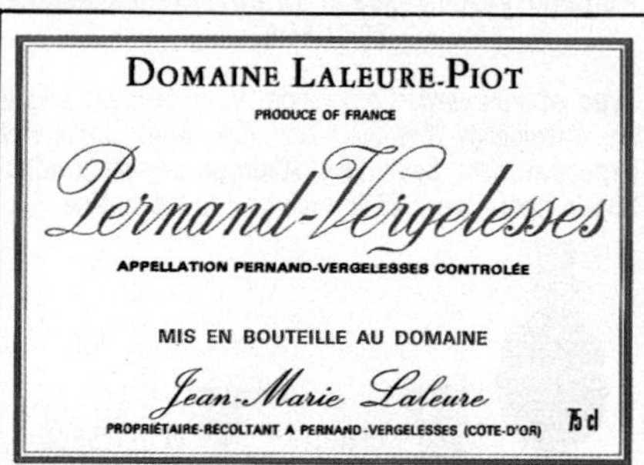

Appellation: Corton, Corton Charlemagne, Pernand Rouge and Pernand Blanc, Village 1er Cru, Savigny 1er Cru, Les Vergelesses, Côtes de Nuits Village, Chorey-lès-Beaune. **Type:** Red, white. **Technique:** Traditional. **Maturing:** In oak casks. **Alcohol content:** 13%. **Characteristics:** Very aromatic and yet quite supple. **Serving temperature:** White: 12° - Red: 17-18°. **Vintages available in 89/90:** 1987.

Characteristics of vintages

1987: Red: supple, beautiful color, concentrated red berry aroma - White: very flowery, full, lingering afterstaste.

Sales volume:
- Wholesale: 60%. - Retail: 15%. - Restaurants: 25%.

Sales in France: 30%.
Export sales: 70%.
Main trading partners : Switzerland, Germany, Belgium, Japan, USA, United Kingdom.

References in France

Restaurants: Lameloise, Georges Blanc, Billoux, Crocodile.

Abroad

United States
Bercut Vandervoort Co., 1405 Sutter St. San Francisco CA 94109.

United Kingdom
Friarwood, 26 New King's Road, London SW 64 St. Tel: 01 736 2628.

Germany
Alpina Burkard Bovensiepen 8938, Buchloe Alpenstrasse 3537. Tel: 08241 3071.

Switerland

Reichmuth Stanffecherstrasse 14 Ja. 8004 Zurich. Tel: 01 241 56 38.

Belgium

SPRL Thorrout Vins, rue de la Saluche 8A. 5830 Mazy. Tel: 081 633852.

Others

Denmark: DZ Wine Mileparken 34, DK 2730 Herlev. Tel: 02844433.

SAVIGNY-LES-BEAUNE

DOMAINE SIMON BIZE ET FILS

12, rue Chanoine Donin
21420 Savigny-lès-Beaune
80 21 50 57

Type of vineyard: Family-owned. **Vine stocks:** Pinot Noir, Chardonnay. **Soil:** Chalky clay. **Exposure:** South, South-East. **Average annual production in hectoliters:** 200 barrels.

Savigny-les-Beaune
APPELLATION CONTROLÉE
750ml
13% vol.
MISE AU DOMAINE
Simon Bize & Fils
Vignerons-Propriétaires à Savigny-les-Beaune (Côte-d'Or)
PRODUIT DE FRANCE

Appellation: 1er Cru Savigny-lès-Beaune, Bourgogne. **Type:** Red, white. **Technique:** Traditional. **Maturing:** In barrels. **Characteristics:** Elegant, fine and fruity "Nourishing, theological and life prolonging" as indicated on the wall of the Château de Savigny. **Serving temperature:** 18°. **Served with:** Fish, lamb, red meat. **Vintages available in 89/90:** 1986.

Characteristics of vintages

1986: Red: fruity, balanced, long. White: excellent, rich and fragrant. Price range (pre-tax, ex-warehouse): 30 to 50 F.F. – 50 to 80 F.F.

Sales volume:
– Wholesale: 50 %. – Retail: 15%. – Restaurants: 35%.

Sales in France: 50%.

Export sales: 50%.

References in France

Restaurants: Guy Savoy, Taillevent, Crillon, Arpège, Loiseau, Georges Blanc, Maxim's, Girardet.

Abroad

United States

Chambers and Chambers, 645 Marioposa St. San Francisco 626 2121.

United Kingdom

Lay and Wheeler Culver St., West Cochester 67 261. Domaine Direct 29, Wilmington Square, London WC1 837 3521.

Germany

Segnitz Lowenhof 2, 2800 Bremen 1.

Switzerland

Reichmuth Stauffacherstraase 145a, 8026 Zurich – Tel. 1241 56 38.

Belgium

Dewit Steenweg Brussel 254, 1900 Overrijse, 687 84 75.

The Netherlands

Van Ouverkerk Susterhuis 1, 4201 Eh Gorinchem, 01830 31150.

Far East

Toyo Menka Kaisha P.O. Box. 61 Osaka Japan.

Comments

Excellent family enterprise where great care is given to the vinification of the Savigny (remarkable 83 and 86) and Burgundy wines.

DOMAINE CHANDON DE BRIAILLES

Comte et Comtesse de Nicolay
1, rue sœur Goby, 21420 Savigny-lès-Beaune
80 21 52 31 – Telex: 204 944 Paris

Type of vineyard: Agricultural Association. **Established:** 1967, vineyard since 1834. **Number of employees:** 5, **Vine stocks:** Pinot Noir and Chardonnay. **Soil:** Chalky clay. **Exposure:** East – South-East. **Average annual production in hectoliters:** 450.

PRODUCE
OF FRANCE
12,5% Vol.
75 cl
MISE EN BOUTEILLES AU DOMAINE
PERNAND
ILE DES VERGELESSES 1er CRU
APPELLATION PERNAND 1er CRU CONTROLÉE
G.F.A. DOMAINE CHANDON DE BRIAILLES
PROPRIÉTAIRE A SAVIGNY-LES-BEAUNE COTE-D'OR FRANCE

Appellation: Savigny-lès-Beaune, Pernand Vergelesses, Corton. **Type:** Red, white. **Technique:** Traditional, slow, temperature control. White: at low temperature. **Maturing:** In oak casks 1/5 new. **Alcohol content:** 12 to 13°. **Characteristics:** Élegant, substantial, aromatic and rich, concentrated, good keeping. **Serving temperature:** 17°. **Served with:** Savigny-lès-Beaune: meat. Corton: meat cooked in sauce, venison. **Vintages available in 89/90:** 1986 and 1987.

Characteristics of vintages

1988: Not yet available. Concentrated, good color and aroma, superb. **1987:** Rich, concentrated, elegant, very serious, great style, good keeping. **1986:** Élegant, subtle and yet quite substantial, very promising. **1985:** Up to now undeveloped, very concentrated, substantial, keep for 10 years. Superb, great vintage. Price range (pre-tax, ex-warehouse): 30 to 50 F.F. – 50 to 80 F.F. – 80 to 120 F.F. – 120 to 160 F.F.

Sales volume:
– Retail: 15%. – Restaurants: 15%. – Other: 70% foreign importers and French wholesalers.
Sales in France: 30%.
Export sales: 70%.
Main trading partners : UK, Switzerland, Benelux countries, Germany, Denmark, USA, Canada, Bermuda, Japan, Hong Kong.

References in France

Restaurants: Maxim's, Lucas Carton, Jules Verne, Beauvilliers, Lasserre, La Marée, Les Trois Marches.
Shops: Caves Madeleine, Repère de Bacchus, Caves Besses, Caves de Nîmes, etc.

Abroad

United Kingdom
Heyman Brothers, London, Berkman Wine Cellars, London.

Germany
Seignitz-Bremen, Champavins Français, Cologne.

Switzerland
Elie Gazzar SA, Lausanne.

Belgium
A. Mampaey, Brussels.

Canada
Goodyear, Toronto (Ontario).

The Netherlands
Bart Vijnimport, Vos Vijnimport.

Far East
Toyomenka – Tokyo, De Villamon Far East – Hong Kong.

Others
Bermuda: Gosling Brothers, Hamilton.

Comments

In the same family since 1834, the estate now belongs to the Count and Countess Aymard-Claude de Nicolay, to their children and to other associated families. It was bequeathed to the Count de Nicolay by his grandmother, the Countess Chandon de Briailles, herself related to the well known Champagne house, Moët & Chandon. The wines are superb (sublime Corton, particularly the 83, 85 and 86 vintages),typical, rich, well colored and will develop beautifully.

DOMAINE ANTONIN GUYON

Dominique and Michel Guyon
21420 Savigny-les-Beaune.
Office: 26 rue Chabot-Charny 21000 Dijon
80 67 13 24 – Telex: 283 155 F

Type of vineyard: Family Agricultural Association. **Number of employees:** 18. **Vine stocks:** Pinot Noir and Chardonnay. **Soil:** Chalky clay. **Exposure:** South-East. **Average annual production in hectoliters:** 1,875.

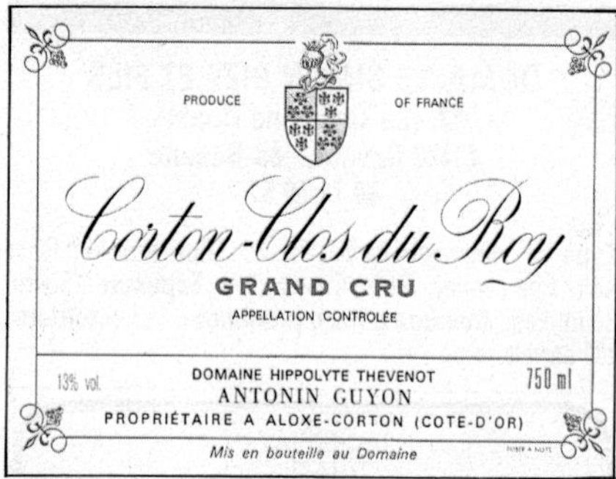

Appellation: Corton Charlemagne, Corton Clos du Roy, Corton Renardes, Corton Bressandes, Aloxe-Corton 1er Cru, Gevrey-Chambertin, Chambolle-Musigny, Volnay-Clos des Chênes, Meursault-Charmes, Savigny-lès-Beaune, Pernand-Vergelesses 1er Cru, Beaune, Haute-Côtes de Nuits. **Type:** Red, White. **Technique:** Traditional fermentation on skins in wooden vats for 12 days. **Maturing:** 18 months in oak casks (40% to 50% new). **Alcohol content:** 13%. **Characteristics:** Long, beautiful color, very fragrant and aromatic. Strawberry, raspberry and vanilla aromas. Tannic, but not too much so, to avoid dominating the characteristics of the various wines. **Serving temperature:** Red: 18°. White: 12°. **Vintages available in 89/90:** 1988, 1987, 1986, 1984.

Characteristics of vintages

1988: Exceptional. A very great year. Fruity and tannic. To be kept. **1987:** Good year, elegant wines. **1986:** Very good year, well balanced. Remarkable white wine. **1985:** Exceptional, a very great year, fruity and long. **Other:** 1984: Very fine and fruity. Easy to dring young. Price range (pre-tax, ex-warehouse): between 50 and 250 F.F.

Sales volume:
– Retail: 20%. – Restaurants: 80%.
Sales in France: 20%.
Export sales: 80%.
Main trading partners : Switzerland, United Kingdom,

United States, Netherlands, Belgium, Germany, Canada, Denmark, Japan.

References in France

Restaurants: Lucas Carton, Tour d'Argent, La Marée, Le Crillon, Le Ritz, Maxim's, Lasserre, Lameloise, Troisgros, La Mère Blanc, Le Négresco, etc.
Shops: Fauchon, Le Verger de la Madeleine.

Abroad

United States

Château & Estate Wines Co., 375 Park Avenue, New York, N.Y. 10152. Shops: Sherry Lehmann, Zachy's. Restaurants: Lutèce, Le Bernardin.

United Kingdom

Michael Druitt Wines, 9 Deanery Street, London W1Y 5LF. Restaurants: Le Gavroche, Waterside Inn.

Germany

Jacques Wein Depot, Dusseldorf. Marwede, Hamburg. Hawesko.

Switzerland

Coop-Suisse, Basel.

Belgium

Ets Breuval, Brussels.

Canada

Société des Alcools de Québec.

The Netherlands

Ets Louis Bogaers, Tilburg.

Far East

Japan: Izumi Trading, Tokyo. Hong Kong: Foods from France.

Others

Denmark: Molt Wengels Vinimport, Copenhagen.

JEAN-MARC PAVELOT

Jean-Marc Pavelot
1, chemin des Guettottes
21420 Savigny-lès-Beaune
80 21 55 21

Type of vineyard: Family-owned. **Vine stocks:** Pinot noir. **Soil:** Chalky clay. **Exposure:** South and South-East. **Average annual production in hectoliters:** 30 to 40. **Appellation:** Savigny-lès-Beaune Village and Savigny 1er cru. **Type:** Red. **Technique:** Traditional. **Maturing:** 12 to 14 months in oak casks, 25 to 50% new for the 1er cru. **Alcohol content:** 13%. **Characteristics:** Balanced wines, combining grace, delicacy, elegance, distinction and an incomparable bouquet. **Serving temperature:** 16°. **Vintages available in 89/90:** 86, 87, 88.

Characteristics of vintages

1988: In casks at the present time. Certainly a wine to keep.

1987: Beautiful color, well balanced, rich, fragrant, quite long. **1986:** Good year, elegant, fine and fruity, excellent keeping.
Sales volume:
– Wholesale: 15%. – Retail: 20%. – Restaurants: 15%. – Other: 50% agents.
Sales in France: 40%.
Export sales: 60%.
Main trading partners: Switzerland, Belgium, United Kingdom, United States, Netherlands.

References in France

Restaurants: Troisgros and others.

Abroad

United States

Diamond Wine Merchants, Albany, California. Silenus Wines, Inc., Waltham 02151, Mass.

United Kingdom

J.T. Davies and Son LTD, Croydon. Domaine Direct, 29 Wilmington Square, London. Tel: 01 837 3521.

Switzerland

F. Banchet SA, J.P. Mathieu & Cie, E. Gazzar SA, P. Cretegny SA.

Belgium

Pro Vino 3520 Zonhoven, R. Goffard, Brussels.

The Netherlands

Sauter Wijnen, Maastricht.

Comments

Winemakers from father to son for several generations, very attached to the Burgundy tradition, they produce fruity and classic wines in their appellation.

• *In 1985, the wines of the following regions received the A.O.C. (Appellation d'Origine Contrôlée) classification: Minervois, Coteaux-des-Baux, Coteaux-d'Aix-en-Provence, Coteaux-du-Lyonnais and Coteaux-du-Languedoc.*

DOMAINE SEGUIN

Pierre Seguin
Rue Paul Maldant, 21420 Savigny-lès-Beaune
80 21 50 42 - Telex: SMVIN 350 407

Type of vineyard: Family-owned. **Established:** 1720. **Number of employees:** 9. **Vine stocks:** Pinot Noir. **Soil:** Chalky clay. **Exposure:** South-East. **Average annual production in hectoliters:** 200.

SEGUIN-MANUEL

PRODUCE OF FRANCE

vin récolté par Pierre Seguin
propriétaire à
Savigny-les-Beaune (Côte-d'Or)

SAVIGNY GODEAUX

APPELLATION SAVIGNY CONTROLÉE

élevé et mis en bouteilles par
SEGUIN-MANUEL, Négociant à Savigny-les-Beaune (Côte-d'Or) France

Appellation: Savigny-lès-Beaune & Savigny-lès-Beaune 1er Cru. **Type:** Red. **Technique:** Traditional, in oak casks. **Maturing:** In new oak casks. **Alcohol content:** 12.5%. **Characteristics:** Light and fragrant. **Serving temperature:** 17°. **Served with:** White meat and light cheese. **Vintages available in 89/90:** 1985, 1986, 1987, 1988.

Characteristics of vintages

1986: Fragrant, goes down well, to be kept for 10 years. **1985:** Fragrant and tannic, lingering flavor, can age at least 15 years. **Other:** 1984: low alcohol content, fine, very pleasant, excellent vinification. Price range (pre-tax, ex-warehouse): 30 to 50 F.F.
Sales volume:
- Wholesale: 50%. - Retail: 50%.
Sales in France: 50%.
Export sales: 50%.
Main trading partners: Switzerland, Belgium, Luxemburg, Netherlands, UK, Austria, Germany.

Comments

On the facade of the fermenting room there is an inscription engraved in 1772 by the Monks of Citeaux indicating the five ways to drink the wine of Savigny: "If I remember well, there are five reasons to drink: the arrival of a guest, present thirst, future thirst, as well as the quality of the wine and any other appropriate reason".

• *Watch out for certain confusing labels: "Bottled at the Château", the wine is produced on the estate; "bottled on the estate", the wine comes from a cooperative... (See Chapter "Labeling").*

BEAUNE

MAISON ALBERT BICHOT

Wine merchant, winegrower
Bernard Bichot
6 bis, boulevard J.-Copeau - B.P. 49
21202 Beaune Cedex
80 22 17 99 - Telex: 350 864
TELEFAX: 80 22 24 64

Type of vineyard: Corporation. **Established:** 1831. **Number of employees:** 85. **Average annual production in hectoliters:** 9,000,000 bottles.
Appellation: Complete range of A.O.C. (Chablis, Burgundy, Maconnais, Beaujolais, Vallée du Rhône). Table wines (red, white, rosé). Chablis: Domaine Long Depaquit. Vosne Romanée: Domaine du Clos Frantin.

Characteristics of vintages

1988: Excellent vintage to be sold next year. **1987:** To be tasted: the Chablis and Corton Charlemagne of high quality, rich and structured, to be aged. **1986:** To be tasted: the Chablis and a white Corton Charlemagne of high quality, rich and structured, to be aged. **1985:** Remarkable reds, notably the Richebourg, the Vosne-Romanée and the Nuits-St-Georges. Do not hesitate.
Sales in France: 15%.
Export sales: 85%.
Main trading partners: 90 countries approximatively. Canada, UK, Germany, Switzerland, the Benelux Countries, USA, Japan, the Scandinavian countries, the Far East.

Abroad

United Kingdom

Laurence Hayward and Partners, Sevenoaks, Kent.

MAISON BOUCHARD PÈRE ET FILS

Mr. Claude Bouchard
Domaines du Château de Beaune
21202 Beaune Cedex
80 22 14 41 - Telex: 350 830 - Fax: 80 22 55 88

Type of vineyard: Family-owned. **Established:** 1731. **Number of employees:** 170. **Vine stocks:** Pinot Noir, Chardonnay, Aligoté, **Soil:** Clay with calcium carbonate, sub-soil chalky or marly. **Exposure:** East and Southeast. **Appellation:** Meursault 1er Cru et Village, Chambertin, Corton Charlemagne, Montrachet, Bourgogne Aligoté Bouzeron, Chambolle, Aloxe-Corton, Savigny, Beaune, Pommard, Volnay. **Type:** Red, white. **Technique:** Fermentation in self-pressing vats, temperature control. **Maturing:** In casks, some new. **Alcohol content:** 12.5% to 13.5%. **Characteristics:** Fresh white wines, silky, elegant, dry but soft and rich, good for ageing. Red wines, with good color, harmoniously combining body and finesse, should be aged to fully develop the aroma of the Pinot Noir. **Vintages available in 89/90:** 1981, 1982, 1984, 1985, 1986, 1987.

Characteristics of vintages

1986: Good year for whites; reds more supple, fine, pronounced bouquet. **1985:** Great year for reds (Volnay, Pommard) rich, to be aged. **1984:** Starts being pleasant now. Certain vats truned out well. **1983:** To be aged. Price range (pre-tax, ex-warehouse): From 30 F.F. to 500 F.F.
Sales in France: 40%.
Export sales: 60%.
Main trading partners : USA, Germany, Switzerland, UK, Canada, Belgium, Nordic Countries, Far East.

References in France

Restaurants: In 90% of the better French Restaurantswith Michelin Stars: Troisgros, Lameloise, Ritz, Orsi, Le Grand Véfour, L'Auberge de l'Ile, L'Oustau de Beaumanière.
Shops: Fauchon, Hédiard. Paris. Globus (CH), Dallmayr (D).

CHANSON PÈRE ET FILS

François and Philippe Marion-Chanson
10, rue Paul-Chanson - B.P. 19 - 21200 Beaune
80 22 33 00 - Telex: 350 568

Type of vineyard: Corporation. **Established:** 1750. **Vine stocks:** Pinot Noir and Chardonnay. **Soil:** Clay with calcium carbonate. **Exposure:** East and East by Southeast. **Average annual production in hectoliters:** 1,500. **Appellation:** Sixteen 1st Cru in Beaune, Savigny les Beaune and Pernand Vergelesses. **Type:** Red, white. **Technique:** Classic. Total or partial destemming, according to the harvest. Temperature regulated, automatic pressing. **Maturing:** New or one year old casks and large casks, depending on category. **Alcohol content:** 12% to 13.5% according to the vintage. **Characteristics:** Typically Côte-de-Beaune, rich, well-balanced, but maturing, relatively early light and supple, fresh. **Vintages available:** 1982 to 1986.

Characteristics of vintages

1986: Natural and fragrant. **1985:** Very pleasant, soft, rich and fruity, quite early maturing. **1984:** Well made, develops slowly. **1983:** Rich and well-balanced, wines with character which will age well. **1982:** Quite subtle, supple, fragrant. Price range (pre-tax, ex-warehouse): From 20 F.F. to over 160 F.F.
Sales volume:
- Wholesale: 8%. - Retail: 13%.
- Restaurants: 14%. - Other: 65% (export).

Sales in France: 35%.
Export sales: 65%.
Main trading partners : UK, USA, Belgium, Switzerland, Germany.

References in France

Restaurants: La Côte d'Or (Nuits-St-Georges), Relais de Saulx (Beaune), Georges Blanc (Vonnas), Lameloise (Chagny), Haeberlin (Illhaueusern), Moulin de Mougins (Mougins), Tour d'Argent (Paris), Jacques Lainé (Beaune).
Shops: Denis Perret, Place Carnot - 21200 Beaune. Fauchon - Paris.

Abroad

United States

Slocum & Sons Inc., Westhaven (Conn.), Grapevine Imports, Medford (Mass.). Baron François Ltd., New York (N.Y.).

United Kingdom

U.K. Sales Manager: Richard Banks, tél: 01 622 7437 etc.

Germany

Firma K. Burgard GmbH, Gumprecht von Schlieben, etc.

DOMAINE BOUCHARD AINE & FILS

36, rue Ste-Marguerite - 21203 Beaune
80 22 07 67 - Telex: 350 163 F

Type of vineyard: Family-owned. **Vine stocks:** Pinot Noir. **Soil:** Clay/Limestone. **Exposure:** South/South-west. **Average annual production in hectoliters:** 87. **Appellation:** Mercurey. **Type:** Red. **Technique:** Traditional. **Maturing:** Oak barrels. **Alcohol content:** 12.8%. **Characteristics:** Good color, full fruit, tannic for the first number of years. **Serving temperature:** 16/18°C. **Served with:** Burgundian Chicken, rib steak with mushrooms. **Vintages available in 89/90:** 1984, 1985,

Characteristics of vintages

1985: Full-bodied and round. **1984:** Well balanced, full perfume. Price range (pre-tax, ex-warehouse): 30 F.F.-50 F.F.
Main trading partners : Canada, England, USA, Switzerland, Denmark, Germany.

• *Would you like to know to recognize the caracteristic fragrances of certains wines, their woodland, fruity, flowery or leather aromas, the evaluate the level of acidity or the presence of tannins, to ascertain the mellowness or the color of a wine...? See the Chapter entitled "The Art and Manner of Wine Tasting".*

DOMAINE JOLIETTE

Maurice Joliette
Domaine les Pierres-Blanches - 21200 Beaune
80 22 26 45

Type of vineyard: Family-owned. **Established:** 1950. **Vine stocks:** Chardonnay Blanc, Pinot Noir. **Soil:** Calcium carbonate. **Exposure:** Southeast. **Average annual production in hectoliters:** 1,300.

Domaine des
Pierres Blanches
APPELLATION COTE DE BEAUNE CONTROLÉE
75 cl
75 cl
M. JOLIETTE propriétaire récoltant à Beaune (Côte-d'Or)
mise en bouteille à la propriété
Product of France

Appellation: Aloxe-Corton, Côte-de-Beaune. **Type:** Red, white. **Technique:** Slow, in Oak casks - late harvest. **Maturing:** 2 years. **Alcohol content:** 12.7%. **Characteristics:** Aloxe-Corton: natural, supple, soft and full bodied when mature. White: well-balanced, good fruity aromas. Red: extreme finesse. **Serving temperature:** Red: 17°. White: 8°. **Served with:** Red: white red meat. White: fish preferably served hot. **Vintages available in 89/90:** 1982, 1983, 1984, 1985, 1986.

Characteristics of vintages

1986: Very promising... **1985:** Good year, very classic wine. **1984:** Very special, very typical of the area. **1983:** Good wine for ageing, rich and fragrant. **1982:** Drink now. Price range (pre-tax, ex-warehouse): Between 50 F.F. and 120 F.F.
Sales volume:
- Retail: 30%. - Restaurants: 40%. - Other: 30% (export).
Sales in France: 70%.
Export sales: 30%.
Main trading partners : UK, Belgium, Germany, Switzerland, Netherlands and Japan.

References in France

Restaurants: Restaurants with Michelin Stars.

Abroad

United Kingdom

London.
Shops: Gavroche - London.

The Netherlands

Van Poucke, Bercham 2600.

Far East

Japan: Threes - Tokyo.
Luc Corporation, Tokio.

Comments

Trained by Paul Chanson, The Group Captain (World war) has given new birth to the Montagne de Beaune area. The Domaine in the vineyard and their home is open to all wine connoisseurs.

LYCÉE AGRICOLE ET VITICOLE DE BEAUNE

David Vincent, director
16, avenue Charles-Jaffelin - 21200 Beaune
80 22 34 77

Type of vineyard: Associated with a public institution. **Established:** 1884. **Number of employees:** 4. **Vine stocks:** Pinot Noir, Gamay, Chardonnay, Aligoté. **Soil:** Clay with calcium carbonate, limestone. **Average annual production in hectoliters:** 900.
Appellation: Beaune 1er Cru, Beaune, Puligny Montrachet, Burgundy. **Type:** Red, white. **Technique:** Traditional. **Maturing:** In oak casks. **Alcohol content:** 12.5%. **Characteristics:** To be kept. Rich and well-balanced, lots of finesse. **Serving temperature:** Red: 16°. White: 8 to 12°. **Served with:** Grilled meat or meat sauce, game and fine game birds. **Vintages available in 89/90:** 1983, 1984.

Characteristics of vintages

1984: Average vintage but, nevertheless, not without quality. **1983:** Great wine for keeping. Excellent vintage, especially Beaune 1er Cru. Price range (pre-tax, ex-warehouse): Between 20 F.F. and 80 F.F.
Sales volume:
- Wholesale: 20%. - Retail: 80%.
Sales in France: 90%.
Export sales: 10%.
Main trading partners : Belgium, Switzerland, Germany.

DOMAINE MAILLARD PÈRE ET FILS

Daniel ou Pascal Maillard
Chorey-lès-Beaune, 21200 Beaune
80 22 10 67

Type of vineyard: Family corporation. **Established:** 1952 - Corporation in 1978. **Number of employees:** 5. **Vine stocks:** Pinot Noir, Aligoté (very little). **Soil:** Chalky clay. **Exposure:** Mostly East-West. **Average annual production in hectoliters:** 35 to 40.
Type: Red, white. **Technique:** Traditional. **Maturing:** In oak casks, 1/3 new. **Alcohol content:** 12.5 to 13%. **Characteristics:** Lightly tannic wines, developing a bouquet after a few years. **Serving temperature:** 16°. **Vintages available in 89/90:** 1982, 1983, 1984, 1985, 1986, 1987, 1988 according to the appellations.

Characteristics of vintages

1988: Wine which will very soon be good to drink, in about 4 years. Good year. **1987:** Good year, quickly developing, can be kept for 12 to 13 years. **1986:** Very supple, great finesse can be kept 10 to 12 years. **1985:** Round, beautiful color, to be drunk in 3 to 4 years, according to the appellations. **Other:** 1984 – to be consumed in a few more years. 1982 – good keeping in general, still rather tannic, not yet developed. 1982 – breed, can be drunk now or kept a bit longer. Price range (pre-tax, ex-warehouse): 20 to 30 F.F. – 30 to 50 F.F. – 50 to 80 F.F. – 80 to 120 F.F.

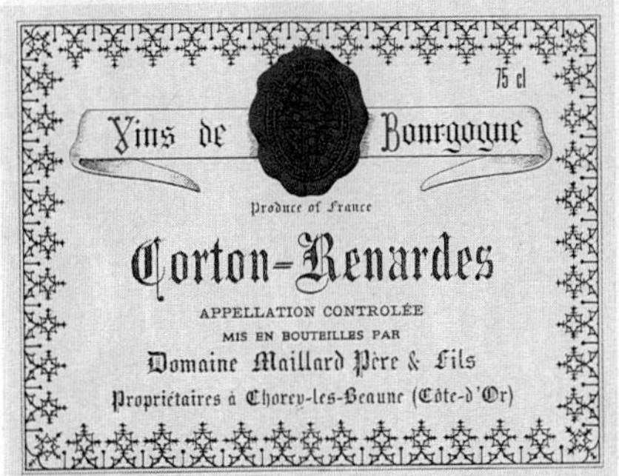

Sales volume:
– Wholesale: 20% and cellars. – Retail: 15%. – Restaurants: 5%.
Sales in France: About 30%.
Export sales: 70%.
Main trading partners: USA, United Kingdom, Germany, Belgium, Switzerland, Netherlands, Japan.

References in France

Restaurants: Brittany, Normandy, Lyonnaise region, Burgundy, Paris, Alsace.
Shops: Brittany, Normandy, Parisian region, Burgundy.

Comments

The domain was established in 1952 as the result of the purchase of a number of properties in several communes. In 1978 a limited liabilities corporation was set up with sons Alain and Pascal.

TOLLOT BEAUT & FILS

rue Alexandre Tollot – Chorey-lès-Beaune
21200 Beaune
80 22 16 54

Type of vineyard: Family-owned for five generations. **Established:** 1880. **Vine stocks:** Pinot Noir, Chardonnay, Aligoté. **Soil:** Chalky clay. **Exposure:** East, South-East. **Average annual production in hectoliters:** 900. **Appellation:** Chorey-lès-Beaune, Savigny-lès-Beaune, Savigny Champ Chevrey, Savigny Lavières, Beaune, Beaune Clos du Roi, Beaune Grèves, Aloxe Corton, Corton, Corton Bressandes, Corton Charlemagne. **Type:** Red, white. **Technique:** Traditional. **Maturing:** In oak casks (18 months). **Alcohol content:** 12 to 13.5%. **Characteristics:** Long keeping, full, round, harmonious, very fine. **Serving temperature:** 15 to 16°. **Served with:** Red meat, game, poultry. **Vintages available in 89/90:** 1987.

Characteristics of vintages

1987: Well balanced, delicate red berry aromas, good keeping, quite successful in this difficult year, supple and well colored. Price range (pre-tax, ex-warehouse): 50 to 80 F.F.
Sales in France: 40%.
Export sales: 60%.
Main trading partners: United Kingdom, Benelux, USA, Switzerland.

References in France

Restaurants: Lameloise, Chapel, Mère Blanc, L'Espérance, Côte St-Jacques, L'Oustau de Baumanière, Taillevent, Jung Strasbourg, Pic Valence, etc.
Shops: Paris, Willi's Wine Bar, Retrou, Legrand.

Abroad

United States

Seagram Château Estate Wines Co., New York.

United Kingdom

Loeb – Berkmann, etc.

Germany

France Vinicole – Weincontor.

Switzerland

Fisher – Baur au Lac – Barisi, etc.

Belgium

Pirard – Thiran.

The Netherlands

Colaris – Okuysen – Du Mée.

Comments

The whole range of the best Burgundy curs, from the most affordable (AOC Bourgogne) to the most prestigious (Corton).

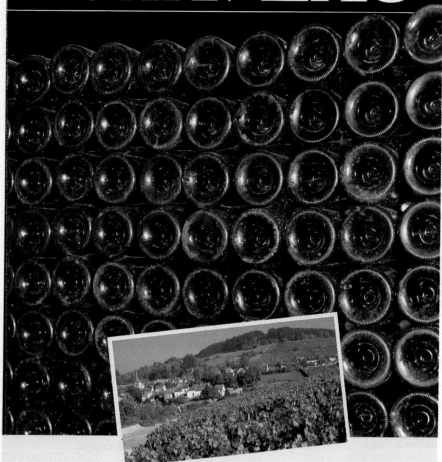

MAISON ROGER RAVEAU

Dominique Raveau
BP 90 21203 Beaune Cedex
80 22 68 00 – Telex: 350 232 F

Wine Merchant: Family-owned. **Established:** 1935. Domaine Wines Distributor.
Number of employees: 10.
Appellation: Bourgogne, Beaujolais. **Type:** Red, White.

Technique: Traditional. **Maturing:** In casks. **Serving temperature:** 10 to 16°. **Served with:** White: fish, and shellfish. Red: meat. **Vintages available in 89/90;** 1987, 1986, 1985.

Characteristics of vintages

1986: Good year. Excellent whites, fruity and fine. **1985:** Very successful reds, rich color, well-balanced good ageing potential (Gevrey-Chambertin, Pommard...).
Sales in France: 85%. **Export sales:** 15%.
Main trading partners : UK, Germany, Switzerland.

Comments

The enterprise was founded in the 1930's by Mr. Roger Raveau. At its head until 1979, he passed the direction to his two children who had been his associates. The facilities becoming too limited, Dominique Raveau, decided to move to the Industrial Zone of Savigny-lès-Beaune. On a 7, 000 square meter terrain, a modern building was built, divided into several work areas: ground floor – offices, bottling, storage, shipping; basement – a very large cellar for maturing and ageing the wines in casks and bottles.

MAISON LOUIS JADOT

André Gagey
5 Samuel Legay - B.P. 121
21204 Beaune Cedex
80 22 10 57 – Telex: 350 881 – Telefax: 80 22 56 03

Type of vineyard: Wholesale wine merchant. **Established:** 1859. **Number of employees:** 49. **Average annual production in hectoliters:** 45,000.
Appellation: Meursault, Blagny, Nuits, Beaune, Corton, etc. **Type:** Red, white. **Technique:** Oak casks. **Alcohol content:** 13%-14%. **Serving temperature:** 11°-15°. **Vintages available in 89/90:** 1982, 1983, 1984, 1985, 1986.

Characteristics of vintages

The whole range of great Burgundy Wines, vinified with utmost care. Remarkable Corton, Meursault, Beaune and Nuits. Average pre-tax, ex-warehouse price: 1984: 131 F.F., 1985: 166 F.F.
Sales volume:
– Retail: 15%. – Restaurants: 65%. – Other: 20% (cellars).
Sales in France: 15%.
Export sales: 85%.
Main trading partners : USA, UK, Netherlands, Japan, Switzerland, Germany, Denmark, Italy, Canada, Brazil, Hong Kong, Singapore, Belgium, etc.

References in France

Restaurants: Bocuse, Lameloise, La Mère Blanc, Troisgros, Auberge de l'Ill, Moulin de Mougins, L'Espérance, A la Côte St-Jacques, La Tour d'Argent, etc.
Shops: Hédiard, Fauchon... Paris.

Abroad

Germany

Langenbach GMBH, Alzereystrasse 31, D 6520 Worms. Tel: (06241) 5002 0.

POMMARD

GAEC JOILLOT JEAN-LUC

Jean-Luc Joillot
Rue de la Métairie, 21630 Pommard
80 22 10 82 or 80 22 47 60

Established: 1987. **Number of employees:** 1. **Vine stocks:** Pinot Noir. **Soil:** Chalky clay. **Exposure:** South, South-East. **Average annual production in hectoliters:** 400.

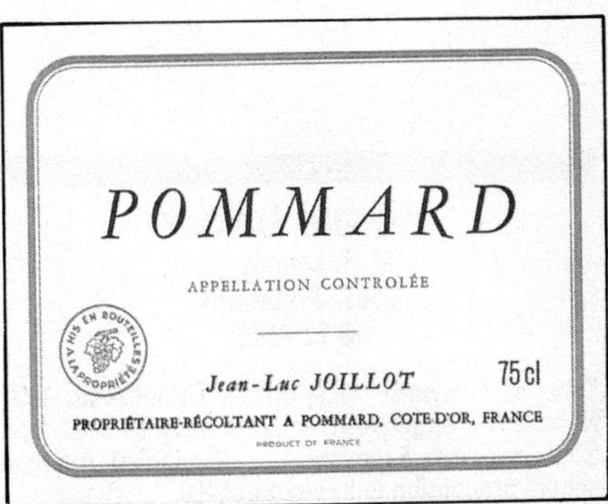

Appellation: Pommard, Pommard Épenots 1er Cru, Bourgogne Hautes Côtes de Beaune, Bourgogne. **Type:** Red. **Technique:** Traditional. **Maturing:** 18 months in casks, 30% new. **Alcohol content:** 12.5 to 13%. **Characteristics:** Full and vigorous wine, for keeping. **Serving temperature:** 17°. **Served with:** Meat in sauce, cheese. **Vintages available in 89/90:** 1986, 1987.

Characteristics of vintages

1987: Rich in color and alcohol, long. **1986:** Although still young, developing its fruity aromas for which it can already be appreciated. Price range (pre-tax, ex-warehouse): between 50 and 80 F.F.
Sales volume:
– Wholesale: 40%. – Retail: 50%. – Restaurants: 10%.
Sales in France: 70%.
Export sales: 30%.
Main trading partners : United States, United Kingdom, Belgium, Switzerland.

References in France

Restaurants: Restaurant "Le Parc" (Illzach 68), Restaurant Hôtel Claret (bld de Bercy, Paris).
Shops: Les Toques Gourmandes (Paris), La Maison de Vin (Martigues).

Abroad

United States

Mr. Peter Vezan, Julienne Importing Company, Chicago. Wine Import, Ltd.

United Kingdom

Bancroft and Associates, Gresham House, 4/7 Gt. Pulteney Street, London W1R 3DF. Tel: 01434 9919.

Belgium

Vinea, Stuivenbergstraat 20, B.1686 6001K. Tel: 532 052 01.

Comments

Winemakers from father to son. In order to achieve high quality, the wine is vinified using traditional methods such as treading and long fermentation on skins (10 days) followed by maturing in casks, some of which are new, for 18 months. The production of each wine is kept track of to determine the need for pruning which is done to concentrate the raw material, the grape, at the expense of the juice.

DOMAINE LAUNAY

R. Launay
21630 Pommard
80 22 12 23

Type of vineyard: Family-owned. **Established:** 1908. **Number of employees:** 4. **Vine stocks:** Pinot Noir. **Soil:** Chalky clay. **Exposure:** East – South-East. **Average annual production in hectoliters:** 400.

Appellation: Pommard, Santenay, Chambertin. **Type:** Red. **Technique:** Traditional Burgundy vinification – long fermentation on skins with treading. **Maturing:** In oak casks. **Alcohol content:** 13%. **Characteristics:** Long keeping. **Serving temperature:** 17°. **Served with:** Roasts and game. **Vintages available in 89/90:** 1980, 1981, 1982, 1984, 1985, 1986, 1987.

Characteristics of vintages

1988 : Exceptional. **1987:** More supple wines, well colored, well made. **1986:** Rich, structured, good development. **1985:** Exceptional. Price range (pre-tax, ex-warehouse): Santenay 40 to 60 F.F., Pommard 80 to 120 F.F., Chambertin 120 to 180 F.F.

Sales in France: 60%.
Export sales: 40%.
Main trading partners: Germany, Switzerland, USA.

References in France

Restaurants: Pré au Clerc (Dijon).

Comments

The Launay family has been in the winemaking business for several generations. Originally from Chassagne-Montrachet, the family is proud to show authentic marriage documents contracted under Louis XVI and Napoleon I.

CLAUDE MARÉCHAL

Claude Maréchal
Route de Chalon-sur-Saône
21880 Bligny-lès-Beaune
80 21 44 37

Type of vineyard: Family-owned. **Established:** 1981. **Vine stocks:** Pinot Noir, Chardonnay. **Soil:** Chalky clay. **Exposure:** South, South-East. **Average annual production in hectoliters:** 230.

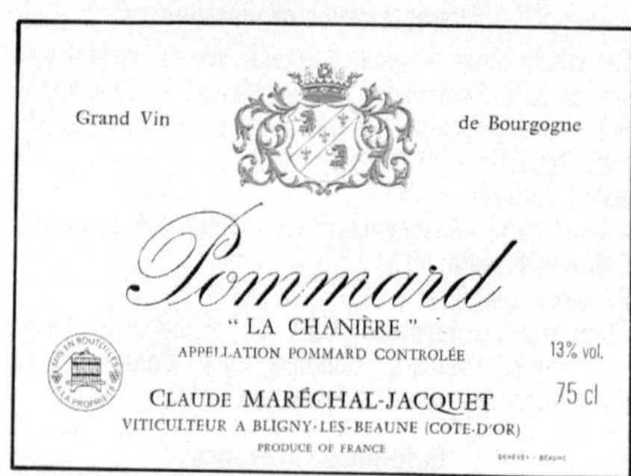

Appellation: Pommard, Savigny-lès-Beaune, Auxey Duresses (Rouge & Blanc) Ladoix, Bourgogne. **Type:** Red, white. **Technique:** Traditional. **Maturing:** In casks (1/3 new). **Alcohol content:** 13%. **Characteristics:** Pommard: rich and well balanced, tannic. Savigny, Ladoix & Auxey Duresses: supple, fruity, more delicate. Auxey Duresses (white): flowery aromas (honey & spices). **Serving temperature:** 15-16°. **Served with:** White: white meat cooked in sauce, or fish. Red: grilled game and poultry, red meat. **Vintages available in 89/90:** 1987, 1988.

Characteristics of vintages

1988: Substantial, rich and well balanced, beautiful color, very good ageing potential. Wait. **1987:** Rich and well

balanced, beautiful color, very pleasant, good ageing potential. Price range (pre-tax, ex-warehouse): 30 to 50 F.F. – 50 to 80 F.F.
Sales volume:
– Wholesale: 20%. – Retail: 50%. – Restaurants: 20%. – Other: 10% shops and delicatessens.
Sales in France: 70%. **Export sales:** 30%.
Main trading partners : USA, Switzerland, Germany, etc.

Comments

Enterprise created in 1981. Warehouse constructed during 1984 and 1985 and equipped for quality production (harvest separator, grape conveyor, casks). Real crafstmen, creative producers of quality wines.

DOMAINE ANDRÉ MUSSY

André Mussy
21630 Pommard
80 22 05 56

Type of vineyard: Family-owned. **Established:** 1756. **Vine stocks:** Pinot Noir. **Soil:** Clay with calcium carbonate. **Exposure:** Southeast. **Average annual production in hectoliters:** 32 to 35 hl. per hectare.

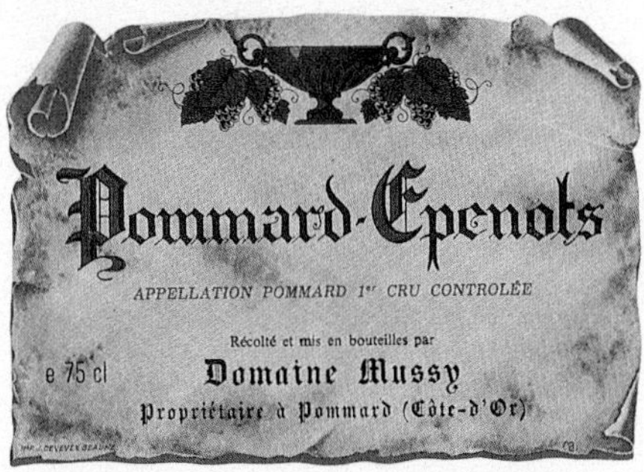

Appellation: Pommard Grand 1er Cru, Pommard Epenots 1er Cru, Pommard 1er Cru Pézerolles, Beaune Montremenots 1er Cru, Beaune Eprenotier 1er Cru, Volnay. Pommard, Beaune, Beaune Montremale 1er Cru, Burgundy Pinot. **Type:** Red. **Technique:** Traditional, Oak vats. **Maturing:** Oak casks. **Alcohol content:** 12.8 to 13%. **Characteristics:** Great wines for ageing. Firm, Higly-colored. Our ancestors used to say, honest, mellow and marketable. **Serving temperature:** 16°. **Served with:** Roasts, game, cheese. **Vintages available in 89/90:** 1985.

Characteristics of vintages

1986: Very promising in the Spring of 1988. To drink in about 12 years. **1985:** Great vintage, well-balanced, fruity, long, for long a life. **1984:** Wonderful success, to be drunk a bit young. Finesse and fragrance. **Note:** Some old vintages in small quantities. Price range (pre-tax, ex-warehouse): between 50 and 80 F.F.

Sales volume:
– Retail: 38%. – Restaurants: 10%. – Other: 52% (export)
Main trading partners : USA, UK, Canada; Netherlands, Belgium, Switzerland, Germany, Australia, Japan.

References in France

Restaurants: Vishnou Indra, L'Écu de France, Taillevent (Paris), Le Vaccarès (Arles), etc.

Abroad

United States
Diamond Wine Merchants, San Francisco. Consolitated Distillers, Birent Vanderwoort, Haynes, Hanson and Clark. Le Courtier du Vin. Charie Import.
United kingdom
Haynes, Hanson and Clark.
The Netherlands
Die Wijnkamer Rosmaken.
Far East
Japan – Mainicki Build, Tokyo.
Others
Australia: The de Burgh Day Wine Company, Melbourne. Belgium: Van den Bussche, Gent, Verhelle 3009, Herent.

Comments

Old family vineyard. Twelve generations of winemakers; 59 years in the business.

S.A. DOMAINE PARENT

Jacques & François Parent
Place de l'Église – 21630 Pommard
80 22 15 08 or 80 22 61 85

Type of vineyard: Family-owned. **Established:** 1680 – became a family corporation in 1974. **Number of employees:** 5. **Vine stocks:** Pinot Noir. **Soil:** Calcium carbonate. **Average annual production in hectoliters:** About 500.
Appellation: Pommard. **Type:** Red. **Technique:** Traditional, in wooden vats for 8 to 10 days. **Maturing:** Traditional. **Alcohol content:** 12.8°, 13°, 13.2°. **Characteristics:** Rich and well-balanced, yet extremely delicate. **Serving temperature:** 16°. **Served with:** Meat, game, cheese. **Vintages available in 89/90:** 1986, 1987.

Characteristics of vintages

1988: Very promising, but to early to tell – not yet. **1987:** Bottled. **1985:** Very good, but still very young. **1983:** Beautiful wine, very successful year. **1982:** Good year – wine rich in aroma and well-balanced, good for ageig.
Sales volume:
Sold exclusively to individuals, clients, restaurants and cellars and specialized shops.
Sales in France: 30%. **Export sales:** 70%.
Main trading partners : Switzerland, UK, Germany, Benelux Countries, Denmark, Netherlands, USA, Japan, Australia.

CHÂTEAU DE POMMARD

Jean-Louis Laplanche
21630 Pommard
80 22 07 99

Type of vineyard: Personal property. **Established:** 1726. **Number of employees:** 6. **Vine stocks:** Pinot Noir. **Soil:** Chalky clay. **Average annual production in hectoliters:** 600.
Appellation: Château de Pommard. **Type:** Red. **Technique:** Open oak vats for 12 days. Crushing 3 times a day. **Maturing:** In new oak casks for 2 years. **Alcohol content:** 12 to 12.9%. **Characteristics:** Long keeping (15 to 40 years), tannic, robust, well-balanced. Pronouced aromas, long fragrant and full bodied. **Serving temperature:** 17°. **Served with:** Game, meat in sauce, cheese (munster etc.). **Vintages available in 89/90:** 1978, 79, 82, 83, 84, 85, 86.

CHATEAU
DE POMMARD
One of Burgundy's most beautiful Domaines. Also produces one of its most prestigious wines.
1976
CHATEAU
DE POMMARD
Sole U.S. Importers : KOBRAND

Characteristics of vintages

1986: Great year, very well balanced. **1985:** Very great vintage. **Other:** 1984: lighter and more supple, ready. 1983: good keeping wine for the cellar, well-balanced and complex, dense. 1979: very beautiful vintage, now at its peak. 1978: very great vintage. Price range (pre-tax, ex-warehouse): 120 to 160 F.F. – 160 F.F. and over.
Sales volume: – Retail: 85% France and Europe (Switzerland & Germany). – Restaurants: 1%. – Other: 14% export (USA, Japan, Germany).
Sales in France: 65%. **Export sales:** 35%.
Main trading partners : Switzerland, USA, Japan, Germany.

References in France

Restaurants: Bocuse, Lasserre.

Abroad

United States

Kobrand – NDW York. Shops: All Better Shops and Restaurants Via Kobrand.

Germany

Direct sales.

Switzerland

Direct sales.

Canada

Regie Liqueurs Ontario.

The Netherlands

Direct sales.

Far East

Japan – Nikko Trading, Nikkei Shoji.

Comments

The largest estate belonging to a single wine producer in Burgundy. Meticulous maintenance of the vineyard and refined technique have only one aim: quality. Visits to the Estate: daily from the end of March to the third Sunday in November.

DOMAINE DU CLOS DES ÉPENEAUX

P: Comte Armand. R: Pascal Marchand
Place de l'Église – 21630 Pommard
80 24 70 50

Established: Over a hundred years ago. **Number of employees:** 2. **Vine stocks:** Pinot Noir. **Average annual production in hectoliters:** 33.
Appellation: Pommard 1er Cru "Clos des Épeneaux". **Type:** Red. **Technique:** Traditional in wooden vats (10 to 15 days), destemming. **Maturing:** 18 to 20 months in Oak casks (30% new). **Characteristics:** Forthcoming. Lots of structure, the weaker vintages lean towards finesse and elegance rather than dilution (1979 and 1982). Wines which always require a bit of ageing in the bottle (minimum 5 years).

VOLNAY

DOMAINE MARQUIS D'ANGERVILLE

Jacques d'Angerville
Volnay - 21190 Meursault
80 21 61 75 - Telex: 350020 F

Type of vineyard: Family-owned. **Vine stocks:** Pinot Noir and Chardonnay. **Soil:** Chalky. **Exposure:** South-East. **Average annual production in hectoliters:** 450.

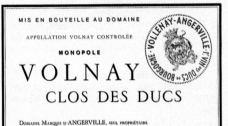

MIS EN BOUTEILLE AU DOMAINE
APPELLATION VOLNAY CONTROLÉE
MONOPOLE
VOLNAY
CLOS DES DUCS
VOLLENAY-ANGERVILLE-1ᵉʳ VIN des DUCS de BOURGOGNE
DOMAINE MARQUIS D'ANGERVILLE, SEUL PROPRIÉTAIRE
PROPRIÉTAIRE-RÉCOLTANT A VOLNAY, COTE-D'OR, FRANCE

Appellation: Volnay premiers crus, Meursault, Santenots. **Type:** Red, white. **Technique:** Traditional. **Maturing:** In oak casks. **Alcohol content:** 13%. **Vintages available in 89/90:** 1983, 1984, 1985.

Characteristics of vintages

1988: Great year, very well balanced, perfectly sound, beautiful color, long evolution. **1987:** Over abundant harvest, good balance, very fragrant, beautiful ruby color. **1986:** Beautiful wines, tannic, will develop well. **1985:** Really great vintage, to be aged. **Other:** 1984: fruity, balanced, to be consumed within 5 years. Excellent Meursault. 1983: very tannic, rich and well balanced, superb Volnay, combining structure and elegance, to be aged. Price range (pre-tax, ex-warehouse): 80 to 120 F.F.
Sales volume:
- Retail: 5%. - Restaurants: 25%.
Sales in France: 30%. **Export sales:** 70%.
Main trading partners : USA, UK, Switzerland, Germany, Belgium, Netherlands, Austria, Sweden, Japan.

References in France

Restaurants: Taillevent, Robuchon, Lucas Carton, Faugeron, Tour d'Argent, la Marée, Hôtel Grillon, Côte St-Jacques, Espérance, Loiseau, Lameloise.
Shops: Hédiard, Caves de la Madeleine.

Abroad

United States
Château & Estate Wines Co., 375 Park Av., New York, N.Y. 10152. Restaurants: Lutèce, Côte Basque, La Grenouille, Le Cygne.

United Kingdom
Ow Loeb & Co 64 Southwark Bridge Road, London SEI OAS, Corney 1 Barrow 12 Helmet Row, London ECIV 3 QJ.

Germany
Franz Keller Oberbergen, Segnitz 2 2800 Bremen 1.

Switzerland
Entrepôts vins spiritueux, 1181 Vinzel.

Far East
Fuji Hakko Kogyo 31-4 Motoyoyogicho Shibuyaku, Tokyo, Japan.

Comments

Splendid wines (fantastic 83 and 86 vintages), remarkably vinified, well bred, for keeping.

DOMAINE DE MONTILLE

Hubert de Montille
21190 Volnay
80 21 62 67 and 80 41 71 79

Type of vineyard: Family-owned. **Established:** Before the Revolution. **Number of employees:** 3 to 4. **Vine stocks:** Pinot Noir. **Soil:** Chalk, limestone. **Exposure:** Southeast. **Average annual production in hectoliters:** 200.
Appellation: Volnay, Mitans. **Type:** Red. **Technique:** Traditional vinification, long, intensive crushing, several times a day. Vinification in Oak vats at high temperature. (between 32° and 34°). **Maturing:** Traditional Oak, 1/4 new. **Alcohol content:** 12%. **Serving temperature:** Between 15° and 17°. **Served with:** Red meat, poultry. **Vintages available in 89/90:** 1986 in 1989 and 1987 in 1990.

Characteristics of vintages

1988: Exceptional year, deep color, lingering taste, concentrated bouquet, perfect balance, good keeping, to be considered amongst the greatest - alcohol content: 12.2 %, will be put on the market end of 1990 beginning of 1991. **1987:** Fruity, well developed bouquet, red berry aroma, well-balanced. To be drunk between 1992 and 1997. Good year, alcohol content: 12 %. Will be on the market end of 1989/ beginning of 1990. **1986:** Wait several months before expressing an opinion. **1984:** Beautiful color, light and supple, fragrant. Ready to drink between 1988 and 1990. Average pre-tax, ex-warehouse price: 1984: 72 F.F. Price range (pre-tax, ex-warehouse): Between 50 F.F. and 120 F.F.
Sales volume:
- Retail: 30%. - Restaurants: 30%. - Other: 40% (export).
Export sales: 40%.
Main trading partners : UK, Japan, Germany, Switzerland, Belgium, Netherlands, USA, Australia.

References in France

Restaurants: Rebuchon, Savoy, Faugeron, Tour d'Argent, etc. Troisgros, Chapel, Blanc, Meneau, Lameloise, etc.
Shops: Marks and Spencer, Fauchon, Harrods.

SCE DU DOMAINE DE LA POUSSE D'OR

Gérard Potel
Volnay, 21190 Meursault-Pousse-d'Or
80 21 61 33

Type of vineyard: Corporation half owned by family. **Established:** 1964. **Number of employees:** 5. **Vine stocks:** Pinot. **Soil:** Oxfordian marl and Bathonian lime. **Exposure:** East. **Average annual production in hectoliters:** 35 to 40 hl/ha.
Appellation: Volnay 1er Cru Clos de la Beaune d'Or, Clos des Caillerets, Clos des Ourrier, Caillerets, Clos d'Audignac, Pommard 1er Cru, Les Jarollières, Santenay 1er Cru, Les Gravières, Clos Tavanner. **Type:** Red. **Technique:** In open vats. **Maturing:** In oak casks 30% new each year. **Alcohol content:** 12 to 13.5% depending on the year. **Characteristics:** Volnay: Wines from the best vineyards, combining breed, nobility, distinction, finesse, elegance, lightness and an incomparable bouquet. Pommard: rich and well-balanced, vermilion color, bouquet or ripe plum. Santenay: firm, soft and rich, typical bouquet. **Serving temperature:** 18 to 19°. **Vintages available in 89/90:** 1984, 1986, 1987 (in November 89).

Characteristics of vintages

1986: Good harvest at Santenay, small production at Volnay due to bad weather in June. Wines of a beautiful vermilion color, full-bodied, grapy, round, and harmoniously balanced. **1985:** Promising evolution, confirmation of a great year much like the 1978 and 1966 vintages, full bodied, rich and well balanced, tempered by a very elegant roundness and a long and harmonious persitance. Price range (pre-tax, ex-warehouse): 50 to 80 F.F. (Santenay 1er Cru), 80 to 120 F.F. (Volnay 1er Cru and Pommard 1er Cru).
Sales in France: 30%.
Export sales: 70%.
Main trading partners: USA, Switzerland, Belgium, Netherlands, Luxemburg, Germany, UK, Sweden, Japan, Australia.

References in France

Restaurants: Troisgros, Le Grand Véfour, La Tour d'Argent, Maxim's, Les Crayères (Gérard Boyer), Greuze, A. Chapel.
Shops: Lucien Legrand, Chemin des Vignes, La Cave de Longchamps, Les Grandes Caves du Sahel, Les Caves du Châtelet (Annemasse), Les Caves de l'Ardières (Belleville-sur-Saône).

Abroad

United States

By Rebecca Wasserman à Bouilland, France. Diamond Wine Merchants, 1320 A Solano Avenue, Albany, USA 94706 California. Prestige Wine Corp. 21 East 40th St. New York NY 10016, USA.

United Kingdom

Domaine Direct, London. Anthony Byrne Fine Wines, Huntington Cmabridgeshire. Atkinson à Londres. I.E.C. à Stevenage.

Germany

Schwartzer Adler Franz Keller 7818 Vogtsburg-Oberbergen. Fergers et Unterberg à Koeln. Georg Schmidt à Bunde. Grand Cru Select à Bonn. Paul Starosky à Hodenhagen. Waldhotel Krautkramer à Munster.

Switzerland

Fischer-Rihs 17, rue des Marchandises 2502 Bienne.

Belgium

J. Pirard, 1, rue de Glabais 1470 Genappe.

Australie

Mark Fesq à Botany N.S.W. Liberty liquors à Perth W.A.

Far East

Japan: Jardine Matheson CO ltd., Tokyo 105. Toyo Menka Kaisha à Tokyo.

Others

Luxemburg: Caves Weber, Rosport. Austria: E.U.M. Muller Gross-St Florain. Hollande: Vos Wijnimport à Tilburg. Norvège: Vinmonopolet à Oslo.

Comments

Formerly Domaine Duvaut Bloché, then De Lavoreille and Chavigné, the present company (50% family capital, 50% Australian capital) started up in 1964 by re-using the principal vines of the Domaine de Lavoreille and Chavigné and taking over the house and wine warehouses at Volnay.

JOSEPH VOILLOT

Volnay 21190 Meursault
80 21 62 27

Type of vineyard: Family-owned. **Vine stocks:** Pinot noir. **Soil:** Brown, chalky, on sub-soil of hard Jurassic chalk and alluvial gravel. **Exposure:** South-East. **Average annual production in hectoliters:** 340.

MIS EN BOUTEILLES A LA PROPRIÉTÉ
Volnay
LES FREMIETS
APPELLATION D'ORIGINE CONTROLÉE
75cl JOSEPH VOILLOT
VIGNERON A VOLNAY (COTE-D'OR) FRANCE

Appellation: Volnay, Volnay Fremiets, Volnay Champans, Volnay Cailleret, Pommard, Pommard Rugiens, Pommard Pezerolles, Pommard Clos Micault. **Type:** Red. **Technique:** Traditional, open vats, 10 day maceration with temperature control, treading. **Maturing:** In oak vats, 15 to 18 months. **Alcohol content:** Bourgogne 12.8%, Village 13.3%, 1er Cru 10.5%. **Characteristics:** Bourgogne: light red wine, fruity. Volnay and 1er Cru fine, flowery and red berry aromas. Pommard and 1er Crus: full-bodied, tannic, spicy aroma. **Serving temperature:** 16°. **Served with:** Volnay: white meat, feathered gams. Pommard: red meat, furry game. **Vintages available in 89/90:** 1986, 1987.

Characteristics of vintages

1988: Excellent vintage, extremely promising, good color and structure. **1987:** Good balance, great wine, good keeping. **1986:** Very fragrant, not to be aged more than 8 years in order to keep its fruitiness. Price range (pre-tax, ex-warehouse): 20 to 30 F.F. – 50 to 80 F.F.

Sales volume:
– Wholesale: 50%. – Retail: 40%. – Other: vinothèques, wine cellars*.
Sales in France: 50%.
Export sales: 50%.
Main trading partners : Switzerland, Belgium, Netherlands, United Kingdom, Germany, Canada, USA.

References in France

Shops: Millésimes Fontviele, Vinothèque (Tours), Vinothèque (Poitiers), L'Arbre à Vin (Paris), Maison Branque (Limoges).

Abroad

United States

World Shippers & Importers Co. 1420 Walnut Street, Philadelphia.

United Kingdom

Robert Rolls Market Winters 11-12 West Smithfield EC 1A 9 JR.

Switzerland

Bourgeois Frères 1338 Ballaigues-Danzeisen Payerne - J.Savary Weinhandel 8580 Amriswil.

Begium

Jean Engels Kerweg 28 – 2980 Boortmeerbeck.

Canada

The Wine Cellar 12421 – 102 Avenue Edmonton Alberta.

The Netherlands

Wynkoperij HFA Okhuysen BV Gierstraat 34-36-38 – 2011 GE Haarlem.

Comments

Remarkable Volnay and Pommard (1983-1988) typical, well made, seductive, lingering flavor, good keeping.

MONTHELIE

BOUZERAND

Xavier Bouzerand
Monthelie – 21190 Meursault
80 21 20 08

Type of vineyard: Family-owned. **Established:** 1959. **Vine stocks:** Pinot Noir, Chardonnay, Burgundy Aligoté, Gamay. **Soil:** Clay with clacium carbonate. **Exposure:** South, Southwest. **Average annual production in hectoliters:** 200.
Appellation: Red: Monthelie 1er Cru, Monthelie, Beaune.

White: Meursault, Auxey. **Type:** Red, white. **Technique:** Traditional. **Maturing:** In Oak casks. **Alcohol content:** 12.5%. **Characteristics:** Fruity, fine, bouquet... **Serving temperature:** Red: 17°. White: 15°. **Served with:** White: fish, delicatessen, snacks. Red: meat in light sauces, cheese. **Vintages available in 89/90:** 1984, 1985.

Characteristics of vintages

1985: Richer and better balanced than average, will improve with ageing. **1984:** Light, goes down well, pleasant to drink. Very successful vinification. Price range (pre-tax, ex-warehouse): between 30 F.F. and 50 F.F.
Sales volume:
– Retail: 70%. – Restaurants: 30%.
Sales in France: 70%.
Export sales: 30%.
Main trading partners: Netherlands, Switzerland, Germany, Belgium.

References in France

Restaurants: Lucas Carton (Paris), Restaurant de la Gare (In Hirson with – Mr. Feutry, first ranking sommelier of France), Hotel Lutetia (Paris).

DOMAINE DENIS BOUSSEY

Denis Boussey
Grande Rue, Monthélie, 21190 Meursault
80 21 21 23

Type of vineyard: Family-owned. **Established:** 1971. **Number of employees:** 2. **Vine stocks:** White: Chardonnay. Red: Pinot Noir. **Soil:** Chalky clay. **Exposure:** South, South-East. **Average annual production in hectoliters:** 400.

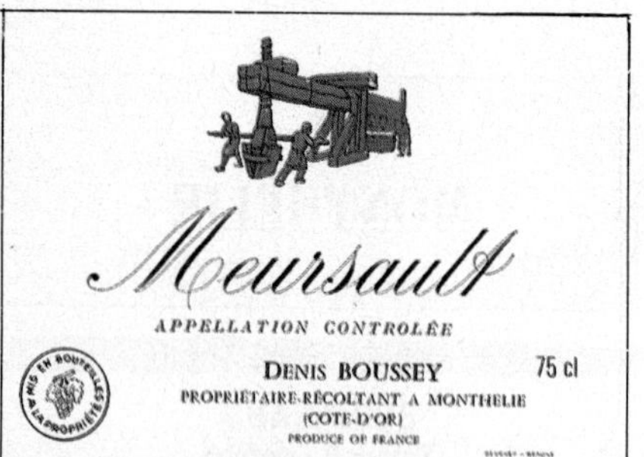

Appellation: Meursault. **Type:** White. **Technique:** Alcoholic fermentation with temperature control, in vats. **Maturing:** Oak casks (1 to 6 years old) for 10 to 12 months. **Alcohol content:** 13%. **Characteristics:** Dry white wine that keeps well for 6 to 12 years. **Serving temperature:** 12 to 13°. **Served with:** As an aperitif and with warm first courses, fresh water fish, snails. **Vintages available in 89/90:** 1987, 1988.

Characteristics of vintages

1988: Great year. Fruity, fine, soft and full, long. **1987:** Good year. Very fine, dry, very good keeping, long. Honey and vanilla aromas (next casks). Price range (pre-tax, ex-warehouse): between 50 and 80 F.F.
Sales volume:
– Wholesale: 10%. – Retail: 50%. – Restaurants: 10%. – Other: 30% wholesale export.
Sales in France: 50%.
Export sales: 50%.
Main trading partners: Switzerland, United Kingdom, Germany, Belgium.

References in France

Restaurants: Troisgros (Roanne).

Abroad

United Kingdom

Mr. Bewicke, Knaphill, Woking, Surrey. Tel: 4867 2732.

Comments

A family domain for four generations which offers excellent, typical Meursault, marked by its soil and capable of a good evolution. Other appellations of the domain: Monthélie red and white, 1er Cru red and white, Meursault 1er Cru, Volnay, Pommard, Aloxe-Corton and Savigny les Beaune.

MARCEL DESCHAMPS

M. Deschamps
Monthélie, 21190 Meursault
80 21 28 60

Type of vineyard: Family-owned. **Established:** 1961. **Number of employees:** 1. **Vine stocks:** Pinot Noir. **Soil:** Chalky clay. **Exposure:** South-East and South. **Average annual production in hectoliters:** 40.
Appellation: Monthélie. **Type:** Red. **Technique:** Traditional. **Maturing:** In casks. **Alcohol content:** 12.8%. **Characteristics:** Ruby color, red berry aroma, rich and well balanced, can be kept for 10 years. **Serving temperature:** 17°. **Served with:** Red meat, cheese. **Vintages available in 89/90:** 1987.

Characteristics of vintages

1988: Rich, promising, good keeping. **1987:** Good year, well made wine, good color, full, fruity, good development. Price range (pre-tax, ex-warehouse): 30 to 50 F.F.
Sales volume:
– Wholesale: 20%. – Retail: 60%. – Other:20% (cellars, etc.).
Sales in France: 80%.
Export sales: 20%.
Main trading partners: Belgium, Switzerland, UK, Netherlands.

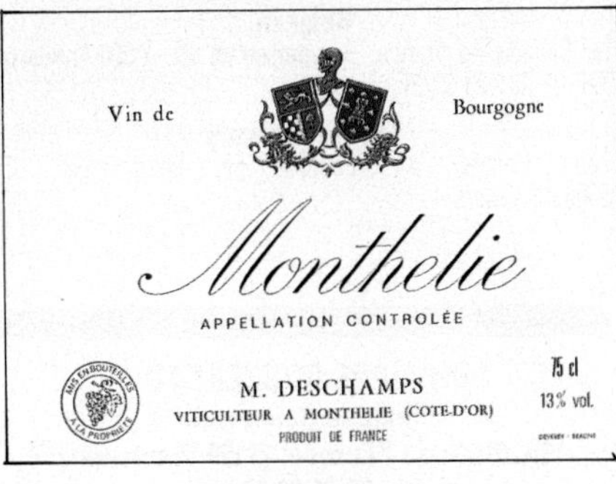

References in France

Restaurants: In Paris, Langon, Tanney, Nasac, Plerin.

Abroad

Switzerland

Private clientèle.

Belgium

Le Millésime 2 Hakin. Vinéa Stunnebergstraat B. 16 96 Gooik.

The Netherlands

Tjia, Haven 40 A 2312 NK Leiden.

Comments

Visit the superb winecellars.

AUXEY-DURESSES

DOMAINE MICHEL PRUNIER

Michel Prunier
Route Nationale, Auxey-Duresses
21190 Meursault
80 21 21 05

Type of vineyard: Family-owned. **Established:** 1968. **Number of employees:** 3. **Vine stocks:** Pinot Noir, Chardonnay, Aligoté. **Soil:** Clay and chalky clay. **Exposure:** East-south. **Average annual production in hectoliters:** 400.
Appellation: Auxey-Duresses, Meursault, Beaune, Volnay. **Type:** Red, white. Other: Cremant de Bourgogne. **Technique:** Traditional, no destemming. **Maturing:** Red: in oak casks (1/4 new). White: in vats and 1/4 in casks. **Alcohol content:** 12-14%. **Characteristics:** Auxey-Duresses (red): full bodied and tannic, average keeping (5-10 years). Auxey-Duresses (white) 1987: fruity still lively, will fully develop in about 2 years. Auxey Duresses 1[er] Cru: finer and more complete than the village appellation. **Serving temperature:** Auxey-Duresses white: 10-12°. Auxey-Duresses red and 1[er] Cru: 16-18°. **Served with:** Auxey (white): fish (trout, sole). Auxey (red): red meat. **Vintages available in 89/90:** 1986 and 1987.

Characteristics of vintages

1988: Maturing, will be put on the market in 1991. **1987:** Beautiful purple color, well developed bouquet, will be ready in 2-3 years. **1986:** Supple, delicate and harmonious, taste now. **1985:** Stock depleted. **Other:** 1984: average structure, pleasant right now though slightly astringent. Price range (pre-tax, ex-warehouse): 30 to 50 F.F. – 50 to 80 F.F. – 80 to 120 F.F.
Sales volume:
– Wholesale: 15%. – Retail: 80%. – Restaurants: 5%.
Sales in France: 55%. **Export sales:** 45%.
Main trading partners : UK, USA, Switzerland, Germany, Netherlands, Belgium.

References in France

Shops: Arôme des Vins (Antibes).

Abroad

United States

Grape Expectations 4097 Harlan Street, Emerville – Calif 94608.

United Kingdom

Justerini and Brooks LTD 214 Upton Lane Forest Gate London E7 – Balls Brothers LTD 313 Cambridge Heath Road, London E2 9LQ.

Switzerland

Sordet SA Case Postale 90 1211 Geneva 18, Switzerland.

The Netherlands

De Wijnkammer Postfus 2218 5202 CE'S – Hertogenbosch.

Comments

Passed down from father to son since 1820 (four generations) the Domaine Michel Prunier extends over more than 8 hectares from Beaune to Merusault, via Volnay and Auxey-Duresses.

MEURSAULT

MICHEL BUISSON-CHARLES

Michel Buisson-Charles
3, rue de la Velle, 21190 Meursault
80 21 22 32

Type of vineyard: Family-owned. **Established:** 1958. **Number of employees:** 1. **Vine stocks:** Pinot Blanc, Chardonnay, Pinot Noir. **Soil:** Chalky clay. **Exposure:** South-East. **Average annual production in hectoliters:** 250 to 300.

Appellation: Meursault, Tessons, Charmes, Goutte d'Or, Bouches Chères, Volnay, Santenots, Bourgogne Rouge. **Type:** Red, white. **Technique:** Traditional. **Maturing:** Oak casks. **Alcohol content:** 13%. **Characteristics:** White: dry and fruity. Red: average color, quite fragrant, not too tannic. **Serving temperature:** White: 12°. Red: 14°. **Served with:** Fish, white meats, foie gras. **Vintages available in 89/90:** 1987, 1988.

Characteristics of vintages

1988: White: fine, fragrant, great year. **1987:** White: dry, still young; to be drunk after 3 years. Price range (pre-tax, ex-warehouse): between 80 ans 120 F.F.
Sales volume:
– Wholesale: 2/3. – Retail: 1/3.
Sales in France: 80%.
Export sales: 20%.
Main trading partners : Belgium, United Kingdom.

References in France

Restaurants: Hostellerie La Poularde (Montrond les Bains), Sousceyrac (rue Faideherbe, Paris), Le Menozzi (Montrouge), Augusto (Deauville).

Abroad

United Kingdom

John Sandell Wines, 12 Field Close, Locks Heath, Southampton, Hampshire SO3 6TX. Tel: 048 95 77128.

Belgium

Le Caveau de France, Bervoetsstraat 22, 2 000 Antwerp. Tel: 03 231 33 32/31.

The Netherlands

Léon Colaris, b.v. Postbus 55, Emmasingel 15, 6000 AB Weert.

PHILIPPE BOUZEREAU

Philippe Bouzereau
15, Place de l'Europe, 21190 Meursault.
80 21 20 32

Type of vineyard: Family-owned. **Vine stocks:** Chardonnay 60%, Pinot Rouge 30%, Gamay Aligoté 10%. **Soil:** Chalky clay. **Exposure:** Rising sun.
Appellation: Meursault, Puligny, Chassagne, Beaune, Corton, Santenay. **Technique:** Traditional. **Maturing:** Oak casks, renewed every 5 years. **Characteristics:** Wide variety going from Bourgogne Aligoté to Corton Bressandes. **Vintages available in 89/90:** Red: 1987. White: 1988.

Characteristics of vintages

1988: Very successful, especially in red. Forthcoming year, for keeping. **1987:** Light wines, very well balanced, delicate. Excellent, fragrant whites that are quite harmonious.

Price range (pre-tax, ex-warehouse): between 20 and 160 F.F.
Sales volume:
– Wholesale: 50%. – Retail: 40%. – Restaurants: 10%.
Sales in France: 30%.
Export sales: 70%.

Abroad

United States

Chadderdon, New-York. Martine's Wines, San Francisco.

United Kingdom

David Baillie.

Far East

Japan: Luc Corporation, Tokyo.

Comments

A domain derived from an exploitation of the proprietor's father, itself passed on from generation to generation since the 17th century, divided and increased in size over the years according to the opportunities provided. Some excellent vintages, notably in whites (Puligny, Meursault).

J.-F. COCHE - DURY

Jean-François Coche
9, rue Charles-Giraud - 21190 Meursault
80 21 24 12

Type of vineyard: Family-owned. **Established:** 1972. **Vine stocks:** Aligoté, Chardonnay, Pinot Noir. **Soil:** Chalk and clay with calcium carbonate. **Exposure:** East and Southeast. **Average annual production in hectoliters:** 250. **Appellation:** Burgundy. **Type:** Red, white. **Technique:** Traditional. **Maturing:** In casks for 18 to 22 months. **Characteristics:** Keeps the character of each locality. **Serving temperature:** Whites: about 14°, reds: 16 to 18°. **Vintages available in 89/90:** Available only by reservation.

Characteristics of vintages

Sales in France: 55%.
Export sales: 45%.
Main trading partners : UK, Netherlands, Belgium, Norway, Germany, Switzerland, Italy, USA, Japan, Australia.

FRANÇOIS CHARLES

François Charles
Nantoux 21190 Meursault
80 26 01 20

Type of vineyard: Family-owned. **Established:** 1961. **Number of employees:** 2. **Vine stocks:** Pinot Noir. **Soil:** Chalky clay. **Exposure:** South, South West. **Average annual production in hectoliters:** 200.

Bourgogne
Hautes Côtes de Beaune
APPELLATION CONTROLÉE
Récolté et mis en bouteilles par
75 cl
FRANÇOIS CHARLES
PROPRIÉTAIRE-VITICULTEUR A NANTOUX (COTE-D'OR)

Appellation: Bourgogne Haute Côtes-de-Beaune. **Type:** Red. **Technique:** Traditional with temperature control. **Maturing:** In oak casks. **Alcohol content:** 12.8%. **Characteristics:** Very fruity and very good color. **Serving temperature:** 12 to 13°. **Served with:** Game, cheese. **Vintages available in 89/90:** 1986, 1987.

Characteristics of vintages

1987: Tannic, good keeping, very surprising for the vintage. **1986:** Fruity, light and supple. Price range (pre-taxe, ex-warehouse): 20 to 30 F.F.
Sales volume:
– Wholesale: 10%. – Retail: 70%. – Other: 20%.
Sales in France: 80%.
Export sales: 20%.
Main trading partners : Germany, Netherlands.

References in France

Shops: Les Spécialités, 44 Chateaubriant – Le Cellier de Longchamps, 35 Rennes – Terroir 52, 52100 St-Didier.

Abroad

Germany

La Cave Steines, 8058 Erding.

The Netherlands

Henri Bloem, S 8011 XH Zwolle.

Comments

Successful enterprise which produces other wines as well: Bourgogne Aligoté, Bourgogne Hautes Côtes-de-Beaune Blanc, Bourgogne Passetoutgrain and some great crus – Volnay 1er Cru, Beaune 1er Cru and Pommard (very successful in 1983 and 1986).

DOMAINE J. JOLIOT ET FILS

Jean-Baptiste Joliot
Nantoux - 21190 Meursault
80 26 01 44

Type of vineyard: Family-owned. **Established:** Has always existed from father to son. **Vine stocks:** Pinot Noir, Chardonnay. **Soil:** Clay with calcium carbonate. **Exposure:** East, Southeast. **Average annual production in hectoliters:** 400.
Appellation: Pommard, Meursault, Hautes Côtes de Beaune. **Type:** Red, white. **Technique:** Traditional. **Maturing:** In Oak casks. **Alcohol content:** 12.5 to 13.5%. **Characteristics:** Pommard: firm and forthcoming, fullness, body, spicy fragrance. Meursault: very soft and rich, with just enough acidity, very fragrant. Hautes Côtes de Beaune: small fruit taste, delicate aroma, beautiful color. **Serving temperature:** Red: 15 to 16°, white: 10 to 12°. **Served with:** Red: eggs in wine sauce (meurette), Coq au Vin, meat in sauce, roast meat, cheese. White: parsley, ham, fish. **Vintages available in 89/90:** 1981, 1983, 1984, 1985, 1986.

Characteristics of vintages

1986: Very successful thanks to lots of care. Beautiful amber color. Fragrant red. **1985:** Easy year, very good. To be drunk young, very fragrant. **1984:** To be kept, although already good to drink. Will age well. **1983:** Tannin, forthcoming, good quality, good year, great wine. **1982:** Stock exhausted. **Other: 1981:** Astonishing fragrance, great bottles that will surprise you. Price range (pre-tax, ex-warehouse): between 20 F.F. and 80 F.F.
Sales volume:
- Wholesale: 40%. - Retail: 40%. - Restaurants: 5%.
- Other: 15% (specialized shops and clubs).
Sales in France: 60%.
Export sales: 40%.
Main trading partners : Belgium, Germany, Netherlands, Switzerland. Some to the UK and the USA.

DOMAINE GUY ROULOT

Mrs. Jean-Marc Roulot
1 rue Charles-Giraud - 21190 Meursault
80 21 21 65

Type of vineyard: Family-owned. **Established:** 1951. **Number of employees:** 6. **Vine stocks:** Chardonnay, Bourgogne Aligoté, Pinot Noir. **Soil:** Chalky clay. **Exposure:** East-West.

MIS EN BOUTEILLES A LA PROPRIÉTÉ
Meursault
"Les Luchets"
APPELLATION MEURSAULT CONTROLÉE
75 cl
Domaine Guy ROULOT
13% vol.
PROPRIÉTAIRE A MEURSAULT (COTE-D'OR) FRANCE

Appellation: Meursault, Auxey, Bourgogne Chardonnay. **Type:** Red, White. **Technique:** Separate vinification for each variety in the appellation. **Maturing:** In oak casks (20% new) - on lees for 8 months, bottled in September. **Serving temperature:** 12°. **Served with:** Fish and shellfish, certain vintages with white meat and fois gras. **Vintages available in 89/90:** 1987.

Characteristics of vintages

1987: Flowery aromas, more subdued than the 1985 or 1986 - Bottled relatively recently (September 1988). Wait. **Other:** Marc and Fine distilled and produced by the Domain are also for sale (see Comments).
Sales volume:
- Retail: 45%. - Restaurants: 55%.
Sales in France: 60%.
Export sales: 40%.
Main trading partners : USA, UK, Germany, Switzerland, Netherlands.

References in France

Restaurants: Pierre Gagnaire, La Mère Blanc, Loiseau, Saulieu, Marc Meneau, Lameloise, Rostang, Troisgros, Comme Chez Soi.
Shops: Caves Retrou, Caves Notre-Dame.

Abroad

United States
Importers: Parliament Import Company - Atlantic city.

United Kingdom
Domaine Direct, London.

Germany
Klaus Fetzner.

Switzerland
Fischer.

The Netherlands
Van Nieulande.

Others
Australia, Japan, New Zealand.

Comments

Guy Roulot founded his enterprise during the 1950s. He was one of the first Meursault winemakers to vinify the harvests from various parcels separately. Since his death in 1982, Geneviève Roulot and her children have taken over the operation of the domain. Master distiller since 1860. Production of Marc and Fine Bourgogne, aged for 10 years in oak casks.

ROPITEAU FRÈRES

François Mariotte Director
Jean-Marc Pusset Export manager
21190 Meursault
80 21 23 94 - Telex: 350 951

Type of vineyard: Agricultural Association. **Established:** 1848. **Number of employees:** 30. **Average annual production in hectoliters:** 18,750.
Appellation: Main. **Type:** White. **Maturing:** In new casks. **Alcohol content:** 13%. **Characteristics:** Elegant, dry, soft and rich, vanilla and toasted aroma. **Serving temperature:** 12°. **Served with:** Fish and shellfish. **Vintages available in 89/90:** 1986, 1987, 1988. **Others:** Vins de Chablis, de la Côte-de-Nuits et Côte-de-Beaune, Maçonnais, Beaujolais et Côtes-du-Rhône, Meursault de Ropiteau.

Characteristics of vintages

1988: Perfect acidity balance, soft and full, delicate. **1987:** Fresh honey and vanilla aroma - good keeping. **1986:** Great

finesse, class. Price range (pre-tax, ex-warehouse): 80 to 120 F.F.
Sales in France: 20%.
Export sales: 80%.
Main trading partners: UK, Germany, USA, Canada, Netherlands, Belgium, Switzerland, etc.

References in France

Restaurants: Fouquet's, Royal Monceau, La Tour Eiffel, La Coupole, Bœuf sur le Toit, L'Estournel.
Shops: Flo Prestige, Hediard.

Abroad

United States
Palm Bay Imports Inc. P.O. BOX 1026, Long Island City, N.Y. 11101 (Tel: (718) 274 4900).

United Kingdom
Waverley Vintners Agencies, P.O. BOX 22, Crieff Road, Perth PH1 2SL (Tel: 0738 29621).

Germany
M. Munz, Schafgarten 25, 7000 Stuttgart 75. Mrs. Collong, Friedenplatz 6, 6227 Oestrichwinkel (Tel: 711 47 77 67 & 672 350 36). Mr. Foglino, Ingolstädterstr 68 c 8000 München 45. Tel: (089) 3 16 40 15.

Switzerland
Agence Tritten, JM Beausoleil, Borex Soleil, 1261 Borex (Tel: (022) 67 17 16).

Belgium
Ets Tamines, Strephenson Straat 80/84, 1020 Brussels (Tel: 2 241 94 64).

Canada
United Distillers Group Ltd. 180 Bloor Street West, Toronto, Ontario M5S 2V6 (Tel: (416) 964 2880).

Quebec
Vins Philippe Dandurand, 251, rue St Jacques Ouest, Montreal Quebec M2Y 1H6.

The Netherlands
Intercaves BV, Marsweg 43, Postbus 517, 8000 An Zwolle (Tel: 38 69 69 69).

Far East
Japan: Nisshoku Co, Ltd, 9-10 Nozaki-Cho, Kita-Ku, Osaka (Tel: 6 313 0689).

Comments

In 1848, Jean Ropiteau, descended from a very long line of winemakers (his ancestors are at the head of the oldest civil register of the commune, dated 1580) foresaw that improvements in transportation and simplification of travel could bring a great deal to Burgundy. The Ropiteau Brothers' establishment moved to Meursault in 1930, setting up shop in the "Caves de l'Hôpital", former property of the Hospices de Beaune (17th century property of the President of Massol). For five generations, they have been distributing wines from the best located domains of the region.

DOMAINE JACQUES PRIEUR

Jean and Martin Prieur
Rue des Santenots, 21190 Meursault
80 21 23 85

Type of vineyard: Corporation.
Appellation: Meursault, Puligny-Montrachet, Clos-Vougeot, Beaune, Volnay, Musigny, Chambertin, Montrachet. **Type:** Red, white. **Technique:** Traditional. **Maturing:** In oak casks. **Serving temperature:** Room temperature.

Characteristics of vintages

1988: Not yet ready, very promising year. **1987:** Small harvest, good year. **1986:** Same. **1985:** Same. **Other:** 1982, 1983: in small quantities. Price range (pre-tax, ex-warehouse): between 20 and 160 F.F.
Sales in France: 20%.
Export sales: 80%.

References in France

Restaurants: L'Oustau de Beaumanière, Georges Blanc, etc.

Abroad

United States
Vintners International, New York.

United Kingdom
Heyman Brothers, London.

Switzerland
Ste Pam, Beaune.

Belgium
Louis Cooreman, Brussels.

Canada
Ontario and Quebec Monopolies.

The Netherlands
Verlinden, AG's Hertogenbosch.

PULIGNY-MONTRACHET

DOMAINE LAROCHE

Claude Laroche
Château de Puligny-Montrachet
21190 Meursault
86 42 14 30 – Telex: 800 029

Type of vineyard: Corporation. **Established:** Bought in 1985. **Number of employees:** 7. **Vine stocks:** Chardonnay, Pinot Noir. **Soil:** Clay with calcium carbonate. **Exposure:** East, Southeast. **Average annual production in hectoliters:** 50 hectoliters/hectare.
Appellation: Puligny-Montrachet, Meursault, Pommard, Monthelie, Côtes-de-Nuits, Clos du Château (white). **Type:** Red, white. **Technique:** Fermentation in casks (white), vinification with crushing, temperature control (red). **Maturing:** Traditional. **Alcohol content:** 12.5 to 13%. **Characteristics:** White: rich, full, forthcoming. Red: tannic, fine, to be kept. **Serving temperature:** White: 12 to 15°. Red: 14 to 17°. **Served with:** White: fish, poultry. Red: roasts, cheese. **Vintages available in 89/90:** 1986, 1985.

Characteristics of vintages

1986: Good year for whites. **1985:** Excellent vintage, especially for reds. Château de Puligny, not yet tasted. Price range (pre-tax, ex-warehouse): Between 60 F.F. and 150 F.F.
Sales volume:
– Retail: 10%. – Restaurants: 70%. – Other: 20% (airlines).
Sales in France: 20%.
Export sales: 80%.
Main trading partners: UK, Germany, USA, Japan, Canada.

References in France

Restaurants: 200 restaurants with Michelin stars.
Shops: Fauchon, etc.

DOMAINE HENRI CLERC

Bernard Clerc
Puligny Montrachet – 21190 Meursault
80 21 32 74

Type of vineyard: Family-owned. **Established:** Several centuries. **Number of employees:** 14. **Vine stocks:** Chardonnay, Aligoté, Pinot Noir, Gamay. **Soil:** Clay with calcium carbonate. **Exposure:** Hillsides and plains – Southeast. **Average annual production in hectoliters:** 1,000 to 1,500.

Appellation: Grands Crus, 1er Crus, Villages, Appellations Régionales. **Type:** Red, white, rosé. **Technique:** Classical Burgundy. **Maturing:** In Oak, casks, one year before bottling. **Characteristics:** White and red wines from harvested in the communes of: Vougeot, Beaune, Meursault, Puligny, Chassagne, Corpeau. **Serving temperature:** White: 14° to 16°. Red: 18 to 20°. **Served with:** White: as an aperitif or with warm and cold first courses, seafood, fish, white meat, goat cheese and swiss cheese. Red: red meat-grilled or in sauce. **Vintages available in 89/90:** 1985 and 1986.

Characteristics of vintages

1986: Good whites (Puligny, Meursault). **1985:** Remarkable Beaune and Vougeot reds, robust and supple at the same time, dense, to be aged. Average pre-tax, ex-warehouse price: Between 23 and 220 F.F.
Sales volume:
– Wholesale: 1/2. – Retail: 1/4. – Restaurants: 1/4.
Sales in France: 1/2.
Export sales: 1/2.
Main trading partners: Benelux Countries, Germany, UK, Switzerland, USA, Japan, Australia.

SCE DU DOMAINE ÉTIENNE SAUZET
Gérard Boudot
Puligny Montrachet – 21190 Meursault
80 21 32 10

Type of vineyard: Family corporation. **Established:** Beginning of the Century. **Vine stocks:** 100% Chardonnay. **Soil:** Clay with calcium carbonate. **Exposure:** Southeast. **Average annual production in hectoliters:** 650. **Appellation:** Puligny-Montrachet. **Type:** White. **Technique:** Oak casks, 1/3 new each year. **Maturing:** 11 months in casks. **Alcohol content:** 13%. **Characteristics:** Balanced, subtle, long. **Serving temperature:** 12°. **Served with:** Fish, shellfish. **Vintages available in 89/90:** 1986.

Characteristics of vintages

1986: Beautiful balance. Consistant, will age well in the bottle. A very successful white, soft and supple, with complex aromas, full. Price range (pre-tax, ex-warehouse): Between 80 and 140 F.F.
Sales volume:
– Retail: 15%. – Restaurants: 30%. – Other: 55% (export).
Sales in France: 45%.
Export sales: 55%.
Main trading partners: USA, UK, Japan, Netherlands, Belgium, Australia.

References in France

Restaurants: Nearly all of the Michelin 3 stars Rest. in France.
Shops: Numerous shops in Paris.

Abroad

United States
Vineyard Brands, Inc. (Robert Haas Selections), Chester, Vermont 05143.

United Kingdom
O.W. Loeb (London). Ingletons Wines (Maldon, Essex). Lay and Wheeler (Colchester, Essex). Adnams, etc.

Germany
Restaurants: Tantris (Munich), Le Canard (Hamburg), Krautkrämer (Münster).

the Netherlands
Okhuysen (Haarlem).

Others
R. Goffard (Belgium). Cellarcraf (Sydney, Australia). Mitsubishi (Japan).

• *The naturally sweet wines of the Loire region, such as Quarts-de-Chaume or Coteau-du-Layon, offer the possibility of some very lovely wine tastings. Very fruity, full, supple and harmonious, they will keep well. (See the Chapter on the Loire Valley).*

DOMAINE
ÉTIENNE SAUZET

PROPRIÉTAIRE A
PULIGNY-MONTRACHET
COTE-D'OR

SAINT-AUBIN

DOMAINE AIME LANGOUREAU

Gilles Bouton
Gamay Saint-Aubin, 21190 Meursault
80 21 32 63

Type of vineyard: Family-owned. **Established:** Family owned since 1740 – present owner Gilles Bouton. **Number of employees:** 1. **Vine stocks:** Chardonnay, Pinot Noir, Gamay, Aligoté. **Soil:** Chalky clay. **Exposure:** South, South-East. **Average annual production in hectoliters:** 300.

Appellation: Saint Aubin (Cru De Bourgogne et 1er Cru), Blagny 1er Cru, Chassagne Mr., Puligny 1er Cru "Les Garennes". **Type:** Red, white. **Technique:** Temperature control, fermentation on skins (12 days for red wine). **Maturing:** Casks and vats. **Alcohol content:** 12.5%. **Characteristics:** Red: rich and well balanced, good keeping – White: very fragrant, beautiful golden color. **Serving temperature:** Red: 15° – White: 12°. **Served with:** Delicatessen, fish. Red: coq au vin. **Vintages available in 89/90:** Red: 1987, 1988. White: 1988.

Characteristics of vintages

1988: Red: tannic, beautiful ruby color White: very fruity.
1987: Red: very fragrant, and pleasant. To be drunk young.
Price range (pre-tax, ex-warehouse): 30 to 50 F.F.

Sales volume:
– Wholesale: 20%. – Retail: 50%. – Restaurants: 5%. – Other: 25% export.
Sales in France: 67%.
Export sales: 33%.
Main trading partners : Netherlands, Belgium, Switzerland, United Kingdom.

References in France

Restaurants: Vanel (31000 Toulouse), Les Petits Plats (75 Pontoise), Diana (67000 Molsheim).

Abroad

United Kingdom
Kurs, 12 Littleton Road, Harrow Middlesex HA 135 V.

Germany
Weinagesstur Wiethasestrasse 67, 5000 Koln 41.

Switzerland
Pultter (importer), Résidence St-Jacques, 21200 Beaune.

Belgium
René Verhelle, Mechelsesteenweg 1987, 3009 Herent.

The Netherlands
W. Van der Linden Postbus 31041, 3003 HA Rotterdam.

Other
Luxemburg: European Parliament, Plateau de Kirchberg, 2929 Dutch West Indies: Le Coq Traditionnel – French Wines N.V. 90 Orange Grove, Cole Bay – St. Maarten N.A.

Comments

Visit the arched cellars and the tasting room.

- *The 1980 vintage is badly understood. In Bordeaux the wines are already quite surprising and will do quite well while waiting for the development of the other vintages. See "The last five vintages" in the Chapter on Bordeaux wines.*

DOMAINE DU CHÂTEAU CHARLES BLONDEAU-DANNE PÈRE

Denis Blondeau-Danne
Château de Saint-Aubin 21190 Saint-Aubin
80 21 31 46

Type of vineyard: Family-owned. **Established:** 1977 – previous manager Charles Blondeau-Danne. **Number of employees:** 3. **Vine stocks:** Pinot noir, Chardonnay, Aligoté. **Average annual production in hectoliters:** 300. **Appellation:** Saint-Aubin 1er Cru, Puligny Montrachet 1er Cru, Meursault 1er Cru, Volnay, Chassagne Montrachet, Criots Batard Montrachet. **Type:** Red, white. **Technique:** Traditional. **Maturing:** In oak vats. **Characteristics:** Red: beautiful color, complex aromas, tannic, good keeping – White: very fruity, graceful and delicate. **Serving temperature:** Red: 16°. White: 8°. **Vintages available in 89/90:** 1984, 1985, 1986, 1987.

Characteristics of vintages

1987: White: very fragrant, pleasant, to be aged, great year. **1986:** Red: tannic, very aromatic. White: fine, delicate aroma, exceptionnal year. **1985:** Red: tannic, supple, rich. White: aromatic, fullbodied, to be drunk, great year.
Sales volume:
– Retail: 70%. – Restaurants: 30 %.
Sales in France: 70%.
Export sales: 30%.
Main trading partners : Switzerland, Belgium, Netherlands, Denmark.

Comments

Excellent white wines (Meursault and Puligny), and typical red wines of the appellation. Vinification always very well controlled.

MARC COLIN

St-Aubin 21190 Meursault
80 21 30 43

Type of vineyard: Family-owned. **Established:** 1979. **Vine stocks:** Aligoté, Pinot Noir, Chardonnay. **Soil:** Chalky on chalk and chalky clay. **Exposure:** South, South-East. **Average annual production in hectoliters:** 400.

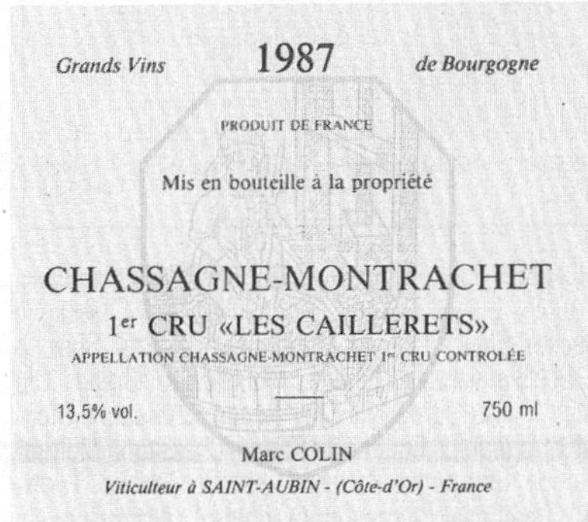

Grands Vins 1987 de Bourgogne
PRODUIT DE FRANCE
Mis en bouteille à la propriété
CHASSAGNE-MONTRACHET
1er CRU «LES CAILLERETS»
APPELLATION CHASSAGNE-MONTRACHET 1er CRU CONTROLÉE
13,5% vol.
750 ml
Marc COLIN
Viticulteur à SAINT-AUBIN - (Côte-d'Or) - France

Appellation: Bourgogne Aligoté, St Aubin 1er Cru Blanc & Rouge, Chassagne-Montrachet, Chassagne 1er Cru, Cailleret & Champgains Blanc, Saint Aubin, Santenay, Montrachet. **Type:** Red, White. **Technique:** Traditional. **Maturing:** In vats and casks. **Alcohol content:** 13%. **Serving temperature:** White: 13 to 14°. Red: 14 to 16°. **Vintages available in 89/90:** 1987 & 1988.

Characteristics of vintages

1988: Very rich red and white. **1987:** Very good white. Good red. **1986:** White: stock depleted. Lovely red. **1985:** stock depleted. Price range (pre-tax, ex-warehouse): 20 to 160 F.F. and over.

Sales volume:
– Wholesale: 15%. – Retail: 30%. – Restaurants: 15%. – Other: 40% (export).
Sales in France: 50%.
Export sales: 50%.
Main trading partners : Japan, UK, Belgium, Germany, Netherlands, Italy, Norway, Switzerland, USA.

References in France

Restaurants: Lameloise, Georges Blanc, Taillevent, Montrachet, Loiseau.

DOMAINE BACHELET JEAN-CLAUDE

Jean-Claude Bachelet
Saint-Aubin, 21190 Meursault
80 21 31 01

Type of vineyard: Family-owned. **Vine stocks:** Chardonnay, Pinot Noir. **Soil:** Chalky clay. **Exposure:** South and Southeast.

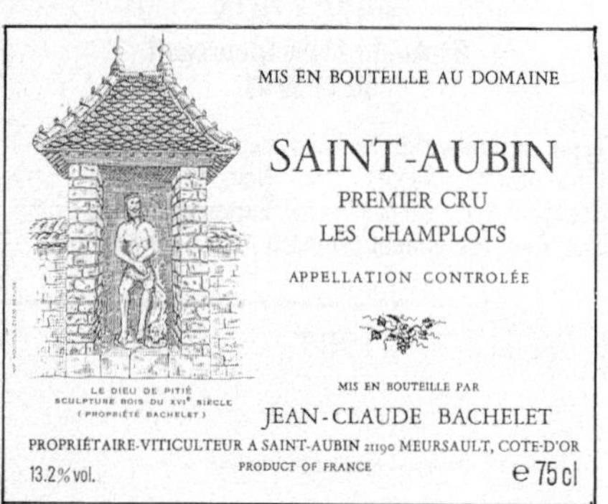

MIS EN BOUTEILLE AU DOMAINE
SAINT-AUBIN
PREMIER CRU
LES CHAMPLOTS
APPELLATION CONTROLÉE
LE DIEU DE PITIÉ
SCULPTURE BOIS DU XVI° SIÈCLE
(PROPRIÉTÉ BACHELET)
MIS EN BOUTEILLE PAR
JEAN-CLAUDE BACHELET
PROPRIÉTAIRE-VITICULTEUR A SAINT-AUBIN 21190 MEURSAULT, COTE-D'OR
PRODUCT OF FRANCE
13.2% vol.
e 75 cl

Appellation: Saint-Aubin 1er Cru, Les Champlots Blanc, Saint-Aubin Blanc, Puligny Montrachet Bl, Chassagne Montrachet Blanc, Puligny Montrachet 1er Cru, Sous le Puits Bl Bienvenues Bâtard Montrachet Grand Cru St. Aubin 1er Cru Derrière la Tour Rouge, Chassagne Montrachet 1er Cru de La Boudriotte Rouge, Chassagne Montrachet Rouge, Bourgogne Rouge. **Type:** Red, White. **Technique:** Traditional, temperature control. **Maturing:** In casks, 1/3 new. **Characteristics:** White: fruity, full-bodied Red: rich and well balanced. **Serving temperature:** White: 12-14° - Red: 16-18°.

Characteristics of vintages

1988: Red: very great year – White: pleasant. **1987:** Red and White: promising. **1986:** White: lively – very good year. Red: pleasant. **1985:** Beautiful year. Good keeping.
Sales volume:
– Wholesale: 50%. – Restaurants: 10%. – Other: 40%. export.
Sales in France: 60%.
Export sales: 40%.
Main trading partners : United Kingdom, Belgium.

References in France

Restaurants: Auberge Bretonne, Jacques Taurel, Restaurant Jean Brouilly, Montrachet, Puligny Montrachet.
Shops: Cellier Saint-Germain.

Abroad

United Kingdom

Mrs. Richard Walford, Manor House Pickwoth, Rutland near Stamford Limes PE9 4DJ Tel: 078081242.

ROUX PÈRE ET FILS

Saint-Aubin – 21190 Meursault
80 21 32 92 – Fax: 80 21 35 00

Type of vineyard: Corporation – family-owned. **Average annual production in hectoliters:** 200,000 bottles. **Appellation:** Meursault, Puligny-Montrachet, Chassagne-Montrachet, Santenay, Bourgogne, St. Aubin. **Type:** Red, white. **Technique:** Traditional with temperature control. **Characteristics:** More than 30 Awards and medals since 1970. White: great wines, rich, full, fragrant, very fine. Red: structured, aromatic, seductive. **Vintages available in 89/90:** Red: 1987, 1988. White: 1988.

Characteristics of vintages

1986: Very good year. Superb whites: Meursault, Chassagne and Puligny to be aged. **1985:** Excellent vintage, complete, well-balanced, elegant, red wines for long ageing, very successful whites.
Sales volume:
– Retail: 30%. – Restaurants: 15%.
– Other: 5% (corporations), 50% (export).
Main trading partners : USA, Japan, EEC (UK, Netherlands, Belgium, Germany, Sweden), Australia, Switzerland.

SANTENAY

CHÂTEAU DE LA CHARRIÈRE

Jean Girardin
21590 Santenay
80 20 61 95

Type of vineyard: Family-owned. **Established:** For three generations. **Vine stocks:** Pinot Noir and Chardonnay. **Soil:** Chalky clay. **Exposure:** South, South-West. **Average annual production in hectoliters:** 900.

Château de la Charrière
Santenay Clos Rousseau
1er Cru
APPELLATION SANTENAY CONTROLÉE
Mis en bouteille au Château par
750 ml e
Domaine Jean GIRARDIN, Propriétaire-Récoltant à Santenay (Côte-d'Or)
PRODUCE OF FRANCE

Appellation: Bourgogne, Côtes de Beaune, Santenay et 1er Cru "Gravières", Commes, Beauregard, Clos Rousseau, Maladière, Passe-Temps, Savigny-lès-Beaune, Blanc et Rouge, Chassagne-Montrachet 1er Cru Morgeot, Clos St. Jean. **Type:** Red, White. **Technique:** Traditional. **Maturing:** Oak casks (1/3 new). **Alcohol content:** 13%. **Characteristics:** Deep color, very fine red berry nose particulary after a few years ageing, rich (full-bodied and tannic) – very good keeping. **Serving temperature:** 16°. **Served with:** Duck, coq au vin, venaison. **Vintages available in 89/90:** 1986, 1987, 1988.

Characteristics of vintages

1988: Exceptional year, color, bouquet and flavor. **1987:** Very good year, rich, long keeping. **1986:** Good year, fruity and supple. Price range (pre-tax, ex-warehouse): 30 to 50 F.F.

Sales volume:
– Wholesale: 73 %. – Retail: 15 %. – Restaurants : 2 %. – Other: 10% (associations).

Sales in France: 25%.

Export sales: 75%.

Main trading partners : Switzerland, UK, Germany, Japan.

References in France

Restaurants: A number of restaurants in Paris.

OLIVIER PÈRE ET FILS

Hervé Olivier
21590 Santenay
80 20 61 35

Type of vineyard: Family-owned. **Number of employees:** 1. **Vine stocks:** Pinot noir, Chardonnay. **Soil:** Chalky and chalky clay. **Exposure:** South-East. **Average annual production in hectoliters:** 40-45 hl/ha. **Appellation:** Bourgogne, Santenay, Santenay 1er Cru, Savigny les Beaune 1er Cru, Pommard. **Type:** Red White (Santenay). **Technique:** Traditional. **Maturing:** 2 years in wooden casks. **Alcohol content:** 13%. **Characteristics:** Aromatic, typical Pinot de Bourgogne, made from vines growing on the upper hillsides. **Serving temperature:** 16 to 18°. **Served with:** Meat in sauce, cheese. **Vintages available in 89/90:** 1987, 1988.

Characteristics of vintages

1988: Excellent red, rich and well balanced, good white, fresh and fragrant. **1987:** White: aromatic, fin Red: quite successful. Price range (pre-tax, ex-warehouse): 30 to 50 F.F. (Bourgogne) – 50 to 80 F.F. (Santenay 1er Cru, Savigny 1er Cru & Santenay Blanc – 80 to 120 F.F. (Pommard).

Sales volume:
– Wholesale: 10%. – Retail: 80%. – Restaurants: 5%. – Other: 5% (agents).

Sales in France: 80%.

Export sales: 20%.

Main trading partners : Belgium, United Kingdom, Switzerland, Denmark, Netherlands.

References in France

Restaurants: Chez Camille (21 Arnay le Duc), Hostellerie du Château de Bellecroix (71 Chagny), La Vigne (58 St Pierre le Moutiers), Ma Cuisine (rue Bayen 17th), Chez Prunières (rue d'Assas, Paris 6th).

Abroad

United Kingdom

Russel and Mac Iver London – High Breck Vintners Hants.

Germany

Der Franzosiche Weinkeller 7032 Harrenberg.

Belgium

Goffard Brussels.

Comments

Successful family exploitation, reputed for the regularity of its wines (Bourgogne, Santenay, Savigny...).

• *To help us improve our next edition, please send in your suggestions and answer our questionnaire.*

DOMAINE PRIEUR-BRUNET

Guy Prieur
21590 Santenay
80 20 60 56 - Telex: 350 376 F

Type of vineyard: Family-owned. **Established:** 1804. **Number of employees:** 10. **Vine stocks:** Pinot Noir Chardonnay. **Soil:** Clay with calcium carbonate. **Average annual production in hectoliters:** 1,000.

Appellation: Santenay, Chassagne Montrachet, Meursault, Volnay, Pommard, Beaune. **Technique:** Long fermentation with skins for reds. Pneumatic press. **Maturing:** In Oak casks - 25% new casks per year. **Alcohol content:** 13%. **Characteristics:** Very aromatic, well balanced for ageing. **Serving temperature:** Whites, 8° to 10°, reds 12° to 16°. **Served with:** Santenay at Volnay - with Leg of Lamb and poultry, Beaune and Pommard - red meat, Chassagne Montrachet - game, Meursault and Chassagne Montrachet - fish served warm, Batard Montrachet - foie gras. **Vintages available in 89/90:** 1985, 1986, 1987.

Characteristics of vintages

1987: Red: fine, very aromatic, color - white: fruity. **1986:** red: robust, fragrant, spicy - white: fragrant, inviting. **1985:** light, aromatic, to be tasted. Price range (pre-tax, ex-warehouse): between 50 F.F. and 80 F.F.

Sales volume:
- Retail: 30%. - Restaurants: 40%. - Other: 30% (export).

Sales in France: 70%.
Export sales: 30%.
Main trading partners : UK, Germany, USA, Switzerland, Japan, Benelux Countries, Canada.

References in France

Restaurants: La Marée, Paris, L'Espérance at St. Père; Lameloise at Chagny; Crocodile at Strasbourg.

• *For an ideal wine cellar, find out what to do and what not to do (see chapter "Organizing a Wine Cellar")*

DOMAINE JOSEPH BELLAND

Joseph Belland
Rue de la Chapelle - 21590 Santenay
80 20 61 13

Type of vineyard: Family-owned. **Established:** For 3 generations. **Number of employees:** 9. **Vine stocks:** Pinot Noir for the red, Chardonnay for the white. **Soil:** Clay with calcium carbonate on a limestone base. **Exposure:** South and Southeast. **Average annual production in hectoliters:** 650.

Appellation: Santenay, Chassagne-Montrachet, Puligny-Montrachet 1er Cru and Pommard. **Type:** Red, white. **Technique:** Traditional. Open vats, floating cap. **Maturing:** In Oak barrels, approx. 2 years. **Alcohol content:** 12 to 13%. **Characteristics:** Very rich and well-balanced, can easily age 10 years or more. Finesse and bouquet develop with ageing. **Serving temperature:** Red: 17 to 18°. White: 12°. **Served with:** Everything, except sweet or vinegary food. **Vintages available in 89/90:** 1986, 1985, 1984, 1983, 1982, 1981, 1980 and 1979.

Characteristics of vintages

1986: Very well balanced wine that will age well, with a fine and elegant bouquet. **1985:** Great year, full, rich, velvety. Lively ruby color, good length. **1984:** Supple, quite mellow, fruity, will develop quite rapidly. **1983:** Very beautiful vintage, rich and well-balanced, very tannic. To drink when it is 10 years old. **1982:** Great vintage which is developing under very good conditions. Begin to drink in 2 years. **Other: 1981:** Beautiful color, very rich and well-balanced, substantial, will age very well. To be drunk around 1988-1990. 1980: Very fine wine, supple, fruity, delicate aroma, already well-developed. 1979: Very good year, pleasant, balanced and harmonious, with body and finesse. Ready to drink. Will easily keep for 4 to 5 years. Price range (pre-tax, ex-warehouse): between 30 F.F. and 160 F.F.

Sales volume:
- Wholesale: 25%. - Retail: 30%. - Restaurants: 25 %.
- Other: 20% (all clients).

Sales in France: 60%.
Export sales: 40%.
Main trading partners : Switzerland, Germany, Luxemburg, Belgium, Netherlands, UK, USA, Japan.

• *The naturally sweet wines of the Loire region, such as Quarts-de-Chaume or Coteau-du-Layon, offer the possibility of some very lovely wine tastings. Very fruity, full, supple and harmonious, they will keep well. (See the Chapter on the Loire Valley).*

• *Paulée - traditional meal which brings winelovers and winegrowers together after the harvest, particularly in Burgundy.*

CÔTE CHALONNAISE

BUXY

ALAIN BERTHAULT
Cercot Moroges - 71390 Buxy
85 47 91 03

Type of vineyard: Family-owned. **Established:** 1976. **Vine stocks:** Pinot Noir – Aligoté – Gamay. **Soil:** Clay with calcium carbonate. **Exposure:** Very favorable – good sunshine. **Average annual production in hectoliters:** 300.
Appellation: Bourgogne Pinot Noir – Bourgogne Aligoté – Crémant de Bourgogne. **Type:** Red, white. **Technique:** Traditional (fermentation with skins and pressing) No machines used. **Maturing:** Oak casks. **Alcohol content:** 12%. **Characteristics:** Aligoté: fresh, fruity, to be drunk young. Pinot Noir: must be aged. **Serving temperature:** Aligoté: 5° to 6°. Bourgogne Pinot Noir: 12° to 15°. **Served with:** Aligoté – seafood, fish, very good for Kir apéritifs Bourgogne Pinot Noir – red meat and cheese; Crémant de Bougogne – as an apéritif. **Vintages available in 89/90:** Aligoté: 1987 – Pinot Noir: 1986.

Characteristics of vintages

1986: The Bourgogne Pinot Noir must be aged for a few more years. **1985:** Fast developing year for the Bourgogne Pinot Noir. Crémant de Bourgogne ready for tasting. Price range (pre-tax, ex-warehouse): between 20 F.F. and 30 F.F. **Sales in France:** 100%.

GUY CHAUMONT
Le Montroy - Rosey - 71390 Buxy
85 47 94 70

Type of vineyard: Family-owned. **Established:** 1850. **Vine stocks:** Pinot Noir, Chardonnay, Gamay, Aligoté. **Soil:** Clay with calcium carbonate and a limestone sub-soil (the Basilor "mother" rock) or silica-clay with clay sub-soil. **Exposure:** Mostly South and Southeast. **Average annual production in hectoliters:** 280.
Appellation: Burgundy, Passetoutgrain, Burgundy Aligoté, Givry Rouge et blanc, Crémant de Bourgogne. **Type:** Red, white. **Technique:** Traditional. **Maturing:** Reds in wood, enamelled steel for the whites. **Characteristics:** Red Burgundy, characteristic of the wines of the Chalon region. Very typical Pinot Noir. Chardonnay wines representative of Givry, fine and fragrant. **Serving temperature:** Reds: 16°. Whites: 8° to 10°. **Served with:** Reds: the usual dishes for an average Pinot Noir. Whites: fine fish dishes, well prepared, poached, etc. Goat cheese. **Vintages available in 89/90:** 1985, 1986.

Characteristics of vintages

1987: Good Fine Whites. **1986:** Good quality whites. Reds quite supple. **1985:** Very good quality, to be aged. Average pre-tax, ex-warehouse price: 20 to 33 F.F.
Sales volume:
– Wholesale: 20%. – Retail: 60%.
– Restaurants: 5% (plus wine shops). – Other: 15% (export).
Sales in France: 85%.
Export sales: 15%.
Main trading partners: Germany, Switzerland, USA, England, Denmark.

JEAN DERAIN
Jean Derain
Bissey-sous-Cruchaud - 71390 Buxy
85 92 10 94

Type of vineyard: Family-owned. **Vine stocks:** Pinot noir, Pinot Chardonnay, Aligoté. **Soil:** Clay with calcium carbonate and granitic silica. **Exposure:** Hillside. **Average annual production in hectoliters:** 250.
Appellation: Burgundy, Burgundy Aligoté. **Type:** Red, white. **Technique:** Temperature control by heat pump. **Maturing:** Oak vats and casks. **Alcohol content:** 12.5%. **Characteristics:** Red Burgundy: forthcoming. White Burgundy: dry and robust. Burgundy Aligoté: dry, young, fruity. **Serving temperature:** Red Burgundy: 15 to 16°, white Burgundy: 8 to 10°. **Served with:** Red: meat and cheese. White: fish, shellfish. Aligoté: apéritif, oysters... **Vintages available in 89/90:** 1983, 1984, 1985, 1986.

Characteristics of vintages

1988: Bourgogne Rouge: Great vintage. **1987:** Bourgogne Rouge: Fruity, pleasant aromas, taste-tested by the Chevaliers du Clos Vougeot. **1986:** Forthcoming, more supple. Good white. **1985:** Exceptional wine, well made, to be kept. **1984:** Ageing agreeably, pleasant to drink. Price range (pre-tax, ex-warehouse): Between 10 and 30 F.F.
Sales volume:
– Wholesale: 50 %. – Retail: 45 %. – Restaurants: 5 %.
Sales in France: 85 %.
Export sales: 15 %.
Main trading partners : USA.

Abroad

United States
Northwind enterprises – 3434 Bladensburg Rd., Md. 20722.

MICHEL GOUBARD

Michel Goubard
71390 Saint-Desert
85 47 91 06

Established: 1963. **Number of employees:** 5. **Vine stocks:** Pinot Noir, Chardonnay, Aligoté. **Soil:** Chalky clay. **Exposure:** South-East. **Average annual production in hectolitres:** Approximately 700.

1986
Mont-Avril
Bourgogne
Appellation Bourgogne Contrôlée
Michel GOUBARD
Propriétaire-Récoltant
71390 SAINT DESERT
FRANCE
Tél. 85 47 91 06
Viticulteur de Père en Fils
depuis 1600
"Par la fenêtre du presbytère, je découvris
le village et le coteau du Mont-Avril dont le vin est renommé"
(Abbé Courtépée, historien de la Bourgogne, 1780)
13% vol.
750 ml
Mis en bouteille à la Propriété

Appellation: Bourgogne Rouge, Bourgogne Aligoté, Bourg Blanc, Bourg P.T.G. **Type:** Red, white, rosé. **Technique:** Traditional. **Maturing:** In oak vats and enamelled and concrete tanks. **Alcohol content:** 12.5 % and 13 %. **Characteristics:** Fruity, tannic. **Serving temperature:** Red: 15°. White: 8°. **Served with:** White: hors d'œuvres and fish. Red: red meat, cheese. **Vintages available in 89/90:** 1986 and 1987, Vins Vieux 1983.

Characteristics of vintages

1988: Very good balance for all Bourgognes. Very good wine, good ageing potential. **1987:** Fruity, to be drunk within 4 years. **1986:** Well balanced, very fruity, drink now. **1985:** Very good year, good keeping. **Other:** 1983: full-bodied, drink now with cheese. Price range (pre-tax, ex-warehouse): 20 to 30 F.F.
Sales volume:
– Retail: 40 %. – Restaurants: 10 %.
Sales in France: 52 %.
Export sales: 48 %.
Main trading partners : USA, Denmark, Germany, Switzerland, Belgium, UK, Netherlands.

References in France

Restaurants: La Brasière (Paris), Chez Annel (Paris), Sarajo (Paris), Restaurant La Grille (Lyon), Hostellerie du Vieux Moulin (Autun), Royal Grey (Cannes), Denis (Chalon-sur-Sâone), etc.
Shops: C.I.D.D. Alain Segelle (Paris), Cellier des Cordeliers (Macon), Sotebi (Le Havre), etc.

Abroad

United States
Dan Kravitz, 226 East Lee Street Warrenton V.A. 22186 – Tel: 1 34911060 – 703 347 3471.

United Kingdom
Cave d'Or Wines LTD. 160 Warstonelane Birmingam Bl86 NN Tel: 21 2364757.

Germany
Les Vignobles Multeimer S.T.R. 103 D.4100 Duisburg, Tel: 203 34 000 56 or 57 or 59. Hanseatische Weinhandelsges M.B.H. Limburgerstr 2900 Bremen M 6.

Switzerland
Club D.I.V.O. rue des Terreaux 2 1003 Lausanne Tel: 21 23 27 42.

Belgium
Club D.I.V.O. Quai au Foin 37 1003 Brussels Tel: 02 217 93 39. Michel Tiran Import rue Eugène Vadenhoff 4030 Grivegnee-Liege Tel: 041 42 68 92.

The Netherlands
Wijnkoperij B.V. Molenstraat 2.4. 8913 Leeunarden Tel: 58 12 58 06. W.C. Paroel Putstraat I 6251 N. Neckerlade.

Others
Denmark, Philipson Wine Aps Holmegardsvej 29 2920 Charlottenlund Tel: 64 50 81 – Otto Svenson Dr Tvaegade 7 1302 Copenhagen.

Comments

Family enterprise since 1600.

DOMAINE VACHET

Jean Vachet
Saint-Vallerin – 71390 Buxy
85 92 12 91

Type of vineyard: Family-owned. **Established:** 1640. **Number of employees:** 2. **Vine stocks:** Chardonnay and Pinot. **Soil:** Clay with calcium carbonate. **Exposure:** East. **Average annual production in hectoliters:** 250. **Appellation:** Montagny. **Type:** White. **Technique:** Traditional. **Maturing:** Vats. **Characteristics:** Fruity, sufficiently rich and well-balanced to age well. **Serving temperature:** 13°. **Served with:** First courses, delicatessen and fish. **Vintages available in 89/90:** 1987 then 1988.

Characteristics of vintages

1988: Beautiful wine, very promising, fruity, delicate, full-bodied, rich and well-balanced. Good keeping. **1987:** Fresh and fruity, as yet undeveloped but will come into its own in a year or so. **1986, 1985:** Two beautiful years combining fruitiness and richness, well-balanced. Price range (pre-tax, ex-warehouse): between 30 and 50 F.F.

Sales volume:
- Retail: 40%. - Restaurants: 20%. - Other: 40% (export).

Sales in France: 60%.
Export sales: 40%.
Main trading partners : Netherlands, Belgium, Germany, USA.

References in France

Restaurants: Billoux la Cloche (Dijon) - Les Trois Marches (Versailles) - Lutetia Concorde (Paris).

DOMAINE DE LA TOUR BAJOLE

Messrs. Roger and Jean-Claude Dessendre
71490 Saint-Maurice-les-Couches
85 49 67 60

Type of vineyard: Family-owned. **Established:** 1742. **Number of employees:** 4. **Vine stocks:** Red: Pinot Noir, Gamay. White: Chardonnay, Aligoté. **Soil:** Clay with calcium carbonate. **Exposure:** South, Southeast. **Average annual production in hectoliters:** 500.
Appellation: Bourgogne, Crémant de Bourgogne. **Type:** Red, white, rosé. **Technique:** Traditional vinification with temperature control. **Maturing:** Large and small oak casks. **Alcohol content:** 12.5%. **Characteristics:** Red: tannic, very fruity, good wine for ageing. Burgundy - sold after 4 years, earlier for the PTG (little). White Burgundy Chardonnay, very fruity and fragrant; Aligoté, drier. Rosé: very fragrant, onion skin color. Crémant, very fine. **Serving temperature:** Red: 16° to 18°. White and rosé: 8° to 10°. Crémant: 5°. **Served with:** Red: meat in sauce, game, certain cheeses. White (Chardonnay) : delicatessen products, fish; (Aligoté) fish and seafood. Rosé: as an apéritif or with dessert (chilled). Crémant: as an apéritif or with dessert. **Vintages available in 89/90:** Red: 1979, 1982. White: 1983 (Aligoté), 1985 (Chardonnay). Rosé: 1986. Crémant: 1986.

Characteristics of vintages

1986: Crémant and rosé: very pleasant. **1985:** Chardonnay: very fruity, similar to the Meursault of the same year. Great finesse. **1983:** Aligoté: very typical. Red: too tannic, needs to age. 20,000 bottles in stock. **1982:** Red: very tannic and fragrant. 2 types: Domaine and Chantefluté (more robust). **Other:** 1979: excellent, ready for consumption, soft, full and heady. Price range (pre-tax, ex-warehouse): Between 20 F.F. and 30 F.F.

Sales volume:
- Wholesale: 30%. - Retail: 40%.
- Restaurants: 25%. - Other: 5%.

Sales in France: 60%.
Export sales: 40%.
Main trading partners : UK, Germany, Benelux countries, Switzerland.

References in France

Restaurants: Restaurants de la Tour Bajole, Le Moulin de Bourg-Château (Tournus).

CHAGNY

MARIE LAFOUGE

Marie Lafouge
Paris L'Hôpital - 71150 Chagny
85 91 12 66

Type of vineyard: Family-owned. **Established:** 1960. **Vine stocks:** Pinot Noir. **Soil:** Clay with calcium carbonate. **Exposure:** Southeast. **Average annual production in hectoliters:** 250.
Appellation: Bourgogne, Hautes Côtes-de-Beaune. **Type:** Red. **Technique:** Traditional. **Maturing:** Large and small wooden casks. **Alcohol content:** 12.9%. **Characteristics:** These wines are initially astringent, characteristic of the wines of the region, but become more light and supple with age. **Serving temperature:** 18°. **Served with:** Meat and cheese. **Vintages available in 89/90:** 1981, 1984, 1985.

Characteristics of vintages

1985: Good vintages, supple and fragrant, awarded a Prize at the Concours de Mâcon. **1984:** Gold Medal at Mâcon, a very successful vintage. **Other:** 1981: Good vintage, quantity limited. Price range (pre-tax, ex-warehouse): Between 20 and 30 F.F.

Sales volume:
- Wholesale: 30%. - Retail: 60%. - Restaurants: 2%.

Sales in France: 90%.
Export sales: About 10%.
Main trading partners : Belgium, Netherlands.

JEAN MORETAUX AND SONS

Jean-Louis Moreteaux
Nantoux - Chassey-le-Camp - 71150 Chagny
85 87 19 10

Established: for 80 years. **Vine stocks:** Pinot Blanc and Pinot Rouge.

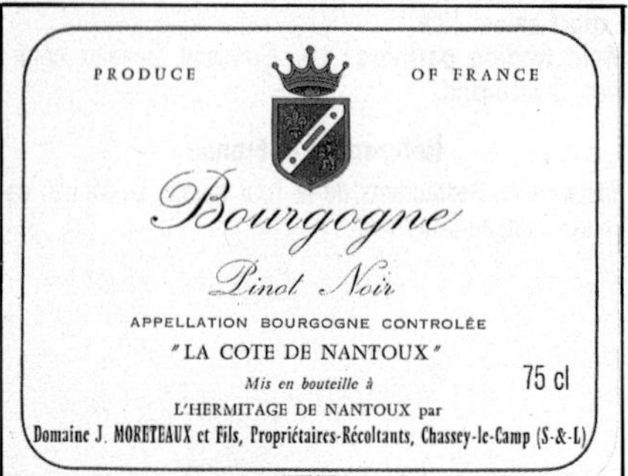

PRODUCE OF FRANCE
Bourgogne
Pinot Noir
APPELLATION BOURGOGNE CONTROLÉE
"LA COTE DE NANTOUX"
Mis en bouteille à
75 cl
L'HERMITAGE DE NANTOUX par
Domaine J. MORETEAUX et Fils, Propriétaires-Récoltants, Chassey-le-Camp (S-&-L)

Appellation: Bourgogne Aligoté – Rully Blanc Premier Cru – Chassagne Blanc. **Type:** Red, white, rosé. **Technique:** Traditional. **Alcohol content:** 12%. **Characteristics:** White: fruity and pleasant – Red: full bodied, keeps well. **Serving temperature:** White: 10° – Red: 12°-14°. **Served with:** Fish – shellfish and fine cooking. **Vintages available in 89/90:** 1985 and 1986.

Characteristics of vintages

1986: Good year. To be aged. **1985:** Very good year – rich, fruity and well-balanced wine. Price range (pre-tax, ex-warehouse): 20-30 F.F., 50-80 F.F.

Abroad

United States

Slect Vinseard.

United Kingdom

A. Colombier.

Belgium

Huyghebeart.

S.C.E.A. LES CHAMPS PERDRIX

Christine Chandesais Ponsot
Château Saint-Nicolas - B.P. 1 - Fontaines
71150 Chagny
85 91 41 77 - Telex: 801 173 c/o Chandesais
Fax: 85 91 40 26

Established: 1980. **Vine stocks:** 70% Pinot Noir, 30% Chardonnay. **Soil:** Clay with calcium carbonate. **Exposure:** South, Southeast. **Average annual production in hectoliters:** 380-400.

Appellation: Burgundy. **Type:** Red, white. **Technique:** Stainless steel tanks with temperature regulation. **Maturing:** Oak casks (20% to 50% new casks each year). **Alcohol content:** 12.5% to 13%. **Characteristics:** Deep, colored reds, well-balanced, typical Pinot Noir, with a touch of new oak flavor. Rather deeply colored whites due to ageing in the cask. Fine, pronounced bouquet, ages rather well. **Serving temperature:** Red 16/17°, white 12/14°. **Served with:** Red with roasts, poultry and fine cheese. White with fine fish cooked in sauce, light first courses. **Vintages available in 89/90:** 1984, 1985, 1986.

Characteristics of vintages

1966: Rather light, pleasant wines, particularly the whites. **1985:** Exceptional year, already agreeable, but may be aged. **1987:** Due to very small crop deep and rich wines with very good ageing potential. 25 F.F.
Sales volume:
– Wholesale: 80%. – Restaurants: 20%.
Sales in France: 30%.
Export sales: 70%.
Main trading partners : UK, Switzerland, Belgium.

References in France

Restaurants: Lameloise in Chagny, Moulin de Martorey in Saint-Rémy, Cogny in Mercurey, etc...
Réservé grande restauration.

Abroad

United Kingdom

I.W.B.C. c/o Terry Platt, Ferndale Road, Liandudno Junction (Gwynedd), Tel: 0492 592 971.
Seligman & Co. Ltd. 401 Walsall Road Perry Barr Birmingham, Tel: 021 331 4949.

The Netherlands

Lion Vins Import, Herenweg 23, CB Noordwijkerhout 2211, Tel: 2523 72 498.

Far East

Daimaru Inc., Midosuji Building, 8 Nishishimizu Machi, Minami-Ku, Osaka 542, Japan, Tel: 06 245 1235.

• *1989 Classification of the Bordeaux Grands Crus : for everything there is to know about the present quality of the various Châteaux, those that are "on the way up", those that have "come down in the world" and the others (see Bordeaux Region).*

• *For an ideal wine cellar, find out what to do and what not to do (see chapter "Organizing a Wine Cellar")*

GIVRY

LUMPP FRÈRES (GAEC DE L'ORCENE) V. ET F. LUMPP

Vincent or François Lumpp
45, rue de Jambles, Poncey 71640 Givry
85 44 33 09 & 85 44 52 00

Type of vineyard: Family-owned. **Established:** 1977. **Number of employees:** 1. **Vine stocks:** Pinot Noir 60%, Chardonnay 25%, Aligoté 15%. **Soil:** Chalky clay – Chalky sub-soil. **Exposure:** East, South-East, South. **Average annual production in hectoliters:** 280 hl total, 90 hl white.
Appellation: Bourgogne Givry appellation (Côte Chalonnaise). **Type:** Red, white. **Technique:** Traditional, continuous œnological attention, temperature control. **Maturing:** Red: 100% wooden casks – 20% new. White: Enamelled steel tanks – 10% in casks. **Characteristics:** Red: ruby color, red berry aroma, very well balanced. White: Brilliant pale green color. Very aromatic (light hazelnut), round and harmonious. **Serving temperature:** Red: 15°. White: 13°. **Served with:** Red: red meat, grilled or cooked in sauce, cheese. White: As an aperitif and with white meat, fish, hors d'œuvres. **Vintages available in 89/90:** 1986 (red) 1987 (red) 1988.

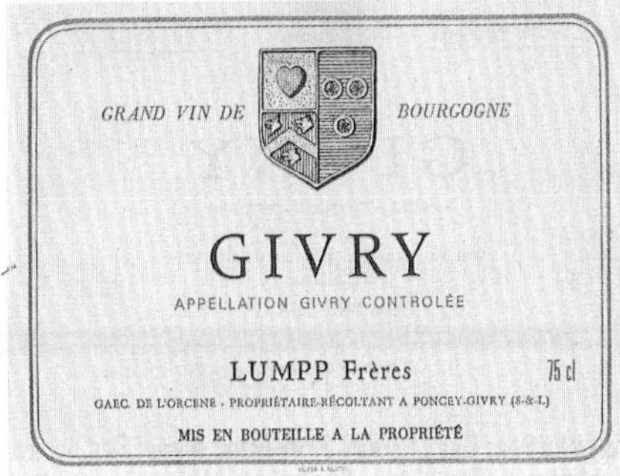

Characteristics of vintages

1988: Very rich and very concentrated wines, flowery aromas, deep red color, good tannin content. Good keeping. **1987:** Aromatic, lots of finesse, round. To drink within 10 years, (similar to 1979). **1986:** Not yet developed, beautiful color, have not yet achieved their final harmony. Good keeping wines which should be ready in one or two years. Price range (pre-tax, ex-warehouse): between 30 and 50 F.F.
Sales volume:
– Wholesale: 5%. – Retail: 80%. – Restaurants: 15%.
Sales in France: 60%. **Export sales:** 40%.
Main trading partners: United Kingdom, Netherlands, Denmark.

References in France

Restaurants: Aux Terrasses (71 Tournus), Hôtel Restaurant de la Halle (71640 Givry).
Shops: Le Cercle des Grands Vins (Avenue des Gobelins, 75005 Paris), Le Tastevin (Nerac 47600).

Abroad

United Kingdom
Big Wines Ltd, Awsworth NG 16 2RR, Nottingham Tel: J. Cross 0602 326040.

The Netherlands
Sauter's Wijnkelders b.v. BP 3011 – 6202 Maastricht. Tel: 31 43 212245.

Others
Denmark: Hoyer Vinimport – Lindevang 19 DK 2660 Brondby Strand. Tel: 02 731711.

Comments

Exploitation created 12 years ago by V. and F. Lumpp immediately after finishing their studies at the Lycée Viticole in Beaune (21200). Major restructuring of the vineyard including purchase, renting and planting of young carefully selected vines (pinot fin). Oak casks renewed frequently. Outlook for the next 3 years: replanting of 3 hectares of vines, 2 for Givry Rouge 1er Cru and 1 for Givry Blanc.

JEAN CHOFFLET

Russily – 71640 Givry
85 44 34 78

Type of vineyard: Family-owned. **Established:** 1710. **Number of employees:** Occasional. **Vine stocks:** Pinot Rouge, Pinot Chardonnay, Aligoté. **Soil:** Clay with calcium carbonate. **Exposure:** South and Southeast. **Average annual production in hectoliters:** 280.
Appellation: Givry Rouge, Givry Blanc, Aligoté, Baury P.T.G. **Type:** Red, white. **Technique:** Fermentation 8 to 10 days, treading. **Maturing:** Concrete vats and oak casks, partial destemming. **Alcohol content:** 12.5% to 13%. **Characteristics:** Fruity, supple, goes down well. To be aged from 5 to 7 years. **Serving temperature:** Red: 17° to 18°, white: 13° to 14°. **Served with:** Red: red meat, game. White: first course, fish. **Vintages available in 89/90:** 1985, 1986.

Characteristics of vintages

1988: Recent racking – beautiful color, balanced and harmonious, reminiscent of the 1985 – will be put on the market in 1990. **1987:** On sale now. Very fruity, very pleasant primary aromas, red berry overtones. Light in color, good ageing potential (minimum 5 years) due to rather strong tannins. **1986:** Promising vintage. The white should be a winner. **1985:** Very fruity and agreeable, but still long. To be kept. **1984:** Fruity, but very short. To be for immediate consomption. **1983:** Very tannic, a bit hard, needs ageing. **1982:** Somewhere between the 1983 and the 1985, a bit disappointing asit ages. **Other:** 1976: Exceptional year.

GÉRARD MOUTON

Gérard Mouton
1, rue du Four, Poncey, 71640 Givry
85 44 37 99 or 85 44 37 14

Type of vineyard: Family-owned. **Established:** 1967. **Number of employees:** 1 full time, others from time to time. **Vine stocks:** Givry red: Pinot Noir. Givry white: Chardonnay. **Soil:** Chalky clay. **Exposure:** South-East. **Average annual production in hectoliters:** 399.

Vin préféré du
Roi HENRI IV
Givry
APPELLATION GIVRY CONTROLÉE
Mis en bouteille à la propriété par
GÉRARD MOUTON
75 cl
PROPRIÉTAIRE-RÉCOLTANT à PONCEY - 71640 GIVRY
PRODUCE OF FRANCE

Appellation: Givry. **Type:** Red, white. **Technique:** Traditional. **Maturing:** Oak casks. **Alcohol content:** 13%. **Characteristics:** Givry red: rich and well balanced wine, with lots of grace and distinction, fruit aromas. Givry white: in the class of the great white Burgundies. **Serving temperature:** Red: 14 to 16°. White: 8 to 10°. **Vintages available in 89/90:** Givry red: 86 and 87. Givry white: 87. Burgundy Aligoté: 86 and 87.

Characteristics of vintages

1988: Superb quality, a great year, not yet for sale. **1987:** Very good quality, needs ageing. **1986:** Good quality. Price range (pre-tax, ex-warehouse): Aligoté: between 10 and 20 F.F. Givry: between 20 and 30 F.F.

Sales volume:
– Retail: 30%. – Restaurants: 20%.

Sales in France: 50%.

Export sales: 50%.

Main trading partners : Denmark, Netherlands, United Kingdom, United States, Switzerland.

References in France

Restaurants: Michel Rostang (Paris 17).

Abroad

United States

Robert Chadderdon Selections, 30 Rockefeller Plaza, Suite 1920, New York 10112.

United Kingdom

Thorman Hunt & Co. Ltd, 4 Pratt Walk, Lambeth, London SE11 6AR.

Switzerland

Jacques Duruz, 1411 Cronay.

The Netherlands

Turkenburg Tradition, Spoorstraat 19, Postbus 96, 2410 AB, Bodegraven.

Denmark

Philipson Wine APS, Holmegaardsvej 29, 2920 Charlottenlund.

DOMAINE RAGOT

Jean-Pierre Ragot
Poncey, 71640 Giury
85 44 38 84

Type of vineyard: Family-owned. **Established:** For five generations. **Number of employees:** 1. **Vine stocks:** Pinot Noir and Chardonnay. **Soil:** Oxfordian and coralline chalky clay. **Average annual production in hectoliters:** 45 hl/ha. (8 hectares).

LE VIN PRÉFÉRÉ
DU ROI HENRI IV
GIVRY
APPELLATION CONTROLÉE
MIS EN BOUTEILLE A LA PROPRIÉTÉ
75 cl
13% vol.
DOMAINE RAGOT
PROPRIÉTAIRE-RÉCOLTANT A GIVRY-PONCEY (SAONE-ET-LOIRE)
PRODUCT OF FRANCE

Appellation: Giury Rouge, Giury Blanc. **Type:** Red, white. **Technique:** Traditional. **Maturing:** White: in stainless steel tanks, red: in oak casks. **Alcohol content:** 13%. **Characteristics:** Red: fruity, well structured, fine bouquet (spices), rich and well balanced, solid, good keeping. White: fruity natural, pleasant, fruity (hazelnut) and flowery flavor. **Serving temperature:** White 8°. Red: 16°. **Vintages available in 89/90:** 1986, 1987.

Characteristics of vintages

1987: White: excellent, lively, fruity, lingering taste. Red: well made. **1986:** Red: excellent, fragrant, well colored, good keeping. Superb white. Price range (pre-tax, ex-warehouse): 30 to 50 F.F.

Sales volume:
– Retail: 60%. – Restaurants: 10%. – Other: 30% export.
Sales in France: 60 to 70%. **Export sales:** 20-30%.
Main trading partners: European community and Japan.

References in France

Restaurants: Lameloise (Chagny), Brasserie de la Paix (Lille).

Abroad

United Kingdom
Domaine Direct – Pierre Hourlier.

Germany
Diete Wissemeck – Gérard Wein Mart.

Belgium
Simon Delvigne.

The Netherlands
Vojacek – Maison du Mée.

Far East
Japan: Toyo Menka.

S.C.V. ÉMILE VOARICK

Pierre Voarick (manager)
Saint-Martin-sous-Montaigu – 71640 Givry
85 45 23 23 – Telex: 530 955 poste N 54

Type of vineyard: Winegrowing Corporation. **Vine stocks:** Pinot Noir, Chardonnay, Gamay, Aligoté. **Soil:** Clay with calcium carbonate. **Exposure:** Hillside. **Average annual production in hectoliters:** 2,500 to 3000 (85% red, 15% white).
Appellation: Corton, Beaune, Mercurey, Burgundy, Crémant of Burgundy, Givry. **Type:** Red, white. **Technique:** Use of harvesting machine. **Maturing:** Traditional. Oak casks, large casks. **Characteristics:** Corton, Beaune: noble wines, heady, with long life. Mercurey: great Chalon Wine, to be aged. Burgundy: genetic appellation, often unappreciated and ignored, but with a good quality-price ratio. Crémant: agreeable apéritif. Givry: earthy smell, very rich, finesse. **Serving temperature:** Red wines at room temperatures. Whites rather cool. Crémant chilled. **Served with:** Whites: Burgundy, Aligoté, Mercurey – first courses, fish, white meat (Mercurey). Reds: game, cheese (Corton, Beaune, Mercurey). Simple dishes with Red Burgundy and Passetoutgrain. **Vintages available in 89/90:** 1983, 1984, 1985, 1986, 1987.

Characteristics of vintages

1986: Light and supple, evolves well, promissing. **1985:** Similar to 1983, to be aged. **1983:** Great quality, will age well quite a long time, keeps well. Price range (pre-tax, ex-warehouse): Burgundy: 20-30 F.F. Mercurey: 30-50 F.F. Beaune: 50-80 F.F. Corton : 80-120 F.F.
Main trading partners : Switzerland, UK, Germany, Belgium.

MERCUREY

DOMAINE DU MEIX FOULOT

Paul de Launay
71640 Mercurey
85 45 13 92

Type of vineyard: Family-owned. **Established:** 1947. **Number of employees:** 4. **Vine stocks:** Pinot, Chardonnay. **Soil:** Chalky clay. **Exposure:** East and South. **Average annual production in hectoliters:** 500.

Appellation: Mercurey. **Type:** Red, White. **Technique:** Traditional, in open vats, crushing and pumping over (8 to 10 days). **Maturing:** 2 years (1 "en masse" (in bulk) and 1 in casks 20-25% new). **Alcohol content:** 12 to 13%. **Characteristics:** rather delicate tannins, long, small berry aroma (mulberry, raspberry, cooked cherry) gamier with ageing. **Serving temperature:** Red: 16 to 18°. White: 12°. **Served with:** Red: grilled meat, roasts, non-fermented cheese. White: fish cooked in sauce. **Vintages available in 89/90:** 1984, 1985, 1986, 1987 (to be bottled Summer of 89).

Characteristics of vintages

1987: Blackcurrant flavor, supple and fruity (available end of 1989). **1986:** Very beautiful color, raspberry aroma. **1985:** Great year for ageing (mulberry, blackcurrant flavor). **Other:** 1984 – fully developed, harmonious, cherry flavor.
Sales volume:
– Wholesale: 15-20%. – Retail: 10%. – Restaurants: 20%. – Other: 55% (specialized shops).
Sales in France: 60%. **Export sales:** 40%.
Main trading partners : UK, USA, Switzerland, Germany, Belgium, Japan.

References in France

Restaurants: Le Père Bise (Talloire), Hôtel du Val d'Or (Mercurey), La Grille (Paris). *Shops:* Le Pavillon des Vins.

Abroad

United States

Importers: Select Vineyards Ltd. Lexington Avenue, New York 10001.

United Kingdom

Castle Wines, Mexboro, Heinkley, Leicester.

Germany

Fred Thalmann, Robert Stab Brassezo, Dusseldorf.

Switzerland

Pierre Muller, CH 4245 Kleinbutze, Postfach 16.

The Netherlands

Turkenburg Tradition – Postbus 96 – 2410AB – Bodegraven.

DOMAINE BRINTET

Luc Brintet & Frédéric Charles
Grande Rue – 71640 Mercurey
85 45 14 50

Established: 1984. **Vine stocks:** Pinot Noir and Chardonnay. **Soil:** Clay with calcium carbonate. **Exposure:** Southeast. **Average annual production in hectoliters:** 450 to 500.
Appellation: Mercurey, Bourgogne. **Type:** Red, white. **Technique:** White: fermentation in casks after pressing. Red: maceration in open vats for 8 to 10 days. **Maturing:** Red: oak casks for 18 months. White: large casks. **Alcohol content:** 12.5 to 13.5%. **Characteristics:** The white Mercurey a pale yellow color, is a dry and fruity wine. The red Mercurey is a good. It is (7 to 15 years). Their ruby color and red fruit aroma as well as their finesse wine for ageing grace the finest tables. **Serving temperature:** Whites: 12° – Reds: 16 to 18°. **Served with:** Bourgogne and Mercurey (white) – fish and seafood. Mercurey (red): red meat, meat in sauce and cheese. **Vintages available in 89/90:** 1984, 1985.

Characteristics of vintages

1985: Very good vintage, good for ageing. **1984:** Good, very fruity wine, pleasant drinking. Price range (pre-tax, ex-warehouse): Between 30 and 50 F.F.

CAVES DU CLOSEAU

Mr. Cohu
71560 Mercurey
85 45 18 66 – Telex: 801 536

Type of vineyard: Corporation. **Established:** May 2, 1979. **Number of employees:** 7. **Vine stocks:** Pinot. **Soil:** Clay with calcium carbonate.
Appellation: Mercurey, Brouilly. **Type:** Red. **Technique:** Stainless steel tanks. **Alcohol content:** 12-13%. **Serving temperature:** 13-14°. **Served with:** Meat, game. **Vintages available in 89/90:** 1985, 1986.

Characteristics of vintages

1986: Mercurey Chanteflute. **1985:** Mercurey Tastevine. Average pre-tax, ex-warehouse price: Brouilly 30 F.F. – Mercurey 45 F.F.
Sales volume:
– Wholesale: 100%.
Sales in France: 90%.
Export sale: 10%.
Main trading partners : USA, Denmark.

MERCUREY – CHÂTEAU DE CHAMIREY

MM. Marquis de Jouernes
and Bertrand Devillard
71640 Mercurey
85 45 22 22 – Telex: 800 307 F

Type of vineyard: Family-owned. **Established:** 1875. **Vine stocks:** Pinot Noir and Chardonnay. **Soil:** Clay with calcium carbonate. **Exposure:** East, Southeast.
Appellation: Mercurey. **Type:** Red, white. **Technique:** Traditional, fermentation with skins, 10 days for reds. **Maturing:** In oak casks, 1/3 renewed each year. **Characteristics:** Reds: exceptional, rich in alcohol and color, well balanced, robust but not devoid of the finesse and elegant characteristics of the neighboring Côtes de Beaune. Whites: more seductive, more fragrant and fruity. **Serving temperature:** Reds: 14°-16° – Whites: 12° – 14°. **Served with:** Red: Game in general, cheese. White: Shellfish, fish, goat cheese. **Vintages available in 89/90:** White: 1986 – Red: 1981, 1982, 1984, 1985.

Characteristics of vintages

1986: With maturity, a very promising vintage. **1985:** Rich, complex, a very good vintage, to te aged. **1984:** At its optimum maturity, ready for tasting well structured. **1982:** Strong red fruit overtone. Supple and well balanced. Price range (pre-tax, ex-warehouse): Between 50 and 80 F.F.
Sales volume:
– Retail: 25% – Restaurants: 65%. – Other: 10% (cellars).
Sales in France: 50%.
Export sales: 50%.
Main trading partners : USA, UK, Germany, Middle East.

References in France

Restaurants: Lameloise (Chagny), Chanteclerc (Nice), Côte d'Or (Saulieu), Blanc (Vonnai), L'Espérance (Vézelay), L'Auberge de l'Ill (Illhausesm).
Shops: La Cloche (Dijon).

• *To help us improve our next edition, please send in your suggestions and answer our questionnaire.*

JEAN MARECHAL

Jean Marechal
71640 Mercurey
85 45 11 29

Type of vineyard: Family-owned. **Established:** 1570. **Vine stocks:** Pinot Noir. **Soil:** Chalky clay. **Exposure:** South, South-East. **Average annual production in hectoliters:** 400.

Appellation: Mercurey, Bourgogne. **Type:** Red. **Technique:** Hand harvesting, partial destemming, crushing in vats 3 times a day, long fermentation on skins. **Maturing:** In oak casks 20% new for 12 to 15 months. **Characteristics:** Charming, delicate, rich and well balanced, well structured, good keeping wines. **Serving temperature:** 16°. **Served with:** Roasts and cheese.

Characteristics of vintages

1988: Full-bodied, intense bouquet (blackcurrant, violet) long, beautiful tannins, great keeping wine. **1987:** Deep color, beautiful red berry aroma (raspberry, blackcurrant) subtle woodland fragrance. **1986:** Fine and intense, cherry and raspberry fragrance, well balanced, perfect right now. **Other:** 1984: Fruity and seductive, dominant cherry fragrance, beautiful color, to be consumed within 5 years or so. Price range (pre-tax, ex-warehouse): 30 to 50 F.F.
Sales volume:
– Retail: 70%. – Restaurants: 10%.
Sales in France: 80%.
Export sales: 20%.
Main trading partners : Switzerland, Belgium, Germany, UK, Denmark.

References in France

Restaurants: In a number of great restaurants.

Comments

Descendants of a long line of winemakers going back 4 centuries. Their objective today, as in the past, is to produce high quality wines. The estate of approximately 10 hectares is located in the best wine area – Clos L'Evêque, Clos Barraut, Naugues and Champs Martin. After manual harvesting the vinification receives attentive care to produce structured, full-bodied, fragrant and forthcoming wines.

MICHEL JUILLOT

Michel Juillot
B.P. 10 – 71640 Mercurey
85 45 27 27 – Telex: ITACH 800 175

Type of vineyard: Family-owned. **Established:** 1958. **Number of employees:** 10. **Vine stocks:** Pinot Noir, Chardonnay. **Soil:** Clay with calcium carbonate. **Exposure:** South, Southeast. **Average annual production in hectoliters:** 1,000.
Appellation: Mercurey – Corton Charlemagne, Corton Perrières, Aloxe Corton. **Type:** Red, white. **Technique:** Traditional. **Maturing:** In oak casks (30% new). **Characteristics:** Supple, small red berry flavor for 1986 and 1984 which complement the great ageing vintages of 1985 and 1983. **Serving temperature:** 14° to 15°. **Served with:** Red meat, game. **Vintages available in 89/90:** 1986: available now. 1987: will be available in sept. 89. 1988: will be available in sept. 90.

Characteristics of vintages

1988: Very well-balanced, to be drunk during the year 2000. **1987:** Good structure, fruity aroma, fresh, pleasant, easy to drink. **1986:** Promising vintage, particularly for whites, Hold. **1985:** Balanced and harmonious, good for ageing. Remarkable Corton. **1984:** Bright, ruby color, fresh, fruit aromas, fine, elegant structure. Its freshness makes it a pleasant and agreeable wine. Price range (pre-tax, ex-warehouse): between 50 and 80F.F.
Sales volume:
– Wholesale: none. – Restaurants: 30%.
Sales in France: 45%.
Export sales: 55%.
Main trading partners : Japan, Australia, USA, UK, Denmark, Switzerland, Belgium, Germany.

Références in France

Shops: Fauchon, Magasin Legrand.

L. MENAND PÈRE & FILS

Georges-Claude Memand
"Chamerose" – 71640 Mercurey
85 45 19 19

Type of vineyard: Family-owned. **Established:** 1850. **Vine stocks:** Pinot Noir, Chardonnay, Aligoté. **Soil:** Clay with calcium carbonate. **Exposure:** South, Southwest.
Appellation: Mercurey (red and white), Aligoté. **Type:** Red, white. **Technique:** Traditional. **Maturing:** Oak casks, about 20 months. **Alcohol content:** 12.5 to 13%. **Characteristics:** Red: beautiful scarlet color, long with a small red fruit flavor (raspberry, blackcurrant). Robust, fragrant wine, long keeping. White: beautiful gold-green color, hazelnut fragrance. Aligoté: limpid, clear color, fine and flowery fragrance. **Serving temperature:** Red: 16 to 18°.

White: 8 to 10°. Aligoté: 6 to 8°. **Served with:** Red: red meat, roasted or in sauce, and, when a little older, with cheese. White: fish, shellfish, all first courses with fish. Aligoté: at the beginning of the meal, alone or with as an aperitif with a bit of Crème de cassis. **Vintages available in 89/90:** 1987 (red and white). 1987 (red, white and Aligoté as of January 1988).

Characteristics of vintages

1987: Red: beautiful purple color, long touch of violet, ver fragrant. **1987:** Very long keeping, touch of small red fruit (raspberry, blackcurrant). **1987:** Very fruity, lots of finesse, already has the attraction of an old wine. No hesitation. Price range (pre-tax, ex-warehouse): Between 30 and 50 F.F.
Sales volume:
– Wholesale: Very little. – Retail: The most. – Restaurants: Very little.
Sales in France: Almost all. **Export sales:** Very little.
Main trading partners : Belgium, Switzerland, Germany, Netherlands, USA.

References in France

Restaurants: Hôtellerie de Val d'Or (Mercurey), Les Petits Plats (Pontoise), Hôtel du Parc (Salbris), Restaurant Dauvergne (Poisson), Les Adrets (Lyon), Hôtellerie Beaurivage (Condrieu), etc.
Shops: Aux Caves du Sergent Hoff (Paris), Dalloyau (rue du Faubourg-St-Honoré, rue de la Convention, rue Godot-de-Mauroy, rue de l'Ingénieur-Keller, rue Edmond-Rostand, Paris), La Cave (Lorient), Le Tastevin (Villefranche-sur-Saône), etc.

DOMAINE DU CHÂTEAU DE MERCEY

Michel and Jacques Berger
71150 Cheilly-les-Maranges
85 91 11 96

Type of vineyard: Family corporation. **Established:** From father to son. **Number of employees:** 14. **Vine stocks:** Pinot Noir. **Soil:** Chalky and pebbly clay. **Exposure:** Southeast. **Average annual production in hectoliters:** 1,800.
Appellation: Burgundy Hautes Côtes de Beaune and Mercurey. **Type:** Red, white. **Technique:** Traditional with temperature control. **Maturing:** Reds: in casks. **Alcohol content:** 12.5% to 13%.**Characteristics:** The red wines have an aroma of fresh red fruit when young. Well-balanced and slightly tannic. They will age well. The white wines, elegant and substancial have a hazel nut perfume. Their firmness is softened by the mellowness of the Chardonnay. **Serving temperature:** Reds: 16° to 18°. Whites: 12° to 14°. **Served with:** Reds: grilled or roasted red meat, feathered game, cheese (not too strong). Whites: fish, shellfish, delicatessen products, strong cheese. **Vingages available in 89/90:** Red: 1983, 1985, 1986, 1987. White: 1987, 1988.

Characteristics of vintages

1987: Rather tannic, good keeping. **1986:** Beautiful color, will be a good year. **1985:** Great year, to be allowed to age. **1983:** Quite tannic, should also be allowed to age. Price range (pre-tax, ex-warehouse): Between 30 and 50 F.F.
Sales volumes:
– Wholesale: 25%. – Retail: 50%. – Restaurants: 10%. – Other: 15% (wholesalers, winecellars).
Sales in France: 70%. **Export sales:** 30%.
Main trading partners : Switzerland, Belgium, Netherlands, UK, USA, RFA, Japan.

Comments

The Domaine du Château de Mercey is a 45 hectare Family vineyard. The Berger's have been proprietors for several generations.

DOMAINE P.M. NINOT

P.M. Ninot
Le Meix Guillaume, Rully, 71150 Chagny
85 87 07 79

Type of vineyard: Family-owned. **Established:** Several generations. **Number of employees:** 3. **Vine stocks:** Red: Pinot Noir. White: Chardonnay. **Soil:** Chalky clay. **Exposure:** South-East. **Average annual production in hectoliters:** 35 hl per hectare.
Appellation: Mercurey Rouge "La Crée" 1987. **Type:** Red. **Technique:** Manual harvesting and traditional vinification in open vats, partial destemming, treading for a good color and maceration. **Maturing:** in oak casks. **Alcohol content:** 12.5%. **Characteristics:** Very pretty deep ruby color, typical Pinot Noir fragrance, fruity with woodland aroma, rich and well balanced, long, a superb wine for keeping. **Serving temperature:** 18 to 20°. **Served with:** Perfect with red meat and feathered game. **Vintages available in 89/90:** Several bottles of Mercurey Rouge Tasteviné "La Crée" 1985, Mercurey Rouge 1986.

Characteristics of vintages

1988: Wine for very long keeping, will be ready in 5 or 6 years (not ready now). **1987:** Supple wine, well balanced, ready for tasting in 3 years. Very lovely wine for keeping. **1986:** Out of stock. **1985:** Remarkable wine, taste tested at the Clos Vougeot, to be drunk in one or two years. Very long keeping wine. There are only a few bottles left. Average pre-tax ex-warehouse price: 46 F.F.
Sales volume:
– Retail: 60%. – Restaurants: 20%. – Other: 20% agents.
Sales in France: 80%. **Export sales:** 20%.
Main trading partners : Switzerland, United Kingdom, Belgium, United States.

References in France

Restaurants: In 12 of the best great restaurants of France.
Shops: In the cellars of a number of shops in Paris.

Comments

An exploitation whose winegrowing origins go back to 1376. Maternal grandfather, Louis Rigaud, was one of the pioneers in reintroducing grapevines in the commune of Rully.
Open every day by appointment. Many medals in competitions. Wines regularly taste tested at the Clos de Vougeot.

RULLY

DUREUIL-JANTHIAL

Raymond Dureuil-Janthial
Rue de la Buisserolle, Rully – 71150 Chagny
85 87 02 37

Type of vineyard: Family-owned, 9 hectares. **Established:** 3 generations. **Vine stocks:** Aligoté, Chardonnay, Pinot Noir. **Soil:** Chalky clay. **Exposure:** Rising sun. **Average annual production in hectoliters:** 350.

Grand Vin
de Bourgogne
RULLY
APPELLATION CONTROLÉE
13% vol.
Mis en bouteille à la Propriété par
75 cl
RAYMOND DUREUIL-JANTHIAL
PROPRIÉTAIRE-VITICULTEUR A RULLY (SAONE-&-LOIRE)
PRODUIT DE FRANCE

Appellation: Rully red and white, Mercurey red, Puligny-Montrachet 1er Cru, Burgundy red and white, Burgundy Aligote. **Type:** Red, white. **Technique:** Traditional. **Maturing:** 2 years in oak casks. **Charateristics:** Tannic reds which soften with ageing. **Serving temperature:** Red: room temperature. White: cool. **Served with:** Red: meat, game, cheese. White: first courses, fish, shellfish. **Vintages available in 89/90:** 85, 86, 87 (autumn 89).

Characteristics of vintages

1987: Rully red: Full of promise, lovely ruby color, tannic, rich and well balanced red fruit flavor, most particularly blackcurrant. Rully white: Pale gold, floral fragrance, hazel nut aftertaste. **1986:** Good quality/price ratio, quite successful wines for the year. **1985:** Rully red: beautiful color, fruity fragrance, aromas of raspberries with round tannins. Rully white: worthy of this exceptional year, produced from 50 year old vines, exotic fruit aromas, lightly woody, round. Price range (pre-tax, ex-warehouse): between 30 and 50 F.F.

Sales volume:
– Retail: 95%. – Restaurants: 5%.
Sales in France: 95%.
Export sales: 5%.

Comments

A family property, dealing almost exclusively with a their own clientele, very attentive to quality. Short pruning to control yields, manual harvesting, selection of grapes in case of rot, long fermentation on stems. A great importance is attached to the reception and contact with clients for whom the heartiest welcome is always reserved.

S.C. HENRI & PAUL JACQUESON

Messrs. Henri & Paul Jacqueson
Rue de Chèvremont – Rully – 71150 Chagny
85 87 18 82 / 85 91 25 00 / 85 91 25 91

Type of vineyard: Family-owned. **Established:** 1975. **Vine stocks:** Pinot Noir (reds), Chardonnay (whites). **Soil:** Hillsides – clay with calcium carbonate. **Exposure:** East. **Average annual production in hectoliters:** 250. **Appellation:** Rully, Rully 1er Cru, Mercurey, Bourgogne Aligoté, Bourgogne Passetoutgrain. **Type:** Red, white. **Technique:** Traditional in vats, without destemming, long fermentation with skins, crushing twice a day. **Maturing:** In oak casks (30% new each year). **Alcohol content:** 12.5% tou 13.5%. **Characteristics:** Red: beautiful ruby color, rich bouquet, tannic, long. White: green gold color, rich bouquet, full-bodied and long. **Serving temperature:** Red: 15°. White: 10° to 12°. **Served with:** Red: red meat, game, creamy cheese (Brillat-Savarin) and goat cheese. White: fish, lobster, rock lobster. **Vintages available in 89/90:** 1986, 1987, 1988 (bottling in autumn 1989).

Characteristics of vintages

1988: Excellent year for Burgundy. Rich and well-balanced. **1987:** Great finesse. **1986:** To be aged – particularly the whites – very promising. Price range (pre-tax, ex-warehouse): Between 30 and 50 F.F.
Sales in France: 40%.
Export sales: 60%.

References in France

Restaurants: Taillevent, Lameloise, Rostang, Les Templiers, La Côte Saint-Jacques, Léon de Lyon, Le Quai des Ormes, La Tour d'Argent.
Shops: Willi's Wine Bar (Paris).

DOMAINE GUYOT-VERPIOT

Hubert Guyot
Rue du Château, 71150 Rully
85 87 04 48

Type of vineyard: Family-owned. **Established:** 1973. **Vine stocks:** Chardonnay, Pinot Noir. **Soil:** Chalky clay. **Exposure:** South-East.

Appellation: Rully. **Type:** Red, white, Crémant de Bourgogne. **Technique:** Traditional. **Maturing:** In vats and casks. **Characteristics:** Rully red: tannic, good keeping. Rully white: fruity. **Serving temperature:** Red: 15°. White: 12°. **Served with:** Red: all meats. White: fish, shellfish. **Vintages available in 89/90:** White: 1987. Rully red: 1984, 1986, 1987.

Characteristics of vintages

1988: Rully white: good year. **1987:** Rully white: rich, fruity. **1986:** Rully red: very promising. **1985:** Rully red: well balanced, beautiful color.
Sales volume:
– Wholesale: 20%. – Retail: 78%. – Restaurants: 2%.
Sales in France: 50%.
Export sales: 50%.
Main trading partners : United States, United Kingdom, Denmark, Germany.

Abroad

United States
Wold Shippers Importers, Philaderphia, Penn.

United Kingdom
Tand W Wines, Thetford. Bishopmead Wine, Dorking.

Germany
Muller, Saarbrück.

Others
Denmark: Philipson Wine, Charlottenlund.

• *To better understand the evolution and adherence to type of the various vintages, consult our "Vintage Code" chart.*

DOMAINE P.M. NINOT

P.M. Ninot
Le Meix Guillaume, Rully 71150 Chagny
85 87 07 79

Type of vineyard: Family-owned. **Established:** Several generations. **Number of employees:** 3. **Vine stocks:** Red: Pinot Noir. White: Chardonnay. **Soil:** Chalky clay. **Exposure:** South-East. **Average annual production in hectoliters:** 35 to 40 hl per hectare.
Appellation: Rully Blanc 1er Cru Grésigny 1988. **Type:** White. **Technique:** Long extraction of first juice at low temperature for concentrated aroma. **Maturing:** Stainless steel tanks until debourbage, then in oak casks. **Alcohol content:** 13.5%. **Characteristics:** Well developed nose, long, extreme finesse, golden color, very rich bouquet. Long keeping vintage. **Serving temperature:** 8 to 12°. **Served with:** Fish, grilled or in cream sauce, chicken in cream. **Vintages available in 89/90:** 1987 Rully Blanc 1er Cru Grésigny.

Characteristics of vintages

1988: Wine for keeping, to be drunk in 2 or 3 years. A very great year, rich and concentrated. **1987:** Well constituted wine, elegant and fine, can be drunk now but deserves one or two more years in the bottle to reach its peak. Average pre-tax ex-warehouse price: about 45 F.F.
Sales volume:
– Retail: 35%. – Restaurants: 35%. – Other: 30% export.
Sales in France: 70%.
Export sales: 30%.
Main trading partners : Germany, United Kingdom, Switzerland, United States, Belgium, Ireland.

References in France

Restaurants: In 12 of the best great restaurants of France.
Shops: In the cellars of a number of shops in Paris.

Comments

It is best to hold onto this wine because we cannot meet the demand. Open every day by appointment. Many medals in competitions. Wine regularly taste tested at the Clos de Vougeot.

LA P'TIOTE CAVE

Guy Mugnier Père et fils
Rully - 71150 Chagny
Cave à Chassey-le-Camp
85 87 15 21

Type of vineyard: Family-owned. **Established:** 1979 - owned by winemaker since 1963. **Number of employees:** 3. **Vine stocks:** Chardonnay, Pinot Noir, Aligoté, Gamay. **Soil:** Variable. **Exposure:** East. **Average annual production in hectoliters:** 300.

Appellation: Bourg Passetoutgrain, Bourg Rosé, Bourg Rouge, Rully Blanc & Rouge, Mercurey Blanc & Rouge, Meursault 1er Cru (plus two grades), Côte de Beaune, Chorey, Crémant, Marc, Fine. **Type:** Red, White, Rosé. Other: Crémant, Marc, Fine. **Technique:** Traditional, in vats (8 to 10 days). **Maturing:** In oak casks. **Alcohol content:** 11.5-13%. **Characteristics:** Very different depending on the appellations. **Serving temperature:** White: 11 to 12° - red: 15 to 17°. **Vintages available in 89/90:** A few 1985 and 1986-1987.

Characteristics of vintages

1988: Still in casks. **1987:** Not enough bottles to judge, looks better than 1986 red. **1986:** Red: lacking balance, White: not bad at all. **1985:** Excellent but it does not look as if it will come up to expectations as far as ageing is concerned. Wait and see. Price range (pre-tax, ex-warehouse): 20 to 120 F.F.

Sales volume:
- Wholesale: only Passetoutgrain and part of the Bourg production - bad year. - Retail: 98-99%. - Restaurants: 1-2%.

Sales in France: 50%. **Export sales:** 50%.
Main trading partners : USA, UK, Netherlands, Belgium.

References in France

Restaurants: Henri (Romainville), La Morvandelle (Villebon), Le Cheval noir (Bougival), Récamier, Ramponneau, Les Champs d'Or (Paris), etc.

Abroad

United States

American Produce & Vegetable Co. 1120, Central Expressway, 2831 Nagles, 7522 Dallas - Continental Distributing Co. Inc. 9800 W Balmoral, 60018 Des Plaines - Rosemont, Illinois - Kiwikai Import Inc., Paustis and Sons, 14330, 21 St. Ave. No. 5544 Minneapolis - Northwind Enterprises Inc. 3434 Bladensburg Road, 2072 Brentwood - Mrr Traders, Division of Legal Sea Foods, 33 Everett Street, 92134 Ma Boston

United Kingdom

Halkin Pharmaceutical Ltd T.AS. Chalfont Wine Shippers, Chalfont House. Misb Chalfont St. Peter Bu - Richards Walford & Co. Ltd. Manor House, Picknorth, Stamford Lines PE94D - K. Colombier Ltd V & S Unit, 9 Kildare Close, Filden Road Ruislip - S & K Management Services Ltd. Manor Farm, Cuddington Chelshire - Squarewalk Ltd - Continental & Overseas Wines, Altricham, Chelshire Timperley.

Belgium

Chais et Entrepôts du Nord, Simon Stevinstraat, Zone 1, 8400 Ostende.

Germany

Château Le Claire, Schnerstrasse 59 - 5650 Solingen.

The Netherlands

Gebr Heisterkamp BV V & S Ootwal 5, 7630 Ootmarsum - Vos Bevolux Netderland BV V & S (Vos Wijnimport BV), Jellingh Ausstraat 3, 5004 Tilburg.

Comments

Born in Rully of parents who made their living from a small enterprise in Meursault, Guy Mugnier lived in Paris for 30 years as a consulting engineer. Then, at the age of 49, he took over the family business which he has been running since 1963. Growing by successive purchases of small parcels, the vineyard produces an impressive variety of wines (15 to 17 appellations) on only 5.5 hectares. It is neither a château nor a domain, it's the P'tiote Cave...
Very friendly welcome, animated. Generous tasting. Faithful clientele always, content with their visit.

- *Watch out for wines that have lost their authenticity, "with neither soul nor virtue", most often the result of specific vinification techniques (carbonic maceration, too long maturing in casks...). See the various Regions: Bordeaux, Languedoc, South-West, Provence...*

- *A good everyday wine for 20 F? See the Bordeaux, Anjou, Touraine, Côtes-du-Rhône or Languedoc Regions.*

- *Help me make the next Guide even more useful. Let me have your advice and tell me about your experiences with the winegrowers and the welcome extended. (See questionnaire "Wine, the Guide and you").*

DOMAINE DE RULLY SAINT MICHEL

Mme de Bodard de la Jacopière
Rue du Château - Rully - 71150 Chagny
85 91 28 63

Type of vineyard: Agricultural Association. **Established:** 1850. **Vine stocks:** (Red) Pinot Noir, (White) Chardonnay. **Soil:** Chalky clay. **Exposure:** East. **Average annual production in hectoliters:** 450-500.
Appellation: Rully Premier Cru - (Red) Champs-Cloups, Clos de Pellerey - (White) Rabource, Les Cloux. **Type:** Red, White. **Technique:** Traditional. Manual harvesting. Slow vinification. **Maturing:** in oak casks and stainless steel tanks, as long as necessary, about 8 to 10 months. **Alcohol content:** 12.5 to 13.5%. **Characteristics:** Red: beautiful red fruit color, rich bouquet, balsam fragrance, very good acid/alcohol balance, long. White: beautiful color, very fruity, rich bouquet, soft, full and long. **Serving temperature:** Red: 15°, White: 10-12°. **Vintages available in 89/90:** White: 1962, 1964, 1969, 1973, 1974, 1977, 1978, 1979, 1980, 1981, 1982, 1985, 1986, 1987, Red: 1978, 1981, 1983, 1984, 1985, 1986, 1987, 1988.

Characteristics of vintages

1987: White: 2nd Prize (Côte Chalonnaise). **1986:** Red: First prize (Côte Chalonnaise) White: Bronze Medal, Paris, first prize (Côte Chalonnaise). **1985:** White: Silver Medal, Paris, First prize Côte Chalonnaise. **Other: 1984:** White: First Prize (Côte Chalonnaise) Red: 2nd Prize (Cote Chalonnaise).
Sales volume:
- Retail: 20%. - Restaurants: 25%. - Other: 12%.

Sales in France: 60%. **Export sales:** 40%.

References in France

Restaurants: Hôtel de la Côte d'Or - Bistrot de Paris - Chez André - Le Bernardin.
Shops: Cave Taillevent - Caves de la Madeleine.

Abroad

United States
Importers: Mossvod Wine - New York.

United Kingdom
Thomas Panton Wine.

Far East
Japan Air Lines.

Others
Luxemburg : European Parliament.

Comments

Estate belonging to the same family for 6 generations, developed by the Treasurer to Napoléon III. Wines conserved in exceptional caves carved into the rock. Their reputation is well established, having been awarded a number of distinctions: Gold Medal at the Universal Exhibition of 1900 and many medals since (Milan, Liège, etc.). Gold Medal at the Concours Général, Paris, in 1987. A number of vintages (between 1962 and 1987) are available.

ANDRÉ DELORME S.A. - DOMAINE DE LA RENARDE

Jean François Delorme
Rue de la République, Rully 71150 Chagny.
85 87 10 12 - Telex: 800 175 - ITACH (for Delorme)

Type of vineyard: Family-owned. **Established:** 1942. **Number of employees:** 30. **Vine stocks:** Pinot Noir and Chardonnay, Aligoté for Bouzeron. **Soil:** Chalky clay. **Soil:** Rising and setting sun, all on hillsides. **Average annual production in hectoliters:** 3,000.

Appellation: Bourgogne Aligoté Bouzeron, Bourgogne Chardonnay, Rully, Rully 1er Cru, Bourgogne Rosé, Givry, Mercury. **Type:** Red, white, rosé, Champagne method, Crémant de Bourgogne. **Technique:** Red: temperature control with heating or cooling as necessary. Fermentation in bulk and partly in casks. **Maturing:** Red: Entirely in oak casks for 8 months. **Alcohol content:** 12.5 to 13%. **Characteristics:** White: very fresh and fruity (early bottling seals in these characteristics; whites generally bottled in May/June following the harvest). Red: without losing freshness, wine and oak are married for 6 to 8 months. Bottling in September. Combined character and suppleness. Sold 6 months later. According to the vintage, a first tasting or additional ageing are recommended. **Serving temperature:** White and rosé: 10°. **Vintages available in 89/90:** Still a little 1985, mostly 1986/1987 and, of course, 1988.

Characteristics of vintages

1988: Very great year, especially in red. **1987:** Lots of distinction, the reds are still firm, the whites are elegant. **1986:** Marvelously blossomed out, the reds are still a bit firm. **1985:** The whites are developing quite slowly. They should be very great in 3 or 4 years. Hazelnut nuances are noticeable. Red: development much more rapid, beautiful finesse and secondary tannins. Price range (pre-tax, ex-warehouse): between 20 and 50 F.F.
Sales volume:
- Wholesale: 7%. - Retail: 40%. - Restaurants: 13%.
- Other: 18% champagnization, 22% export.

Sales in France: 60% + 18% (champagnization).
Export sales: 22%.
Main trading partners: United Kingdom, Belgium, United States, Germany, Sweden.

References in France

Restaurants: La Coupole (Paris 14 th), Paul Bocuse (Collonges au Mont d'Or 69), Lameloise (Chagny 71), Alain Rayé (Paris 8 th), Lucas Carton (Paris 8 th), Élitair Tour Eiffel (Paris 7 th), Hôtel Miramar (Biarritz 64), Greuze (Tournus 71).

Abroad

Canada

Monopoly – Ontario.

Others:

Sweden: Monopoly.

Comments

In 1989, for the first time, the Montagny vineyards will be harvested and a planting program will be begun. (The domain is the only producing all of the wine varieties of the region of the Côte de Chalon.)

L. VITTEAUT ALBERTI

Gérard Vitteaut
Rue du Pont d'Arrot – B.P. N°8
71150 Rully-Chagny
85 87 23 97

Type of vineyard: Family-owned. **Established:** 1951. **Number of employees:** 4. **Vine stocks:** Pinot Noir, Chardonnay, Aligoté. **Soil:** Chalky clay. **Exposure:** South-East. **Average annual production in hectoliters:** 1,250.

VA
Crémant de Bourgogne
APPELLATION CRÉMANT DE BOURGOGNE CONTRÔLÉE
PRODUIT DE FRANCE
12% VOL. 75cl
ÉLABORÉ PAR L.VITTEAUT ALBERTI A 71150 RULLY

Appellation: Cremant de Bourgogne Blanc & Rosé. **Type:** White, rosé. **Technique:** Pressing (whole grapes) at low temperature. **Maturing:** In vats. **Alcohol content:** 11%. **Characteristics:** Very fine and lingering foam, subtle and multiple aromas due to blending of Chardonnay (for finesse and lightness), Pinot Noir (for length, richness and fullness) and Aligoté (for freshness). **Serving temperature:** 6°. **Served with:** As an aperitif and with fish and shellfish. **Vintages available in 89/90:** 1987.

Characteristics of vintages

1987: Remarkable wines – concentrated aromas, very supple, beautiful color, fine foam, lingering taste. Price range (pre-tax, ex-warehouse): 20 to 30 F.F.
Sales volume:
– Wholesale: 10%. – Retail: 80%. – Restaurants: 10%.
Sales in France: 90%.
Export sales: 10%.
Main trading partners: UK, USA, Australia, Belgium, Netherlands, Denmark.

References in France

Restaurants: Lameloise (Chagny 71), Taillevent (Paris).

Comments

Created in 1951 by the present proprietor's father, the Vitteaut Alberti house produces sparkling wines according to the champagne method. Gérard Vitteaut, who now runs the establishement, has organized it so as to produce part of the grapes that contribute to personalize his wines. Modern equipment such as an air conditioned fermenting room and great attention to detail – an essential policy of the house – results in the production of first rate, quality controlled wines. The Cremant de Bourgogne Blanc is characterized by its lightness, its fine bubbles, a beautiful color, a concentration of aromas and its lingering taste. As for the Cremant de Bourgogne Rose, it has a very light but honest color and exudes the aromas of the various red berries characteristic of the Pinot Noir from the Côte de Beaunes and the Côte Chalonnaise.

CÔTE MÂCONNAISE

MÂCON

DOMAINE DE LA COMBE

Henri Lafarge
Bray – 71250 Cluny
85 50 02 18

Type of vineyard: Family-owned. **Number of employees:** 1. **Vine stocks:** Pinot Noir, Chardonnay, Gamay Noir (white juice). **Soil:** Chalky clay 90%, granite 10%. **Exposure:** West. **Average annual production in hectoliters:** 750.
Appellation: Macon-Bray & Bourgogne. **Type:** Red, white. **Technique:** Traditional. **Maturing:** In wooden casks and cement vats. **Alcohol content:** 12.5%. **Characteristics:** Red: fruity, rustic, well colored – White: dry and fruity, fine. **Serving temperature:** White: 8° – Red: 14°. **Served with:** White: fish and shellfish – Red (Mâcon): with the entire meal and (Bourgogne) with meat and cheese. **Vintages available in 89/90:** 1986, 1987, 1988 (red).

Domaine de la Combe
MACON-BRAY
APPELLATION MÂCON CONTRÔLÉE
Produce of France
750 mle
Henri LAFARGE
alc. 12,5% by vol.
PROPRIÉTAIRE-VITICULTEUR, BRAY 71250 CLUNY
Mis en bouteille au Domaine

Characteristics of vintages

1988: Red: great year, good keeping, fragrant, rich and well balanced. **1987:** White: fruity and fine – Red: supple and fruity, faster evolution. **1986:** Red: rich and well balanced, good keeping. Price range (pre-tax, ex-warehouse): 20 to 30 F.F.
Sales volume:
– Wholesale: 65%. – Retail: 15%. – Restaurants: 20%.
Sales in France: 80%.
Export sales: 20%.
Main trading partners: United Kingdom, Netherlands, USA, Belgium and Germany.

Abroad

United States

Handpicked Selections – Virginia, 703 347 3471.

United Kingdom

Richards & Walford – 78081 242.

Germany

Gamintchi Cologne – 221 431 786. Mr Knoblauch – Weinkelleri, Ravensburg – 751 230 37. Vinum Weinfachandel, Bremen – 421 3470 94.

Belgium

Ets Manquoi, Anvers – 3238 0237.

The Netherlands

Vos Wijnimport, Tilburg – 13 674 918.

Comments

Family estate since about 1880 (four generations of winemakers) near the Cluny abbey and facing the community of Taize, where the good wines of the Mâcon region are to be tasted.

VINS PAUL BEAUDET

Jean Beaudet
Pontanevaux 71570 La Chapelle-de-Guinchay
85 36 72 76 – Telex: 351 923 F
Fax: 85 36 72 02

Established: 1869. **Vine stocks:** Chardonnay. **Soil:** Chalky clay. **Exposure:** East – South-East. **Average annual production in hectoliters:** 650.
Appellation: Mâcon-Villages Blanc. **Type:** White. **Technique:** With temperature monitoring. **Maturing:** Early bottling. **Alcohol content:** 12.5%. **Characteristics:** Medium dry – fruity and spicy, mellow, clean finish. **Ser-**

ving temperature: 7°. **Served with:** Appetizers, fish and shellfish. **Vintages available in 89/90:** 1988.

Characteristics of vintages

Other: South Burgundies also available: Pouilly-Fuissé – Pouilly Vinzelles – Beaujolais Blanc – St. Véran – Bourgogne Aligoté. Price range (pre-tax, ex-warehouse): 20 to 30 F.F.
Sales volume:
– Wholesale: 10%. – Retail: 10%. – Restaurants: 80%.
Sales in France: 50%.
Export sales: 50%.
Main trading partners: UK, USA, Canada, Japan, Belgium, Netherlands, Germany.

References in France

Restaurants: Lasserre, Potel & Chabot (Paris).

Abroad

United States

Admiral Wine Merchant (Tel: (201) 371 2211).

United Kingdom

European vintners (Tel: 44 19977030).

Germany

Geibel (Tel: 2 653 6386).

Switzerland

Lignier (Tel: 71888019).

Canada

Monopoles L.C.B.O. (Tel. (514) 873 6788).

The Netherlands

Vos Wijnimport Tilburg (Tel: (013) 6800 75).

Comments

"Specialized since 1869 in Beaujolais and Mâconnais wines, located in the heart of the vineyard, the house of Paul Beaudet has close relationships with the growers. The name of Paul Beaudet is well recognized all over the world for its concern for quality."

CHEVALIER & FILS

Mr. Chevalier
71000 Charnay-lès-Mâcon
85 34 26 74

Type of vineyard: Family-owned.
Appellation: Bourgogne – Mâcon – Crémant de Bourgogne. **Type:** Red, white. **Technique:** Traditional. **Characteristics:** Excellent Crémant de Bourgogne – fine and fruity. **Served with:** Red: meat, roasts. White: fish. **Vintages available in 89/90:** 1985, 1986.

Characteristics of vintages

1986: Good year. Fruity, well structured wines. Excellent whites. **1985:** Good year. Rich, well-balanced red wines. Good for ageing.

CAVE DE LUGNY

B.P. 6 – Rue des Charmes
71260 Lugny (France)
85 33 22 85 – Telex: 800 806 F
Télécopie: 85 33 26 46

Type of vineyard: Cooperative Agricultural Association. **Established:** 1927. **Number of employees:** 26. **Vine stocks:** Chardonnay 2/3, Pinot Noir 1/6, Gamay 1/6. **Soil:** Clay with calcium carbonate. **Exposure:** South, Southeast. **Average annual production in hectoliters:** 65,000.
Appellation: Mâcon Villages (white), Mâcon Supérieur (red and rosé), Bourgogne Pinot Noir, Bourgogne Passe-toutgrain, Crémant de Bourgogne. **Type:** Red, white, rosé. **Technique:** White: traditional. Red: classic, Beaujolais style, Champagne Method. **Maturing:** Vats. **Alcohol content:** 11% to 13%. **Characteristics:** White: dry, but supple, flowery. Red: light, round, well-balanced. Crémant: light, pleasant, fine, much appreciated as an apéritif. **Serving temperature:** White: 8°. Red: 15° to 18°. **Served with:** White: white fish, white meat. Red: with poultry, red meat, cheese. **Vintages available in 89/90:** 1985, 1986, 1987.

Characteristics of vintages

1988: Rich, very fruity, one of the best vintage from these ten years. **1987:** Very fruity, very aromatic. **1985:** Rich, well-balanced, smells of little red fruit. Price range: (pre-tax, ex-warehouse): Between 10 and 30 F.F.
Sales in France: 30%. **Export sales:** 70%.
Main trading partners: USA, UK, Benelux Countries, Germany, South-East Asia, Australia.

CAVE DE VIRÉ

Emmanuel Bène
71260 Viré
85 33 12 64 – Telex: 351 903 F
Fax: 85 33 17 99

Type of vineyard: Agricultural Association. **Established:** 1928. **Number of employees:** 14. **Vine stocks:** Chardonnay (100%). **Soil:** Clay with calcium carbonate. **Exposure:** South, Southeast. **Average annual production in hectoliters:** 20,000.
Appellation: A.O.C. Mâcon Viré and A.O.C. Crémant de Bourgogne 100% Chardonnay. **Type:** White. **Technique:** Champagne method. **Maturing:** Casks, stainless steel and concrete tanks. **Alcohol content:** About 13%. **Characteristics:** Dry, fruity whitewine, very typical Chardonnay, round and long. **Served with:** As an apéritif and with shellfish, white meat, goat cheese. **Vintages available in 89/90:** 1988, 1989.

Characteristics of vintages

1988: Good balance, fruity and round – a very good vin-

tage. Price range (pre-tax, ex-warehouse): Between 20 an 30 F.F
Sales volume:
- Wholesale: 10% - Retail: 20%. - Restaurants: 20%.
Sales in France: 50%.
Export sales: 50%.
Main trading partners : USA, UK, Germany, Belgium, Canada, Australia.

References in France

Restaurants: In many fine restaurants.
Shops: Malaval, Lyon.

ST-VÉRAN

DOMAINE DES DEUX ROCHES

Messrs. Collovray and Terrier
Davaye 71960
85 35 83 29

Vine stocks: Chardonnay. **Soil:** Chalky clay. **Average annual production in hectoliters:** 800.
Appellation: St Veran. **Type:** White. **Maturing:** In vats and oak casks. **Serving temperature:** 12°. **Served with:** As an aperitif and with fish and white meat. **Vintages available in 89/90:** 1987, 1988.

Characteristics of vintages

1988: Abundant fragrance of ripe fruit, very good structure. **1987:** Very fruity, fresh fragrance of fruit and flowers (honeysuckle, pears, peaches). Price range (pre-tax, ex-warehouse): between 20 and 30 F.F.
Sales volume:
- Wholesale: 30%. - Retail: 20%. - Restaurants: 10%.
- Other: 40% (export).
Sales in France: 50%.
Export sales: 50%.
Main trading partners : Germany.

CHÂTEAU DE LEYNES

Jean-Bernard Goussu
Leynes - 71570 La Chapelle-de-Guinchay
85 35 11 59

Type of vineyard: Family-owned. **Established:** Established in 1898. **Number of employees:** 4. **Vine stocks:** Gamay (3/4), Chardonnay (1/4). **Soil:** Granitic with clay and calcium carbonate. **Exposure:** South. **Average annual production in hectoliters:** 1,200.
Appellation: Beaujolais-Villages, St-Véran, Beaujolais Blanc, Beaujolais Rosé. **Type:** White. **Technique:** Red: traditional Beaujolais. Rosé: traditional Saignée. White: traditional Mâcon. **Alcohol content:** 12 to 13%. **Characteristics:** White: dry, fruity, aromatic, ages well. Red: good color, charming, firm, typical of the area. Rosé: fruity, aromatic. **Serving temperature:** White: 14°. Red: 16°. Rosé: 13°. **Served with:** White: fish, first course, seafood, white meat. Rosé: goes with everything except heavy, rich cooking. Red: goes with everything excep game, cheese. **Vintages available in 89/90:** 1987, 1988, 1989.

Characteristics of vintages

1988: Complete wine, rich and well-balanced, with body and fine aromas - precocious, to be kept. **1987:** Well-balanced, very aromatic, can be kept for 5 years.

POUILLY-FUISSÉ

AUVIGUE BURRIER REVEL

Jean-Pierre Auvigue
Le Moulin Du Pont, 71850 Charnay-lès-Mâcon
85 34 17 36 - Telex: B SC ABr 306 254

Type of vineyard: Corporation. **Established:** 1946. **Vine stocks:** Chardonnay. **Soil:** Chalky clay. **Exposure:** South-East. **Average annual production in hectoliters:** 80 hl.
Appellation: Pouilly-Fuissé. **Type:** White. **Maturing:** In wooden casks. **Alcohol content:** 13 %. **Characteristics:** Fruity, round, goes down smoothly. **Serving temperature:** 12°. **Served with:** Fish, shellfish, white meat. **Vintages available in 89/90:** 1986, 1987, 1988.

Pouilly-Fuissé
APPELLATION POUILLY-FUISSÉ CONTROLÉE
Mise en bouteilles par les Ets AUVIGUE-BURRIER & REVEL à 71000 CHARNAY-LES-MACON.
13% vol.
"LA FRAIRIE"
750 ml
ANDRE AUVIGUE, PROPRIETAIRE · SOLUTRÉ-POUILLY (S & L)

Characteristics of vintages

1988: Fruity, very fine, balanced, supple. **1987:** Beautiful color, intense aromas, round, supple. **1986:** Very typical Chardonnay, long, supple, hazelnut butter flavor. Price range (pre-tax, ex-warehouse): 30 to 50 F.F.
Sales volume:
– Retail: 5%. – Restaurants: 25%. – Other: 70% – export.
Sales in France: 30%.
Export sales: 70%.
Main trading partners : USA, United Kingdom, Belgium, Japan, Netherlands, Switzerland.

References in France

Restaurants: La Mère Blanc (Vonnas), Lasserre (Paris), Hôtel de Paris (Monaco), Maxim's (Paris), etc.

Abroad

United States

Seagram – Robert Chadderdon, both in New York.

United Kingdom

European Cellars – Ingletons – Walter Siegel – Ebury Mathiot, Sichel.

Switzerland

Hertig Vins.

Belgium

Feys – Werco – Gilbart – Heenbert – Caves de France – V.P.S. Belgique – L'Hermitage.

The Netherlands

Vojacek Maastrieht.

Far East

Toyo Menka (Japan) – Mitsumi.

Others

Mexico: Ditribuidora Reforma.

Comments

Producers of Pouilly-Fuissé for several generations. Limited liability corporation founded in 1946 by Francis Auvigue.

ANDRÉ FOREST

André Forest-Vergisson
Vergisson 71960 Pierreclos
85 35 84 58

Type of vineyard: Share-cropping. **Established:** For several generations. **Vine stocks:** Chardonnay. **Soil:** Chalky clay. **Exposure:** South-West. **Average annual production in hectoliters:** 50 hl/5 ha.
Appellation: Pouilly-Fuissé. **Type:** White. **Technique:** Hand harvesting. **Maturing:** In oak casks. **Alcohol content:** 13.5%. **Characteristics:** Very dry and very fruity, green gold color. **Serving temperature:** 10 to 12°. **Served with:** All first courses and, especially, with fish. **Vintages available in 89/90:** 1987 and 1988 as from June 1989.

Characteristics of vintages

1988: Dry, and very aromatic. **1987:** On sale right now, very long, still a bit young. **1986:** Very delicate, can be aged a long time. Price range (pre-tax, ex-warehouse): 50 to 60 F.F. including tax.
Sales volume:
– Retail: 25%. – Restaurants: 25%. – Other: 50% (export).
Sales in France: 50%.
Export sales: 50%.
Main trading partners : USA, Ireland, Belgium, Germany.

References in France

Restaurants: Paris: The Ritz Hôtel, Faugeron, Joël Robuchon, Le Toit de Passy, Jacques Cagna, Le Pont Alma, les Trois Marches, etc.

Abroad

United States

Weygandt-Metzler Coatesville Pa. Worldwide Wines, Connecticut.

United kingdom

Kelly's Strand Hotel, Rosslare C° Weford, Ireland.

Germany

Gerwig Import 7014 Kornwestheim.

Belgium

Domaine du Château de Fraineux, 4151 Nandrin.

LUQUET ROGER

Roger Luquet
71960 Fuissé
85 35 60 91
Telex: 800 831 CHAMCO/ATT R. LUQUET
Fax: 85 35 60 12

Type of vineyard: Family-owned. **Established:** 1966 (Luquet family for several generations). **Vine stocks:** Chardonnay. **Soil:** Chalky. **Exposure:** South. **Average annual production in hectoliters:** 600.
Appellation: Pouilly-Fuissé, Saint-Véran "les Grandes Bruyères", Mâcon Blanc "Clos de Condemine". **Type:** White. **Technique:** Traditional, 12 hours debourbage, racking in March, bottling April, May. **Maturing:** Stainless steel tanks. **Alcohol content:** 13° to 13.2°. **Characteristics:** Pouilly-Fuissé: very rich and well-balanced, good color. Saint-Véran: slightly more acidic becoming drinkable rapidly, color with glints of green. Mâcon Blanc: very young, fresh and fruity, can keep for 5 to 6 years. **Serving temperature:** 11° to 12°. **Served with:** Pouilly-Fuissé: fish, foie gras. Saint-Véran: first courses, delicatessen products. Mâcon Blanc: seafood, shellfish. **Vintages available in 89/90:** 1987, 1988.

Characteristics of vintages

1988: Very well-balanced wines, will keep well, fruity and

rich. Excellent Pouilly-Fuissé characteristic of the terrain. Average pre-tax, ex-warehouse price: Pouilly-Fuissé: 39 F.F. per bottle. Saint-Véran: 24 F.F. Mâcon Blanc: 20,50 F.F.
Sales volume:
– Retail: 20%, – Restaurants: 20%.
– Other: 60% (export).
Sales in France: 40%.
Export sales: 60%.
Main trading partners : UK, Netherlands, USA, Belgium, Germany.

References in France

Restaurants: Lasserre, Le Vivarois, Auberge des Templiers, Lamazère, Le Relais de Mougins (more than 100 well known French restaurants).

CHÂTEAU DE FUISSÉ

Jean-Jacques Vincent
71960 Fuissé
83 35 61 44 – Telex: 351 030

Type of vineyard: Family-owned. **Established:** 1850. **Number of employees:** 10. **Vine stocks:** Chardonnay. **Soil:** Chalky clay. **Exposure:** South, South-East. **Average annual production in hectoliters:** 1,500. **Appellation:** Pouilly-Fuissé, Château-Fuissé. **Type:** White. **Technique:** Direct pressing, temperature control. **Maturing:** In oak, partially renewed each year. **Alcohol content:** 12 to 13%. **Characteristics:** Generally supple wines, very full, slightly acid. **Serving temperatrue:** 10 to 12°. **Served with:** All cooked fish, white meats. **Vintages available in 89/90:** 87 and 88.

Characteristics of vintages

1988: Very promising year, very full, very good balance. **1987:** Very tender, rich intense aromas, to be kept for 5 years. **1986:** Very great year, very good balance, good keeping. **1985:** Great richness, a very good year. Price range (pre-tax, ex-warehouse): between 50 and 120 F.F.
Sales volume:
– Retail: 5%. – Restaurants: 10%. – Other: 85% export.
Sales in France: 15%. **Export sales:** 85%.
Main trading partners : United Kingdom, United States, Germany, Japan, Belgium.

References in France

Restaurants: Most of the Michelin 2 and 3 star restaurants; Pic, Sanderans, Troisgros.
Shops: Fief de la Vigne, Angers and Nantes.

Abroad

United States

Frederick Wildam and sons, Ltd.

United Kindgom

Richard-Walford, Domaine Direct, Eldridge Pope.

Germany

Grand Cru Select.

Switzerland

Diffuvins.

Belgium

Jacques Pirard, Ets Raes, Ets P. Dalle.

The Netherlands

"Hommage au Vin", H. Valrhaven.

Far East

Japan: Izuhi Trading Co. Toyo Henka Keisha.

Comments

Family enterprise established in the historic Château de Fuissé. The vineyard extends over Pouilly and Fuissé, half way up the hill, with a large proportion of old vines. The wines of the château and, in particular, the Château Fuissé, are generally wines for keeping which can be tasted when they start to open up after about three years.

DOMAINE MATHIAS

Jean Mathias
71570 Chaintré
Tél. 85 35 60 67

Type of vineyard: Family-owned. **Established:** Successive generations. **Vine stocks:** White: Chardonnay. Red: Gamay. **Soil:** Chalky clay. **Exposure:** East and South-East. **Average annual production in hectoliters:** 500.

mis en bouteilles
à la propriété
Produit
en France
Pouilly-Fuissé
APPELLATION POUILLY-FUISSÉ CONTROLÉE
13,5 % vol.
75 cl
DOMAINE MATHIAS
Propriétaires-Viticulteurs, 71570 CHAINTRÉ - France

Appellation: Pouilly-Fuissé, Pouilly-Vinzelles, Mâcon-Loche, Beaujolais Blanc, Beaujolais-Villages, Marc de Bourgogne. **Type:** Red, White. **Technique:** Traditional. **Maturing:** In vats and casks. **Alcohol content:** 13%. **Characteristics:** Pouilly-Fuissé: fine and fruity, a wine for keeping par excellence. Pouilly-Vinzelles: harmonious and distinguished, it improves with age. Mâcon-Loche: elegant, pleasant, agreeable to the eye and to the taste. Beaujolais Blanc: supple, youthful and very floral. Beaujolais-Village Red: fruity, a wine for friendship that goes down well. **Serving temperature:** White: about 10°. Red: about 12°. **Served with:** White: as an aperitif, with first courses, fish, shellfish, white meats, etc. Beaujolais-Villages: red meat, game. **Vintages available in 89/90:** 1987, 1988.

Characteristics of vintages

1988: A vigorous, hale and hearty wine with a future. **1987:** Fine and fruity, a vintage that will captivate the connoisseurs. Price range (pre-taxe, ex-warehouse): Beaujolais-Villages Red: Between 10 and 20 F.F. Mâcon-Loche, Beaujolais Blanc: between 20 and 30 F.F. Pouilly-Fuissé, Pouilly-Vinzelles, Marc de Bourgogne: between 30 and 50 F.F.

Sales volume:
- Retail: 15%. - Restaurants: 10%.

Sales in France: 60%.
Export sales: 40%.
Main trading partners : United States, United Kingdom, Germany.

References in France

Shops: Hédiard.

V.S.O.P.
FINE
CHAMPAGNE
COGNAC
Otard
FORTIS ET FIDELIS
au Château de Cognac

COGNAC
Otard
V.S.O.P.
FINE CHAMPAGNE
70 cl
40%vol.
au Château de Cognac

CHAMPAGNE

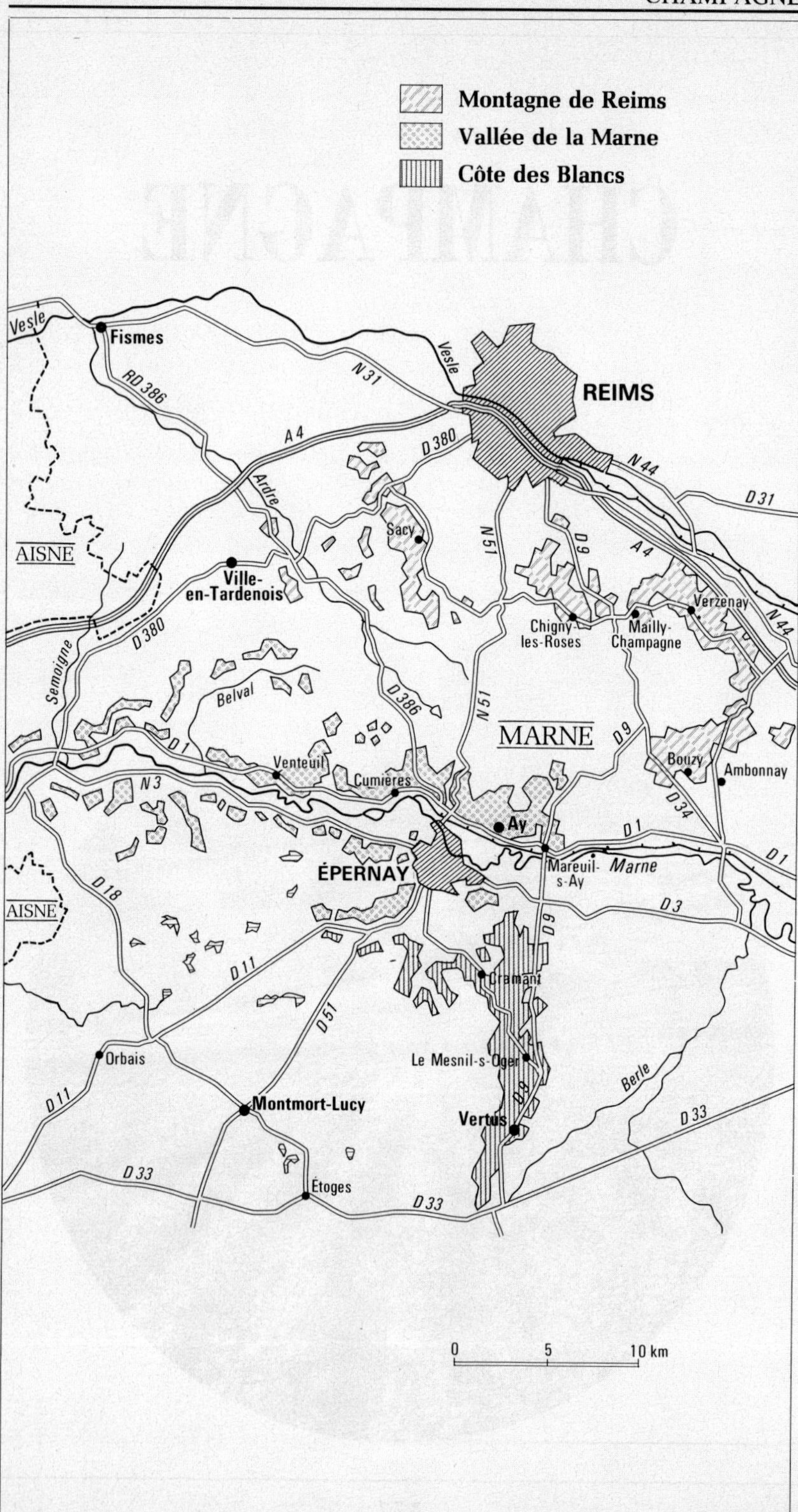
Montagne de Reims
Vallée de la Marne
Côte des Blancs
Vesle
Fismes
RD 386
N 31
Vesle
REIMS
A 4
D 380
N 44
D 31
Ardre
Sacy
N 51
D 9
A 4
AISNE
Ville-en-Tardenois
Verzenay
N 44
Chigny-les-Roses
Mailly-Champagne
D 380
Semoigne
Belval
D 386
N 51
MARNE
D 9
D 1
Venteuil
Cumières
Bouzy
Ambonnay
N 3
D 34
Ay
D 1
D 1
Mareuil-s-Ay
Marne
ÉPERNAY
D 18
D 3
AISNE
D 9
D 11
Cramant
D 51
Orbais
Le Mesnil-s-Oger
Berle
D 11
Montmort-Lucy
D 9
Vertus
D 33
D 33
Étoges
D 33
0
5
10 km

The art of blending

Our Guide is extending its coverage to new producers this year and includes an analysis of the quality of most of the wine lots of the traditional houses, from the greatest to the most "modest". It was all the more necessary because the region is often subject to qualitative changes and I felt it really necessary either to confirm the continuing merit of certain prestigious brands, or at least their status quo, at a time when more and more lesser known brands are appearing on the market.

HISTORICAL BACKGROUND

Initially, little attention was paid to the wines of the Montagne de Reims or those of the Marne Valley, which separates the regions of Ay and Hautevillers. Because the color of the wine was similar to that of burgundies, wines of this region complemented those of Beaune, which were used for the coronation festivities of French kings.

When Nicolas Brûlart inherited the Sillery vineyard in 1587, the wines improved significantly. The appellation "champagne" was introduced in the 17th century. This was advantageous for the winegrowers of Ay. They benefited from the supreme authority of Nicolas Brûlart, whom Henry IV named Chancellor of Navarre in 1605, then Chancellor of France in 1607. A sharp rivalry ensued between "champagne" and "wine from Beaune." Physicians and poets took sides in favor of one or the other. Finally, champagne emerged victorious. It became extremely popular in 1654 when it was served at the coronation festivities of Louis XIV in Reims.

The reputation of wines from Champagne crossed the English Channel when St. Evremond, who had fallen from the court of Louis XIV and was in exile in England, shared his passion for champagne with the entourage of King Charles II. And he did so admirably. In France, the magic of the word champagne reached its height beginning in 1662, and throughout the 18th century, the wine sold at higher prices than Burgundy wines.

In 1668, the Abbey of Hautevillers gave the responsibility for its monastery to Dom Pérignon. When he became administrator at Hautevillers, he ordered the digging of bigger and deeper cellars than those that had existed previously. He looked for a way to make white wine with Pinot Noir, succeeded in doing so, and by 1690 the wines of Hautevillers had become famous. In 1694, the price of white wine was so high that it was inscribed proudly on the abbey's wine press.

Dom Pérignon had a delicate palate and by simply tasting a grape he could tell the vineyard from which it came. He was enthusiastic about Champagne wines with *mousse* or foam and so he developed the art of mastering it. He invented a technique to make the foam take shape and remain firm. Thus he gave the natural qualities of Marne Valley wines the additional feature of indisputable excellence. At the time, this was revolutionary.

He had to deal with the final obstacles which were, first, the fragility of the bottles—a difficult problem to resolve because little was known about the physics of fermentation. Squat, potbellied bottles posed a problem for *dégorgement*—the removal of sediment—which Dom Pérignon used in place of settling. He changed the shape of the wine bottle, making it similar to the bottles we know today. The second obstacle was the plug. Wooden stoppers covered with hemp and dipped in oil had been used to help stop the second fermentation and prevent gas from escaping from the bottle. The cellar master of Hautevillers had the idea of replacing the hemp with cork, and in 1698 he made the first great vintage champagne. In 1700, it was sold for double the price of earlier champagnes. Champagne was the rage in the court of Louis XV and was the preferred wine of the Comtesse du Barry and of Madame de Pompadour, who said : "Champagne is the only wine a woman can drink which will not make her ugly."

Despite heavy customs duties, champagne was also honored at the Court of England where King George II drank it enthusiastically. And as trade barriers were gradually lifted, champagne won over the English completely.

By 1780, because vintage champagnes required aging, the trade of Champagne wines could no longer be handled by individual winegrowers and brockers in Reims and Epernay. Great personalities of the region anticipated the future. Wine houses were established, thereby giving champagne casks an emblem. Five years later, sales totalled 300,000 bottles. Six million bottles were sold by the mid-19th century, and by the early 20th century the number sold had exceeded 28 million. When Dom Pérignon introduced his first bottle of Champagne, he surely had no idea of the success awaiting it—a success story that goes on and on. . .

THE VINEYARD

The Champagne wine growing region is made up of four principal zones: the Reims Mountain, the Marne Valley, the Côte des Blancs and the Aube Vineyard. The first three, which cover the entire districts of Reims and Epernay, in the heart of the Champagne region, are the most important, those producing the most highly reputed crus. Vines meander along the hillside slopes forming winding ribbons 120 kilometers long, varying from 300 meters to 2 kilometers in width. The Reims mountain forms part of the Ile-de-France precipice. It constitutes the southern slope of the Vesle Valley, extending as far as the Marne Valley which it overlooks at Epernay. It is a huge, rather flat plateau, between 20 to 25 kilometers long, and 6 to 10 kilometers wide. Among its best Crus: Ambonnay, Beaumont-sur-Vesle, Bouzy, Louvois, Mailly-Champagne, Sillery, Verzenais and Versy.

In the Marne Valley, vineyards have been established mainly between Tours-sur-Marne and Dormans, and extend as far as Château-Thierry and beyond, even as far as the Aisne. This area produces renowned Crus such as the Ay and the Mareuil-sur-Ay.

The Côte des Blancs, or Côte d'Avize, thus called because it produces almost exclusively white grapes, faces East. It forms a second slope, perpendicular to the Reims Mountain, less high, which extends over 20 kilometers from North to South, south of Epernay and of the Marne. The best Crus are: Avize, Cramant, Oger and Le-Mesnil-sur-Oger. It extends further to the Côte de Vertus, the Congy area and the Côte de Sézanne.

Separated from the Marne by the Champagne plain, the Aube Vineyard is located in the Bar-sur-Seine and Bar-sur-Aube region.

THE "METHODE CHAMPENOISE" (Champagne Method)

The method of secondary fermentation in the bottle is generally associated with the name of Dom Pérignon, the 18th Century gustatory genius, who prepared the first "tumultuous" wines imprisoned in thick bottles capable of withstanding a pressure of as much as 6 kg. It consists in adding to still wine, obtained by subtle selection and blending, a "tirage" liqueur with a particular sugar dosage depending on the type of product one desires, as well as leavens made of selected yeasts. The wine is immediately bottled and placed in a cellar at a temperature of 10° to 12°C. A secondary fermentation then takes place. It lasts a few months, during which the carbon dioxide is kept under pressure in the bottles. The quality of the foam will depend on how well this process is controlled. The bottles are then placed on the shaking racks, invented, it is believed, by the Veuve Cliquot, which allow the bottles to be turned in any orientation. Then begins the shaking, which amounts to inclining and turning the bottles. Certain specialists "handle" from 30,000 to 40,000 bottles a day. When the sediment reaches the neck of the bottle, it is expelled at low temperature. To replace the few centiliters of disgorged liquid (4 to 8) a sweetening liqueur (the expedition liqueur) is added, made of old wines and sugar in varying dosage accordins to the type of sparkling wine desired : brut, dry. . . etc. The bottles are then corked definitively. Note that the champagne method is unique, the blending and chaptalization operations determining, for the most part, the quality of the product.

THE CHARACTERISTICS OF THE VINEYARD

The vineyards of Champagne are located at the eastern end of the Seine River basin, in a region of chalky soil 120 mi. (193 km) long by 274 yd. to 3.2 mi. wide (300 m to 2 km). The four main areas of Champagne are the Montagne de Reims, the Valley of the Marne, the Côte des Blancs and the vineyards of Aube.

Soil

The vines of Champagne are planted in a limestone-concentrated soil which has a thick layer of arable soil. The chalky subsoil insures perfect drainage, protects the soil from humidity, and stores heat which is transferred to the grapes.

Climate

Winter in the Champagne region is mild, spring is unpredictable, and fall and summer are gorgeous. The sun shines ?? days a year; the average temperature is 50°F (10°C). These are the climatic conditions that give Champagne grapes their freshness and acidity—essential for grapes that are picked the very moment they mature.

OBJECTIVE ATTAINED

To have one's enterprise recognized as one of the first five great Champagne producers is not something that just anyone might do. As a result of dedication and ambition, the house of Laurent-Perrier has achieved this distinction, colors flying; a great adventure in which man plays a dominant role.

As of 1812 the destiny of the house was signed and sealed. "Whether by chance or foresight", they say here, "the choice made by the Laurent-Perriers for their red brick establishment at Tours-sur-Marne was remarkable."

Of course, you have to concede that finding yourself surrounded by 100% classified vineyards affords a certain predisposition to quality. "Champagne comes only from Champagne", they continue, "certainly, but as great wine is produced only from great grapes, great Champagne results only from the blending of great Champagne crus."

If La Palice would have approved without reserve, it was still necessary to get together the means and then to succeed in imposing the style of the establishment. For Bernard de Nonancourt, if "vintage Champagne is characterized by a year, the brut is characterized by a house". Hale and hearty, equally at ease at the Court of St. James or in a "bistro" with his friends, he is a legend unto himself. As remarkable a person as you might want to meet, frank, sincere and passionate, gift for human relations and an exceptional competitive spirit, he can go on forever on his favorite subject, the secret of success in Champagne. Assisted by Bernard de La Giraudière and François Philippoteaux, surrounded by a remarkable team—more nearly a "family"—he has managed to promote his establishment from 98th place in the 1960's to among the first five today! Chance had no place in this story. Quality and consistency are behind this success.

The message has been received and understood all over the world.

THE PRODUCTS

Cuvée Grand Siècle:

Top of the line, 100% blended from grands crus of the best vintages, it is a rich and velvety wine, with that touch of freshness, elegance and fruitiness dear to the hearts of well-born souls.

Cuvée Rosé Brut:

Obtained by direct rosé vinification of the best crus of Pinot Noir, followed by fermentation in oak casks. A delicate rosé with a beautiful color, fruity to the nose as well as to the taste.

Brut and Vintage Brut:

Fine and fragrant, produced from crus with an average rating above 90% (the Champagne scale goes from 77 to 100%), to which is added an ultra-brut, unsugared, lively and light. In exceptional years it is assigned a vintage (1973, 1979. . .).

Blanc de Blancs de Chardonnay:

Product of the king of the white vinestocks, from the best terrain and the best crus, a still wine, dry and fruity, light, supple and full to the taste.

CHAMPAGNE HENRI ABELÉ

Henri Lafay (Director)
50, rue de Sillery - B.P. 18 - 51051 Reims
26 85 23 86 - Telex: 842 181 F

Type of vineyard: Corporation. **Established:** 1757. **Wine stocks:** Chardonnay, Pinot Noir, Pinot Meunier. **Average annual production in hectoliters:** About 6,900.
Appellation: Champagne. **Type:** White, rosé. **Technique:** Traditional, champagne method. **Alcohol content:** 11.5 to 12%. **Characteristics:** Fresh, flowery, fine, elegant, beautiful, green-gold color. **Serving temperature:** 6° to 8°. **Served with:** The Brut "Sourire de Reims". As an apéritif and with fine fish, foie gras, poultry. The Brut "Grande Marque Impériale" 1982 with red meat, light sauces. The Brut Rosé as an apéritif and with red meat. The vintage Brut Blanc de Blancs as an apéritif and with very fine meats. **Vintages available in 89/90:** Vintage Brut 1982 – Vintage Blanc de Blancs 1982.

Characteristics of vintages

1986, 1985, 1983: Not yet available. **1982:** Fresh, very well-balanced, beautiful personality holos many pleasant surprises for the future. Also try the Champagne rose. Average pre-tax, ex-warehouse price: 80 F.F. to 136 F.F.
Sales volume: – Wholesale: 30%. – Off-Licence: 30%. – Restaurants: 40%.
Sales in France: 60%.
Export sales: 40%.
Main trading partners: Spain, USA, UK, Germany, Netherlands, Belgium, Portugal, New Zealand.

References in France

Restaurants: In more than 2000 restaurants listed in the Michelin, Champerard, Gault & Millau and Hachett Guide Books.
Shops: Specialized cellars etc., Guilde des Cavistes in Paris, Musée du Vin à Paris.

Abroad

United States

Freixenet USA. 23555 Highway 121. SONOMA 95476. P. Box 1949.

United Kingdom

Direct Wine Supplies Ltd. Culpitt House 74/78 Town Centre Hatfield HERTS AL10 0JW.

Germany

Abele Markenvertrieb. Franz-Abt-Str. 10 D-6200 Wiesbaden.

Others

Spain: Commercial Champañera S.A. – c/Joan Sala s/n – San Sadurni de Noya – Barcelona.

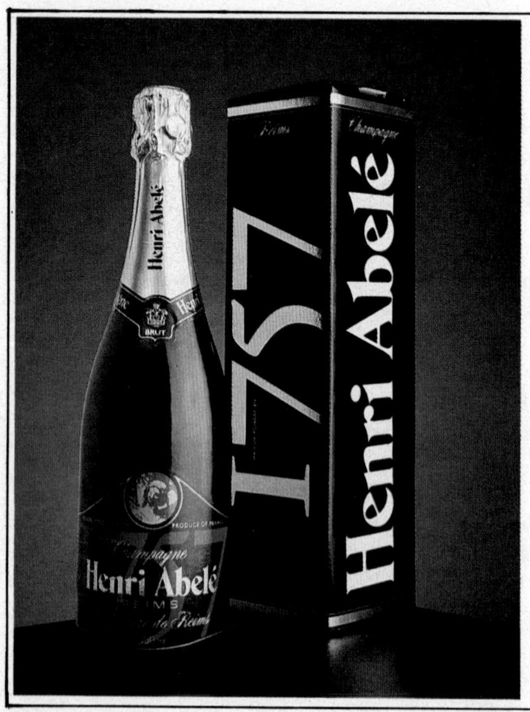

CHAMPAGNE BEAUMONT DES CRAYÈRES

Jean-Paul Bertus
Mardeuil 51200 Épernay
26 55 29 40

Type of vineyard: Cooperative. **Established:** 1955. **Vine stocks:** Pinot noir, Pinot Meunier, Chardonnay. **Soil:** Chalky. **Exposure:** East, South-East. **Average annual production in hectoliters:** 2,300.

Appellation: Champagne. **Type:** White, Rosé.

Characteristics of vintages

Price range (pre-tax, ex-warehouse): 50 to 80 F.F.
Sales volume:
- Wholesale: 10%. - Retail: 80%. - Restaurants: 10%
Sales in France: 90%.
Export sales: 10%.
Main trading partners : Belgium, Italy, Switzerland.

Comments

A "small" cooperative winecellar with 75 hectares in production for 210 members. Jean Paul Bertus directs this establishement with competence and authority. A distinguished œnological technician, he studied for seven years at the Lycée d'Avize. A number of wine lots are available, in particular the Cuvée Prestige Brut (Chardonnay and Pinot) and the Cuvée "Rosé", a fine and lingering Brut with a rapsberry fragrance.

• *Watch out for certain confusing labels: "Bottled at the Château", the wine is produced on the estate; "bottled on the estate", the wine comes from a cooperative... (See Chapter "Labeling").*

• *A dish for each wine. According to the age of your wines, their style, their typical nature, their color, adapt your menu without sticking to stereotypes (see "Wine and Foods".*

LES HAUTES CAVES

Alain Bergere
23 70 29 82 - Telex: 840 704 F T. 0013

Type of vineyard: Family-owned. **Number of employees:** 6. **Vine stocks:** Chardonnay 35%, Pinot Noir 25%, Meunier 40%. **Soil:** Chalk, clay and alluvium. **Exposure:** South - South-East and East. **Average annual production in hectoliters:** 540.
Appellation: Champagne, Vins des coteaux Champenois. **Type:** Red, white, rosé. **Technique:** Champagne method, alcoholic fermentation at 18°. **Maturing:** Partial malolactic fermentation. **Alcohol content:** 12.5%. **Characteristics:** Blanc de Blancs: finesse - selection: fuller-bodied due to Pinot Noir - Reserve: supple. **Serving temperature:** 8°. **Served with:** As an aperitif, and with salmon or white meat (rosé).

Characteristics of vintages

1985: Balanced, delicate and full-bodied. Price range (pre-tax, ex-warehouse): 52 to 90 F.F.
Sales volume:
- Wholesale: 5%. - Retail: 85% - Restaurants: 10%.
Sales in France: 80%. **Export sales:** 20%.
Main trading partners : Canada, Switzerland, Germany, UK.

References in France

Shops: L'Amour du Vin.

Abroad

Canada

Société des Alcohols du Québec, Place d'Armes, Montreal H2Y 3J8 (Telex: 05 828691 SAQ).

Comments

Since the 18th century, the family vineyard has been straddling the Etoges and Ferebrianges localities, 25 km South of Épernay. The chalky soil favors the production of fine, light wines whose character tends to be dominated by the Chardonnay vinestocks. An extension of the vineyard is currently under way in the Marne Valley. The Meunier grapes yield round and supple blends. The 85 vintage contains about 60% Chardonnay, 30%, Pinot Noir and 10% Meunier.

CHAMPAGNE BESSERAT DE BELLEFON

M. Jean-Jacques Bouffard
Allée du Vignoble - 51100 Reims
26 36 09 18 - FAX: 26 36 39 09

Type of vineyard: Corporation. **Established:** 1843. **Number of employees:** 100. **Vine stocks:** Pinots. **Soil:** Chalky. **Exposure:** South. **Average annual production in hectoliters:** 60 hl/ha.

Appellation: Champagne. **Type:** White, rosé. **Technique:** White: temperature control. **Maturing:** In stainless steel tanks. **Alcohol content:** 12%. **Characteristics:** Extreme finesse and lightness. **Serving temperature:** 8°. **Vintages available in 89/90:** 1982, 1983.

Characteristics of vintages

Other: 1982: Very natural wines. Price range (pre-tax, ex-warehouse): 80 to 120 F.F.
Sales volume:
- Retail: 45%. - Restaurants: 35%. - Other: 20% winecellars and wholesalers.
Sales in France: 80%.
Export sales: 20%.
Main trading partners : Switzerland, Belgium, UK.

References in France

Restaurants: Almost all of the great restaurants.
Shops: Luxury cellars and delicatessens in Paris and elsewhere in France.

Abroad

Switzerland

Perisem.

United States

Austin Nichols.

United Kingdom

Campbell distillers LTD.

Germany

I.G.M.

Belgium

Établissements Victor Tamines.

Canada

Distilleries Dumont.
And many others countries all over the world.

Comments

Besserat de Bellefon was founded in 1843 by Edmond Besserat at Ay, a village well known to Champagne lovers, where Henry IV owned several vineyards and a wine press. Since 1970, Besserat de Bellefon has been installed south of Reims, in a modern establishment which provides a capacity for growth in the years to come.
In 1988, Besserat de Bellefon sold almost 2,5 millions bottles for a turnover of 148 millions francs before taxes, an increase of 15% over 1987.

CHAMPAGNE BILLECART - SALMON

Jean Roland-Billecart
40, rue Carnot 51160 Mareuil-sur-Ay
26 50 60 22 - Telex: 840 470 - FAX: 26 50 64 88

Type of vineyard: Corporation. **Established:** 1818. **Number of employees:** 30. **Vine stocks:** Chardonnay 41%, Pinot Noir 29%, Pinot Meunier 30%.
Appellation: Champagne. **Type:** White and Rosé. **Technique:** In cellars. **Maturing:** In bottles. **Alcohol content:** 12.5%. **Characteristics:** Fruity, light, elegant. **Serving temperature:** 8°. **Served with:** As an aperitif, and with fish and white meat. **Vintages available in 89/90:** 1983, 1985.

Characteristics of vintages

1988: Will be bottled in 1989. **1985:** Full-bodied, rich and well balanced, very fresh. **Other:** 1983: Finesse, elegance. Price range (pre-tax, ex-warehouse): 80 to 120 F.F. (Brut S.A. and Rosé), 120 to 160 F.F. (Brut millésime 1983) over 160 F.F. (Blanc de Blancs, Vintage 1983).
Sales in France: 55%. **Export sales:** 45%.
Main trading partners : Italy, UK, Germany, Benelux countries.

References in France

Restaurants: (Paris): Lucas Carton, Drouant, Le Vivarois, Le Grand Vefour. (Cagna): Le Carré-des-Feuillants. (Valence): Pic. (Eugénie-les-Bains): Guérard, etc.
Shops: Caves Bardout, Inno, Caves de la Madeleine, la Cave-aux-Champagnes (Paris).

Abroad

United States

Importers: Robert Chadderdon, New York.

United Kingdom

Windrush Wines. Mr. Mark Savage, Cirencester.

Germany

Champa Vins Français, Mr. Karl Dœrfler, Stolberg.

Switzerland

Maison Favre Tempia. Mr. J.L. Mazel, Geneva.

Belgium

Robert Goffard, Brussels.

Far East

Japan: Asahi, Tokyo.

Champagne
BILLECART-SALMON
BILLECART
BRUT
CHAMPAGNE
BILLECART-SALMON
Mareuil-sur-Ay
BRUT
B.P.8 MAREUIL-SUR-AY-51160 AY-TEL. 26.50.60.22

Others

Italy: V.E.L.I.E.R., Genova. Australia: Domaine Wine Shippers, Victoria. Mexico: Pedro Pinson, Mexico.

Comments

The roots of the Billecart family in Champagne go back to time immemorial as proven by two emblazoned tombs from the 16th century to be found in the Mareuil-sur-Ay church. In 1818, Nicolas-François Billecart, owner of a large vineyard that he inherited from his ancestors, founded his enterprise and registered his Trade Mark: "Billecart-Salmon". Heir to his ancestor Pierre Billecart, Counsellor to the King's Parliament, he made use of the old Coat of Arms, so typical of local taste, to decorate his labels: "from azur to the golden chevron, with three bunches of grapes at the top and a greyhound at the point". He was succeeded in turn by his son Charles Billecart (1823-1888), his grandson Pol Billecart (1888-1916), and then his great grandson Charles Roland-Billecart, whose son Jean Roland-Billecart is currently President and Director General of the Corporation, S.A. Champagne Billecart-Salmon.

CHAMPAGNE BLONDEL

Mr. Blondel
"Les Monts Fournois"
51500 Ludes
26 03 43 92

Type of vineyard: Family-owned. **Vine stocks:** Chardonnay and Pinot Noir.
Appellation: Champagne. **Type:** White – Rosé. **Technique:** Traditional champagne method. **Characteristics:** Excellent Champagne Brut, Carte Or, fine foam, combination of balance and elegance, very seductive. The Rosé and Blanc de Blancs are not to ber missed. **Serving temperature:** 10-12°. **Served with:** As an aperitif and with the entire meal. **Vintages available in 89/90:** 1979, 1983 (if any is left).

Characteristics of vintages

Price range (pre-tax, ex-warehouse): 50-80 F.F.

References in France

Shops: L'Amour du Vin, 94, rue Saint-Dominique, 75007 Paris. Tél: 45 56 12 94.

CHAMPAGNE BOIZEL

Mrs. Evelyne Roques-Boizel
14-16, rue de Bernon – 51200 Épernay
26 55 21 51 – Telex: 830 913 F

Type of vineyard: Corporation. **Established:** 1834. **Vine stocks:** No vineyards, grapes supplied by independent growers under contract. **Average annual production in hectoliters:** 2,000000 bottles.
Appellation: Champagne: Brut Réserve, Brut Blanc de Blancs, Brut Rosé, Brut Millésimé "Joyau de France". **Characteristics:** Complexity and balance, richness and elegance of the champagnes made by traditional blending. Blanc de blanc an delicacy and finesse of great Chardonnay grapes. **Served with:** As aperitif or with fish and white meat. Rosé: tenderloin of beef. **Vintages available in 89/90:** 1982, 1983, 1985.

Characteristics of vintages

1985: Full bodied and yet supple balance and elegance. **1983:** Fruity, elegant, balanced, good acidity. **1982:** Very full and refined, fully matured, long, a perfect success. Buy with complete confidence. Price range (pre-tax, ex-warehouse): Between 50 F.F. and 120 F.F.
Sales volume: – 50% (export).
Sales in France: 50%. **Export sales:** 50%.
Main trading partners : UK, Switzerland, Italy, USA, Belgium, Germany, Australia, Netherlands.

References in France

Restaurants: Royal Champagne (Épernay), La Chunga (Cannes).

Shops: Caves de la Madeleine, Pt. Bacchus, Willi's Paris.

Abroad

United States

Master Wines, Winesellers, 9933 N. Lawler Av., Westmoreland Bldg., Skokie, L11. 60077. Restaurants: Jam's (N.Y.), Bud's (N.Y.), Dixie (Chicago), Hollywood Roosevelt (Los Angeles).

United Kingdom

Hedges & Butler, Three Mill Lane, Bromley by Bow, London E3 3DU. Restaurants: Marlborough Crest, Kettners, Shoppenhangers Manor.

Germany

V. Hafner, Schulstrasse 49, 6630 Saarlouis 2. Barthel Haimhauerst.1 Munchen.

Canada

Le Marchand de Vin, 1538 Ouest rue Sherbrooke, suite 510, Montreal, Quebec H36 1L5.

The Netherlands

Heeren van Heusden, Heusden. Restaurants: Auberge de Kiwitt.

Far East

Sakatsuya Co., 6-12 Chome Chiyoda, Naka Ku, Nagoya, Japan.

Others

Switzerland: Erwal Sonnhaldenstr. 47, hergiswill. Italy: lemmallo, Via A Regolo 2, Milan. Belgium: Mairesse, Rue des Pierres, Brussels.

Comments

Independent family winemakers since 1834.

F. BONNET, PÈRE & FILS

Dupont Alain, œnologue
Route du Mesnil à Oger (Marne) - 51190 Avize
26 57 52 43

Type of vineyard: Agricultural Association. **Established:** 1922. **Number of employees:** 10. **Vine stocks:** White: Chardonnay. Red: Pinot Noir. **Soil:** Chalky. **Exposure:** South. **Average annual production in hectoliters:** 125,000 bottles.
Type: White. **Technique:** Champagne Method. **Maturing:** 4 years in chalk caves. **Alcohol content:** 12%. **Characteristics:** Fine bouquet, harmonious and balanced. Lightness, finesse. **Serving temperature:** 8°. **Served with:** Recommended as an aperitif. Perfect with first courses, shellfish, fish. **Vintages available in 89/90:** 1983.

Characteristics of vintages

1983: Discrete and refined, rich aromas, beautiful lengh, wonderful future. From an exceptional harvest, remarkable in every way. Distinguished flowery touch, it discover with confidence. Price range (pre-tax, ex-warehouse): between 50 F.F. and 80 F.F.

Sales volume:
- Wholesale: 10%. - Retail: 60%. - Restaurants: 30%.
Sales in France: 70%.
Export sales: 30%.
Main trading partners : UK, Germany, Italy, Netherlands, Belgium, Switzerland, Spain.

CHAMPAGNE BRICOUT

Mr. Clément Muller
29 rempart du Midi - 51190 Avize
26 57 53 93 - Telex: 830 695.

Type of vineyard: Corporation. **Number of employees:** 70.

Appellation: Champagne.

Characteristics of vintages

Price range (pre-tax, ex-warehouse): 80 to 120 F.F. - 120 to 160 F.F.
Sales volume: - Retail: 5%. - Restaurants: 80%.
Sales in France: 75%. **Export sales:** 25%.
Main trading partners : Germany, USA, Italy, UK.

References in France

Restaurants: Restaurants with Michelin stars (Joël ROBUCHON, Guy SAVOY, Gérard BOYER, ...).

Abroad

United States

Racke USA.

Switzerland

Bataillard.

West Germany

Racke.

Far East

Japan: Mitsui.

Italy

Meregalli.

England

Boutinot

Comments

In 1979, the Kupferberg house of Mainz and its affiliate Bricout from Avize joined with the Racke holding group of Bingen, in the Rhineland. The Racke group, a leader in the spirits sector in Germany, imports wines from France and Yugoslavia and is a producer for Whisky, Rhum, Armagnac and a number of other products.

CHAMPAGNE A. CHARBAUT & FILS

René & Guy Charbaut
17, avenue de Champagne - B.P. 150
51250 Épernay Cédex
33 26 54 37 55 - Telex: Champac 840 233 F
Fax: 33 26 54 47 12

Type of vineyard: Corporation (private). Family-owned. **Established:** 1948. **Vine stocks:** Pinot Noir, Chardonnay, Pinot Meunier. **Average annual production in hectoliters:** 11,250, or 1,500,000 bottles.
Appellation: Champagne. **Type:** White. Rosé. **Technique:** Traditional. Method champagne. **Alcohol content:** 12%. **Characteristics:** Supple, well-balanced. **Serving temperature:** 6 or 8° / 42 or 48 F. **Served with:** As an aperitif and with the entire meal. **Vintages available in 89/90:** 1982 and 1985.

Characteristics of vintages

Good vintage (notably the '82 vintage), fruity and well-balanced combination, full-taste. Price range (pretax, ex-warehouse): between 80 F.F. and 130 F.F., 60 F.F. and 90 F.F.
Sales in France: 50%. **Export sales:** 50%.
Main trading partners: England, USA, Germany, Belgium, Switzerland, Australia, Japan, Greece, Spain, Italy, Canada, Luxemburg, Mexico, the Netherlands.

References in France

Restaurants: Le Grand Vefour, Paris; Bardet, Tours; Royal Champagne, Épernay; Les Crayères-Boyer, Reims.

Abroad

United States

Wine Markets International, 100 Crossways Park West, Woodbury New York 11787 USA. Tel: (516) 346-1850. Telex: WUI-6852086 (NAT). Fax: (516) 364-1197. Mitchell Nathanson.
Wine Warehouse, 800 E. 9 Th Street, Los Angeles, California 90021. Tel: (415) 588 4575 - (800) 992 Wine. Telex: 686 466.
Heritage Wine Cellars, 6610 W. Howard Street, Niles, Illinois 60648. Tel: (312) 965 3625.
Sigels Wine and Liquor, 2960 Anode Lane, Dallas, TEXAS 75220, M. John Rector.
Shops: Zachys, 16 East Park Way, Scarsdale, New York 10583. Tel: (914) 723 0241. Sherry Lehmann, 679 Madison Avenue, New York 10021.
Tel: (212) 838 7500.

Germany

Gebr. Anraths Gmbh, Bilker Allee 57, Postfarch 260116 4000. Düsseldorf. Tel: 0211 307027. Telex: 85 82 657. Fax: 0211 307029, M. Tintelnot.

Japan

Odex Japan Co. Ltd, Tankanawa Wine Club, 8-9 Tankanawa 4 - Chome, Minato - KU. Tokyo, Japan 108. Tel: 03.445.6895. Telex: 23659. Fax: 03 445 65 88. Odex Mori. M. Toshi Mori.

Switzerland

Solai - Follmi S.A., 25 route des Jeunes 1227 Carouge Suisse. Tel: 022, 42.50.80 M. Solai. Fax: 022 42 33 90.

England

H. Needham & Sons, 123 Saint-Johns Hill, Sevenoaks, Kent. TN 13 3 PE. Rolph Needham. Tel: 0732 740422. Telex: 95571 G Neevin.

Belgium

Chais et entrepôts du Nord, rue Simon Stevin, Z.I. d'Ostende 8400 Ostende. Tel: 059 80 46 69. Telex: 81768 B VANIS. Fax: 059 70 80 88.

Canada

Liquor board of Ontario, Toronto, Ontario.

• *Please note that all temperatures in this book are expressed in degrees Centigrade.*

CHAMPAGNE
CLOS DU MOULIN
CATTIER
BRUT
Cuvée
RENAISSANCE
CHAMPAGNE
CATTIER
BRUT
1982
CHIGNY-LES-ROSES
750 ml
CHAMPAGNE
CATTIER
CHIGNY-LES-ROSES
courrèges
CHAMPAGNE
courrèges
PARIS
CATTIER

CHAMPAGNE CATTIER

Jean-Jacques Cattier
6 et 11, rue Dom Pérignon, Chigny-les-Roses
51500 Rilly-la-Montagne
26 03 42 11 - Telex: 830252 - FAX 26 03 43 13

Type of vineyard: Family-owned. **Established:** Turn of the century. **Vine stocks:** Pinot Noir, Pinot Meunier, Chardonnay. **Soil:** Chalky, typical of the Champagne region. **Average annual production in hectoliters:** 2,000. **Appellation:** Champagne. **Type:** White, rosé, other: Côteaux Champenois (red and white). **Technique:** Traditional champagne method. **Maturing:** In vats. **Alcohol content:** 12%. **Characteristics:** Rich and full bodied, well balanced. Fruitiness associated with Pinot combined with the lightness, finesse and subtlety of the Chardonnay. Perfectly balanced champagne, top quality. **Serving temperature:** 6° to 8°. **Served with:** As an aperitif and with first course, seafood, fish, shellfish, foie gras, caviar, etc.

Characteristics of vintages

1988: Not yet on the market. **1987:** Not yet on the market. **1985 and 1986:** Will be put on sale end of 1989. **Other:** 1983: Rich and full bodied, good potential, a dense and complete wine. 1982: Fruity, lots of finesse, lightness and elegance. Aroma and distinction, very good vinification. Cuvées de prestige: Clos-du-Moulin. Cuvée Renaissance: First rate Champagne combining elegance, richness, balance and distinction. Price range (pre-tax, ex-warehouse): 80 to 120 F.F. - 120 to 160 - 160 and over (Cuvée Clos-du-Moulin).

Sales volume:
- Retail: 70%. - Restaurants: 30%.

Sales in France: 70%. **Export sales:** 30%.
Main trading partners : USA, UK, Japan, Germany, Australia, Switzerland, Austria, Belgium, Netherlands, Mexico, Thailand, Taiwan, Singapore, Hong Kong, Denmark, South Korea, etc.

References in France

Restaurants: Mainly restaurants with Michelin stars in the Champagne region: Boyer (Château des Crayères), Lallemant (L'Assiette Champenoise), Guichaoua (Le Grand Cerf), Maillard (Les Berceaux Épernay).
Shops: Caves Petrissans (30 bis, avenue Niel, 75017 Paris), L'Amour du Vin (94, rue St-Dominique, 75007 Paris).

Abroad

United States
Neal Rosenthal, 56 Drive Maspeth, New York 11378 (Tel: (718) 326 79 90).

United Kingdom
Haughton Fine wine, Chorley (near Cholmondeley), Nantwich, Cheshire CW5 8JR (Tel: 0270 74 537). Ian & Madeleine Trehearne, Wine Merchants, 20 New end Square, London NW3 1LN (Tel: 01 435 6310).

Germany
Gebr. Anraths, Hans Peter Tintelnot, Bilker Allee 57, 4000 Düsseldorf (Tel: (0211) 30 70 27).

Switzerland
Caves Bujard, 1095 Lutry (Tel: (021) 39 13 13).

Belgium
Ets Massaux, 51, rue F. Colon, 5730 Malonne (Tel: 44 44 16).

The Netherlands
Hanos Apeldoorn B.V., Stadhoudersmolenweg 41, 7317 AW Apeldoorn (Tel: (055) 214546).

Far East
Singapore: Fabian Trading, 2 Pandan Road, Singapore 2260 (Tel: 2666411). Hong Kong: Topsy Trading, Flat J 14/7, Yip Cheung Centre, 10 Fung Yip Street, Chai Wan (Tel: 5 568268).

Italia
Fratelli Rinaldi Importatori Via Mascarella 102. Bologne (Tel: (051) 24 09 84).

Austria
Alois V. Stangl, Untersbergstrasse 4. 5020 Salzburg (Tel: (0662) 84 96 84).

Japan
Sanyo Electric Trading 33 Hiyoshi - Cho, 2 Chome Moriguchi-Shi, Osaka Fu.

Mexico
Corporacion Vinicola Angelopolitana S.A. de C.V. Av. Hermanos Serdan 652 72100 Puebla (Estado de Puebla) (Tel: (9122) 49 00 88).

Others
Denmark: Chris Wine, Erling Carl and Sonner, Herstedostervej 21, 2600 Glostrup (Tel: (02) 45 65 00). Australia: Crittendens Fine Wine Merchant, 513-515 Bridge road, Richmond 3121, Victoria (Tel: (03) 429 4800).

Comments

The Cattier family has owned and operated vineyards at Chigny-les-Roses over the generations since 1763. Cattier produces Champagne under the "Courrèges" trademark which is part of the "Gourmet Concept" proposed by the great clothing designer André Courrèges. Some of the main outlets are the Duty Free Shops.

CHAMPAGNE DE CASTELLANE

55, rue de Verdun - 51200 Épernay
26 55 15 33

Vine stocks: Chardonnay and Pinot Noir. **Appellation:** Champagne. **Type:** White. **Technique:** Champagne method. **Characteristics:** Good Vintage Cuvée Commodore. Dense, fragrant, well-balanced. To be tasted: the Brut Sans Année and the Vintage Blanc de Blancs. **Vintages available in 89/90:** 1980 and 1981.

• *Please note that all temperatures in this book are expressed in degrees Centigrade.*

CHAMPAGNE BUSIN BEAUFORT

Jacques Busin
17, rue Thiers, 51360 Verzenay
26 49 40 36

Type of vineyard: Family-owned. **Established:** 1800. **Vine stocks:** Pinot Noir, Chardonnay. **Soil:** Chalky. **Exposure:** East and South-East. **Average annual production in hectoliters:** 600.

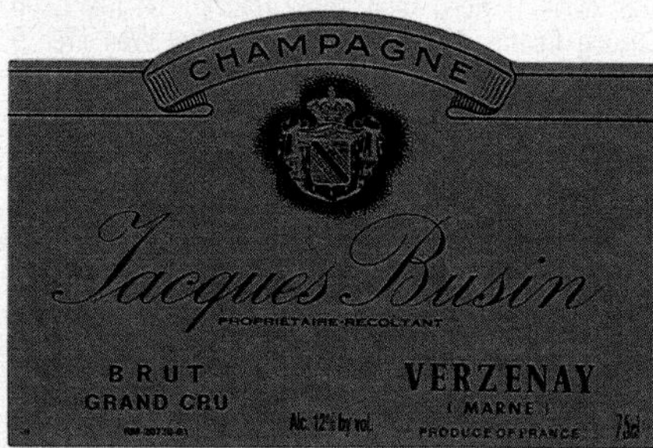

Appellation: Champagne. **Type:** White, rosé. **Technique:** Traditional champagne method, blending of great crus – 70% Pinot Noir for richness and fragrance and 30% Chardonnay Blanc for freshness and finesse. **Characteristics:** 1985: very good year, well balanced, good keeping. **Serving temperature:** 7°. **Served with:** The entire meal, very appreciated as an aperitif. **Vintages available in 89/90:** 1985.

Characteristics of vintages

1985: Very good year, balanced, good keeping. Price range (pre-tax, ex-warehouse): 50 to 80 F.F.
Sales volume:
– Wholesale: 40%. – Retail: 60%.
Sales in France: 70%.
Export sales: 30%.
Main trading partners : Germany, Belgium, Switzerland.

Abroad

Germany
La Petite France, Florentiusgraben 29 D-5300 Bonn 1 – Tel: 0228/691388.

Switzerland
Jean Louis Yenny, 7, rue des Clos, 2022 Bevaix – Tel: 038 46 24 54.

Belgium
Maison Mouliez Weemarkt 92, 8500 Courtray – Tel: 056 22 00 30.

Comments

A vineyard created in 1800 and passed down from farther to son over the generations, which offers a blend of various prestigious wines from its Verzenay, Verzy and Ambonnay vineyards (three among the rare 100% classified grands crus of Champagne).

CHAMPAGNE COLLERY

Collery
2, place de la Libération - 51180 Ay
26 54 01 20

Type of vineyard: Family-owned. **Established:** 17th Century. **Number of employees:** 12. **Vine stocks:** Pinot Noir. **Soil:** Chalk. **Exposure:** Full South. **Average annual production in hectoliters:** 500.
Appellation: Champagne. **Technique:** Traditional. **Maturing:** In the warehouse. **Alcohol content:** 11.5%. **Characteristics:** Fruity and elegant. **Serving temperature:** 10°. **Served with:** as an aperitif or with the entire meal. **Vintages available in 89/90:** 1983. **New:** Cuvée Solange Collery, 100% Blanc de Noir, Ay.

Characteristics of vintages

1983: Bouquet, finesse. Price range (pre-tax, ex-warehouse): between 50 F.F. and 80 F.F.
Sales volume:
– Wholesale: 40% – Retail: 60%.
Sales in France: 70%.
Export sales: 30%.
Main trading partners : UK, Germany, Belgium.

CHAMPAGNE CHARLES DE CAZANOVE

Thierry Lombard, Directeur Général
1, rue des Cotelles, BP 126, 51204 Épernay cedex
26 54 23 46 – Telex: 830 157 Fax: 26 54 16 38

Type of vineyard: Corporation. **Established:** Trade mark established in 1811. **Number of employees:** 49. **Average annual production in hectoliters:** About 2,000,000,000 bottles of 75 cl.
Appellation: Champagne A.O.C. **Type:** White, rosé. **Technique:** Enamelled vats to preserve aromas. **Maturing:** Same. **Alcohol content:** 11.5%. **Characteristics:** Traditional blending of Champagne vinestocks. Chardonnay with a majority of Pinots for strong, round wines. **Serving temperature:** 5 to 6°. **Served with:** As an aperitif and with fish dishes and white meats. **Vintages available in 89/90:** 1981 then 1985.

Characteristics of vintages

1985: Truly exceptional year – beautiful, well balanced wine to be offered for sale at the end of 1989. Price range (pre-tax, ex-warehouse): between 80 and 120 F.F.
Sales volumes:
– Wholesale: 90%. – Retail: 5%. – Restaurants: 5%.
Sales in France: 70%.
Export sales: 30%.
Main trading partners: United Kingdom and the rest of the European Economic Community.

References in France

Restaurants: Les Berceaux (Épernay), Le Vigneron (Reims).

Shops: Les Caves de Passy (Paris), La Boutique des Vins (Toulouse).

Abroad

United Kingdom

U.K. office: Anthony Coles, 9 Canynge Road, Clifton, Bristol. Tel: 7274 5288.

Germany

Freudenreich, Saarbrucken, Hofstattstrasse 24-26, 6620 Volklingai. Tel. 068 98/224 42.

The Netherlands

Huinck, Keizersgracht 18, 1015CP Amsterdam. Tel. 020-265751/260297.

Comments

Generally well made wines (excellent Cuvée millésimée). Good quality/price ratio over the whole range.

• *Keep up with the quality and the real evolution of the vintages. Consult the "VINTAGE CODE" at the beginning of the Guide (see Editorial). For an additional free copy, send a stamped, self-addressed envelope to Patrick DUSSERT-GERBER, 94 rue Saint-Dominique (75007 Paris).*

• *1989 Classification of the Bordeaux Grands Crus: for everything there is to know about the present quality of the various Châteaux, those that are "on the way up", those that have "come down in the world" and the others (see Bordeaux Region).*

CHAMPAGNE DELABARRE

Élisabeth Collignon – Jacky Brochet
19, rue Dom-Pérignon, 51200 Épernay
26 54 78 57 – Telex: 842 780 – Fax: 26 51 06 66

Type of vineyard: Family-owned. **Established:** For three generations. **Vine stocks:** Chardonnay, Pinot Meunier, Pinot Noir. **Soil:** Chalky. **Exposure:** South-West. **Appellation:** Champagne. **Type:** White. **Technique:** Champagne method. **Alcohol content:** 12%. **Characteristics:** Traditional "cuvées": delicate, fruity and light. Cuvée Pierre Balmain: breed, rich bouquet. **Serving temperature:** 9°. **Served with:** As an aperitif and with the entire meal. **Vintages available in 89/90:** 1983.

Characteristics of vintages

Price range (pre-tax, ex-warehouse): Champagne Delabarre: from 55 to 90 F.F. H.T.
Champagne Pierre Balmain: over 135 F.F. H.T.

Abroad

Belgium

Xylander, 12, rue de l'Oratoire, 7700 Mouscron (Tel: 056 33 24 02).

United Kingdom

Franglais Enterprise Ltd, 65, Saddleback Rd Camberley – Surrey GU 15 4DA (Tel: 276 68 46 04.

Other

Hong Kong: International Geotrade Ltd, 22, F Oxford Commercial Building, 494-496 Nathan Rd, Knowloon (Tel: 3-8721522/4). Grèce: Precieux SA, 45 Scoufa Street, 10672 Athènes (Tel: 01 33 60 86 16/18). Japan: International Geotrade Ltd. 8/F Reliance DK Bld 8-3-4 Ginza Chuo Ku, Tokyo 104 (Tel: 03 57 26 290).

Comments

The Champagne Delabarre enterprise has inherited its know-how from the three previous generations, producing their Champagne using the most modern techniques, but with no lack of respect for Champagne tradition. The activities of Champagne Delabarre are currently in a phase of full expansion and are followed with considerable interest by their consumers. Champagne Pierre Balmain is a new product, original, luxuous, for which the producer has selected a special cuvée. For the first time a great "Couturier" has affixed his label to a Champagne bottle.

CHAMPAGNE A. DESMOULINS

Jean Boulore
44 avenue Foch, B.P. 10, 51201 Epernay
26 54 24 24

Established: 1908. **Number of employees:** 7.

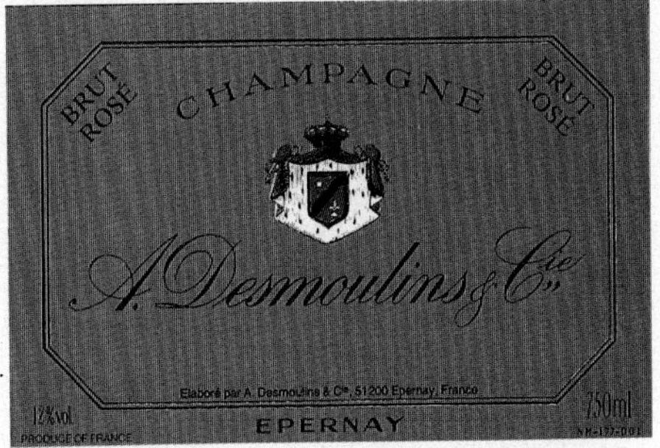

Appellation: Champagne. **Type:** White, Rosé. **Technique:** Traditional Champagne Method. **Characteristics:** Some beautiful lots, generally successful. In particular, a seductive and fruity rosé Champagne, combining finesse, richness and balance. **Served with:** As an aperitif or with the entire meal.

Characteristics of vintages

Price range (pre-tax, ex-warehouse): between 80 and 120 F.F.
Sales volume: – Retail: 100%.
Sales in France: 85%. **Export sales:** 15%.
Main trading partners : Germany, United Kingdom, Belgium.

CHAMPAGNE DEUTZ

André Lallier
16, rue Jeanson - B.P. 9 - 51160 Ay-Champagne
26 55 15 11 - Telex: 840 456
Fax: 26 54 01 21

Type of vineyard: Family Corporation. **Established:** 1838. **Number of employees:** 62. **Vine stocks:** Chardonnay, Pinot Noir, Pinot Meunier. **Soil:** Champagne chalk. **Exposure:** Multiple. **Average annual production in hectoliters:** 8,000.
Appellation: Champagne. **Type:** White, rosé. **Technique:** Champagne Method. **Maturing:** Stainless steel tanks. **Alcohol content:** 12%. **Serving temperature:** 9 to 11°. **Vintages available in 89/90:** Cuvée William Deutz: 1982. Other vintage wines: 1985.

Characteristics of vintages

1988: Very delicate, perfect balance – will not be available until 1992. **1985:** Very great vintage, high quality but in small quantity. Great concentration of aromas, rich and well-balanced, a certain finesse and therefore great elegance. **1982 and 1979:** Two great years for champagne, beautiful wines. Price range (pre-tax, ex-warehouse): non-vintage Brut: between 80 F.F. and 120 F.F. Brut, Rosé and Blanc de Blanc 1982: between 120 F.F. and 160 F.F. William Deutz: over 160 F.F.
Sales in France: 50%.
Export sales: 50%.
Main trading partners : USA, Switzerland, Germany, UK, Belgium, Italy, New Zealand, Australia.

CHAMPAGNE DE TELMONT

André & Serge Lhopital
1 avenue de Champagne - B.P. 17 Damery
51316 Epernay Cedex
26 58 40 33 - Telex: 842 781 F

Type of vineyard: Family-owned. **Established:** Winegrowers from father to son since the origin of the Champagne vineyards. Champagne method since 1920. **Number of employees:** 23. **Vine stocks:** Chardonnay, Pinot Noir, Pinot Meunier. **Soil:** Chalky. **Exposure:** South. **Average annual production in hectoliters:** 7,500.

Appellation: Champagne AOC. **Type:** White, Rosé. **Technique:** traditional. **Maturing:** Fermentation and ageing in bottles. **Alcohol content:** 12%. **Characteristics:** Supple, delicate and fruity. **Serving temperature:** 6-8°. **Served with:** Brut: as an aperitif and with the entire meal – Demi-sec: with dessert. **Vintages available in 89/90:** 1980 – 1983.

Characteristics of vintages

Grande Réserve *Brut and Medium-Dry:* delicate blending of 3 vinestocks – supple and fresh. *Grand Vintage Brut:* Première Cuvée – exceptional quality, finesse and great distinction. *Blanc de Blancs Brut:* Première Cuvée (Chardonnay) – breed, distintiction, great finesse, light and fruity. *Grand Rosé Brut:* Première Cuvée, special selection of superior grapes (destemmed Pinot Noir). *Cuvée Grand Couronnement:* Quality above and beyond classification. Made from selected Chardonnay grapes. For connaisseurs.
Sales in France: 70%.
Export sales: 30%.

Main trading partners : UK, Germany, Belgium, Switzerland.

Abroad

United Kingdom

Majestic Warehouses Ltd., 421 New Kings Road, London SW6 4 RN.

Germany

Miss Richet, Berlin French Sector, Potfach 620651 – 0100 Berlin.

Belgium

Ets. Sotbeleir, 79 Bard, Les Capucins, Brussels 09300 Aalst.

Switzerland

Ste Vinum, 10, rue Renfert, 2501 Bienne.

Comments

Good wines, regularly successful. Proprietors of vineyards at Damery, 5 kms from Epernay, for several generations, the De Telmont family has established itself over the years as a producer of very high quality Champagne. The unequalled quality of its wines is the result of a constant search for perfection, very long experience and love of the vines and the wines that they yield. Meticulous care in the choice of the best grapes suited to the production of the various Cuvée, extreme care in the selection of the harvests, first class equipment, large stocks which make possible ideal ageing in deep cellars – these are the very basis of the richness of the wines, which are nurtured with respect for age old traditions, thus guaranteeing the quality, the origin and the purety of all J. De Telmont Champagnes, equal to the best and sure ot satisfy the most demending winelovers.

CHAMPAGNE ROBERT DOYARD ET FILS

Yannick Doyard

61, av. de Bammental, B.P. 3 – 51130 Vertus

26 52 14 74

Type of vineyard: Family Agricultural Association. **Established:** 1977. **Number of employees:** 4. **Vine stocks:** Chardonnay 93 %, Pinot Noir 7 %. **Soil:** Thin layer of chalky alluvium on chalk. **Exposure:** South, South-East. **Average annual production in hectoliters:** 350.
Appellation: Champagne and Vertus Rouge. **Type:** Red, Rosé, Champagne. **Alcohol content:** 12.5 %. **Serving temperature:** 8 to 10°, according to age and vintage. **Served with:** Mostly as an aperitif. Rosé and Crémant, during the meal. **Vintages available in 89/90:** From 1976 to 1983 in magnums. 1983, in bottles.

Characteristics of vintages

1985: Brut Reserve (blended mostly from the 1985 vintage): Same aromatic range as the 83, fresh with lots of personality. Vin Rouge de Vertus: red fruit, slight cherry and vanilla fragrance, clean tasting. **Other:** 1983: Very aromatic (butter, toast, roasted coffee), very well-balanced, long. Rosé brut: aroma of cooked red fruit, a touch of vanilla, very agreeable. Cuvée spéciale extra brut: very fruity and very supple, with body, long. Price range (pretax, ex-warehouse): between 50 and 80 F.F.
Sales volume:
– Wholesale: 30%. (export) – Retail: 50% (France). – Other: 20% ("Hédiard", de luxe grocery).
Sales in France: 70%.
Export sales: 30%.
Main trading partners : USA, Belgium, UK, Switzerland.

References in France

Shops: Hédiard (Paris and Province).

Abroad

United States

Importers: Trebon Wine & Spirit Corp., 3618 Budd Place, Flushing 11354 New York. Tel: (718) 886 7310.

United Kingdom

Sookias and Bertaut, The Cottage. Cambalt Road, Putney Hill, London SW15 6EW. Tel: 01 788 4193.

Switzerland

S M T Marketing, Chemin du Reposoir 16, 1007 Lausanne. Tel: 02 127 4041.

Belgium

De Wingerd, Valikstraat 2, 3720 Kortessem. Tel: 11 37 77 88.

Comments

The Doyard family has been established at Vertus for four generations. Maurice Doyard was the founder of the Comité Interprofessional de Champagne. As of 1927, commercialization under the estate's trade mark was begun at a time when the great majority of winemakers were selling through dealers. The establishement has continued to be independent, refusing to enter into a cooperative and has remained both a grower and a distributer of fine wines.

CHAMPAGNE NICOLAS FEUILLATTE

Serge Rafflin (President), Jean-Pierre Daraut (Director), Bruno Bocquet (Commercial Director).

B.P. 210 Chouilly, 51206 Épernay Cedex

26 54 50 60 – Telex 830 372

Type of vineyard: Cooperative. **Established:** 1972. **Number of employees:** 90. **Vine stocks:** Chardonnay, Pinot Noir, Pinot Meunier. **Soil:** Chalk. **Average annual production in hectoliters:** 90,000.
Appellation: Champagne. **Type:** Champagne. **Technique:** Champagnization. **Maturing:** Champagne method. **Alcohol content:** 12%. **Characteristics:** Blended from various Champagnes. **Serving temperature:** 7 to 8°. **Served with:** Essentially as an aperitif. **Vintages available in 89/90:** 82 and 83 vintages.

Characteristics of vintages

Other: 1983: Cuvée Spéciale Palmes d'Or. Price range (pre-tax, ex-warehouse): between 80 and 120 F.F.
Sales volume:
– Retail: 20% (including specialized shops). – Restaurants: 40%/ – Other: 40% (GMS).
Sales in France: 67%.
Export sales: 33%.
Main trading partners: United Kingdom, Germany, United States, Italy, Australia.

References in France

Restaurants: Chez Francis, Orêve, Olsson's, Le Cochon d'Or, Restaurant au Quai d'Orsay, etc. (Paris).
Shops: Fauchon (Paris), Le Vintage (Reims).

Abroad

United States

Bonsal Seggerman, New York. Tel: (516) 484-3070. Restaurants: St Pierre, La Côte Basque, Le Chantilly, Les Quatre Saisons.

United Kingdom

Thierry's + Tatham Food + Wine Services The Old Brewery House Portersbridgestreet Romsey Hampshire SO51 8DJ. Tel: 794 515 500. Metronote-Metro House – 2/4 Manor Grove – London SE15 1SX. Tel: 1 252 8111. Spedding Nicolson – Whitchurch road Chester CH3 6AF. Tel: 244 332010. Crown Catering Group – Romford Essex RM7 9EL. Tel: 708 22145. Restaurant: St James Court.

Germany

Weinhandlung, A. Viehhauser, Hamburg. Tel: 40 460 48 30. Gerwig Import, Solitudeallee 123, 7014 Kornwestheim. Tel: 71 54 60 87. Restaurant: Le Canard à Hamburg.

Switzerland

Agrifrance, Genève. Tel: 22 42 97 00. Restaurant: Le Richemond à Genève.

Belgium

Mairesse, rue des Pierres, 1000 Bruxelles. Tel: 2 511 7275. Intercommercial Services, AG Building, 5, place Champ de Mars, Bruxelles. Tel: 2 511 18 95. Restaurants: Le Metropole, Mercure à Bruxelles, Pullman à Bruges.

The Netherlands

De Waal & Zey, J. Van Oldenbarneveltlaan 60, 2582 NW Den Haag. Tel: 70 54 60 11.

Comments

Serious and traditional house which offers a number of very well made wines.

CHAMPAGNE ELLNER S.A.

Jean-Pierre Ellner (Director general)
1 & 6, rue Cote Legris, 51200 Épernay
26 55 60 25 – Telex: 830 755

Type of vineyard: Family-owned. **Established:** Turn of the century. **Vine stocks:** 30. **Soil:** Chalky. **Exposure:** South-East, South-West. **Average annual production in hectoliters:** 3,750.

Appellation: AOC. **Type:** White, rosé. **Technique:** Selection and blending of wines in stainless steel tanks and wooden casks. **Maturing:** In cellars (3 years on the average). **Alcohol content:** 12%. **Characteristics:** Fruity, elegant, well balanced. **Served with:** The entire meal. **Vintages available in 89/90:** 1982, 1983, 1985.

Characteristics of vintages

1985: Lively – goes perfectly well with oysters. Price range (pre-tax, ex-warehouse): 50 to 80 F.F.

Sales in France: 50%.
Export sales: 50%.
Main trading partners: UK, USA, Germany and other European countries.

References in France

Restaurants: La Briqueterie (Vinay 51).

Abroad

United States

Bridge Import 1201 Maine St. Cincinnati, Ohio, Tel: 513 381 8400.

United Kingdom

Lay and Wheeler, J.T. Davies, Peter McKinley.

Germany

Gerard Dubois GMBH. Mainz.

Switzerland

Curti sa Berne and Geneva.

Belgium

Declercq and Petre, Lendelede.

Others

Italy: Distillerie Sari, Gussago. Ireland: Fitzgerald and Co, Dublin.

Comments

The Maison Ellner was founded at the turn of the century by Charles-Emile Ellner who little by little acquired the first parcels of the vineyard. Later, his only son, Pierre Ellner, continued in the same vein, and with the help of his wife and, later, of their four sons, began to develop sales and the trademark. Today, the enterprise is still very much structured around the family and each of the children is responsible for his own particular sector: oenology, management, and operation of the vineyard.

STE GARDET AND CO. CHAMPAGNE

13, rue Georges-Legros, 51500 Chigny-les-Roses
26 03 42 03 - Telex: 830 216 F

Type of vineyard: Corporation. **Established:** 1895. **Average annual production in hectoliters:** 4,500.

Type: Champagne. **Technique:** Traditional. **Alcohol content:** 12%. **Characteristics:** Blending of 30 different wines from 3 vinestocks – Chardonnay, Pinot noir and Meunier. **Serving temperature:** 8 to 10°. **Vintages available in 89/90:** 1976, 1979, 1982.

Characteristics of vintages

Other: 1976: Lots of finesse, delicious lingering flavor. 1979: Good fruit and richness. A complex wine. Fine quality. Will develop. Price range (pre-tax, ex-warehouse): between 50 and 80 F.F.
Sales volume:
– Wholesale: 80%. – Retail: 10%. – Restaurants: 10%.
Sales in France: 80%.
Export sales: 20%.
Main trading partners: United Kingdom, Italy, Netherlands, Belgium, Denmark, Germany, Switzerland.

Comments

Some good wines, notably the 79 vintage. Also, good brut.

CHAMPAGNE RENE GEOFFROY

René Geoffroy
150, rue des Bois des Jots - Cumières
51200 Épernay
26 55 32 31

Type of vineyard: Family-owned. **Established:** From generation to generation since 1600. **Number of employees:** 5. **Vine stocks:** Pinot noir, Meunier, Chardonnay. **Soil:** Chalk. **Exposure:** Hillsides full South. **Average annual production in hectoliters:** 900 to 1,000. **Appellation:** Coteaux Champenois and Champagne. **Type:** Red, white, rosé. **Technique:** Traditional in wooden casks. **Maturing:** In wooden casks and vats with epoxy resin. **Characteristics:** Champagne that ages a long time thanks to production without malolactic fermentation. **Serving temperature:** 8 to 10°. **Served with:** Champagne: as an aperitif. Coteaux Champenois Rouge: red meat, light snacks. **Vintages available in 89/90:** 1982, 1983, 1985.

Characteristics of vintages

1988: Not yet bottled – still in vats. Strongly acid. Should age well. **1987:** Vintage still requiring ageing in chalky cellars, similar to 1986, but with a bit more body. **1986:** Not yet available for sale. Well balanced wine. **1985:** Without doubt one to the best years of the century in quality; a really great bottle. **Other: 1982:** Will soon arrive at its peak. Still a very good bottle thanks to its production without malolactic fermentation. A multitude of aromas that come with ageing. **1983:** Good for tasting now, but can still be left several years in the cellar. More full bodied than the 1982. Price range (pre-tax, ex-warehouse): between 50 and 80 F.F.

Sales volume:
– Retail: 70%. – Restaurants: 30%.
Sales in France: 82%.
Export sales: 12%.
Main trading partners: Germany, Switzerland, Belgium, Netherlands, Japan.

References in France

Restaurants: Le Royal Champagne, Le Florence, Les Berceaux, Le Cheval Blanc, La Briqueterie, Le Continental (all in the Champagne region), Le Restaurant (Lille).

Comments

The house of Geoffroy, for generations and generations, since 1600, has been an establishment where concern for tradition (small volume, maturing in casks, separation of the harvest, if necessary...) is combined with great care in blending and vinification techniques. Cuvée de Réserve: A blend of 70% 86 and 30% 85 is made almost entirely of pinot noir and meunier. Great regularity in this bottle. Cuvée Prestige: Pure 1985, 1/3 pinot noir and 2/3 chardonnay. A very great bottle, ready for tasting but can still age a number of years. Cuvée Sélectionnée: Pure 1982, 1/3 chardonnay and 2/3 pinot noir. Still very fresh. A multitude of aromas from ageing.

CHAMPAGNE H. GERMAIN

General Manager: Bernard Walbaum
Export Manager: Gérard Stasi
Rue de Reims 51500 - Rilly-la-Montagne
Phone: 26 03 40 19 – Telex: 830 171
Fax: 26 03 43 11

Type of vineyard: Corporation. **Established:** 1898. **Vine stocks:** Pinot Meunier, Pinot Noir and Chardonnay. **Soil:** Chalky. **Exposure:** East. **Average annual production in hectoliters:** 7,500.
Appellation: Champagne. **Type:** White, rosé. **Technique:** Tanks. **Characteristics:** Brut: blending of 3 grapes varieties. Natural, strong bouquet. Brut 1983: Well-balanced, elegant blend, fruity, solid structure. Brut rosé: fruity thanks to blending with the famous red wine Cru de Rilly-la-Montagne. Brut Blanc de Blanc 1983: beautiful Chardonnay blend, fine lively sparkle, elegant and fruity. Cuvée Vénus 83: full of character. **Serving temperature:** Cool but not iced. **Served with:** Brut: as an aperitif or with entire meal. Brut 1983: red meat. Brut rosé: as an aperitif and with strong meats (game). Brut Blanc de Blanc: as an aperitif, and with shellfish and fish. Cuvée Vénus 1982: as an aperitif and with red meat.

Characteristics of vintages

1983: Brut and Brut Blanc de Blanc. **1982:** Cuvée Vénus.
Price range (pre-tax, ex-warehouse): 60 F.F.-120 F.F.
Sales volume:
– Retail: 15%. – Restaurants: 20%. – Other: 30% (wholesale), 35% (large distribution).
Sales in France: 70%.
Export sales: 30%.
Main trading partners : USA, Switzerland, Italy, Portugal, Belgium, Germany, UK.
Total Sales: 1,2 million bottles.

CHAMPAGNE PAUL GOERG

Daniel Aubertin
4, place du Mont Chenil, 51130 Vertus
26 52 15 31 – Telex: 840 704 F Code T 0065

Type of vineyard: Cooperative. **Established:** 1950. **Number of employees:** 11. **Vine stocks:** Chardonnay, Pinot Noir. **Soil:** Chalky. **Exposure:** South and South-South-East. **Average annual production in hectoliters:** 5,000 to 6,000.
Appellation: Champagne, Coteaux Champenois. **Type:** White. **Technique:** Champagne method. **Maturing:** In vats, bottle fermentation. **Alcohol content:** 12%. **Serving temperature:** 10°. **Served with:** As an aperitif and with fish. **Vintages available in 89/90:** 1982, 1983.

Characteristics of vintages

Price range (pre-tax, ex-warehouse): 50 to 80 F.F.

Sales volume:
– Wholesale: 38%. – Retail: 2%. – Other: 52% (to co-op members) 8% (export).
Sales in France: 2%.
Export sales: 8%.
Main trading partners: Germany, UK.

Abroad

United Kingdom

Mr. Pascal Granweiler, 103 Cinnamon Wharf Shad Thames, London SE 1 (Tel: 44 13 78 02 08).

Germany

Mr. Robert Diemert, Oberlanderstrasse 6 D 76 40 Kehl (Tel: 49 78 51 77 163 or 49 78 51 75 504).

Belgium

Mr. Guy Godfroid, Résidence Flores Parklaan 66 BP 44K 9000 Gand (Tel: 32 91 22 00 69).

Comments

Good wines vinified by this conscientious cooperative.

CHAMPAGNE MICHEL GONET

Michel Gonet
196, avenue Jean Jaurès, 51190 Avize
26 57 50 56 – Telex: 830 159 GONET MC

Established: 1802. **Vine stocks:** Chardonnay 80%, Pinot Noir 20%. **Soil:** Chalky. **Exposure:** South-East. **Average annual production in hectoliters:** 2,500.
Appellation: Champagne, Blanc de Blancs. **Type:** White. **Technique:** Traditional. **Maturing:** Stainless steel tanks. **Alcohol content:** 12°. **Characteristics:** Finesse, bouquet. **Serving temperature:** 8°. **Served with:** As an aperitif and with fish. **Vintages available in 89/90:** Brut 1981, Brut 1983, Club 1985.

Characteristics of vintages

1986: Some excellent lots.

Other

1983: Club bottles: rich and well-balanced, needs ageing.
1981: Blanc de Blancs Grand Cru: finesse, well developed.
Price range (pre-tax ex-warehouse): 50 to 80 F.F. – 80 to 120 F.F.

Sales in France: 50%.
Export sales: 50%.
Main trading partners: Germany, UK, Belgium, USA, Japan.

Abroad

United Kingdom

Brewer 51 Oakdale Road, London SW16 2HL.

Canada

Liquor Control Board of Ontario, Toronto (Ontario).

Comments

The vineyards cover 40 hectares (100 acres) spread over six of the most prestigious villages and were built up over the generations: Avize-Oger – Le Mesnil-sur-Oger the 100% classified first growths of the Côtes des Blancs reputed for the delicacy of their chardonnay grapes, Vindey (Vinum Dei) the wine of the Gods, Montgueux a fruity and full bodied Chardonnay. Excellent wines (Special Club) like the Blanc de Blancs (100% Chardonnay), fine and flowery, with a lingering sparkle.

CHAMPAGNE HUSSON JEAN-PIERRE

Jean-Pierre & Marie-Christine Husson
2, rue Jules-Lobet – 51160 Ay-Champagne
26 55 43 05

Type of vineyard: Family-owned. **Established:** 1975. **Number of employee:** 1 (permanent) plus temporary staff. **Vine stocks:** Pinot Noir. **Soil:** Clay whith calcium carbonate. **Exposure:** South. **Average annual production in hectoliters:** 250.
Appellation: Champagne (white and rosé) and Coteaux Champenois "Ay Rouge". **Technique:** Ay rouge (Foating cap, submerged cap, selected and destemmed by hand). **Maturing:** In Oak casks. **Alcohol content:** 11%. **Characteristics:** Cuvée Réservée is a fruity, 3 year old Champagne. It is available as Brut intégral (no sugar added) and as demi-sec. (0.5% sugar added). Champagne Grande Réserve is 5 years old and is available in half bottles, bottles and magnums. The Champagne Rosé Madame Husson is a mixture of Grande Réserve and Ay Rouge. **Serving temperature:** Should be served cool, not iced, preferably in a Champagne bucket. **Served with:** Champagne Cuvée Réservée or Grande Réserve: foie gras, fish served warm or cold, white meat. Champagne rosé (more frafrant): Spicyer dishes. Ay Rouge: red meat, cheese. **Vintages available in 89/90:** None for the moment.

Characteristics of vintages

1986: Wines of even quality, well vinified. Excellent rosé.
Price range (pre-tax, ex-warehouse): 50 F.F.-80 F.F.
Sales volume:
– Retail: 95%. – Restaurants: 5%.
Sales in France: 90%. **Export sales:** 10%.
Main trading partners: UK, Germany, Belgium.

CHAMPAGNE JEEPER

Christian Goutorbe
8 rue Georges Clémenceau, Damery par 51200 Epernay.
26 58 41 23 - Telex: 300 121 Att: Jeeper

Type of vineyard: Agricultural Association and Corporation. **Established:** 8th generation. **Number of employees:** 25. **Soil:** Micaceous chalk. **Exposure:** South, South-East, South-West. **Average annual production in hectoliters:** 2,400.
Appellation: AOC Champagne. **Type:** White, Rosé. **Technique:** Fermentation with temperature control, clarification at low temperature. **Maturing:** In stainless steel tanks. **Alcohol content:** 12%. **Characteristics:** Blending of Pinot and Chardonnay. **Serving temperature:** 6 to 8°. **Served with:** As an aperitif and with the entire meal. **Vintages available in 89/90:** 1982, 1983, 1985.

Characteristics of vintages

1985: Well balanced, light and fruity. **Other:** 1982: Harmonious, fine sparkle, lingering. Price range (pre-tax, ex-warehouse): 50 to 80 F.F.
Sales volume:
- Wholesale: 30%. - Retail: 40%. - Restaurants: 30%.
Sales in France: 90%.
Export sales: 10%.
Main trading partners : Germany, UK, Switzerland, Belgium, USA.

Abroad

United States

Vica Vines 1910 NW 44ST, Pompano Beach 33064 Florida. St-Honore, The Harbour, Second Floor, BD Palm Beach Garden, Florida.

United Kingdom

South Wales, West of England, Bon Ding Co, Ltd, 2 Building Curran Road, Cardiff.

Germany

Ets. Peter Bush, Bastionstrasse 9, 4000 Dusseldorf.

Comments

Winemakers from father to son for 8 generations, the Jeeper family reorganized the entreprise as a corporation in 1973.

CHAMPAGNE JACQUART

Christian Doisy
5, rue Gosset - B.P. 467 - 51066 Reims Cedex
26 07 20 20 - Telex: 830 984

Established: 1962. **Number of employees:** 95. **Vine stocks:** Chardonnay, Pinot Noir, Pinot Meunier. **Soil:** Clay with calcium carbonate. **Exposure:** Various. **Average annual production in hectoliters:** 75,000.
Appellation: Champagne. **Type:** White, rosé. **Technique:** Champagne Method. **Maturing:** In bottles. **Alcohol content:** 12%. **Characteristics:** Forthcoming, rich and well-balanced, subtle and elegant. **Serving temperature:** 6° to 8°. **Served with:** Fish and white meat, but may accompany the entire meal. **Vintages available in 89/90:** 1989, 1983.

Characteristics of vintages

Jacquard 1983: Apples, lemons, floral notes in the nose with underlying light yeast character. Tart and delicate in the mouth with good crisp fruit and a clean, sharp finish. Lighter style with good fruit, nicely balanced flavors. **Cuvée Renommée de Jacquart 83:** A big wine in the full bodied style with lots of toastt yeast and fruit in the bouquet. Creamy mouth feel with flavors carried across the palate gracefully, excellent balance, lengthy finish. **Cuvée Renommée de Jacquart Rosé 83:** Beautifully complex bouquet of biscuity yeast with lashings of pinot noir aromas: black cherries, raspberries, mushrooms,

spice. Very intense, concentrated flavors in the mouth with cherry fruit and toast perfectly balanced. The finish blends all the elements together wonderfully with lingering hints of plums, cherries and toasty yeast. Still young, this great wine should develop even more complexity and richness with age. Also a beautiful rosé. By with confidence. Price range (pre-tax, ex-warehouse): Between 80 F.F. and 160 F.F.
Sales volume:
– Retail: 20%. – Restaurants: 35%. – Other: 45%.
Sales in France: 67%.
Export sales: 33%.
Main trading partners : USA, Germany, Belgium, Switzerland, Netherlands, New Zealand, Italy, Great Britain.

CHAMPAGNE JEANMAIRE

Gérard Tisserand
12, rue Roger-Godart - B.P. 256
51207 Épernay Cedex
26 54 60 32 – Telex: 830 712

Type of vineyard: Corporation. **Established:** 1947 (in a different form). **Number of employees:** 40. **Vine stocks:** Chardonnay, Pinot Noir, Pinoy Meunier. **Soil:** Chalky. **Exposure:** East, South. **Average annual production in hectoliters:** 70 hectoliters per hectare.
Appellation: Champagne. **Type:** Red, rosé. **Technique:** Low temperature vinification (16°), kept in the cellar at 10°. **Maturing:** Bottle fermentation. **Alcohol content:** 12%. **Characteristics:** Elegant and light, with lots of Chardonnay in the blends. **Serving temperature:** 8°. **Served with:** Blanc de Blancs: as an aperitif or with shellfish, fish. Rosé: meat, cheese, desserts. Blanc de Noirs: meat, cheese. Blanc de Blancs Millesimé: foie gras, cheese. **Vintages available in 89/90/** 1982, 1983.

Characteristics of vintages

1982: The Wines are rich, well balanced, fine and elegant. **1983:** The wines have a very good constitution, harmonious and typical. Price range (pre-tax, ex-warehouse): 80 F.F. and 120 F.F.
Sales in France: 40%.
Export sales: 60%.
Main trading partners : USA, Belgium, Netherlands, Sweden, Norway, Luxemburg, Germany, Switzerland, Italy, spain, UK.

KRUG S.A.

5, rue Coquebert – 51100 Reims
26 88 24 24

Average annual production in hectoliters: ± 40,000 cases.
Appellation: Champagne, Krug Grande Cuvée. **Type:** White. **Technique:** First fermentation in oak casks. **Characteristics:** Very elegant, well-balanced, fruity and complex (40 to 50 different wines of 8 to 10 different years. Multi vintage). **Serving temperature:** 8° to 9°.

Characteristics of vintages

Krug Vintage 1982: Wines of excellent ripeness and fairly full character. Full bodied, the long aging of 7 years brings some depth and intensity allied with elegance.

CHAMPAGNE RENE LALLEMENT

Mr. René Lallement
22, rue Gambetta – 51 Bouzy
26 57 00 68

Type of vineyard: Family-owned. **Established:** 1950. **Vine stocks:** Pinot Noir. **Soil:** Chalky. **Exposure:** South. **Average annual production in hectoliters:** 450.
Appellation: Bouzy Rouge, Champagne, Champagne Rosé. **Technique:** Traditional Champagne Method. **Maturing:** Kept in cellars carved into the chalk for at least 3 years. **Alcohol content:** 12%. **Characteristics:** Very supple wines – regular quality – champagne produced exclusively by 3 different vineyards renowned for the production of quality grapes. The blending of "crus" is known to be conducive to making of good Champagne. **Serving temperature:** 8-9°. **Vintages available in 89/90:** 1983 Champagne Carte d'Or and Carte Blanche, Champagne Brut Rosé.

Characteristics of vintages

1985: White gold color – very fine bubbles – combines finesse and vinosity, full taste and distinguished. **1983:** Millésimé 1983 – The 1985 vintage will be available at the beginning of 1990. Golden color – lots of fine bubbles – fine nose – food acidity balance. A very special wine. Price range (pre-tax, ex-warehouse): 60 F.F. to 90 F.F.
Sales volume:
– Retail: 80%. – Other: 20% (Works Committee).
Sales in France: 95%.
Export sales: 5%.
Main trading partners : Belgium, Switzerland, Germany, Luxemburg.

Comments

Winegrowers from father to son for several generations, the Lallement family began exploiting their own vineyard as early as 1928, improving their technique through the years. The 1988 harvest may be selected for a vintage champagne and that of 1987 will be fresh and elegant.

• *Paulée – traditional meal which brings winelovers and winegrowers together after the harvest, particularly in Burgundy.*

CHAMPAGNE LANSON

BSN
12 bd. Lundy BP 163 51056 Reims Cedex
26 40 24 40 - Telex: 830 624 F
Télécopie: 26 47 00 70

Vine stocks: Chardonnay, Pinot Noir.
Appellation: Champagne. **Type:** White, rosé. **Technique:** traditional (long maturation) **Characteristics:** Very traditional wines, well made. **Finest jewel of the collection:** the "Cuvée Black Label"! **Serving temperature:** 8°. **Served with:** The entire meal. **Vintages available in 89/90:** 1981, 1983.

CHAMPAGNE GUY LARMANDIER

Guy Larmandier
30, rue du Général Kœnig - 51130 Vertus
26 52 12 41

Type of vineyard: Family-owned. **Established:** Vineyard in 1962, first harvest in 1977. **Number of employees:** 4. **Vine stocks:** Chardonnay, Pinot Noir. **Soil:** Clay. **Average annual production in hectoliters:** 450.

Appellation: AOC Champagne Grand Cru Blanc de Blancs & Premier Cru Blanc & Rosé, Coteaux Champenois (Rouge). **Maturing:** in vats. **Alcohol content:** 12%. **Characteristics:** Champagne Brut Premier Cru: blended from various wines of the establishment, delicate and light wine. Champagne Blanc de Blancs Cramant Brut: made from Chardonnay de Cramant, light and elegant, fine bouquet. Champagne Rosé Premier Cru: blended from Chardonnay and Pinot Noir (20%). Champagne Cramant Blanc de Blancs: fine and light foam, excellent Champagne for elegant dining. **Served with:** This champagne is very much appreciated when served as an aperitif and is an excellent choice with fish and shellfish. **Vintages available in 89/90:** 1985.
Sales in France: 80%.
Export sales: 20%.
Main trading partners : USA, Belgium, Germany, Japan, Switzerland.

References in France

Restaurants: Grand Écuyer (Cordes 81), Veneto (Saint-Dié), Relais de la Poste (Vaucouleurs), Les 3 Marches (Nancy 54), Les Luthiers (Mire 88), Le Dauphin (Nogent-le-Rotrou 28).
Shops: J.-P. Peyre (26600 La Roche-de-Glun), Dyonisos (26 Crest), Caves Serpent Volant (37 Tours).

Abroad

United States

Importers: Rosenthal Wine Merchant – Select Vinyards 56-31, 56th Drive Maspeth, New York 11378 – Tel: (718) 326-79-90.

Belgium

M.S. Bygodt-111, rue de la Libération, 7498 Hennuyères - Tel: 67 55 36 67.

Far East

Japan: Mitsumi Co Ltd, 8 7 6 Chome, Ginza Cho-Ku, Tokyo 104 – Tel: 571 42 28.

Comments

The vineyard is located in the best winegrowing area of the Côte des Blancs Cramant-Chouilly-Vertus.

CHAMPAGNE LAURENT PERRIER

Bernard de Nonancourt
51500 Tours-sur-Marne
26 58 91 22

Type of vineyard: Family-owned. **Vine stocks:** Chardonnay and Pinot Noir.
Appellation: Champagne and Bouzy. **Type:** Red – White – Rosé. **Technique:** Traditional Champagne Method. **Characteristics:** Rigorous selection and blending, and careful vinification guarantee the quality and regularity of the product of this exceptional establishment. **Serving temperature:** 10-12° for Bouzy. **Served with:** As an aperitif and with the entire meal. **Vintages available in 89:** 1982 (Superb!).

Characteristics of vintages

1986: No hesitation: fabulous Cuvée Grand Siècle, perfect selection and blending of the best crus of the vineyard and of the best vintages. Vinous and velvety, very elegant, incomparable freshness and fruitiness. Excellent rosé, lively, pleasant flavor. And an Ultra Brut, with no sugar added, light and fruity.

• Help me make the next Guide even more useful. Let me have your advice and tell me about your experiences with the winegrowers and the welcome extended. (See questionnaire "Wine, the Guide and you").

CHAMPAGNE LECLERC-BRIANT

Pascal Leclerc-Briant
Cumières - 51200 Épernay
26 54 45 33 - Telex: 240 777 Leclerc-Briant

Type of vineyard: Private enterprise. **Established:** 1872. **Number of employees:** 23. **Vine stocks:** Pinot Noir 50%, Chardonnay 30%, Pinot Meunier 20%. **Soil:** Chalk and chalky clay. **Exposure:** 90% facing full South. **Average annual production in hectoliters:** 1,500. **Appellation:** Champagne. **Type:** White, Rosé. **Technique:** Traditional champagne method, control of fermentation temperature. Rosé: made from Pinot Noir – maceration 8 days. **Alcohol content:** 12.5%. **Characteristics:** Fruity, and fresh thanks to high percentage of Pinot Noir, lingering taste. **Serving temperature:** 6 to 8°. **Vintages available in 89/90:** 1983.

Leclerc Briant,
le Champagne-Tradition.
Pascal LECLERC BRIANT in his cellars.
CHAMPAGNE
Leclerc Briant
BRUT RÉSERVE
SCRIPTØ
DOMAINE Leclerc Briant
CUMIÈRES - 51200 ÉPERNAY (France) - Tél : 26.54.45.33

Characteristics of vintages

Other: 1983: Remarkable, combining finesse and structure, very aromatic. Price range (pre-tax, ex-warehouse): 80 to 120 F.F.

Sales volume:
– Wholesale: 10%. – Retail: 30%. – Restaurants: 10%. – Other: 10% (private companies), 40% (export).

Sales in France: 60%.

Export sales: 40%.

Main trading partners : European community, Switzerland, USA, Japan.

References in France

Restaurants: Le Royal Champagne (Épernay), Les Armes de Champagne (Châlons-sur-Marne).
Shops: Hédiard, L'Amour du Vin, etc.

Abroad

United States

Baron François Ltd, New York. Champely, Playa del Rey, CA.

United Kingdom

Colombier, Ashby de la Zouch. Hall & Bramley, Liverpool.

Germany

Newman Vin (Agent in Beaune). Ets Bross Richard, Appenweier.

Switzerland

Sanini Sulmoni, Ligornetto. Édouard Mahler Fils Frères SA, Zurich. La Maison du Champagne, Geneva. Divo SA, Lausanne.

Belgium

Armand Ell, Brussels. Asbach Uralt, Brussels.

The Netherlands

Hosman Frères BV, Schiedam. Erik Sauter, Maastricht.

Others

Italy: Istituto Enologico Italiano, Verona.

Comments

Vinegrower since 1664, the Leclerc family produced its first bottle of Champagne in 1872. The vineyards are still cultivated without chemical fertilizers and, for the most part, are plowed and worked in the traditional manner. Preparation of special wine lots: The Collection Historique Leclerc-Briant includes the following "cuvées" 1986: Cuvée de la Liberté, in honor of the hundredth anniversary of the Statue of Liberty; 1987: Cuvée du Millénaire, for the thousandth anniversary of the crowning of Huges Capet; 1989: Cuvée du Bicentenaire des Droits de l'homme, celebrating the two hundredth anniversary of the Declaration of the Human Rights. Construction of pyramids and monuments in Champagne flutes: they hold the world's record for the highest Champagne flute pyramid (14.444 flutes - 8,5 m). A reproduction of the Eiffel Tower for the competition "Le Commerce Fête Eiffel" won first prize in December 1988.

CHAMPAGNE CLAUDE LEMAIRE

Mr. & Mrs. Claude Lemaire
19, rue Pasteur, 51200 Damery
26 58 41 31

Type of vineyard: Family-owned. **Established:** 1924. **Vine stocks:** Pinot Meunier, Pinot Noir, Chardonnay. **Soil:** Chalky. **Exposure:** South. **Average annual production in hectoliters:** 200 to 250.
Appellation: Champagne. **Type:** White, rosé. **Technique:** Traditional champagne method. **Alcohol content:** 12%. **Characteristics:** Cuvée de Réserve: brut exclusively (in the bottle for a minimun of 3 years). Champagne Carte d'Or: brut, extra-dry, demi-sec – half bottles, magnums, jeroboams – brut exclusively. Rosé Brut. **Serving temperature:** 6 to 8°. **Served with:** Blanc Brut: as an aperitif. Demi-Sec: with dessert. Rosé: with meat. **Vintages available in 89/90:** 1986 and 1985.

Characteristics of vintages

1986: Excellent brut – lovely rosé, flowery and fine.
1985: Excellent vintage – limited quantity. Price range (pre-tax, ex-warehouse): 50 to 80 F.F.
Sales volume:
– Retail: 98%. – Restaurants: 2%.
Sales in France: 95%.
Export sales: 5%.
Main trading partners : Germany, Belgium, Switzerland.

References in France

Restaurants: Le St-Vinvent, Péronne (Somme).

CHAMPAGNE A R LENOBLE

J.M. Malassagne
35 rue Paul Douce 51480 Damery
26 58 42 60 – Telex: 842 793

Type of vineyard: Family-company. **Established:** 1920. **Number of employees:** 12. **Vine stocks:** Chardonnay, Pinot Noir, Pinot Meunier. **Soil:** chalky. **Average annual production in hectoliters:** 78 hl per hectare.

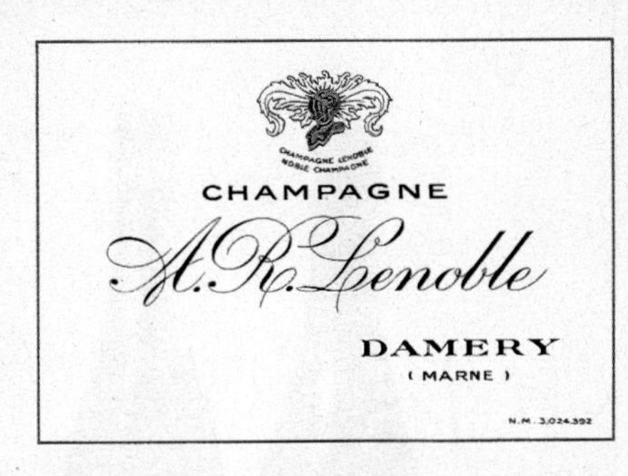

Appellation: Champagne. **Type:** Red, Blanc de Blanc. **Technique:** Traditional Champagne Method. **Maturing:** Traditional. **Alcohol content:** 12%. **Characteristics:** The finesse, lightness and elegance of the Chardonnay combined with the fruity richness of the Pinots. **Serving temperature:** 8 to 9°. **Vintages available in 89/90:** 1979, 1982 exclusively Blanc de Blancs de Chardonnay.

Characteristics of vintages

1985: Very beautiful color in a white bottle, light and fruity. Rosé: delicate (blend of red Pinot Noir and white Chardonnay).
Sales volume:
– Wholesale: 25%. – Retail: 50%. – Restaurants: 25%.
Sales in France: 65%.
Export sales: 35%.
Main trading partners : United Kingdom, Belgium, Luxemburg, Switzerland, Germany, Netherlands, United States.

References in France

Shops: Verger de la Madeleine (Place de la Madeleine, Paris).

Abroad

United States
Importers: Magnums Corp., North Hollywood.

United Kingdom
Champagne Agencies Ltd, Windsor.

Switzerland
Fischer et Rihs, Munsterkellerei Bern.

Belgium
Importers: Topvins, Bruxelles.
Restaurants: Mon Manège à toi (Bruxelles), Eddy Vandekerckhove (Courtrai).

The Netherlands
De Meulmeester, Jean Arnaud.

• A good everyday wine for 20 F? See the Bordeaux, Anjou, Touraine, Côtes-du-Rhône or Languedoc Regions.

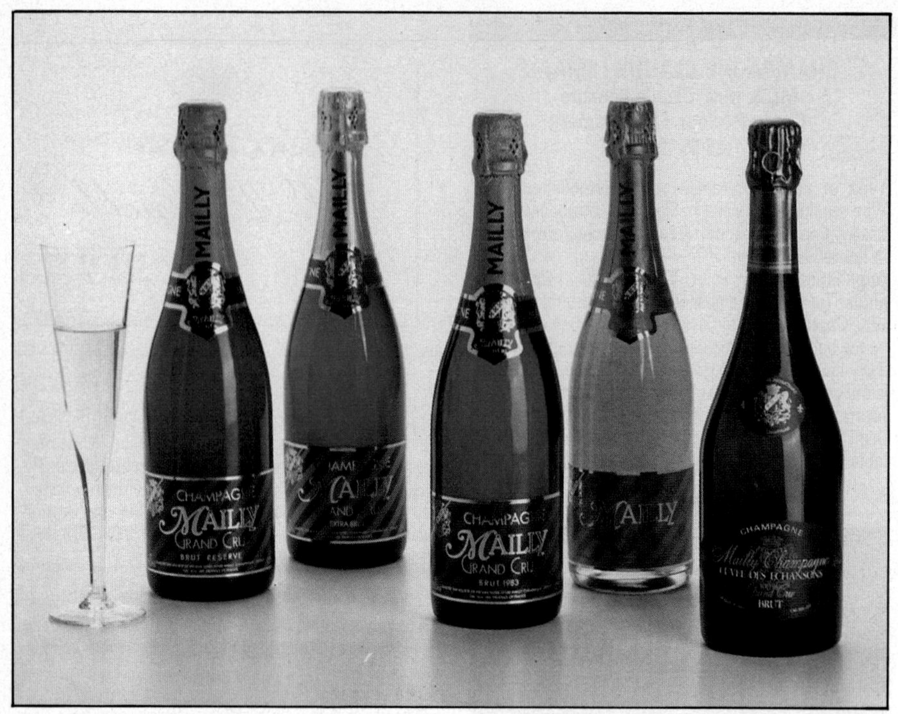

CHAMPAGNE MAILLY GRAND CRU

Gérard Fremaux
Rue de la Libération, B.P. 1
51500 Mailly Champagne
26 49 41 10 - Telex: Mailly 842 156 F
FAX: 26 49 42 27

Type of vineyard: Producer's association. **Established:** 1929. **Number of employees:** 18. **Vine stocks:** Pinot Noir 75%, Chardonnay 25%. **Soil:** Chalky. **Exposure:** North, South, East. **Average annual production in hectoliters:** 4,000.
Appellation: Champagne. **Technique:** Traditional. **Maturing:** Stored in cellar for an average of 4 years. **Alcohol content:** 12%. **Serving temperature:** 6 to 8°. **Vintages available in 89/90:** Brut 1983.

Characteristics of vintages

1988: Most probably a great vintage. **1987:** Good year, elegant, very much like 1988. **1986:** Average year. **1985:** Excellent year - in line with 1983 wines. Price range (pre-tax, ex-warehouse): 80 to 160 F.F.
Sales volume:
- Retail: 50%. - Restaurants: 20%. - Other: 30% (cellars).
Sales in France: 50%.
Export sales: 50%.

Main trading partners : All European countries, Japan, USA, Hong Kong, Australia, etc.

References in France

Restaurants: Assiette Champenoise (Tinqueux), Les Crayères (Reims), La Tour d'Argent (Paris), D'Chez Eux (Paris), Le Madigan (Paris), etc.
Shops: Cave de la Citadelle (12, rue de la Citadelle, 95300 Pontoise).

Abroad

United States:
Rolar Imports LTD 10 Cutter Mill Road, Great Neck 11021, New York.

United Kingdom
Desborough and Brown LTD Brewmaster House, The Mailings Chequer Street, St Alban Heris.

Germany
Kieffer DFW Blumenstrasse 3 6600 Saarbrucken 3 Kafer, Munich.

Switzerland
Reichmuth, Zurich.

Belgium
Feys., Bruges - Bvba De Wijngalerij, Courtrai - Deldaele, Mouscron - Lovens, Limbourg - Van Orshoven, Leopoldsburg - Goosens, Tirlemont - Fryns, Hasselt - Vimaco, Ternat.

Canada

LCBQ, Toronto.

The Netherlands

La Française d'Exportation, Maartensdijk.

Far East

Izumi Trading Co, Tokyo – Mrs Longtime Co, Hong Kong.

Comments

Founded in 1929 to deal with the severe crisis in Champagne at the time, the enterprise owned only about 30 hectares and the building which had been constructed was intended to press the member's grapes in order to stock the wines and sell them to the Champagne houses at a more propitious time. The winemakers of Mailly Champagne have always been ready, even in difficult times, to sacrifice everything to quality, which is the reason why the champagne produced is made entirely from a single Grand Cru, Mailly Champagne.

CHAMPAGNE MARIE STUART-C.V.C.

Francis Fourchet
8, place de la République – BP 268
51059 Reims Cedex
26 47 92 26 – Telex: 830 543 F

Type of vineyard: Family-owned. **Established:** 1867. **Number of employees:** 25. **Vine stocks:** Pinot Noir, Chardonnay, Pinot Meunier. **Soil:** Blending of harvests from 3 different soil types. **Average annual production in hectoliters:** 1,700,000 bottles.
Appellation: Champagne. **Type:** White, rosé. **Technique:** Champagne method. **Alcohol content:** 12%. **Serving temperature:** 8-10°. **Vintages available in 89/90:** 1982, 1983, 1985.

Characteristics of vintages

1985: Fruity, full-bodied. **Other:** 1982: Light, still fresh. Price range (pre-tax, ex-warehouse): 50 to 80 F.F.
Sales volume:
– Wholesale: 80%. – Retail: 10%. – Restaurants: 10%.
Sales in France: 60%.
Export sales: 40%.
Main trading partners: Germany, Switzerland, Italy, USA, UK, Japan.

References in France

Restaurants: Chaine Altea-Pullman.

Abroad

United States

Depot/Groskopf Warehouse – 20580 8TH Street East, Sonoma, CA. 95476.

United Kingdom

Marblehead trading LTD – Macleod Building – Lovat Place Queen Elizabeth Ave. – Hillington – Glasgow G52 4TW – Scotland. Germany: Weinwelt Mack & Schule – Neue Strasse 45 – 7311 Owen.

Switzerland

Trosag-Handels Ag – Rorschacherstr. 150 – 9006 St Gallen.

The Netherlands

Gysbert van Bilsen's – Korvelseweg 45 – 5025 JB Tiburg.

Far East

Million Trading Co. Tokyo Office, 15-2/I-Chome, Shinkawa Chuo-Fu – Tokyo – Japan.

Comments

The origin of this House goes back to 1867; the official registration of the trademark to 1909; and, the new development to 1964 – date at which it moved to a new, more functional location, while conserving the old cellars, cradle of its trademark. The brand "Marie Stuart" is still little known but is valued for its remarkable quality/price ratio, in particular for its "Rosé", its "Millésime" or its "Cuvée R.G." (made from Chardonnay).

CHAMPAGNE MUMM

29, rue du Champ-de-Mars - 51100 Reims
26 40 22 73

Vine stocks: Chardonnay and Pinot Noir.
Appellation: Champagne. **Type:** Champagne method. **Characteristics:** Highly reputed House, known for its famous Cordon Rouge and the super Cuvée René Lalon 1979. Great finesse. Beautiful rosé champagne. **Serving temperature:** 11°. **Served with:** As an aperitif and with the entire meal. **Vintage available in 89/90:** 1979 and 1982.

GRAND CHAMPAGNE NAPOLEON

Ch. & A. Prieur SARL
Managers: Etienne et Vincent Prieur
2, rue de Villers-aux-Bois, 51130 Vertus
26 52 11 74 - Telex: 830 173 PRIEUR

Type of vineyard: Family Corporation. **Established:** 1825. **Number of employees:** 10. **Vine stocks:** Chardonnay, Pinot, Meunier. **Average annual production in hectoliters:** 150,000 bottles × 75 cl.
Appellation: Champagne. **Type:** White, rosé. **Technique:** Champagne Method. **Vintages available in 89/90:** 1979, 1981.

Characteristics of vintages

Other: Blending of Champagne Grands Crus (45% Chardonnay). Price range (pre-tax, ex-warehouse): 50 to 80 F.F. and 80 to 120 F.F.
Sales volume:
- Retail: 85% (France).

Sales in France: 40%.
Export sales: 60%.
Main trading partners : Germany, Belgium, Netherlands, Luxemburg, Italy, Switzerland, North and Central America.

Comments

Family estate founded in 1825 at VERTUS, member of the Syndicat de Grandes Marques de Champagnes (Champagne producers union), independent establishment with its own cellars and storerooms in VERTUS, doing business under the trademarks GRAND CHAMPAGNE NAPOLEON and BONAPARTE. Blending and distribution of Grands Crus de Champagne.

SOCIÉTÉ MOËT ET CHANDON

20, avenue de Champagne - 51200 Épernay
26 54 71 11 - Telex: 830 941

Type of vineyard: Corporation. **Established:** 1743. **Number of employees:** 1400. **Vine stocks:** Pinot Noir, Pinot Meunier, Chardonnay. **Soil:** Tertiary debris and chalky fragments on a limestone sub-soil. **Average annual production in hectoliters:** 25,000.
Appellation: Champagne. **Type:** White, rosé. **Technique:** Alcoholic Champagne fermentation, second malolactic fermentation. **Alcohol content:** 12% to 12.5%. **Characteristics:** blending of different varieties. Chardonnay: finesse. Pinot Noir: strength, body. Pinot Meunier: freshness, vitality. **Serving temperature:** 6°. **Served with:** all kinds fo dishes. **Vintages available in 89/90:** 1982.

Characteristics of vintages

1982: White and rosé. **Other:** Dom Pérignon 1980. Price range (pre-tax, ex-warehouse): more than 160 F.F.

Sales volume:
– Wholesale: 100 % (except a few personnal clients).
Sales in France: 23.5 %. **Export sales:** 76.5 %.
Main trading partners : UK, USA, Germany, Switzerland, Italy, Belgium, Austria, Netherlands, Canada.

Sales volume:
96 % of the production exported to restaurants, clubs and specialized shops and winecellars, no supermarkets.
Sales in France: 4 %.
Export sales: 96 %.
Main trading partners : Belgium, Switzerland, USA, UK, Germany, Italy, Netherlands.

CHAMPAGNE BRUNO PAILLARD

Bruno Paillard
Avenue de Champagne et rue Jacques-Maritain
51100 Reims
26 36 20 22 – Telex: 830 458 Telefax: 26 36 57 72

Type of company: Family Corporation. **Established:** 1981. **Number of employees:** 7. **Average annual production in bottles:** 342,000 (1988).
Appellation: Champagne. **Type:** Brut, White, Rosé. **Technique:** Traditional champagne method. **Maturing:** Stainless steel tanks, then bottles. **Alcohol content:** 12 %. **Serving temperature:** 7 to 8° in an ice bucket. **Served with:** Mostly as an aperitif, but also with all simple or refined dishes, if not too seasoned or sweet. **Vintages available in 89/90:** 1976-1979-1983-1985 (recent and dated disgorging for all).

Characteristics of vintages

1976: The year of the drought – great concentration of aromas, perfect balance and maturity. **1979:** Influence of the Chardonnay: fine and rich at the same time. **1983:** A Blanc de Blancs (100 % Chardonnay) fresh, lively and very elegant. **1985:** A blend of Pinot Noir and Chardonnay, rich and fruity from a year of perfect ripeness/acidity balance. There are also a Brut non vintage, a Rosé non vintage and a Cremant blanc de blancs non vintage. Price range (pre-tax, ex-cellars): 90 to 200 F.F.

Abroad

United States
Calvert & Woodley, 4339 Connecticut Ave NW, Washington DC, 20008 Tel: (202) 966 4400 – Grape Expectations 4097 Harlan St., Emeryville, Cal. 94 Tel: (415) 658 8891.

United Kingdom
Berkmann Wine Cellars Ltd, 12 Brewery RD, London N7 9 NH Tel: 1 609 4711.

Germany
A. Segnitz & Co, Löwenhof 2, Postfach 101506, 2800 Bremen 1 Tel: 04 21/388007.

Switzerland
Ets. Degusta, Schmiedengasse 17, 4500, Solothurn Tel: 65 236630.

Belgium
Ets Velu Vins, 215 rue Bollinckx, 1070, Brussels TE Tel: 5206068 – Import Masure, 11 Rampe Est Kursaal, 8400 Ostende Tel: 59 70 19 60.

The Netherlands
Wijnimport Van Broekhuizen, Gerrit V.D. Veenstraat 49 HS 1077 Amsterdam – Tel: 20 662 62 08.

Italy
Flli Gancia & C, SpA. Corso Liberta, 16,14053 Canelli Tel: 0141/8301.

Comments

The youngest Champagne enterprise, concentrating only on the top of the line.

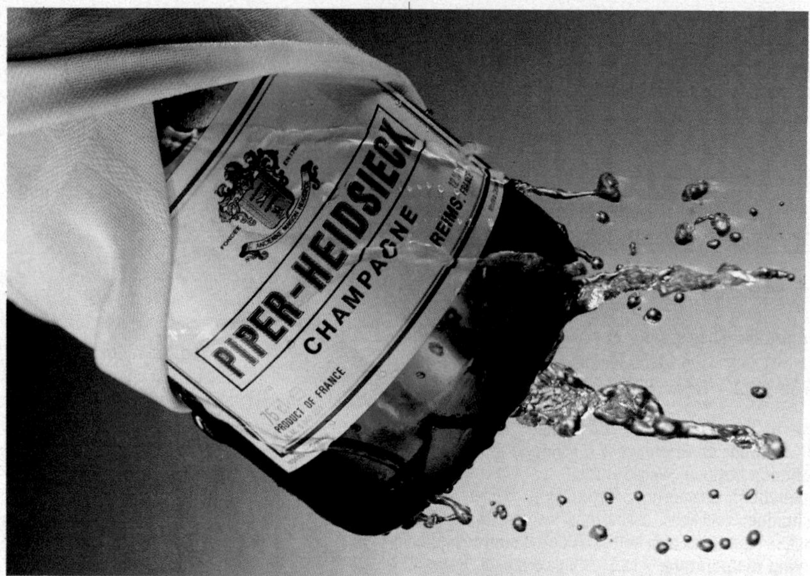

CHAMPAGNE PIPER-HEIDSIECK

Marquis François d'Aulan
51, Bd Henri-Vanier 51100 Reims
2 6 85 01 94 - Telex: 830 024

Established: 1785. **Number of employees:** 190. **Average annual production in hectoliters:** 5,000,000,000 bottles.
Appellation: Champagne. **Type:** White, Rosé. **Technique:** In white. **Alcohol content:** Between 11 and 12%.
Characteristics: Remarkably matured wines, covering the whole range, whose principal characteristics are elegance and persistance. **Serving temperature:** 6 to 8°.
Vintages available in 89/90: 1979, 1982 and 1985.

Characteristics of vintages

Price range (pre-tax, ex-warehouse): from 80 to more than 160 F.F.
Sales volume:
- Wholesale: 16%. - Retail: 55%. - Restaurants: 24%. - Other: 5% tax free shops.
Sales in France: 40%.
Export sales: 60%.
Main trading partners: United States, Germany, United Kingdom, Italy, Belgium, Switzerland, Netherlands.

References in France

Restaurants: In most first rate restaurants and shops.

Abroad

United States

Importers: Première Wine Merchants, Inc. 888, Seventh Avenue, New York NY 10106

United Kingdom

Percy Fox I.D.V., Gilbey House, Fourth avenue Harlow, Essex CM20 1DX

Germany

Piper-Heidsieck Deutschland, Postfach 4746, 6200 Wiesbaden.

Switzerland

Marmot Kellerei, 8832 Wollerau am Zurichsee.

Belgium

Mampaey & Co., Gossetlaan 21, B-1720 Groot Bijgaarden.

The Netherlands

Martini & Rossi Nederland nv, Verrijn Stuartlaan 32, 2288 El Rijswijk.

Others

Italy: Martini & Rossi Ivlas Spa, Corso Vittorio Emanuele 42, 10123 Turin.

Comments

The house of Piper-Heidsieck (successor to Heidsieck) was founded in 1785. The Company owns Piper-Heidsieck and Heidsieck (alone). Piper-Heidsieck is one of the oldest Champagne trademarks. One of the most beautiful Champagne Houses and some remarkable wines: The Brut "Sauvage", without expedition liqueur, lively and dry, superb. The Cuvées Millésimées (82 and 79), still perfect. The exceptional "Cuvée Rare", unusual elegance, rare and dense, very harmonious, a must.

CHAMPAGNE PERRIER-JOUET

26 avenue de Champagne - 51200 Epernay
26 55 20 53 - Telex: 840 204

Type of vineyard: Corporation. **Established:** 1811. **Number of employees:** 110 plus sales force. **Vine stocks:** The three Champagne vinestocks, Chardonnay, Pinot Noir and Pinot Meunier (mostly Chardonnay).

Appellation: Champagne. **Type:** White, Rosé. **Technique:** Champagne Method. **Alcohol content:** 12 to 12.5%. **Serving temperature:** Cool, between 5 and 10°. **Served with:** As an aperitif and with the whole meal. **Vintages available in 89/90:** 1983 and 1985.

Characteristics of vintages

Price range (pre-tax, ex-warehouse): Grand Brut and Brut Millésimé: between 100 and 120 F.F. Blason de France and Blason de France Rosé: between 120 and 160 F.F. Belle Epoque and Belle Epoque Rosé Millésimé: over 200 F.F.
Sales in France: 30%.
Export sales: 70%.
Main trading partners : United States, U.K., Switzerland, Italy, Germany, Belgium.

References in France

Restaurants: In most of the great restaurants.
Shops: In most of the specialized shops in Paris and elsewhere in France.

Abroad

United States
Importers: Seagram Chateau & Estate Wines, 375 Park Avenue, New York, N.Y. 10152-0192. Tel: (212) 572 7057.

United Kingdom
Seagram United Kingdom Ltd, Seagram Distillers House, 17 Dacre Street, London SW1H ODR. Tel: (44) 1 222 43 43.

Germany
Epikur - Deinhard, Deinhard Platz, Postfac 509, D 5400 Koblenz/Rheim. Tel: (49) 261 1040.

Switzerland
Ets Robert Maeder A.G., Seestrasse 510, 8038 Zurich.

Belgium
Seagram Belgium, Plantin & Moretuslei 12, B 2000 Anvers.

Others:
Italy: Seagram Italia, Centro Direzionale Paul Bernini, Milan 2, 20090 Segrate. Tel: (39) 2 21 26 1.

Comments

The house of Perrier-Jouet was founded in 1811 by Pierre-Nicolas Marie Perrier-Jouet. It owns one of the most beautiful vineyards in the Champagne region, well known for its excellent vinestocks: Cramant, Avize in the heart of the Côte des Blancs; Ay, Dizy in the Marne Valley; Mailly on the Reims Mountain.

CHAMPAGNE POL ROGER

Messrs. Christian Pol-Roger & Christian de Billy
1, rue Henri Lelarge - 51200 Épernay Marne
26 55 41 95 - Telex: 840 260 F

Type of vineyard: Family-owned. **Established:** 1849. **Number of employees:** 60. **Average annual production in hectoliters:** Approx. 1,000.

Characteristics of vintages

Some excellent lots. Very traditional and in the family image. Good breeding, distinguished, generally well blended and successful. You may have complete confidence.
Sales in France: 35%.
Export sales: 65%.
Main trading partners : UK, USA, Belgium, Switzerland.

References in France

Restaurants: Nearly all restaurants with Michelin Stars.
Shops: Hédiard, Fauchon.

CHAMPAGNE POMMERY

Hubert Louis
5, place du Général Gouraud, 51000 Reims
26 05 71 61

Vine stocks: Chardonnay, Pinot Noir.
Appellation: Champagne. **Type:** White, rosé. **Technique:** Traditional (long maceration). **Maturing:** Traditional. **Characteristics:** Superb "cuvées" (Louise Pommery), perfect and regularly successful blendings. **Serving temperature:** 8°. **Served with:** The entire meal. **Vintages available in 89/90:** 1983, 1982 "cuvée".

• *A great naturally sweet wine with Roquefort? Try a Sauternes, of course, a Grand Cru from a late Alsacian harvest, a mellow Anjou or a Banyuls.*

R.RENAUDIN
BRUT
1976
CHAMPAGNE
R.RENAUDIN
Grande Réserve
MOUSSY ÉPERNAY

R.RENAUDIN

CHAMPAGNE R. RENAUDIN

Dominique Tellier

Domaine des Conardins 51200 Moussy - Épernay

26 54 03 41 - Telex: 842 060 - TELEFAX: 26 54 31 12

Type of vineyard: Corporation. **Established:** 1935. **Number of employees:** 18. **Vine stocks:** Pinot, Chardonnay. **Exposure:** South. **Average annual production in hectoliters:** 2000.
Appellation: Champagne. **Type:** White. **Technique:** Traditional. **Maturing:** In vats. **Alcohol content:** 12%. **Serving temperature:** 7°. **Vintages available in 89/90:** 1981, 1983.

Characteristics of vintages

Price range (pre-tax, ex-warehouse): 65 to 85 F.F. - 100 to 120 F.F.
Sales volume:
- Retail: 15%. - Restaurants: 30%. - Other: 55% (export).
Sales in France: 45%.
Export sales: 55%.
Main trading partners: USA, Germany, Netherlands, Singapore, Switzerland.

References in France

Restaurants: Taillevent, Besson, Grande Cascade, Cazaudehore, Garnier, Le Duc, Château-de-Brecourt.
Shops: Caves Taillevent, Caves St. Georges.

Abroad

United States

Bill Deutsch, 400 King Street Chappaqua, New-York, 10514.

United Kingdom

David Peppercorn, 2 Bryanston Place London W1 - Serena Sutcliffe.

Germany

Firma Otmar Federl, Forst Kasten Allee 123 8000 Munchen 71.

Switzerland

Jacques-Vins-Champagne, 176 route d'Hermance, C Postal n° 29-2111 Genève.

The Netherlands

Ets. Otto Lenselink Winjimport 1E Loswal 2A - 1216 BE Hilversum.

CHAMPAGNE RUINART

4, rue des Crayères - 51100 Reims

26 85 40 29

Vine stocks: Chardonnay and Pinot Noir, Pinot Meunier. **Appellation:** Champagne. **Type:** White, rosé. **Technique:** Champagne Method. **Characteristics:** Exceptionnal Dom Ruinart Blanc de Blancs Vintage 1982, made from Chardonnay grapes, and Dom Ruinart Rosé Vintage 1981, long in flavour with great aromatic fineness. "R" de Ruinart Brut 1983: a powerful wine with presence and roundness. "R" de Ruinart Rosé: red fruits aroma. **Vintages available in 89/90:** 1978, 1979 and 1981.

Champagne ALAIN ROBERT Père & Fils

Alain Robert

25, avenue de la République, Le Mesnil-sur-Oger

51190 Avize

26 57 52 94 - Telex: 842 753

Average annual production in hectoliters: 800.

Appellation: Champagne. **Type:** White. **Technique:** Traditional. **Vintages available in 89/90:** 1978 & 1979.

Characteristics of vintages

1978: Mesnil Tradition 78: a great vintage, very long, very fine sparkle. **1979:** Mesnil Réserve 79: to be enjoyed with friends. **Other:** Mesnil Sélection (6 years old), for all occasions. Brut non vintage (5 years old), lively, very fresh, very pleasant as an aperitif, will improve with age. Price range (pre-tax, ex-warehouse): 50 to 80 F.F. (Brut non vintage). 80-120 F.F. (Mesnil Selection) - over 160 F.F. (Mesnil Réserve & Tradition).
Sales volume:
- Retail: 100%.
Sales in France: 50%.
Main trading partners: European countries.

Comments

Winemakers in Mesnil, from father to son, since the 17th century with vineyards in 3 Champagne regions, 7 villages, 31 localities, who produce Champagne made from grapes grown exclusively on their own property. The AOC wines referred to as Grand Cru Blanc de Blancs are made exclusively from Mesnil. The blends are made from 6 other noble vinestocks.

• *A good everyday wine for 20 F? See the Bordeaux, Anjou, Touraine, Côtes-du-Rhône or Languedoc Regions.*

CHAMPAGNE TAITTINGER

9, place Saint-Nicaise – 51100 Reims
26 85 45 35

Vine stocks: Chardonnay, Pinot Noir, Pinot Meunier. **Appellation:** Champagne. **Type:** White, rosé. **Technique:** Champagne Method. **Characteristics:** Superb Comtes de Champagne Blanc de Blancs, combining finesse, elegance and complexity of aromas. To be tasted: the vintage Rosé Brut. For drinking pleasure: the bottles marked Arman and Vasarely. **Served with:** As an aperitif and with the entire meal. **Vintages available in 89/90:** 1982 and 1983.

CHAMPAGNE BERNARD TORNAY

Bernard Tornay
51150 Bouzy
26 57 08 58

Type of vineyard: Family-owned. **Vine stocks:** 2/3 Pinot Noir, 1/3 Chardonnay. **Soil:** Chalky. **Exposure:** South. **Average annual production in hectoliters:** 800 to 900. **Appellation:** Champagne. **Type:** White, rosé. **Technique:** The must is stored in large enamelled tanks. Sugar is added, if necessary, and then the enzymes to start the alcoholic fermentation. Vinification then proceeds in vats, the wines are separated by years, except for the vintage wines. **Alcohol content:** 12.5 to 13%. **Characteristics:** Fruity and light. Brut: five year blending. Perfect continuity from one year to the next. Brut Rosé: raspberry fragrance. The richness in Bouzy gives, balance and body. Brut V. Réserve: Blend of five years improves by a longer agein period. **Serving temperature:** 8°. **Served with:** Brut: as an aperitif, or with an entire meal. Brut Rosé: as an aperitif, or with an entire meal. Brut Rosé: as an aperitif or with hors d'œuvres. Can be used like the Vintage Bruts. Brut V. Réserve: as an aperitif or with fish. **Vintages available in 89/90:** 1981, 1985.

Characteristics of vintages

1985: Rich and well-balanced wine, fresh, pleasant to drink. **Other:** 1981: Very fragrant wine, very fine sparkle. Price range (pre-tax, ex-warehouse): between 50 and 80 F.F.

• Keep up with the quality and the real evolution of the vintages. Consult the "VINTAGE CODE" at the beginning of the Guide (see Editorial). For an additional free copy, send a stamped, self-addressed envelope to Patrick DUSSERT-GERBER, 94 rue Saint-Dominique (75007 Paris).

CHAMPAGNE TROUILLARD

Bertrand Trouillard
B.P. 272 – 2, avenue Foch, 51200 Épernay Cedex
26 55 37 55 – Telex: 842 748

Type of vineyard: Family-owned. **Established:** 1896.

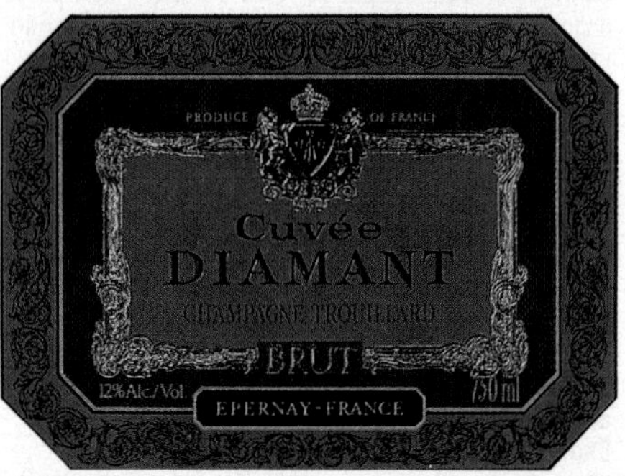

Appellation: Champagne. **Type:** White, Rosé. **Characteristics:** Fruity, light, fresh. **Serving temperature:** 7 to 8°. **Vintages available in 89/90:** 1982, 1983.

Characteristics of vintages

Other: 1983: Blanc de Blancs, rich and well balanced, fruity, long. Price range (pre-tax, ex-warehouse): between 50 and 120 F.F.

Sales volume:
– Wholesale: 50%. – Retail: 40%. – Restaurants: 10%.
Sales in France: 35%.
Export sales: 65%.
Main trading partners : European Economic Community, Africa, Canada, Australia.

Abroad

United Kingdom

Speyside Distellery, Glasgow. The Hilbre Wine Co., Liverpool. Prospero Wines, London.

Germany

Wein Fuchs, Hamburg.

Switzerland

Banchet, Geneva. Gastronomie Rustique, Lausanne.

Belgium

Van Peteghem, Brussels. Boon, Bornem.

Canada

L.C.B.O.

The Netherlands

Select Drink, Breda.

Comments

Family estate whose principal desire is to remain, above all, in the Champagne tradition. Personal relationships are sought with foreign dealers based on mutual confidence and an interest in marketing quality Champagne.

GEORGES VESSELLE

Mr. Georges Vesselle
16, rue des Postes - 51150 Bouzy-Champagne
26 57 00 15 - Telex: 842 094 F

Type of vineyard: Family-owned. **Established:** 15th Century. **Number of employees:** 14. **Vine stocks:** 90% Pinot Noir, 10% Chardonnay. **Soil:** Champagne chalk. **Exposure:** South. **Average annual production in hectoliters:** 1875.
Appellation: Bouzy Champagne. **Type:** Red, white, rosé. **Technique:** Champagne: steel tanks. Bouzy: fermentation in skins in pressurized tanks. **Alcohol content:** 12.5%. **Characteristics:** Champagne: each lot is a blend of carefully selected vintage wines. Bouzy: light wine, with finesse and elegance. **Serving temperature:** Champagne: 10°. Bouzy: 13°. **Vintages available in 89/90:** Red Bouzy: 1985 and 1983. Non-vintage (white Bouzy) - Blend of a red Bouzy with a 100% grand cru.

Characteristics of vintages

1985: Bouzy – rich and well-balanced. Hold. **1983:** Finesse, a bit too light. **Other:** Remarkable Champagnes, rich and well-balanced, finesse and structure. The "Juline" is a blend of old wines, full and successful. Exceptional Bouzy reds, balanced, the best of which is the "Véronique-Sylvie", dense, rich and well-balanced, long. Price range (pre-tax, ex-warehouse): Between 50 F.F. and 120 F.F.
Sales volume:
– Wholesale: 5%. – Retail: 15%. – Restaurants: 80%.
Sales in France: 80%.
Export sales: 20%.
Main trading partners : Benelux Countries, Switzerland, Germany, USA.

CHAMPAGNE VEUVE CLIQUOT

12, rue du Temple - 51100 Reims
26 40 25 42

Vine stocks: Chardonnay and Pinot Noir.
Appellation: Champagne Type: White, rosé. **Technique:** Champagne Method. **Characteristics:** Exceptional vintage rosé, flowery nose, made by blending white wine and Bouzy. Regularly successful. To be tasted: the Cuvée Spéciale Grande Dame and the Vintage Carte Or.

• *The quality of the 1987 vintage, particularly in Bordeaux, is questionable. Much of the Merlot suffered from coulure and a good bit of the harvesting was done in the rain. Only a few vineyards will produce a good vintage (see the Chapter on Bordeaux wines and the "Vintage Code").*

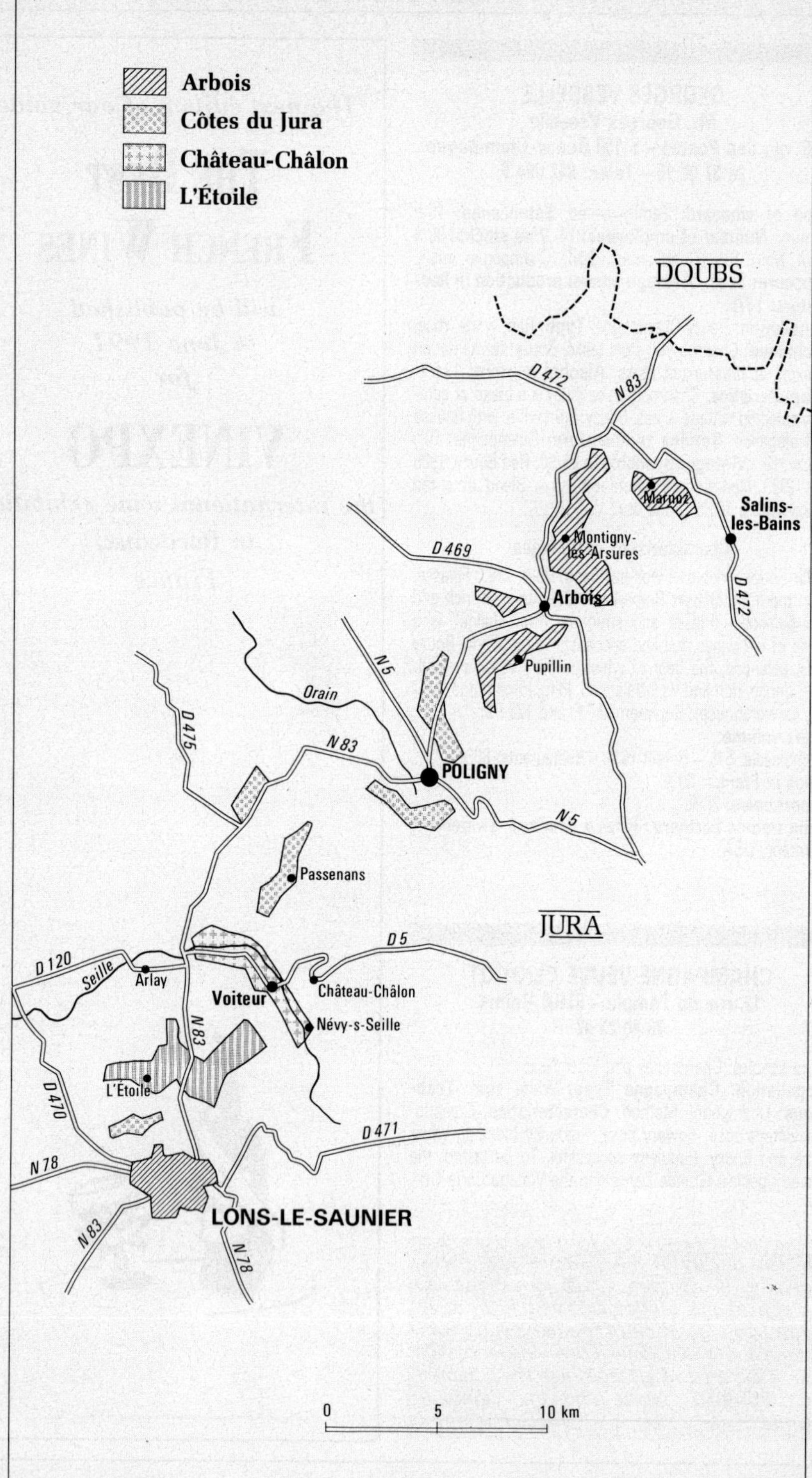
Arbois
Côtes du Jura
Château-Châlon
L'Étoile
DOUBS
JURA
D 472
N 83
Marnoz
Salins-les-Bains
Montigny-les-Arsures
D 469
Arbois
D 472
Pupillin
N 5
Orain
D 475
N 83
POLIGNY
N 5
Passenans
D 5
D 120
Seille
Arlay
Voiteur
Château-Châlon
Névy-s-Seille
N 83
L'Étoile
D 470
D 471
N 78
LONS-LE-SAUNIER
N 83
N 78
0
5
10 km

JURA

THE WINES

— **Vin Jaune.** Made exclusively from the Savagnin (also called "Naturé") grape variety, reminiscent of the Traminer of the Rhine Valley. Harvested late in the year, the overripe grapes are pressed and left for primary fermentation. The following spring, the wine is racked and left to mature in small oak casks for 6 years (minimum authorized) to 10 years. Soon after this transfer, a thin airtight film develops on the surface of the wine. This film, which absorbs oxygen, makes topping up unnecessary and prevents oxidation. It goes without saying that this wine-making technique, a difficult one, not easily mastered, owes much to the talent of the Jura proprietors, and it is not surprising that the wines are expensive. The wine now ready to drink is bottled exclusively under the Arbois Jaune and Château-Chalon appellations, also called "Clavelin" (63 cl).

How to describe it? It is a wine for connoisseurs which must be discovered little by little, without reference to other wines and scents, until one learns to appreciate its extraordinary flavor suggestive of nuts and honey. A wine of rare distinction—unique in the world—it can be aged indefinitely and never spoils.

— **Vin de paille.** Originally, wine made from grapes dried on straw mats or hung up before destemming, the "vin de paille" is made today with grapes spread out on wooden slats in a dry and well ventilated room. This "drying technique" lasts two to three months during which the wine acquires a natural unctuosity, which, after a few years in the cask, permits very long keeping. Some can be superb!

— **White wines.** Made essentially from Chardonnay, topped up with Savignin and Pinot Blanc, the white wines we have tasted were pleasant, fruity and very aromatic after ageing a few years. The best come from Arbois and Etoile.

— **Red wines.** We found the Côtes-du-Jura (made from Poulsard, Trousseau and Pinot Noir) pleasant and fragrant, but our preference is definitely for the Arbois reds, made from the same grape varieties, which while delicate and supple are nonetheless vigorous and well-balanced.

— **Rosés.** If one can talk of great rosés, those from the Jura, grey, pink or coral in color depending on the relative length of the vinification process, or whether or not they have been made from blended red and white grapes, are about the best one can find. Lively and vigorous, with a pronounced bouquet, they should be drunk cool or close to room temperature (14-15°) with rich food. The best come from Arbois and Arlay.

GRAPES VARIETIES:

• **POULSARD OR POUSSARD.** Red grapes typical of the Jura. The long, soft, indented violet bunches bear ovoid, translucid, flavorful grapes which yield a very fine rosé. It can be recognized by its deeply cut leaves.

• **TROUSSEAU.** Beautiful velvety grapes with thick skins, sweet, pungent and abundant pulp. The leaves are round and slightly blistered. Makes wines with body and color.

• **SAVIGNIN.** Small crispy grapes, golden yellow in color, in short bunches. Its leaves, a beautiful dark green, are cottony, with white and fluffy buds. Makes the famous "vin jaune".

• **PINOT NOIR.** Round grapes in small and tight clusters. The glory of Burgundy, it can very well make a well-balanced wine, all on its own. Here, it is blended with Poulsard and Trousseau giving the wine richness, structure and ageing potiental.

• **CHARDONNAY OR MELON D'ARBOIS.** Round grapes growing in average size clusters, of a beautiful pale yellow color, with a thin skin and particularly fine leaves. Basic component of the better whites of the area.

THE CHARACTERISTICS OF THE VINEYARD

The French *département* of the Jura is located in the winegrowing region of the ancient province of Franche-Comté. The Jura vineyard covers approximately ?? acres (1,000 hectares) on the hillsides of the Jura plateau.

Soil

Limestone is the main component of the Jura plateau. Marl is found in the prized vineyards of Arbois and Château-Chalon.

Climate

The Jura is in a continental climate. The annual temperature averages 50°F to 51.8°F (10-11°C). Rainfall is relatively high and frost and hailstorms are not uncommon.

CÔTES DE JURA

CHÂTEAU D'ARLAY

Comte R. de Laguiche
Arlay - 39140 Bletterans
84 85 04 22 - Telex: 360 075 F Attn: S.E.D.A.

Type of vineyard: Corporation. **Established:** 1970. **Number of employees:** 12. **Vine stocks:** Pinot Noir, Chardonnay, Trousseau, Poulsard, Savagnin. **Soil:** Clay and calcium carbonate with marl. **Exposure:** South, Southwest, Southeast.
Appellation: A.O.C. Côtes-du-Jura. **Type:** Red, white, rosé. Other: "Vin Jaune" (Yellow Wine). **Technique:** Traditional. **Maturing:** In casks (2 years), 6/7 years for Yellow Wine. **Alcohol content:** 12% – yellow 13.5%. **Characteristics:** Red: delicate. Rosé (coral): full and good wine for ageing. White: typical, elegant. Yellow: rich and well-balanced, fine. **Serving temperature:** Red/rosé/white: cool – yellow: room temperature. **Served with:** Poultry in mushroom and cream sauce, white meat, delicatessen products, shellfish, fish, cheese. **Vintages available in 89/90:** Red, Rosé-Corail, White: 1986, 1987, Jaune de Garde: 1982.

Characteristics of vintages

1988: Still ageing but quite promising, good color, fruity aromas, substantial, good keeping. All the more so as harvesting techniques have been much improved with the introduction in 87/88 of automatic crushing, the Kreyer heat pump, new vats, with a view to improve the quality of the Château d'Arlay Red and Rosé-Corail wines.

JEAN-MARIE & HÉLÈNE SALAÜN

Passenans 39230 Seillières
84 85 24 15

Type of vineyard: Family-owned. **Established:** 1978. **Number of employees:** Seasonal help. **Vine stocks:** Savagnin & Chardonnay. **Soil:** Blue Marl and clay. **Average annual production in hectoliters:** Augmenting, aiming at 400 hl.
Appellation: A.O.C. "Côtes du Jura". **Type:** Red, white. **Ohters:** "Vin Jaune" (yellow wine) & "Vin de Paille" (straw colored wine). **Technique:** Traditional. **Maturing:** In Oak casks. **Alochol content:** 12.5%. **Characteristics:** Must be aged, full bodied, nutty flavor. **Serving temperature:** Cellar temperature – 16°. **Served with:** White: with fish, white meats, terrines. "Vins de Paille" & "Vins Jaunes": with foie gras, fresh salmon, oysters (cooked), mushrooms (morels variety). **Vintages available in 89/90:** White and Red, 1985. Vin Jaune, 1980.

Characteristics of vintages

1986: Not yet on the market. **1985:** Very good year, young wine but well balanced. **1984:** Average year, still in Oak casks, promising. **1983:** Exceptional year, stock fast depleting. **1982:** Stock depleted. **Note:** 1980: Fragrant "Vin Jaune"; to be aged. Price range (pre-tax, ex-warehouse): 20 F.F. – 120 F.F.
Sales volume:
– Wholesale: 5%. – Retail: 70%. – Restaurants: 25%.
Main trading partners : Germany – Belgium.

References in France

Restaurants: La Guerlande (Montmartre).
Shops: "Flo Prestige" – L'Œnothèque – Caves Estève, Paris.

Comments

Recently created Estate (1978), products already eliciting a certain interest on the part of professionnals; eager to increase increasing marketing opportunities with specialized shops and delicatessens in France and abroad.

ARBOIS

DOMAINE JACQUES TISSOT

Jacques Tissot
39, rue de Courcelles - 39600 Arbois
84 66 14 27

Type of vineyard: Family-owned. **Established:** Commercial since 1969; 2 generations old. **Number of employees:** 7. **Vine stocks:** Savagnin, Chardonnay, Poulsard, Trousseau, Pinot. **Soil:** Clay and chalky marl. **Exposure:** Hillside South. **Average annual production in hectoliters:** 450 to 1 000.
Appellation: Arbois A.O.C. **Type:** Red, white, rosé and "Vin Jaune " Yellow: Wine (dry), "Vin de Paille" straw colored wine (sweet). **Technique:** Traditional, in cool cellars. **Maturing:** Oak casks. **Alcohol content:** 12% to 13%. **Characteristics:** White: typical. Rosé: fruity. Yellow: very typical. **Serving temperature:** 12° on the average. **Served with:** Red and rosé: red meat and light cheeses. White: fondue, shellfish. Yellow: salmon, "Truit Saumonée" (Sea Trout with pink flesh); as an aperitif, with "Comté" cheese. **Vintages available in 89/90:** Yellow: 1975, 1976, 1977, 1978, 1979. Red, rosé, white: 1982, 1983, 1984, 1985, 1986.

Characteristics of vintages

1986: Good, red Arbois but especially excellent white. **1985:** A lovely rosé, light, supple and lively. Good whites and reds, fragrant and full. **Other:** Good Yellow Wines, especially the 1975 and 1978 vintages. Price range (pre-tax, ex-warehouse): Between 25 F.F. and 35 F.F. Yellow: between 120 F.F. and 160 F.F.
Sales in France: 90%.
Export sales: 10%.

ROLET PÈRE ET FILS

M. Rolet
Montigny - 39600 Arbois
84 66 00 05

Established: 1968. **Number of employees:** 7. **Average annual production in hectoliters:** 2300.
Appellation: Arbois and Côtes-du-Jura. **Type:** Red, White, Rosé. Other: "Vin Jaune" (Yellow) and "Vin de Paille" (Straw-colored). **Technique:** In stainless steel tanks with temperature control. Destemming. **Maturing:** In Oak casks for 12 to 18 months - 6 years for Yellow Wines. **Characteristics:** Whites: good for ageing wines (8 to 10 years). Rosé: specific to the Jura, obtained by red wine vinification of the Poulsard Grape Variety. Single variety reds: Poulsard, Pinot or Trousseau (from the lightest to the most robust), good for ageing, 8 to 10 years. Yellow: for very long ageing (more than 50 years), very marked, nutty aroma. **Vintages available in 89/90:** 1985, 1986, 1987.

VIN JAUNE

CAVES JEAN BOURDY

Christian Bourdy
Arlay - 39140 Bletterans
84 85 03 70 - Telex: 360 443 ITAJR - poste 152

Type of vineyard: Family-owned. **Established:** 1741. **Number of employees:** 4. **Vine stocks:** Red: Poulsard, Trousseau, Pinot. White: Chardonnay. Yellow: Savagnin. **Soil:** Clay with calcium carbonate, Jurassic lias. **Exposure:** South, South west. **Average annual production in hectoliters:** 42 hl per hectare (35 hl per hectare for the Château-Chalon).
Type: Red, White, Rosé, Yellow, and Château-Chalon. **Technique:** In heated tanks at 18° to trigger the fermentation of malic to lactic acid. **Maturing:** Ageing in Oak casks 3 years for the red and white, 7 years for the yellow. **Alcohol content:** 12% to 13.5%. **Characteristics:** Reds: aroma of flowers and small fruit, very rich and well-balanced, long keeping. Whites: dry and fruity with a bouquet of hazel nuts an grilled almonds. Yellows: heady with an aroma of hazel nuts, green nuts and grilled almonds. **Serving temperature:** Reds: 14°. Whites: 10 to 12°. Yellows: 15°. **Served with:** Reds: roast meat. Whites: as an aperitif or with first courses and fish. Yellows: shellfish, foie gras, Franche-Comté cheese. **Vintages available in 89/90:** Reds and Whites: 1986 and 1986. Yellow and Château-Chalon: 1982.

CHASSOT MAURICE

Mr. Chassot
15, route de Lyon, 39600 Arbois
84 66 15 36

Type of vineyard: Family-owned. **Established:** 1955. **Vine stocks:** Poulsard, Chardonnay, Trousseau, Savagnin. **Soil:** Clay with calcium carbonate. **Exposure:** South - Southeast. **Average annual production in hectoliters:** 130.
Appellation: A.O.C. Savagnin and «Vin jaune». **Type:** White, rosé. **Technique:** In tanks (rosé). **Maturing:** in wooden containers. **Alcohol content:** 12 to 13%. Vin Jaune: 14%. **Characteristics:** White and rosé: Dry wines, for keeping. Vin Jaune: very rare. Its price, which may seem exorbitant, is justified because production is low and carried out under difficult conditions. **Serving temperature:** Rosé: 16° - White: 12°. Vin Jaune: at room temperature (16-17°). **Served with:** Rosé: roasts, delicatessen. White: hors-d'œuvre, cheese. Vin Jaune: as an aperitif, or at the end of the meal - with cheese. **Vintages available in 89-90:** Rosé: 81, 82, 83, 85, - 86 at the end of the year. White: 82, 85, 86 at beginning of '88. Vin Jaune: '76 (Gold Medal), '73 and '78.

Characteristics of vintages

1986: Excellent year. Very promising young wine. **1985:** Excellent year. Very promising young wine. **1983:** Very good wine (very sunny year). For keeping. **1982:** Vin Jaune - awarded Bronze Medal at the Concours général de Paris, 1989. Lighter wines, of average quality. **Other:** Vin Jaune 1976: excellent year. Vin Jaune 1973: also very good. Vin Jaune 1978: somewhat inferior to the other years. Price range (pre-tax, ex-warehouse): Rosé and White: 20-32 F.F. Vin Jaune: 80-120 F.F.
Sales volume: - Retail: 80%. - Restaurants: 20%.
Sales in France: 70%. **Export sales:** 30%.
Main trading partners: Denmark, Germany, Belgium, Switzerland.

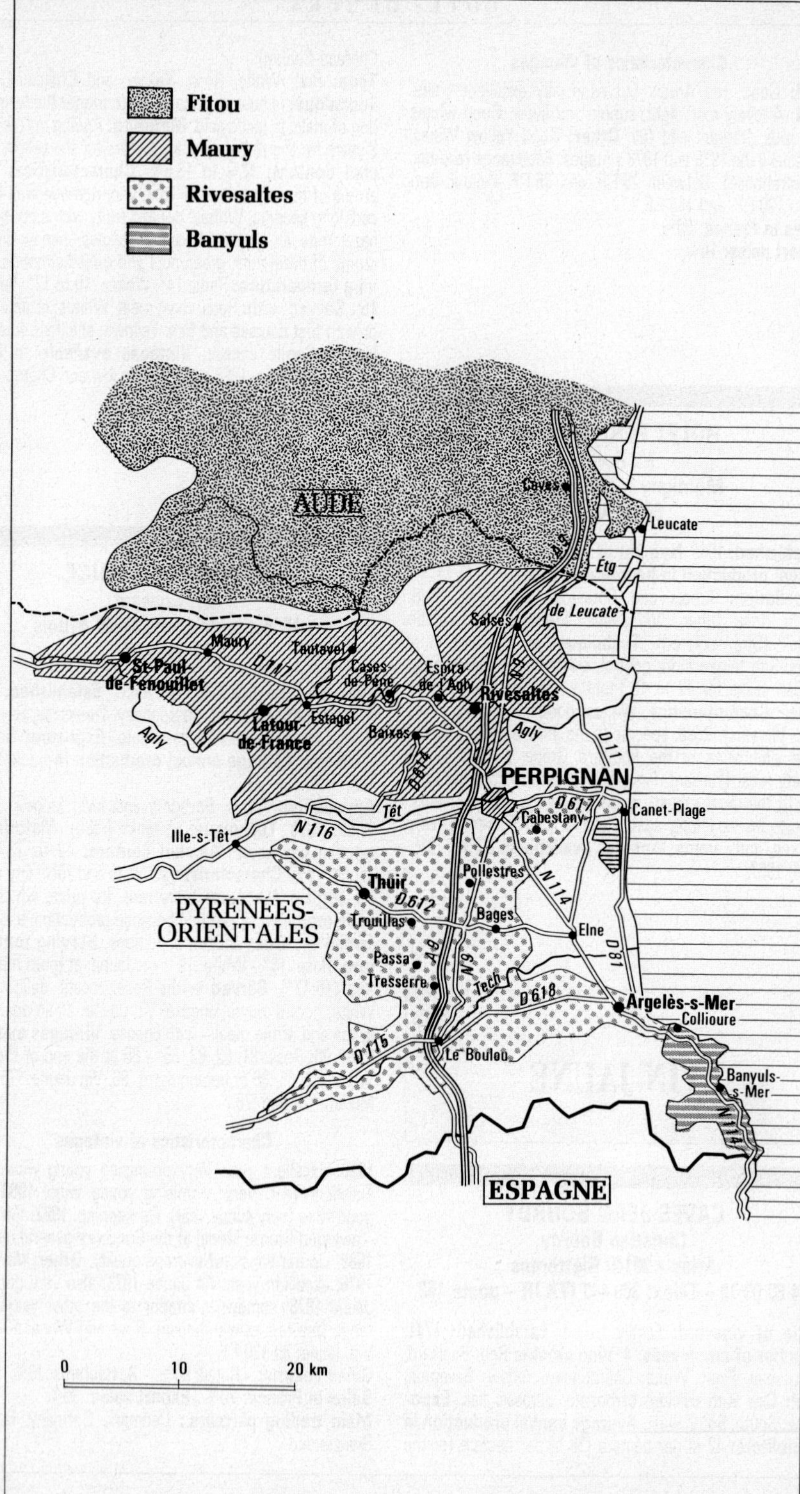

Fitou
Maury
Rivesaltes
Banyuls
AUDE
Caves
Leucate
A9
Étg
de Leucate
Salses
Maury
St-Paul-de-Fenouillet
Tautavel
Cases-de-Pène
Espira de l'Agly
Rivesaltes
D 117
N9
Latour-de-France
Estagel
Baixas
Agly
Agly
D 614
D 11
PERPIGNAN
D 617
Canet-Plage
Têt
Cabestany
N 116
Ille-s-Têt
Pollestres
N 114
Thuir
D 612
PYRÉNÉES-ORIENTALES
Trouillas
Bages
Elne
D 81
Passa
A9
N9
Tresserre
Tech
D 618
Argelès-s-Mer
Collioure
D 115
Le Boulou
Banyuls-s-Mer
N 114
ESPAGNE
0
10
20 km

LANGUEDOC ROUSSILLON

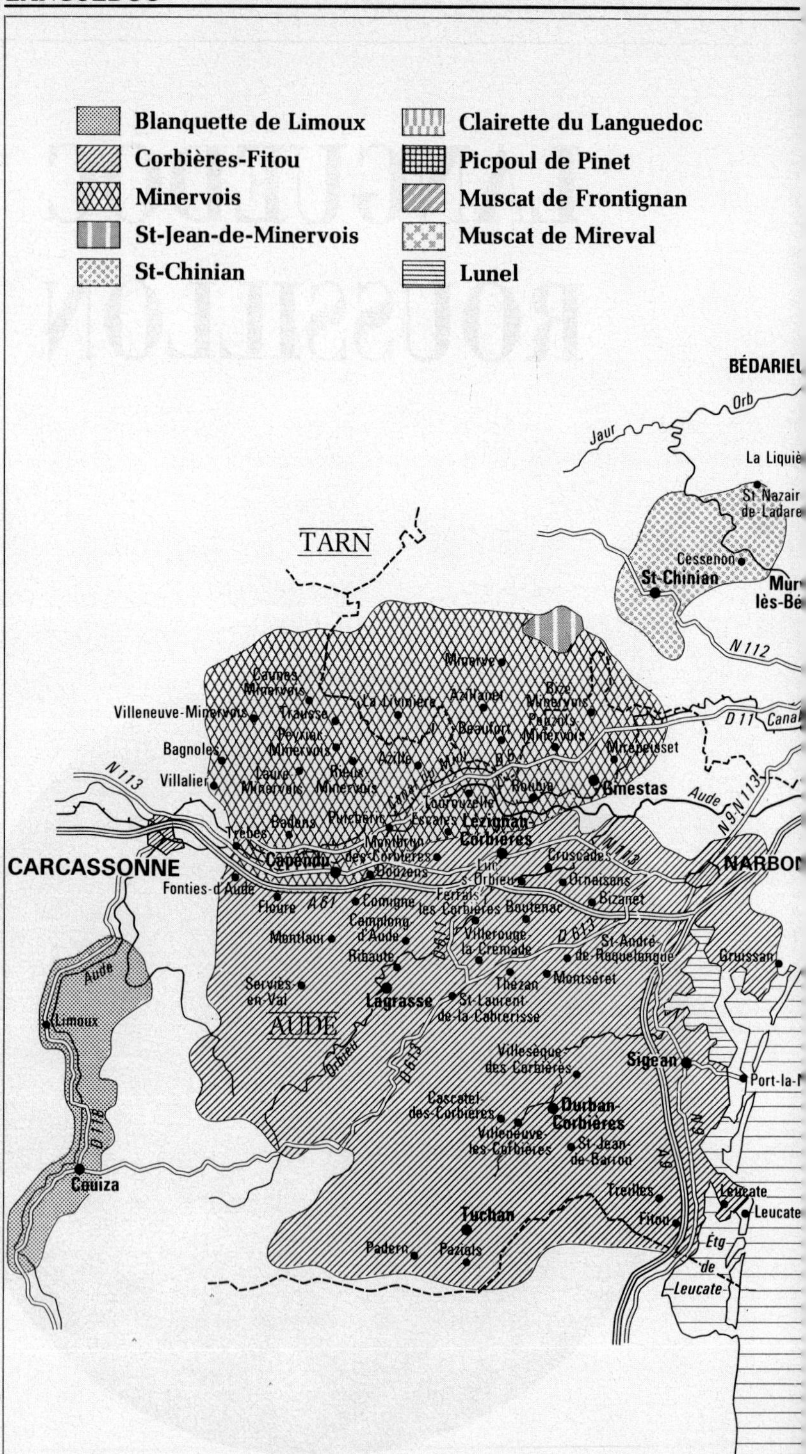

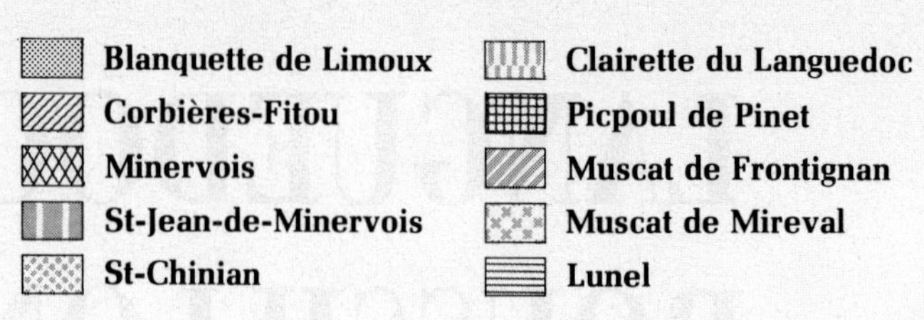
Blanquette de Limoux
Corbières-Fitou
Minervois
St-Jean-de-Minervois
St-Chinian
Clairette du Languedoc
Picpoul de Pinet
Muscat de Frontignan
Muscat de Mireval
Lunel
BÉDARIEU
Orb
Jaur
TARN
Cessenon
St-Chinian
N 112
Minerve
Caunes-Minervois
Villeneuve-Minervois
Trausse
La Livinière
Azillanet
Bize-Minervois
Peyriac-Minervois
Beaufort
Pouzols-Minervois
Bagnoles
Azille
Mirepeisset
Laure-Minervois
Rieux-Minervois
Villalier
N 113
Roubia
Ginestas
Aude
D 11
Canal
N 9-N 113
Trèbes
Badens
Puichéric
Escales
Lézignan-Corbières
Montbrun-des-Corbières
CARCASSONNE
Capendu
Douzens
Cruscades
Ornaisons
NARBON
Fonties-d'Aude
Floure
A 61
Comigne
Ferrals-les-Corbières
Boutenac
Bizanet
Camplong-d'Aude
Montlaur
Villerouge-la-Crémade
D 613
St-André-de-Roquelongue
Gruissan
Ribaute
Thézan
Montséret
Servies-en-Val
Lagrasse
St-Laurent-de-la-Cabrerisse
Limoux
AUDE
Orbieu
Villesèque-des-Corbières
Sigean
Port-la-
Cascatel-des-Corbières
Durban-Corbières
Villeneuve-les-Corbières
St-Jean-de-Barrou
Couiza
D 118
Treilles
Leucate
Tuchan
Fitou
Paderne
Paziols
Étg. de Leucate

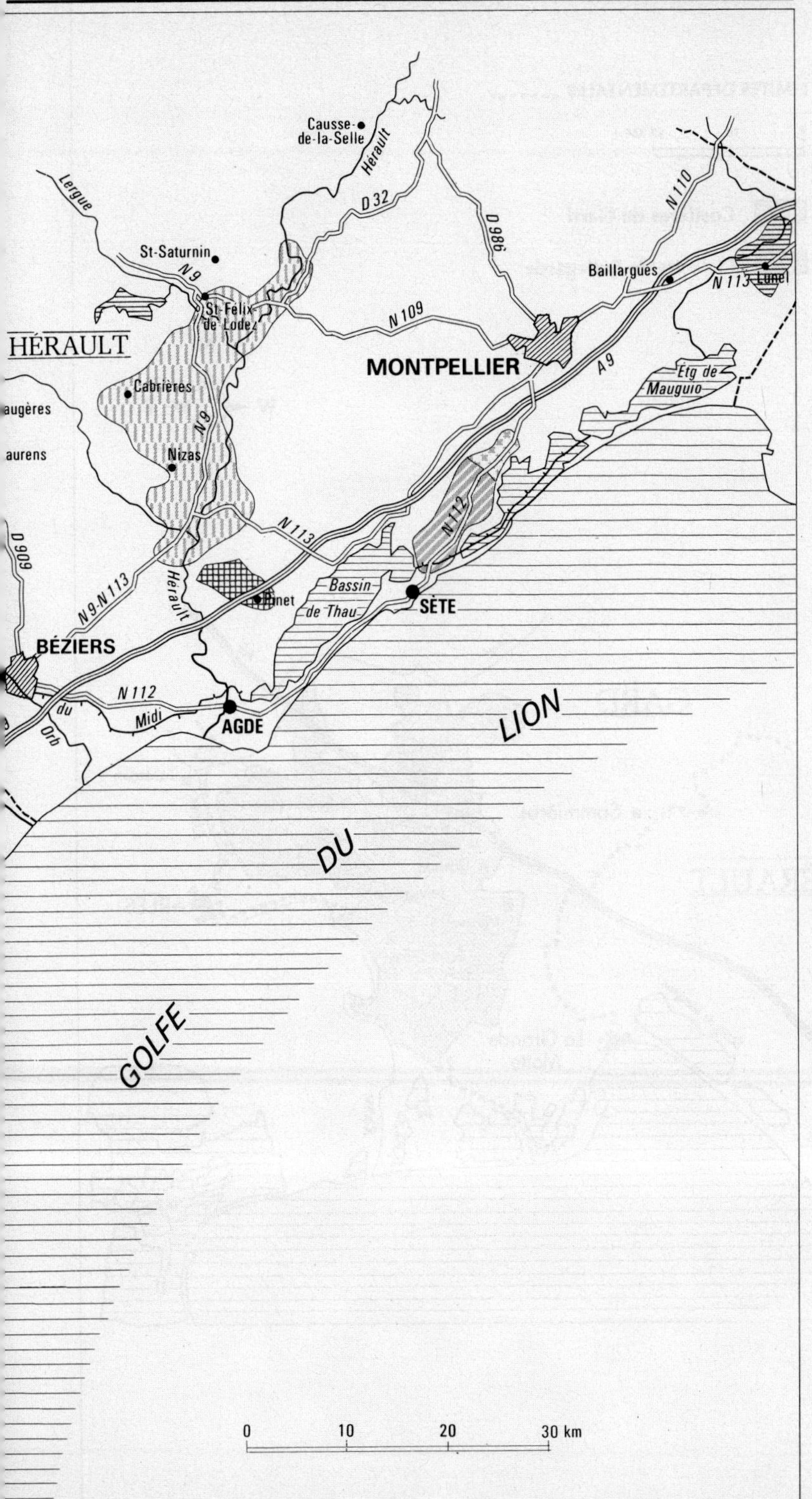
Causse-de-la-Selle
Hérault
Lergue
D 32
D 986
St-Saturnin
N 9
St-Félix-de-Lodez
N 109
N 110
Baillargues
N 113
Lunel
HÉRAULT
MONTPELLIER
A 9
Étg de Mauguio
Cabrières
augères
aurens
N 9
Nizas
N 112
N 113
D 909
Hérault
Pinet
Bassin de Thau
SÈTE
N 9-N 113
BÉZIERS
N 112
du
Midi
Orb
AGDE
LION
DU
GOLFE
0
10
20
30 km

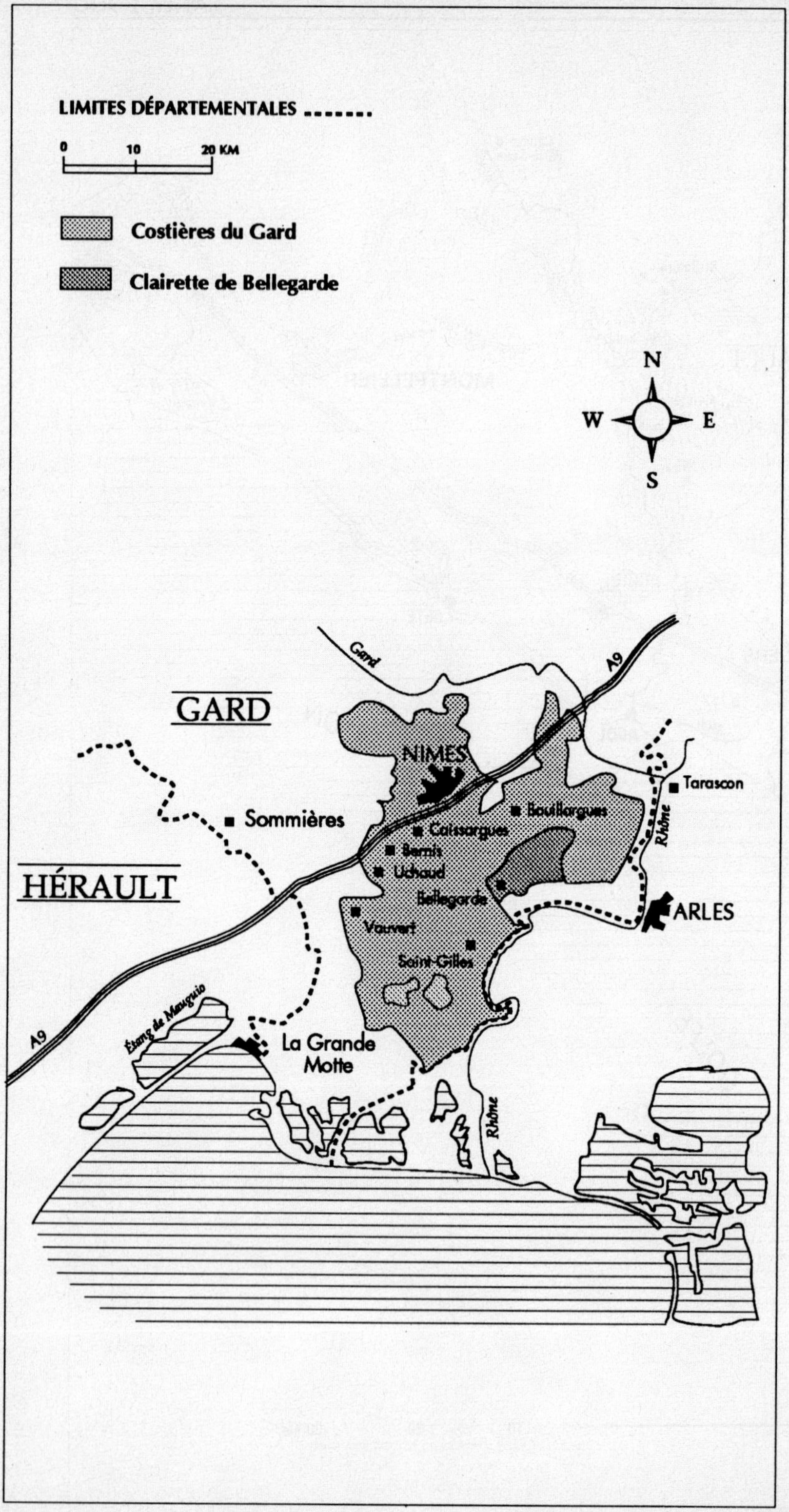

LIMITES DÉPARTEMENTALES

0 10 20 KM

Costières du Gard

Clairette de Bellegarde

Gard

A9

GARD

NIMES

Tarascon

Bouillargues

Sommières

Caissargues

Bernis

Uchaud

Rhône

HÉRAULT

Bellegarde

ARLES

Vauvert

Saint-Gilles

A9

Étang de Mauguio

La Grande Motte

Rhône

The birth of a vineyard

It is the largest wine-growing region in France, the most extensive and the most productive. Apart from the table wines, which are entirely without interest, one now regularly comes upon, at least during the last three or four years, some remarkable crus in all appellations, from the Corbières to the Coteaux-du-Languedoc, from the Costières-du-Gard to the Minervois, from the notheworthy Blanquette de Limoux (which is now beginning to be properly appreciated) to certain local wines. As in other French regions, the appellations are becoming less important than the efforts of certain producers who increasingly deserve our respect and encouragement.

When in Roussillon, you absolutely must try an old Rivesaltes or a Banyuls – remarkable typical wines, produced in their own very special way, yawning chasmes of aroma and fragrance, which quite obviously deserve to be better received. You will also find some fine reds (the Côtes-du-Roussillon in particular) many of which are very well made, well-colored and warm with a spicy fragrance.

HISTORICAL BACKGROUND

After Marseilles but well before the rest of Gaul, the region of Narbonne, nicknamed "Narbonnaise," was so prosperous that Pliny the Elder said, "It is not a province, but Italy itself." When in 120 B.C. Narbonnaise lost its status as an empire and became a province, the climate of the region prompted the province to plant vineyards.

Narbonnaise wines, which traveled as far as Lugdunum (the former name of Lyon), continued on to new directions following halts of varied duration in the shops of dealers of the city. Then the wine trade was subjected to various types of taxation: *octroi* or city tax, entry and exit customs dues and circulation duties. These taxes seemed in actual fact to be a form of harassment and might be considered a misappropriation of funds. In any case, they were abusive practices.

A trace of this illegal tax on wine may be found in pleas made by Cicero for Fonteius. Fonteius was the propraetor or chief administrator of Narbonnaise from 78 B.C. to 73 B.C. In the 10th century, the Moors wrecked havoc in the vineyards in some of the regions of the south, including vineyards in Tarn which were uprooted completely. The Abbey of St. Michel, which was founded in Gaillac in 960 by Count Raymond I of Toulouse, helped bring life back to the vineyards through the unrelenting work of the abbey's monks. This marked the beginning of a prosperous new city. Gaillac wines were shipped as far as Bordeaux, and from there on to such countries as England and Germany where they were greatly appreciated.

The Ancient French provinces of Languedoc and Roussillon are better known today by the compound name of Languedoc-Roussillon, which refers to their status as an administrative area in the south of France. Languedoc-Roussillon comprises three *départements*—Gard, Hérault and Aude—and as a winegrowing area has the largest number of vineyards in France: 30% of the vineyards in the entire country. Grapes for winemaking may not be the only, but is certainly the principal agricultural pursuit of the region.

THE WINES

LANGUEDOC

• **FITOU.** Full-bodied red wines, rather tannic, rich, well-balanced and typical, with good ageing potential.

• **CORBIERES.** 35,000 hectare vineyard producing red, rosé and white wines that can be quite aromatic, full-bodied and harmonious, especially after some time in the cask.

• **MINERVOIS.** Reds that merit consideration. Light (when produced in the valley), to be drunk within a year, supple and fruity if made by carbonic maceration, well-balanced, fine and full-bodied when they come from mountainous areas and have been cask-aged.

• **COTEAUX DU LANGUEDOC.** Only rosés and reds, fruity and often very attractive.

• **COSTIERES DU GARD (V.D.Q.S.).** Full-bodied and well-balanced reds and rosés.

ROUSSILLON

• **CÔTES-DU-ROUSSILLON. (A.O.C.).** A recent appellation (22 March 1977) just waiting to be discovered. Superb reds, of a beautiful ruby color. Round and fruity, scents of Morello cherry and rasberry. The Côtes-du-Roussillon-Villages (covering 25 communes) have even more class and subtlety, a good tannic structure and they keep well. A sure thing. Also, very pleasant white wines, with flowery bouquet, firm, vigorous and fresh, made from Maccabéo grape variety.

• **VINS DOUX NATURELS (fortified sweet red wines).** The Rivesaltes (upper river bank in the Catalan language) vineyard, which extends from Corbières on the Mediterranean, through the Aspres terraces, to Albères, covers the entire production area of Roussillon sweet red wines, except for Banyuls. Vinestocks include: Malvoisie, Grenache Blanc, Gris and Noir, and Maccabéo. Perhaps the most diversified of all sweet red wines they improve with age.

• **MUSCAT DE RIVESALTES.** Made from a blend of Muscat d'Alexandrie and a small Muscat variety, the Muscat de Rivesaltes cannot leave you indifferent whether you are a connoisseur or juste a wine lover. Historically, it is the most famous French wine of its category. Finesse, breed and fruitness are characteristics of this fiery and deliciously aromatic wine which dates back from the time when the Roussillon was a Spanish province.

• **BANYULS.** The Banyuls is made for the most part from the Grenache (Noir and Gris) grape variety which clings to the last schistose terraces of the Albères on the Spanish border. Generous, vigorous and of velvety texture, it is a wine of great distinction, which acquires with age a rustic flavor and a topaze-yellow color, with golden highlights. Maurice Sailland Curnonsky, gastronomic crown Prince was often heard to say that Banyuls had "the warmth and roundness of the Saracens."

• **MAURY.** The Maury vineyard, nestled in the Agly Valley, at the foot of the ruins of the Catharian citadel of Quéribus is the cradle of the "vins doux naturels." Grown on sun drenched schistose soil, Grenache noir grapes produce a red wine, which after a few years of ageing, becomes vigorous and firm and acquires a characteristic deep amber color.

BANYULS

DOMAINE DU MAS BLANC

Docteur André Parce
9, avenue du Gén.-de-Gaulle
66650 Banyuls-sur-Mer
68 88 32 12 or 68 38 10 05 – Office: 68 34 28 72 – Telex: 500 024 SCA PARCE & Fils

Type of vineyard: Family Corporation. **Established:** 1635. A Corporation since 1975. **Number of employees:** 3. **Vine stocks:** Banyuls: 80% Grenache Noir. Collioure: Syrah. **Soil:** Cambrian schist. **Exposure:** South and Southeast. **Average annual production in hectoliters:** 420. **Appellation:** Banyuls A.O.C., Collioure A.O.C. **Type:** Red. **Technique:** Classic, maceration in vats with crushing. Long fermentation with the skins, thermo-regulation. **Alcohol content:** Banyuls: 17%. Collioure: 12.3%. **Characteristics:** Banyuls: fleshy, tannic, concentrated, substantial. Poor soil, low yield (18 hl. per hectare). Collioure: good reds for ageing, fine, rich and well-balanced, aromatic and full. **Serving temperature:** 14°. **Served with:** Banyuls: as an aperitif, and with dessert, red fruit. Rimage: bottled very young, with Chocolate Desserts. Collioure: with cheese, etc. **Vintages available in 89/90:** Banyuls: 1980, 1978, 1974. Rimage: 1985. Collioure: 1984 & 1985.

Characteristics of vintages

1985: Great vintage. **1984:** Excellent vintage (Collioure). **Others:** Banyuls: all vintages mentioned above are great.

BLANQUETTE DE LIMOUX

MAISON ANTECH

Mr. Antech
Domaine de Flassian – Route de Carcassonne
11300 Limoux
68 31 15 88

Type of vineyard: Family-owned. **Vine stocks:** Mauzac, Chardonnay and Chenin.
Appellation: Blanquette de Limoux. **Type:** White. **Technique:** Traditional Champagne Method. **Characteristics:** The best Blanquette-de-Limoux. Very fine, well-balanced and fruity, excellent quality/price ratio. **Serving temperature:** 10-12°. **Served with:** As an aperitif and with the entire meal.

Characteristics of vintages

Price range (pre-tax, ex-warehouse): 20-30 F.F.

References in France

Shops: L'Amour du Vin, 94, rue Saint-Dominique, 75007 Paris. Tél: 45 56 12 94.

CLAIRETTE DU LANGUEDOC

CHÂTEAU LA CONDAMINE BERTRAND

Bernard Jany
Avenue d'Ormesson – Lezignan – La Cèbe
67 25 27 96

Type of vineyard: Family-owned. **Established:** By great grandfather. **Number of employees:** 4. **Vine stocks:** Syrah, Grenache, Mourvèdre, Carignan, Clairette, Chenin, Roussane. **Soil:** Chalky clay. **Exposure:** Facing full south. **Average annual production in hectoliters:** 60 hl/ha.

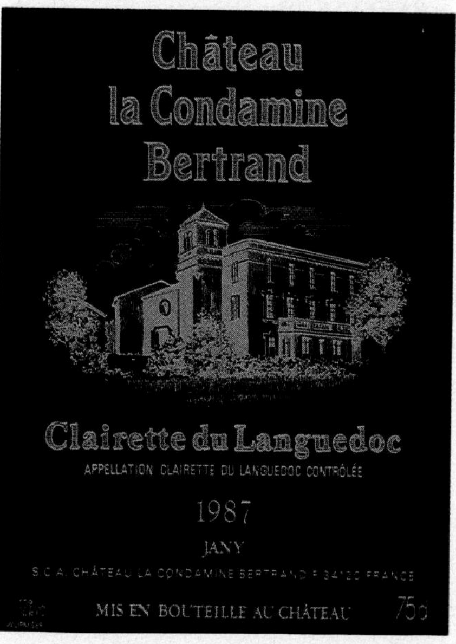

Appellation: Château Condamine Bertrand. **Type:** Red, white, rosé. **Technique:** Red: Temperature control, maceration (16 days) – White: low temperature (16° for 22 days). **Maturing:** instainless steel tanks. **Alcohol contents:** 12%. **Characteristics:** Red: rich and well-balanced, rip fruit flavor – white: Pear fragrance, very pleasant, not aggressive. **Serving temperature:** Red: 16° – bottle should be opened an hour before serving. White: 10°. **Vintages available in 89/90:** Red: 1988. White & Rosé: 1989.

Characteristics of vintages

Price range (pre-tax, ex-warehouse): 10 to 20 F.F. red & rosé. 20 to 30 F.F. white.
Sales volume:
– Wholesale: 50% (Côteau du Languedoc). – Retail: 35%.
– Restaurants: 15%.
Sales in France: 90%.
Export sales: 10%.
Main trading partners : Netherlands, Germany, UK.

References in France

Restaurants: Michel Bras (Laguiole), P. Pages (Chantoiseau), Le Réverbère (Narbonne).

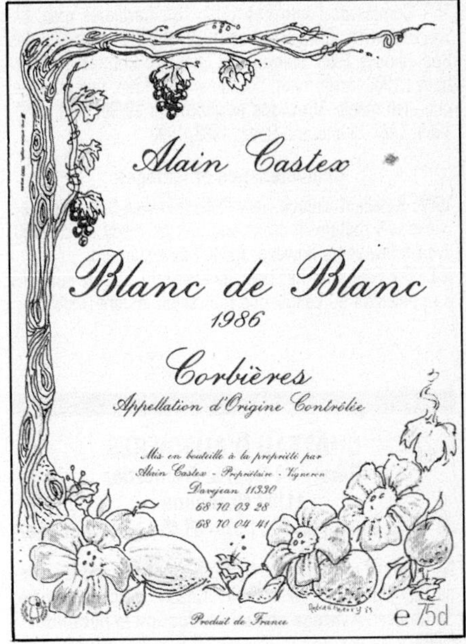

Alain Castex
Blanc de Blanc
1986
Corbières
Appellation d'Origine Contrôlée
Mis en bouteille à la propriété par
Alain Castex - Propriétaire - Vigneron
Davejean 11330
68 70 03 28
68 70 04 41
Produit de France
e 75cl

CORBIÈRES

DOMAINE DES AMOURIES

Alain Castex
Place de l'Église, Davejean – 11330 Mouthoumet
68 70 04 28

Type of vineyard: Family-owned. **Established:** 1981. **Vine stocks:** Carignan, Cinsault, Grenache, Syrah, Pinot Noir, Chardonnay. **Soil:** Schistic clay and schist. **Average annual production in hectoliters:** 450.
Appellation: Corbières. **Type:** Red, white, rosé. **Technique:** Red: partly by carbonic maceration, partly by crushing. Rosé: by drawing off. **Maturing:** White, rosé: conservation 5 months in stainless steel tanks. Red: conservation 8 months in concrete vats. **Alcohol content:** 11.5% to 13% according to type. **Characteristics:** Red: Mulberry and woodland fragrances, bright red color, prune and cherry aromas, great length of fruit in alcohol. Rosé: salmon pink color, fragrance of raspberries, blackcurrants and orange blossoms, very fruity, good length. White: brilliant green glint, exotic fruit and plant fragrance, fresh and lively. **Serving temperature:** Red: 15° to 17°. Rosé: 10° to 12°. White: 7° to 8°. **Served with:** Red: stews, leg of lamb, Cassoulet, cheese. Rosé: throughout a summer meal, fish, delicatessen or as an aperitif. **Vintages available in 89/90:** Red: 1985, 1986. Rosé: 1986. White: 1986.

Characteristics of vintages

Sales volumes: – Retail: 80%. – Restaurants: 20%.
Sales in France: 75%. **Export sales:** 25%.

References in France

Restaurants: Fine restaurants in the Department of the Aude and neighboring departments.
Shops: Fine shops in the Department of the Aude and neighboring departments.

CAVES DES CÔTES D'ALARIC

Odile Denat (Director)
Camplong d'Aube – 11200 Lézignan Corbières
68 43 60 86 – Telex: LARA 500 370

Type of vineyard: Cooperative Agricultural Association. **Established:** 1932. **Number of employees:** 4. **Vine stocks:** Grenache, Cinsault, Mourvèdre, Syrah, Carignan. **Soil:** Clay with calcium carbonate. **Exposure:** Full South. **Average annual production in hectoliters:** 12000.
Appellation: A.O.C. Corbières. **Type:** Red, white, rosé. **Technique:** Red: carbonic maceration. **Maturing:** vats and Oak casks. **Alcohol content:** 11.8%. **Characteristics:** Corbières Vert 1986: Apple aroma, dry and fresh; Vin des Républiques 1985: Cherry color, ripe fruit fragrance, goes down well; Comtes de Fontbaries 1982: rich and well-balanced, truffle and blackcurrant aromas, elegant. Corbières rosé 1986: fresh and round. **Serving temperature:** Corbières Vert 1986: 6° to 8°. Vin des Républiques 1985:

15°. Comtes de Fontbaries 1982: 18°. Corbières rosé: 8°. **Served with:** Corbières Vert 1986: shellfish, fish. Vin des Républiques 1985: steaks, soft cheeses. Comtes de Fontbaries 1982: roast meat. Corbières rosé 1986: first courses, one-dish meals. **Vintages available in 89/90:** Red: 1985, 1986, 1988. White and Rosé: 1988, 1990.

Characteristics of vintages

1988: Excellent vintage, very fruity and well-balanced. Red wines will mature in casks and will be ready as of 1990. Wait a few years however for full development.
N.B. The Fonbories has been awarded the "Oscar des Vins d'Appellation du Languedoc Roussillon in June 1988".

CHÂTEAU D'AUSSIÈRES

Gérard et Sophie Dumortier
11100 Narbonne
68 45 10 65 and 68 45 11 97 – 68 45 17 04 (manager)

Number of employees: 10. **Vine stocks:** Carignan, Grenache, Cinsaut, Syrah. **Soil:** Chalky clay. **Exposure:** South-East. **Average annual production in hectoliters:** 5 500.
Appellation: Corbières. **Type:** Red. **Technique:** carbonic maceration. **Alcohol content:** 12%. **Characteristics:** Elegant, typical of the Corbières Maritimes region, fruity, silky texture, goes down smoothly. **Serving temperature:** 17°. **Vintages available in 89/90:** 1988.

Characteristics of vintages

1988: Excellent year, colored, dense, pronounced bouquet, good development. Price range (pre-tax, ex-warehouse): 20 to 30 F.F.
Sales volume:
– Wholesale: 89%. – Retail: 10%.
Sales in France: 70%. **Export sales:** 30%.

References in France

Restaurants: The Société Générale branch offices and consumer cooperatives.

Comments

Site of pre-historic habitations, then Gallo-Roman villa, finally a Cistercian barn and, currently a modern winemaking enterprise of 700 hectares, 177 of which are planted with grapevines. The domain was acquired in 1791 by the Count Daru, Minister and General Intendant of the house of the Emperor Napoleon 1st. This date of course brings to mind the forthcoming celebration of the bicentennial of the French Revolution. For many years, the Château d'Aussières has been making and selling Corbières. Direct personal management of the family enterprise since 1985.

CHÂTEAU D'AUSSIÈRES

CHÂTEAU DE CABRIAC

Jean de Cibeins
11700 Douzens
68 77 16 12 - Telex: CCI CARC: 500 379 F

Type of vineyard: Family Agricultural Association. **Established:** 1802, by the Family; Association 1962. **Vine stocks:** Syrah, Mourvèdre, Grenache, Cinsault, Carignan, Macabeu. **Soil:** Clay with calcium carbonate, poor and shallow, numerous outcroppings. **Exposure:** Various. **Average annual production in hectoliters:** 6000. **Appellation:** Château de Cabriac, A.O.C. Corbières. **Type:** Red, white, rosé. Also Cépage Merlot, a regional wine. **Technique:** 50% carbonic maceration, 50% traditional. **Maturing:** Concrete vats and large casks. **Alcohol content:** 12% to 12.7%. **Characteristics:** Typical for the aromatic varieties such as Syrah and Mourvèdre as well as for the Syrah, Mourvèdre and Carignan wines, produced by carbonic maceration. Very pleasant to drink after the 1st year, optimum development 2 to 4 years. **Serving temperature:** 1984: 16° to 17°. 1985 and 1986: 18° to 19°. **Served with:** White: trout form the Montagne Noire. Rosé: Guinea Hen with green peas. Red A.O.C. 1984: Croustade with Roquefort. Red A.O.C. 1985: Cassoulet. Cépage Merlot: tenderlion of beef with mushrooms. **Vintages available in 89/90:** 1984, 1985, 1986.

Characteristics of vintages

1986: Full, rich, well-balanced, round and very fragrant. **1985:** Red: full, rich and well-balanced, intense color. Rosé and white: elegant and lively. **1984:** Fine and fragrant, fully developed, ready to drink.

CHÂTEAU DE CARAGUILHES

Lionel Faivre
Saint-Laurent de la Cabrerisse - 11220 Lagrasse
68 43 62 05 - Telex: 500 920 Perpignan

Type of vineyard: Family Association. **Established:** 1958. **Number of employees:** 12. **Vine stocks:** Carignan, Grenache, Cinsault, Syrah, Malvoisie. **Soil:** Hillsides, clay with calcium carbonate, pebbly. **Exposure:** South. **Average annual production in hectoliters:** 5500. **Appellation:** Corbières A.O.C. **Type:** Red, white, rosé, V.D.N. **Technique:** Red: whole grapes. White: direct pressing, debourbage and fermentation at low temperature. Rosé: by drawing off, fermentation at low temperature. **Maturing:** Red: large Oak casks. White and rosé: in tanks under inert gas. **Alcohol content:**12 to 12.5%. **Characteristics:** Red: fruity, aromatic, light and supple. White: fragrant, easy to drink. Rosé: fruity, fine and limpid. **Serving temperature:** Red: 18°. Rosé and white: 8°. **Served with:** Blanc de Blancs: shellfish. Rosé and the Gris: grilled fish, fish in sauce, smoked salmon, delicatessen. Red 1979: meat in sauce. Red 1983: white meat. Red 1985: roast meat, cheese. **Vintages available in 89/90:** White: 1986. Rosé: 1986. Red: 1979, 1983, 1985, 1986.

Characteristics of vintages

1986: Red: nicely balanced, light and supple, already very agreeable to drink. **1985:** Red: a very great vintage to be rediscovered with great pleasure in several years. Rich, well-balanced and fragrant. Blanc de Blancs: to drink with shellfish, dry and fruity.

CHÂTEAU DU GRAND-CAUMONT

Mme Françoise Rigal
11200 Lézignan Corbières
68 27 10 82 - Telex: 500 920 Telex Public Perpignan

Vine stocks: Corbières, Vin de Pays 1986, 1988.

1988
Château du
Grand Caumont
CORBIÈRES
APPELLATION CORBIÈRES CONTROLÉE
MIS EN BOUTEILLE AU CHATEAU
12%Vol
e 75cl
LOUIS RIGAL, PROPRIÉTAIRE
CHATEAU DU GRAND CAUMONT, 11200 LUC-s/ORBIEU
FRANCE
PRODUIT DE FRANCE

Appellation: Corbières AOC. **Type:** Red. **Technique:** Traditional with carbonic maceration. **Maturing:** Oak casks. **Alcohol content:** 12%. **Serving temperature:** 16 to 18°. **Served with:** Game, red meat, cheese. **Vintages available in 89/90:** 1986 and 1988.

Characteristics of vintages

1988: Intense color, very soft and full, concentrated, long, great future. **1986:** Ruby color, good balance, soft tannins, very pleasant for drinking now. Price range (pre-tax, ex-warehouse): between 10 and 20 F.F.
Main trading partners: Germany, United Kingdom, Netherlands, Belgium, England, Philippines, Bermudes.

CHÂTEAU GLEON MONTANIE

Jean-Pierre & Philippe Montanie
Villesèque des Corbières, 11360 Durban
68 48 28 25

Type of vineyard: Family-owned. **Established:** 1861. **Vine stocks:** Red and Rosé: Grenache, Carignan, Cinsaut, Syrah. White: Malvoisie. **Soil:** Chalky clay of the secondary era (Jurassic, Triassic), (terraces and hillsides). **Exposure:** South. **Average annual production in hectoliters:** 1,200.

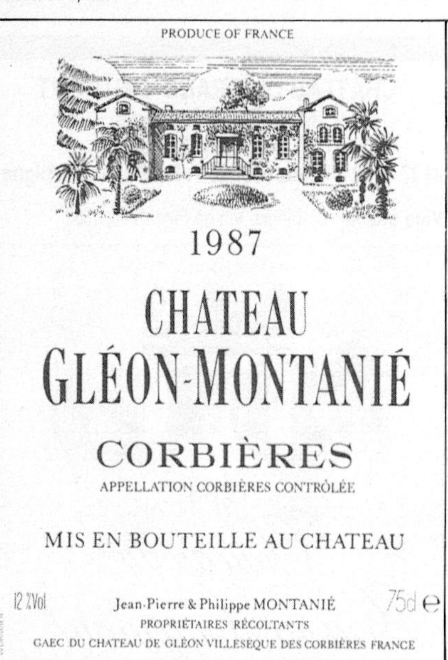

PRODUCE OF FRANCE
1987
CHATEAU
GLÉON-MONTANIÉ
CORBIÈRES
APPELLATION CORBIÈRES CONTRÔLÉE
MIS EN BOUTEILLE AU CHATEAU
12 %Vol
Jean-Pierre & Philippe MONTANIÉ
75cl e
PROPRIÉTAIRES RÉCOLTANTS
GAEC DU CHATEAU DE GLÉON VILLESÈQUE DES CORBIÈRES FRANCE

Appellation: AOC Corbières. **Type:** Red, white, rosé. **Technique:** Hand harvesting – vinification of whole grapes, carbonic maceration. **Maturing:** In vats and bottles. **Alcohol content:** 12%. **Characteristics:** Red: primary (red berry), secondary (vegetal-garrigues) aromas, structured, aromatic, complete and long. White and rosé: flowery aroma, fruity, fragrant, elegant. **Serving temperature:** Red: 16 to 18°. Rosé: 8 to 10°. White: 8°. **Served with:** Red: venison, game, red meat, cheese (roquefort). Rosé: delicatessen, buffet country style, small game. White: as an aperitif and with fish. **Vintages available in 89/90:** 1986, 1987, 1988.

Characteristics of vintages

1988: Excellent year for red white and rosé. **1987:** Good year. White and red: successful, fragrant. **1986:** Richer year, well colored and supple wines. Price range (pre-tax, ex-warehouse): 10 to 20 F.F.

Sales volume:
– Wholesale: 80%. – Retail: 20%.

Sales in France: 100%.

References in France

Shops: Établissements Rouanet (34500 Béziers).

Comments

The origins of the Domaine de Gleon go back to earliest antiquity as attested to by the numerous Gallo-Roman and Visigothic vestiges (pottery, pre-Roman chapel from the 4th century). It belonged to the Treille Gleon Druban Narbonne family for a thousand years. The Château de Gleon defended the entrance to the Hautes Corbières. The last Marquis of Gleon sold it to the ancestors of the present owner in 1861.

DOMAINE DE COUDERC

Paul Herpe
Route de Marcorignan – 11100 Narbonne
68 32 03 25 – Telex: 500 421

Type of vineyard: Agricultural Association. **Established:** 1970. **Vine stocks:** Grenache, Cinsault, Carignan. **Soil:** Clay with calcium carbonate. **Average annual production in hectoliters:** 1 000.

Appellation: Corbières A.O.C. **Type:** Red. **Technique:** Traditional. **Maturing:** Oak casks. **Alcohol content:** 12%. **Characteristics:** Supple, fragrant, balanced. **Serving temperature:** 16° to 18°. **Served with:** Red meat, white meat, cheese. **Vintages available in 89/90:** 1988, 1987.

Characteristics of vintages

1988: Too young at the moment – wait. **1987:** Fine, distinguished, well-balanced.

DOMAINE DE GRAFFAN

Henri Barthez
11200 Ferrals-les-Corbières
68 43 60 02

Type of vineyard: Family-owned. **Established:** 1873. **Number of employees:** 3. **Vine stocks:** Carignan, Grenache, Syrah, Mourvèdre, Malvoisie, Terret. **Soil:** Pebbly chalk. **Exposure:** Hillsides. **Average annual production in hectoliters:** 1,900.

Appellation: Corbières. **Type:** Red, White. **Technique:** Traditional, carbonic maceration. **Maturing:** A year and a half. **Alcohol content:** 11.8%. **Characteristics:** Supple, fruity, aromatic. **Serving temperature:** Red: 16°. Rosé, White: 8°. **Served with:** Red: cassoulet, cheese. **Vintages available in 89/90:** Red: 1986, 1987. White and Rosé: 1987, 1988.

Characteristics of vintages

1987: Rosé (Gris) – obtained by devatting, made from "vin gris" vinestocks, salmon color, fruity, fresh. **1986:** Round

and well balanced, will age well – beautiful ruby color. Price range (pre-tax, ex-warehouse): 10 to 20 F.F.
Sales volume:
– Wholesale: 20%. – Retail: 10%. – Restaurants: 60%. – Other: 10% (cellars).
Sales in France: 95%. **Export sales:** 5%.
Main trading partners : Belgium, Germany.

References in France

Restaurants: Midi-Pyrénées, Languedoc.

Abroad

Germany

Y. Risacher (Restaurant), Savignyplatz II, 1000 Berlin 12. Tel: 313 86 97.

Belgium

Descheemaeker, Brussels Fromages & Vins de France, 106 rue du Bailli. Tel: 537 66 53.

Far East

South East Asia: E.G.E. 32, rue Gabrielle 94220 CHARENTON. Tél. 43 68 00 04 - Télex EGEXPO 262851 F.

Comments

Winecellar built in 1873. A number of ageing casks. Bottling as of 1974 – pioneers in Languedoc.

CHÂTEAU HÉLÈNE

Marie-Hélène Gau
11800 Barbaira
68 79 00 69

Type of vineyard: Family-owned. **Established:** 1750. **Number of employees:** 1. **Vine stocks:** Carignan, Syrah, Cinsault, Grenache, Sauvignon, Macabeu. **Soil:** Clay with calcium carbonate and gravel. **Exposure:** Hillsides. **Average annual production in hectoliters:** 1600. **Appellation:** A.O.C. Corbières – Vin de Pays des Coteaux de Miramont. **Type:** Red, white, rosé. **Technique:** Traditional, carbonic maceration at low temperature. **Maturing:** Red Corbières: in tanks (2 years) or in new Oak casks. **Alcohol content:** 12%. **Characteristics:** Red: aromatic, red berry and spicy aromas. **Serving temperature:** Red: 16° – Rosé and white: 10°. **Served with:** A.O.C. '83: meat cooked in sauce, cheese. Red A.O.C. '85: meat in sauce, grilled steaks. Rosé: delicatessen products, grilled steaks. White: fish in sauce, shellfish. **Vintages available in 89/90:** Red: '83 (aged in casks); '85; '86. Rosé and white.

Characteristics of vintages

1985 and **1986:** Long and full-bodied. Ready, bu tannic enough to be kept 3-4 years. **1983** and **1984:** Aged in new casks. Round, well-balanced, goes down smoothly. Very fine, already excellent but will certainly age well. **Other:** White and rosé: "Vin d'une Nuit"; wine to be consumed preferably within the year. Price range (pre-tax, ex-warehouse): 10 F.F. – 20 F.F.

Sales volume:
– Retail: 20%. – Restaurants: 30%. – Other: 25% (distributors). 25% (export).
Sales in France: 75%.
Export sales: 25%.
Main trading partners : Germany, Denmark, Belgium.

CHÂTEAU LE BOUIS

Pierre Clément
11430 Gruissan
68 49 00 18 – Telex: 500 428 Clément

Type of vineyard: Personal. **Established:** 1977. **Number of employees:** 5 to 10. **Vine stocks:** 45% Carignan, 10% Cinsault, 8% Syrah, 7% Mouvèdre, 7% Grenache, 10% Malvoisie, 8% Clairette, 5% Terrets. **Soil:** Clay with calcium carbonate. **Exposure:** South. **Average annual production in hectoliters:** 1,800.
Appellation: Corbières A.O.C. and Vin de Pays de l'Aude. **Type:** Red, white, rosé. **Other:** Blanc Moelleux, Rosé Perlant, Cartagène. **Technique:** Red: carbonic maceration. White: pressing. **Maturing:** For 3 to 10 years. **Alcohol content:** 11.5% to 12.5%. **Characteristics:** Red: soft and full, rich and well-balanced, well-structured. Rosé: very fine, pleasant, very good rosé. White: soft and full, fine and delicate, very good with fish and shellfish. **Serving temperature:** Red: 14° to 18°. Rosé: 9° to 11°. White: 8° to 10°. **Served with:** Red: hors-d'œuvre and dessert, but especialy meat, spicy sauces, cheese. Rosé: hors-d'œuvre, dessert, fish or even the entire meal. White: hors-d'œuvre, fish, shellfish. White ("doux" – sweet): foie gras and pâtés, white sauce, meat, cheese. **Vintages available in 89/90:** Red: 1982 and 1986. White & Rosé: 1987.

Characteristics of vintages

1988: Excellent Rosé, and specially the Blanc de Blancs, great finesse of aroma. **1985:** Excellent Red. Hold. **Other:** Red 1982: Matured in Oak casks, soft and full, rich in alcohol, complex aroma. Price range (pre-tax, ex-warehouse): Between 10 F.F. to 60 F.F.
Sales volume:
– Retail: 40%. – Restaurants: 20%. – Other: 40% (local shops, cellars etc.).
Sales in France: 92%.
Export sales: 8%.
Main trading partners : UK, Belgium, Netherlands, Germany.

References in France

Restaurants: Nearly all the better restaurants of the Langudoc-Roussillon and of the Haute-Garonne. Areas.

Comments

Three Medals – Gold, Silver and Bronze – at the Concours Agricole (Agricultural Competition), in 1987. Four prizes at the Concours Corbières (Corbières Competition), in 1986 and 1987.

CHÂTEAU DE LASTOURS

Jean-Marie Lignères
11490 Portel-des-Corbières
68 48 29 17

Number of employees: 100 among whom 60 are mentally handicapped. **Soil:** Pebbly clay. **Exposure:** Slopes overlooking the sea. **Average annual production in hectoliters:** Approximately 6,000.
Appellation: Corbières. **Type:** Red, white, rosé. Other: Vin Gris – Sweet Fortified Wines (Muscat). **Technique:** Temperature control. **Maturing:** In vats, oak casks and bottles. **Alcohol content:** 12%. **Characteristics:** Well balanced and supple wines. **Serving temperature:** Red: 17-18°. White: 6 to 8°. **Served with:** White: foie gras, fish. Red: red meat, game. **Vintages available in 89/90:** 1985, 1986, 1988, 1987 (white).

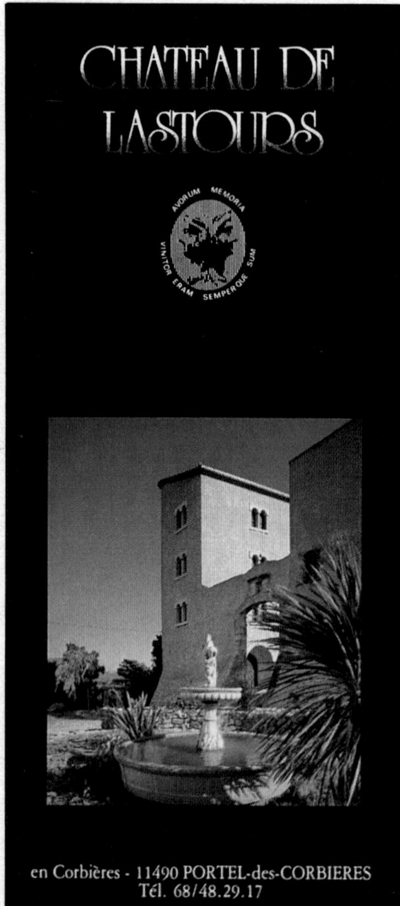

Characteristics of vintages

1988: White: very successful vintage – Red: promising. **1987:** White: excellent, well done, flowery and lively. Lovely red. **1986:** Red: remarkable, developing special truffle aroma, full flavor, rich and well balanced, full bodied and lingering taste, excellent development. Price range (pre-tax, ex-warehouse): 20 to 30 F.F.
Sales volume:
– Retail: 100%.
Export sales: 10%.
Main trading partners : UK, Japan, USA.

References in France

Shops: L'Amour du Vin (94, rue St-Dominique, 75007 Paris).

Abroad

United Kingdom

Paul Boutinot Wines LTD. Stockport.

Comments

Lastours extends over more than 700 hectares of mountain ous terrain, deep canyons and vines. The grounds are used by Mitsubishi, Peugeot and others for 4×4 practice in preparation for races such as the Paris-Dakar. This Centre d'Aide par le Travail, a very unusual establishment, allows mentally handicapped persons to work while at the same time receiving an essential medical and psycho-social support. Congratulations are also in order for having made Lastours into a major cultural center offering many concerts ("Les Cuivres d'Aquitaine...") and an ideal practice area for automobile racing champions (Metge, Jabouille, Lafitte...).

CHÂTEAU LES OLLIEUX

Françoise Surbezy-Cartier
Montseret T.M. 14-11200 Lézignan Corbières
68 43 32 61

Type of vineyard: Family-owned. **Established:** 1856. **Number of employees:** 6. **Vine stocks:** Carignan, Grenache, Syrah, Cinsault. **Soil:** Clay and calcium carbonate, gravel. **Exposure:** Facing full South. **Average annual production in hectoliters:** 3200.
Appellation: Corbières. **Type:** Red, rosé. **Technique:** Rosé: drawing off – Red: carbonic maceration. **Alcohol content:** 11.5%. **Characteristics:** Rosé: beautiful, blackcurrant color, light. Woodland and anis seed aromas. Heady. Elegant "Vins Gris", typical of the Mediterranean area. Red: Fresh, deep color. Full, complex nose (small red fruit flavor). Very well-structured wines, very promising. **Serving temperature:** Rosé: 5°-6°. Red: 16°-17°. **Served with:** Rosé: with fish, delicatessen products, or an entire Summer meal. Young cheese. Red: stews (like Daubes etc.) Cassoulet, red meat, i.e. rich food. Goat cheese, Cantal, etc. **Vintages available in 89/90:** Rosé: 1986. Red: 1985 and 1986.

Characteristics of vintages

Average pre-tax, ex-warehouse price: between 12 F.F. and 20 F.F.
Main trading partners : Denmark, Germany, UK, Portugal, Luxemburg.

References in France

Restaurants: Auberge d'Auriac (Carcassonne) – Le Réverbère (Narbonne) – Le Pont Levis (Carcassonne) – La Tamarissière (Agde) – Darroze (Toulouse).
Shops: Comtesse du Barry – Vitrine de France.

Comments

Baptized by the Romans, "les Ollieux", this property used to be a Cistercian Monsastery for women, and was part of the famous Abbaye de Fontfroide. Vineyards have been cultivated here since 1311. Madame Françoise Surbezy-Cartier perpetuates a Family Tradition which dates back to 1856.

PIERRE SALLES

Château d'Olivery – Cruscades
11200 Lézignan-Corbières
68 27 08 66 and 68 32 04 64

Type of vineyard: Family-owned. **Vine stocks:** Carignan, Grenache Noir, Cinsault, Syrah, Mourvèdre. **Soil:** Clay with calcium carbonate. **Average annual production in hectoliters:** 3,000 hl. Corbières, 2,000 hl regional wine.
Appellation: Corbières A.O.C. and Vin de Pays de l'Aude. **Type:** Red. **Technique:** Carbonic maceration and traditional. **Alcohol content:** 12%. **Characteristics:** Robust, fleshy, fragrant, well-structured. **Serving temperature:** To be drunk cool. **Served with:** Delicatessen, poultry, game, roasts, cheese. **Vintages available in 88/89:** 1986 and 1988.

Characteristics of vintages

1988: Beautiful year, aromatic, fleshy, full. **1986:** Dense, red, good color. **Note:** Also available in plastic containers. Prices upon request.
Disponible 1986 et 1988

DOMAINE DE VILLEMAJOU

Georges Bertrand
11200 Saint-André-de-Roquelongue
68 45 10 43 – Telex: DIVIMER 505 514

Type of vineyard: Family-owned. **Established:** 1969. **Number of employees:** 5. **Vine stocks:** Carignan, Grenache, Syrah. **Soil:** Clay with calcium carbonate and gravel. **Exposure:** Full South.
Appellation: "Domaine de Villemajou" A.O.C. Corbières. **Type:** Red. **Technique:** Carbonic maceration. **Maturing:** In Oak casks. **Alochol content:** 12.3%. **Characteristics:** The Villemajou is deep red. Its bouquet owes its complexity to the subtle balance on the grape varieties used, to the very elaborate technique of vinification and to the delicate marriage of Oak and wine. The Domaine de Villemajou belongs to the family of great wines born out of complicity with the soil, men, grapes and adroit technology. **Serving temperature:** 18° to 19°. **Served with:** All meats, grilled or in sauce, cheese. **Vintages available in 89/90:** 1979, 1983, 1985.

Characteristics of vintages

1985: Beautiful color, tannic structure, very substantial, with light and supple tannins and an aroma of red fruit. **1983:** Deep red color, fine tannins, light, supple and peppery, spicy aromas, taste of honey, good persitence.

CHÂTEAU DE SAINT LAURENT ET DOMAINE DES MOULINS DE SAINT-LAURENT

Joël de Bermond
Saint-Laurent de la Cabrerisse – 11220 Lagrasse
68 44 01 93 – Telex: VINI 67 69 699 559
Type of vineyard: Family-owned. **Established:** 1940. **Number of employees:** 3. **Vine stocks:** 60% Carignan, 15% Grenache, 10% Syrah, 4% Cinsault, 11% Cabernet and others. **Soil:** Clay with calcium carbonate, poor soil, sunny. **Exposure:** Hillsides, local micro-climate. **Average annual production in hectoliters:** 4500.
Appellation: A.O.C. Corbières Château de Saint Laurent, A.O.C. Corbières Domaine des Moulins de Saint-Laurent, plus a regional red wine, "Coteaux de la Cabrerisse". **Type:** Red, white, rosé. **Technique:** Red: carbonic maceration. **Maturing:** Cement vats. **Alcohol content:** 11% to 12%. **Characteristics:** A.O.C. red: harmonious, round, fleshy, very long. Intense nose, beautiful, deep red-tile color. A.O.C. white: lively attack, light sparkle, lovely, brilliant, very clear. A.O.C. rosé: light, fruity, persistant. Regional wine (red): fruity, due to the Cabernet Sauvignon. **Serving temperature:** A.O.C. red: 16° to 18°. White: cool but not cold. Rosé: quite cool. **Served with:** A.O.C. red: delicatessen products, game, roasts, cheese. White: sauerkraut, shellfish. Rosé: hors-d'œuvre, throughout the meal during the Summer. **Vintages available in 89/90:** 1986 (Corbières A.O.C. and regional wine).

Characteristics of vintages

1986: Suppleness and character, round, fruity and fleshy, a very successful vintage for all three wines, to enjoy with complete confidence.

COSTIÈRES DU GARD

MAS AUPELLIÈRE

Léo Grootemaat
Gallician - 30600 Vauvert
66 73 30 75

Established: 1979. **Number of employees:** 2. **Vine stocks:** Mourvèdre, Syrah, Grenache, Cinsault, Carignan. **Soil:** Rhone Valley sandstone. **Exposure:** South. **Average annual production in hectoliters:** 1,200.
Appellation: A.O.C. Costières-du-Gard. **Type:** Red, rosé. **Technique:** Traditional, fermentation. **Maturing:** 18 months in large casks and vats. **Alcohol content:** 12° to 12.5%. **Characteristics:** Red Syrah: slow maturing, quite tannic. Red Mourvèdre: more subtle, mature more rapidly. Rosé: dry, very refreshing. **Serving temperature:** Red: 14° to 16°; cooler for the rosé. **Vintages available in 89/90:** Reds: 1983, 1984, 1985, 8% Rosé. 1988.

Characteristics of vintages

1985: Lovely red Mourvèdre, supple, aromatic, already developed. **1983:** Successful vintage, more complex, full and well-balanced (Syrah). Average pre-tax, ex-warehouse price: 18 F.F to 20 F.F.
Sales in France: 90%.
Main trading partners : Netherlands, Germany.

CHÂTEAU DE CAMPUGET

30129 Manduel
Chais: 20 34 92 - Bureau: 20 20 15

Type of vineyard: Family owned Corporation (private). **Soil:** Pebbly, kind of villafranchien. **Average annual production in hectoliters:** 7500.
Appellation: Costières-du-Gard. **Type:** Red, White, Rosé. **Technique:** Temperature control with cooling machines. **Maturing:** In tanks. **Alcohol content:** 12.5%. **Characteristics:** Red: good color, with spicy and fruity aromas, soft and full, with tenacity. White: flowery, full, original flavor. **Serving temperature:** White and Rosé: 8 to 10°. Red: 16 to 18°. **Vintages available in 89/90:** Red: 1985. White, Rosé: 1986.

Characteristics of vintages

1986: Gold Medal – White Mâcon 1986. Gold Medal – Red, Concours Général Agricole Paris 1986 (Principal Agricultural Competition). Price range (pre-tax, ex-warehouse): between 10 F.F. & 20 F.F.
Sales in France: 66%. **Export sales:** 33%.
Main trading partners : Europe.

CHÂTEAU FONTEUIL

Jean-Pierre Manquillet - Geneviève Fayet
Château Fonteuil - Gallican - 30600 Vauvert
66 73 33 13 & 66 73 31 45

Type of vineyard: Agricultural Association. **Established:** 1983. **Vine stocks:** Syrah 25%, Grenache 25%, Vieux Carignan 20%, Cinsault 20%, Mourvèdre 10%. **Soil:** Tertiary terminal moraine, alluvial deposits of the Rhône River, sandstone. **Exposure:** North-South. **Average annual production in hectoliters:** 5000.
Type: Red, white, rosé. **Note:** Primeurs. **Technique:** Harvest done by hand. Separate vinification. Temperature control. White and rosé: 3 weeks (17°C). Red: traditional, 6-10 days, carbonic maceration. **Maturing:** White and rosé in stainless steel tanks. Red in Oak casks and concrete tanks. **Alochol content:** 11.5-12.5%. **Characteristics:** White: pale gold color, dry but not overly acid. Hazelnut and undergrowth fragrance. Rosé de Saignée: natural, ample and fruity. Delicately spicy (Mourvèdre flavor). Red: ruby color, natural and fruity, touch of raspberry. Supple tannins, ripe fruit aroma, woodland aftertaste. **Served temperature:** Red: 14-17°C. White & rosé: 5-7°C. **Serving with:** Red: duck steaks, beef cooked in sauce, red mullet, cheese. White: as an aperitif and with shellfish, fish and young rabbit. **Vintages available in 89/90:** 1985, 1986, 1987.

Characteristics of vintages

1986: Good red. Quite successful white and rosé, very aromatic. **1985:** Red: beautifully structured, well made. Price range (pre-tax, ex-warehouse): 10-20 F.F.
Sales volume:
– Retail: 5%. – Restaurants: 10%. – Other: 85% (export).
Sales in France: 15%.
Export sales: 85%.
Main trading partners : Germany, Belgium, Netherlands.

CHÂTEAU DE ROZIER

Mr. Louis de Belair
30129 Manduel
66 01 11 87 - Telex: 572 093 F CHROZIER

Type of vineyard: Family-owned. **Established:** 1977 (taken over from the aunt of Monsieur de Belair, Mademoiselle de Bernis). **Number of employees:** 2. **Vine stocks:** Grenache, Syrah, Carignan, Cinsault. **Soil:** Sandstone, Villafranchien gravel. **Exposure:** High plateau. **Average annual production in hectoliters:** 1,200.
Appellation: Costières-du-Gard. **Type:** Red. **Technique:** Classic, in stainless steel tanks. **Maturing:** Stainless steel tanks and bottles. **Alcohol content:** 12%. **Characteristics:** Garnet red, tannic, red fruit and spices. **Serving temperature:** 16 to 17°. **Served with:** Red meat, cheese. **Vintages available in 89/90:** 1989, 1987, 1988.

Characteristics of vintages

1985: Gold Medal, Concours Agricole de Paris, 1986, rich, fragrant. **1984:** Prizewinner, Mondial du Vin, Brussels 1986, very successful vintage. **1983:** Second prize, Concours du Congrès National des Sommeliers de France, 1985. **1982:** Bronze Medal, Paris 1983. Average pre-tax, ex-warehouse price: 18.55 F.F. Price range (pre-tax, ex-warehouse): Between 10 F.F. and 20 F.F.
- **Wholesale:** 100% in tank 50%
- **Retail:** 30% in bottles 50%
- **Restaurant:** 12% in bottles 50%
- **Export:** 58% in bottles 50%

100% production A.O.C.

Export: In Germany, Holland, Switzerland, Luxemburg, Denmark, Belgium and this year Great Britain in London

CAVE PILOTE DE GALLICIAN

M. Meizonnet (chairman of the board)
Gallician - 30600 Vauvert
66 73 31 65

Type of vineyard: Cooperative Agricultural Association. **Established:** 1951. **Number of employees:** 15. **Vine stocks:** Carignan, Cinsault, Ugni Blanc, Syrah, Mourvèdre and various others. **Soil:** Very fertile dry soil, pebbly. **Exposure:** Hillsides, maximum sunshine. **Average annual production in hectoliters:** 70,000.

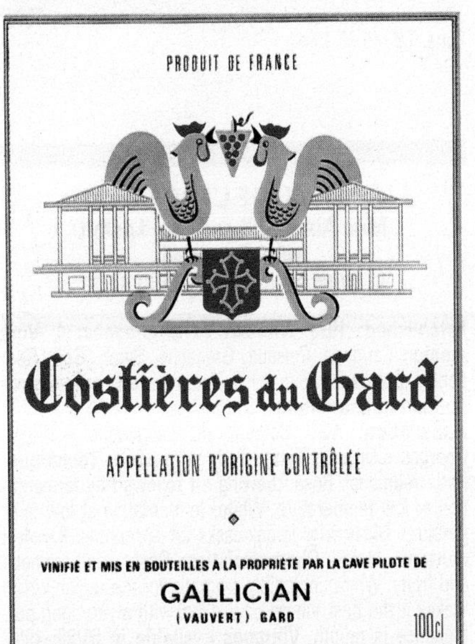

Appellation: Gris, sparkling, Champagne Method, Blanc de Blancs and Rosé. **Type:** Red, white, rosé. **Technique:** Short or traditional. **Maturing:** Selection according to variety, color, alcohol content, classification of the soil and even the age of the vine. **Alcohol content:** 12%. **Characteristics:** Because the sunshine favors maturity, the wines of the Cave Pilote have little acidity which gives them a pleasant suppleness. **Serving temperature:** Red: room temperature. Rosé, white, gris: cool. **Served with:** Red: cheese, steak. Gris: pâté, delicatessen. White: fish, shellfish. Rosé: goes with everything. **Vintages available in 89/90:** 1986.

Characteristics of vintages

1986: Red "Cuvée Majoral": fruity. Rosé: Good and fruity.

DOMAINE DE MOURIER

Mr. Campfrancq
Chemin des Canaux 30000 Nîmes
66 38 05 27

Type of vineyard: Agricultural Association. **Established:** 1979. **Vine stocks:** Syrah, Grenache, Carignan, Cinsaut. **Soil:** Pepply. **Exposure:** South, South-West. **Average annual production in hectoliters:** 800.

Appellation: Costières de Nîmes. **Type:** Red, Rosé. **Technique:** Traditional. **Maturing:** On the estate. **Alcohol content:** 11.8 to 12°. **Characteristics:** Deep color, aromatic, develops well with age. Rosé: fruity and lively. **Served with:** Meat in sauce, roasts, cheese. **Vintages available in 89/90:** 1986, 1987, 1988.

Characteristics of vintages

1988: Deep color, aromatic, very promising. **1987:** Elegant

and fruity. **1986:** Supple, ages well. Price range (pre-tax, ex-warehouse): 10 to 20 F.F. – 20 to 30 F.F.
Sales volume:
– Wholesale: 70%. – Retail: 20%. – Restaurants: 10%.
Sales in France: 60% winecellars.
Export sales: 40%.
Main trading partners: Netherlands, Belgium, Denmarks, Germany, UK.

CHÂTEAU DE TOURELLES

Hervé Durand
30300 Beaucaire
66 59 22 69

Type of vineyard: Family-owned. **Established:** More than 250 years old. **Number of employees:** 4. **Vine stocks:** 11% Syrah, 48% Grenache, 15% Cinsault, 18% Carignan, 8% Mourvèdre. **Soil:** Pebbles (Alpine dilluvium). **Exposure:** Hillside along the Rhône River. **Average annual production in hectoliters:** 2,500.
Appellation: Costières-du-Gard. **Type:** Red. **Technique:** Traditional fermentation with skins 5 to 7 days. **Maturing:** Ageing in stainless steel tanks, then bottling. **Alcohol content:** 12%. **Characteristics:** Color: ruby red tending towards vermillion, brilliant. Very aromatic and warm with vegetal overtones (woodland, scrub bushes), touch of spice (pepper, vanilla). Flavor: supple, forthcoming, tastes of pitted fruit (plum, prune), spicy finish. **Served with:** Beef, mutton, Roquefort, Causses Blue Cheese. **Vintages available in 89/90:** 1985, 1986.

Characteristics of vintages

1988: Very beautiful vintage, deep ruby red color, very aromatic, red fruit, roasted coffee fragrance, round, full, rich and well-balanced taste. **1987:** Good year, elegant and fruity, good color. **1985:** Good vintage, rich and well-balanced, forthcoming, ages well, dense. Price range (pre-tax, ex-warehouse): Between 10 F.F. and 20 F.F.
Sales volume:
– Wholesale: 50%. – Retail: 50%.
Sales in France: 60%.
Export sales: 40%.
Main trading partners: Germany, Switzerland, Netherlands.

Comments

Hervé Durand is the creator of the first vineyard in Quebec, Canada; "Le Vignoble de l'Opailleur".
The white Quebec wines are as original and interesting as are his red wines of the Costières-du-Gard.

> • *Blending – a method consisting of mixing different wines from different lots or different vintages in order to obtain a more homogeneous product.*

CÔTEAUX DU LANGUEDOX

CHÂTEAU DE CARRION-NIZAS

Bernard Gaujal
Nizas – 34320 Roujan
67 25 15 44

Type of vineyard: Family-owned. **Vine stocks:** (30 hectares): Grenache, Cinsault, Syrah and Carignan. **Soil:** Hillsides of primary sandstone. **Exposure:** South.
Appellation: Côteaux-du-Languedoc. **Type:** Red. **Technique:** Traditional. **Characteristics:** The best Côteaux-du-Languedoc: soft and full, red berry and humus bouquet, well-structured, wine that keeps well (excellent quality/price ratio). **Serving temperature:** 15°. **Served with:** Roasts, game, spicy dishes. **Vintages available in 89/90:** 1983, 1984 and 1985.

Characteristics of vintages

1986: Very promising. **1985:** Remarkable wine, rich in color and aroma, full-bodied, good for ageing. **1984:** Beautiful year, more supple. Price range (pre-tax, ex-warehouse): 20-30 F.F.

References in France

Shops: L'Amour du Vin, 94, rue Saint-Dominique, 75007 Paris. Tél: 45 56 12 94.

CHÂTEAU DE L'ENGARRAN

Mrs. Alain Grill and Mrs Losfelt
34880 Laverune
67 27 60 89 and 16 (1) 42 61 11 20

Established: 1923. **Number of employees:** 4. **Vine stocks:** Carignan, Cinsault, Grenache, Syrah. **Soil:** Red: pebbly. **Exposure:** Sunny hillsides. **Average annual production in hectoliters:** 60 hl/ha.
Appellation: AOC Coteaux du Languedoc – Saint-Georges d'Orques. **Type:** Red, rosé, white. **Technique:** Red: traditional. Rosé: drawing off followed by fermentation at low temperature. White: fermentation at low temperature. **Maturing:** In oak casks for 18 months. **Alcohol content:** 11.8%. **Characteristics:** Rosé: very aromatic and fruity. White: incredibly aromatic for the region which makes it the best Vin de pays d'Oc, with a very long permanence in mouth. **Vintages available in 89/90:** 1984, 1985, 1986, 1987, 1988.

Characteristics of vintages

1988: Gold Medal at Concours général agricole de Paris

(March 1989). **1985:** A great vintage for ageing, aromatic and dense. **Other:** 1984: A relatively unknown year. Character which develops very well in the bottle, quite successful.
Sales in France:
Export sales: 55%.

References in France

Restaurants: Le Cochon d'Or (Paris), Restaurant A. Morel (Paris), Léonce, Florensac.

Abroad

United States

Poseidon, Miami.

United Kingdom

Harvey House, Bristol.

Germany

J. 2 Houdeyer - Les Vins Français.

Switzerland

Schenk.

Belgium

De Comminck.

Far East

Japan: Nihon Olivier.

PECH REDON

Christophe & Mireille Bousquet
route de Gruissan - 11100 Narbonne
68 90 41 23

Type of vineyard: Agricultural Association. **Established:** 1988. **Vine stocks:** Syrah, Grenache, Cinsault, Carignan, Chardonnay. **Soil:** Chalky silica clay. **Exposure:** South-West. **Average annual production in hectoliters:** 2,000.
Appellation: AOC Coteaux du Languedoc La Clape. **Type:** Red, white, rosé. **Technique:** Red: carbonic maceration - White and Rosé: low temperature. **Maturing:** Red: in oak casks. **Alcohol content:** 12-12.5%. **Characteristics:** Red: red berry and strong vanilla aroma, well structured. White and Rosé: very lively and very flowery. **Serving temperature:** Red: 18-19°; White and Rosé: 11-13°. **Served with:** Red game, red meat. Rosé: delicatessen. White: fish cooked in sauce and certain types of cheese.

Characteristics of vintages

1988: Red: rich tannins, already lingering taste of blackcurrant and liquorice. Will be a great vintage. **1987:** Red: Fine tannins, light red berry aroma, good development. Price range (pre-tax, ex-warehouse): 10 to 20 F.F. - 20 to 30 F.F.
Sales in France: 25%.
Export sales: 75%.
Main trading partners : United Kingdom, Netherlands, Germany, Belgium, USA.

References in France

Restaurants: Narbonne, Montpellier, Paris.
Shops: Paris, Nantes, Montpellier.

Abroad

United States

Europvin (Texas and Massachussets).

United Kingdom

Bordeaux Direct Reading Berkshire.

Belgium

Sté. Grands Magasins Rob, Brussels.

The Netherlands

N.C.K. Rijndijk.

1987
Château
de Pech Redon
Côteaux du Languedoc
La Clape
Appellation Côteaux du Languedoc Contrôlée
Mis en bouteilles au Domaine par C. & M. BOUSQUET
Propriétaires au Château de Pech Redon 11100 Narbonne France
Produit de France
11,7 % alc./vol.
75 cl e
L'ÉPERVIER
1re mise
15.000 bouteilles
bouteille
Nº 02020
MÛRI EN FÛTS DE CHÊNE

Comments

This land was ceded by Caesar to a centurion of the 10th legion. Remains of the Roman villa can still be found on the domain. Later, the Abbot of Valvernière, Christophe Bousquet, winegrower and oenologist, took over the Domaine de Pech Redon after the death of J. Demolombe. Harvesting is always done by hand, in hampers, in order to bring whole grapes to the vats. Care is taken to conserve the aromas of the grapes grown on these 300 hectares of garrigues and chalky rocks. The reds, matured in oak casks, develop aromas of red berries, vanilla and woodlands. Lovely, fine and fragrant whites.

• *To better understand the evolution and adherence to type of the various vintages, consult our "Vintage Code" chart.*

CHÂTEAU RICARDELLE

Anne-Marie Lafforgue
Route de Gruissan – 11100 Narbonne
68 65 21 00 – Telex: 470 673 Flash Vin

Type of vineyard: Family-owned. **Established:** 1935. **Number of employees:** 6. **Vine stocks:** Carignan 60%, Grenache 25%, Cinsaut 5%, Merlot 5%, Syrah 5%. **Soil:** chalky clay. **Exposure:** South-East. **Average annual production in hectoliters:** 3,500.

Appellation: AOC Coteaux du Languedoc, La Clape, Vin de Pays de l'Aude. **Type:** Red, rosé. Other: Vin gris. **Technique:** Traditional. **Maturing:** In warehouses. **Alcohol content:** 11 and 13%. **Characteristics:** Good color, aromatic, combining finesse, richness and balance. **Serving temperature:** Red: 18°. Vin gris: 9°. **Served with:** delicatessen, meat, cheese.

Characteristics of vintages

1987: Château Ricardelle rosé: fine, delicate, fragrant – to be drunk cool (9°). **1986:** Château Ricardelle red. **1985:** Château Ricardelle red.

References in France

Restaurants: Hôstellerie du Maine Brun, Mr. Ménager (Angoulême) – Restaurant Jean Bardet, Tours Concorde Lafayette (Paris) – Le Réverbère (Narbonne).

• To help us improve our next edition, please send in your suggestions and answer our questionnaire.

CAVE COOPÉRATIVE

Neffies – 34320 Roujan
67 24 61 98

Type of vineyard: Cooperative Agricultural Association. **Established:** 1937. **Number of employees:** 2. **Vine stocks:** Carignan, Syrah, Grenache. **Soil:** Schistic hillsides. **Average annual production in hectoliters:** 2500. **Appellation:** Coteaux du Languedoc. **Type:** Red. **Technique:** Carbonic maceration. **Maturing:** Oak casks. **Alcohol content:** 12.5%. **Characteristics:** Fleshy, soft and full, fine tannins, touch of pepper and vanilla, round. **Serving temperature:** 17°. **Served with:** Meat in sauce, game. **Vintages available in 89/90:** 1986.

CHÂTEAU ROUQUETTE S/MER

Jacques Boscary
11430 Gruissan
68 49 80 01 and 68 32 56 53

Type of vineyard: Family-owned. **Established:** 1969. **Number of employees:** 6. **Vine stocks:** Grenache, Cinsault, Syrah, Carignan, Bourboulenc. **Soil:** Chalky. **Exposure:** Full South, on cliff overlooking the sea. **Average annual production in hectoliters:** 2400.
Appellation: Coteaux-du-Languedoc, La Clape. **Type:** Red, white, rosé. **Technique:** Traditional, carbonic maceration, rigorous temperature control. **Maturing:** Oak casks. **Alcohol content:** 11.5% to 12%. **Characteristics:** Rosé: supple and fruity. White: very aromatic. Red: structured, tannic and fruity. **Vintages available in 89/90:** 1983, 1985, 1986.

Characteristics of vintages

1986: Vintage not tasted. **1985:** Good year for all three wines. Fruity. **1983:** Good red, aged in casks, intense, complex bouquet, full, well made.

VINS DE PAYS

MAS DAUMAS GASSAC

Véronique Guibert de la Vaissière
34150 Gignac
67 57 71 28 – Telex: 485 347

Established: 1970. **Number of employees:** 10. **Vine stocks:** 80% Cabernet Sauvignon – old plants, not cloned. **Soil:** Glacial powder. **Exposure:** North. **Average annual production in hectoliters:** Red: 35 to 40. White: 20 to 25.

Appellation: Vin de Pays de l'Hérault. **Type:** Red, white. **Technique:** Médoc tradition. **Maturing:** 20 months in casks. **Alcohol content:** 13%. **Characteristics:** For very long keeping. Rich, well balanced, complex, tannic. **Serving temperature:** Red: 17.5 to 18°. White: 10 to 12°.

Characteristics of vintages

1987: A lighter Daumas, soft, supple and seductive. **1986:** Deep ruby color, spicy nose, beautiful roundness. **1985:** Very full and fragrant. To be drunk in 1999. Price range (pre-tax, ex-warehouse): between 80 and 100 F.F.

Sales volume:
– Wholesale: 80%. – Retail: 20%.
Sales in France: 30%.
Export sales: 70%.

References in France

Shops: Nicolas (Paris) and the 50 best shops.

Abroad

United States
Kermit Lynch, San Francisco. Tel: 415 524 1524.

United Kingdom
Mistral, London. Tel: 01 262 5437.

Germany
Nagel, Aix-la-Chapelle. Tel: 241 34 455.

Switzerland
La Cave, Geneva. Tel: 22 76 20 63.

Belgium
L'Art et la Mer, Brussels. Tel: 32 24 65 7217.

The Netherlands
Ockwysen, Harlem. Tel: 23 31 22 40.

Far East
G. Sorne, Paris. Tel: 4202 4197.

Comments

Mas Daumas Gassac was discovered between 1970 and 1972 by the geographer Henri Engelbert of Bordeaux. In 1989 Daumas Gassac is distributed in 25 countries and is known the world over. In France, however, their table wine is still little known.

DOMAINE DE LAVAL

Mr. Jean Chazottes
Tourbes – 34120 Pézenas
67 98 15 11 – Telex: 490 267

Established: 1968. **Vine stocks:** Red: Cabernet Sauvignon 20%, Merlot 30%, Cinsault 30%, Carignan 15%, Syrah 5%. White: Sauvignon 25%, Ugni Blanc 75%. Rosé: Cinsault 60%, Grenache 40%. **Soil:** Clay with calcium carbonate and gravel. **Exposure:** South-west. **Average annual production in hectoliters:** 5200.
Appellation: Vin de Pays de l'Hérault, Vin de Pays de Pézenas, Vin de Pays des Côtes de Thongue. **Type:** Red, white, rosé. **Technique:** Traditional with temperature control. **Alcohol content:** 11.5%. **Characteristics:** Rosé: fruity, young and lively. Red: peppery, lively and very well balanced – peony and citrus fruits aromas. White: dry, very aromatic (peach-pear), supple, fruity. **Serving temperature:** White: 10°. Rosé: 14°. Red: 20°. **Served with:** White: as an aperitif ("kir") – seafood – shellfish. Rosé: white meat (chicken, veal) – first courses. **Vintages available in 89/90:** 1985, 1986.

Characteristics of vintages

1986: Good year. Reds: supple, deep color. Beautiful whites. Price range (pre-tax, ex-warehouse): Less than 10 F.F.

Sales volume:
– Wholesale: 20%. – Retail: 10%. – Restaurants: 10%.
– Other: 60% (export).
Sales in France: 20%.
Export sales: 80%.
Main trading partners : Belgium, Netherlands, Denmark, UK, Germany, USA, Japan.

DOMAINE DE LUCH

Count Guy de Fleurieu
Route de Narbonne, 34500 Béziers
67 28 36 66

Type of vineyard: Family-owned. **Established:** 1858. **Number of employees:** 8. **Vine stocks:** Merlot, Cabernet Sauvignon, Syrah, Chasan, Chardonnay. **Soil:** Slightly sloping soil on chalky sub-soil. **Exposure:** South. **Average annual production in hectoliters:** 6,500.

Appellation: Vin du Pays de l'Hérault. **Type:** Red, white, rosé. **Technique:** Red: traditional. White: refrigeration. **Maturing:** In oak casks. **Alcohol content:** 11 to 12%. **Characteristics:** Rosé: fruity. Red: Merlot and Cabernet Sauvignon well balanced and aromatic. **Serving temperature:** Red: 18°. Rosé: 8°. **Vintages available in 89/90:** 1985, 1986, 1987, 1988.

Characteristics of vintages

1988: Merlot, Cabernet Sauvignon, exceptional year. **1987:** Cabernet Sauvignon. **1986:** Merlot, very much appreciated abroad. **1985:** Merlot, Cabernet Sauvignon (Cuvée Spéciale), of which only a few thousand bottles remain. Price range (pre-tax, ex-warehouse): between 10 and 20 F.F.

Sales volume:
– Wholesale: 99%. – Retail: 1%.
Sales in France: 90%.
Export sales: 10%.
Main trading partners: Germany, United Kingdom, Netherlands, Denmark, Belgium.

References in France

Restaurants: Le Castelet (route de Narbonne, Béziers).

Abroad

United Kingdom

Goujon and Sons, London.

Germany

Fremery and Dyckerhoff, Cologne. Wilke Weinimport, Datteln.

Belgium

Vinothèque, Brussels.

The Netherlands

Appeldoorn, Velp. Rotteveel, Uden.

Others

Denmark: Jaegersborg Vinimport, Gentofte.

Comments

Family estate for 130 years and 4 generations. In the 17th century, the property was cut in two by the Canal du Midi.

DOMAINE DE MONTMARIN

Emmanuel and Paule de Bertier
Montblanc – 34290 Servian
67 77 42 20

Type of vineyard: Family-owned (1976). **Established:** Vineyard has remained in the same family since 1488. **Vine stocks:** Grenache, Syrah, Mourvèdre, Merlot, Cabernet, Marsanne. **Soil:** Clay with pebbles, alluvium and sand. **Exposure:** South and South-west. **Average annual production in hectoliters:** 7000.
Appellation: Vin de Pays des "Côtes-de-Thongue". **Type:** Red, white, rosé. **Technique:** Classic. **Alcohol content:** 11.5%. **Characteristics:** Merlot: round and supple. Marsanne: freshness and finesse.

Characteristics of vintages

1987: Marsanne – awarded Gold Medal at the Concours général Agricole, Paris 1988. **1986:** Merlot: very successful, Marsanne: seductive.

CHÂTEAU DE PENNAUTIER

Countess Amédée de Lorgeril
Pennautier – 11610
68 25 02 11

Vine stocks: Cabernet Sauvignon, Merlot, Cot, Grenache, Carignan, Cinsault.
Appellation: Cabardes V.D.Q.S. **Type:** Red. **Technique:** Classic vinification with temperature regulation. **Serving**

temperature: 17° to 18°. **Vintages available in 89/90:** 1985.

Characteristics of vintages

1987: Beautiful ruby color, extra sheen, intense and complex aromas (red berry), spicy note, round attack, soft and full, mellow tannins, full-bodied, lingering taste. **1985:** Pleasant red, good color, rich and well-balanced, quite supple.

DOMAINE DE PUECHREDON

Michel Cuche
30610 Sauve
(16) 66 77 31 25

Type of vineyard: Family owned. **Established:** 1973. **Average annual production in hectoliters:** 4000. **Varieties of grapes used:** traditional varieties of the Region Grenache, Carignan, Cinsault, Syrah, Alicante. **Bordeaux varieties:** Cabernet, Merlot. **White grapes:** Chardonnay, Sauvignon blanc, Uni blanc.
Terroir: The vineyard has west/south-west hillside exposure. Soil red, argilo-calcerous with pebbles.
Appellation: Vin de pays du Gard. **Types:** Rouge, Rosé, White. **Technique:** Traditional. **Maturing:** 6 months in Oak aging casks. **Alcohol content:** 12°. **Characteristics:** Rouge: Ruby color, well-balanced, red berry aroma. Rosé: Fruity. White: Very aromatic. **Vintages available in 89/90:** 86, 87, 88.

Characteristics of vintages

Price range: 20 F.F.
Sales volume:
– Wholesale: 10%. – Retail: 65%. – Restaurants: 20%.
Sales in France: 95%.
Export sales: 5%.
Main trading partners: Belgium, Canada, Germany, Netherlands.

References in France

Restaurants: 40 in Languedoc. Stores: more than 50 boutiques in Languedoc. Paris: 10 references.

Comments

Puechredon is a picturesque estate located at the foot of the Cévennes mountains, between the Gardon river and the Vidourle valley, several Kilometers from the medieval town of Sauve.

• *Please note that all temperatures in this book are expressed in degrees Centigrade.*

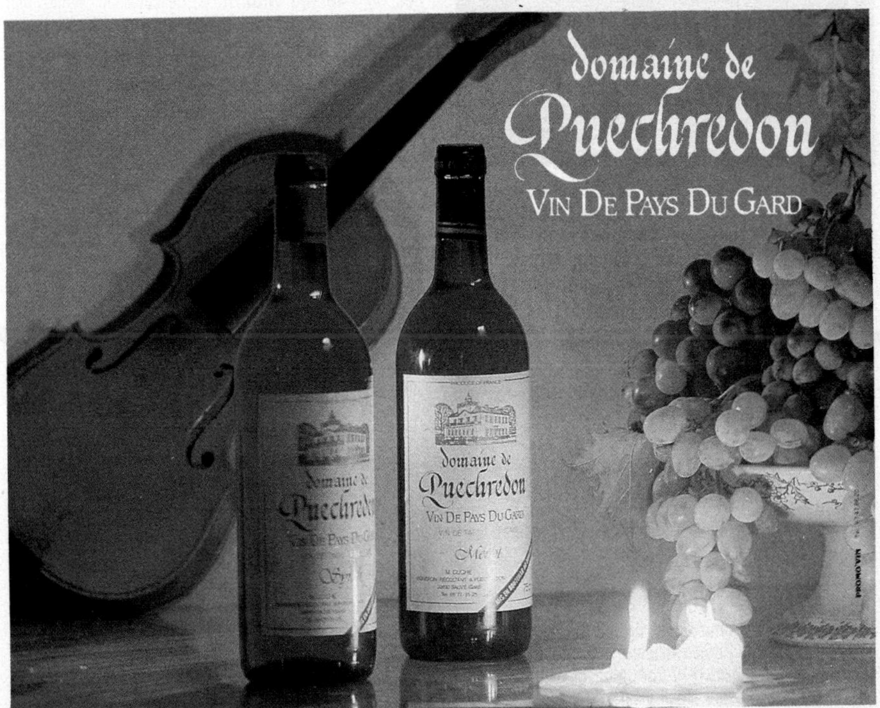

domaine de
Puechredon
VIN DE PAYS DU GARD

LA VERNÈDE

Mme Ribet
34440 Nissan-Lez-Ensérune
67 37 00 30 or 68 33 61 62

Type of vineyard: Agricultural Association. **Established:** 1872. **Number of employees:** 5. **Vine stocks:** Mourvèdre, Grenache, Carignan, Syrah, Cinsaut. **Soil:** Pebbly brown chalky marl. **Exposure:** East, South-East, South. **Average annual production in hectoliters:** 2,750.

Appellation: Vin de Pays des Coteaux d'Enserune. **Type:** Red, Rosé. **Technique:** Traditional, temperature control with refrigeration equipment. **Maturing:** In stainless steel tanks. **Alcohol content:** 11.5%. **Serving temperature:** 16 to 18°. **Served with:** Red meat, game, cheese. **Vintages available in 89/90:** 1986-1988.

Characteristics of vintages

1988: Young wine, supple and fruity, well balanced. **1986:** round, fruity and well balanced. Price range (pre-tax, ex-warehouse): 10 to 20 F.F.
Sales volume:
- Wholesale: 50%. - Retail: 50%.

References in France

Restaurants: A number of restaurants in Toulouse.
Shops: "Busquet & Bacquier" Toulouse.

Comments

The history of the domain goes back to the Roman epoch (vestiges of a large Roman villa are to be found). The château was purchased in 1870 from Monsignor d'Hulst, Bishop of Narbonne. Very small yields (less than 50 hl per hectare) due to the poor hillside soil. The Mourvèdre is responsible for the unique bouquet, the Syrah for character, the Grenache, roundness, the Cinsault, suppleness and balance, and the Carignan, richness. The five vinestocks combined, grown in the arid Languedoc soil, yield warm, fragrant and fruity wines.

UNION DES CAVES DES COTEAUX DU PONT DU GARD

Alain Jaussaud
30210 Vers Pont du Gard
66 22 80 35 - Telex: 490 551 F

Type of vineyard: Family-owned. **Established:** 1974. **Number of employees:** 3 (office), 14 (cellars). **Vine stocks:** Carignan, Grenache, Cinsault, Syrah, Ugni Blanc, Grenache Blanc. **Soil:** Clay with calcium carbonate. **Exposure:** Mostly South. **Average annual production in hectoliters:** 60000 (Vins de Pays).
Appellation: Vins de Pays des Coteaux du Pont du Gard. **Type:** Red, white, rosé. **Technique:** Traditional. **Maturing:** Stainless steel and concrete lined tanks. **Alcohol content:** 12%. **Characteristics:** Red: light ruby color. Nose light, fine. Fruity. Rosé: intense rosé color, fruity and full flavor. White: golden color, discrete, fresh, goes down smoothly. **Serving temperature:** Rosé and white: 8°. Red: 14°. **Served with:** Rosé: delicatessen. White: fish and shellfish. Red: meat (grilled and roasted). **Vintages available in 89/90:** 1988.

Characteristics of vintages

1988: Good vintage for reds, whites and rosés. Fine and fruity wines. Good vinification. Average pre-tax, ex-warehouse price: Between 7 and 10 F.F.
Sales volume:
- Wholesale: 75%. - Retail: 15%. - Restaurants: 10%.
Sales in France: 90%.
Export sales: 10%.
Main trading partners : Germany, Belgium.

CÔTES DU ROUSSILLON

DOMAINE CAZES

André & Bernard Cazes
4, rue Francisco-Ferrer 66600 Rivesaltes
68 64 08 26 - Telex: 506 230 F

Type of vineyard: Agricultural Association and Corporation. **Established:** 1971. **Number of employees:** 20. **Vine stocks:** Carignan, Sauvignon, Cabernet Sauvignon, Merlot, Grenache Noir & Blanc, Macabeu, Syrah, Mourvèdre, Chardonnay. **Soil:** Pebbly clay, terraces (Quaternary era) **Exposure:** Plain (Roussillon). **Average annual production in hectoliters:** 5,000-6,000.

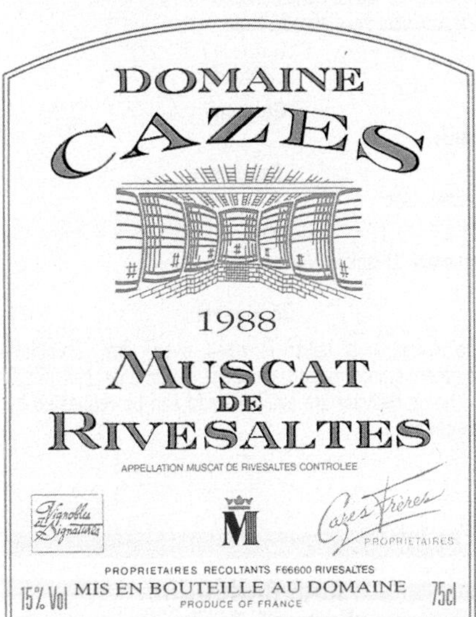

Appellation: Rivesaltes - Muscats de Rivesaltes - Vin de pays catalan - Côtes du Roussillon & Villages. **Type:** Red, White, **Others:** naturally sweet wine. **Maturing:** In lined stainless steel tanks, new and old wooden vats - air-conditioned cellars. **Serving temperature:** White & Rosé: 6-8°. Red: 16-18°. Muscat & Rivesaltes: 10-12°. **Vintages available in 89/90:** 1973, 1978, 1986, 1987, 1988.

Characteristics of vintages

1988: Comparable quality to other wines of this vintage in general. **1987:** Good average wine, harvested under perfect sanitary conditions. **1986:** Very good level on the whole. **1985:** Superb in all categories.

Marketing Information

Price range (pre-tax, ex-warehouse): 10 to 20 F.F. - 30 to 50 F.F. - 20 to 30 F.F. - 80 to 120 F.F.
Sales volume:
– Retail: 40%. – Restaurants: 40%. – Other: 20% (export).
Sales in France: 80%.
Export sales: 20%.
Main trading partners: Europe, USA, Japan, French overseas territories, Canada.

References in France

Restaurants: (Paris) Tour d'Argent, Lucas Carton, Crillon, La Marée Laurent, Pavillon Élysées, Chapel, Blanc, Boyer. (Cannes) Gray d'Albion. (Monte-Carlo) Hôtel de Paris, Lameloise, etc.
Shops: Fauchon, Hédiard, etc.

Abroad

United States

Importers: Handpicked Selection (Maryland).

United Kingdom

Enotria, London. Windrush wines Urencester.

Switzerland

Club Divo (Lausanne), Fischer & Richs (Bienne).

Belgium

Marc François (Petit Enghein), La Maison d'Echanson (La Hulpe), Lambert (Brussels).

Canada

SA Quebec Montréal, Parent (Reserve & Selection), Montréal.

The Netherlands

Hersterkamp Ootmarsum, Jos Beres Gronignen, etc.

Far East

Japan: Takachimaya (Tokyo).

Others

Denmark: Vinicole-Vinimport (Copenhagen) - Vingaarden (Odense). Ireland: Findlater, Dublin.

Comments

Family enterprise (150 hectare vineyard) directed by André and Bernard Cazes, the former being in charge of marketing, and the latter of the running of the estate and vinification process. Production in bottles since 1955.

CHÂTEAU DE CAP DE FOUSTE

André Cavaille
66200 Villeneuve de la Raho
68 55 91 04

Established: 5 type of vineyard? **Vine stocks:** Malvoisie, Maccaber, Grenache Blanc, Noir, Syrah, Cabernet Sauvignon, Carignan Noir, Muscat Alexandrie. **Soil:** Terraces of clay with calcium carbonate. **Exposure:** Northeast, Southwest. **Average annual production in hectoliters:** 2000.

Appellation: Côtes du Roussillon (red and white), Plus a naturally sweet wine, the Muscat de Rivesaltes. **Technique:** Traditional, destemming, carbonic maceration, temperature control. **Maturing:** Vats, Oak barrels, bottles. **Alcohol content:** 12.5 to 17.5%. **Characteristics:** Red: deep red color with glints fo tile-red, finished aroma, touch of venison, robust, long, round. Muscat or pale: finished aroma, fruity, soft, full, long unctuous. **Serving temperature:** Red: 13 to 15°. Muscat Alexandrie: 9 to 12°. **Served with:** Everything, meat, sauces, delicatessen. Product Muscat Alexandrie: as an aperitif or with dessert. Try it also with foie gras and Roquefort.

Characteristics of vintages

1985: Good reds and, above all, an excellent Muscat, full and very fruity.

Sales volume:
– Wholesale: 74%. – Retail: 26%.

Sales in France: 70%.

Export sales: 30%.

Main trading partners: UK, Germany, Netherlands, Switzerland.

DOMAINE DU MAS ROUS

Pujol
66740 Montesquieu
68 89 64 91

Type of vineyard: agricultural association (tenant farming). **Established:** 1976. **Number of employees:** 1. **Vine stocks:** Syrah, Grenache, Carignan, Mourvèdre. **Soil:** Schist, granite, clay. **Exposure:** North. **Average annual production in hectoliters:** 1,800.

PRODUIT DE FRANCE
Domaine du Mas Rous
Côtes du Roussillon
APPELLATION COTES du ROUSSILLON CONTROLEE
12% vol.
1986
e75cl
J. PUJOL PRODUCTEUR-ELEVEUR A MONTESQUIEU
MIS EN BOUTEILLE AU DOMAINE

Appellation: Côtes de Roussillon. **Type:** Red. **Technique:** Carbonic maceration and traditional. **Maturing:** Reserve in oak casks. **Alcohol content:** 12%. **Characteristics:** Fruity, cherry, mulberry, black currant flavor. Moderately rich and well-balanced, goes down well. **Serving temperature:** 14°. **Served with:** Grilled lamb and beef. **Vintages available in 89/90:** 1986, 1987.

Characteristics of vintages

1987: Ruby red color, very fruity, vanilla, woody flavor, slightly tannic, will arrive at its maturity in 1990. **1986:** Garnet red color, very fruity, cherry, mulberry flavor, slightly spicy, a touch of venison, goes down well. Price range (pre-tax, ex-warehouse): between 20 F.F. and 30 F.F.

Sales volume:
– Wholesale: 70%. – Retail: 5%. – Restaurants: 10%.
– Other: 15%.

Sales in France: 70%.

Export sales: 30%.

Main trading partners: Belgium, Germany, Denmark.

References in France

Restaurants: Local restaurants.
Shops: Local specialized shops.

Abroad

Germany

Transvin, G.B.R.

Belgium

Saillart, Geel.

Others

Denmark: Daugaart Vinimport.

Comments

The winetasting cellar is open every day. Complete commercial information, technical documents, and prices for home delivery are available and can be requested by telephone.

MAS RANCOURE

Docteur E. Pardineille
Laroque des Albères – 66740 Roussillon
68 89 03 69

Type of vineyard: Family-owned. **Established:** Same family for 3 centuries. **Vine stocks:** Grenache Noir, Syrah, Carignan. **Soil:** Pebbly, silica-clay. **Exposure:** Terraces. **Average annual production in hectoliters:** 1 000. **Appellation:** Côtes-du-Roussillon. **Type:** Red. **Technique:** Carbonic maceration. **Maturing:** Wooden vats and stainless steel tanks. **Alcohol content:** 12.5%. **Characteristics:** Cherry color, aromas of cooked fruit and spices, very round, soft tannins, fully developed aroma, fine and lingering wines, will age well. **Served with:** Delicatessen, grilled steaks, light sauces. **Vintages available in 89/90:** 1983, 1985 Cuvée Vincent, 1987.

Characteristics of vintages

1986: Reminiscent of the 1985, but more pronounced woody aroma. **1985:** Marked Syrah and Grenache overtones, fine, well-structured, very successful vintage.

Characteristics of vintages

1988: White, rosé: very fine, very flowery, well developed aroma. **1987:** Red: very aromatic, fine, supple and delicate. **1986:** Red Tannic colored, well balanced, aroma developed. **Ohters:** Rivesaltes: 20 years of age. Try as an aperitif.

MAS CHICHET

Jacques Chichet
Chemin Charlemagne - 66200 Elne
68 22 16 78

Type of vineyard: Family-owned. **Number of employees:** 6. **Vine stocks:** Cabernet Franc, Sauvignon, Syrah, Merlot, Grenache. **Average annual production in hectoliters:** 1,300.
Appellation: Vin de Pays. **Type:** Red, rosé, other: Cuvée Cabernet. **Technique:** Red and Rosé: maceration. Cuvée Cabernet: destemming. **Alcohol content:** Red: 11,8%. Rosé: 11,7%. Cuvée Cabernet: 12%. **Vintages available in 89/90:** 1987-1986.

Characteristics of vintages

1986: Good vintage, very fresh and fruity. **1985:** More robust vintage, well-colored, youthful, supple and fine. Excellent rosé. Average pre-tax, ex-warehouse price: 11,8 F.F. and 20,24 F.F.
Sales in France: 84%.
Export sales: 16%.
Main trading partners: Belgium, Germany, UK, Denmark, Switzerland.

DOMAINE SARDA-MALET

S.-M. Malet
Mas Saint-Michel
12, Chemin Sainte-Barbe
66000 Perpignan
68 56 72 38 - Fax: (33) 68 56 47 60

Type of vineyard: Family-owned. **Established:** A long time ago. **Number of employees:** 4. **Vine stocks:** Grenache Noir, Syrah, Mourvèdre, Carignan, Malvoisie, Roussanne, Marsanne, Viognier. **Soil:** Clay with calcium carbonate, silica-clay. **Exposure:** South, South-west. **Average annual production in hectoliters:** 2,200.
Appellation: Côtes-du-Roussillon, Rivesaltes. **Type:** Red, White, Rosé. **Technique:** Destemming, temperature control. **Maturing:** Partly in casks (for 12 months), partly in new Oak casks. **Alcohol content:** 12% to 12.5%. **Characteristics:** Red: fleshy, very fine tannins, aromatic. Rosé: very fine, wines produced by drawing off. White: flowery, flinty. **Serving temperature:** Red: 14° to 15°. Rosé: 10° to 12°. White: 8° to 10°. **Vintages available in 89/90:** 1985.

STÉ COOPÉRATIVE AGRICOLE DES VINS FINS

Alain Carsassonne, director
66600 Salses-le-Château
68 38 62 08 - Telex: 506 058

Established: 1929. **Number of employees:** 20. **Vine stocks:** Carignan 70%, Grenache Noir 20%, Syrah 8%, Maccabéo 2%. **Soil:** Chalky clay. **Exposure:** Full South. **Average annual production in hectoliters:** 80,000.

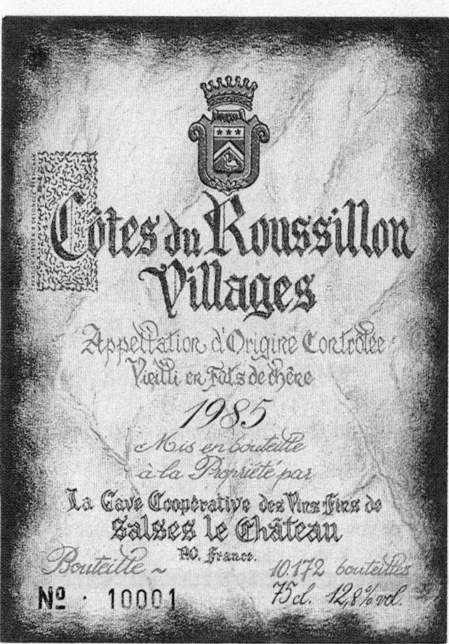

Appellation: Rivesaltes, Muscat, Côtes de Roussillon, Côtes de Roussillon Villages.

Characteristics of vintages

1988: Limited production, available only in white and rosé. **1987:** Red Côtes de Roussillon. **1986:** Côtes de Roussillon Villages 1986 will be available in 1990. **1985:** Côtes de Roussillon Villages aged in oak casks. **Other:** Old Rivesaltes vintages ("tile red"), 8 to 10 years old. Price range (pre-tax, ex-warehouse): Côtes and Villages: between 10 and 20 F.F. Rivesaltes and Muscat: between 20 and 30 F.F.
Sales volume:
- Wholesale: 80%. - Retail: 10%. - Other: 10% (export).

Abroad

United Kingdom

Ets Boutinot (Muscat).

Germany

Wein aus dem Roussillon, Fribourg.

Belgium

Ets André, Charleroi.

The Netherlands

Ets Bouvigne, Breda (100 resale outlets).

Others

Luxemburg: Chaîne Cactus. Denmark: Ets Vingsolen, Kobe.

Comments

Through an agreement with the Historical Monuments Authority, wines have been aged in casks and in bottles in the royal stables of the Château since July 1988, in recognition of which, the "Roc du Gouverneur" wine was created.

FAUGÈRES

DOMAINE DU FRAISSE

Jacques Pons
Rue du Chemin-de-Ronde – Autignac
34480 Magalas
67 90 23 40

Type of vineyard: Family-owned. **Established:** For five generations. **Vine stocks:** 18% Syrah, 48% Carignan, 26% Grenache, 8% Cinsault. **Soil:** Schist and sandstone with calcium carbonate interstratification – dry and porous soil, rich in magnesium. **Exposure:** Mediterranean climate (no frost), dry in summer, maximum sunshine. **Average annual production in hectoliters:** 40-50.
Appellation: Faugères A.O.C. **Type:** Red. **Technique:** semi-carbonc, for about 10 days. **Maturing:** Enamelled tanks. **Alcohol content:** 12%-13.5%. **Characteristics:** Limpid, bright color. **Serving temperature:** 17°. **Served with:** Leg of lamb, meat in sauce or marinated duck. **Vintages available in 89/90:** 1987, 1988.

Characteristics of vintages

1987: Faugères – Domaine du Fraisse: beautiful ruby color, brown-tinged - clear, bright. **1986:** Red fruit and woodland tastes and aromas. Full-bodied, peppery. **1985:** Dark garnet color, strong nose, red fruit aroma, strong tannins.

CHÂTEAU DE GREZAN

Michel Lubac
Laurens, 34480 Magalias
67 90 28 03

Type of vineyard: Corporation. **Established:** 1976. **Number of employees:** 8. **Vine stocks:** Grenache, Syrah, Mourvèdre, Cabernet, Merlot, Carignan, Chardonnay. **Soil:** Schist and chalky clay. **Exposure:** South. **Average annual production in hectoliters:** 7,000.

Appellation: AOC Fougères and Coteaux Languedoc. **Type:** Red, white, rosé. **Technique:** Traditional. **Maturing:** In wooden casks (partly new). **Alcohol content:** 12%. **Characteristics:** Red: fruity (red berry) – well balanced, tobacco and animal fragrance, lingering taste, fine tannins. **Serving temperature:** 15 to 17°. **Served with:** Large game, feathered game, meat in sauce. **Vintages available in 89/90:** 1988.

Characteristics of vintages

1988: Very good structure, good keeping. **1987:** Graceful and delicate, to be drunk in 4 years or so. **1986:** Depleted stock. Price range (pre-tax, ex-warehouse): 10 to 20 F.F. – 20 to 30 F.F.
Sales in France: 60%. **Export sales:** 40%.
Main trading partners : UK, Belgium, Netherlands, Germany, Switzerland, Canada.

B. & C. VIDAL

Bernard and Claudie Vidal
La Liquière – 34480 Magalas
67 90 29 20

Type of vineyard: Family-owned. **Established:** 1971. **Number of employees:** 5. **Vine stocks:** Grenache, Carignan, Cinsault, Syrah, Mourvèdre, Teret, Chazan. **Soil:** Schistic. **Exposure:** South. **Average annual production in hectoliters:** 1,500-1,800.

Appellation: Faugères. **Type:** Red, rosé. **Technique:** Carbonic maceration in casks for rosés and whites. **Alcohol content:** 12.5%. **Characteristics:** Very typical wines, garnet color. Rosés: light and supple, taste of pitted fruit, very aromatic. **Served with:** Red: game, red meat. But excellent also with white meat. White: all fihs, light meals, dessert. **Vintages available in 89/90:** 1988.

Characteristics of vintages

1986: Good Faugères (red and rosé) and Blanc des Schistes. Finesse and aroma.

FITOU

TERRE ARDENTE

Aimé Fontanel
11510 Caves-en-Fitou
68 45 71 05

Type of vineyard: Family-owned. **Established:** 1960. **Number of employees:** 3. **Vine stocks:** Muscat, Grenache Noir, Maccabeu, Carignan. **Soil:** Very pebbly clay with calcium carbonate. **Exposure:** Southeast. **Average annual production in hectoliters:** 700.
Appellation: Fitou, Muscat de Rivesaltes, Rivesaltes. **Type:** Red, white, rosé. **Technique:** Traditional. **Maturing:** Rivesaltes: casks. Others: tanks and bottles. **Alcohol content:** Between 12% and 14%. **Characteristics:** Rich, well-balanced, lots of tannins, very aromatic (Muscat). **Serving temperature:** White and rosé: 6° to 8°. Fitou: 18°. **Served with:** Muscat de Rivesaltes: goes well with foie gras and ice cream, pastry or sherbet desserts. Fitou: goes very well with meat, game and cheese. **Vintages available in 89/90:** Fitou: 1985. Rivesaltes: 1984, 1985.

Characteristics of vintages

1986: The Muscat is at its best for drinking. **1985:** The Fitou and the Rivesaltes will improve dramatically with ageing.
Average pre-tax, ex-warehouse price: Filou: 13 F.F. Rivesaltes: 21 F.F. Muscat de Rivesaltes: 24 F.F.
Sales volume:
- Wholesale: 20%.
- Retail: 80%.

Sales in France: 80%.
Export sales: 20%.
After a number of commercial disappointments, the proprietor is more interested in producing a good wine than in selling it.

CAVES DES PRODUCTEURS DE FITOU

Jean-Luc Meurisse
R.N. 9 - 11510 Fitou
68 45 71 41 - Telex: 550 129

Type of vineyard: Cooperative Agricultural Association. **Established:** 1933. **Number of employees:** 7. **Vine stocks:** Carignan, Grenache Noir, Muscat d'Alexandrie. **Soil:** Clay with calcium carbonate. **Exposure:** South-Mediteranean. **Average annual production in hectoliters:** 18,000.

Appellation: Fitou, Muscat de Rivesaltes, Von Rivesaltes. **Type:** Red, white. **Technique:** Traditional and carbonic maceration. **Maturing:** vats. **Alcohol content:** 13%. **Characteristics:** Fitou: rich and well-balanced. Muscat: fruity and velvety. **Serving temperature:** Fitou: 15°. Muscat: 8°. **Served with:** Fitou: game, red meat and cheese. Muscat: as an aperitif or with dessert. **Vintages available in 89/90:** Fitou: 1977 (old reserve), 1985, 1986. Muscat: 1986.

Characteristics of vintages

1986: Fitou - aromatic, rich and well-balanced, elegant. Gold Medal (Concours agricole 1988). **1985:** To be aged, rich, well-balanced, full. Gold Medal at the Concours Général, 1987. **Other:** Muscat de Rivesaltes: to be tasted.

PAUL COLOMER

Tuchan - 11350 Aude
68 45 46 34

Type of vineyard: Family-owned.**Vine stocks:** Carignan, Grenache, Muscat, Cinsault, Syrah. **Soil:** Schistic. **Exposure:** Hillside facing South. **Average annual production in hectoliters:** 800.
Appellation: A.O.C. Fitou, Muscat de Rivesaltes A.O.C., Rivesaltes (red). **Type:** Red, white. **Technique:** Carbonic maceraton for the Fitou. **Maturing:** Concret vats, stainless steel and enamelled tanks. **Alcohol content:** 12.5 to 13%. **Characteristics:** Fitou: "purple-black" color, taste of

"black" fruit, balanced, rustic, non-agressive. Muscat: Unctuous and aromatic. **Serving temperature:** Fitou: room temperature. Muscat: cool. **Served with:** Fitou: Coq au Vin, Wild Boar Stew, game. Muscat: dessert. Rivesaltes: with melon or as an aperitif. **Vintages available in 89/90:** Fitou: 1986. Muscat: 1985. Rivesaltes: 1984.

Characteristics of vintages

1986: Fitou: Gold Medal at the "Concours Général Agricole". Principal Agricultural Competition. **1987:** Complex and spicy, rich and well-balanced, keeps well. Excellent Muscat. To be tasted.

MINERVOIS

CHÂTEAU FABAS
Jean-Pierre Ormières
11800 Laure-Minervois
68 78 17 82

Type of vineyard: Family-owned. **Established:** 1938. **Number of employees:** 3. **Vine stocks:** Grenache, Syrah, Mourvèdre, Carignant, Cinsautl, Maccabeu. **Soil:** Clay with calcium carbonate, gravel and flinty marl. **Exposure:** South. **Average annual production in hectoliters:** 2,000.
Appellation: Minervois. **Type:** Red, Rosé. **Technique:** Destemming, fermentation on skins for 22 days. Traditional with rigorous temperature control. **Maturing:** Vats, Oak casks and bottles. **Alcohol content:** 12%. **Characteristics:** Red: spicy, round tannins wooldland aroma. Rosé: dry and very aromatic, flowery. **Serving temperature:** Red: 15° to 17°. Rosé: 10°. **Served with:** Red: red meat, sauces. Rosé: delicatessen products, fish, shellfish, white meat. **Vintages available in 89/90:** (In 1989): Red: 1986, 1987. Rosé: 1988 – (In 1990): Red: 1986, 1987, 1988. Rosé: 1989. White: 1989.

Characteristics of vintages

1988: Very good structure, good tannins, round, soft and full, very aromatic, beautiful color, excellent year. **1987:** Limited stock – good balance, good structure, average keeping. **1986:** Excellent year for reds. **1985:** Very good year, soft and full wines, complex. **1984:** Quite good year, lively and fruity wines.
Represented by: T.P. Marshall, Nuits-Saint-Georges, 21700 France. Telex: 350 622 Tim Nuisg. Tel: 80 61 11 62 and H. Newman Vins Export 21200 Beaune – Telex: 350177 Newins – Tel: 80 22 70 87.

CAVE DES PRODUCTEURS
Jean Escande
11120 Pouzols – Minervois
68 46 13 76

Established: 1936. **Number of employees:** 3. **Vine stocks:** Carignan, Grenache, Cinsault, Syrah, Mourvèdre. **Average annual production in hectoliters:** 27000. **Appellation:** A.O.C. Minervois. **Type:** Red, white, rosé. **Technique:** Traditional, carbonic maceration. **Maturing:** In stainless steel tanks and large Oak casks. **Alcohol content:** 12.2%. **Characteristics:** White, dry, bright, fruity. Elegant, macerated red, ruby color. **Serving temperature:** Red tradition: 18/19°. Red (macerated): 17/18°. Rosé tradition: 10/12°. White tradition: 8°. **Vintages available in 89/90:** Red: 1983, 1985.

Characteristics of vintages

1988: Red: elegance and breed. White and Rosé: delicate and fruity - A great vintage. **1983** Red wine aged in Oak casks, denser, fragrant.

LES VIGNERONS DU HAUT MINERVOIS
34210 Azillanet
68 91 22 61

Type of vineyard: Cooperative Agricultural Association.

Established: 1922. **Number of employees:** 4. **Vine stocks:** Syrah, Grenache, Cinsault, Carignan. **Soil:** Hillsides. **Exposure:** South. **Average annual production in hectoliters:** 55,000.
Appellation: A.O.C. Minervois, Vin de Pays "Côtes-du-Brian". **Type:** Red, Rosé. **Technique:** Carbonic maceration. **Maturing:** Under inert atmosphere. **Alcohol content:** 11.5%. **Characteristics:** Fragrant, good color, red fruit taste. **Serving temperature:** Red: 14° to 15°. **Served with:** Red meat, game, cheese. **Vintages available in 89/90:** 1985, 1986, 1988.

Characteristics of vintages

1988: Deep color, red berry aromas, pleasant tannins. **1986:** Deep purple color, fruity, animal aroma.

DOMAINE DES HOMS
Bernard de Crozals
Rieux – 11800 Minervois
68 78 10 51

Type of vineyard: Family-owned. **Established:** 1930. **Number of employee:** 1. **Vine stocks:** Syrah, Carignan, Cinsault. **Soil:** Pebbly terraces, quartzite and sandstone.

Exposure: South. **Average annual production in hectoliters:** 1,300.
Appellation: A.O.C. Minervois. **Type:** Red. **Technique:** Long maceration after crushing. **Maturing:** In Oak casks and traditional. **Alcohol content:** 12.5%. **Characteristics:** Produced from a mixture of 60% Carignan, 10% Cinsault and 30% Cinsault, ruby color, elegant, balanced structure and aroma of small wild berries, mostly blackcurrant and rapsberry. Full, goes down well. **Serving temperature:** 16° to 18°. **Served with:** Red, meat, game, Cassoulet, stew. **Vintages available in 89/90:** 1980, 1981, 1982, 1984, 1985, 1986.

Characteristics of vintages

1986: Full of promise. **1985:** Very beautiful cherry color, supple, rich and well-balanced, fine bouquet, very aromatic. Ready to drink now but it can be aged. **1984:** Beautiful color, well-balanced, long, spicy, quite successful for this difficult vintage. **1982:** Beautiful, deep ruby color, fruit aromas with a touch of violet, very long. **Other:** 1981: Beautiful ruby color, soft and full, round, rich, well-balanced and full, at its peak (goes with all dishes).

LE PECH D'ANDRÉ

Marc and Germaine Remaury
Azillanet - 34210 Olonzac
68 91 22 66

Type of vineyard: Family-owned. **Established:** Approx. 300 years ago. **Number of employees:** 2. **Vine stocks:** 30% Carignan, 25% Syrah, 25% Mourvèdre, 20% Grenache. **Soil:** Clay with clacium carbonate. **Exposure:** South. **Average annual production in hectoliters:** 2,200 of which 1,000 are A.O.C.
Appellation: Minervois "Domaine du Pech d'André." **Type:** Red, rosé. **Technique:** Traditional with temperature control. **Maturing:** In bottles. **Alcohol content:** 12%. **Characteristics:** Fine and fruity. Principal aromas: pepper, liquorice for the Mourvèdre based wines, small red fruity for the Syrah based wines. **Serving temperature:** 16°. **Served with:** Grilled steak, delicatessen products, Cassoulet. **Vintages available in 89/90:** 1987.

Characteristics of vintages

1988: Minervois, very well developed, long, fine and elegant, with a bouquet of "wild" blackberries, very successful. Price range (pre-tax, ex-warehouse): Between 10 F.F. and 20 F.F. **1987:** Cuvée Jacques d'André: Syrah base, finesse, Lilac fragrence, long, aromatic. Minervois du Domaine: Mourvèdre base, rich and full-bodied, liquorice aroma, high quality tannin.
Sales volume:
- Retail: About 150 hectoliters. - Other: 600 hectoliters, sold by agents.
Sales in France: 75%.
Export sales: 25%.

Abroad

United Kingdom

Importers: - Majestic wines. - The Wine Schoppen Limited (Sheffield).

CHÂTEAU LA GRAVE

J. Orosquette
11800 Badens
68 79 01 69 or 68 79 16 00

Type of vineyard: Family-owned. **Established:** From father to son.
Appellation: A.O.C. Minervois, Vin de Pays des Hauts de Badens. **Type:** Red, white, rosé, cartagène. **Vintages available in 89/90:** 1983, 1985, 1986.

Characteristics of vintages

1985: Good red, pleasant flavor and aroma. Try the rosé. Price range (pre-tax, ex-warehouse): Between 10 F.F. and 20 F.F.
Sales volume:
- Retail: Yes. - Restaurants: Yes. - Other: Retailers, fine groceries.
Export sales: Increasing.
Main trading partners : Canada, Belgium, Netherlands.

CHÂTEAU VILLERAMBERT JULIEN

Lucette & Marcel Julien
11160 Caunes-Minervois
68 78 00 01 - Telex: 500 379 Chamco-Carca

Type of vineyard: 1850. **Number of employees:** 5. **Vine stocks:** 50% Carignan, Syrah, Grenache, Mourvèdre, Cinsault. **Soil:** Clay with calcium carbonate, schistic hillsides. **Exposure:** South. **Average annual production in hectoliters:** 3,500.
Appellation: Minervois A.O.C., Château Villerambert Julien. **Type:** Red, rosé. **Technique:** Classic and with maceration. **Maturing:** In Oak casks. **Alcohol content:** Red: 11.5%. Rosé: 12%. **Characteristics:** Rich and well-balanced aroma with nuances. Balanced taste, firm and vigorous, harmonious structure which will allow it to develop without losing any of its quality. **Serving temperature:** Red: 17°. Rosé: Cold. **Served with:** Red: the entire meal. Rosé: salads, first coursed, fish, dessert. **Vintages available in 89/90:** 1986.

Characteristics of vintages

1988: Rosé: extremely promising - same characteristics as the Rosé 1986. **1987:** Rosé: almost out of stock - Cuvée Prestige - matured in new oak casks, awarded Gold Medal at the Concours Général Agricole de Paris: long, fruity, good alcohol/tannin/aroma balance. Beautiful dark ruby color. Described as "silky" by the English. **1986:** Rosé: out of stock. Red: now on sale.

DOMAINE MARIS JACQUES

34210 La Livinière
68 91 42 63

Type of vineyard: Family-owned. **Established:** For several generations. **Vine stocks:** Red and rosé: Carignan and Cinsault. The Grenache and Syrah produce breeding and warmth. White: Maccabera for an abundant flowery aroma. **Average annual production in hectoliters:** 3,500.
Appellation: Minervois, Vin de Pays Coteaux de Peyriac. **Type:** Red, white, rosé. Other sparkling, champagne method. **Maturing:** Oak casks. **Alcohol content:** 12%. **Characteristics:** Red: good color, rich and well-balanced, red fruit and woodland fragrance. White: dry, flowery, quite long. **Vintages available in 89/90:** 1986, 1987.

Characteristics of vintages

1986: Good wines, specially the reds. Typical and fragrant.

DOMAINE DE LA SEICHE

Suzanne de Faucompret
La Livinière - 34210 Olonzac
68 91 42 87 - 59 62 71 21

Type of vineyard: Family-owned. **Established:** 1420. **Number of employee:** 1. **Vine stocks:** Carignan, Cinsault, Grenache, Syrah. **Soil:** Chalky hillsides, alluvial soil, schistic, granitic, gravel, rich in mineral salts. **Exposure:** South, very sunny dry climate. **Average annual production in hectoliters:** 1,000.
Appellation: A.O.C. Minervois. **Type:** Red. **Technique:** Traditional and natural. **Maturing:** In Oak casks. **Alcohol content:** 11,5% to 13%. **Characteristics:** Light, supple and velvety red wine, will age, well fragrant. **Serving temperature:** 18°. **Served with:** Red meat in sauce, cheese, game, Cassoulet. **Vintages available in 89/90:** 1982.

PICPOUL DE PINET

DOMAINE GAUJAL

Claude Gaujal
B.P. N° 1 - 34850 Pinet
67 77 02 12

Type of vineyard: Family-owned. **Established:** 1743. **Number of employees:** 3. **Vine stocks:** Picpoul 25%, Sauvignon 10%, Merlot 20%, Others 45%. **Soil:** Clay with calcium carbonate. **Exposure:** South. **Average annual production in hectoliters:** 5,000.
Appellation: Picpoul de Pinet. **Type:** White. **Maturing:** In vats. **Alcohol content:** 12.5%. **Characteristics:** The Gaujal wines are known for their fine aroma, character, and length. Light straw color. **Serving temperature:** 6° to 8°. **Served with:** Seafood, shellfish, fish, asparagus. **Vintages available in 89/90:** 1988.

Characteristics of vintages

1988: Beautiful wine, fine, soft and harmonious, good color, pronounced aroma, gold medal.

SAINT-CHINIAN

CHÂTEAU COUJAN

Guy et Peyre
34490 Murviel
67 37 80 00

Type of vineyard: Family-owned. **Established:** For six generations. **Vine stocks:** Mourvèdre 40%, Grenache 30%, Cinsaut 30%. **Soil:** Miocene pebbles on coral base.
Appellation: AOC Saint-Chinian. **Type:** Red. **Technique:** destemming, temperature control, fermentation (10 days). **Alcohol content:** 11.5%. **Characteristics:** Light, long finish, full-bodied, blackcurrant and cooked rasberry aromas, wines that age well and can be kept for 10 years. **Serving temperature:** 14 to 17°. **Vintages available in 89/90:** 1988, 1987, 1986, 1985, 1983.

Characteristics of vintages

1987: Light in color, ripe cherry aroma, elegant, bottled in october 1988. **1986:** Strength and finesse, bottled in October 1987. **1985:** Excellent but must be aged. Price range (pre-tax, ex-warehouse): 20, 30, 50, 80 F.F.
Sales volume:
– Retail: 50%. – Restaurants: 25%. – Other: 25% (cellars).
Sales in France: 80%.
Export sales: 20%.
Main trading partners : UK, Germany, Belgium, Switzerland.

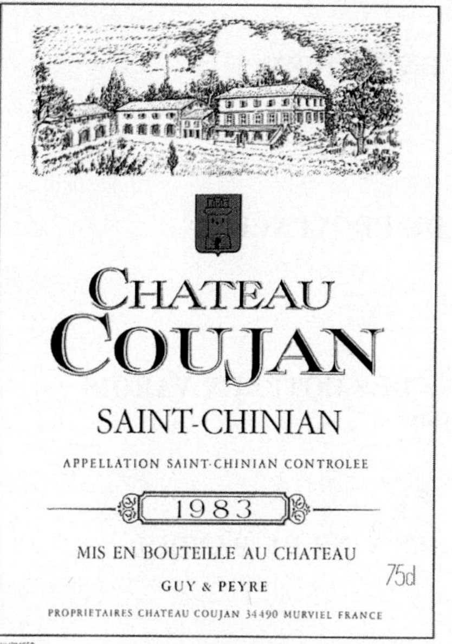

References in France

Restaurants: All good restaurants of the region.

Abroad

United Kingdom

Eldridge Pope & Co.

Comments

This Gallo-Roman estate, inhabited since time immemorial, has been recognized by the media as producing the zenith of the Appellations. In this peaceful setting, well shaded, is also a bird sanctuary where hunting is prohibited. Excellent wine for tasting, a warm welcome and good conversation are all provided by the proprietor and his family.

• Watch out for wines that lose their authenticity, most often because of carbonic maceration (see Roussillon, South-west, Périgord...).

LANGUEDOC ROUSSILLON

COMITÉ INTERPROFESSIONNEL DES COSTIÈRES DU GARD
Domaine de la Bastide
Président : Jack Darboux
30000 NIMES - Route de Générac
Tél. : 66.38.02.23

CONSEIL INTERPROFESSIONNEL DES VINS DE FITOU, CORBIÈRES, MINERVOIS
Coteaux occitans
Président : Yves Barsalou
11200 LÉZIGNAN-CORBIÈRES
Route Nationale 113
Tél. : 68.27.03.64

COMITÉ INTERPROFESSIONNEL DES COTEAUX DU LANGUEDOC
Domaine de Maurin
Président : Jean-Claude Bousquet
34972 LATTES
B.P. 9 - Tél. : 67.27.84.11

GROUPEMENT INTERPROFESSIONNEL DES CÔTES DU ROUSSILLON ET DES CÔTES DU ROUSSILLON VILLAGES
19, avenue de Grande-Bretagne
Président : M. Salies
66000 PERPIGNAN - Tél. : 68.51.31.81

SYNDICAT DE LA BLANQUETTE DE LIMOUX
29, route de Carcassonne
Président : Achille Gayda
Directeur : Georges Pous
11300 LIMOUX - Tél. : 68.31.67.77

SYNDICAT DE LA CLAIRETTE DU LANGUEDOC
Aspiran
34800 CLERMONT-L'HÉRAULT
Tél. : 67.96.50.37

SYNDICAT DES COTEAUX DU LANGUEDOC
Domaine de Maurin - B.P. 9
34970 LATTES - Tél. : 67.27.84.11

SYNDICAT DU CRU CORBIÈRES
Route Nationale 113
Boîte Postale 111 - M. Bergès
11200 LÉZIGNAN-CORBIÈRES
Tél. : 68.27.04.34

SYNDICAT DE DÉFENSE DU FITOU
Route Nationale 113
11200 LÉZIGNAN-CORBIÈRES
Tél. : 67.86.00.09

SYNDICAT DU CRU MINERVOIS
10, boulevard Louis-Blazin
34210 OLONZAC - Tél. : 68.91.21.66

PROVENCE-CÔTE-D'AZUR

COMITÉ INTERPROFESSIONNEL DES VINS
DE CÔTES DE PROVENCE
Maison des Vins - Route Nationale 7
Président : Guy Négrel
83460 LES ARCS-SUR-ARGENS
Tél. : 94.73.33.38

SYNDICAT DES COTEAUX D'AIX-EN-PROVENCE
Avenue H.-Pontier
13626 AIX-EN-PROVENCE
Tél. : 42.23.57.14

SYNDICAT DES VINS DE CÔTES DE PROVENCE
M. André Garnoux
83460 LES ARCS-SUR-ARGENS
Tél. : 64.73.31.01

SYNDICAT DE DÉFENSE DES VINS DES COTEAUX VAROIS
15, avenue Maréchal-Foch - M. Régnier
83170 BRIGNOLES
Tél. : 94.69.02.08

SYNDICAT DES PRODUCTEURS DES VINS DE BANDOL
Le Prieuré - Avenue J.-Soulin
83740 LA CADIÈRE-D'AZUR
Tél. : 94.90.00.89

CORSE

GROUPEMENT INTERPROFESSIONNEL DES VINS
DE L'ILE DE CORSE
6, rue Gabriel-Péri
Président : François Orsucci
20200 BASTIA
Tél. : 95.31.37.36

CIVAM
6, rue Gabriel-Péri
20200 BASTIA
Tél. : 95.31.36.30

PROVENCE
CÔTE D'AZUR
CORSE

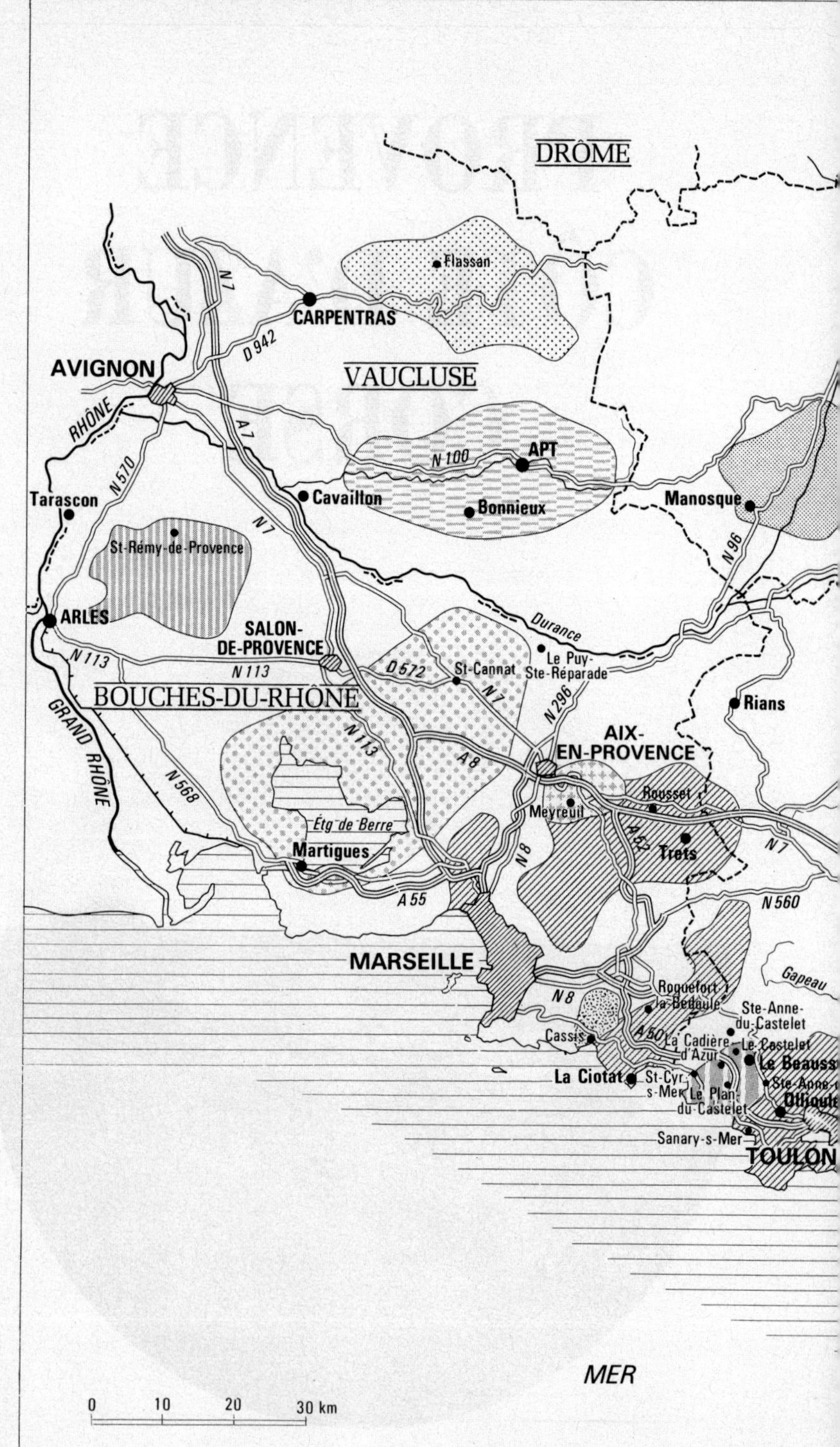
DRÔME
Flassan
CARPENTRAS
N7
D 942
AVIGNON
VAUCLUSE
RHÔNE
A7
N 100
APT
N 570
Tarascon
Cavaillon
Bonnieux
Manosque
N7
St-Rémy-de-Provence
N 96
ARLES
SALON-
DE-PROVENCE
Durance
Le Puy-
Ste-Réparade
N 113
N 113
D 572
St-Cannat
N7
BOUCHES-DU-RHÔNE
N 296
Rians
GRAND RHÔNE
N 113
AIX-
EN-PROVENCE
A8
N 568
Rousset
Meyreuil
Étg de Berre
A 52
Trets
N7
N8
Martigues
A 55
N 560
MARSEILLE
Gapeau
Roquefort-
la-Bédoule
N8
Ste-Anne-
du-Castelet
Cassis
A 50
La Cadière-
d'Azur
Le Castelet
Le Beauss
La Ciotat
St-Cyr-
s-Mer
Le Plan-
du-Castelet
Ste-Anne-
Ollioule
Sanary-s-Mer
TOULON
MER
0
10
20
30 km

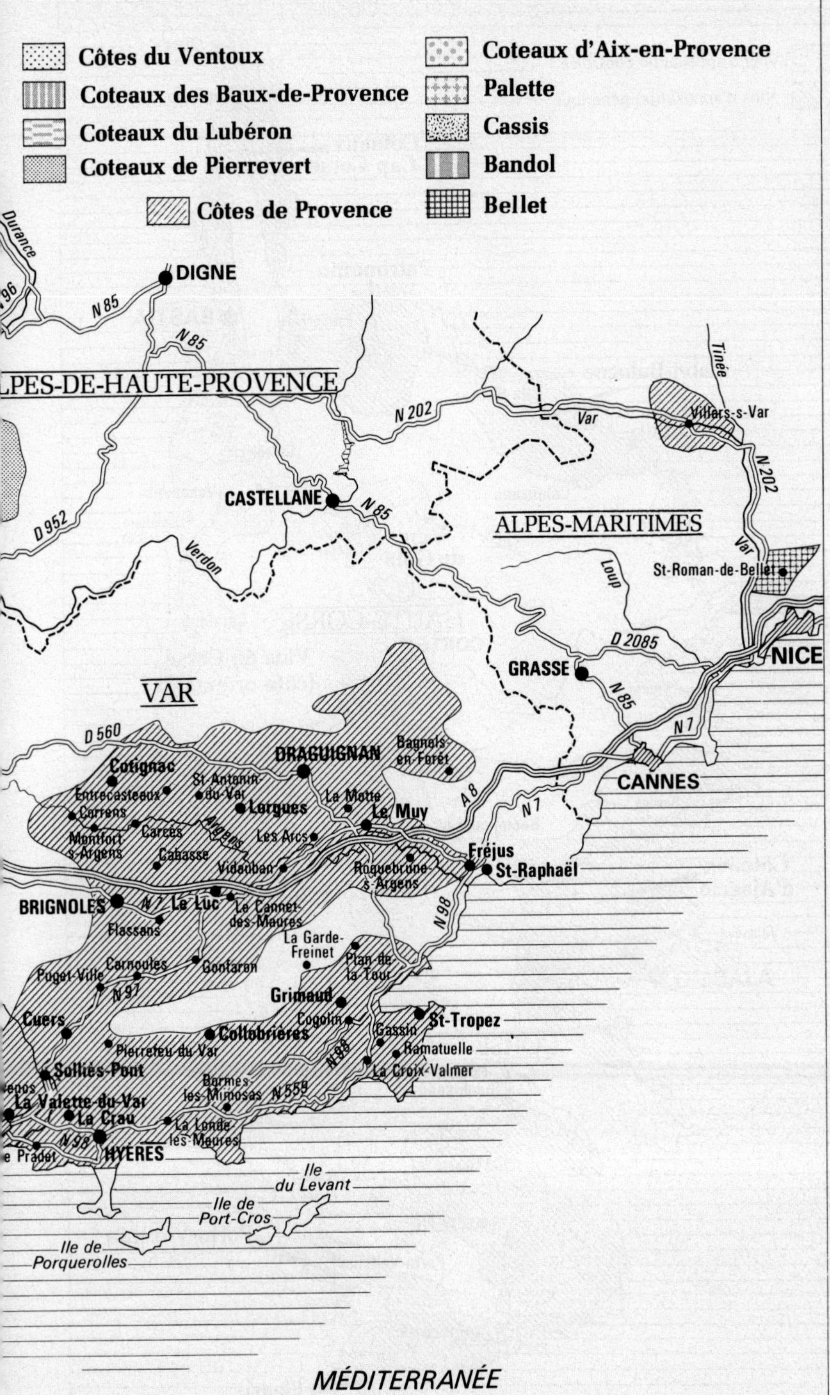

Côtes du Ventoux
Coteaux des Baux-de-Provence
Coteaux du Lubéron
Coteaux de Pierrevert
Côtes de Provence
Coteaux d'Aix-en-Provence
Palette
Cassis
Bandol
Bellet
Durance
DIGNE
N 85
N 85
LPES-DE-HAUTE-PROVENCE
N 202
Var
Tinée
Villars-s-Var
N 202
CASTELLANE
N 85
D 952
Verdon
ALPES-MARITIMES
Var
Loup
St-Roman-de-Bellet
D 2085
NICE
GRASSE
N 85
VAR
D 560
DRAGUIGNAN
Bagnols-en-Forêt
N 7
CANNES
Cotignac
St-Antonin-du-Var
Entrecasteaux
Correns
Lorgues
Le Motte
Le Muy
A 8
N 7
Montfort-s-Argens
Carcès
Argens
Les Arcs
Cabasse
Vidauban
Roquebrune-s-Argens
Fréjus
St-Raphaël
BRIGNOLES
N 7
Le Luc
Le Cannet-des-Maures
Flassans
N 98
La Garde-Freinet
Plan-de-la-Tour
Puget-Ville
Carnoules
Gonfaron
N 97
Grimaud
Cogolin
Cuers
Collobrières
Gassin
St-Tropez
Ramatuelle
Pierrefeu-du-Var
N 98
Solliès-Pont
La Croix-Valmer
Bormes-les-Mimosas
N 559
La Valette-du-Var
La Crau
La Londe-les-Maures
N 98
HYÈRES
Ile du Levant
Ile de Port-Cros
Ile de Porquerolles
MÉDITERRANÉE

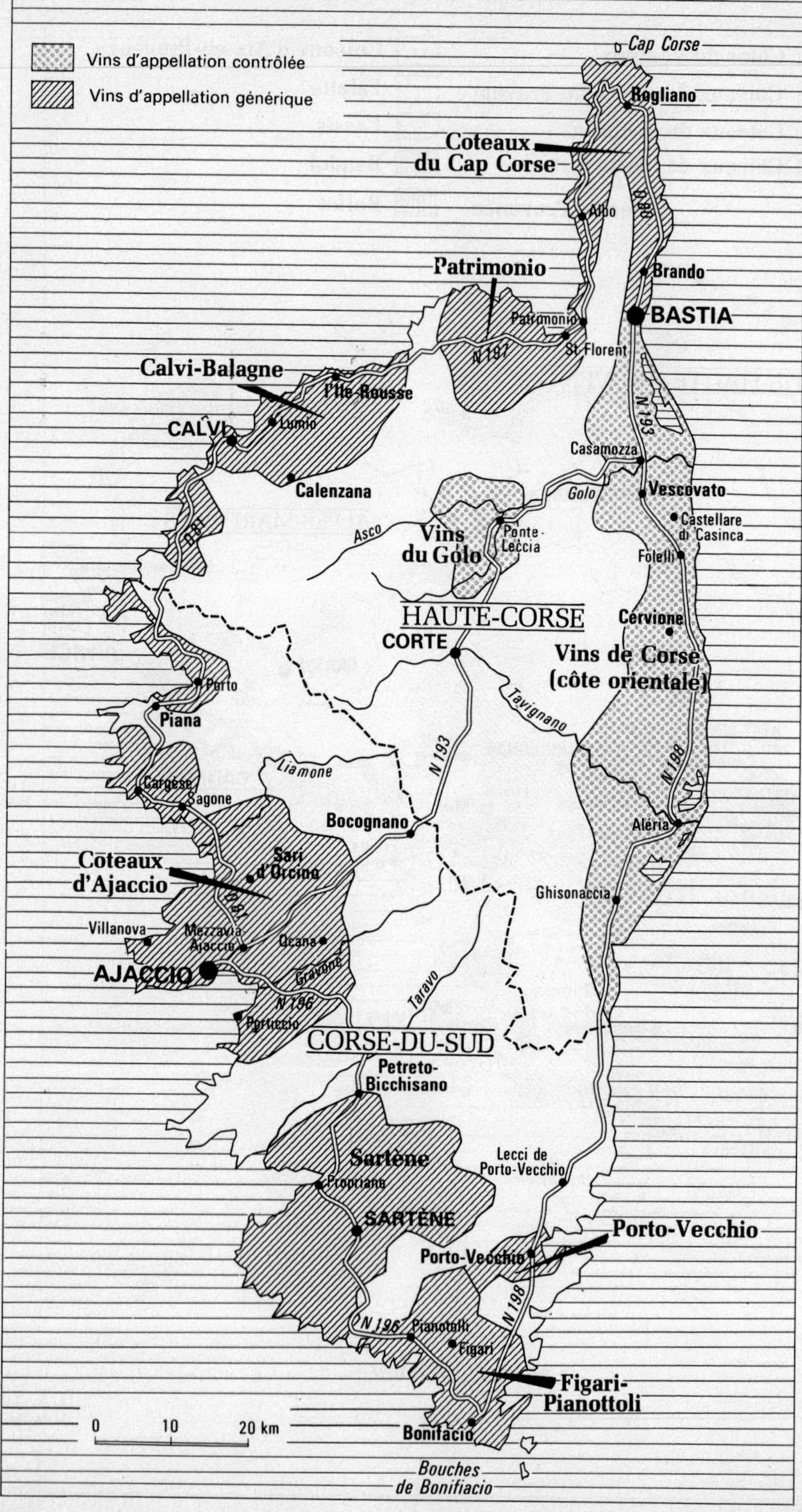
Vins d'appellation contrôlée
Vins d'appellation générique
Cap Corse
Rogliano
Coteaux du Cap Corse
Albo
Brando
BASTIA
Patrimonio
St Florent
N 197
Calvi-Balagne
l'Ile-Rousse
Lumio
CALVI
Calenzana
Casamozza
Golo
Vescovato
Castellare di Casinca
Folelli
Asco
Vins du Golo
Ponte-Leccia
N 193
HAUTE-CORSE
CORTE
Cervione
Vins de Corse (côte orientale)
Tavignano
Porto
Piana
Liamone
N 198
Cargèse
Sagone
Bocognano
Aléria
Coteaux d'Ajaccio
Sari d'Orcino
Ghisonaccia
Villanova
Mezzavia
Ajaccio
Ocana
AJACCIO
Gravone
N 196
Taravo
Porticcio
CORSE-DU-SUD
Petreto-Bicchisano
Sartène
Propriano
Lecci de Porto-Vecchio
SARTÈNE
Porto-Vecchio
Pianotolli
Figari
Figari-Pianottoli
0
10
20 km
Bonifacio
Bouches de Bonifiacio

The good wines and the others

Although the entire region, with all of its appellations taken into consideration, now produces exceptional wines, it remains exceedingly perplexing for the consumer. In fact, on this very extensive territory (extending from Arles to Nice, from Marseille to Avignon!) you can find just about everything: reds, whites, rosés, a few quality wines, some very ordinary wines and some great ones, about ten appellations, wines that don't deserve them and others that deserve better. That is why – for the first time – I have prepared a classification of the Provence-Côte d'Azur wines starting in 86 (see "89/90 Classification"), which makes it abundantly clear that the AOCs don't mean a thing and that only a few isolated producers are really right up there... The best are in this year's Guide.

HISTORICAL BACKGROUND

The vineyards of Provence were planted as early as 600 B.C., but they were destroyed by the Moors in the 10th century. The fact that Marseilles—or Massalia at it was called in ancient times—was founded by the Greeks is a strong indication that they took part in planting and caring for the vineyards. They also bequeathed a vocabulary of vine-growing terms as well as the technique of wine pruning, a key to improving grapes.

The Greeks were equally skillful merchants. They used the port of Marseilles to export the ceramic amphoral jars they made. The amphoras were used as wine containers.

The wine trade flourished. A cluster of grapes was even depicted on coins. Vineyards were originally concentrated around Massalia, then little by little they spread to Cavaillon and Avignon. Several centuries later the Romans followed the example of the Greeks by expanding wine trading in the eastern part of the Mediterranean.

Monks, especially the Benedictines, brought their skills to the vineyards of Provence. In 1023, someone by the name of Stéphane donated the vineyards of La Cadière, near Bandol, to the Abbey of St. Victor. The abbey has existed officially since 1715 thanks to Boyer Foresta who signed the act of foundation, anticipating that the city would grow to a more than adequate size. Foresta brought onto these lands a variety of merchants, including a distiller and a transporter.

The act of foundation allowed the lord to be granted a tithe on the peasants' harvests. He also gave himself the right to open a tavern in July where he could sell his wines on a wholesale as well as retail basis. In the 1750s, the port of Bandol gave the wine trade impressive opportunities for expansion.

The name that remains dear to the residents of Provence is that of King René, count of Provence. He made Marseilles a free port, thus further favoring the wine trade. He introduced the Muscat grape and helped develop *claret* and rosé wines.

THE WINES

• **COTES DE PROVENCE (A.O.C.).** The Côtes de Provence vineyard has its roots in the Bouches du Rhône department, at the foot of the Sainte Victoire Mountain. It then works round the Sainte-Baume massif and finds its way in the Var, where, after skirting the shores of the Mediterranean, it runs into the foot-hills of the Estérel. Here it is the art of man that counts.

• **BANDOL (A.O.C.).** The reds lead the way. Made from the fabulous Mourvèdre (which provides bouquet, body and roundness) the good Bandol reds can prove exceptional indeed. Full-bodied, elegant, soft, rich and aromatic, they must be aged to give their full measure. The rosés, natural and fruity, deserve a gold star, and so do the whites.

• **CASSIS (A.O.C.).** Whites, rosés and reds favored, like those of Bandol, by an exceptionnaly good climate and the kindly disposition of the Mistral Winds which clean the plants and provides, each year, almost unvarying temperatures.

• **PALETTE (A.O.C.).** Appellation assigned to a very small region near Aix en Provence whose soil is mainly crumbled limestone.

• **BELLET (A.O.C.).** Very old and confidential vineyard consisting mainly of local varieties (Folle noire, Braquet for reds, mostly Rolle for whites) planted on soil rich in silica.

Another thing: a few propretors of the Coteaux d'Aix make wine a far cry above those of their neighbors. Make sure to taste the Côtes du Lubéron (See classification).

THE CHARACTERISTICS OF THE VINEYARD

The winegrowing region of Provence, as distinct from the former province of the same name, includes four main regions: the Massif de Maures; the depression extending from Toulon to Saint-Raphaël; the plateaus which stretch from Cotignac to Draguignan; and Arc, bordered on the north by the Montagne Sainte Victoire.

Soil

In Provence, the soil is a mixture of formations representing the full range of maritime and continental geological ages. The soil also contains crystalline rock mineral deposits.

Climate

The vineyards of Provence are protected from cold winds by the ?? Mountains and consequently thrive in a mild and sunny climate. The region is one of France's most fortunate, with over ?? days of sunshine annually and very little rainfall.

CORSICA IN BRIEF

Corsica is an island (the third largest in the Mediterranean). It is also a mountain growing right out of the sea. This mountain, which slashes the island from North-West to South-East for almost 200 kilometers, has 20 peaks more than 2,000 meters high, with two very different mountainsides.

To the West lies the Hercynian Corsica. Sharp crests springing from the long dorsal ridge plunge abruptly into the sea. It is a compartmented Corsica, made up of a number of small valleys bathed by torrents which, tumultous in the winter and sping, turn to a mere trickle in summer. The coastline is extraordinary, with capes, long deep gulfs, headlands and beaches giving on incomparably pure waters.

To the East the predominant features are the Alpine folds which create a disorderly proliferation of hills and cliffs and very varied hillsides. The narrow, alluvial coast, is the only plain on the island and is rather limited in surface. This is not Sardinia, nor even Majorca. Its waters, which abound with fish, extend inland into large salt lakes (Diana, Biguglia, Urbino). These geographical features are confirmed by geological data.

There is a crystalline Corsica: it lies on the West coast (reminiscent of the soil of the Upper-Beaujolais) with its various granites (prophyroids in Calvi and Ajaccio, mixed with biotite around Calvi, more on the granulite side in the Sartène region).

- With its granulites bearing two kinds of mica and others composed of salt.
- With its diorites near Ajaccio and Figari.
- With its crystalline schists at Ajaccio and South-East of Porto-Vecchio.

There is a schistous Corsica: to the East, with its sericite mica schists, its glaucophane schists and its more or less serpintine green ophites.

There is a sedimentary Corsica: in the zone that connects la Balagne to Corte.

There is, finally, a limestone Corsica: At Bonifacio, but also at Patrimonio.

The climate, on the other hand, is a unifying factor, condusive to winegrowing. It is a temperate maritime Mediterranean climate, with mild temperatures, relatively abundant precipitation and remarkable sunshine. The lighting is exceptional and is associated with an average of at least 2,450 hours of sunshine per year, which in some places exceeds 2,760 hours (1958 - Ajaccio, 2,763 hours - Bastia, 2,688). It is, therefore, not surprising that, thanks to such favorable climatic conditions over 62% of the island, extending even to the bottoms of the valleys, the vines have scaled the hillsides and are even cultivated at altitudes of 400 and 500 meters. The island geography has divided the country into valleys, providing plenty of sunshine for cultivation and other economic activities and pretty much fragmenting the growing regions, differentiating processing techniques and creating an overall diversity.

THE WINE GRAPES

Local vinestocks: Their implantantion makes it possible to distinguish the regions of traditional cultivation from the recent vineyards which only represent 8% of the total.

— **Nielluccio** (red), inseparable from the wines of Patrimonio, yields fragrant, rich and well-balanced wines that keep well.

— **Sciacarello** (red), cultivated, for the most part, at Sartène, Ajaccio, Balagne and in the Figari and Porto-Vecchio regions. Its wine is light and distinguished.

— **Vermentino** (white) which acquires a very rich sugar content when overripe. It must be harvested rapidly to avoid its tendency to over-oxidation.

Complementary vinestocks: Syrah and Cabernet (1 to 2%).

Provence vinestocks: Grenache, Cinsault, Alicante, Carignan represent 60 to 70% of the varieties in the recent vineyards.

Other vinestocks: Malvoisie (for the Muscats), Ugni Blanc, Genovese, Barbarossa, Riminese (a little on Cap Corse). . . .

PROVENCE-CÔTE D'AZUR CLASSIFICATION
(In alphabetical order)

RED WINES

	BANDOL	CÔTES-DE-PROVENCE
①	Domaine LAFRAN-VEYROLLES Domaine LA LAIDIÈRE Château PRADEAUX Domaine TEMPIER Domaine des TERRES BRUNES	Château MINUTY Dom. de ST-ANDRÉ-DE-FIGUIÈRES Château SAINT-PIERRE Château SAINTE-ROSELINE
②	Domaine de L'HERMITAGE Mas de LA ROUVIÈRE Moulin des COSTES Domaine de L'OLIVETTE* Domaine de PIBARNON Château ROMASSAN Château SAINTE-ANNE	Domaine de LA BERNARDE Domaine des BAUX Domaine de CASTEL ROUBINE Commanderie de PEYRASSOL Château de ROUX Domaine de ST-BAILLON Château de SELLE Château SAINT-GEORGES
③	Domaine du CAGUELOUP Domaine LE GALANTIN Château VANNIÈRES**	Château BARBEYROLLES* Domaine de LA CRESSONNIÈRE Domaine CURÉBÉASSE Domaine de GRAND-BOISE Domaine du JAS D'ESCLANS* Domaine de LA MARTINETTE Domaine de LA NAVARRE Château du ROUET
④	Domaine de la FRÉGATE Domaine des SALETTES	Mas CADENET Château MENTONE

	COTEAUX	DIVERS
Beyond Classi-fication	Château VIGNELAURE (Coteaux d'Aix)	
①	Commanderie de LA BARGEMONE (Coteaux d'Aix) Château LA COSTE (Cot. d'Aix)	Château de BELLET (Bellet)
②	Dom. de FONSCOLOMBE (Cot. d'Aix) Dom. de LA VALLONGUE (Cot. des Baux)*	Château SIMONE (Palette)
③	Château LA CANORGUE (Côtes-du-Lubéron) Ch. de CALISSANNE (Cot. d'Aix) Ch. SAINT-ESTÈVE (Coteaux Varois) Domaine des TERRES BLANCHES* (Coteaux des Baux) Dom. de TREVALLON (Cot. des Baux)	
④	Mas de LA DAME (Coteaux des Baux) Dom. de DEFFENDS (Cot. Varois)* Château de la GAUDE (Coteaux d'Aix) Mas de GOURGONNIER (Cot. des Baux)* Ch. de MILLE (Côtes-du-Lubéron) Château du SEUIL (Coteaux d'Aix)	

*** Might deserve a better rating in certain vintages.**

WHITE WINES

	BANDOL	CÔTES-DE-PROVENCE
Beyond Classi-fication		Clos MIREILLE
①	Domaine BASTIDE BLANCHE	Domaine LA BERNARDE Dom. de CASTEL ROUBINE Domaine des FERAUD Château MINUTY
②	Domaine de L'HERMITAGE Domaine LA LAIDIÈRE Domaine de L'OLIVETTE Château SAINTE-ANNE	Domaine des ASPRAS Dom. de MALHERBE Château de ROUX Château SAINTE-ROSELINE*
③	Domaine de LAFRAN-VEYROLLES Domaine de PIBARNON*	Domaine de l'AUMERADE Domaine de CAMPDUMY Domaine de CURÉBÉASSE Château MENTONE Château SAINT-PIERRE*
④		Château des BORMETTES Domaine de RIMAURESCQ*

	COTEAUX	DIVERS
Beyond Classi-fication		Château SIMONE (Palette)
①		Château de FONTBLANCHE
②	Château LA COSTE (Coteaux d'Aix)	Domaine du BAGNOL (Cassis) Clos BOUDARD (Cassis)
③	Château de BEAULIEU (Cot. d'Aix) Domaine les BASTIDES (Cot. d'Aix)	

*** Might deserve a better rating in certain vintages.**

**** Should be "marked down" a bit because it lacks the typical nature of the other great wines of the appellation.**

ROSÉ WINES

	BANDOL	CÔTES-DE-PROVENCE
①	Moulin des COSTES	Château de BARBEYROLLES
②	Domaine LAFRAN-VEYROLLES Domaine de l'OLIVETTE Château SAINTE-ANNE Domaine TEMPIER	Domaine de LA BERNARDE Domaine CASTEL ROUBINE* Mas CADENET Château de GRAND-BOISE Château de GRAND-PRÉ Domaine de MALHERBE Commanderie de PEYRASSOL* Château SAINT-PIERRE
③	Domaine des SALETTES Château SAINTE-ANNE	Domaine de LA CRESSONNIÈRE* Domaine de CURÉBÉASSE Château de SELLE Château LA BEGUDE Château REDON* Domaine SAINT-BAILLON*
④	Château VANNIÈRES	Château de SAINT-MARTIN

	COTEAUX	DIVERS
①	Château LA COSTE (Cot. d'Aix) Domaine de LA VALLONGUE	Château de BELLET (Bellet)
②	Domaine de LOOU	Château SIMONE (Palette)
③	Mas de LA DAME Château du SEUIL (Cot. d'Aix) Domaine des TERRES BLANCHES	Domaine du BAGNOL (Cassis)

*** Might deserve a better rating in certain vintages.**

CÔTES DE PROVENCE

DOMAINE DE L'ABBAYE

Petit Franc
83340 Le Thoronet
94 73 87 36 – Telex: 970 842

Type of vineyard: family-owned. **Established:** 1979. **Number of employees:** 3 plus an engineer and laboratory assistant. **Vine stocks:** Ugni, Rolle, Clairette, Cinsault, Grenache, Cabernet, Syrah. **Soil:** Chalky clay. **Average annual production in hectoliters:** 1,250 and increasing.

Appellation: Côtes de Provence. **Type:** Red, white, rosé. **Technique:** Blanc de Blanc and rosé: by drawing off. **Maturing:** in vats and new casks. **Alcohol content:** 12%. **Characteristics:** Blanc de Blancs: fruity, harmonious, can be kept 4 years. Rosé de Saignée (known as «one nigth» rosé): natural vinification, pale color. Red: very aromatic, great wine, rich and balanced, for keeping. **Serving temperature:** White, rosé: 10°. **Served with:** Rosé: shellfish, fish, white meat, aubergine salad. White: oysters, shellfish. Red: grilled meat in sauce, game. **Vintages available in 89/90:** Red: 1982-1983-1984-1985-1986. White: 1984-1987-1988. Rosé: 1987-1988.

Characteristics of vintages

1987: Blanc de Blanc: Dry, fruity, gun flint aroma. Rosé de Saignée: round, elegant, goes down well. **1986:** Red: toast, coffee (grilled meat). **1985:** Red: good to drink now or to keep. Price range (pre-tax, ex-warehouse): between 30 F.F. and 50 F.F.

Sales volume:
– Wholesale: 15% (in bulk). – Retail: 10%. – Restaurants: 40%. – Other: 15% (winecellars), 20% (export).
Sales in France: 80%.
Export sales: 20%.
Main trading partners: Hong Kong, Japan, Germany, Antilles.

References in France

Restaurants: La Corniche, Les Roches, Cap Brune Restaurant, Lustrin, Byblos, Palm-Beach, Hostellerie de l'Abbaye, La Bouillabaisse, Le Régal, Royal, la Mère Besson, Compostalle, Le Flambart, le Queen Victoria, Arvèdre.
Shops: Tastevin (Wagram), Musée du Vin (Paris), Cave à Nemorois, Malun, etc.

Abroad

Germany

Baldauf (Cologne).

Far East

Japan: Ken Internationale; President Club. Hong Kong: Lucullus. Vin dans le Group Peninsula.

Others

Antilles: St. Barth, Mr. Courtois, Tahiti.

Comments

The estated belonged to a 12th century Cistercian Abbey. It was abandoned for 40 years, then sold and subdivided. In 1979, it was entirely redone – cellars, warehouse, museum, residence, park, etc. Originally cultivated by the monks of the Abbey, the estate was entirely renovated, new cellars and a museum created. All of the vines are well exposed to the sun. Manual harvesting yields 40 hectoliters per hectare. This all confirms the estate's motto which is to make quality, distinguished wines, respecting tradition and natural procedures.

DOMAINE DE LA BERNARDE

Mr. Meulnart
83340 Le Luc
94 60 07 31

Type of vineyard: Family-owned. **Vine stocks:** (33 hectares): Syrah, Cabernet, Mourvèdre, Grenache, Cinsault. **Soil:** Clay with calcium carbonate.
Appellation: Côtes-de-Provence. **Type:** Red, white, rosé. **Technique:** Hand harvesting, rigorous vinification. **Maturing:** Traditional. **Characteristics:** Red: beautiful color,

very fragrant, combining balance and finesse, keeps well. White: dry and vigorous, very flowery (see Classification) Rosé: clean and supple taste, fragrant. **Served with:** the entire meal. **Vintages available in 89/90:** 1985, 1986 and 1987.

Characteristics of vintages

1986: Good year. Excellent whites and reds, supple and structured. **1985:** Remarkable red, good ageing potential.

References in France

Shops: L'Amour du Vin, 94, rue Saint-Dominique, 75007 Paris. Tél: 45 56 12 94.

MAS DE CADENET

13530 Trets
42 29 21 59 Telefax: 42 61 32 09
Telex: 430 301 F poste 213

Type of vineyard: Family-owned. **Vine stocks:** Grenache, Cinsautl, Syrah, Cabernet, Mourvèdre, Ugni Blanc, Clairette, Rolle. **Exposure:** hillsides facing full South at the foot of the Ste. Victoire Mountain. **Average annual production in hectoliters:** 2500.

Appellation: AOC Côtes de Provence. **Type:** Red, White, Rose. **Technique:** traditional, devatting for rosé. **Maturing:** Red: in oak casks. **Alcohol content:** 12%. **Characteristics:** Red: peppery nose, deep color, full-bodied and well-balanced. White: almond and nut flavor, lively and fresh. Rosé: firm, light and supple, very aromatic. **Serving temperature:** Rosé and white: 8° – Red: 15°. **Served with:** the entire meal. **Vintages available in 89/90:** 1988-1987-1986.

Characteristics of vintages

1988: Red: very deep color, complex and rich bouquet with multiple flowery and fruity aromas. Full-bodied, admirable finish. Well made wine that must be aged. A very great year. Rosé: beautiful bright color, flowery aroma (broom) and citrus fruit, fresh, fine and fruity (red berry) excellent aromatic finish. White: beautiful crytalline color, very fruity nose, touch of exotic aromas, fresh, lingering flavor. Price range (pre-tax, ex-warehouse): 15 F. and 25 F.
Sales in France: 80%.
Export sales: 20%.
Main trading partners : Switzerland, Belgium, Germany, Netherlands, Denmark, Austria, USA.

Comments

Paleontological mini-exhibition (dinosaur eggs, various fossils). Receptions in the winecellars.

DOMAINE DE BRIGUE

Fernand Brun
2, place Pasteur – 83340 Le Luc
94 60 74 38

Type of vineyard: Family-owned. **Established:** Old family property. Wine-cellar in 1972. **Number of employees:** 5. **Vine stocks:** Grenache, Cinsault, Mourvèdre, Syrah, Cabernet, Sauvignon, Tibouren. **Soil:** Clay with calcium carbonate on crumbly red soil. **Exposure:** Southeast. **Average annual production in hectoliters:** 3,500.
Appellation: Côtes-de-Provence. **Type:** Red, white, rosé. **Technique:** Traditional. **Alcohol content:** 12%. **Characteristics:** Supple, pleasant tasting, very typical rosé. **Serving temperature:** 15-28°. **Served with:** The rosé goes well with hors-d'œuvre, meat, fish and cheese. **Vintages available in 89/90:** 1985 (red), 1988 (red, rosé, white).

Characteristics of vintages

1988: Good rosé, pleasant and fragrant, seductive. Red: good color, rich and well-balanced, typical of the area. **1985:** Red Cuvée Spéciale: very successful. Price range (pre-tax, ex-warehouse): Between 11 F.F. and 30 F.F.
Sales volume:
– Wholesales: 5%. – Retail: 90%. – Restaurants: 5%.
Sales in France: 100%.

References in France

Restaurants: Palm Beach Restaurant, Cannes.

L'ESTANDON
J. BAGNIS & FILS
CUERS
CÔTES DE PROVENCE
27, rue Verdi, 06000 NICE - Tél. : 93.88.97.61 - Télex : 470232 - Télécopie : 93.16.05.38

"L'ESTANDON"

Bagnis family
27-29 rue Verdi 06200 Nice (Headquarters)
93 88 97 61 (Nice) – 94 48 55 20 (Cuers)
Telex: 470 232 (Nice) – 400 281 (Cuers)

Type of vineyard: Corporation. **Established:** 1900 (corporation since 1981). **Number of employees:** 40. **Vine stocks:** Rolle, Cinsaut, Grenache, Carignan, Clairette. **Soil:** Clay.
Appellation: A.O.C. Côtes-de-Provence. **Type:** Red, white, rosé. **Technique:** Traditional. Rosé and white: fermentation at 17°. **Maturing:** Red: in oak casks. White and rosé: stainless steel and enamelled concrete tanks. **Alcohol content:** 12 to 12.5%. **Characteristics:** Very representative of the appellation thanks to the traditional vinestocks. Rosé and white: very aromatic, fresh and vigorous. Red: elegant, supple, not too tannic. **Serving temperature:** Rosé, white: 7 to 8°. Red: 14 to 16°. **Served with:** Red, rosé: meat, grilled and in light sauce. White: shellfish, grilled fish. **Vintages available in 89/90:** Red, white, rosé, Cuvée white and rosé: 1987 an 1988. Cuvée red: 1985.

Characteristics of vintages

Price range (pre-tax, ex-warehouse): between 20 and 30 F.F.
Sales in France: 85%.
Export sales: 15%.

References in France

Restaurants: Fouquet's SBM, Negresco.
Shops: Hédiard, Cave de la Madeleine.

Abroad

United States
Château Estate Wines, Park Avenue, New York.

United Kingdom
Thoman Ltd, London. Yapp Brothers.

Switzerland
Manuel et Lassueur, Lausanne.

Belgium
Renglet, Brussels.

Canada
ARVin, Montreal.

The Netherlands
Fourcroy Nederlands.

Far East
Japan: Suntory.

Comments

L'Estandon is a very old Côtes de Provence trademark, having been registered by Mr. Jean Bagnis in 1936. Since, 4 generations have labored for its quality. L'Estadon has been playing an important role as ambassador for the Côtes de Provence, both in France and abroad, for more than 50 years.

CHÂTEAU DE LA COULERETTE

Mrs. Sylvette Brechet
83250 La Londe-les-Maures
90 65 86 09 – Telex: 431 803

Type of vineyard: Corporation. **Established:** 1967. **Number of employees:** 7. **Vine stocks:** Grenache, Syrah, Mourvèdre, Cinsault, Carignan. **Soil:** Chalky marl and sandy clay. **Exposure:** Northwest, Southeast. **Average annual production in hectoliters:** 4,500.
Appellation: A.O.C. Côtes-de-Provence. **Type:** Rosé. **Technique:** Rosé: vinification by drawing off. **Alcohol content:** 12.5%. **Characteristics:** A rosé very representative of the Côtes-de-Provence; bright, fresh, intense fragrance. **Serving temperature:** Cool but not ice old. **Served with:** Goes well with any meal in the summer. **Vintages available in 89/90:** 1986.

Characteristics of vintages

1986: Flowery fragrance with a touch of violet and heather, pleasant freshness. Price range (pre-tax, ex-warehouse): Between 10 F.F. and 20 F.F.
Sales volume:
– Wholesale: 70%. – Restaurants: 30%.
Sales in France: 70%.
Export sales: 30%.
Main trading partners : Belgium, Switzerland, Germany, Netherlands, Japan, USA, Canada, Denmark.

References in France

Restaurants: Pullman Hotel, Baumanière, Armes de Champagne.
Shops: Marché aux Vins, La Sommelière.

Abroad

United States
Importers: Stacole, Miami – Wine Warehouse, Los Angeles.

United Kingdom
Importers: Hawkins & Nurick, London.

Germany
Importers: Vinotheka, Bischofsheim.

The Netherlands
Importers: Verlinden en Zoon AG's Hertogenbosch.

Far East
Importers: Jardine Matheson, Tokyo for South-East Asia.

Others
Importers: Switzerland: Riotton & Gillieron SA – Geneva.

DOMAINE DE LA CRESSONNIÈRE
A.M. Paganelli
R.N. 97 – 83790 Pignans
94 48 85 80 – Telex: 403 245 F

Type of vineyard: Agricultural Association. **Established:** 1982. **Number of employees:** 4. **Vine stocks:** Mourvèdre, Syrah, Grenache, Cinsault. **Exposure:** South. **Vine stocks:** 500 to 600.
Appellation: A.O.C. Côtes-de-Provence. **Type:** Red, white, rosé. **Technique:** Red: Semi-carbonic. Rosé: Traditional, with drawing off. **Maturing:** Red: Large casks for 6 months. **Alcohol content:** 11.8%. **Vintages available in 89/90:** Red: 1985, 1986. Rosé: 1986. White: 1985, 1986.

Characteristics of vintages

1986: Excellent rosé, Silver Medal at Paris and Mâcon. Lovely red, Bronze medal Paris, fruity, supple, well-made.
1985: Red: rich, well-balanced, aromatic. Average pre-tax, ex-warehouse price: 18 F.F., tax included. Price range (pre-tax, ex-warehouse): Between 10 an 20 F.F.
Sales volume:
– Wholesale: 15% (only abroad). – Retail: 60%. – Restaurants: 25%.

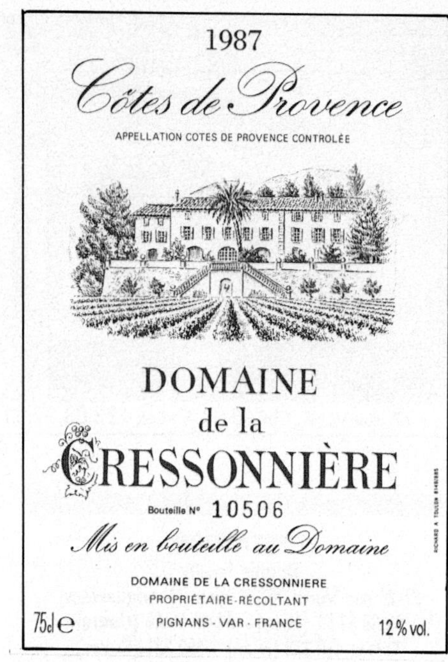

1987
Côtes de Provence
APPELLATION COTES DE PROVENCE CONTROLÉE
DOMAINE
de la
CRESSONNIÈRE
Bouteille N° 10506
Mis en bouteille au Domaine
DOMAINE DE LA CRESSONNIERE
PROPRIÉTAIRE-RÉCOLTANT
75cl e
PIGNANS - VAR - FRANCE
12 % vol.

Sales in France: 85%.
Export sales: 15%.
Main trading partners : Germany, Belgium.

References in France

Restaurants: 12 regional restaurants.
Shops: 8 regional shops.

DOMAINE DE CUREBEASSE
Jean Paquette
Route de Bagnols 83600 Frejus
94 52 10 17 – New number (autumn 89): 94 40 87 90

Type of vineyard: Family-owned. **Established:** Already existed in the 18th century. **Number of employees:** 3. **Vine stocks:** Red: Mourvèdre, Cinsault, Grenache, Cabernet Sauvignon, Syrah, Tibouren – White: Rolle, Ugni Blanc. **Soil:** Direct product of the superficial decomposition of dolerite mother rock and of rhyolite sandstone (Permian lava). **Exposure:** South. **Average annual production in hectoliters:** 800.
Appellation: AOC Côtes de Provence. **Type:** Red, Rosé, White. **Technique:** Red: long fermentation on skins (4 weeks) Rosé: maceration with skins at low temperature, temperature controlled fermentation. White: maceration with skins at low temperature, temperature controlled fermentation. **Maturing:** Red: in new casks. White: on fine lees. **Characteristics:** Red: good keeping, complex aromas (red berry, mulberry, spices, vanilla and touch of

cocoa) pronounced tannins, velvety texture. Rosé: noticeable presence of exotic fragrances (mango, litchie) raspberry, cinnamon, supple, soft and full, lingering taste. White: rich and well-balanced fresh accacia and bloom flower fragrance, lilac and mango flavor, touch of hazelnut due to maturation on fine lees. **Serving temperature:** Red: 16-18°. Rosé: 10-12°. White: 10°. **Served with:** Red: game, red meat (on the grill) – Rosé: cold cuts, shellfish, smoked ham, cheese – White: white meat, goat cheese. **Vintages available in 89/90:** Red: 87-88. Rosé: 88. White: 88.

Characteristics of vintages

Price range (pre-tax, ex-warehouse): Red (Roches Noires), Retail: 29 F.F., Export/wholesale: 23 F.F. Rosé (Angelico), Retail: 28 F.F., Export/wholesale: 22 F.F. White (Blanc de Blancs), Retail: 29 F.F., Export/wholesale: 23 F.F. Others (red & rosé): 15 F.F. to 20 F.F.

Sales volume:
- Wholesale: 5%. – Retail: 55%. – Restaurants: 20%.
- Other: 20% (export, UK, Germany, Belgium, Netherlands).

References in France

Restaurants: Vieux Four, Potiers, Toque Blance, Pastorel (Fréjus-Saint Raphael).

Abroad

United Kingdom

The Panton Wine Merchants – Tetbury, Gloucestershire – Tel: 066 53088.

Germany

H. Scheibe, Bunzlauerstr, Hamburg – H. Schmid, Tizianweg, Stuttgart – Tel: 071 855220. Weltenburg Vinotek, Kelheim – Tel: 0944 13682.

Belgium

R. Van Hove, Industrie Str, Lier, 03 4806825.

The Netherlands

Wijnimport J. Bart, Purmerend 02 998 3650.

Comments

The Curebasse domain, appears already on the Map of France drawn by Cassini, in the 18th century. Its present owners undertook its restoration, starting in 1952. The vineyard is characterized by: – the soil (direct decomposition of the mother rock composed of sandstone and Permian dolerite). – the climate (the domain is situated, between Les Maures and L'Esterel about 4 km from the sea) – the proximity of the pine forest. For several years, under the direction of the œnologist Jérome Paquette, new vinestocks have been selected (Mourvèdre, Tibouren, Rolle) and wine making techniques have been developed (very long fermentation on skins, short maturing in wooden casks – mostly new, maceration with skins, maceration on fine lees) in order to obtain whay could be called the "climax wine" of Curebasse, that is to say the highest quality wine that can be produced on a given soil.

DOMAINE DE LA GARNAUDE

Mr. or Mrs. J.P. Guinand
83590 Gonfaron
94 78 20 42

Type of vineyard: Family-owned. **Established:** 1982. **Vine stocks:** Syrah, Cabernet-Sauvignon, Grenache, Cinsault, Mourvèdre, Vieux Carignan, Vieil Ugni Blanc. **Soil:** Permotriassic on a base of Permian sandstone and clay sediment. **Exposure:** South by Southeast. **Average annual production in hectoliters:** 1,200.
Appellation: Côtes-de-Provence A.O.C., Vin de Pays des Maures. **Type:** Red, white, rosé. **Technique:** White: clarification of the must and fermentation at low temperature. Rosé: drawing off, followed by fermentation at low temperature. Red: No crushing, destemming. **Maturing:** Rouge Cuvée Santane: in new oak casks (225 liters). **Alcohol content:** 12.5%. **Characteristics:** White: Fresh, fruity and lively. Rosé: Fresh, fruity, goes down smoothly. Red: Fleshy, robust, well-balanced. **Serving temperature:** White and rosé: 8-10°C – Red: 18°C. **Served with:** White: as an aperitif and with first course, fish, shellfish. Rosé: first course, delicatessen, pastry, etc. Red: Main course, beef, lamb, poultry, game, cheese. **Vintages available in 89/90:** 1988 (Red, Rosé and White) – 1987 Rouge Cuvée Santane.

Characteristics of vintages

1987: Red – Gold Medal at the Concours Général de Paris, 1988. **1987:** Red – Gold Medal at the Concours de Vins,

Mâcon 1988. Price range (pre-tax, ex-warehouse): 15-25 F.F.
Sales volume:
– Retail: 30%. – Restaurants: 20%. – Other: 50% (Export).
Sales in France: 50%.
Export sales: 50%.
Main trading partners: USA, Germany, Luxemburg, Denmark, Netherlands, Belgium, Switzerland.

References in France

Restaurants: Gold Hôtel de Valescure, St-Raphaël. Le Manuscrit, Vallauris. La Foucado, La Garde Feinet.
Shops: Marché aux Vins, Reims – Marché aux Vins, L'Épine – Les Vins du Var SA, Saint-Raphaël.

Abroad

United States

Happy's Import Dist. 296 Main Street, Everett, Mass. 02149 – Consolidated Distilled Products, Chicago, Illinois 60623 – Wine Imports Ltd. 655 Suttei St., San Francisco, CA 94102 – Ideal Wines Spirits Co. Inc. 3890 Mystic Valley... Medford, MA. 02155.

Germany

Robert Diemert Import – Kriemhildstrasse 6, D 7640 Kehl.

Others

Belgium – Luxemburg.

Switzerland

La Vigneronne SA, Genève – Loew et Cie SA, Neuchâtel – Crelier SA, Neuchâtel.

COMMANDERIE DE PEYRASSOL
94 69 71 02 – Telex: Comdrag 970 842

Type of vineyard: Agricultural association. **Established:** 1981. **Number of employees:** 9. **Soil:** Chalky clay. **Exposure:** North-East and South-East. **Average annual production in hectoliters:** 2,500.
Appellation: Côtes de Provence. **Type:** Red, white, rosé. **Technique:** Red: traditional. White and rosé: maceration on skins. **Maturing:** White and rosé: 3 to 6 months in stainless steel tanks. Red: vats and casks, partly new. **Alcohol content:** 12 to 13%. **Characteristics:** White and rosé: fine and elegant. Red: rich and well-balanced, for ageing, but very fruity and aromatic in their youth. **Serving temperature:** White and rosé: 8 to 12°. Red: 16 to 17°. **Vintages available in 89/90/** 1985, 1986, 1987, 1988.

Characteristics of vintages

1988: Rosé and white: great finesse, only slightly acid. Red: very rich and well-balanced. Wait a while. Very, very great wines. **1987:** White and rosé: very fine and balanced. Red: lacking in richness and fullness. Pleasant now. **1986:** Rosé: average. Red and white: very fruity. **1985:** Great year for all three colors. Full-bodied. The reds are still a bit closed. Wait a while. Price range (pre-tax, ex-warehouse): between 20 F.F. and 30 F.F.

Sales volume:
– Wholesale: 25%. – Retail: 15%. – Restaurants: 30%. – Other: 30% (export).
Sales in France: 70%.

Export sales: 30%.
Main trading partners: Europe, USA, Japan, Antilles.

References in France

Restaurants: Hôtel Byblos (St-Tropez), Gray d'Albion (Cannes), Château St-Martin (Vence), La Chèvre d'Or (Eze), Le Louis XV (Hôtel de Paris, Monte Carlo), Le Mas d'Artigny, Sofitel Vieux Port and Sofitel Marignane (Marseille), Gérard Besson (Paris 1er).

Abroad

United States

Selected Vineyard, 56-31 56th Drive, Maspeth, New York 11378. Tel: 718 326 7990. Mr. Neal Rosenthal, 1230 East 223 Street, Suites 206-207, Carson, Calif. 90745. Tel: 213 834 5755. Shops: 976 Lexington Avenue, New York, N.Y. 10021.

United Kingdom

Scotland: Cokburn and Co. (Leith) Ltd, 19 Dublin Street, Lane South, Edinburgh EH1 3PX. Tel: 031 557 3071. Telex: 72153. Vessel du Vin, Mr. Molinari, Thurland Castle, Tunstall, Via Carnforth, Lancashire LA6 2QR. Tel: 046 834 360.

Germany

Les Grands Vins de France, Weinkontor, GmbH, Wengenstrasse 79, 7412 Eningen, U.A. Tel: 07121/82196. Wein Bauer, Alte Langgasse 2, 6450 Hanau 9. Tel: 06181/573137. Feinkost Kafer, Schummanstrasse 1, 8000 Munich 80. Tel: 089/4168 237.

Belgium

Six, S.A., 38 rue de la Bascule, 8900 Ypres. Tel: 57 200 545. Bal and Meeus, Autolei 107, 2222 Wommelgen. Tel: 03/322 2220. Chais et Entrepots du Nord, Simon Stevinstrat, Industrie Park, B 8400, Ostende. Tel: 059 80 46 69.

Far East Japan

Izumi, Itabashi 1, Chome, Itabashi Ku, Tokyo 173. Tel: 03 964 8255 and 2272.

Others

Antilles: Barnes & Sons, Boite Postale 2, Gustavia 1, 97133 St. Barthélemy, Guadeloupe. Tel: 590 27 60 33.

CHATEAU GRAND-BOISE

Nicole Gruey
BP 2 - 13530 Trets - Provence
42 29 22 95 - 42 29 33 12 - Telex: 430 301 304

Type of vineyard: Corporation. **Established:** 1983. **Number of employees:** 11. **Vine stocks:** Grenache, Cinsault, Cabernet-Sauvignon, Syrah, Ugni Blanc, Rolle, Sémillon. **Soil:** Sedimentary limestone. **Exposure:** 2/3 facing North - 1/3 facing South. **Average annual production in hectoliters:** 2,000.

Appellation: Côtes de Provence A.O.C. **Type:** Red, white, rosé - Other: Vin de Pays (Red and Rosé). **Technique:** Traditional or carbonic maceration at low temperature. **Maturing:** Red: in oak casks for 18 months. **Alcohol content:** 11.5%. **Characteristics:** Red: ruby color, finesse and bouquet, strong blackcurrant fragrance, slightly tannic. Rosé: supple, fresh, flowery aroma (English candy). Blanc de blancs sec: fine, intense flower and fruit aroma. **Serving temperature:** Red: 14-16° - Rosé and white: 8-10°. **Served with:** Red: meat, poultry, game and cheese. Rosé: hors-d'œuvre, provençal cuisine, goat cheese. White: better with fish and shellfish than with seafood. Excellent as aperitif. **Vintages available in 89/90:** Red: '86 - '87. Rosé and white: '88. White: '88.

Characteristics of vintages

1986: Not yet on sale except for a small lot prepared by carbonic maceration (very much in demand). **1985:** Excellent year, developing well, on sale at present. **1984:** No red wine produced at Grand Boise. Very bad year. **1983:** Good year that has aged better than the 1982 (out of stock). **1982:** Very good year for red wines that have aged very well (out of stock). **Other:** Whites and Rosés are sold

in the year following production, currently 1986-1987. Price range (pre-tax, ex-warehouse): 18 F.F.
Sales in France: 70%. **Export sales:** 30%.
Main trading partners: EEC countries (Germany, UK, Belgium, Switzerland, Netherlands), Canada (Ontario), USA (California, Illinois).

Comments

Grand Boise is above all a 400 hectare forest, planted with wines on 43 hectares, perpendicular to the Mistral as a protection against fire. Because of its Northern orientation and its altitude, the Château Grand-Boise is the most mountainous of the Provence vineyards and has a rather unusual soil.

DOMAINE DU JAS D'ESCLANS

R. Lorques
Route de Callas
83920 La Motte
94 70 27 86

Type of vineyard: Family-owned. **Established:** 1835. **Established:** 1936. **Number of employees:** 8. **Vine stocks:** Cinsault, Grenache, Mourvèdre, Syrah, Ugni Blanc, Clairette, Rolle. **Soil:** Chalky clay. **Exposure:** South, Southeast. **Average annual production in hectoliters:** Around 2,300.

CRU CLASSÉ
Domaine du
JAS D'ESCLANS
CÔTES DE PROVENCE
APPELLATION CÔTES DE PROVENCE CONTRÔLÉE
FRANCE
1983
e 750ml
LORGUES-LAPOUGE
Propriétaire-Récoltant, route de Callas La Motte (Var) France
MIS EN BOUTEILLE AU DOMAINE
Vin en provenance de vignes cultivées, sans engrais chimiques, ni herbicides, ni insecticides de synthèse.

Appellation: Côtes-de-Provence. **Type:** Red, white, rosé. **Technique:** Red: traditional, during 6 days. Rosé: by drawing off. **Maturing:** Red: in casks for 3 years. **Alcohol content:** 12%. **Characteristics:** Rosé and white: dry and fruity. Red: rather tannic, good for ageing, fragrance of red berries and "herbes de Provence". **Serving temperature:** Rosé and white: 9 to 10°. Red: 18°. **Served with:** White: fish. Rosé: fish, delicatessen and smoked dishes. Red: meat, game and cheese. Wine by Champagne method: as an aperitif or with dessert. **Vintages available in 89/90:** Red: 85, 86 (in 1990). Rosé and white: 88 (until the 1990 harvest).

Characteristics of vintages

1988: Rosé and white: very well-balanced, in keeping with the preceding years. **1986:** Rosé and white: fruity and dry. The rosé has a typical Grenache aroma, the white, an aroma of Rolle. **1985:** Red: well-balanced, wild fruit aroma (made from Cinsault, Grenache, Mourvèdre, Syrah - no Cabernet). **Other:** 1984: Robust wine, beautiful ruby color, sustained bouquet. Gold medal, Mâcon. 1983: Sustained color, wild fruit fragrance. Gold medal, Paris.
Price range (pre-tax, ex-warehouse); between 20 and 30 F. Special quotations for large quantities.
Sales volume:
Sales in France: 75% – Export sales: 25% – Retail: 50% – Restaurants: 25% – Other: 25%.
Main trading partners: Germany, Denmark, Switzerland, Benelux Countries, UK.

Abroad

United Kingdom
Bowtie Wine Co., 5 Blackheath Vale, SE30TX, London – Tel: 4418580787.

Germany
Agents for 15 large towns: Mr. Northum, 72 av. 10 September, Luxembourg – Tel: 352452232.

Switzerland
Cave Monségur, 98 Spalering, 4055 Bâle – Tel: 4161392944.

Belgium
W. Slangen, Constitutierstraat 69, 2008 Anvers – Tel: 3232357495.

The Netherlands
J. Berger, 7 Swalmerstraat, 6041 Roermond – Tel: 31475032966.

Others
Denmark: G.O Wine Import, 278 Jonstrupvez, 3500 Varlose – Tel: 452659040.

CHÂTEAU MINUTY

Etienne or Jean-Pierre Matton
Gassin 83990 Saint-Tropez
94 56 12 09

Type of vineyard: Family-owned. **Established:** 1936. **Number of employees:** 30. **Vine stocks:** Grenache, Tibourin, Mourvèdre, Cabernet Sauvignon, Cinsault, Ugni Blanc, Rolle, Sémillon, Clairette. **Soil:** Micaceous schist. **Exposure:** rising sun 1/2 – setting sun 1/2.

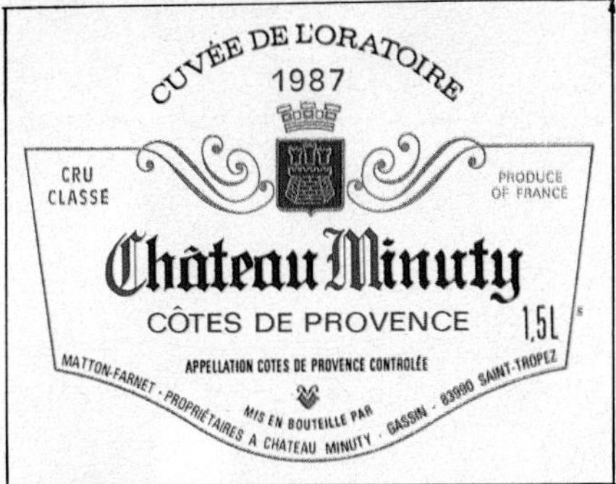

Appellation: Côtes-de-Provence. **Type:** Red, White, Rosé. **Technique:** Traditional, whole grapes. **Maturing:** Red: partly in wooden casks. White and rosé: in metal and concrete tanks. **Alcohol content:** 12.5%. **Characteristics:** Fruity, soft and full, long. **Serving temperature:** Red: 12°. White and rosé: 7-8°. **Served with:** Rosé : "salades gourmandes", dishes from the South of France and white meat. **Vintages available in 89/90:** Red 1987, Rosé and White 1988.

Characteristics of vintages

1988: Rosé and white: fuity, soft and full, light, long. **1987:** Red fruity, soft and full, light, long, delicate tannins, harmonious. Price range (pre-tax, ex-warehouse): 20 to 30 F.F. – 30 to 50 F.F.

Sales volume:
– Wholesale: 5%. – Retail: 20%. – Restaurants: 65%.
– Other: 10% (export).

Sales in France: 90%.
Export sales: 10%.
Main trading partners : Germany, UK, Switzerland, Belgium, former French colonies.

References in France

Restaurants: Hôtel de Paris (Monte Carlo), Reserve, Beaulieu Carlton, Cannes, etc.

Abroad

United Kingdom
Michael Druitt, 9 Deanery Street, Park Lane, London W 1Y 5LF.

Germany
A. Segritz & Co, Lovenhof 2 2800 Bremen 1.

Switzerland
Fisher Metral 20 Champ Prevost 1214 Ernier-Geneve C.4.

Belgium
Cesva – Zoning Industriel, Ave, des Etats Unis 6200, Charleur.

Others
Luxembourg: Sunnen Hoffmann – Negociant Viticulteur, Remerschem – Moselle – Grand Duché du Luxembourg.

Comments

The Château Minuty property was purchased in 1936 by Mr. Gabriel Farnet, then operated by his daughter and son-in-law, Mr. and Mrs. Etienne Matton, who restored the domain as it was under Napoléon III. It was quickly taken over by the third generation, the two sons of Mr. and Mrs. Etienne Matton, Jean Etienne, 26 years old, and François, 20 years old. A combination of traditional vinification – manual harvesting, transportation of the whole grapes by elevator to the vats, gravity feeding – and modern techniques – pneumatic pressing, refrigeration of the vats.

DOMAINE DE LA MALHERBE

Mrs. Serge Ferrari
83230 Bormes-les-Mimosas
94 64 80 11 – Telex: 900 411

Type of vineyard: Family-owned. **Established:** 1930. **Number of employees:** 6. **Soil:** Sand, alluvion, schist and clay. **Exposure:** Seaside. **Average annual production in hectoliters:** 700.
Appellation: A.O.C. Côtes-de-Provence. **Type:** Red, white, rosé. **Technique:** White: pressing at low temperature (17°). Rosé: crushing, maceration, pumping over – at low temperature (17°) – Red: Traditional: maceration (12-15 days). **Alcohol content:** 12%. **Serving temperature:** Rosé and White: 12° – Red: 17°. **Vintages available in 89/90:** White, rosé: 1988. Red: 1987. Altogether 100,000 bottles which will probably be gone by the end of 1989.

Characteristics of vintages

Price range (pre-tax, ex-warehouse): 40 F.F. to 50 F.F.

Sales volume:
– Retail: 25%. – Restaurants: 75%.

Sales in France: 90%.
Export sales: 10%.
Main trading partners : Switzerland, Italy.

• *In 1985, the wines of the following regions received the A.O.C. (Appellation d'Origine Contrôlée) classification: Minervois, Coteaux-des-Baux, Coteaux-d'Aix-en-Provence, Coteaux-du-Lyonnais and Coteaux-du-Languedoc.*

Domaine F. Ravel

CHATEAU MONTAUD

VIGNOBLES ET VERGERS, FRANÇOIS RAVEL
Château Montaud-Pierrefeu 83390 CUERS F-Tél.94/28.20.30-Télex:40035
400 hectares de Vignobles au cœur de la Provence

CHÂTEAU MONTAUD

François Louis Ravel
83390 Pierrefeu
94 28 20 30 - Telex: 400 359

Type of vineyard: Family-owned. **Established:** 1963. **Number of employees:** 53. **Vine stocks:** Red: Cabernet Sauvignon, Syrah, Merlot, Mourvèdre – Rosé: Tibouren, Grenache, Syrah, Cinsault, Mourvèdre, Carignan – White: Sémillon, Ugni Blanc, Sauvignon Blanc, Chardonnay. **Soil:** Schist of the Maures Mountains cultivated in long terraces in order to avoid erosion, to respect the water table and to permit a regular development of the vineyard. **Exposure:** North-West. **Average annual production in hectoliters:** around 20,000.

Appellation: Côtes de Provence. **Type:** Red, Rosé Blancs de Blancs. **Technique:** For all wines: continuous temperature control by flowing cold water over large, very high stainless steel tanks to maximize the heat exchange surface, and suppression of the natural carbon dioxide resulting from the vinification. Rosé: long drawing off by gravity. Red: traditional vinification, long fermentation on skins, submerged cap and closed vat. White: direct pressing and cold debourbage. **Maturing:** in vats. **Alcohol content:** Red: 12.2%. Rosé: 11.8%. White: 11.6%. **Characteristics:** Red: well-colored, full-bodied, rich and well-balanced, can be kept 2 to 3 years. Rosé: dry but not acid, fruity, fragrant with a touch of "gun flint" and woodland. They should be drunk within 12 months of bottling. White: fresh, light, fruity wines to be drunk within 8 months of bottling. **Serving temperature:** Red: room temperature. Rosé and white: cool but not cold. **Vintages available in 89/90:** 1988.

Characteristics of vintages

Price range (pre-tax, ex-warehouse) between 10 F.F. and 20 F.F.
Sales in France: 35% (2% retail, 20% restaurants, 13% wholesale.) **Export sales:** 65%.
Main trading partners: Belgium, Germany, Denmark, Luxemburg, Netherlands, Switzerland, Austria, UK, Japan, Malasia, Hong Kong.

Comments

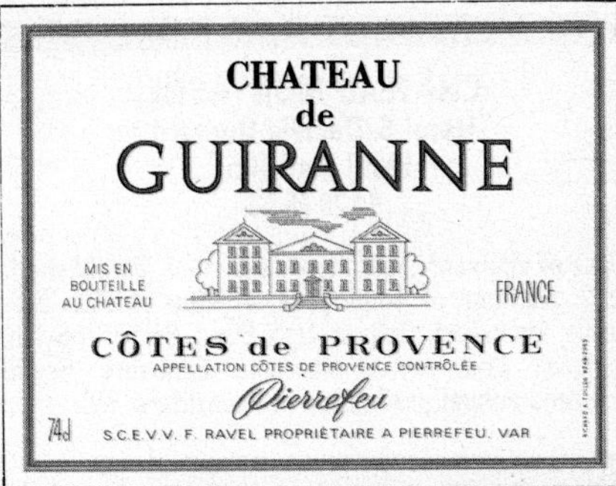

The Vignobles François Ravel company has been established at Pierrefeu in the Var since 1963. It manages a number of vineyards spread over a radius of about 20 kilometers around Pierrefeu, on the foothills of the Massif des Maures: Château Garamache, Château la Guiranne, Côteau des Lettes, Domaine du Fenouillet, Château la Mandrive, Domaine du Haut Plan de Loube. Located between Pierrefeu and Collobrieres, on the site of an ancient Roman Villa whose pressing stone has been rediscovered and carefully preserved, Château Montaud is the compagny headquarters. Its winecellar, with a capacity of 30 000 hectoliters and equipped for the most modern vinification techniques, receives the harvest of all of the vineyards under the best of conditions.

FONDATION LA NAVARRE DOMAINE

Michel de Louvencourt
Domaine de la Navarre - 83260 La Crau
94 66 04 08

Established: 1878. **Vine stocks:** Clairette, Rolle, Syrah, Cabernet, Mourvèdre, Cinsault, Grenache, Ugny... **Soil:** Silica clay. **Exposure:** South. **Average annual production in hectoliters:** 50 hectoliters/hectare.
Appellation: A.O.C. Côtes-de-Provence. **Type:** Red, white, rosé. **Technique:** Traditional. **Maturing:** Oak casks. **Alcohol content:** 12.5%. **Characteristics:** Red (Cuvée Réservée): supple, fruity, pleasant, well-balanced. Some reds age very well. Very fruity rosé and white. **Serving temperature:** Red: room temperature (17°). Rosé and white: 8°. **Served with:** Red: meat and cheese. Rosé: paëlla, hors-d'œuvre. White: fish, seafood, bouillabaise and for Kir aperitifs. **Vintages available in 89/90:** Red: 84, 87. Rosé: 88. White: 87, 88.

Characteristics of vintages

1988: Rosé: quite fruity. White: fruity. Cuvée Les Roches, Cuvée Darrie li Frais, wines aged in red Oak casks were awarded 3 Gold Medals. White Cuvée Don Bosco in commemoration of the hundredth anniversary of the Founder's death.
Sales volume:
- Retail: 90%. - Restaurants: 3%. - Other: 27% (Export).
Main trading partners: Germany, Denmark, Belgium, Luxemburg.

CHÂTEAU MONTAGNE

Henri & Danièle Guerard
83390 Pierrefeu
94 28 68 58

Type of vineyard: Agricultural Association. **Established:** 1982. **Number of employees:** 1. **Vine stocks:** Grenache, Mourvèdre, Cinsault, Ugni Blanc, Sémillon, Syrah, Carignan. **Soil:** alluvial sandstone. **Exposure:** South. **Average annual production in hectoliters:** 780.

Appellation: Côtes de Provence. **Type:** Red, White, Rosé. **Technique:** Red: semi-carbonic maceration – Rosé: drawing off, temperature control. **Maturing:** Red: in Oak casks (18 months). **Alcohol content:** 12%. **Characteristics:** Red: ruby color, intense and delicate nose – Rosé: depth of color, fruity, supple, well-balance – White: intense flowery nose, lively and firm. **Serving temperature:** Red: room temperature – Rosé and white: 8-10°. **Served with:** Red: game, dishes cooked in sauce – Rosé: exotic cuisine – White: fish, bouillabaise and ailloli. **Vintages available in 89/90:** Red: 1987 – Rosé and white: 1988.

Characteristics of vintages

1988: Rosé: fruity, supple – White: intense flowery nose. **1987:** Red: round, goes down smoothly. **1986:** Red: pleasant, full of flavor. Price range (pre-tax, ex-warehouse): 13 F.F. to 20 F.F.

Sales volume:
– Retail: 15%. – Restaurants: 75%. – Other: 10% (cellars).

Sales in France: 80%. **Export sales:** 20%.
Main trading partners: UK, Belgium, Switzerland, Japan.

References in France

Restaurants: Restaurants of the Var region.
Shops: regional cellars.

Abroad

United Kingdom
Maison Colombier Bucks Tel: 889339.

Switzerland
Cave Bingelli – Morrens 7312445.

Belgium
Cave de Brunehaut – 37 rue Norga, Brussels – SPRL East-Vin 4750 Weywertz – SPRL Crouquet-Dubois, Verviers.

Comments

Large provincial country house going back to the end of the 17th century, located on the plain North of Toulon and Hyères on the foothills of the Maures Mountains at Pierrefeu on the most highly regarded soil of the Côtes de Provence. Vinification and bottling are done at the château under the control of a œnologist. Château wines are mostly sold in provincial wasp-waist bottles, decorated in 4 color enamel.

DOMAINES DE RASQUE DE LAVAL

Baron de Rasque de Laval
Château Sainte-Roseline
83460 Les Arcs/Argens
94 73 32 57 – Telex: COMDRAG 970 842 F

Type of vineyard: Family-owned. **Established:** 1921. **Number of employees:** 15. **Vine stocks:** Sémillon, Grenache, Tibourenc, Cinsault, Mourvèdre, Cabernet-Sauvignon. **Soil:** Permotriassic of the tertiary era. **Exposure:** Slopes. **Average annual production in hectoliters:** 40 hectoliters/hectare.
Appellation: A.O.C. Côtes-de-Provence Cru Classé. **Type:** Red, white, rosé. **Technique:** White and rosé: at low temperature. Red: long fermentation. **Maturing:** White and rosé: 3 years. Red 6 years. **Alcohol content:** 12.8%. **Characteristics:** White: goes down well, fruity. Rosé: rich color, very fruit. Red: Robust, truffle and undergrowth fragrance. **Serving temperature:** White and rosé: 9-13° maximum. Red: 15° maximum. **Served with:** White and rosé: shellfish, fish, seafood. Red: red meat, game, cheese. **Vintages available in 89/90:** White and rosé: 1985. Red: 1983.

Characteristics of vintages

1987: Excellent whites, fresh and dense, very fragrant. Beautiful rosés. **1983:** Rich well-colored reds, complex aroma, good keeping wines. Price range (pre-tax, ex-warehouse): 35 F.F.-60 F.F.

Sales volume:
- Retail: 15%. - Restaurants: 35%.
Sales in France: 50%.
Export sales: 50%.
Main trading partners : Canada, Germany, Luxemburg, Belgium, Switzerland, Denmark.

References in France

Restaurants: Carlton, Cannes. SBM, Monte Carlo. Moulin de Mougins. Gray d'Albion, Cannes. Aquilon, Nantes. Réserve, Annecy.

Abroad

Germany

Importers: Frankhof Kellerei Burgeffstrasse 19 6203 Hochleim/Main Germany - Tel: 061464051; Sigmund Schlott Handelsagentu Möwenweg 31 6680 Neunkirchen - Tel: 0681/6006 221.

Canada

Importers: S.A.Q. CP 10058 Place d'Armes Montréal Canada H2Y 3J8 Tel: 5148733816. LCBO 55 Lake Shore Toronto Ontario M5E 1A4 Tel 416/9631866.

Others

Denmark, Switzerland, Belgium, Luxemburg. Importers: Babette Vin Straedet 6 Lystrup 3550 Slangerup, Denmark. Tel: 02278577. Balsiger Bernstrasse 19 3122 Kehrsatz, Bern, Switzerland. Tel: 031543344. Au Coq d'Or, 5 Molard 1204, Geneva, Switzerland. Tel: 022/284311. Soced, Square Sainctelette 11/12 1000 Brussels, Belgium. Tel: 02/2177910. Rommes A. Sarl, ZI Hirebesch 8320 Cap, Luxemburg. Tel: 310 811.

Austria

Morandell 6300 Worgl/Tirol.

Italia

Gemi S.A.S. Mondovi (CN).

CHÂTEAU REAL MARTIN

Jacques Clotilde
83143 Le Val
96 86 40 90 - Telex: 403 901 F

Type of vineyard: Family-owned. **Established:** 1980. **Vine stocks:** Syrah, Grenache, Cinsault, Ugni Blanc, Mourvèdre. **Soil:** Calcium carbonate. **Exposure:** Hillsides facing Southeast. **Average annual production in hectoliters:** 1,200.
Appellation: A.O.C. Côtes-de-Provence. **Type:** Red, white, rosé. **Technique:** Fermentation with skins in stainless steel and concrete tanks for 10 to 12 days with temperature control, devatting for rosés. **Maturing:** White and rosé - 1 year: red - 3 years. **Characteristics:** Red: aromatic, structured, red fruit aroma. White: quince aroma. **Serving temperature:** White and rosé: 7°-8°. Red: 17° to 18° (15° with lamb). **Served with:** White & rosé; fish and shellfish. Red: red meat and game, lamb. **Vintages available in 89/90:** 1982, 1983, 1984, 1985, 1986.

Characteristics of vintages

1985: Rosé: Prize for Excellence, "Vinalis" 1987. **1983:** Red: Bronze Medal in Mâcon - Rosé: Prize for Excellence, "Vinabis 1985". **1982:** Red: First Prize in Mâcon - White: Silver Medal in Mâcon - Rosé: Prize for Excellence, "Union des Œnologues". Price range (pre-tax, ex-warehouse): between 30 F.F. and 50 F.F.

CHÂTEAU DU ROUET

Bernard Savatier
Le Rouët 83490 Le Muy
94 45 16 00 - Telex: Comdrag 920 842 F

Type of vineyard: Agricultural Association. **Established:** 1965. **Number of employees:** 14. **Vine stocks:** Grenache, Ugni Blanc, Syrah, Mourvèdre. **Soil:** Acid silica clay (Permian depression and rhyolite). **Exposure:** South. **Average annual production in hectoliters:** 3,000.

Appellation: Côtes de Provence. **Type:** Red, white, rosé, sparkling wine. **Maturing:** Red: in oak casks. **Alcohol content:** 12%. **Characteristics:** White: dry fut fruity. Rosé: fruity and long. Red: full-bodied.
Serving temperature: White and rosé: 10 and 12°. Red: 16 to 18°. **Served with:** White: Fish, seafood, Roquefort, etc. Rosé: Regional and traditional cooking. Red: meat. **Vintages available in 89/90:** White and rosé: 87, 88. Red: 86, 87.

Characteristics of vintages

Sales volume:
- Wholesale: 8%. - Retail: 50 %. - Restaurants: 30%.
- Other:12% (purchasing group).
Sales in France: 90%.
Export sales: 10%.
Main trading partners : Germany, Switzerland, Belgium, Netherlands.

References in France

Restaurants: Restaurant La Volta (Cannes), Le St. Pierre (Villefranche), Hôtel de Parfum (Grasse).
Shops: Camif (Niort).

Abroad

United States

Importers: Slocum and Sons, Inc., West Haven, Conn. 06516. Tel: 94 45 15 00.

United Kingdom

Layton's Wine Merchants Limited, London.

Germany

Kiefer, 3 Blumenstrasse, D6600 Saarbrucken.

Switzerland

W. Staiger, 46 ctre Morges, Lausanne 244452, 1004.

Canada

Alberta Liquor Control, St. Albert, T8N 3T5 (50 Corriveau. AV.)

The Netherlands

Henri Van Iersel, Kerkstraat 2, Waspik 5165 GG.

Comments

By special appointment to the court of Louis XVI. The vineyard forms a fire-break in the Esterel Forest in the Fréjus region and is part of the estate of the Château de Fréjus.

DOMAINE DE REILLANNE

Comte G. de Chevron Villette
Route de Saint-Tropez
83340 Le Cannet-des-Maures
94 60 73 31 - Telex: 402 200 Code 812 Reillanne

Type of vineyard: Family-owned. **Established:** Turn of the century. **Average annual production in hectoliters:** 3,000.
Appellation: A.O.C. Côtes-de-Provence. **Type:** Red, white, rosé. **Serving temperature:** Red: 16-18° - White and Rosé: 10-12°. **Vintages available in 89/90:** Red: 1985, 1986 - Rosé: 1988, 1989 - White: 1988, 1989.

Characteristics of vintages

1988, 1987: Two very good years in all three colors. Similar to the 1985 and 1986. **1986:** Very good year for red and white wines. Medals at Mâcon. Average pre-tax, ex-warehouse price: 13 F.F.-15 F.F. Price range (pre-tax, ex-warehouse): 12 F.F.-20 F.F.
Sales volume:
- Wholesale: 25%. - Retail: 10-15%. - Restaurants: 20-30%.- - Others: 30% (traders, work councils, wholesalers).
Sales in France: 75%. **Export sales:** 25%.
Main trading partners : Denmark, Germany, Belgium, and other EEC countries.

CHÂTEAU DE ROUX

Mr. Paul Dyens - Giraud
Cannet-des-Maures - 83340 Le Luc
94 60 73 10

Type of vineyard: Family-owned. **Established:** 1952. **Vine stocks:** Grenache, Cinsault, Syrah, Cabernet, Mourvèdre, Rolle. **Soil:** Clay with calcium carbonate. **Average annual production in hectoliters:** 1,200.
Appellation: A.O.C. Côtes-de-Provence. **Type:** Red, white, rosé. **Technique:** Rosé de Saignée. Red: traditional. **Maturing:** In bottles. **Alcohol content:** 12%. **Characteristics:** Fine tannin balance thanks to good blending of Cabernet-Sauvignon, Syrah and Grenache. The Mourvèdre now coming of age (22 years old) help make wines with good ageing potential, particulary Rosés. **Serving temperature:** Rosé: 8° - Red: 17-18°. **Served with:** Rosé: Bouillabaisse, Bourride (another type of fish soup) and Provençal cuisine in general. Red: meat, leg of lamb, game. White: shellfish, fish. **Vintages available in 89/90:** 1984, 1985, 1986.

Characteristics of vintages

1986: Well-structured. Fine tannin, harmonious, great keeping wine. **1985:** Firm, beautiful color, typical Provence wine. **1984:** Very round, lovely nose, forth-coming. Very good year for our area. **Other:** Blanc de Blancs 1986: very typical, citrus fruit aroma. Price range (pre-taxe, ex-warehouse): 20 F.F.-30 F.F.
Sales volume:
- Retail: 50%. - Restaurants: 50%.
Sales in France: 95%.
Export sales: 5%.
Main trading partners : Belgium, Germany.

DOMAINE ST-ANDRE DE FIGUIERE

A. & André Daniel Connesson
83250 La Londe
94 66 92 10

Type of vineyard: Agricultural Association. **Established:** 1979. **Number of employees:** 4. **Vine stocks:** Grenache, Mourvèdre, Cinsault, Rolle, Sémillon, Ugni Blanc, Carignan. **Soil:** schistic. **Exposure:** 50% South, 50% variable. **Average annual production in hectoliters:** 800.
Appellation: Côtes De Provence (biological cultivation). **Type:** Red, White, Rosé. **Technique:** drawing off, short maceration, temperature control. **Maturing:** in vats (use of inert gas). **Alcohol content:** 12%. **Characteristics:** fruity, delicate, long, easy to drink, low SO_2 content (less than 30 mg on average). **Serving temperature:** White and rosé: cool but not iced. Red: room temperature. **Served with:** according to classical criteria. **Vintages available in 89/90:** White & Rosé: 1988 - Red: 1987-1988.

Characteristics of vintages

1988: White & Rosé: finesse, elegance and beauty - Red: harmonious, lingering taste, class. **1987:** White & Rosé: out of stock Red: beautiful development, promising, wait a few years. **1986:** out of stock. **1985:** out of stock. Price range (pre-tax, ex-warehouse): 20 F.F. to 30 F.F., 30 F.F.
Sales in France: 60%.
Export sales: 40%.
Main trading partners : Germany, Switzerland, Belgium, Netherlands, UK, USA.

Domaine Saint André
de Figuière
1987
CUVEE SPECIALE
Mis en bouteille au Domaine
COTES DE PROVENCE
APPELLATION COTES DE PROVENCE CONTROLEE
G.F.A. DOMAINE SAINT ANDRE DE FIGUIERE
- 83250 - LA LONDE LES MAURES
e 75cl
Product of France
12% vol

Abroad

United States

Importers: Robert Kacher Selection – 3015 V Street N.E. Washington D.C. 20018.

United Kingdom

Morris and Verdin – 28 Chruton Street – London SWIV 2LP.

Germany

Weinimport U Hartl (Tubingen) – M. Schmiedberger (Stuttgart).

Switzerland

A. G. Denner – Grubenstrasse 10 CH 804S Zurich.

Belgium

Vajra – 62 rue J. Baus Wezembeek Oppem – 1970 – Brussels.

Comments

Created in 1979. Starting with no clients at all, average sales have been increasing by 100000 bottles per year since 1985, a result of rigorous discipline in the cultivation, vinification, maturing, presentation and marketing of the product. The quality of the wines and the almost total absence of SO_2 certainly contribute a great deal to this success.

PALETTE

CHÂTEAU SIMONE

René Rougier
13590 Meyreuil
42 66 92 58

Type of vineyard: Family-owned. **Established:** For 2 centuries. **Number of employees:** 8. **Vine stocks:** Red: Grenache, Mourvèdre, Cinsaut and 10 others. White: Clairette, Ugni Blanc, Grenache Blanc, Muscadet. **Soil:** Chalky clay scree. **Exposure:** North. **Average annual production in hectoliters:** 550.

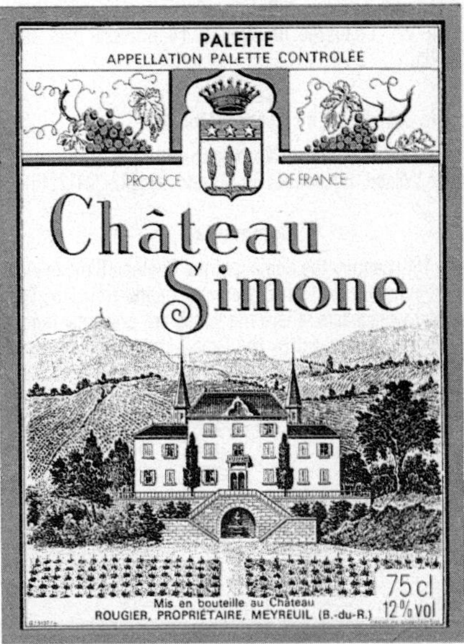

PALETTE
APPELLATION PALETTE CONTROLEE
PRODUCE
OF FRANCE
Château
Simone
75 cl
12 % vol
Mis en bouteille au Château
ROUGIER, PROPRIÉTAIRE, MEYREUIL (B.-du-R.)

Appellation: Palette. **Type:** Red, White, Rosé. **Technique:** Traditional. **Maturing:** In oak casks. **Alcohol content:** 12%. **Characteristics:** Rich and well balanced and structured, great keeping wines. **Serving temperature:** White and Rosé: 11°. Red: 17°. **Served with:** White: fish cooked on the grill or in sauce. Red: meat in sauce, game. Rosé: delicatessen, poultry. **Vintages available in 89/90:** Red: 1985. White: 1986. Rosé: 1987.

Characteristics of vintages

1986: Structure, finesse, distinction. **1985:** Rich and well balanced wines, fine color, complex aromas. Price range (pre-tax, ex-warehouse): 50 to 80 F.F.

Sales volume:

– Retail: 25. – Restaurants: 40%. – Other: 35% (export).

Sales in France: 65%.
Export sales: 35%.
Main trading partners: UK, Germany, USA, Canada, Belgium, Netherlands, Switzerland.

References in France

Restaurants: Restaurants with Michelin Stars.
Shops: Hédiard, Nicolas, Fauchon.

Abroad

United States:
Robert Chadderdon Selection, 30 Rockefeller Plaza, Suite 1920 New York (Tel: (212) 757 8185). .

United Kingdom
Yapp Brothers, Mere Wiltshire (Tel: 4474 7860676).

Germany
Frankofkellerei Gmbh Burgeffstrasse 19 (Tel: 06146/4051).

Switzerland
Devigny, 1373 Chavonay (Tel: 024411407).

Belgium
France Vin, Chaussée de Wennel 64 Brussels (Tel: 322 4277406).

Canada
Société des alcools du Québec, Montréal.

The Netherlands
Sauter Wijnen, Rechstraat 55 Maastricht (043-22412245).

Comments

In the 16th century the domain of the Château Simone was the property of the "Grands Carmes" monks from Aix. The splendid winecellars where the wines are presently matured were hollowed out by the Grand Carmes themselves. The domain has belonged to the Rougier family for 2 centuries. At Château Simone, the golden rule of production is the absolute respect for the local winemaking traditions.

CASSIS

LA FERME BLANCHE

François Paret
B.P. 57 - 13260 Cassis
42 01 00 74

Type of vineyard: Family-owned. **Established:** 1714. **Number of employees:** 6. **Vine stocks:** Ugni Blanc, Grenache, Mourvèdre, Cinsault, Clairette, Sauvignon, Marsanne. **Soil:** Clay with calcium carbonate. **Exposure:** Mostly hillsides. **Average annual production in hectoliters:** 1,000.
Appellation: Cassis. **Type:** Red, white, rosé. **Technique:** Traditional. **Maturing:** in wooden casks (for reds). **Alcohol content:** 13%. **Characteristics:** White: finesse and character. Full bodied wine. Red: Aromatic and tannic. Rosé: Firm and fruity. **Vintages available in 89/90:** White and rosé 1986, Red 1985.

Characteristics of vintages

1986: Good white wines – typical, aromatic, combining firmness and freshness, lingering farewell. **1985:** Excellent red wines, solid and well-structured, good keeping. Price range (pre-tax, ex-warehouse): 30 F.F.-50 F.F.
Sales volume:
– Retail: 15%. – Restaurants: 50%. – Other: 35% (shops).
Sales in France: 95%.
Export sales: 5%.
Main trading partners: EEC countries, USA.

MAS DE FONTBLANCHE

Jean-Jacques Bontoux-Bodin
Route de Carnoux - 13600 Cassis
42 01 01 62 - 42 01 00 11

Type of vineyard: Family-owned. **Established:** 1900. **Number of employees:** 7 fulltime. **Vine stocks:** Silica, clay covered. **Exposure:** South, Southeast. **Average annual production in hectoliters:** 1,700.
Appellation: A.O.C. Cassis. **Type:** Red, white, rosé. **Technique:** Traditional, with temperature control (20-21°). **Maturing:** Stainless steel tanks. **Alcohol content:** 11°5. **Characteristics:** Dry, fruity, fragrant, very cool. Young wines for marketting, which permits fragrant wines. **Serving temperature:** 8° and 11°. **Vintages available in 89/90:** 1987 Rosé, 1985 and 1986 Red.

Characteristics of vintages

1986: End of marketing. **Others: 1987:** Very promising, marketing January 1988. Price range (pre-tax, ex-warehouse): between 30 F.F. and 50 F.F.
Sales volume:
– Retail: 20%. – Restaurants: 80%.
Sales in France: 90%.
Main trading partners: USA, Switzerland, England, Scandinavia.

BANDOL

DOMAINES BUNAN
CHÂTEAU LA ROUVIÈRE
MOULIN DES COSTES

Paul & Pierre Bunan
83740 La Cadière-d'Azur
94 98 72 76 - Telex: 404 620 - FAX: 94 98 60 05

Type of vineyard: Family owned. **Established:** 1962. **Number of employees:** 15. **Vine stocks:** Mourvèdre, Cinsault, Grenache, Syrah, Clairette, Sauvignon. **Soil:** Chalky clay. **Exposure:** Facing full South. **Average annual production in hectoliters:** 35 hl/ha.

MIS EN BOUTEILLE A LA PROPRIETE
CHATEAU LA ROUVIÈRE
BANDOL
MÉDAILLE D'ARGENT
CONCOURS GÉNÉRAL AGRICOLE
PARIS 1987
APPELLATION BANDOL CONTROLEE
13% vol.
1985
75 cl
BUNAN PROPRIETAIRE-RECOLTANT, LE CASTELLET, VAR - FRANCE

Appellation: AOC Bandol controlée. **Type:** Red, white, rosé. **Technique:** Fermentation at low temperature. **Maturing:** In casks – 18 months (red) and 9 months (rosé and white). **Alcohol content:** 12.5%. **Characteristics:** Rosé: fine and elegant, English candy flavor, slight salmon color. Red: rich nose, flowery aroma, touch of sloe, good attack, pleasant tobacco and green oak fragrance, harmonious, marked Mourvèdre flavor. White: good lively attack, grilled spice fragrance. **Served with:** White and rosé: grilled fish and seafood. Red: roasts, leg of lamb, game. **Vintages available in 89/90:** 1989, 1986, 1985, 1984, 1982.

Characteristics of vintages

1987: Rosé – rose petal and apricot fragrance. **1986:** Red – firm with peppery finish, liquorice bouquet. The Domaines Bunan have been described by Robert Parker as "Excellent producers" and their rosé wines "the finest in the world!". **1985:** Red – beautiful deep garnet color, rich and and harmonious, beautiful wine. **Other: 1987:** Extremely refreshing and elegant.

Sales volume:
– Retail: 20%. – Restaurants: 60%. – Other: 20% (export).
Sales in France: 80%.
Export sales: 20%.
Main trading partners : UK, Belgium, Switzerland, Germany, Denmark, USA.

References in France

Shops: Cave Legrand, (Paris), Maison du Fromage, (Paris), Galerie des Vins, Great Grape Traders, (Paris), Master Wines, (Paris).

Abroad

United States

Direct Import Chicago.

United Kingdom

Yapp Brothers Mere – Soho Wine Market, London.

Germany

Connaisseur de Paris, Munich.

Switzerland

Rieger Melingen.

Canada

Gill Vinette de Laval, Montreal.

The Netherlands

Kersten.

Comments

The Bunans, who own Moulin des Costes and Château la Rouvière, are one of the leading families of Bandol. They own three important estates in Bandol comprising 173 acres altogether. Paul Bunan, a serious, soft-spoken man, purchased Moulin des Costes (a vineyard near La Cadière) in 1961. His brother Pierre, a broad-faced, affable, gregarious man, bought Château la Rouvière (near Le Castellet) in 1969. Subsequently, they added another vineyard at Le Castellet called Bélouvé. The Bunan family work as an enthusiastic, strong team, not only to make their wines but to market them as well. Their hillside vineyards are in impeccable condition, as is the wine cellar. They use a blend for their red wine of 65% Mourvèdre, 14% Grenache, 6% Syrah, and 15% Cinsault. The rosé is made from 70% Cinsault, 24% Mourvèdre and 6% Grenache. For the white wine the blend is 45% Clairette, 45% Ugni Blanc and 5% each of Sauvignon and Bourboulenc. The Bunans also produce a good Marc de Bandol from the skins of the grapes.

DOMAINE DE FRÉGATE

Comte de Pissy, Comtesse de la Fite
Route de Bandol 83270 St Cyr-sur-Mer
94 26 17 02

Type of vineyard: Agricultural Association (family-owned). **Established:** 1966. **Number of employees:** 5. **Vine stocks:** Mourvèdre 50%, Grenache, Cinsault, Ugni, Clairette. **Soil:** Silica, clay. **Exposure:** South, South-East – waterfront. **Average annual production in hectoliters:** 800.

Appellation: Bandol. **Type:** Red, White, Rosé. **Technique:** Red: fermentation on skins (8/10 days) Rosé/ White: direct pressing. **Maturing:** Red: in oak vats (15 months). **Characteristics:** Red: rich and well balanced, full but not heavy, aromatic, good keeping. Rosé: supple and fruity. White: dry and fruity. **Serving temperature:** Red: 18°. Rosé and White: 8°. **Vintages available in 89/90:** Red 1986, 1987. Rosé: 1988.

Characteristics of vintages

1988: Lovely rosé, fresh and flowery, rather long. **1986:** Good red, beautiful color, fruity, ageing well. Price range (pre-tax, ex-warehouse): 20 to 30 F.F.
Sales volume:
- Retail: 20 %. - Restaurants: 80 %.
Sales in France: 95 %.
Export sales: 5 %.
Main trading partners : USA, Belgium, Netherlands.

Abroad

United States
Select Vineyards Ltd, New York.

Belgium
Dussart P & F, Brussels.

The Netherlands
Van-Nieulande, Breda.

DOMAINE LE GALANTIN

Achille Pascal
Le Plan du Castelet 83330
94 98 75 94

Type of vineyard: Family-owned. **Vine stocks:** Mourvèdre over 50%, Cinsault, Grenache. **Soil:** Clay with calcium carbonate. **Average annual production in hectoliters:** 500.
Appellation: Bandol. **Type:** Red, white (some). **Others:** Rosé. **Technique:** Traditional without destemming. **Maturing:** Stainless steel tanks for rosé and white. Wood for red. **Characteristics:** Tannic. Rich and well-balanced. To be aged. **Serving temperature:** 12° Rosé. Red 17°-18°. **Served with:** Rosé: Pork, light meals. Red: red meat, lamb, game, cheese. **Vintages available in 89/90:** Red: 1984, 1985. Rosé: 1986.

Characteristics of vintages

1986: Excellent rosé, firm and fruity. **1985:** Red: rich, typical, combines structure and elegance, to be aged. Price range (pre-tax, ex-warehouse): Between 30 F.F. and 35 F.F.
Sales volume:
- Retail: 30 %. - Restaurants: 30 %. - Other: 10 % (export).
Sales in France: 70 %.
Export sales: 10 to 15 %.
Main trading partners : Germany, Belgium, Holland.

DOMAINES OTT (CHÂTEAU DE SELLE, CLOS MIREILLE AND CHÂTEAU ROMASSAN 22)

Olivier Ott
22, bd d'Aiguillon - 06600 Antibes
93 34 38 91 - Telex: 970 915 OTFRERE

Established: 1986. **Vine stocks:** Cabernet-Sauvignon, Grenache, Cinsault, Sémillon. **Soil:** Schist and clay with calcium carbonate. **Exposure:** Hillsides. **Average annual production in hectoliters:** 4,500.
Appellation: Côte-de-Provence and Bandol. **Type:** Red, white, rosé. **Technique:** in Oak barrels. **Maturing:** in wooden casks - (white): 4 months - (rosé): 6 months (red): 18 months. **Alcohol content:** 12.5 %. **Characteristics:** Supple, soft and rich, charming with lingering taste. **Serving temperature:** White: 6°-8° Red: 16°-18° - Rosé: 8°-10°. **Served with:** White: fish, crayfish, mushrooms - Rosé: salmon (marinated), shellfish, fish soup, exotic dishes - Red: lamb, meat, cheese. **Vintages available in 89/90:** Rosé and white: 1986 - Red: 1985-1981-1979.

Characteristics of vintages

1986: Superb rosés. Great elegance. **1985:** Delicious reds. **Other:** 1981 - Red: for very long ageing. 1979 - Red: superb with game. 1978 - Red: for long ageing.
Sales volume:
- Retail: 25 %. - Restaurants: 75 %.
Sales in France: 75 %.
Export sales: 25 %.
Main trading partners : Germany, Switzerland, Belgium, UK, Italy, Luxemburg, Netherlands, Scandinavia, USA, Japan, Southeast Asia.

References in France

Restaurants: Most Restaurants with Michelin Stars.
Shops: Fauchon - Hédiard.

Abroad

United States
Importers: The House of Burgundy Inc., 534 West 58th Street, New York, N.Y. 10019 - Tel: (212) 2470550. Shops: Sherry Leeman, Morrel: New York. Restaurants: Great restaurants.

United Kingdom
Importers: Mentzendorff 1 Co., Westminster, 31 Great Peter Street, London SWI 3LS Tel: (01) 222 2522/9. Shops: Harrods. Restaurants: Great London restaurants, Relais & Châteaux.

Germany
Importers: Monopole Goertz, Gustav-Heinemann-Strasse, 4044 Kaarst 1 (BEI Düsseldorf) Tel: (02101) 60060. Shops: Kafer. Restaurants: Great restaurants.

Japan
Importers: Weinkeller K.K. Takarada Building 6.13, Shintomi 1, Chome, Chuo-Ku - Tokyo. Shops: Luxury shops. Restaurants: Great international restaurants.

Others
Belgium - Luxemburg - Hong Kong - Spain.

LAFRAN-VEYROLLES

Mrs. Jouve-Ferec
Route de l'Argile, 83740 La Cadière d'Azur
94 90 13 37 or 94 98 72 59

Type of vineyard: Family-owned. **Established:** 1641, Bandol appellation in 1941. **Number of employees:** 5, some part time. **Vine stocks:** Mourvèdres, Cinsault, Grenache, Clairettes, Ugnis Blancs. **Soil:** Chalky clay produced by deposits of marine formations. **Exposure:** Full South and South-East. **Average annual production in hectoliters:** 200.

Appellation: Bandol Aoc. **Type:** Red, Rosé, White. **Technique:** Traditional, long (25 to 30 days), pumping over every other day. **Maturing:** Red: in the old style, in oak casks for 18 to 24 months, according to the vintage. **Alcohol content:** 12.6 to 13.2%. **Characteristics:** With slight variations associated with the year's climate, they are robust wines, like the soil from which they come, with a beautiful deep ruby color, mulberry, violet and liquorice aromas, long, spicy and complex like Cashmere wool. **Serving temperature:** Red: 16 to 18°. Rosé and White: 9 to 10°. **Served with:** White: fish and shellfish. Rosé: almost everything – as an aperitif or with bouillabaisse and exotic dishes. Red (classical): grilled or roasted meat and poultry. More full-bodied Reds: venison, wild boar or deer stew but also with monkfish ragout with fresh thyme.

Characteristics of vintages

1988: Rosé and White: dry and fruity, as expected, with pleasant, fresh aromas. Fine and full at the same time. **1987:** Red: very, very promising but you will have to wait. **1986:** Red: beginning to be sold. Although still a bit young, they are very well-structured, rich and well-balanced, with pleasant liquorice aromas and a certain persistance. Because of their tannins and their strength, they will age well. **1985:** Red: splendid wines with marvelously balanced tannins, round and harmonious. Keeping wines par excellence, they are fine and elegant. Great year. Gold Medal at Mâcon, **1987:** Price range (pre-tax, ex-warehouse): between 30 and 50 F.F.

Sales volume:
– Retail: 65%. – Restaurants: 35%.
Sales in France: 80%.
Export sales: 20%.
Main trading partners : Germany, Denmark.

References in France

Restaurants: La Côte de Bœuf et les Arcenaulx (Marseille), Le Shabu-Shabu (only Japanese restaurant in Marseille), Le Relais Saint-Victoire (Aix).
Shop: All fine shops in the region. L'Amour du Vin (94, rue Saint-Dominique, Paris 7th), Vins et Privilèges (Grasse).

Abroad

Germany

Weindepot Les Vignobles, Mulheimer Strasse 103 D, 4100 Duisburg I.

Others

Denmark: Babette Vin Import, Straedet 6, Lystrup, Slangerup DK 3550.

Comments

It is a small estate, but faithful to the rigid principles that it set for itself at the birth of the "Bandol" appellation in 1941, and always desirous to perfect the reputation that it has since acquired. Its wines, fruit of a privileged soil (on the Mediterranean coast, between Bandol and La Cadière d'Azur) and of an exceptional climate, are very much appreciated by connoisseurs. They are prepared from vinestocks cultivated with no herbicides or chemicals, except for the oligo-elements. The grapes are harvested manually, selected once in the vineyard and a second time in the winecellar. They are vinified in the old style except for temperature control by semi-modern techniques. The reds, rich in tannin, are aged for 18 months in oak casks. They are only offered for sale after 2 1/2 to 3 years. All that for the good of the wines and the satisfaction of those who honor them in the drinking.

DOMAINE DE LA LAIDIÈRE

Jules & Freddy Estienne
Sainte-Anne d'Evenos 83330 Evenos
94 90 37 07 or 94 90 35 29

Type of vineyard: Family-owned Agricultural Association. **Established:** 1941. **Vine stocks:** Mourvèdre, Cinsaut, Grenache, Clairette, Ugni Blanc. **Soil:** Sandy Marl. **Exposure:** South, South-East. **Average annual production in hectoliters:** 650.

Appellation: Bandol. **Type:** Red, White, Rosé. **Technique:** Traditional without destemming. **Maturing:** Red: in casks. Rosé and White: in vats. **Alcohol content:** 12.5 to 13%. **Characteristics:** Fragrant, long, very fine. **Serving temperature:** Red: 16°. White and Rosé: 8°. **Served with:** Red: red meat and game. Rosé: spicy dishes, oriental cuisine. White: fish, shellfish, seafood, or as an aperitif. **Vintages available in 89/90:** Red: 1986, 1987. White and Rosé: 1988.

Characteristics of vintages

1988: Rosé and White: very fruity, fresh, graceful, delicate. **1987:** Exceptional richness and grace, perfect harmony. **1986:** Same. Price range (pre-tax, ex-warehouse): between 30 and 50 F.F.

Sales volume:
– Retail: 30%. – Restaurants: 30%. – Other: 40%. (distributors).

Sales in France: 90%.

Export sales: 10%.

Main trading partners : Belgium, Germany, Switzerland, Netherlands, Denmark, United States, Japan.

Abroad

United States

Alliance du Vin 53 D Street SE, Whashington DC.

Germany

Joseph Zink Gmbh, Vogesenstrasse 2 A, 7580 Buhl.

Switzerland

Bruger von Tobel, Bern-Steinholzli, 3001 Bern.

Belgium

Maison Jean Straetmans, Zemstaan 148, 2800 Mechelen.

The Netherlands

Intercaves B.V., Marsweg 43, Postbus 517, 8000 A M Zwolle.

Far East

Japan: Daiei Sangyo Kaisha 18, 4 Chome Honjindori Nakamura-Ku, Nagoya 453.

Others

Norway: A/S Vinmonopolet, Haslevengen 16, 0502 Oslo. Denmark: Jysk Vinlager, Egegordsvej 43, DK 8900, Ronders.

Comments

Family estate for several generations. In 1941, Édouard Estienne, one of the founders of the Bandol appellation, and his son Jules, reconstituted the vineyard by replanting only noble grape varieties. From a first harvest of 6 hl in 1941, the production has increased to 650 hl on 17 hectares and will probably further increase to 850 to 900 hl on 24 hectares in 1992. The domain has always strived to produce very high quality wines. With the passage of time, improvements in vinification methods and new technologies have contributed to the production of some great vintages.

• *Glycerine – wine component responsible for its unctuosity. It appears in the course of the alcoholic fermentation but, in the case of mellow and naturally sweet wines, can also come from the favorable action of noble rot on the grapes. See Sauternes.*

• *Classification of the great Bordeaux wines in 1988. The ratings of Châteaux Lascombes (Margaux), Mazeris-Bellevue (Canon-Fronsac) and Haut-Maco (Côtes-de-Bourg) are improving, as well as those of certain other surprising crus (Châteaux Trocard, Melin, Gazin, Chantegriue, Gloria, La Croix-Saint-André, Fombrauge...). See the 1988 Classification in the Chapter on Bordeaux wines.*

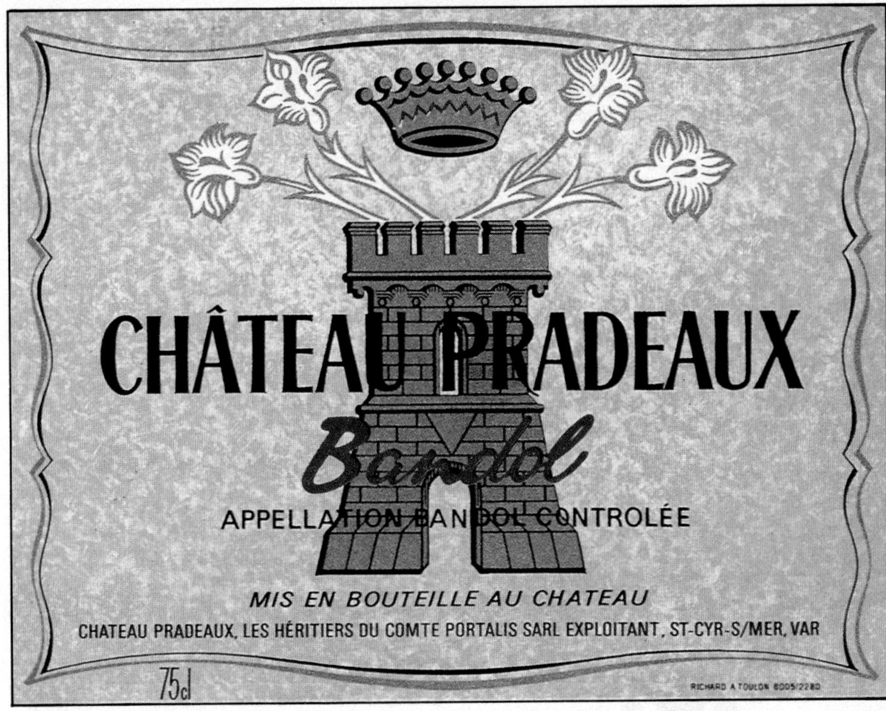

CHÂTEAU PRADEAUX

Mr. Portalis
83270 St Cyr-sur-Mer
94 26 10 74 - 94 32 00 13

Type of vineyard: Corporation managed agricultural association. **Established:** 1964. **Vine stocks:** Mourvèdre 80%, Grenache 10%, Cinsault 10%. **Soil:** Very chalky clay. **Exposure:** Facing the sea. **Average annual production in hectoliters:** 450.
Appellation: Bandol. **Type:** Red, rosé. **Maturing:** Red: in casks. White: in vats. **Alcohol content:** 13°. **Characteristics:** Red: tannic, well-balanced, very aromatic. Rosé: fresh and fruity. **Serving temperature:** Red: 18°. Rosé: 13°. **Served with:** Rosé: with fish, salads, white meat. Red: red meat, game, cheese. **Vintages available in 89/90:** Red: 1984. Rosé: 1988.

Characteristics of vintages

1988: Rosé: (Mourvèdre 15%, Cinsault 85%) fruity and fresh wines. **Other: 1984:** Red (Mourvèdre) rather tannic, can wait but can also be drunk now. **1983:** Red very limited stock. Price range (pre-tax, ex-warehouse): 30 to 50 F.F.
Sales volume:
- Wholesale: 30%. - Retail: 50%. - Restaurants: 20%.
Export sales: 15%.
Main trading partners : European community, USA.

References in France

Restaurants: Moulin de Mougins, La côte de Bœuf, (Marseille), Negresco, (Nice), Casino de Monaco.

Abroad

United States

Importers: Selected Vineyards, New York.

Germany

Frankof Kellerei.

Belgium

Mr. Coolse.

Comments

The estate was brought into the family in 1752 by Jean-Marie-Etienne Portalis, minister under Napoléon, co-author of the Civil Code and author of the Concordat. After the war, Baron Portalis and his daughter, the Countess Arlette Portalis, entirely replanted the vineyard, after which Cyril Portalis, great nephew of Miss Portalis took over. The 25 hectare estate, of which 18 are planted with vines, is located on very chalky soil in a seaside climatic zone. The time-honored cultivation style includes goblet pruning and natural fertilization assured by a herd of sheep. Whole bunches of grapes are vinified in the traditional style, after which the wine is aged in oak casks for 4 to 5 years.

CHÂTEAU STE-ANNE

François Dutheil de La Rochere
83330 Ste-Anne d'Evenos
94 90 35 40

Type of vineyard: Family-owned. **Established:** A vineyard for several generations. First bottling in the Château dating to 1962. **Number of employees:** 3. **Vine stocks:** Mourvèdre, Grenache, Cinsault. **Soil:** Clay with calcium carbonate. Silica in subsoil. **Exposure:** Southeast. **Average annual production in hectoliters:** 860. **Appellation:** Bandol. **Type:** Red, white, rosé. **Technique:** Traditional for red. Direct pressing for rosé and white. **Maturing:** 18 months in oak casks. **Alcohol content:** 12.5°. **Characteristics:** Rosés: good color, amber, richness of aromas with flowery fragrance. Great suppleness. White: very aromatic. Reds: rich and well-balanced, long keeping. Dark red color. Red fuit aroma, liquorice fragrance. **Serving temperature:** 12° (rosé, white), 18° reds. **Served with:** White: Seaeel Terrine, with Cresson Sauce. Rosé: grilled fish. Red: Roast lamb.

Marquis et Marquise Dutheil de la Rochère
propriétaire-récoltant à Sainte-Anne-d'Evenos, Var, tél. 94 90.35.40
CHATEAU Ste ANNE
BANDOL
appellation Bandol contrôlée
MIS EN BOUTEILLE AU CHATEAU
75cl
FRANCE

Vintages available in 89/90: Red: 1985, 1984, 1982. Rosé and white: 1986.

Characteristics of vintages

1985: Great vintage. Good garnet color. Rich aromas. Full of reserve. Very promising. **1984:** Very aromatic. Elegant. Well-balanced body. **1982:** Rich and well-balanced. Exceptional vintage. Very good evolution. Blackcurrant and red fruit aromas. Price range (pre-tax, ex-warehouse): Between 30 F.F. and 50 F.F.

Sales volume:
– Wholesale: 10%. – Retail: 30%. – Restaurants: 30%. – Other: 30% (export).
Sales in France: 70%.
Export sales: 30%.
Main trading partners: Germany, Benelux.

References in France

Restaurants: Auberge de Noues (Avignon).

Abroad

Germany

Vinco 5500 Trler.

The Netherlands

Caves Bernard – Massard – Grevenmacher.

CHÂTEAU DE PIBARNON

Count and Countess de Saint Victor
83740 La Cadière d'Azur
94 90 12 73

Type of vineyard: Family-owned. **Established:** 1954. **Number of employees:** 6. **Vine stocks:** Mourvèdre, Cinsault, Grenache, Bourboulenc, Ugni, Clairette. **Soil:** Clay with calcium carbonate and a number of trace metals. **Exposure:** Southwest. **Average annual production in hectoliters:** 1,400.
Appellation: A.O.C. Bandol. **Type:** Red, white, rosé. **Technique:** long (3 weeks at 30°C for reds) with daily crushing. **Maturing:** in oak vats. **Characteristics:** Red (1985): Rich color, complex nose, bilberry, blackberry flavor, with notes of liquorice cinnamon, pepper and spices. Hint of truffles that will become more noticeable with age. Very fine tannins. Good keeping wine. White (1986): very flowery. Peach flavor. Rosé (1986): very fruity and dry. **Serving temperature:** Red: 16-17°, rosé and white: 6-7°. **Served with:** Red (young): grilled meat, especially lamb, goose or duck preserve, grilled fish. Red (5-6 year old): game, veal kidneys, mushrooms and especially truffles. Rosé 1986: all spicy foods, curry bouillabaisse, roquefort cheese. White 1986: remarkable with seafood, shellfish. **Vintages available in 89/90:** 1985 (Red) – 1986 (Rosé and white).

Characteristics of vintages

1986: Rosé and white: still very fruity, very fresh, to be drunk young. **1985:** Exceptional year for reds, fine tannins, elegance, remarkable ageing potential. **1984:** Out of stock. **1983:** Out of stock. **1982:** Out of stock. Price range (pre-tax, ex-warehouse): 30 F.F.-50 F.F.
Sales volume:
– Retail: 60%. – Restaurants: 30%. – Other: 10% (well known clients).
Sales in France: 90%.
Export sales: 10%.
Main trading partners: UK, Germany, Switzerland, Netherlands, USA, Japan.

References in France

Restaurants: Auberge de Kochersberg, Gagnaire, Oustau de Beaumanière, Chapel, Blanc, Dutournier, La Maison Blanche, Jouteux, etc.
Shops: Paris – Les Caves de la Madeleine, Chez Estève, rue de la Cerisaie, Vins rares et de collection, Rue Laugier.

Abroad

United States

Importers: Wine Imports Ltd. San Francisco – Direct Import Wine Cie., Chicago – Maubert, Florida – Draper & Esquin, San Francisco – Connaisseur Wines, Chicago – Consolidated Distilled Products, Chicago.

United Kingdom

Importers: Wine and Cuisine – Berkmann Wine Cellars. Restaurants: Le Gavroche, Tante Claire (London), Les Quatre Saisons (Oxford).

Germany

Importers: Weinhandlung (Hamburg) – France Vinicole, Hafenstrasse 20, Postfach 1730, 7640 Kehl/Rhein.

The Netherlands

Importers: Wijnkoperij H.F. Okhuysen B.V., Haarlem.

Far East

Importers: Halta Schoten Ltd (Tokyo) Japan.

Switzerland

Importers: Maison Zanchi (Lausanne) – Martel A.G. (Saint-Galen). Restaurants: Le Duc (Geneva).

Comments

The Pibarnon red is known as one of the most typical wines of the Bandol appellation. Cultivated on high ground, sheltered from the wind, the Mourvèdre contributes all its fullness and a veritable fireworks display of fragrances. Also true for the rosé.

DOMAINE TEMPIER
Lucien Peyraud
G.A.E.C. PEYRAUD, DOMAINE TEMPIER, LE PLAN-DU-CASTELLET, 83330 Le Beausset
94 98 70 21

Type of vineyard: Family agricultural association since 1973. **Established:** 1834. **Number of employees:** 6. **Vine stocks:** Mourvèdre, Cinsault, Grenache. **Soil:** Chalky clay. **Exposure:** South. **Average annual production in hectoliters:** 800.
Appellation: Bandol AOC. **Type:** Red, rosé. **Technique:** Traditional. **Maturing:** In 50 hl oak casks. **Alcohol content:** 13%. **Characteristics:** Rosé: aromatic and fruity. Red: full round, supple tannins, long. **Serving temperature:** Rosé: 10°. Red: 16°. **Served with:** Rosé: fish, bouillabaisse, grilled shrimp. Red: red meat, game, cheese. **Vintages available in 89/90:** Rosé: 1987 and 1988. Red: 1984, 1986, 1987.

Characteristics of vintages

1988: Superb vintage, rich, full, round, long, tannic. **1987:** Quite successful, good balance. **1986:** Good year, supple. **1985:** Out of stock. **Other: 1984:** Good year, elegant, soft tannins, fully developed. Price range (pre-tax, ex-warehouse): between 30 and 50 F.F.
Sales volume:
– Retail: 40%. – Restaurants: 60%.
Sales in France: 47%
Export sales: 43%
Main trading partners: USA, Japan, Switzerland, Belgium, UK, Canada.

References in France

Restaurants: Moulin de Mougins, Beaumanière, Lucas Carton, Troisgros, Côte St. Jacques, La Mère Blanc.
Shops: Caves de la Madeleine.

Comments

The Domaine Tempier has belonged to the same family since 1834. Lucien Peyraud married Lucie Tempier and their sons Jean-Marie and François joined them in 1960 to form an agricultural association, Gaec Peyraud, in 1973. The Peyraud family cultivates, vinifies and markets exclusively the Bandol red and rosé wines of the Domaine Tempier under an authentic and respected appellation.

• *The quality of the 1987 vintage, particularly in Bordeaux, is questionable. Much of the Merlot suffered from coulure and a good bit of the harvesting was done in the rain. Only a few vineyards will produce a good vintage (see the Chapter on Bordeaux wines and the "Vintage Code").*

• *In 1985, the wines of the following regions received the A.O.C. (Appellation d'Origine Contrôlée) classification: Minervois, Coteaux-des-Baux, Coteaux-d'Aix-en-Provence, Coteaux-du-Lyonnais and Coteaux-du-Languedoc.*

CÔTEAUX D'AIX ET DES BAUX

CHÂTEAU DE CALISSANNE

Denis Langue, director
Philippe Desruelles, commercial manager
13680 Lançon de Provence
90 42 63 03

Type of vineyard: Agricultural Association. **Number of employees:** 15. **Vine stocks:** Red: Cabernet, Sauvignon, Syrah, Grenache, Mourvèdre – White: Sémillon, Sauvignon, Ugni Blanc. **Soil:** Chalk and chalky clay. **Exposure:** South. **Average annual production in hectoliters:** 40-45.

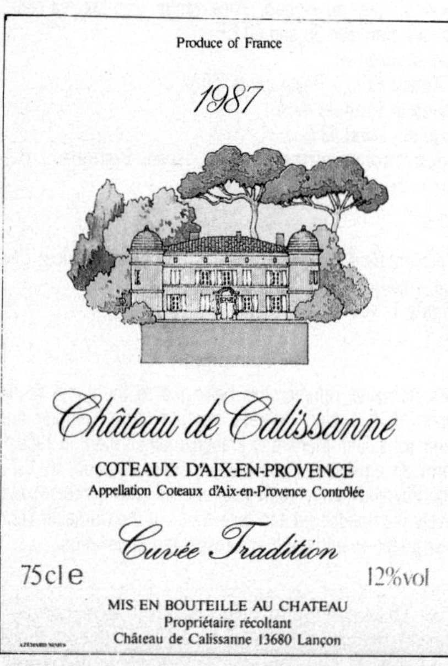

Produce of France
1987
Château de Calissanne
COTEAUX D'AIX-EN-PROVENCE
Appellation Coteaux d'Aix-en-Provence Contrôlée
Cuvée Tradition
75cle
12%vol
MIS EN BOUTEILLE AU CHATEAU
Propriétaire récoltant
Château de Calissanne 13680 Lançon

Appellation: Coteaux d'Aix en Provence. **Type:** Red, White, Rosé. **Maturing:** In Oak casks (Cuvée Prestige Rouge). **Alcohol content:** 12%. **Characteristics:** Red wines for keeping – white and rosé to be consumed within the year. **Serving temperature:** Red: 17°. White & Rosé: 9-12°. **Vintages available in 89/90 :** 1986-1987-1988.

Characteristics of vintages

1988: Excellent vintage particularly for red wines. **1987:** Light and supple, but very fruity. **1986:** Red: very good structure, good keeping. Price range (pre-tax, ex-warehouse): 15 F.F. (Cuvée Tradition), 25 F.F. (Cuvée Prestige).
Sales volume:
– Wholesale: 40% (20% for export). – Retail: 50%. – Restaurants: 10%.
Sales in France: 80%.
Export sales: 20%.
Main trading partners : Netherlands, UK, Luxemburg, Switzerland, Germany, USA.

References in France

Restaurants: Paris: Méridien Hotel, Porte Maillot – Altea-Pullman hotels, Boffinger – Carry Le Rouet: L'Escale.

Abroad

United States
Ideal Wines (Massachusetts), tel. 617 395 3300.

United Kingdom
Bordeaux direct, tel. 0734 48 17 13.

Switzerland
Jean Pierre Mathieu and Co., tel. 021 22 76 67.

The Netherlands
Kerstens, Alliance Vinicole, tel. 017 20 72 645.

Luxemburg
Ets Cactus, tel. 352 31 03 71.

Comments

The Château de Calissanne is a very old estate. A Celto-Ligurian hilltop fortification is still visible. For centuries, the château belonged to the Knights of the Order of Malta. The buildings go back to the 17th century.

MAS DE LA DAME

Les Baux-de-Provence – 13520 Maussane
90 54 32 24

Type of vineyard: Family-owned. **Established:** 1948. **Vine stocks:** Grenache, Cabernet, Cinsault, Syrah, Carignan. **Soil:** Clay with calcium carbonate. **Exposure:** Hillsides facing South. **Average annual production in hectoliters:** 2,500.
Appellation: Coteaux d'Aix-en-Provence – Les Beaux – Contrôlée. **Type:** Red, rosé. **Technique:** Traditional with temperature control. **Maturing:** in Oak casks (for reds). **Characteristics:** Rosé '87: Bright ruby, very fragrant, fruity, strong red berry aroma (cherry, very fine, long for a rosé. Red: 1984: Beautiful color, good alcohol balance, fine bouquet. Red 1985: Beautiful dark red color, tannic, long finish, strong personality, very fine and heady with ageing. Good keeping (10-12 years). **Serving temperature:** Rosé du Mas: cool (12°) – Cuvée Gourmande of the Year: (16°) – Réserve Rouge '84 & '85: at room temperature (18-20°). **Served with:** Rosé du Mas: fish and shellfish – Réserve Rouge 84: with poultry and light sauces – Réserve Rouge 85: red meat, cheese. **Vintages available in 89/90:** Rosé du Mas 1987 – Rouge Cuvée Gourmande, Rouge Réserve 1984, 1985, 1986.

Characteristics of vintages

1987: Rosé du Mas 87: very fine, good year. Réserve 86: promising year, strong aroma, very fine and long finish. **1985:** Réserve 1985: will improve. **1984:** Réserve 1984: very much appreciated by wine lovers – still a few bottles in stock. Hurry. Price range (pre-tax, ex-warehouse): 15 F.F.-25 F.F.

Abroad

Mistral Wines

5 Junction Mews, Sale Place, London W2 1PN. Tel: 01 262 5437/8 – Telex: 267 681 Mistra G.

CHÂTEAU DE FONSCOLOMBE

Marquis de Saporta & Brigitte Grivet
13610 Le Puy Sainte-Reparade
42 61 89 62 – Telex: 441 371

Type of vineyard: Agricultural Association. **Established:** 1720. **Number of employees:** 35. **Vine stocks:** Grenache, Cinsault, Syrah, Cabernet, Carignan, Clairette, Grenache Blanc, Sauvignon, Ugni Blanc. **Soil:** Chalky clay. **Exposure:** Hillsides, South and South-West. **Average annual production in hectoliters:** 10,000.

Château de Fonscolombe
COTEAUX D'AIX EN PROVENCE
APPELLATION COTEAUX D'AIX-EN-PROVENCE CONTRÔLÉE
PRODUCE OF FRANCE
Cuvée Spéciale
12 % vol.
1988
e 75 cl
MIS EN BOUTEILLE AU CHATEAU
Société Civile Agricole Fonscolombe viticulteur,
Marquis de Saporta, administrateur 13610 Le Puy-Ste-Réparade - France

Appellation: A.O.C. Côteaux d'Aix-en-Provence. **Type:** Red, white, rosé. **Technique:** Traditional. **Maturing:** In casks. **Alcohol content:** 12%. **Characteristics:** Fruity, aromatic, light, easy to drink. **Serving temperature:** Red: 17-18°. White/Rosé: 13°. **Served with:** Red: grilled meat. White: fish and as an aperitif. **Vintages available in 89/90:** 1987, 1988.

Characteristics of vintages

1988: Very fruity, juicy, deep color, well-balanced. **1987:** Supple, light, fruity, aromatic. Price range (pre-tax, ex-warehouse): 10 to 20 F.F.

Sales volume:
– Wholesale: 65%. – Retail: 5%. – Restaurants: 30%.

Sales in France: 65%.

Export sales: 35%.

Main trading partners: UK, Germany, Benelux countries, Denmark, Japan, USA, Mauritius, Honduras.

DOMAINE DE LAUZIÈRES

Les Filles – 7 – Boyer
Le Destet – 13890 Mouriès
42 04 70 39

Type of vineyard: Family-owned. **Established:** 1960. **Vine stocks:** Cinsault, Grenache, Carignan, Mourvèdre. **Soil:** Clay with calcium carbonate. **Exposure:** Hillsides. **Average annual production in hectoliters:** 1,500. **Appellation:** Coteaux des Beaux-de-Provence. **Type:** Red, rosé. **Technique:** Traditional. **Maturing:** In Oak casks. **Alcohol content:** 13%. **Characteristics:** Fine, fruity, full of roundness, full taste, supple and meaty. **Serving temperature:** Between 16 and 18°. **Served with:** Red meat and game. **Vintages available in 89/90:** Red: 1983, 1985, 1986 and 1988. Rosé: 1988.

Characteristics of vintages

1988: Red: Well-balanced, rich, soft, full and long. **1987:** Out of stock. **1986:** Red fruit aroma, full and supple. **1985:** Same quality, to be drunk in 3 years. **1984:** Wines are maturing very well, regularly. They have a good quality-price ratio. Price range (pre-tax, ex-warehouse): between 10 F.F. and 20 F.F.

Sales volume:
– Retail: 95%. – Restaurants: 5%.

Sales in France: 90%.

Export sales: 10%.

Main trading partners: Germany, Belgium, Switzerland.

References in France

Restaurants: Restaurants of the region.

Comments

The vineyard is located at the foot of the Baux, in the very middle of the Alpilles. This is now a family-owned property.

RÉCOLTE 1986
MISE DU DOMAINE
DOMAINE DE LA VALLONGUE
Coteaux d'Aix en Provence
Les Baux
Appellation Coteaux d'Aix en Provence Contrôlée
Ph. PAUL-CAVALLIER
PROPRIÉTAIRE-RÉCOLTANT
A SAINT-RÊMY DE PROVENCE, 13810 EYGALIÈRES
e 75 cl
PRODUCE OF FRANCE
PHOTO CHOLLEY - AVIGN

DOMAINE DE LA VALLONGUE

Philippe Paul-Cavallier
BP No. 4 - 13810 Eygalières
90 95 91 70 – Telefax: 90 95 98 31

Type of vineyard: Family-owned. **Established:** 1962. **Vine stocks:** Cinsault 10%, Counoise 3%, Carrignan 8%, Grenache 45%, Syrah 19%, Cabernet 15%. **Exposure:** East, West. **Average annual production in hectoliters:** 1,800.
Appellation: Coteaux d'Aix-en-Provence, Coteaux d'Aix-en-Provence Les Baux. **Type:** Red, Rosé. **Technique:** Red: traditional. Rosé: drawing off (as low a temperature as possible), no malolactic fermentation. **Maturing:** Red: in 22 hl barrels. **Alcohol content:** 12%. **Characteristics:** Fruity, very aromatic. **Serving temperature:** Red: 18°. Rosé: 8 to 10°. **Served with:** Traditional cuisine. **Vintages available in 89/90:** Red: 1985, 1986, 1988. Rosé: 1988.

Characteristics of vintages

1988: Very pleasant, natural and fruity, improves with age. **1986:** Typical aroma, fruity. **1985:** Typical wild fruit aroma.
Price range (pre-tax, ex-warehouse): 30 to 50 F.F.
Sales volume:
– Wholesale: 95%. – Retail: 2.5%. – Restaurants: 2.5%.
Sales in France: 5%.
Export sales: 95%.
Main trading partners : Switzerland, Germany, Belgium, UK.

References in France

Restaurants: La Giberne (Paris), Hôtel de la Poste, Hôtel Central (Beaune), Greuze (Tournus), Beaumanière, Riboto de Taveny (Les Baux), Coupe Chou (Verquière).
Shops: L'Amour du Vin, (Paris).

Abroad

United Kingdom
Paul Boutinot Wine LTD Stockport.

Switzerland
Ed. Renevier S.A. Lausanne.

Canada
Chase international, Ontario.

Comments

The winecellar, created in 1971 makes use of both traditional and modern techniques of vinification and filtration. Planted in 1962, the vineyard has a good balance of vinestocks which, with increasing age, provide more and more typical wines that are natural, sound and aromatic.

• *To better understand the evolution and adherence to type of the various vintages, consult our "Vintage Code" chart.*

CHÂTEAU DU SEUIL

Carreau Gaschereau
13540 Puyricard
42 92 15 99 – Telex: 441 571

Type of vineyard: Family-owned. **Established:** 1973. **Vine stocks:** Cabernet Sauvignon, Syrah, Cinsault, Grenache, Sauvignon, Ugni, Counoise. **Soil:** Marine and volcanic deposits, chalk, clay. **Exposure:** South. **Average annual production in hectoliters:** 2,200.

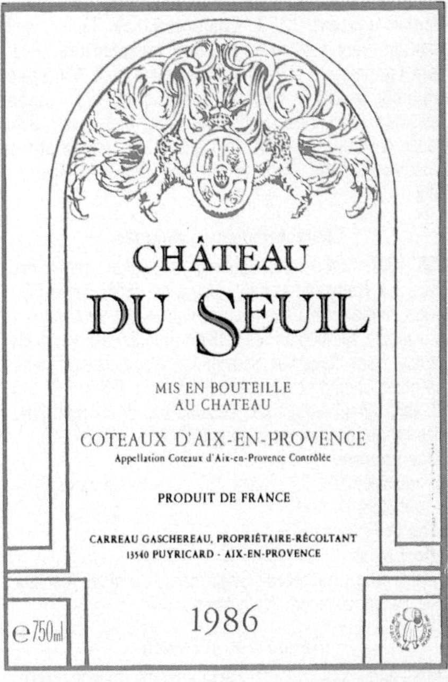

Appellation: Coteaux d'Aix-en-Provence. **Type:** Red, white, rosé. **Technique:** Traditional. **Alcohol content:** 12%. **Characteristics:** Fruity. **Serving temperature:** Red: 16°. Rosé: 12°. White: 10°. **Served with:** Lamb (cooked on the gril), mediterranean style and exotic cuisine. **Vintages available in 89/90:** Red: 1985, 1986, 1987. Rosé: 1988. White: 1988.

Characteristics of vintages

Price range (pre-tax, ex-warehouse): 20 to 30 F.F.
Sales in France: 85%.
Export sales: 15%.
Main trading partners : Germany, Belgium, UK, Denmark, Switzerland.

References in France

Restaurants: Alain Morel (Paris), Le petit Nice, Passedat (Marseille), Le Jules César (Arles).

CHÂTEAU PIGOUDET

Mr. V. Sciré - P. Bitouzet
Route de Jouques
B.P. 5 - 83560 Rians
94 80 31 78 - Telex: 400 126 F

Established: 1975. **Number of employees:** 8. **Vine stocks:** Cabernet-Sauvignon, Syrah, Grenache, Cinsault. **Soil:** Clay with calcium carbonate. **Exposure:** Facing full South. **Average annual production in hectoliters:** 3,000.
Appelation: Coteaux d'Aix-en-Provence A.O.C. **Type:** Red, rosé. **Technique:** Traditional. **Maturing:** Oak casks. **Alcohol content:** 12,5%. **Characteristics:** Tannic, well balanced, very rich color. **Serving temperature:** Red: room temperature (18°-20°). Rosé: quite cool. **Vintages available in 89/90:** Grande Réserve (red) 1985. Cuvée Descartes (red) 1986. Red: 1987. Red and rosé: 1988. Medals awarded in 1988: Gold and Silver Medals at the Concours Général, Paris. Silver and Bronze Medals at Mâcon.

Characteristics of vintages

1988, 1987: Made from Cabernet Sauvignon, Syrah and Grenache. Fruity and slightly spicy wine. **1986:** Cuvée Descartes: made from Cabernet Sauvignon and Syrah. It is a soft, supple, full-bodied wine. **1985:** Grande Réserve: made entirely from Cabernet Sauvignon. Well-balanced wine, rich color, should be aged about 10 years. **Other:** '81 and '78: very tannic - must be decanted and drunk right now.
Price range (pre-tax, ex-warehouse): 20 F.F.-50 F.F.
Sales volume:
- Wholesale: 25%. - Retail: 10%. - Restaurants: 20%.
- Other: 45% (export).

Sales in France: 55%.
Export sales: 45%.
Main trading partners : Switzerland, Germany, Canada, USA, Japan, Denmark, Netherlands, UK.

References in France

Restaurants: Polo de Paris (Paris) - Beach Regency (Nice) - Gray d'Albion (Cannes) - Palais des Congrès (Nice) - Cottage Hôtel (Sté Cottel).
Shops: A.T.C.A. Nice Airport - Maystoril & Supply Store (Monaco) - Sun Shine (Cannes).

Abroad

United States
Importers: Stewart Hill - New Jersey.

United Kingdom
Importers: Ehrmanns Wine Shippers - London.

Germany
Importers: Eggers & Franke - Bremen - Weinhaus Groehl - Hambourg.

Canada
Importers: Opimiam Society - Montréal.

The Netherlands
Importers: Delcave - NL-AK Delft.

Switzerland
Et Mosca.

Others
Importers: Toyo Henka Kaisah - Tokyo (Japan). Globus - Zurich (Switzerland). Logismose - DK-Harby (Denmark).

TERRES BLANCHES

Noël Michelin
Georges Hubert Dutel
RN 99 13210 St. Rémy de Provence
90 95 91 66 - Telex: 420 763 F
Fax: 90 95 99 04
CCI ARLE Attn. of Terres Blanches

Type of vineyard: Family-owned. **Established:** 1968. **Number of employees:** 8. **Soil:** Clay with calcium carbonate, Würmian and post Würmian alluvium, gravel. **Exposure:** Northern slope of the Alpilles, plenty of sunshine. **Average annual production in hectoliters:** 2,000.
Appellation: Coteaux des Beaux (A.O.C. Coteaux d'Aix-les-Baux). **Type:** Red, white, rosé. **Technique:** Red: classic; white and rosé: low temperature. **Maturing:** Red in oak casks for 1 year. **Serving temperature:** Red: 16 - 17°. Rosé and white: 10 - 12 °. **Served with:** Red: lamb. Rosé and white: grilled fish. **Vintages available in 89/90:** Red 1985 and 1986. Rosé 1987 and White 1987 as of March 1988.

Characteristics of vintages

1987: Very mature red, ready now, rather supple but full with a good aromatic density. Can be drunk now or kept another 3 years. **1986:** Red not to be drunk before 1990. Great finesse, a wine for connoisseurs.

CHÂTEAU VIGNELAURE

Georges Brunet
Route de Jouques - 83560 Rians
94 80 31 93 - Telex: 404 614

Type of vineyard: Corporation. **Number of employees:** 30. **Vine stocks:** Cabernet Sauvignon, Syrah, Grenache. **Exposure:** Clay with calcium carbonate. **Exposure:** Mostly South, some vineyards North, some East and some West. **Average annual production in hectoliters:** 35/hectare.
Appellation: Côteaux d'Aix-en-Provence et des Baux. **Type:** Red. **Technique:** Very slow in stainless steel tanks. **Maturing:** 24 months in oak casks. **Alcohol content:** 12.3%. **Characteristics:** Superb wines made for very long ageing, reaching full maturity monly after 7-8 years (see classification). Kept in oak containers for 24 months. Spice and rapsberry fragrance. **Serving temperature:** 14°-15°. **Served with:** Some vintages go well with light meals,

such as white meat, for exanple, while other richer vintages go with other dishes. **Vintages available in 89/90:** 1982, 1983, 1984, and older vintages on demand, 1985 as of February 1988.

Characteristics of vintages

1986: Elegance and breed – Very promising. Order now. **1985:** Very good year – to be set aside for drinking in 1990. **1984:**Supple wines. May be drunk now or aged for at least 10 years. **1983:** Very good year, but not yet developed. Ready in 4 years time. **1982:** Very good year, somewhat similar to the previous year. **Other:** A few bottles of old vintages may be provided for wine lovers.

Abroad

United States

Château Estate Wines, Park Avenue, New-York.

United Kingdom

Thoman Ltd, London. Yapp Brothers.

Switzerland

Manuel et Lassueur, Lausanne.

Belgium

Renglet, Brussels.

Canada

Arvin, Montreal.

The Netherlands

Fourcroy Nederlands.

Far East

Japan: Suntory.

Comments

Very old French A.O.C. (1941). The vineyard was rescued by Mr. Jean Bagnis during the 40s and since, for almost 50 years, the Bagnis family has been striving to maintain it among the ranks of the great wines of Provence.

BELLET

CHÂTEAU DE CREMAT

Charles Bagnis
442 Chemin de Crémat 06200 Nice
93 37 80 30 or 93 37 82 08 – Telex: 470 232

Type of vineyard: Agricultural Association. **Established:** 1945. **Number of employees:** 4. **Vine stocks:** Rolle, Folle Noire, Braquet, Chardonnay, Grenache, Cinsaut. **Soil:** Conglomerate: sand and stones. **Exposure:** South, South-West. **Average annual production in hectoliters:** 450. **Appellation:** A.O.C. Bellet. **Type:** Red, white, rosé. **Technique:** Traditional. **Maturing:** Red: in new casks, renewed every 3 years. **Alcohol content:** 12%. **Characteristics:** Very typical due to the Bellet vinestocks. Each color has its own character. **Serving temperature:** Red: 18°. White, rosé: 7 to 8°. **Served with:** Red: All meats, even in sauce, and cheese. White and rosé: With local specialities and fish. **Vintages available in 89/90:** Red: 1985, 1986. Rosé and white: 1987, 1988.

Characteristics of vintages

Price range (pre-tax, ex-warehouse): between 40 and 60 F.F.

Sales volume:
– Retail: 20%. – Restaurants: 80%.
Sales in France: 80%.
Export sales: 20%.
Main trading partners : USA, UK, Japan, Belgium, Switzerland.

References in France

Restaurants: SBM, Negresco, Martinez, Carlton and all of the other great restaurants of the Côte d'Azur.

CÔTES DU LUBÉRON

CHÂTEAU LA GANORGUE

J.P. Margan
Route du pont Julien 84480 Bonnieux
90 75 81 01

Type of vineyard: Family-owned. **Established:** 1976. **Number of employees:** 2. **Vine stocks:** Syrah 80%, Grenache 10%, Mourvèdre 5%, Cinsault 5%, Clairette 50%, Bourboulenc 50%. **Soil:** Chalky clay. **Average annual production in hectoliters:** 40 hl/ha (on 15 ha). **Appellation:** Côtes du Luberon. **Type:** Red, White, Rosé. **Technique:** Red: traditional – White and Rosé at low temperature. **Maturing:** Red in casks – White and Rosé in stainless steel tanks. **Alcohol content:** 12%. **Characteristics:** Very fruity and light, personality, elegance – can be consumed in their youth but are also good keeping wines. **Serving temperature:** Red: 16°. White and Rosé: 12-14°. **Served with:** Red: game, poultry, lamb, pasta with truffles. White: fish and shellfish and certain cheeses. **Vintages available in 89/90:** Red: 1986, 1987, 1988. White and Rosé: 1988.

Characteristics of vintages

1988: Red: excellent keeping, supple, round, lingering flavor. White and Rosé: fruity, firm and vigorous, Rosé very light in color. **1987:** Red: light, very delicate, fruity, (Gold Medal at the Concours Général Agricole). **1986:** Tannic enough to make a good keeping wine but can be drunk young, supple and rich. Price range (pre-tax, ex-warehouse): 10 to 20 F.F. (export and restaurants) – 20 to 30 F.F. (Private clientele).
Sales volume:
– Retail: 50%. – Restaurants: 30%. – Other: 20% (export).
Sales in France: 80%.
Export sales: 20%.
Main trading partners : UK, Netherlands, Germany, Belgium.

Abroad

United Kingdom

Yapp Brothers mere Wiltshire.

Belgium

De Wijnkoffer Strooistraat Meise (Tel: 02/269 80 86).

The Netherlands

Ockhuysen Gierstraat 34 36 38, 2011 Haarlem.

Comments

Fief established as an earldom by Pope Benoît XIV, the Château La Ganorgue will enchant you by its charm and simplicity. The fountains protected by Neptune and his Dolphins, the little chapel, the majestic terrace from which one has a magnificent view of the Luberon, the Ventoux and Lacoste and its Château which once belonged to the Marquis de Sade, all this is in perfect harmony. You will love this old place.

VINS DE CORSE

CLOS DE BERNARDI

P. de Bernardi
20243 Patrimonio
95 37 01 09

Type of vineyard: Family-owned. **Established:** 1880. **Vine stocks:** Malvoisie, Ugni Blanc, Nielluccio. **Soil:** Silica-clay with pebbles and chalky stones over a conglomerate sub-soil. **Exposure:** Hillsides facing South and Southeast. **Average annual production in hectoliters:** 400.
Appellation: A.O.C. Patrimonio. **Type:** Red, white, rosé. **Technique:** Classic, traditional. Reds: destemming and fermentation with skins for 8 days. **Maturing:** In vats, casks and bottles. **Alcohol content:** 13%. **Characteristics:** Typical, fine and long wines. Ageing less than 10 years for the reds, and less than 5 for the whites and rosés. **Serving temperature:** Red: 17°. White and rosé: 10°. **Served with:** Red: meat and cheese. White: fish and seafood. Rosé: game, poultry, etc. **Vintages available in 89/90:** 1986.

Characteristics of vintages

1986: Very fine, typical vintage. Good, aromatic red, rather full bodied, good vinification. White: light and supple, fruity. Price range (pre-tax, ex-warehouse): between 20 and 30 F.F.
Sales volume: – Retail: 70%. – Restaurants: 30%.
Sales in France: 100%.

References in France

Restaurants: In the best Corsican Restaurants.

CLOS CULOMBU

Etienne Suzzoni
Chemin de la Chapelle Saint Pierre 20260 Lumio
95 60 70 68

Type of vineyard: Privately owned. **Established:** 1973. **Number of employees:** 5. **Vine stocks:** Niellucciu 50%, Sciacarellu 30%, Grenache 20%. **Soil:** Quartz sand. **Exposure:** South-West. **Average annual production in hectoliters:** 1,000.
Appellation: Vins de Corse – Calvi. **Type:** Red, Rosé. **Technique:** Traditional, with temperature control. **Maturing:** In vats and bottles. **Alcohol content:** 13%. **Characteristics:** Red: spicy aromas, solid structure. **Serving temperature:** Red: 18°. Rosé: 10°. **Served with:** Red:

meat cooked in sauce. Rosé: delicatessen, white meat, fish. **Vintages available in 89/90:** 1986, 1987, 1988 – Red and Rosé.

Characteristics of vintages

1988: Exceptional rosé, delicate and aromatic; red already pleasant. **1987:** Red: very typical tannic structure, maquis fragrance. **1986:** Spicy aromas (pepper, cinnamon, tobacco), well balanced. **1985:** Depleted stock. Price range (pre-tax, ex-warehouse): 10 to 20 F.F. – 20 to 30 F.F.
Sales volume:
– Retail: 70%. – Restaurants: 30%.
Sales in France: 99%.
Export sales: 1%.
Main trading partners : Switzerland.

Comments

Created in 1973 on undeveloped land, the Suzzoni Brother's vineyard is still growing, proving that the invasion of the maquis is not a foregone conclusion in Corsica. Culombu, where the winecellar is located, is represented by the Marine Conch (on the label), a symbol of communication. The wines are a product of traditional cultivation (no herbicides, chemical fertilizers, synthetic pesticides, but only copper and flowers of sulphur), severe pruning, manual desuckering and removal of excess leaves to assure the health and optimum ripening of the grapes.

DOMAINE PERALDI

Comte de Poix
20167 Ajaccio
95 22 37 30

Established: For more than four Centuries. **Number of employees:** 12. **Vine stocks:** Sciaccarello, Grenache, Cinsault, Carignan and Vermentino. **Soil:** Quartz, sand. **Exposure:** All directions. **Average annual production in hectoliters:** 2000-3000.
Appellation: Ajaccio. **Type:** Red, white, rosé. **Technique:** Red: 100 to 150 hl vats. Rosé: stainless steel. **Maturing:** Casks. **Alcohol content:** Rosé, white: 12%. Red: 12.5%. **Characteristics:** Light, long and fragrant. **Serving temperature:** Red: 16°. Rosé and white: 11°. **Vintages available in 89/90:** Red: 1985, 1986. Rosé, white: 1986 & 1987.

Characteristics of vintages

Sales in France: 80% (mostly to cellars).
Export sales: 20%.
Main trading partners : Belgium, UK, Netherlands, Germany, Switzerland, USA (2 States only).

Abroad

United States

American Wine (Texas) Terlato Import (Illinois).

United Kingdom

Wine Club – London.

Germany

Poulig – Dusseldorf.

The Netherlands

Alliance Française.

CLOS REGINU

Mr. Raoust
20 225 MURO
95 61 72 11

Type of vineyard: Family-owned. **Established:** 1975. **Number of employees:** 3. **Vine stocks:** Nielluccio, Sciacarello, Vermentino, Grenache, Syrah, etc. **Soil:** Sandy clay on moraine. **Exposure:** North-South. **Average annual production in hectoliters:** 1 000.
Appellation: Vin de Corse Calvi. **Type:** Red, White, Rosé. **Technique:** Traditional. **Maturing:** Vintage Red: in stainless steel tanks, wooden vats and bottles. **Alcohol content:** 12%. **Characteristics:** White and Rosé: fruity, fresh – Red: rich and well balanced. **Serving temperature:** 17° – 18°. **Vintages available in 89/90:** Red: 1985, 1987, 1988. White and Rosé: 1988.

Characteristics of vintages

1988: Beautiful Whites very much marked by their vinestocks very fruity. **1985:** Excellent Red, good color, full, typical, good development.
Sales volume:
– Wholesale: 60%. – Retail: 40%.
Sales in France: 100%.

DOMAINE DE TORRACCIA

Christian Imbert
20137 Lecci de Porto Vecchio – Corse
95 71 43 50

Type of vineyard: Family-owned. **Established:** 1964. **Number of employees:** 12. **Vine stocks:** Nielluciu, Sciacarellu, Grenache, Malvoisie de Corse. **Soil:** Quartz sand. **Exposure:** Southeast. **Average annual production in hectoliters:** 1 800.
Appellation: Vin de Corse – Porto Vecchio. **Type:** Red, white, rosé. **Technique:** Classic, low temperature for whites and rosés. **Maturing:** In vats, later in bottles. **Alcohol content:** 12% (natrual, no sugar added). **Characteristics:** Very typical Corsican wine. **Serving temperature:** Red: 14°. **Vintages available in 89/90:** Rosé and white: 1986, Red: 1984, Rouge Réserve ORIU: 1981.

Characteristics of vintages

1986: Rosé and white: dry and fruity. Red: fleshy, nose characteristics of the Corsican "maquis" (bush), keeps rather well.

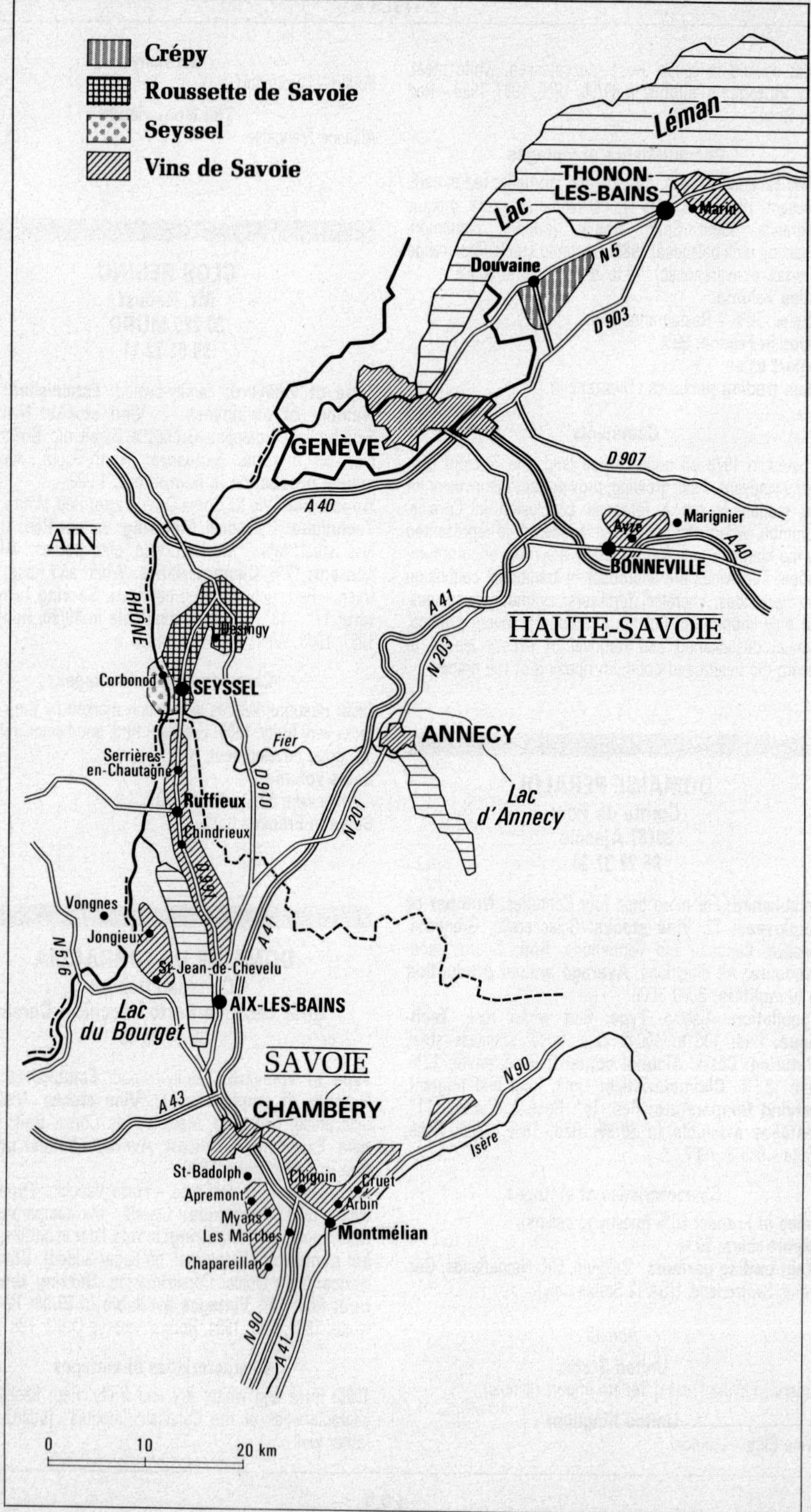

Crépy
Roussette de Savoie
Seyssel
Vins de Savoie
Léman
Lac
THONON-LES-BAINS
Margin
Douvaine
N 5
D 903
GENÈVE
D 907
Marignier
Ayze
BONNEVILLE
A 40
AIN
A 40
RHÔNE
A 41
N 203
HAUTE-SAVOIE
Vesingy
Corbonod
SEYSSEL
ANNECY
Fier
Serrières-en-Chautagne
D 910
Lac d'Annecy
Ruffieux
N 201
Chindrieux
D 991
Vongnes
Jongieux
A 41
N 516
St-Jean-de-Chevelu
Lac du Bourget
AIX-LES-BAINS
SAVOIE
N 90
A 43
CHAMBÉRY
Isère
St-Badolph
Chignin
Cruet
Apremont
Arbin
Myans
Les Marches
Montmélian
Chapareillan
N 90
A 41
0
10
20 km

SAVOIE

THE WINES

• **ROUSSETTE-DE-SAVOIE (A.O.C.).** Although the Roussette-de-Savoie is generally made from a blend of Altesse (finest variety), Chardonnay and Mondeuse Blanche, it includes four crus (Frangy, Marestel, Monterminod, Montheux) which should be made exclusively from Altesse. Wines of a pale yellow color that take up a golden glow with age. Fruity and with a flowery aroma, our taste tests confirm that the Roussette can become delicate and subtle. Excellent quality/price ratio.

• **CRÉPY (A.O.C.).** Along the French right bank of Lake Léman, between Thonon-les-Bains and Geneva lies the 100 hectare Crépy vineyard. Produced in a fertile soil (limestone moraine) with exceptional exposure—the hours of sunshine being accentuated by the reflection in the waters of Lake Léman—and made solely from Chasselas Vert (or Roux) grapes, the Crépy wines are refreshing, slightly sparkling, dry, with a strong hawthorn fragrance. They are diurectic and thirst quenching.

• **SEYSSEL (A.O.C.).** It is regarded, in Savoie, as the best white wine. Supple and well-bred, beautiful straw-yellow color, violet fragrance. Even more delightful, the Seyssel made by the champagne method (a blend of Molette + at least 10% of Altesse) impressed us by its charm and delicate aroma. One of the best French sparkling wines, easily worth an **ABYMES** or an **APREMONT** (Vins de Savoie A.O.C.). These two crus which are produced under the Vins de Savoie A.O.C. must be harvested on delimited plots in the communes of Apremont, Chapareillan, Les Marches, Myans and Saint-Baldoph. The diversity of soils, produced by the mixing of materials from the collapse of Mont-Granier in 1248, the remains of which today form vine-covered hillocks known as the "Abymes of Myans", is perfectly suited to the local vine variety, Jacquière. It is fermented as a "primeur", that is to say at low temperature, and bottled on lees. This yields a fresh and light, slightly sparkling wine. Generally fruity with very little color and a very characteristic gun-flint taste, they are wines to be drunk during their first year with fish and brook trout.

AYSE (Vin de Savoie A.O.C.) White wine made from Gringet (related to yellow Savignin or Traminer) Roussette from Ayse (or white Mondeuse). Lightly or fully sparkling, depending on whether it is fermented by the rural method or the Champagne method, it is very aromatic, natural and exudes freshness. The local restaurateurs delight in serving it with cheese fondues. An excellent quality/price ratio.

• **VINS DE SAVOIE (Chignon, Cruet, Fréterive, Montmélian and Saint-Jeoire-Prieuré A.O.C.).** They are white wines whose most typical varieties (Chignin, for example) are characterized by a brilliant color and a discreet fruitiness with a suggestion of hazel nut. They should be drunk during the year following the harvest.

• **THE RED WINES.** They can be divided into two types. Those coming from the white juice Gamay noir are generally cultivated near the lac du Bourget on soil formed by collapsed limestone or glacial deposits. The good ones are examples of what can be expected from the Gamay wines, fruity but robust, rich, well-balanced and vigorous. Chautagne is the most expressive among them. The other red wines are produced from Mondeuse grapes, planted on stoney crumbled limestone and clay soil, between Chignin and Fréterive. They are firm, typical reds, with strawberry and violet aromas, whose bouquet develops beautifully on ageing. Also available are excellent Pinot wines, fine and fruity.

THE CHARACTERISTICS OF THE VINEYARD

Also in southern France, the vineyards of Savoie are located at the foot of the snow-covered ?? Mountains, along river banks from Lac Leman to Val d'Isère.

Soil

At the subsoil level, limestone is the main component although it is mixed with soft tertiary sandstone and glacial deposits.

Climate

Climatic variations are a function of altitude. The temperature averages 50°F (10°C).

CRÉPY

DOMAINE DE LA GRANDE CAVE DE CREPY

M. Claude Mercier
Loisin - B.P. 7 - 74140 Douvaine
Office: 50 94 00 01
Estate: 50 94 01 23 & 50 94 00 46
Telex: 385 201

Type of vineyard: Family-owned. **Number of employees:** 5. **Vine stocks:** Chasselas. **Soil:** Calcium carbonate (old moraine). **Exposure:** South, southeast. **Average annual production in hectoliters:** 1500 - 2000.

Appellation: Crépy A.O.C. **Type:** White. **Technique:** Classic, alcoholic fermentation, malo-lactic fermentation at low temperature. **Maturing:** Glass casks. **Alcohol content:** Between 11% and 12%. **Serving temperature:** Cool - between 8° and 12° maximum. **Served with:** Fish, shellfish, Fondues, cheese, or as an aperitif with or without blackcurrant liqueur (Cassis). **Vintages available in 89/90:** 1985, 1986.

Characteristics of vintages

1986: A bit young, but lots of fruit. **1985:** Very fruity, very pleasant sparkle, a rather successful vintage.

Sales volumes:

- Wholesale: 30%. - Retail: 10%. - Restaurants: 60%.

Sales in France: 95%.

Export sales: 5%.

SCEA COTEAU DE LUTNY

Pierre Goy
74140 Ballaijon
50 94 31 29

Type of vineyard: Family-owned. **Vine stocks:** Chasselas.

Appellation: Crépy. **Type:** White. **Technique:** Traditional. **Characteristics:** Golden color, lively and fruity. **Serving temperature:** 12°. **Served with:** Fondue Savoyarde, cheese, delicatessen products. **Vintages available in 89/90:** 1985, 1986.

Characteristics of vintages

1986: Pronounced bouquet, very fruity, long and pleasant.

VIN DE SAVOIE

DOMAINE JEAN PERRIER
JEAN PERRIER & FILS

Gilbert Perrier
Saint-André-les-Marches - 73800 Montmélian
79 28 11 45 - Telex: 980 246

Type of vineyard: Family-owned. **Established:** 1946. **Number of employees:** 20. **Vine stocks:** White: Jacquère, Altesse. Red: Gamay, Pinot, Mondeuse. **Soil:** Chalky clay. **Exposure:** South-East.

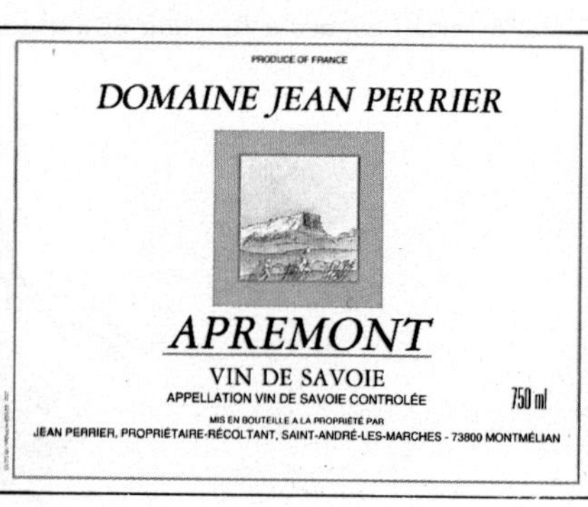

PRODUCE OF FRANCE
DOMAINE JEAN PERRIER
APREMONT
VIN DE SAVOIE
APPELLATION VIN DE SAVOIE CONTROLÉE
750 ml
MIS EN BOUTEILLE A LA PROPRIÉTÉ PAR
JEAN PERRIER, PROPRIÉTAIRE-RÉCOLTANT, SAINT-ANDRÉ-LES-MARCHES - 73800 MONTMÉLIAN

Appellation: Vin de Savoie - Crus: Apremont, Abymes, Chignin, Roussette de Savoie. **Type:** Red, white. **Technique:** White: fast, immediate pressing, selection of juice, fermentation at low temperature. Gamay, Pinot Mondeuse, Arbin. Red: in tanks, for 5 to 8 days, according to the vine-stocks. **Maturing:** Metal and concrete tanks. **Characteristics:** White: Apremont, Abymes and Chignin: light and dry with typical gun flint and honeysuckle aromas. Red: Gamay and Pinot: fine and fruity, spicy, tannic and balanced. The Mondeuse has a very sustained purple color and the aroma of wild berries. **Serving temperature:** White: 8 to 10°. Red: 14°. **Vintages available in 89/90:** 1987 and 1988.

Characteristics of vintages

Price range (pre-tax, ex-warehouse): Between 15 and 25 F.F.

Sales volume:

- Wholesale: 15%. - Retail: 5%. - Restaurants: 60%.
- Other: 20% (department stores, specialized shops).

Sales in France: 95%.

Export sales: 5%.

Main trading partners: Canada, Belgium, Germany, South Africa, Netherlands, UK, Spain, Italy.

References in France

Restaurants: Gastronomic inns and châteaux. Various traditional chains.
Shops: Chesse shops and fine groceries.

Comments

A fifth generation winemaker and a major wine dealer, Gilbert Perrier, through care, rigorous selection and know-how, has given his wines an image of solidity and has maintained their typical nature.

DOMAINE DE L'IDYLLE

Philippe & François Tiollier
GAEC Tiollier Cruet – 73800 Montmelian
79 84 30 58

Type of vineyard: Family-owned. **Vine stocks:** Jacquère, Roussette, Mondeuse. **Soil:** Clay with calcium carbonate – eroding pebbles on sloping hillsides. **Exposure:** South, Southeast. **Average annual production in hectoliters:** 50000.
Appellation: Vin de Savoie (Mondeuse, Cruet, Roussette). **Type:** Red, White, Rosé. **Alcohol content:** 11 – 12.5%. **Characteristics:** Cruet: fruity, lively – Roussette: soft and rich, fruity – Mondeuse (red): typical, rich color, tannic, good balance. **Serving temperature:** White 8° – 12° – Red: 12° – 15°. **Served with:** White: as an aperitif and with fish and seafood. Red: red meat, cheese, country style buffet. **Vintages available in 89/90:** Cruet 1986 – Roussette 1986 – Mondeuse 1986.

Characteristics of vintages

Price range (pre-tax, ex-warehouse): between 10 et 20 F.F..
Sales volumes:
– Retail: 33%. – Restaurants: 33%. – Other: 33% (cellars, etc.).
Sales in France: 100%.

J.-C. PERRET

Jean-Claude Perret
St André-les-Marches – 73800 Montmelian
79 28 13 32 & 79 28 05 08

Type of vineyard: Family-owned. **Established:** 1975. **Vine stocks:** Jacquère. **Soil:** Clay with calcium carbonate. **Exposure:** Hillsides. **Average annual production in hectoliters:** 400.
Appellation: Gamay Apremont, Gamay Abymes. **Type:** Red, white, rosé. **Other:** Champagne Method. **Technique:** Long – low temperature, stainless steel tanks for whites. **Maturing:** In casks all winter, bottling in the spring. **Alcohol content:** White: 11.5%. Red and rosé: 12.5%. **Characteristics:** White (Apremont & Abymes): limpid. Honeydew fragrance, flinty taste, refreshing. Red and rosé (Gamay): light, fruity, typically Gamay, red fruit aroma, good alcohol acidity balance, tannic. **Serving temperature:** Apremont Blanc and Abymes: 8°-10°. **Served with:** Whites: fish, raclette, cheese fondue, as an aperitif (the kir). Gamay Rouge: with red meat (grilled), or throughout the meal. **Vintages available in 89/90:** 1986.

DOMAINE RAYMOND QUENARD

Raymond Quenard
Le Villard Les Tours 73800 Chignin
Cidex 4804 - 79 28 01 45

Type of vineyard: family-owned. **Established:** 4 generations. **Vine stocks:** Jacquère, Roussanne, Gamay, Mondeuse. **Soil:** Chalky clay. **Exposure:** South, South-West. **Average annual production in hectoliters:** 600.

vin de savoie
CHIGNIN
BERGERON
appellation vin de savoie contrôlée
mis en bouteille à la propriété
Domaine « Les Tours »
12% vol.
75 cl
PRODUIT DE FRANCE
Raymond Quenard / Viticulteur / Les Tours / Chignin / Savoie
Tél. 79 28 01 46
modèle déposé

Appellation: Chignin. **Type:** Red, white. **Technique:** Harvesting towards mid-October at optimum maturity. Red: Horizontal pressing. Debourbage after 48 hours. Slow fermentation under temperature control followed by malolactic fermentation. Red: Traditional fermentation on skins for 8 days under temperature regulation, followed by malolactic fermentation. **Alcohol content:** White: 11%. Red: 12%. **Characteristics:** Chignin Bergeron (made from Roussanne): Brilliant golden color, distinct fragrance of banana, mulberrry, pear and mango. Harmonious bouquet dominated by exotic fruit. Chignin (Côteaux-les-Châteaux): Fresh, very round, fruity aroma. Gamay: beautiful cherry color, red berry nuance. Mondeuse: Deep red purple color, aromatic, delicately spicy, tannic, raspberry and violet aroma. **Serving temperature:** Chignin Bergeron: 14°. Chignin Blanc: 12°. Gamay: 12°. Mondeuse: 14°. **Served with:** Bergeron: fish in sauce. Chignin Blanc: shellfish, seafood, fried fish. Gamay: white meat, ham (uncooked or mountain style), cheese. Mondeuse: game, meat in sauce, mountain cheese. **Vintages available in 89/90:** 1988.

Characteristics of vintages

1988: Excellent vintage, harmonious and balanced wine. Price range (pre-tax, ex-warehouse): between 20 F.F. and 30 F.F.

Sales volume:
– Wholesale: 35%. – Retail: 25%. – Restaurants: 40%.
Sales in France: 90%.
Export sales: 10%.
Main trading partners : Sweden.

References in France

Restaurants: Restaurant Lucas Carton (Paris).
Shops: Les Caves d'Edgar (Paris), le Relais des Caves (Paris, Lyon, Montpellier, Annecy, Bourg-en-Bresse, Grenoble, Voiron), L'Esprit du Vin.

Abroad

Other

Sweden: Ab-Vin Spritcenralen, Stockholm – Sergel Plaza. Stockholm Continental, Stockholm, Portalen Jonkoping.

Comments

Quite a few members of the Quenard family are winemakers, so given names – in this case Raymoned – are necessary to distinguish the vineyard. Medals: 1 prize for excellence, Vinalies 88. 2 grand prizes at Mâcon (82, 86). 5 Gold Medals, Paris – Mâcon. 7 Silver Medals, Paris – Mâcon. Visitors received in the wine cellar on Saturdays, preferably by appointment.

QUENARD CLAUDE

Claude Quenard
Le Villard – 73800 Chignin
79 28 12 04

Type of vineyard: Family-owned. **Vine stocks:** Jacquère, Bergeron, Mondeuse. **Soil:** Clay with calcium carbonate. **Exposure:** South, Southwest. **Average annual production in hectoliters:** 600.
Appellation: Vin de Savoie. **Type:** Red, white. **Technique:** Traditional. **Characteristics:** Whites: wines sold "en primeur", fresh, drawn on fine lees. Reds: robust, fruity, can be aged 5 years. **Serving temperature:** White: 9° – Red: at room temperature. **Served with:** White: delicatessen, fish, fondues, cheese fondues, or as an aperitif. Red: red meat, cheese. **Vintages available in 89/90:** 1986 and 1987 Chignin, Bergeron and Mondeuse.

Characteristics of vintages

1986: Lovely wines, fresh, natural and fruity, seductive.
Sales volume:
– Wholesale: 30%. – Retail: 30%. – Restaurants: 30%. – Other: 10%.
Sales in France: 100%.

Comments

Entire production sold in France. Interested in export outlets.

VARICHON & CLERC S.A.

Les Séchallets – 01420 Seyssel
50 59 23 15
Telex: 385 406 - Fax: 50 59 05 35

Type of vineyard: Corporation. **Established:** 1901. **Vine stocks:** Altesse and Jacquère. **Soil:** Fluvio-glacial alluvium. **Exposure:** Both banks of the Rhône. **Average annual production in hectoliters:** 1,700.
Appellation: Seyssel, Pétillant de Savoie, Seyssel Mousseux. **Type:** White. **Technique:** Traditional. **Alcohol content:** 12%. **Characteristics:** Dry wine with a violet fragrance – citrus flavor. Pétillant: refreshing wine with a light sparkle. **Serving temperature:** 10°. **Served with:** First course, fish served hot or cold, shellfish and local specialties such as Fondue. **Vintages available in 89/90:** 1985 and 1986.

Characteristics of vintages

Sales volume:
– Wholesale: 80%. – Mail: 10%. – Restaurants: 10%.
Sales in France: 50%.
Export sales: 50%.
Main trading partners : USA, Italy, UK, Germany, Japan.

Abroad

United States

IVW – Subsidiary of Heublein Inc., Farmington, Connecticut – Sherry Lehman, New York.

United Kingdom

Ernst Gorge - Wine Shippers, 245 Whitechapel Road, London E1 1DB.

Canada

Featherstone an Co. Ltd 1033 Davie Street – Vancouver BC – Canada.

Others

Italy: Velier, SRL, Via Garibaldi, 12, 16124 Genova.

Japan

Tomoe Engineering, 9-2 Nihonbashi 3-Chome Chuo-Ku - Tokyo.

LE VIGNERON SAVOYARD

Robert Dupraz
73190 Apremont
79 28 33 23

Type of vineyard: Agricultural Association. **Established:** 1966. **Vine stocks:** Jacquère, Chardonnay, Gamay, Mondeuse. **Soil:** Clay with calcium carbonate. **Exposure:** Southeast. **Average annual production in hectoliters:** 3000.
Appellation: Vin de Savoie "Apremont" "Abymes" A.O.C. **Type:** Red, White. **Technique:** White – low temperature, bottled on fine lees. **Maturing:** Stainless steel casks, air-conditioned cellars. **Alcohol content:** 11%. **Characteristics:** Light and fruity white wines, slight sparkle. **Serving temperature:** White: 8° – Red: 12-15°. **Served with:** White: fish and sea food, cheese fondue. Red: Cheese (Savoy) meat. **Vintages available in 89/90:** 1988, 1989.

Characteristics of vintages

Price range (pre-tax, ex-warehouse): between 18 and 26 F.F.
Sales volumes:
– Wholesale: 45%. – Retail: 5%. – Restaurants: 7%. – Other: 5% (cellars), 31% (department stores).
Export sales: 7%.
Main trading partners : USA, Germany, UK, Belgium.

BUGEY

LE CAVEAU BUGISTE

Mr. Henri Guillon, Mr. Jean Chaudet,
Mr. Guy Premillieu
01350 Vongnes
79 87 92 37 or 79 87 92 32

Type of vineyard: Agricultural Association. **Established:** 1968. **Number of employees:** 8. **Vine stocks:** Gamay, Pinot, Chardonnay, Aligoté, Jacquère, Altesse, Molette. **Soil:** Clay with calcium carbonate. **Exposure:** Southeast. **Average annual production in hectoliters:** 2000.
Appellation: Bugey. **Type:** Red, white, rosé. Other: sparkling wine (Champagne Method). **Maturing:** Stainless steel and enamelled tanks – sold young. **Alcohol content:** 11%-12.5%. **Characteristics:** Light, fruity. **Vintages available in 89/90:** 1986.

Characteristics of vintages

1986: Red: supple, goes down well. Drink cool. Beautiful white, natural, fruity sparkling wines, very refreshing. Price range (pre-tax, ex-warehouse): between 10 F.F. and 30 F.F.
Sales volume:
– Retail: 45%. – Restaurants: 40%. – Other: 5-10% (wholesale, export, etc.).
Sales in France: 99%.
Export sales: 1%.
Main trading partners : Switzerland, Germany, UK.

MAISON EUGÈNE MONIN ET FILS

Eugène Monin
Vongnes – 01350 Culoz
79 87 92 33

Type of vineyard: Family-owned. **Number of employees:** 2 permanent and a few seasonal workers. **Vine stocks:** Chardonnay, Aligoté, Pinot, Gamay, Mondeuse. **Soil:** Clay with calcium carbonate. **Exposure:** Southeast. **Average annual production in hectoliters:** 800-1000.
Appellation: Vin du Bugey. **Type:** Red, White, Rosé. Others: Brut & Blanc de Blancs (Champagne Method). **Technique:** Red: semi-carbonic maceration. White: thermo-regulation. **Maturing:** In enamelled casks. **Alcohol content:** 11.5% to 12.2%. **Characteristics:** Dry, fruity and long wines. Good vintage whites are not subjected to malo-lactic fermentation. Their natural acidity after the winter cold varies between 4,5° to 5,5°, with slight traces of CO_2 which accounts for their regional character. **Serving temperature:** White: very cool, around 7°-8°. Red (Gamay du Bugey): around 10° (Pinot 1 Mondeuse): 12°. **Served with:** White: fish, oysters, shellfish. Red: meat and cheese. **Vintages available in 89/90:** Bugey Gamay (red): 1988. Bugey Pinot Rouge & Mondeuse: 1988. Bugey Chardonnay: 1988. Bugey Brut-Blanc de Blancs: 1986.

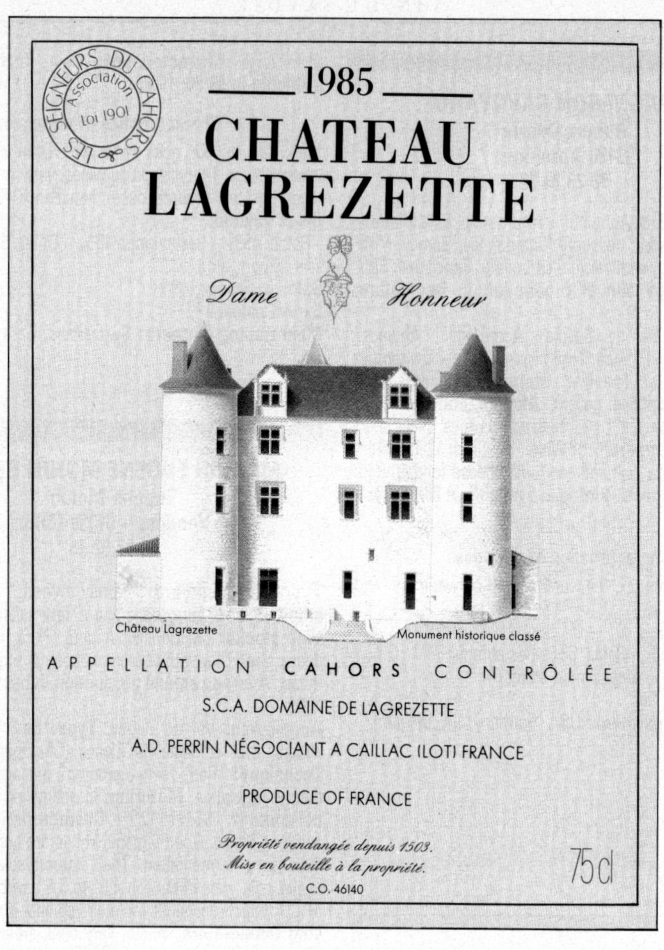

LES SEIGNEURS DU CAHORS
Association
Loi 1901
1985
CHATEAU
LAGREZETTE
Dame
Honneur
Château Lagrezette
Monument historique classé
APPELLATION CAHORS CONTRÔLÉE
S.C.A. DOMAINE DE LAGREZETTE
A.D. PERRIN NÉGOCIANT A CAILLAC (LOT) FRANCE
PRODUCE OF FRANCE
Propriété vendangée depuis 1503.
Mise en bouteille à la propriété.
C.O. 46140
75cl

Alain-Dominique PERRIN- négociant

DOMAINE DE LAGREZETTE

CAILLAC 46140 LUZECH - FRANCE Téléphone : Répondeur 65.20.07.42 Télex : 530667

THE SOUTHWEST

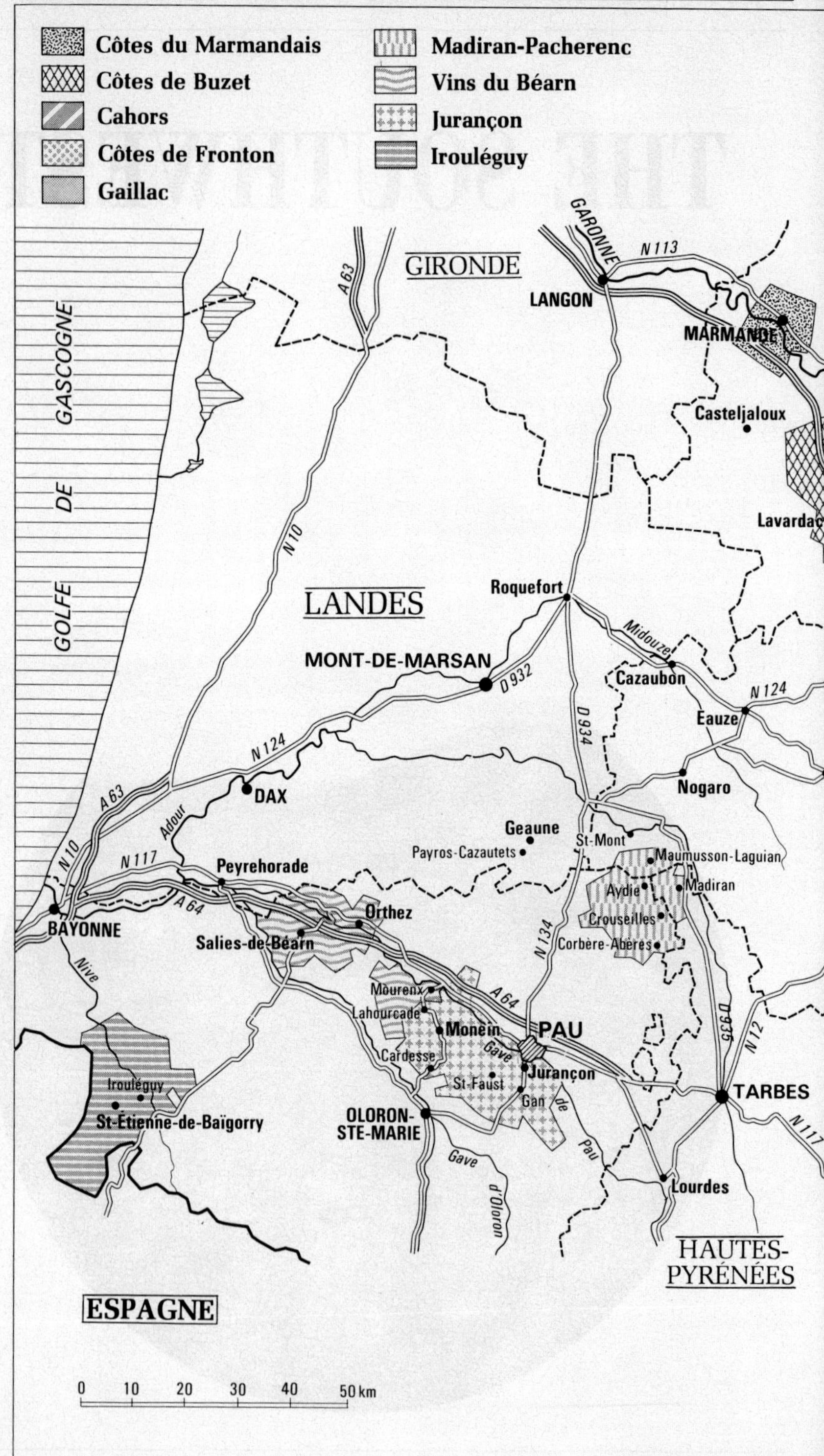
Côtes du Marmandais
Côtes de Buzet
Cahors
Côtes de Fronton
Gaillac
Madiran-Pacherenc
Vins du Béarn
Jurançon
Irouléguy
GOLFE DE GASCOGNE
GIRONDE
LANDES
HAUTES-PYRÉNÉES
ESPAGNE
GARONNE
LANGON
MARMANDE
Casteljaloux
Lavardac
Roquefort
MONT-DE-MARSAN
Midouze
Cazaubon
Eauze
Nogaro
DAX
Adour
Geaune
Payros-Cazautets
St-Mont
Maumusson-Laguian
Aydie
Madiran
Crouseilles
Corbère-Abères
Peyrehorade
Orthez
BAYONNE
Salies-de-Béarn
Nive
Mourenx
Lahourcade
Monein
PAU
Cardesse
Jurançon
St-Faust
Gan
Gave de Pau
Irouléguy
St-Étienne-de-Baïgorry
OLORON-STE-MARIE
Gave d'Oloron
TARBES
Lourdes
A 63
N 113
N 10
D 932
D 934
N 124
N 117
A 64
N 134
D 935
N 12
0 10 20 30 40 50 km

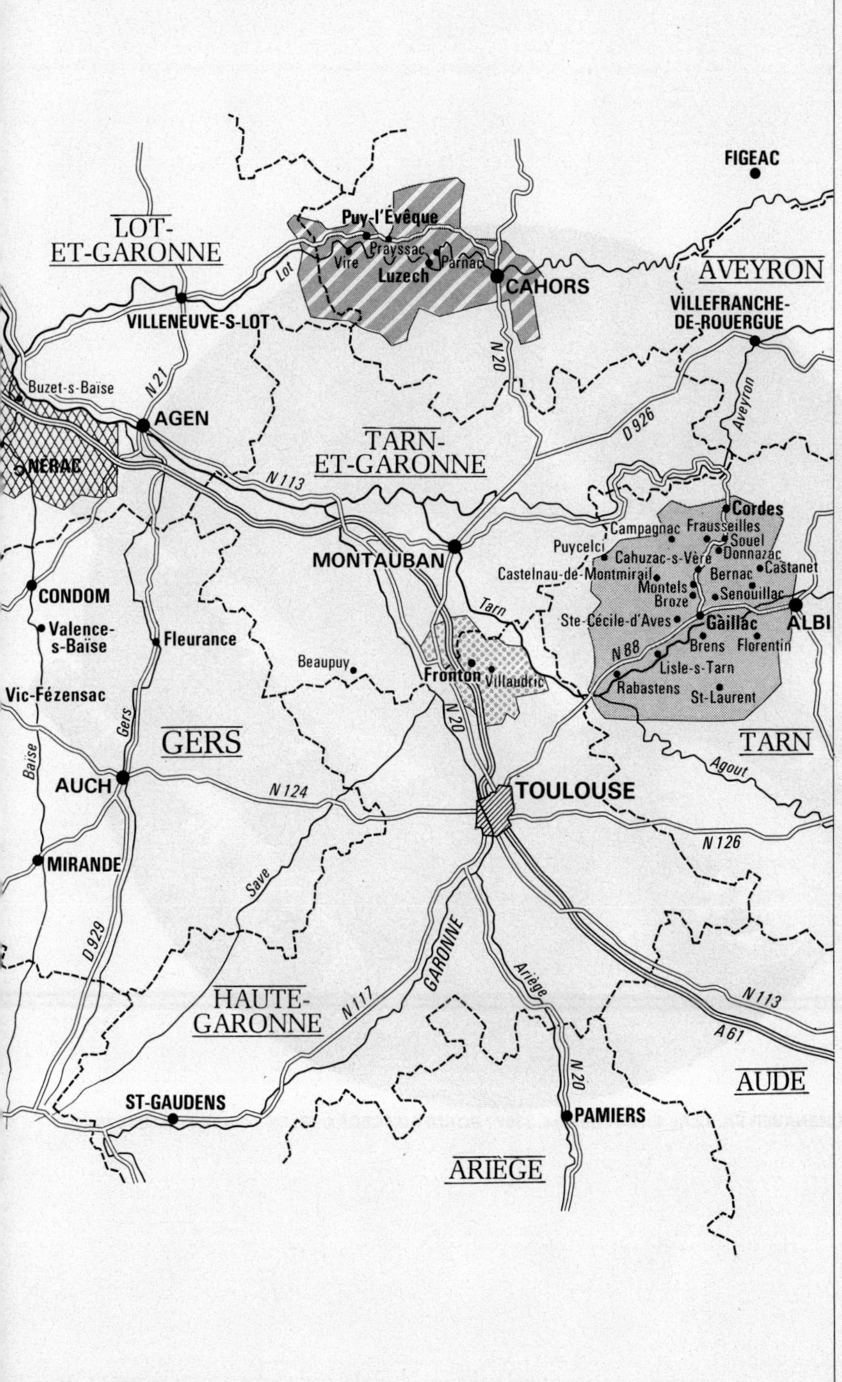
FIGEAC
LOT-
ET-GARONNE
Puy-l'Évêque
Vire
Prayssac
Luzech
Parnac
Lot
CAHORS
AVEYRON
VILLEFRANCHE-
DE-ROUERGUE
VILLENEUVE-S-LOT
N 20
N 21
Buzet-s-Baïse
AGEN
NERAC
TARN-
ET-GARONNE
D 926
Aveyron
N 113
Cordes
Campagnac
Frausseilles
Souel
Donnazac
Puycelci
Cahuzac-s-Vère
Castanet
Bernac
Castelnau-de-Montmirail
Montels
Senouillac
Broze
MONTAUBAN
Tarn
CONDOM
Valence-
s-Baïse
Fleurance
Ste-Cécile-d'Aves
Gaillac
ALBI
Brens
Florentin
N 88
Lisle-s-Tarn
Beaupuy
Fronton
Villaudric
Rabastens
St-Laurent
Vic-Fézensac
Gers
GERS
TARN
Baïse
Agout
AUCH
N 124
TOULOUSE
N 126
MIRANDE
Save
D 929
GARONNE
HAUTE-
GARONNE
N 117
Ariège
N 113
A 61
N 20
AUDE
ST-GAUDENS
PAMIERS
ARIÈGE

1987
BORDEAUX
1985

The typical nature of each terrain

A great wine-growing region that is, unjustifiably, too little known. And it is all the more unfortunate because there are typical crus to be discovered, well marked by the soil in which they are grown, which have their own particular style, thanks to the terrain and the vinestocks (Merlots, Malbecs, Sémillons or Ugni Blanc combined with the traditional Cabernets and Sauvignons). Superb red wines are to be found in all the appellations, from the Pécharmant to the Côtes-de-Bergerac, from the Cahors to the Madiran or Gaillac, all of which age extremely well. One can also find "behind the wood pile" a few bottles of excellent whites, soft, supple and complex, that keep beautifully (Monbazillac, Montravel). I advise you to take advantage of the excellent quality-price ratio characteristic of the region and of the very successful 85 to 88 vintages.

HISTORICAL BACKGROUND

At the decline of the Roman Empire in the 4th century A.D., there were vineyards in nearly every region. But massive invasions took their toll and winegrowing suffered severely. Gaillac wines were extremely popular and in the 12th century they sold at high prices. Consequently they had nothing to fear from high taxes.

Regional wines like Bergerac, Cahors, Gaillac and Pamiers were shipped to England from Bayonne or Dax. But Bayonne was not able to keep up with the expansion achieved by La Rochelle and thus made smaller profits.

In 1215, John Lackland authorized the residents of Bayonne to organize *communes* (free towns) and in 1351 Edward III granted them privileges for the transport and sale of their wines in England. The result was increased trade with Great Britain.

The Carthusian monks left behind traces of the time they spent in Cahors. The vineyards grown at their monastery, which was founded in 1328, produced wine that was highly appreciated. Great men including the novelist and playwright Alexandre Dumas and the writer Jean Ingres savored the fine taste.

Jurançon wine, which was produced in the province of Navarre, gained assured celebrity in 1553 when Prince Henry was born; he would later become King Henry IV. It is said that his father, who loved Jurançon wine, baptized his son with it to give him strength and vigor.

It seems that Henri IV never forgot his baptism because he continued to have that first wine he ever drank delivered to the Louvre Palace. Perhaps he owed his courage, valor and good humor, which stayed with him all his life, to this unusual baptism.

Jurançon wine was also the wine of the monarchs of Aragon and Béarn. It reached foreign markets as well. English sailors came to pick up Jurançon wine at Bayonne. The Dutch shipped Jurançon as far as the Scandinavian countries where the people absolutely loved it.

To seal the Union of Kalmar alliance, the Swedish, Norwegian and Danish delegates brought up from the palace's cellars—the annals mention this—several old bottles of Jurançon wine.

THE WINES

Southwest France is an interesting wine-growing region which boasts a variety of vineyards, all of excellent quality, representing a total production area of 20,000 hectares. They divide into six appellations: Bergerac, Côtes du Frontonnais, Cahors, Gaillac, Jurançon, and the wines from the Bearn and the Basque Country.

1. The BERGERAC REGION

This region, located east of the Bordeaux region, is made up of a mosaic of small vineyards.
1-1-The soil is particulary chalky, sometimes mixed with clay.
The wines, fruity and of excellent quality, are made from Bordeaux grapes, such as Cabernet.
As for the whites, they are dry and smooth, and are made from Sauvignon or Muscadelle.
Pécharmant, another typical red wine of the region, is rich, well-balanced and full-bodied.
Monbazillac is an excellent white wine for keeping.
Côtes de Duras and Côtes de Buzet are also two excellent wines.

2. CÔTES DU FRONTONNAIS

South of Toulouse, this region mainly produces a red wine made from Négrette, a local grape variety.

3. CAHORS

This region, located on the banks of the Lot, is made up of forty comunes which produce red wines exclusively. They are rather tannic, well-balanced and keep well.

4. GAILLAC

Wine growing area bordering the Tarn. Produces wines of good quality.

5. JURANÇON

Vineyard to the South of Pau. Produces wines that are mellow and firm thanks to its sandy and pebbly soil.

6. BÉARN AND BASQUE-COUNTRY

Two main appellations are produced in these regions: one for whites, Pacherec-du-Vic-Bilh, and one for reds, Madiran, which is a robust wine, harvested essentially in the Pyrénées Atlantiques, and well worth keeping.

RED WINES

- **Cahors.** "Black" wines, made from the substantial Malbec grape, and rounded out by the addition of Merlot. Very fragrant, dense, soft and full.
- **Madiran.** Full-bodied, rustic and robust, a wine with some of the roughness of the soil on which it is grown, just right with game.
- **Irouleguy.** Exclusively vinified and marketed by the cooperative cellar of Saint-Etienne de Baigorry.
- **Gaillac.** Wines with character, fruity and fine, quite harmonious.

WHITE WINES

- **Jurançon.** Made from grapes harvested late in the year and selected with the utmost care, the sweet and liquorous wines of the appellation are harmonious, well-balanced, lively, beautifully flowery and fruity, and come into their own after 7 to 15 years, with an incomparable bouquet. Full of the fragrance of the old Pyrenean vinestocks, the dry Jurançon wines that we tasted were subtle, lively and fruity. Should be drunk when young and fresh.
- **Pacherenc-du-Vic-Bilh.** A confidential appellation producing mostly dry, rather typical and charming wines.
- **Gaillac.** White wines, easy to drink, that come from one of France's oldest vineyards and are made from Mauzac, a very aromatic grape variety. Try, by all means, the sparkling ("perlés") and bubbly wines, made by the rural Gaillac method or the champagne method. You will find them pleasant and very refreshing.

BERGERAC

CHÂTEAU DU BLOY

Guillermier Brothers
Bonneville-et-Saint-Avit-de-Fumadières
24230 Vélines
53 27 50 59

Type of vineyard: Family-owned. **Vine stocks:** Reds (Merlot and Cabernets) – Whites (Sauvignon, Sémillon and Muscadelle). **Soil:** Clay with calcium carbonate. **Appellation:** Côtes-de-Bergerac and Montravel. **Type:** Red, white. **Technique:** Traditional. **Characteristics:** Red: the best of the appellation. Tannic and well-balanced, fragrant typical wine that keeps well. White: Montravel, dry and fruity, a rich and velvety mellow wine, ideal when served as an aperitif or with foie gras. **Serving temperature:** White: 10° – Red: 15°. **Served with:** White (dry), with fish. Naturally sweet white, with foie gras. Red, with meat and game. **Vintages available in 89/90:** 1983, 1984, 1985 and 1986.

Characteristics of vintages

1986: Excellent whites, very fragrant. **1985:** Remarkable red, combining balance and finesse, good for ageing. Price range (pre-tax, ew-warehouse): 20-30 F.F.

References in France

Shops: L'Amour du Vin, 94, rue Saint-Dominique, 75007 Paris. Tél. 45 56 12 94.

CHÂTEAU DE LA JAUBERTIE

Henri-Nicolas Ryman
Colombier – 24560 Issigeac
53 58 42 11 – Telex: 570 418

Type of vineyard: Family Corporation. **Established:** 1974. **Number of employees:** 9 to 11. **Vine stocks:** Sauvignon, Semillion, Muscadelle, Cabernet Sauvignon, Franc, Merlot, Chardonnay. **Soil:** Clay with calcium carbonate. **Average annual production in hectoliters:** 4,000. **Appellation:** Bergerac, Monbazillac. **Type:** Red, white, rosé, Monbazillac. **Technique:** Red: traditionnal. Rosé and white: Australian Method. **Maturing:** Vats and barrels. **Alcohol content:** 11.5% to 13%. **Characteristics:** White: very intense, typical aroma, Sauvignon apparent, very soft and full, round, will age. Red: fruity, supple. Reserve: Red: 1 year in barrels, 80% Cabernet, to be kept. Rosé: exceptional. **Serving temperature:** 8° to 15°. **Served with:** White: as an aperitif or with fish, raw vegetable salad. Rosé: with everything in Summer. Red: white meat. Red reserve: red meat, game, cheese. **Vintages available in 89/90:** Red, red reserve: 1986. Rosé, white, Sauvignon: 1988.

Characteristics of vintages

1988: Good for white and rosé. Excellent for red. Invested in more barrels to make far greater quantity of "reserve" quality. **1987:** Very good for white and rosé. Small quantity of red made after severe selection. Good for early drinking. **1986:** Very good year for white and red, very aromatic (rare). Good maturity. **1985:** Excellent wine for ageing. Surmuri – typical, a soft and full red wine, dense, rich and well-balanced. Price range (pre-tax, ex-warehouse): between 20 F.F. and 30 F.F.
Sales volume:
– Retail: 6%. – Restaurants: 4%. – Other: 90% (export).
Sales in France: 10%.
Export sales: 90%.
Main trading partners: UK, Germany, Netherlands, Belgium.

References in France

Les Relais & Châteaux.

Abroad

United Kingdom

Marks and Spencer plc* – J. Sainsbury plc* – Western Wines Ltd. – Glazeley, Bridgenorth – Salop – Majestic Wine Warehouses, 421 New Kings Road, London SW6 4RN. Tel. 01 731 3131.
Restaurants: Scotts Restaurant, 20 Mount Street, London W1.
* Branches all over England.

Germany

Weinkauf GmbH, Charlottenstrasse, 4300 Essen 17, Brugaltendorf. Tel. (0201) 570057.

The Netherlands

Oudwynkopers & Hustinx BV, Postbus 586, 2003 RN, Haarlem. Tel. 23 259201.

Comments

A philosophy since 1984, vinification with the Australian Method of M. Brian Croser of Petaluma has been usedit with a great deal of success. Better protection agianst oxidation, fermentation at very low temperature for a long time. The wines obtained are more typical. Very high class wines.

• *In 1985, the wines of the following regions received the A.O.C. (Appellation d'Origine Contrôlée) classification: Minervois, Coteaux-des-Baux, Coteaux-d'Aix-en-Provence, Coteaux-du-Lyonnais and Coteaux-du-Languedoc.*

CLOS DE LA CROIX BLANCHE

Michel Brouilleaud
Monestier - 24240 par Sigoules
53 58 45 82

Type of vineyard: Family-owned. **Established:** 1910. **Soil:** Clay with calcium carbonate. **Exposure:** Hillsides. **Average annual production in hectoliters:** 600.
Type: Red, white, rosé. **Technique:** Traditional with temperature control. **Maturing:** In the warehouse. **Alcohol content:** Red: 12.5%. Dry white: 12%. Mellow: 14%. Rosé: 12%. **Characteristics:** Rich, well-balanced wines, easy to drink. **Serving temperature:** Red: room temperature. White: mellow, rosé: cool. **Served with:** Red: meat and cheese. Dry white: fish and delicatessen products. Mellow: as an aperitif and with dessert. Rosé: goes with the whole meal. **Vintages available in 89/90:** Red: 1987, 1988. Dry white: 1988. Mellow: 1988.

Characteristics of vintages

1988: Red: exceptional year, reminiscent of 1985. Dry white: very fruity, Sauvignac (Mellow): very much like the 1985. Price range (pre-tax, ex-warehouse): Between 10 F.F. and 20 F.F. **Sales volume:**
- Retail: 98%. - Restaurants: 2%.

Sales in France: 100%.
Export sales: Sold to forreign tourists.

DOMAINES DE BOSREDON

Mr. Laurent de Bosredon
Château Belingard-Chayne Pomport 24240 Sigoules
53 58 28 03 - Telex: 572 179 F

Type of vineyard: Agricultural Association. **Established:** Turn of the century. **Number of employees:** 14. **Vine stocks:** Red: Cabernet Sauvignon, Cabernet Franc, Merlot, Malbec. White: Sauvignon, Sémillon, Muscadelle. **Soil:** Gravel and chalky clay. **Exposure:** Hillsides South - South-East. **Average annual production in hectoliters:** 4 500.
Appellation: Côtes de Bergerac, Bergerac Sec, Monbazillac. **Type:** Red, white. **Technique:** Naturally sweet wines: racking, fermentation (18-20°) chemical sterilization of must at low temperature. Red: destemming, crushing, maceration (15 to 18 days at 28/30°). White (dry): maceration before fermentation (16-18°). Maturing: Wood: Rouge Réserve, Blanc Sec Réserve, Monbazillac. Vats: Rouge Standard. On lees: Blanc Sec. **Alcohol content:** Red: 12.3%. Dry white: 11.9% - Monbazillac: 15°. **Characteristics:** Red: soft and full, fruity and long. White (dry): supple, fresh, complex. Naturally sweet wine: full, fat and rich and yet somewhat vigorous. **Serving temperature:** Red: 16-18°. White (dry): 10-12°. Monbazillac: 8-10°. **Served with:** Red: red meat, cheese, delicatessen. White (dry): oysters, fish, salad. Monbazillac: as an aperitif and with foie gras, white meat, blue cheese. **Vintages available in 89/90:** Red: 1988, 1987, 1986. White (dry): 1988, 1989. Monbazillac: 1986, 1983 old vintages.

Characteristics of vintages

1988: Red: rich and well balanced, deep color, still maturing. White (dry): balanced, fresh and long. **1987:** Red: successful for a "difficult" year - well balanced, with a good structure, developing well.White (dry): lovely wine, complex and harmonious. **1986:** Red: supple and well structured, red berry fragrance, long. White (dry): stock depleted. White (naturally sweet) soft and full, full-bodied, beautiful, to be kept in the cellar. Price range (pre-tax, ex-warehouse): 10 to 20 F.F. - 20 to 30 F.F..
Sales volume:
- Retail: 15%. - Restaurants: 10%. - Other: 75% (export).

Sales in France: 25%.
Export sales: 75%.
Main trading partners : Netherlands, UK, Belgium, Germany, Denmark, USA, Australia, Canada.

References in France

Restaurants: Relais et Châteaux.
Shops: Caves Taillevent.

Abroad

United States

Europvin, 65 Cours St Louis 33000 Bordeaux.

United Kingdom

Martyn Barker, 15 Bell Street, Sawbridgeworth, Herts CM21 9AR.

Germany

Kaven, Leinpfad 83 2000 Hamburg 60.

Belgium

Brasserie de landsheer, Mandekenstraat 209 9360 Buggenhout.

Canada

LCBO - SAQ.

The Netherlands

De Wall & Zey - Johan Van Oldenbarneveltlaan 60 2582 NW DEN HAAG.

Comments

The Domaine de Bosredon is established at the Château Bélingard-Chayne at Pomport. It is the site of an ancient Celtic religious center more than 3000 years old. There, is still to be found a carved stone in the form of a chair which is an ancient Druid sacrificial throne. At the time the Druids gathered the fruit of the "lambrusque" (wild vine) which grew like ivy on the sacred oaks. The drink obtained is the ancestor of the wine to which the Bosredon family has been devotin itself for seven generations.

• *Watch out for wines that lose their authenticity, most often because of carbonic maceration (see Roussillon, Southwest, Périgord...).*

DOMAINE DU GRAND BOISSE

Jean-Pierre Destombes
Saint-Foy-les-Vignes, 24100 Bergerac
53 57 16 27

Type of vineyard: Family-owned. **Vine stocks:** Cabernet Sauvignon 70%, Merlot 30%. **Average annual production in hectoliters:** 40 000 bottles.
Appellation: Côtes-de-Bergerac. **Type:** Red. **Technique:** Traditional, concrete vats. **Maturing:** Vats. **Alcohol content:** 11.5%. **Characteristics:** 1985: Beautiful deep red color, elegant fragrance, pleasant and forthcoming. **Served with:** Meat, cheese and the Gastronomic Specialities of the Périgord.

Characteristics of vintages

1986: Quite promising vintage. Hold. **1985:** Domaine du Grand Boisse: Silver Medal in Paris. A full red, rich and well-balanced, well made, good for ageing.

DOMAINE DE LIBARDE

Jean-Claude Banizette
Nastringues – 24230 Vélines
53 24 77 72

Type of vineyard: Family-owned. **Established:** 1897. **Number of employees:** 2. **Vine stocks:** Semillon, Sauvignon, Muscadelle (for the white). **Soil:** Clay with calcium carbonate. **Exposure:** Northern and southern slopes on the right band of the Dordogne. **Average annual production in hectoliters:** 1 100 to 1 200.
Appellation: Bergerac, Montravel and Haut Montravel, Moelleux. **Type:** Red, white. **Technique:** Traditional with temperature control. **Maturing:** White: stainless steel tanks. Red: concrete. **Alcohol content:** Dry white: 11.5% to 12%. Red: 12% to 12.5%. **Characteristics:** Red Bergerac: slightly tannic, harmonious structure, fine aroma. Dry Montravel: Very pale yellow, rich aroma, quite well-balanced, soft, full and light at the same time. Haut Montravel Moelleux: lively, harmonious, round and long. **Serving temperature:** Red Bergerac: 15 to 16°. Dry white: 7 to 8°. Mellow: 10 to 12°. **Served with:** Red: white meat, poultry. Dry white: first courses, fish, delicatessen products. Mellow: as an aperitif ou with melon, dessert. **Vintages available in 89/90:** Red: 1985, Dry white: 1985, 1986. Mellow: 1982, 1985.

Characteristics of vintages

1986: Good year, fragrant and substantial. **1985:** Lovely red, combining finesse, richness and balance. Taste the mellow '85: full and heady, long, very aromatic, to be aged.

CAHORS

DOMAINE DE BOVILA

Mr. Jean-Claude Valière
Bovila – 46800 Fargues (B.P. 26 – 46001 Cahors)
65 36 91 30

Vine stocks: Auxerrois 70%, Merlot 10%, Jurançon Noir, Sémillon, Mauzac Tannat 20%. **Soil:** Hillsides, clay with calcium carbonate. **Exposure:** South. **Average annual production in hectoliters:** 45.
Appellation: Cahors A.O.C. **Type:** Red. **Technique:** Traditional in enamelled tanks, prior to ageing in OAK casks. **Maturing:** In barrels. **Alcohol content:** Around 12%. **Characteristics:** Good body, ruby color, tannic, lingering taste, very fruity, aroma of prune, OAK, blackcurrant and spices, great finesse, supple, generous taste. Average lifetime: 10 to 15 years. **Serving temperature:** 15-16°. **Served with:** Red meat, game, mushrooms, truffles, preserved duck or goose conserve, cheese. **Vintages available in 89/90:** 1985, 1986. 1982 and 1983 in small quantities.

Characteristics of vintages

1986: Promising. **1985:** Rich, good color, supple and fine at the same time. A success.
Main trading partners: Netherlands, Japan, USA.

Comments

The vineyard is cultivated in the old, traditional style. No weed killers nor chemical fertilizers are used (humus in the wines). No pesticides. Manual harvesting. The wine is not processsed – no additives of any kind nor filtration. Occasionally, fining with egg whites.

BARATSIGAUD

Liliane Sigaud
Métairie Grande du Théron – 46220 Prayssac
65 22 41 80

Type of vineyard: Family-owned. **Established:** 1980. **Vine stock:** Cot. Auxerrois, Merlot Taunat. **Soil:** Clay with calcium carbonate. **Exposure:** South. **Average annual production in hectoliters:** 800.
Appellation: Cahors. **Type:** Red. **Technique:** Stainless steel tanks. **Marketing:** In vats. **Alcohol content:** 13%. **Characteristics:** Beautiful color, warm and fruity (currant) with flower nuances. **Served with:** Duck steak, goose liver. **Vintage available in 89/90:** 1985, 1986.

Characteristics of vintages

1987: Very good vintage, substantial, intense color. **1986:** Promising. **1985:** Very good vintage, will age well.

CHÂTEAU DE TRIGUEDINA

Jean Baldes
46700 Puy l'Évêque
65 21 30 81 – Telex: 533 738

Type of vineyard: Family-owned. **Established:** 1830. **Number of employees:** 6. **Vine stocks:** Cot 70%, Merlot 25%, Tanat 5%. **Soil:** Silica clay. **Exposure:** South-West. **Average annual production in hectoliters:** 50 hl per hectare.

Appellation: Cahors AOC. **Type:** Red. **Technique:** Traditional. **Maturing:** Clos Triquedina: vats. Prince Probus: casks. **Alcohol content:** 12%. **Characteristics:** Robust, fruity wines, can age a long time. **Serving temperature:** 15 to 18°. **Served with:** Products of the South-West, cheese, game, red meat. **Vintages available in 89/90:** 1980, 1985, 1986, 1987, 1988. Prince Probus: 1983, 1985, 1986.

Characteristics of vintages

1986: Triquedina: Vanilla and fruity aromas, substantial, very beautiful color. **1985:** Triquedina: Aromas of black-currant and dark fruit conserves, beautiful persistance. Prince Probus: Fruity fragrance. Should reveal the fullness of its vanilla and woody bouquet. Other: 1983: Prince Probus: Very beautiful nose, substantial, concentrated, balanced, beautiful persistance. 1980: Triquedina: Aroma or the region, fleshy, pleasant. Price range (pre-tax, ex-warehouse): Clos Triquedina: between 20 and 30 F.F. Prince Probus: between 30 and 80 F.F.
Sales in France: 80%.
Export sales: 20%.
Main trading partners : Germany, United Kingdom, Belgium, Netherlands, Switzerland, United States.

References in France

Restaurants: Le Quercy (Paris 9th), Le Chat Grippé (Paris), Le Souceyrac.
Shops: Comtesse du Barry.

Abroad

United States

Dreyffus Ashby.

United Kingdom

Sandgate Cellar Hotel, Intervine Vintners.

Germany

Ludwig Von Kapff, Heinz Potthof.

Switzerland

Hammel.

Belgium

Fina.

Canada

Sté des Alcools de Québec.

The Netherlands

Colaris.

Comments

The Château Triquedina is one of the oldest Cahors vineyards. It has been in operation since 1830 with a succession of 8 generations of winemakers. The Clos Triquedina is a traditional wine, very representative of the Cahors (member of the "Seigneurs du Cahors"). The Prince Probus is the result of rigorous selection and has been aged in new oak casks.

• *Paulée – traditional meal which brings winelovers and winegrowers together after the harvest, particularly in Burgundy.*

CHÂTEAU DE HAUTE-SERRE

Georges Vigouroux
Cieurac 46230 Lalbenque
65 22 30 20 – Telex: 521 833

Type of vineyard: Agricultural Association. **Established:** 1971. **Number of employees:** 10 permanent. **Vine stocks:** 75% Auxerrois, 15% Merlot, 10% Tannat. **Soil:** Very pebbly chalky clay. **Exposure:** Hillsides facing all directions. **Average annual production in hectoliters:** 45 hl per hectare.
Appellation: Cahors. **Type:** Red. **Technique:** Long (21 days) in stainless steel tanks. **Maturing:** In stainless steel tanks the first winter, then in oak casks for 18 months. **Alcohol content:** 12%. **Characteristics:** Particularly rich, full bodied and well balanced wines, with a sustained red color. These qualities are due mainly to the extremely rocky terrain of the Causses du Lot. **Serving temperature:** Old wine: 17°. **Served with:** Young wine: foie gras, delicatessen. Old wine: red meats, game, conserves, cassoulet, cheese. **Vintages available in 89/90:** 1982, 1983, 1985, 1986, 1987.

Characteristics of vintages

1987: A soft and full wine, rich, fragrant, well colored with very fine tannins. **1985:** Extremely fine tannins, fragrance of the vintage, deep ruby color, pronounced nose. **Other: 1983:** Pronounced nose, sustained red color, a very great year. Price range (pre-tax, ex-warehouse): between 20 and 30 F.F.
Sales volumes:
– Wholesale: 30%. – Retail: 10%. – Restaurants: 60%.
Sales in France: 90%.
Export sales: 10%.
Main trading partners : United Kingdom, Germany, Belgium, United States, Canada, Japan.

References in France

Restaurants: Trois Gros (Roanne), Georges Blanc, Le Doyen, Delaveyne, Lesousceyrac, Daguin (Auch), Vanel (Toulouse), Orsi (Lyon).
Shops: Fauchon (Paris), Coq d'Or (Geneva), Sherry Lehmann (New York), etc.

Abroad

United States

Grapevine, Medford, Mass. Shops: Sherry Lehmann.

United Kingdom

Michael Druitt. Shops: Harrod's.

Germany

Frankhof Kellerei, Hocheim. Interpartner, Hamburg.

Belgium

Sobelvin SA, Liège. Shops: Rob SA, Brussels.

Canada

SAQ – LCBO Restaurants: La Rapierre, Montreal. L'Espress, Montreal.

The Netherlands

Wijn Verlinden, AG's Hertogenbosch.

Far East

Foods from France, Hong Kong. Izumi Trading, Tokyo.

Comments

Among the proprietors who were the first to replant the Cahors vinyards on the Cahors hillsides, at the beginning of the 70's, at a time when the vineyard was entirely in the Lot valley.

GAEC DOMAINE EUGÉNIE

Jean et Claude Couture vignerons
46140 Albas
65 30 73 51

Type of vineyard: Family-owned. **Established:** 1470. **Number of employees:** 2. **Vine stocks:** Cot. 80%, Merlot 18%, Tannat 2%. **Soil:** Deep silica-clay, gravel, rocky clay with calcium carbonate. **Exposure:** Southwest. **Average annual production in hectoliters:** 1,000.
Appellation: Cahors. **Type:** Red. **Technique:** Traditional – 12 to 15 days, destemmed. Thermoregulation. Pumping over. **Maturing:** The entire harvest in OAK vats and casks (half new). Bottling at the estate. **Alcohol content:** 12%. **Characteristics:** Deep red color. Very aromatic nose. Tannic, fruity and round, improves with ageing. Excellent soil. The Russian Tsars used to reserve their Cahors at the village castle. **Serving temperature:** 16-17°. **Served with:** Substantial dishes, Cassoulet, red meat, game , duck and goose conserve, foie gras, "mushrooms", cheese. **Vintages available in 89/90:** 1987 C.R.T., C.R.A., E.N., 1988 E.N.

Characteristics of vintages

1988: Aromatic, fruity, tannic, well-balanced, good keeping, but can be consumed young. **1987:** Firm, fruity, good constitution, comparable to the 1986, to be kept. **1986:** Fruity, aromatic, supple, well-balanced tannins. **1985:** Aromatic, fruity, tannic, well-balanced, good keeping but wine that can be consumed young. **1984:** Fruity but a little bit firmer, robust, good keeping wine, developing now.

CHÂTEAU LA COUSTARELLE

Michel Cassot
46220 Prayssac
65 22 40 10

Type of vineyard: Family-owned. **Established:** More than 3 generations. **Number of employees:** 2. **Vine stocks:** Cot. Noir 80%, Merlot 10%, Tannat 10%. **Soil:** Clay with calcium carbonate and gravel (thin sand). **Exposure:** Facing South, hillside terraces. **Average annual production in hectoliters:** 1 000.

Appellation: Cahors. **Type:** Red. **Technique:** Fermentation with skins in stainless steel for 15 to 20 days. **Maturing:** Large ans small OAK casks for 5 to 18 months. **Alcohol content:** 12.5%. **Serving temperature:** 15 to 17°. **Vintages available in 89/90:** 1985 (limited stock), 1986, 1987, 1988.

Characteristics of vintages

1988: Very great year (exceptional), ripe red berry aroma, tannic, full (rich in extract), for long ageing. **1987:** fruity, tannic, long, good ageing potential. **1986:** Very supple, fine tannins, to be consumed right now. **1985:** Exceptional year, fleshy, typical of the region, rich and well-balanced. Excellent wine for ageing. **1983:** Very good year, supple, soft, and full, round, will age well.

CHÂTEAU LA CAMINADE

Mr. Resses and Son
46140 Parnac
65 30 73 05

Type of vineyard: Family Agricultural Association. **Established:** 1985 (vineyar goes back 4 generations). **Number of employees:** 1. **Vine stocks:** Cot. Auxerrois 70%, Merlot 20%, Tanna 10%. **Soil:** Silica-clay with sandy gravel interspersed with clay patches. **Exposure:** South and Southwest. **Average annual production in hectoliters:** 900.
Appellation: A.O.C. Cahors. **Type:** Red. **Technique:** Crushing and 100% destemming. Fermentation and maceration under temperature control (12 to 15 days). **Maturing:** In stainless steel and lined concrete tanks, then 225 liter OAK casks. **Alcohol content:** 12 to 12.5%. **Characteristics:** In general, very high color. Rich and well-balanced nose that is soft and full at the same time. The tast as well with tannins evident. Altogether quite soft and harmonious. **Serving temperature:** Young Cahors: 16 to 17°. 17 to 18° for the others. **Served with:** Pâtés and other delicatessen products and, of course, foie gras. Warm duck preserves, which call for an older Cahors. Also vith lamb, truffle omelettes, etc. And finally, cheese ex: Cabécou, Roquefort. **Vintages available in 89/90:** 1986, 1985, 1984.

Characteristics of vintages

1986 Good year. Fruity wine, full, fine tannins (8 to 10 years). **1985:** Great year. Deep color, rich, well-balanced nose, with promise (10 years). **1984:** Rather mixed year. Here it is well-ballanced, with sustained color, nose evolving well, long. Very good and up now to 7/9 years.

• Blending – a method consisting of mixing different wines from different lots or different vintages in order to obtain a more homogeneous product.

INGANELS

Jean Galbert
46700 Puy-l'Évêque
65 21 32 64

Type of vineyard: Family-owned. **Established:** 1971. **Number of employees:** 1. **Vine stocks:** Cot 86%, Merlot 10%, Tannat 4%. **Soil:** Alluvia silica. **Exposure:** Plateau. **Average annual production in hectoliters:** 600.

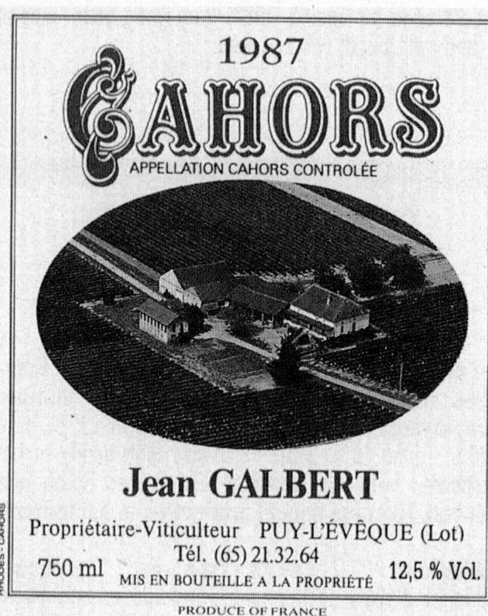

Appellation: Cahors. **Type:** Red. **Technique:** Traditional. **Maturing:** In stratified cement vats. **Alcohol content:** 12%. **Characteristics:** Fruity, aromatic, goes down well. **Serving temperature:** 14 to 18° according to age. **Served with:** Meats, game, cheese, etc. **Vintages available in 89/90:** 1986, 1987, 1988.

Characteristics of vintages

1988: Full bodied, rich color, typical, classic, to be kept. **1987:** Aromatic, beautiful color, can be kept. **1986:** Pleasant finish, fruity and quite supple. Price range (pre-tax, ex-warehouse): between 10 and 30 F.F.
Sales volume:
– Retail: 95%. – Restaurants: 4%. – Other: 1% export.
Main trading partners: United States.

References in France

Restaurants: Fermette du Sud Ouest (75), Rest Entoto (75).
Shops: Vigneron à Bercy.

Comments

Excellent winemaker who conscientiously produces one of the best wines of the appellation. Beautiful 86, 85 and 83 vintages.

CHÂTEAU LAGREZETTE

Alain-Dominique Perrin
Caillac – 46140 Luzech
65 20 07 42

Type of vineyard: Family-owned. **Vine stocks:** Malbec 70%, Merlot and Tannat.
Appellation: Cahors. **Type:** Red. **Technique:** Traditional. **Maturing:** 14 months in casks. **Characteristics:** Exceptional Cahors, typical, representative of the best wines of the appellation, ripe red berry and humus nose, fine woody aroma, rich and well-balanced, good keeping. Member of the "Seigneurs du Cahors", an Association created by Alain-Dominique Perrin (President of Cartier). **Serving temperature:** 18°. **Served with:** Roasts, game. **Vintages available in 89/90:** 1985, 1986, 1987 and 1988.

Characteristics of vintages

1986: Very promising year. To be aged. **1985:** Superb. Very successul, combining structure and finesse. Full taste, good keeping. Price range (pre-tax, ex-warehouse): 30 to 40 F.F.

References in France

Shops: L'Amour du Vin, 94, rue Saint-Dominique, 75007 Paris. Tel. 45 56 12 94.

DOMAINE DE LA PINERAIE

Burc and son
Leygues – 46700 Puy-L'Évêque
65 30 82 07

Type of vineyard: Family-owned. **Established:** 1630. **Number of employees:** 3. **Vine stocks:** Malbec 85%, Merlot 15%. **Soil:** Clay with calcium carbonate. **Exposure:** Southwest. **Average annual production in hectoliters:** 1 200.
Appellation: Cahors. **Type:** Red. **Technique:** Traditional with maceration for at least 15 days. **Maturing:** In OAK casks (10% new each year). **Characteristics:** Very aromatic, with all the fragrance that the barrels contribute. **Served with:** Goes well with all the cooding of the Quercy region as well as roasts, game, cheese. **Vintages available in 89/90:** 1983, 1984, 1985.

Characteristics of vintages

1985: Very soft and full, rich and well-balanced, fine fragrance, will open up in several years. **1984:** Pleasant to drink young, very fruity. **1983:** Very typical Cahors, will age a long time.

• *A good everyday wine for 20 F? See the Bordeaux, Anjou, Touraine, Côtes-du-Rhône or Languedoc Regions.*

DOMAINE DE PAILLAS

Mr. Lescombes
Floressas – 46700 Puy l'Évêque
65 21 34 42

Type of vineyard: Agricultural Association. **Established:** 01-04-82. **Vine stocks:** 82% Cat Noir, 16% Merlot, 2% Tannat. **Soil:** Chalky. **Exposure:** Slight slope to the south. **Average annual production in hectoliters:** Approximately 1,500.
Appellation: Cahors controlée. **Type:** Red. **Technique:** Red: traditional, pumping over 8-10 days. **Maturing:** Stainless steel tanks. **Alcohol content:** 12.4%. **Characteristics:** Extremely complex aroma and bouquet, full-bodied, soft and rich, very fine tannins, strong and complex bouquet. **Serving temperature:** 16 to 18°. **Served with:** Young: almost everything. Aged: meat, game, cheese (Roquefort) or foie gras. **Vintages available in 89/90:** 1983, 1985, 1986, 1987, 1988.

Characteristics of vintages

1988: Average color, fruity nose with good aroma, fruity taste, quite soft and full, already quite pleasant. **1986:** Young and fine aromas, fruity, supple yet with rich tannins. **1985:** Complex, rich and powerful aromas, great vintage. **Other:** 1983 – Very strong tannin content to start with, now just right. Price range (pre-tax, ex-warehouse): between 20 an 30 F.F.
Sales volume:
– Wholesale: 80%. – Retail: 10%. – Restaurants: 10%.
Export sales: about 10%.
Main trading partners : Belgium, United Kingdom, Germany, New Zealand, New Caledonia, Netherlands.

References in France

Restaurants: Michel Bras (Laguiole), Le Sarladais, M. Tartrou (Paris).
Shops: Comtesse du Barry, Lyon.

Abroad

United Kingdom
Sookias et Bertaut ltd., The Cottage, Cambalt Road, Putney Hill, London SW 156 EW – Tel: 017884193.

Germany
Weinimport Handels QMBH – Tizianweg 8-7000 Stuttgart 1 - Tel (0711) 85 52 20 Neue Vinothek untere Clignetstrape Postfach 1510-6800 Mannheim 1. – Tel (0621) 379960.

Belgium
Entrepots Vins Manquoi: Arsenaalstraat 3-2000 Antwerpen – Tel: 032380237 – Telex 73383 Manvin.

New Caledonia
Ets. Ballande – Nouméa – Bordeaux Tel: 5644 4658 – Telex 570304 Ballan.

The Netherlands
Maison Heisterkamp – Rue Oostwal 5, 7631 Egootmarsum. Tel: 05419 2222.

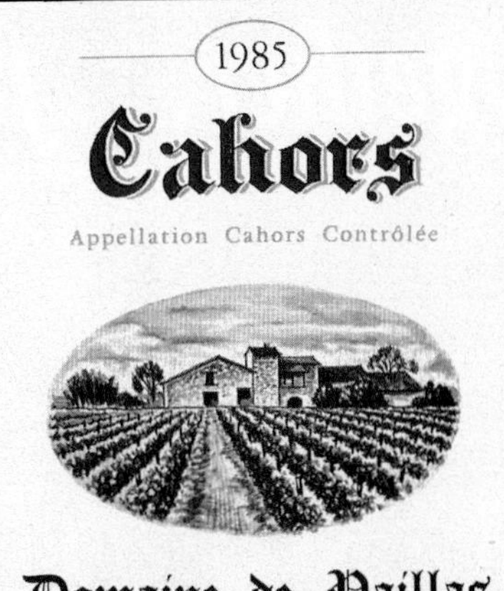

Domaine de Paillas

SCEA DE SAINT-ROBERT
12% Vol. FLORESSAS - LOT - FRANCE 75 cl
MISE EN BOUTEILLE A LA PROPRIÉTÉ

PAILLAS 1982
MÉDAILLE D'OR CONCOURS GÉNÉRAL 1984
GRAND PRIX D'EXCELLENCE VINALIES 1984
PAILLAS 1983
HIGH COMMENDATION
1987 INTERNATIONAL WINE CHALLENGE
PAILLAS 1985
GRAND PRIX D'EXCELLENCE VINALIES 1987

SCEA DE SAINT-ROBERT
FLORESSAS - LOT - FRANCE

Far East
New Zealand: Allied Liquor Merchants Ltd. P.O. Box. 815 Auckland – Tel: (9) 773999 – Telex 60837 Baltray.

Comments

In spite of the youth of the vines (11 years on the average), and thanks to the particular soil of the Causse hillsides, the Paillas is considered by professionals as one of the greatest Cahors wines, as demonstrated by numerous prizes in various national competetions as well as in foreign competitions.

- *Watch out for wines that lose their authenticity, most often because of carbonic maceration (see Roussillon, South-west, Périgord...).*

CAHORS AOC PRIEURÉ DE CÉNAC

Franck Rigal
Parnac - 46140 Luzech
65 30 70 10 - Telex: 520 281

Type of vineyard: Agricultural Association. **Number of employees:** 10. **Vine stocks:** Auxerrois 80%, Merlot 20%. **Soil:** Gravelly, pebbly clay. **Exposure:** South-East. **Average annual production in hectoliters:** 40-45 hl/ha. **Appellation:** Cahors. **Type:** Red. **Technique:** Traditional, with temperature control. **Maturing:** In new oak casks. **Alcohol content:** 12-12.5%. **Characteristics:** Soft and full, complex, round tannins. **Serving temperature:** 17 to 18°. **Served with:** Red meat, game, cheese. **Vintages available in 89/90:** 1985, 1986, 1987.

Characteristics of vintages

1987: Not yet bottled. **1986:** Red berry aromas, soft and full, lingering taste. **1985:** Excellent, complex, very well balanced, good keeping. Price range (pre-tax, ex-warehouse): 30 to 50 F.F.
Sales in France: 80%.
Export sales: 20%.
Main trading partners: European countries, Canada, Japan.

References in France

Restaurants: La Maison du Cantal.
Shops: Caves des Gobelins, Caves de Passy.

Abroad

United States
Importers: Surfluh - Tel: 58 72 80 17.

United Kingdom
Ste Adel - Tel: 46 24 07 01 (France).

Germany
Louge - Tel: 49 22 41 217 55.

Belgium
Cordonnier - Tel: 32 27 70 29 18.

Canada
Le Marchand de Vin: TLX 3727136 after dialing 023000.

The Netherlands
BP de Waal - Tel: 31 70 54 60 11.

Comments

Member of the "Seigneurs de Cahors".

> • *Watch out for certain confusing labels: "Bottled at the Château", the wine is produced on the estate; "bottled on the estate", the wine comes from a cooperative... (See Chapter "Labeling").*

CHÂTEAU DE MERCUES

Georges Vigouroux
Mercues 46090 Cahors
65 20 00 01 - Telex: 521 307

Type of vineyard: Agricultural Association. **Established:** Reestablished in 1983. **Number of employees:** 10 permanent. **Vine stocks:** Auxerrois 75%, Merlot 20%, Tannat 5%. **Soil:** Gravelly terraces. **Exposure:** South. **Average annual production in hectoliters:** 1,000.
Appellation: Cahors. **Type:** Red. **Technique:** Long (21 days) in stainless steel tanks. **Maturing:** The first winter in stainless steel tanks. Then 18 months in oak casks. **Alcohol content:** 12%. **Characteristics:** Full bodied, rich and well balanced wines. **Serving temperature:** Old wine: 17°. **Served with:** Delicatessen, red meat, game, conserves, cheese. **Vintages available in 89/90:** 1987.

Characteristics of vintages

1987: Sustained red color, fine tannins indicating an excellent aptitude for ageing. **1987:** Seul millésime disponible. Price range (pre-tax, ex-warehouse): between 20 and 30 F.F.
Sales volume:
- Retail: 20%. - Restaurants: 80%.
Sales in France: 80%.
Export sales: 20%.

References in France

Restaurants: Vanel (Toulouse), Lamazere, Le Sousceyrac Daguin (Auch).

Comments

The Château de Mercues vineyard is terraced on the gravelly hillcrests of the commune of Mercues, quite close to Cahors. The great reputation of the region was established during the last century. It still provides one of the best Cahors, matured in oak casks.
The Château de Mercues is classified as a historical monument, the only one in the Cahors appellation region. The Château is a 4 star luxury hotel. Visits can be made to the unique Romano-Byzantine caves. It is the only inn and château in France where the client can go directly down from his room and see wine being made and aged in casks and participate in the harvest. Member of the "Seigneurs du Cahors".

CHÂTEAU PECH DE JAMMES

Georges Vigouroux
Flaujac-Poujols 46090 Cahors
65 38 81 98 - Telex: 521 833

Type of vineyard: Agricultural Association. **Established:** 1976. **Vine stocks:** Auxerrois 80%, Merlot 15%, Tannat 5%. **Soil:** Very pebbly on chalky clay sub-soil. **Exposure:**

Full South. **Average annual production in hectoliters:** 50 hl per hectare.
Appellation: Cahors. **Type:** Red. **Technique:** Long (21 days) in stainless steel tanks. **Maturing:** In stainless steel tanks the first winter, then in oak casks for 18 months. **Alcohol content:** 12%. **Characteristics:** Deep red color, firm, full bodied, astringent. These qualities are mostly due to the extremely rocky soil of the Causses du Lot. **Serving temperature:** Old wine: 17°. New wine: 15°. **Served with:** Young wine: foie gras. Old wine: conserves, cassoulets, game, cheese. **Vintages available in 89/90:** 1983, 1984, 1985, 1986, 1987.

Characteristics of vintages

1987: Very promising. **1986:** Rich red fruit aroma, sustained red-violet color, tannic, not agressive. **1985:** Very distinguished nose and color. A certain agressivity to the taste. A good future. **Other:** 1983: Agreeably open, tannins rounding out. Keeps its rich aroma of blackcurrant and mulberry. Price range (pre-tax, ex-warehouse): between 20 and 30 F.F.
Sales in France: 70%.
Export sales: 30%.
Main trading partners : Belgium, Germany, Switzerland, United States.

References in France

Restaurants: Restaurant Vanel (Toulouse), Restaurant de L'Assemblée Nationale.

Abroad

United States
Paramount Brands, Port Chester, N.Y.

Comments

Perched on the Cahors mountain, close to the Château de Haute-Serre, the Château Pech de Jammes has a full Southern exposure on an arid and pebbly hillside. A product of very sweet grapes, the wine is solid and aromatic. This small domain is like a pulpit exposed to the sun overlooking the gravel of the Causse. All of the greats of the worlds of politics, science and art have visited the Château Pech de Jammes.

DOMAINE DE QUATTRE

Mme Philippe Heilbronner
Bagat-Quercy – 46800 Montcuq
65 36 91 04

Established: 1976. **Vine stocks:** Auwerrois 78%, Merlot 13%, Tannat 9%. **Soil:** Chalky plateau. **Exposure:** Plateau – sunny all day. **Average annual production in hectoliters:** 1,000.
Appellation: A.O.C. Cahors. **Type:** Red. **Technique:** Destemming, fermentation with skins for about 15 days, open vats, traditional. **Maturing:** Stainless steel tanks. **Alcohol content:** 12%. **Characteristics:** Hillside vineyard, very fruity when young, well-balanced. To be drunk young (2 years) or after ageing for 4 to 5 years. **Serving temperature:** 14°-16°. **Served with:** All specialties of the Southwest France and, of course, with grilled steaks. Drink young with Couscous, poultry, etc. **Vintages available in 89/90:** 1983, 1984, 1986, 1987 (as of september 1989).

Characteristics of vintages

1988: Superb structure and fruit. Extremely promising. **1987:** Very fruity, pleasant, easy to drink young, can age. **1986:** Magnificent fragrance, young and spirited, in the flush of youth. **1984:** Has been locally acclaimed as the most successful of this vintage (Gold Medal at Mâcon, 3 First Prizes in the Southwest). **1983:** Very structured, nose still undeveloped. Needs ageing (Gold Medal at Mâcon).

DOMAINE DU PORT

Duchamp
Duraviel 46700 Puy-L'Évêque
65 36 56 01

Type of vineyard: Family-owned. **Established:** 1975. **Vine stocks:** Malbec, Merlot, Tannat. **Soil:** Silica & clay. **Exposure:** South, South-West. **Average annual production in hectoliters:** 60.

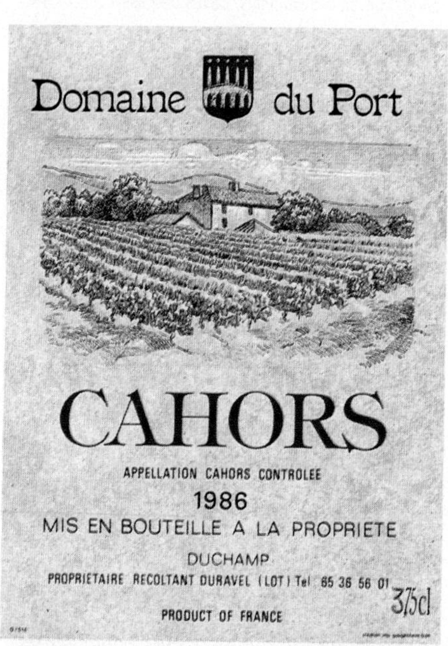

Domaine du Port
CAHORS
APPELLATION CAHORS CONTROLEE
1986
MIS EN BOUTEILLE A LA PROPRIETE
DUCHAMP
PROPRIETAIRE RECOLTANT DURAVEL (LOT) Tel 65 36 56 01
37,5cl
PRODUCT OF FRANCE

Appellation: Cahors. **Type:** Red. **Technique:** Traditional. **Maturing:** In vats and bottles. **Alcohol content:** 12%. **Characteristics:** Tannic, deep color. **Serving tempera-**

ture: 13-14°. **Served with:** Specialties of the South-West: duck, goose, goose liver, mushrooms (cèpes) etc. **Vintages available in 89/90:** 1987, 1988.

Characteristics of vintages

1988: Tannic, full, deep color. **1987:** Tannic, delicate, fruity. Price range (pre-tax, ex-warehouse): 20 to 30 F.F.
Sales volume:
- Wholesale: 60%. - Retail: 18%. - Restaurants: 18.3%.
- Other: 3.2% (EEC countries).

Sales in France: 100%.

References in France

Restaurants: Restaurants serving South-West style cuisine in and around Paris.
Shops: Shops specializing in the products of the South-West, in and around Paris.

Comments

Enterprise that has been in the same family for three generations. The entire harvest is sold in bottles (50000 bottles/year), 80% in and around Paris.

CHÂTEAU DE SOULEILLOU (as of 1989)

Jean-Pierre Raynal
46140 Douelle
65 20 01 88

Type of vineyard: Family-owned. **Established:** End of 17th century. **Number of employees:** 1 part time. **Vine stocks:** Auxerrois (80%), Merlot (15%), Tannat (5%). **Soil:** Chalky clay and gravel. **Exposure:** South, South-West, on terraces. **Average annual production in hectoliters:** 50 hl/hectare.
Appellations: Cahors. **Type:** Red. **Technique:** Traditional, long fermentation, at least 15 days, separately by vinestock, in stainless steel tanks. **Maturing:** In cement vats (12 to 18 months) and oak barrels (Cuvée de Diane). **Alcohol content:** 12%. **Characteristics:** A superb Cahors, sustained bright red color, fragrant, long and well-balanced, with red fruit aromas. Typical, keeps well. **Serving temperature:** 16 to 18°. **Served with:** Regional cooking, conserves, foie gras, red meat, cheese. **Vintages available in 89/90:** 1987, 1988.

Characteristics of vintages

1988: Rich and well-balanced, aromatic, very successful, will age well. **1987:** Bronze Medal at Mâcon. Definite red fruit aroma, beautiful balance. La Cuvée de Diane 1987 (matured in new oak barrels) is superb. Balanced and harmonious, an elegant wine with subtle, lingering perfumes. Prince range (pre-tax, ex-warehouse): between 10 and 20 F.F.
Sales volume:
- Wholesale: 60%. - Retail: 40%.

Main trading partners: Belgium.

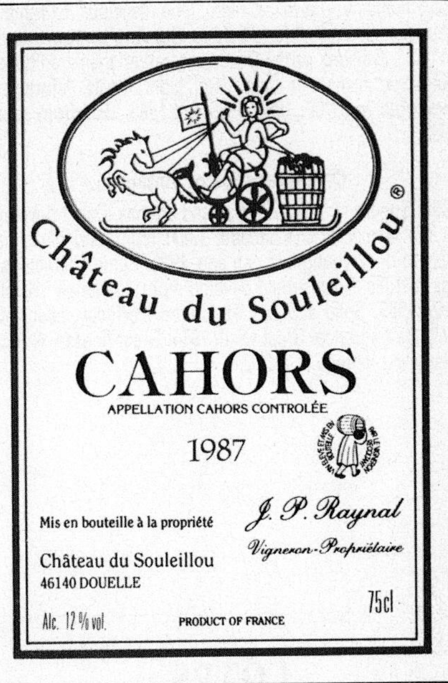

Abroad

Belgium

Millésimes, Jean-Pierre Vanderhende, rue Marché aux Poulets 52, 1000 Brussels. Tel: 02217 46 99.

Comments

From a family of winemakers deeply involved with wine and their vineyards for generations, Jean-Pierre Raynal replanted the vineyard with noble vinestocks 23 years ago. Today he produces typical wines, authentic Cahors, which are regularly awarded prizes at Toulouse and Mâcon as well as Blaye and Bourgeais. In addition to a bronze medal at Mâcon, the 1987 received a second prize at Toulouse.

CHÂTEAU TREILLES

Marquise de Portes
Bagat-en-Quercy - 46800 Montcuq
65 36 91 04

Established: 1980. **Vine stocks:** Auxerrois 75%, Merlot 20%, Tannat 5%. **Soil:** Calcium carbonate with a bit of copper. **Average annual production in hectoliters:** 800 in 1988.
Appellation: A.O.C. Cahors. **Type:** Red. **Technique:** Detemming, long fermentation with skins. **Maturing:** Stainless steel tanks, then new casks, then again in stainless steel tanks. **Alcool content:** 12%. **Characteristics:** Hillside vinyard, complex nose, mixture of fruit, woody,

spicy (cinnamon) aromas. Rich , long, delicious. Extremely fine tannins, unusual for a Cahors. **Serving temperature:** 14°-16°. **Served with:** Delicacies rather than traditional preserved dishes or Cassouset. Light meals. **Vintages available in 89/90:** 1984, 1985 and 1986, 1987 from sept. 1989.

Characteristics of vintages

1988: Superb structure finesse and aromas. Could develop as the winner of the decade. **1987:** Fruity and pleasant. Easy to drink young, but can age. **1986:** Same characteristics as 1985. Nose should develop more. Extremely promising. **1985:** Solid and well structured. Perfectly balanced. Delicate fragrance. Great wine. **1984:** Great finesse. A success. First vintage in A.O.C.

CÔTES DU FRONTONNAIS

DOMAINE DE FAOUQUET

Robert Beringuier
Bouloc – 31620 Fronton
61 82 06 66

Type of vineyard: Family-owned. **Established:** 1850. **Vine stocks:** Negrette, Gamay, Syrah, Cabernet, Jurançon, Mauzac... **Soil:** Sand, alluvial clay, gravel, red, sandy clay. **Exposure:** South. **Average annual production in hectoliters:** 700.

Appellation: Côte du Frontonnais Villaudric. **Type:** Red, rosé. **Technique:** Semi-carbonic. **Maturing:** Concrete vats, stainless steel and enamelled tanks. **Alcohol content:** 11.5%. **Characteristics:** Rich in alcohol, typical of the region, taste of black-current, mulberry, raspberry. Colorful, rich in tannins, balanced and harmonious due to the small yield (30 hl per hectare). Lively, tannic, warm. **Serving temperature:** Rosé: 8° to 10°. Red 1986: 12°. Red 1985: 17°. **Served with:** Rosé: hors-d'œuvre, delicatessen and even the entire meal in Summer time. Young red; grilled or roasted meat, Pyrenean cheese. Red 1985: Cassoulet, preserved duck ou goose. **Vintages available in 89/90:** 1985 and 1986.

Characteristics of vintages

1986: Young wine, supple, aromatic, goes down well. **1985:** Richer vintage with lots of color, well-balanced, rich bouquet.

CHÂTEAU DE BEL AIR

Mrs Andrée Bonhomme
Château de Bel Air, route de Campsas
31620 Fronton
61 82 45 75

Type of vineyard: Family-owned. **Established:** one of the oldest of the Fronton Vintages – bought by the Bonhomme family in 1972. **Vine stocks:** Négrette 50%, Gamay, Cabernet, Mérille, Syrah, Mauzac 50%. **Soil:** Reddish gravel and sand with pebbly red silt, clay, on a subsoil of clay with oxides of iron and manganese on hardpan and alluvium. **Exposure:** Hillsides East/West, terraces, all directions. **Average annual production in hectoliters:** 1,000.

Appellation: Côtes du Frontonnais, Fronton. **Type:** Red, white (Sémillon), rosé. **Technique:** Traditional – long fermentation with skins without destemming. **Maturing:** in concrete tanks. **Alcohol content:** About 11.7%. **Characteristics:** Elegant wines with breed that go down well. Ruby color for the young wines, turning to a darker shade with age. The taste of ripe red berries, with a touch of liquorice. Aged wines with subtle bouquet. **Serving temperature:** 16°-17°. **Served with:** Young wines: regional dishes, roasts and red meat (grilled). Aged wines: game. Rosé of the year: white meat, delicatessen products.
Sémillon: fish, seafood, particularly good with cakes and pastries. **Vintages availables in 89/90:** 1986, 1985, a few 1983 and 1979 bottles.

Characteristics of vintages

1985 and **1986:** Good years, combining balance, suppleness, bouquet and elegance – good for ageing. Price range (pre-tax, ex-warehouse): 10 F.F.-20 F.F.

Sales volume:
– Wholesale: starting only this year...
Main trading partners: Belgium, Germany, Luxembourg.

Comments

Wines sold primarily in regional markets in order to avoid wholesale operations in which wines are sold below costs. The present aim is to sell as much wine as possible in bottles, in France and overseas as well.

CHÂTEAU BELLEVUE LA FORÊT

Patrick Germain
31620 Fronton
62 82 43 21 – Telex: 530 591 – FAX 61 82 39 70

Type of vineyard: Agricultural Society. **Established:** 1974. **Number of employees:** 17. **Vine stocks:** 50% Negrette, 25% Cabernet Franc and Sauvignon, 25% Gamay and Syrah. **Soil:** Gravelly alluvial soil. **Exposure:** Hillside, full East. **Average annual production in hectoliters:** about 6,300.
Appellation: Côtes du Frontonnais. **Type:** Red, rosé. **Technique:** Red: Bordeaux tradition with temperature regulation. Rosé: Drawing off, low temperature vinification. **Maturing:** Vats and casks. **Alcohol content:** 12%. **Characteristics:** Red: Fruity, supple, silky texture, harmonious tannins. Rosé: Very fruity, supple attack, fresh wine, very fragrant, firm and vigorous. **Serving temperature:** Red 14°, Rosé 8°. **Served with:** Red: Grilled meat, poultry, hard cheese. Rose: First courses, delicatessen and fish. **Vintages available in 89/90:** Red: 1987, 1988. Rosé: 1988.

Characteristics of vintages

1988: Excellent Rosé de Negrette, suggestion of mulberry, strong fruity fragrance. **1987:** Prestige Rouge: Matured 6 months in new oak casks. Superb ruby color and a bouquet combining spices and ripe fruit, fleshy and round in body. Rouge traditionnel: Beautiful ruby color, strong floral aromas, a beautiful balance between fruit and tannins. Price range (pre-tax, ex-warehouse): between 16 and 35 F.F./HT.
Sales volumes:
– Wholesale: 0%. – Retail: 30%. – Restaurants: 40% – Other: 30% winecellars.
Sales in France: 65%.
Export sales: 35%.
Main Trading partners: Canada, Switzerland, Germany.

References in France

Restaurants: Hôtel de France (Auch), Grand Hôtel de l'Opéra (Toulouse), Hôtel du Palais (Biarritz), Gray d'Albion (Cannes).
Shops: Nicolas and Vignes Pasquier (Paris).

CHÂTEAU LES PEYREAUX

Vovette Linat de Bellefonds
Villematier-les-Peyreaux - 31340 Villemur
61 35 36 48

Established: In 1650. **Vine stocks:** Négrette, Cabernet Franc, Cabernet Sauvignon, Sirah, Mérille. **Appellation:** Côte du Frontennais, Château des Peyreaux, Vins Pays: Le Vin d'Antan, Vin de Fête. **Type:** Red, white, rosé. **Technique:** Traditional, in the old fashion: 3 rackings during the first year, 2 during the second year. Wine from the first pressing is kept munder nitrogen. Bottling the third year. **Alcohol content:** 12%, A.O.C. **Characteristics:** Typical Fronton: character due to the very specific taste of the Negrette. Wines for long keeping (up to 30 years). **Serving temperature:** Red: 20°-22°. Rosé: 18°. White: 16°. **Served with:** Red: meat, game, cheese. Rosé: fish, shell-fish and white meat. White: as an aperitif, with foie gras or dessert. **Vintages available in 89/90:** 1985, 1986.

Characteristics of vintages

1986: Lots of character. **1985:** Supple and fruity. Price range (pre-tax, ex-warehouse): 20-30 F.F.

CHÂTEAU LA PALME

Martine Ethuin
31340 Villemur-sur-Tarn
61 09 02 82

Type of vineyard: Corporation. **Established:** 1961. **Number of employees:** 6. **Vine stocks:** Negrette 50%, Gamay 20%, Cabernet 20%, Syrah 10%. **Soil:** Silica-clay, reddish alluvium. **Average annual production in hectoliters:** 1,400.
Type: Red, rosé. **Technique:** Classic. **Maturing:** Red: classic. Rosé: low temperature. **Alcohol content:** 11,5%. **Characteristics:** Fruity. **Serving temperature:** 16°. **Served with:** Red: dishes with sauce, steaks. Rosé: hors d'œuvres, foie gras. **Vintages available in 89/90:** 1986, 1987, 1988.

Characteristics of vintages

1988: Fruity, well-balanced, forthcoming. **1987:** Fruity, goes down well. **1986:** Good balance between alcohol, aroma and acidity. **1985:** Fruity, rich and well-balanced. **Other:** Vintages: Rosé: Fruity.

• *A dish for each wine. According to the age of your wines, their style, their typical nature, their color, adapt your menu without sticking to stereotypes (see "Wine and Foods".*

DURAS

DOMAINE DE DURAND

Michel Fonvielhe
47120 Saint-Jean-de-Duras
53 89 02 04 and 53 83 00 48

Type of vineyard: Family-owned. **Established:** 17th Century. **Number of employees:** 2. **Vine stocks:** Red: Merlot, Cabernet Franc, Cabernet Sauvignon. **Soil:** Clay with calcium carbonate. **Exposure:** Southeast. **Average annual production in hectoliters:** 1 200.
Appellation: Côtes-de-Duras. **Type:** Red, white, rosé. **Technique:** Traditional. **Maturing:** 2 years before bottling. **Alcohol content:** 11.5% to 12.5%. **Characteristics:** Red: ruby color, rich, well-balanced fragrance, with a touch of spice and red fruit, tannins still present. Dry white: pale with green glints, very supple, very fruity fragrance. **Serving temperature:** Red: 16° to 17°. White, rosé: 6° to 8°. **Served with:** Red: grilled meat, light cheese. White: fish, shell-fish, oysters. **Vintages available in 89/90:** 1985, 1986, 1987, 1988.

Characteristics of vintages

1988: Great year– wait a little, will be perfect with game and cheese. **1987:** Already pleasant, the choice wine to accompany delicatessen. **1986:** Well-colored, fruity red, quite dense. Good white. **1985:** Excellent vintage, rich and well-balanced with fine tannins, relatively mature. Price range (pre-tax, ex-warehouse): between 20 F.F. and 30 F.F.
Sales volume:
- Wholesale: 20%. - Retail: 30%. - Restaurants: 40%.
- Other: 10% (export).

Sales in France: 90%.
Export sales: 10%.
Main trading partners : Belgium, Germany, USA.

CHÂTEAU LA GRAVE BÉCHADE

Daniel Bensoussan
Baleyssagues - 47120 Duras
53 83 70 06 - Telex: 572 324 F

Type of vineyard: Agricultural Association. **Established:** 1962. **Vine stocks:** Cabernet Franc, Cabernet Sauvignon, Merlot, Sauvignon Blanc. **Soil:** Clay with calcium carbonate and red alluvial clay. **Average annual production in hectoliters:** 3,800.
Appellation: Côtes-de-Duras. **Type:** Red, white, rosé. **Technique:** Traditional. **Maturing:** Oak casks. **Alcohol content:** 12%. **Characteristics:** Red: wine for ageing,

forthcoming, full, round, well-balanced. Sauvignon white: fruity, pleasant to drink. Rosé: made from Cabernet Franc, tasty, cherry colored. **Serving temperature:** Red: room temperature, 18°. **Served with:** Red: meat and game. White: fish and shellfish. Rosé: goes with the whole meal, a good wine for Summer. **Vintages available in 89/90:** Red: from 1979 to 1986. Rosé: 1985 and 1986. Dry white Sauvignon: 1984, 1985, 1986.

Characteristics of vintages

1988: Excellent year for both red and white. Red: full-bodied, long, will be very good keeping wines. Very promising. White: very fragrant, agreeable to drink. **1986:** Very good year, especially for the white. **1985:** Exceptional year, lovely red, good color, dense, to be aged. Price range (pre-tax, ex-warehouse): between 20 F.F. and 30 F.F.
Sales volume:
– Retail: 40%. – Restaurants: 20%. – Other: 40% (export).
Sales in France: 60%.
Export sales: 40%.
Main trading partners: USA, UK, Germany, Belgium, Netherlands, Denmark, Switzerland, Sweden.

References in France

Restaurants: Lucas-Carton, Michel Trama, Daguin, Les Jardins de l'Opéra, Claude Lafitte.
Shops: Duhau (Paris).

Comments

The wines are made in a cellar considered to be the most modern in Europe.

GAILLAC

DOMAINE DE LABARTHE

Jean Albert and son
Castanet – 81150 Marssac-sur-Tarn
63 56 80 14

Type of vineyard: Agricultural Association. **Established:** 1985. **Vine stocks:** White: Mauzac, Len de l'el, Sauvignon. Red: Dures, Fer, Cabernet, Merlot. **Soil:** Clay with calcium carbonate. **Exposure:** South. **Average annual production in hectoliters:** 1 600.
Appellation: Gaillac. **Type:** Red, white, rosé. **Technique:** Traditional. **Maturing:** In vats. **Serving temperature:** Dry white or pearly: 8°. Mellow: 6°. Sparkling (Champagne method) 6°. **Served with:** Dry white or pearly: fish, seafood. Mellow: as an aperitif or with foie gras, desserts. Sparkling: as an aperitif or with desserts. Red: meat, cheese. **Vintages available in 89/90:** 1985, 1986.

Characteristics of vintages

1986: Promising. **1985:** Very beautiful year, wine supple and fragrant. Taste the mellow wine.

DOMAINE DE PIALENTOU

Jean-Louis Ailloud
81600 Brens
63 57 17 99

Type of vineyard: Family-owned. **Established:** 1964. **Number of employees:** 1. **Vine stocks:** Duras, Syrah, Cabernet Sauvignon, Gamay – Mauzac, Sauvignon. **Soil:** Terraces, gravel. **Exposure:** Left bank of the Tarn, South, Southwest. **Average annual production in hectoliters:** 700.
Appellation: A.O.C. Gaillac. **Type:** Red, white, rosé, sparkling. **Technique:** Red: long fermentation with skins. Rosé and white: classic. **Maturing:** In vats. **Alcohol content:** 11.5%. **Characteristics:** Beautiful deep color, with the soft aroma of ripe red fruit. May be aged a long time. **Served with:** Red meat and meat in sauce, typical local dishes, Cassoulet, preserved duck. **Vintages available in 89/90:** 1982, 1983, 1984, 1985.

Characteristics of vintages

1985: Full and round, a beautiful vintage, for ageing. **1984:** Will age well. **1983:** All the qualities of a young wine, lots of fragrance. **1982:** Very beautiful deep color, robust, dense, successful.

DOMAINE DE ROUMAGNAC

Jean-Louis Ribot
Chemin des Balitrans
Roumagnac – 81600 Gaillac
63 57 06 53

Type of vineyard: Family-owned. **Vine stocks:** Traditional vine stocks of the Gaillac.
Appellation: Gaillac. **Type:** Red White. **Technique:** Traditional. **Characteristics:** Red: Very fruity, supple and full, awarded numerous Gold Medals. White: excellent slightly sparkling wine, to be tasted. **Serving temperature:** white: 10°. Red: 154°. **Served with:** As an aperitif and with seafood. Red: with roasts and poultry. **Vintages available in 89/90:** 1985, 1986 and 1987 (white).

Characteristics of vintages

1986: Good year, for white as well as red. **1985:** Excellent red, supple and tannic, well made. Price range (pre-tax, ex-warehouse): 10-20 F.F.

References in France

Shops: L'Amour du Vin, 94, rue Saint-Dominique, 75007 Paris. Tél. 45 56 12 94.

DOMAINE DES TERRISSES

Alain and Joseph Cazottes
Saint-Laurent – 81600 Gaillac
63 57 16 80 or 63 57 09 15

Type of vineyard: Family Agricultural Association. **Vine stocks:** Red: Syrah, Duras, Braucol. White: Mauzac, Len de l'el, Sauvignon. **Soil:** Clay with calcium carbonate; terraces. **Exposure:** South, Southwest. **Average annual production in hectoliters:** 1,800.
Type: Red, white, rosé, mellow, sparkling (Gaillac method). **Technique:** Red: fermentation with skins 8 to 10 days, temperature control. **Maturing:** Red and white: concrete vats. **Alcohol content:** 12%. **Characteristics:** Red: based on a local grape variety (Braucol). They are very fruity, rich and well-balanced. May age 8 to 10 years. Dry white: very flowery, supple and lively at the same time. Mellow: soft and full but not pasty, pleasant Mauzac fruitiness. Gaillac method brut, half dry and sweet: method which preserves all the fruitness in a sparkling wine. **Serving temperature:** Mellow: 6°. Dry: 8°. Sparkling: 8° to 10°. Red: 18°. **Served with:** Red: meat, other dishes depending upon the vintage. Dry: for "Kir" aperitif, hors-d'œuvre. Mellow: as an aperitif or with dessert. Gaillac Method Brut: as an aperitif in the evening. Half dry and half sweet: mostly with dessert. Petillant de Raisin: (100% Mauzac) 3% alcohol (mawimum), should be kept cool.

Characteristics of vintages

1986: Red rich and well-balanced, fleshy, rich in color, to be aged. **1985:** Aromatic, goes down well, can age.

JURANÇON

BURGUÉ

Henri Burgué
64110 Saint-Faust
59 83 05 91

Type of vineyard: Family-owned. **Established:** 1930 by (Joseph Burgué, taken over by his son in 1975). **Number of employees:** 3 family members. **Vine stocks:** Petit Manseng and Gros Manseng. **Soil:** Clay with silica-clay. **Exposure:** South. **Average annual production in hectoliters:** 100.
Appellation: Jurançon. **Type:** White. **Technique:** Traditional. **Maturing:** 3 years in Oak casks. **Alcohol content:** 14%. **Characteristics:** Bouquet reminescent of camomile, lively and forthcoming at the same time. **Serving temperature:** 10°. **Served with:** As an aperitif or with foie gras, fresh or half-cooked, preserved, duck or goose or with a good Ewe's Milk Cheese. **Vintages available in 89/90:** 1985, 1986.

Characteristics of vintages

1985: Well-made vintage.

MADIRAN

BARREJAT

Maurice Capmartin
Maumusson – 32400 Riscle
62 69 74 92

Type of vineyard: Family-owned. **Established:** Several generations. **Number of employees:** 1. **Vine stocks:** Red Madiran: Tannat 50%, Cabernet 50%. White Pacherenc: Memsenc Gros 50%, Memsenc Petit 50%. **Soil:** Sandy alluvial clay and gravel on tufa subsoil. **Exposure:** South, Southeast. **Average annual production in hectoliters:** 45.
Appellation: Madiran, Pacherenc Vilbilh. **Type:** Red, white. **Technique:** Traditional, stabilization at low temperature, 5%, 3 weeks. **Maturing:** Wood 6 months and stainless steel tanks. **Alcohol content:** 12.5 to 13%. **Characteristics:** Madiran: very deep color, fleshy. Rich and well-balanced, tannic, typical of the appellation. Wine to be kept – Open after 7 ou 8 years. Pacherenc du Vilbilh: very fruity. **Serving temperature:** Madiran: 16 to 17°. **Served with:** Red meat, game, cheese from the Pyrenees Mountains, as well as duck preserve, duck filets, steak with Béarnaise Sauce. **Vintages available in 89/90:** 1987, 1988.

Characteristics of vintages

1987: Similar to the preceding years, beautiful deep color, fleshy, well-balanced, tannic, typical of the appellation - to be aged. **1986:** Very good quality, very young, similar to previous years. **1985:** Very robust, also similar to previous years, full, to be aged.

LABRANCHE-LAFFONT

Marcel Dupuy
Maumusson 32400 Riscle
62 69 74 90

Established: For three generations. **Vine stocks:** Tannat 60%, Cabernet Franc 20%, Cabernet Sauvignon 20%. **Soil:** Sand and reddish clay silt with pebbles. **Exposure:** Facing full South. **Average annual production in hectoliters:** 400.

Appellation: Madiran Pacheren. **Type:** Red, white. **Technique:** Traditional. **Maturing:** In stainless steel tanks. **Alcohol content:** 12.8%. **Characteristics:** Tannic, very fruity, spicy and robust. Ages well (about 10 years). **Serving temperature:** 15-16°. **Served with:** Red meat, game, cheese. **Vintages available in 89/90:** Madrian 1987-1988, Pecheren 1988-1989.

Characteristics of vintages

1986-1985: Two exceptional vintages due to lots of sunshine. Price range (pre-tax, ex-warehouse): 10-20 F.F.

CHÂTEAU MONTUS

Alain Brumont
32400 Maumusson
62 69 74 67 - Telex: 532 894

Type of vineyard: Family-owned. **Established:** 1858. **Number of employees:** 10. **Vine stocks:** Tannat 60%, Cabernet Sauvignon 20%, Fer-Servadou 20%. **Exposure:** South. **Average annual production in hectoliters:** 40. **Appellation:** Madiran. **Type:** Red. **Technique:** Destemming, fermentation 3 weeks. **Maturing:** In new barrels. **Alcohol content:** 12.5%. **Characteristics:** Very rich and well-balanced, deep color (brilliant red). Vanilla, fruity, blackcurrant, spicy, animal towards 15 years of age. To drink in 5 to 10 years. May age 30 years. **Serving temperature:** 16°. **Served with:** Ducks, the cuisine of the southwest, game, red meat. **Vintages available in 89/90:** 1985.

Characteristics of vintages

1985: Excellent wine, good color, complex fragrance of macerated red fruit, to be the aged.

CHÂTEAU PEYROS CORBÈRES

64350 LEMBEYE
Denis de Robillard
Office: 83, av. Trespoey - 64000 Pau
59 02 45 90 - Telex: ITAB 530 955 F - PO2

Type of vineyard: Family Agricultural Association. **Number of employees:** 5. **Average annual production in hectoliters:** 1 200.
Appellation: Madiran. **Type:** Red. **Technique:** Traditional. **Characteristics:** Beautiful wines, rich and well-balanced, rich in aroma; age brings, in compensation for moderation in ardor, a supplement of finesse and elegance. **Serving temperature:** 18°. **Served with:** Perfect for game, the Château Peyros is the perfect companion for "Magret de Canard" (duck steaks), Cassoulet, preserved duck and goose, red meat and dishes served with sauce. With age it becomes appropriate for white meat and foie gras. **Vintages available in 89/90:** 1982, 1983, 1985, 1986 (end of 1988).

Characteristics of vintages

1986: Almost a twin brother to the 1985, with a more supple attack, will develop a bit more rapidly. **1985:** Beautiful purple wine, round, robust, balanced. A perfect wine for ageing. Time will confirm its exceptional beauty. **1983:** Very aromatic and fruity, deep purple color, well developed, sound authentic. **1982:** Beautiful wine, not fully developed yet, fruit fragrance, round, fleshy, long. A beautiful bottle.

MARCILLAC

DOMAINE DU CROS

Teulier
Le Cros Goutrens - 12390 Rignac
65 72 71 77

Type of vineyard: Father and son. **Vine stocks:** Mansoi or Fer-Servadou. **Soil:** Permian and chalky. **Exposure:** South. **Average annual production in hectoliters:** 350. **Appellation:** Marcillac. **Type:** Red. **Technique:** Tratidional, manual, on foot. **Maturing:** In wood, from 6 months to 2 years. **Characteristics:** Deep, red color, typical, pronounced woodland aroma. Raspberry and blackcurrant aroma, typical of the region, fruity and sound. **Serving temperature:** 14° to 15°. **Served with:** Regional cooking (red meat and meat in sauce). **Vintages available in 89/90:** 1985, 1986.

CAVE DES VIGNERONS DU VALLON

Metge
Valady - 12330 Marcillac
65 72 70 21

Type of vineyard: Cooperative Agricultural Association. **Established:** 1966. **Vine stocks:** Fer-Servadou, called "Mansoi". **Average annual production in hectoliters:** 3,500.
Appellation: Marccillac. **Type:** Red, rosé. **Technique:** Traditional, long fermentation without destemming. **Alcohol content:** 11%. **Characteristics:** Red: with good color, fruity with a taste of raspberry or blackcurrant depending upon to the year. A bit tannic. **Serving temperature:** 14° to 16°. **Served with:** Goes with the entire meal. **Vintages available in 89/90:** 1985, 1986.

MONBAZILLAC

CHÂTEAU MONBAZILLAC
CCM Monbazillac
24240 Monbazillac
53 57 06 38 – Telex: 550 049 F

Type of vineyard: Cooperative. **Established:** 1942. **Vine stocks:** Sémillon, Muscadelle, Sauvignon. **Soil:** Clay with calcium carbonate. **Exposure:** Plateau North, Northeast. **Average annual production in hectoliters:** 600 (40000 hl in total for the cooperative).
Appellation: Monbazillac. **Type:** White. **Technique:** Traditional, liqueur-like white, total control. **Maturing:** In stainless steel tanks under inert gas. **Characteristics:** Liqueur-like white: beautiful amber color, furity, soft and full, aromatic, toasty aftertaste. **Serving temperature:** 6°. **Served with:** As an aperitif or with foie gras, white meat, cheese. **Vintages available in 89/90:** 1986, 1987, 1988.

Characteristics of vintages

1987: Young, fragrant, but promising, to be aged, complex, fruity. **1986:** Very aromatic, rich and well-balanced, soft and full, flowery aftertaste. Price range (pre-tax, ex-warehouse): between 20 F.F. and 50 F.F.
Sales volume:
– Retail: 80%. – Restaurants: 20%.
Sales in France: 70%. **Export sales:** 30%.
Main trading partners : UK, Germany, Netherlands, Bergium, Canada, USA, Japan.

References in France

Restaurants: The great restaurants of France.
Shops: Fauchon... Paris.

Abroad

United States
Ideal Sarl, Carolis Deal, Gloria Thorpe, 1145 Siskiyou Blvd., Ashland, Oregon 97520. Tel: (503) 482 2561.

United Kingdom
Agent: Mr. Henri Quancard, BP60, 33008 Bordeaux Cedex.

Germany
Same.

Canada
Distribution BLD, Marc Bissonnette, 4 rue Notre Dame Est, Suite 304, Montreal, Quebec. Tel: 514 861 0753. Telex: CHOULE MTL 055 61862.

Luxemburg
Commercial Agent: Mr. Johny Decker, 58, rue Franz Erpelding, L4553 Niebderkorn.

Denmark
Agent: Mr. Olivier Sublett, Château de Roques Export, Roques 33570 Puisseguin. Tel: 57 74 68 73. Telex: ROQUES 571 379 F.

Ohter
Free Agent: Mr. Paul-André Barriat, Culot du Vieux Pré 3, 4051 Plainevaux, Belgium.

PECHARMANT

DOMAINE DU HAUT PECHARMANT
24100 Bergerac
53 57 29 50

Type of vineyard: Agricultural Association (family-owned). **Number of employees:** 5. **Vine stocks:** Cabernet Sauvignon, Cabernet Franc, Merlot, Malbec. **Soil:** Perigord sand and gravel, clay and iron subsoil. **Exposure:** Hillsides facing South. **Average annual production in hectoliters:** 1,500.
Appellation: Pecharmant. **Type:** Red. **Technique:** Traditional, harvested by hand. **Maturing:** Long-3 years, with racking. **Alcohol content:** 12.5%. **Characteristics:** For ageing wine, robust and forthcoming, rich in tannins, interisting development, full maturity in 5 to 7 years. **Serving temperature:** 17 – 18°. Uncork bottle 1 – 2 hours before serving, or better still, allow to settle in carafe. **Served with:** Game in general. **Vintages available in 89/90:** 1984, 1985.

Characteristics of vintages

1986: Maturing – probably comparable to the 1983 vintage. **1985:** Very good structure, nose fruity and fleshy, mellow but strong tannins – Very good vintage. **1984:** Aromatic, lively, supple, goes down well, full maturity towards 1989.
Sales volume:
– Retail: 6%. – Restaurants: 25%. – Other: 20% (export).
Sales in France: 80%.
Export sales: 20%.
Main trading partners : Denmark, Belgium, Switzerland.

References in France

Restaurants: Relais – Châteaux de Dordogne and all of the 3 and 4 star restaurants: Amour du vin.
Shops: Hédiard (Paris) and fine winecellars.

• *To better understand the evolution and adherence to type of the various vintages, consult our "Vintage Code" chart.*

CHÂTEAU DE TIREGAND

Comtesse François de Saint-Éxupéry
Creysse – 24100 Bergerac
53 23 21 08

Type of vineyard: Family Agricultural Association. **Established:** 1830. **Number of employees:** 5. **Vine stocks:** Merlot 35%, Cabernet Sauvignon 35%, Cabernet Franc 20%, Malbec 10%. **Soil:** Périgord sand and gravel with some flint. **Exposure:** South, right bank of the Dordogne river. **Average annual production in hectoliters:** 1,350.
Appellation: Pecharmant. **Type:** Red. **Technique:** Traditional, in vats with maceration for 8 to 12 days with temperature control. **Maturing:** In used oak barrels. **Alcohol content:** 12.5%. **Characteristics:** Tannic, good color, combines finess and roundness with a good, rich taste. Fine blackcurrant fragrance. **Serving temperature:** 16° to 18°. **Served with:** Spicy red meat, game, duck steaks. **Vintages available in 89/90:** 1985, 1986.

Characteristics of vintages

1986: Appears to be fine and aromatic. Ageing in barrels should reveal its character. **1985:** Rich, good balance between its finess and aroma, intense color. **1984:** Light, balanced, a bit acidic, discreet tannin. **1983:** Finesse and elegance, a wine for long ageing, developed tannins. **1982:** Very rich and well-balanced. Very mature, for long ageing.
Sales volumes:
– Wholesale: 25%. – Retail: 50%. – Restaurants: 25%.
Sales in France: 67%. **Export sales:** 33%.
Main trading partners : Switzerland, Belgium, UK, USA.

CHÂTEAU LA RENAUDIE

Olivier Quesnel
La Renaudie Lembras – 24100 Bergerac
53 57 06 38 – Telex: 550 049 F

Type of vineyard: Family-owned. **Established:** 1980. **Vine stocks:** Canernet Franc, Merlot, Malbec. **Soil:** Silica-clay. **Exposure:** South. **Average annual production in hectoliters:** 1,500.
Appellation: Pecharmant. **Type:** Red. **Technique:** Red: maceration. **Maturing:** Stainless steel tanks, bottles. **Characteristics:** Red wine, fruity, rich, lightly tannic, woody aroma. **Serving temperature:** 16 to 18°. **Served with:** Red meat, game, cheese. **Vintages available in 89/90:** 1985, 1986.

Characteristics of vintages

1985: Beautiful color, bouquet, fleshy, rich. Gold Medal at Paris 1987. A wine to discover, to be aged, fine structure. Price range (pre-tax, ex-warehouse): between 15 F.F. and 20 F.F.
Sales volume:
– Retail: 80%. – Restaurants: 20%.
Sales in France: 70%. **Export sales:** 30%.
Main trading partners : UK, Germany, Netherlands, Belgium, Canada, USA.

Abroad

United States
Ideal Sarl, Carolis Deal, Gloria Thorpe, 1145 Siskiyou Blvd., Ashland, Oregon 97520. Tel: (503) 482 2561.

United Kingdom
Agent: M. Henri Quarcard, B.P. 60, 33008 Bordeaux Cedex.

Germany
Same as above.

Canada
Distribution BLB, Marc Bissonnette, 4 rue Notre Dame Est, Suite 304, Montreal, Quebec. Tel. 514 861 Q0753. Telex: CHOULE MTL 055 6186.

Luxemburg
Commercial Agent: M. Johny Decker, 58 rue Franz Erpelding, L4553 Niebderkorn.

Denmark
Agent: M. Olivier Sublett, Château de Roques Export, Roques 33570 Puisseguin. Tel. 57 74 68 73. Telex: ROQUES 571 379 F.

Others
Free Agent: M. Paul-André Barriat, Culot du Vieux Pré 3, 4051 Plainevaux, Belgium.

TURSAN

LES VIGNERONS DU TURSAN

J. Baque (President), B. Paraillous (Director)
40320 Geaune
58 44 51 25

Type of vineyard: Cooperative Agricultural Association. **Established:** 1957. **Number of employees:** 12. **Vine stocks:** White: Barroque. Red: Tannat and Cabernet. **Soil:** Clay with calcium carbonate. **Exposure:** South. **Average annual production in hectoliters:** 20,000.
Appellation: D'origine Tursan – V.D.Q.S. **Type:** Red, white, rosé. **Technique:** Traditional. **Maturing:** Vats. **Alcohol content:** 11%. **Characteristics:** White: touch of almond, rustic aroma, warm affertaste, ripe fruit flavor, dry and lively. Rosé: supple, fruity, goes down well. Red: Deep color, light, structured but supple, representative of the region. **Serving temperature:** White and rosé: 12° – Red: 14°. **Served with:** Country-style: cooking, the traditional cuisine of the Southwest. Sélection: light dishes.

Domaine La Moussière
ALPHONSE MELLOT
Propriétaire Viticulteur
Vignerons de Père en Fils depuis 1513
1985

THE LOIRE VALLEY

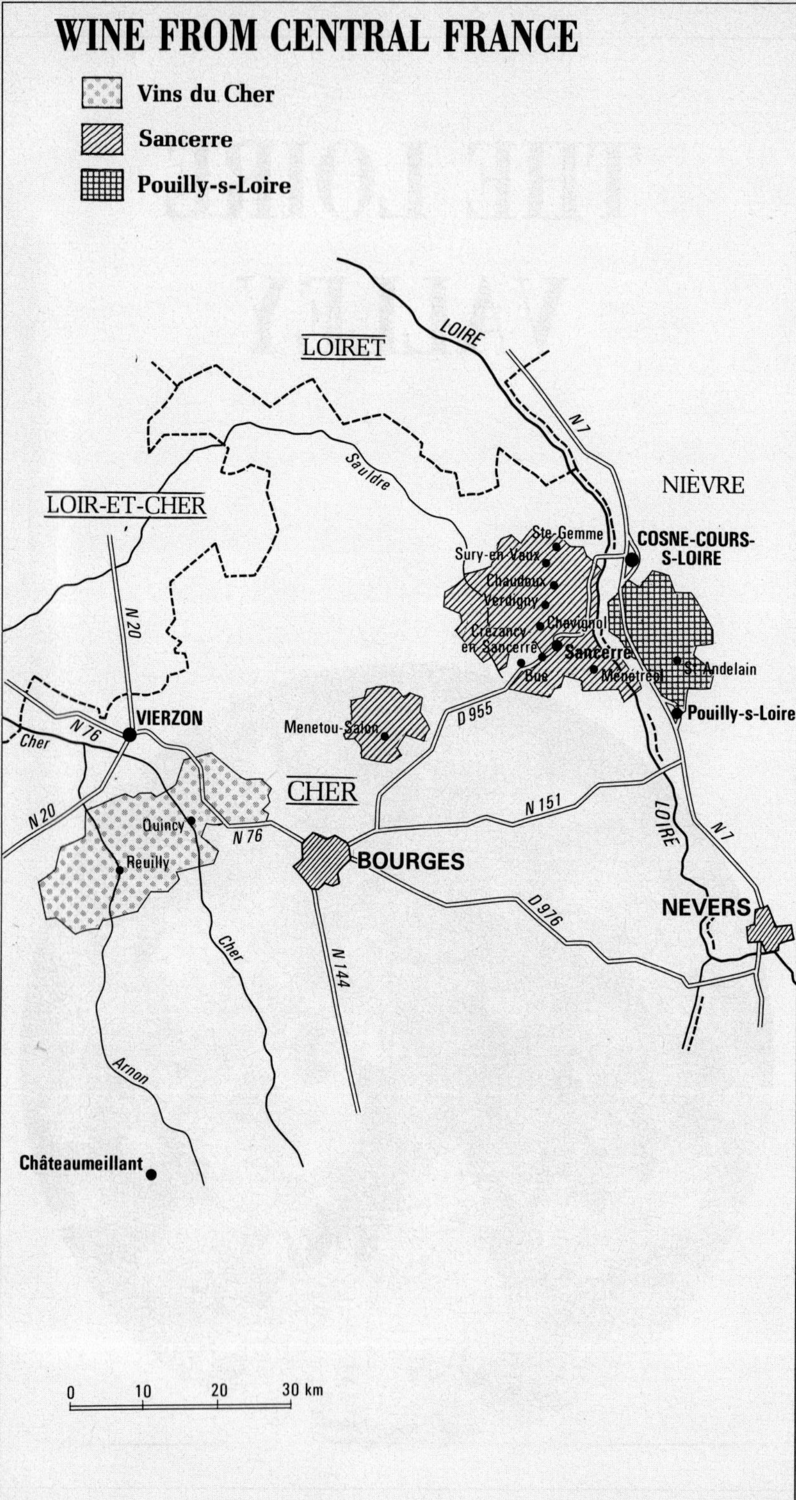
WINE FROM CENTRAL FRANCE
Vins du Cher
Sancerre
Pouilly-s-Loire
LOIRE
LOIRET
N7
Sauldre
NIÈVRE
LOIR-ET-CHER
Ste-Gemme
COSNE-COURS-S-LOIRE
Sury-en-Vaux
Chaudoux
Verdigny
N 20
Chavignol
Crézancy en Sancerre
Sancerre
Bué
Ménétreol
St-Andelain
Pouilly-s-Loire
VIERZON
N 76
D 955
Cher
Menetou-Salon
CHER
N 20
N 151
Quincy
N 76
LOIRE
N7
Reuilly
BOURGES
NEVERS
D 976
Cher
N 144
Arnon
Châteaumeillant
0 10 20 30 km

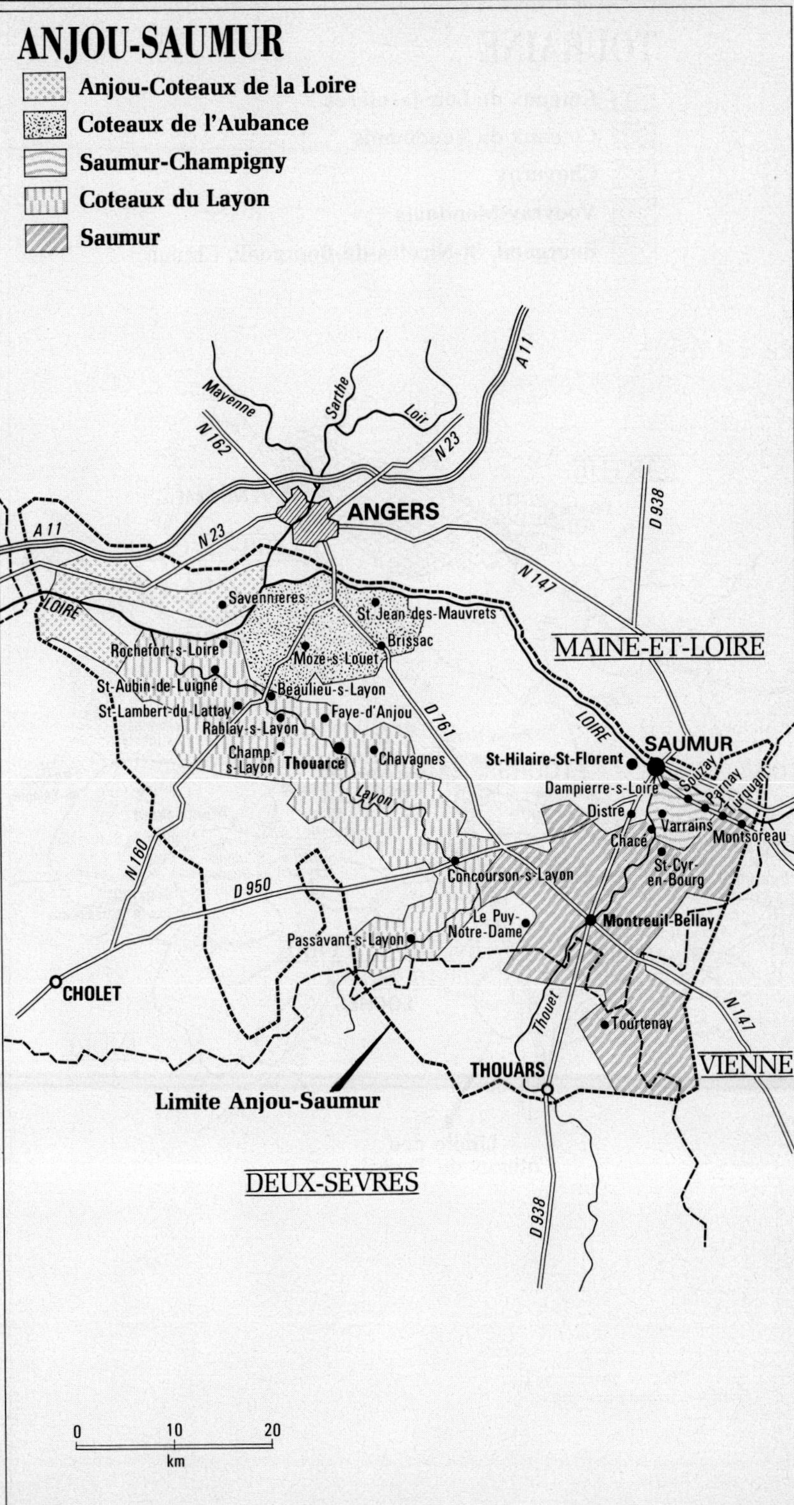
ANJOU-SAUMUR
Anjou-Coteaux de la Loire
Coteaux de l'Aubance
Saumur-Champigny
Coteaux du Layon
Saumur
Mayenne
Sarthe
Loir
A 11
N 162
N 23
ANGERS
D 938
N 147
LOIRE
Savennières
St-Jean-des-Mauvrets
Brissac
Rochefort-s-Loire
Moze-s-Louet
MAINE-ET-LOIRE
St-Aubin-de-Luigné
Beaulieu-s-Layon
St-Lambert-du-Lattay
Faye-d'Anjou
Rablay-s-Layon
D 761
Champ-s-Layon
Thouarcé
Chavagnes
SAUMUR
St-Hilaire-St-Florent
Souzay
Parnay
Turquant
Dampierre-s-Loire
Layon
Distre
Varrains
Montsoreau
Chacé
St-Cyr-en-Bourg
N 160
Concourson-s-Layon
D 950
Le Puy-Notre-Dame
Montreuil-Bellay
Passavant-s-Layon
CHOLET
Thouet
Tourtenay
N 147
VIENNE
THOUARS
Limite Anjou-Saumur
DEUX-SÈVRES
D 938
0
10
20
km

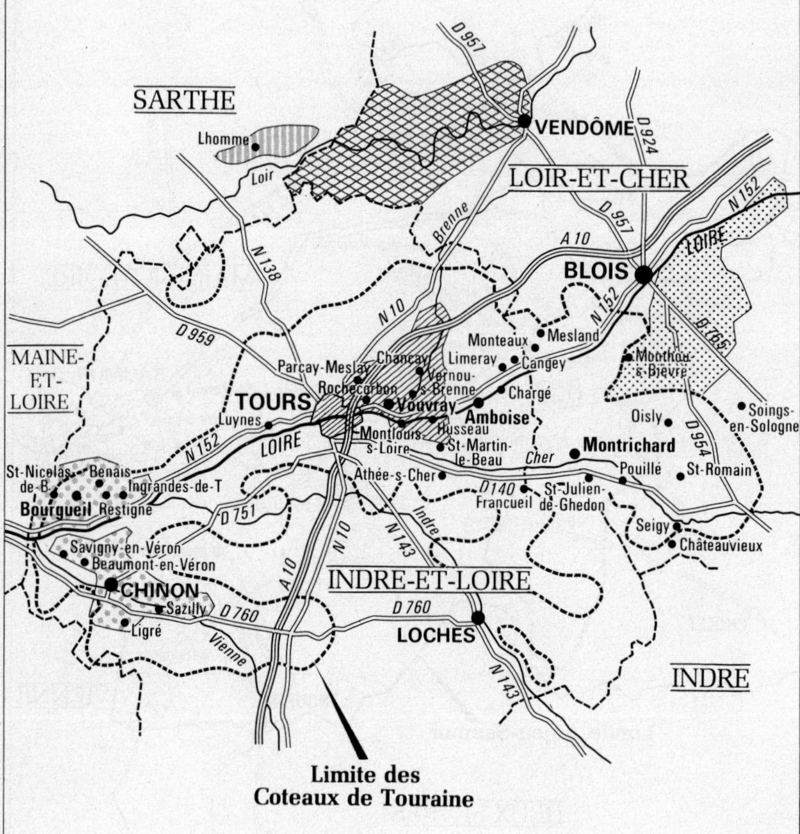
TOURAINE
Coteaux du Loir-Jasnières
Coteaux du Vendômois
Cheverny
Vouvray-Montlouis
Bourgueil, St-Nicolas-de-Bourgueil, Chinon
SARTHE
Lhomme
Loir
D 957
VENDÔME
D 924
LOIR-ET-CHER
N 138
Brenne
D 957
A 10
N 152
LOIRE
BLOIS
D 959
N 10
N 152
D 765
MAINE-ET-LOIRE
Monteaux
Mesland
Parcay-Meslay
Chançay
Limeray
Cangey
Vernou-s-Brenne
Rochecorbon
Monthou-s-Bièvre
TOURS
Vouvray
Chargé
Amboise
Luynes
Montlouis-s-Loire
Husseau
Oisly
Soings-en-Sologne
D 954
N 152
LOIRE
St-Martin-le-Beau
Montrichard
Cher
St-Nicolas-de-B.
Benais
Athée-s-Cher
D 140
Pouillé
St-Romain
Ingrandes-de-T
Francueil
St-Julien-de-Ghedon
Bourgueil
Restigné
D 751
Indre
Seigy
Châteauvieux
Savigny-en-Véron
N 10
N 143
Beaumont-en-Véron
CHINON
INDRE-ET-LOIRE
A 10
Sazilly
D 760
D 760
Ligré
LOCHES
Vienne
N 143
INDRE
Limite des Coteaux de Touraine
0
10
20
30 km

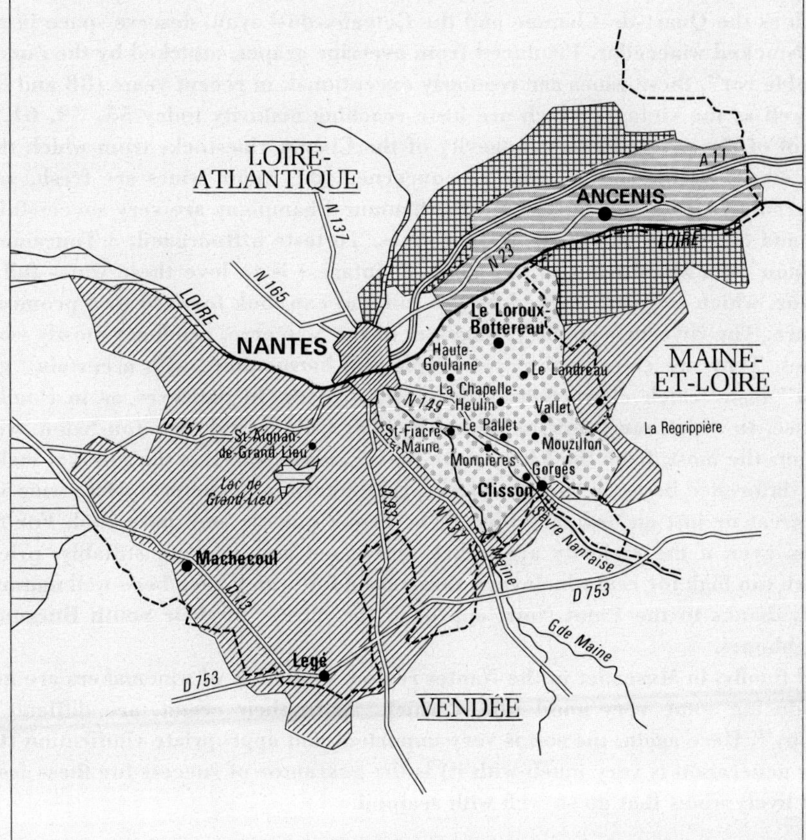
NANTES REGION
Muscadet des coteaux de la Loire
Coteaux d'Ancenis
Muscadet de Sèvre-et-Maine
Muscadet et Gros-plant du pays nantais
LOIRE-ATLANTIQUE
MAINE-ET-LOIRE
VENDÉE
NANTES
ANCENIS
LOIRE
A 11
N 137
N 165
N 23
N 149
D 751
D 937
N 137
D 12
D 753
D 753
Le Loroux-Bottereau
Haute-Goulaine
La Chapelle-Heulin
Le Landreau
Vallet
Le Pallet
Mouzillon
St-Fiacre-s-Maine
Monnières
Gorges
Clisson
La Regrippière
St-Aignan-de-Grand-Lieu
Lac de Grand-Lieu
Machecoul
Legé
Sèvre Nantaise
Maine
Gde Maine
0
10
20
30 km

The château country

Among the Anjou-Saumur wines (in addition to the Savennières, of which there are, unfortunately, only very small quantities) the great naturally sweet wines such as the Quart-de-Chaume and the Coteaux-du-Layon, deserve space in any wellstocked winecellar. Produced from overripe grapes, attacked by the famous "noble rot", these wines are regularly exceptional, in recent years (88 and 86) as well as the vintages which are juste reaching maturity today 55, 59, 61...), proof of the extraordinary longevity of the Chenin vinestocks from which they are made. As far as the reds are concerned, the Anjou wines are fresh, very fragrant, delicate and supple and the Saumur-Champigny are very successful in 87 and 88, much like the Touraine wines. To taste a Bourgueil, a Touraine, a Chinon or a Montlouis (86, 87 and 88 vintages) is to love these wines full of flavor, which are well marked by the soil and can look forward to a promising future. The Nivernais country, kingdom of the Sancerre, produces mostly white wines. They are elegant, dry, yet supple and harmonious, with a certain "gun flint" taste which characterizes the best of them. In Sancerre as in Pouilly-Fuissé, to which must now be added Reuilly, Quincy and Meneton-Salon, what counts the most, from the Cher to the Nièvre, is the soil. It is the soil that makes the difference between two producers, that determines wheter a white wine will be great or just an ordinary wine to be drunk quickly and quite cool. For the reds, even if the majority are largely overrated and are, unjustifiably, priced much too high for real winelovers, there are a few which have been well matured and, thanks to the Pinot Noir, approach the quality of their South Burgundy neighbours.

And finally, in Muscadet in the Nantes region, a number of winemakers are now producing some very good whites which, all to their credit, are difficult to "copy". Here again, the soil is very important and appropriate vinification (the new generation is very much with it) is the guarantor of success for these fresh and lively wines that go so well with seafood.

HISTORICAL BACKGROUND

In the 11th century, winegrowing was a major business in Anjou which contributed to the wealth of the region. Until that time only the lord of the vineyard had the right to sell wine, and this was done at a specific time of the year. This privilege, called "droit de banvin" ( ), was lifted in 1135 by Geoffroy the Handsome, Count of Anjou, thereby giving impetus to the wine trade. Merchants were allowed to come from other regions to purchase wine and the merchants of Anjou showed their expertise in shipping wines up and down the Loire River.

The vineyards of Saumur, located a little farther away, suffered the effects of competition from Anjou. The residents of Saumur therefore asked the count of Anjou to decrease their feudal taxes. He consented in 1138; he lifted his *droit de banvin* and replaced the vine tax with an annual tax payable on St. Martin's Day. Sacrifices often pay off, and the residents of Saumur were rewarded by having their wine served in 1241 at the royal dinner organized for Alphonse de Poitiers, brother of King Louis IX.

The Benedictine monks planted vines in the region of Nantes, including the *Melon-de-Bourgogne* variety which was imported from Burgundy. The vines gave birth to the Muscadet variety of wine. People became more familiar with Muscadet wines in 1930. Their popularity continued in France as well as in other countries.

In 990, the first vines in Bourgueil were those produced by a Benedictine abbey. The monks produced wines of great renown such as *Le Clos de l'Abbaye* and *Le Grand Clos*. These friars were proud of their wines and kept the watch over them for fear workers would drink too much.

Another famous monk was St. Martin, bishop of Tours. In 372 he founded the Monastery of Marmoutier and planted the first vines in Vouvray, on a hillside overlooking the abbey.

A stone's throw away is the Abbey of Fontevrault, which is famous for its vines as well as for the illustrious persons who are buried there: Henry II, the first Plantagenet king; his wife, Eleanor of Aquitaine; and Richard the Lion-Hearted, one of their sons. Anjou has thus paid homage to the King of England for having loved and appreciated its wines and for having made them known and appreciated in his kingdom.

Sancerre, another region along the Loire River, grew wines which became popular instantly. Its vineyards date back to the Capetian period. In the 12th century the biggest vineyards were owned by the Abbey of St. Satur which produced wines of great renown. It is said that Sire de Saccel bought five barrels of the wine at the Orleans Fair of 1335. The commercial success of the wine was off and running. Poets sang of it, in particular, Guillaume le Breton who sang its praises in 1180 at the court of Philip Augustus.

THE "NIVERNAIS" REGION WHITE WINES

Such a marvelous area, here the men know how to blend together perfectly with the style of the wine, vigorous and frank, typical of the sub-soil which knows how to produce its very best when in good hands. Superb tastings with these dry white wines derived from the Sauvignon grape (Sancerre, Pouilly-Fumé, Quincy), labeled savage or wild because of their typically flinty flavor due to the soil, incomparable, dray and vigorous at the same time, very fruity, fills the palate. In this case it's the varietal which has adapted itself to the soil... producing dry, aromatic wines in the Sancerre area, yet spicy, musky wines within a few kilometers in Pouilly-sur-Loire (Appellation : Pouilly-Fumé).

ANJOU SAUMUR

— **REDS.** The best reds of the area are from Saumur, produced mainly in the vicinity of the commune of Champigny. Seductive, velvety, violet and raspberry aromas.

— **WHITES.**

- **Dry wines.** Fine and robust, the crus from Savennières are always splendid.
- **Softer wines.** (Bonnezeaux, Coteaux-du-Layon, Quarts-de-Chaume). As for the Sauternes, growers bank on the favorable effects of noble rot on the grapes during harvesting. The results are unequivocal: perfectly balanced in fruitiness and acidity, elegant and fragrant, the soft wines of the area are just wonderful. To be tasted every twenty years, as an aperitif and with foie gras.

The SAUMUR D'ORIGINE

A few highly reputed houses offer a large range of bubbly wines (Saumur d'origine) prepared under rigorous conditions in the traditional champagne method which deserve to be appreciated in their own right. Lively, fragrant and elegant, they should certainly not be dismissed as second rank sparkling wines, something like a lesser champagne. Comparison would be inappropriate since they each have their authenticity, their particular soil and blending. These foamy wines, matured with the greatest care, are really astounding. Try them on any occasion, as an aperitif or during the meal, with dessert or even foie gras.

TOURAINE

- **Chinon.** (1,200 hectares). Reds, made from Cabernet Franc, with a scent of wild strawberry and red currant.
- **Bourgueil and Saint-Nicolas-de-Bourgueil.** (1,400 hectares). The wines produced on alluvium and gravel should be drunk when young and light. Those grown on micaceous chalk are for keeping. They are well-colored, rich and well-balanced, with a very special raspberry dominated bouquet.
- **Vouvray.** (1,600 hectares) and **Montlouis** (300 hectares). The sweet wines, mainly those from Vouvray, that sometimes keep remarkably long, are wines of distinction with a lovely flowery aroma.
- **Touraine.** The Touraine appellation extends from the Sologne to the Vienne border, on hillsides flanking the banks of the Loire, the Cher and the Indre.

NANTES REGION

The Nantes vineyard, which produces Muscadet, Gros-Plant and Coteaux d'Ancenis-Gamay, covers a surface of about 12,600 hectares.

The production area extends along the banks of the Loire upstream from Nantes, and to the East and Southwest of the Loire-Atlantique department. Only a small part of the production extends as far as the Vendée and the Maine et Loire rivers.

• **MUSCADET. (A.O.C.).** Covering a 9,800 hectare vineyard with an average production of about 400,000 hectoliters.

• **GROS-PLANT DU PAYS NANTAIS CLASSIFIED V.D.Q.S.** (Vin délimité de qualité supérieure) since 1954. A 2,600 hectare vineyard with an average yield of 100,000 hectoliters.

• **COTEAUX D'ANCENIS-GAMAY CLASSIFIED V.D.Q.S.** Since 1954. A 200 hectare vineyard with a production barely exceeding 8,000 hectoliters.

THE CHARACTERISTICS OF THE VINEYARD

ANJOU-SAUMUR

The vineyard lies between Ingrandes and Fontevrault, South of the Loire.

Soil

The soil composition is very varied, consisting mainly of schists, marl, round stones, and limestone (micaceous chalk).

Climate

It owes its mild climate, like the whole of the Loire region, to the influence of the ocean. Hours of sunshine do not exceed 1894 a year, with rather frequent precipitation.

TOURAINE

The vineyards of the Touraine region, to the South-East of the Paris basin, extend from the Sologne to the Anjou border.

Soil

Its soil, like that of the Anjou-Saumur, is very varied. One finds a mixture of clay, flint, sand and limestone derivatives.

Climate

Touraine has a maritime climate.

NANTES REGION

The Nantes region, located on either side of the Loire, is the cradle of Muscadet.

Climate

The region is characterized by mild and temperate weather conditions, the so-called Armorican climate. However, if the temperature is moderate, averaging 11.5°C, the rainfall is heavy (785 mm per year). The prevailing Westerly winds are largely responsible for the rain.

The Loire valley divides into two quite distinctive regions: Anjou-Saumur, and Touraine.

WINE FROM CENTRAL FRANCE

CHATEAUMEILLANT

DOMAINE DE FEUILLAT

Maurice Lanoix
Beaumède – 18370 Châteaumeillant
48 61 33 89

Type of vineyard: Family-owned. **Established:** 1925. **Number of employees:** 2. **Vine stocks:** Gamay, Beaujolais, Pinot de Bourgogne. **Soil:** Sandy and pebbly. **Exposure:** Hillside. **Average annual production in hectoliters:** 650.
Appellation: V.D.Q.S. Châteaumeillant. **Type:** Red, rosé. **Technique:** Red: in temperature regulated tanks after destemming. **Alcohol content:** 12%. **Characteristics:** Red: supple, low acidity (long fermentation), beautiful, sustained color, special fragrance. Dry wine, not very tannic. The Pinot is fruity and lighter in color. **Serving temperature:** Quite cool for the young wine, older wine at room temperature. **Served with:** Red meat and cheese. **Vintages available in 89/90:** 1987.

Characteristics of vintages

1986: Red: Gold Medal, at a competion in Paris, 1987. Rosé: Silver Medal, at a competion in Paris, 1987. Average pre-tax ex-warehouse price: 20 F.F. including tax.
Sales volume:
– Retail: 40 %. Restaurants: 40 %.
Export sales: 20 %.
Main trading partners : Germany.

CÔTES DU FOREZ

LES VIGNERONS FOREZIENS

D. Cheze & A. Coudurier
Le Pont Rompu – Trelins
42130 Boen-sur-Lignon
77 24 00 12

Type of vineyard: Agricultural Association. **Established:** 1962. **Number of employees:** 6 permanent, 2-3 seasonal workers. **Vine stocks:** Gamay. **Soil:** Silica-clay, granitic subsoil. Some vulcanic soil (Basalt). **Exposure:** Southeast. **Average annual production in hectoliters:** 8 000.
Appellation: Côtes-du-Forez (V.D.Q.S.), Vin de Pays d'Urfe (V.D.P.). **Type:** Red, rosé. **Technique:** Semi-carbonic vinification. **Maturing:** Stainless steel tanks, temperature control. **Alcohol content:** 12.5 %. **Characteristics:** Tannic, flinty, raspberry taste. **Serving temperature:** Cellar temperature. **Served with:** All delicatessen products, white meat, cheese (Fourme de Montbrison).

CÔTE ROANNAISE

ROBERT SÉROL

Robert Sérol
Les Estinaudes – 42370 Renaison
77 64 44 04

Type of vineyard: Family-owned. **Established:** Several generations. **Number of employees:** 0. **Vine stocks:**

Gamay. **Soil:** Granitic. **Exposure:** South, Southeast. **Average annual production in hectoliters:** 300.
Appellation: Côtes Roannaises V.D.Q.S. **Type:** Red. **Technique:** Beaujolais style: semi-carbonic. **Maturing:** In vats and in tanks. **Alcohol content:** 12%. **Characteristics:** Fruity and light. **Serving temperature:** 12°. **Served with:** Delicatessen products, red meat, cheese. **Vintages available in 89/90:** 1987.

Characteristics of vintages

1986: Supple. Price range (pre-tax, ex-warehouse): Between 10 F.F. and 20 F.F.

References in France

Restaurants: Le Château d'Esclimont, 28700 St-Symphorien-le-Chateau. Le Relais, Bracieux. La Clé des Champs 45320 Courtenay. Les Caves du Bois Hibout, 14160 Dives-sur-Mer.

CÔTEAUX DU GIENNOIS

PAULAT ALAIN

Alain Paulat
Villemoison CNE de St-Père
58200 Cosne-sur-Loire
86 28 22 39 or 86 26 75 57

Type of vineyard: Family-owned. **Established:** 1974. **Vine stocks:** Gamay Noir, Pinot Noir, Sauvignon. **Soil:** Clay with calcium carbonate, clay subsoil. **Exposure:** Full South. **Average annual production in hectoliters:** 50 ha × 6 ha = 300.
Appellation: Coteaux du Giennois V.D.Q.S. **Type:** Red, white, rosé. **Technique:** Fermentation with skins with 15 days for red (stainless steel and cement), pressing. **Maturing:** Racking of the must for rosé and white. Casks 600 l. for red; stainless steel tanks for white and rosé. **Alcohol content:** 12.5%. **Characteristics:** Red: tannic aromatic. Rosé and white: fruity. Easy to drink, smooth. **Serving temperature:** Red: 15°-17°. White and rosé: 8° to 10°. **Served with:** Red: cuisine with sauce, red meat, cheese. Rosé: fish, pork. White: fish, shellfish. **Vintages available in 89/90:** 1986, 1987, 1988.

Characteristics of vintages

1988: White and rosé: fresh, fruity. Easy to drink, smooth. **1987:** Red: tannic, typical and harmonious. **1986:** Red: tannic, forthcoming. Price range (pre-tax, ex-warehouse): Between 18 F.F. and 20 F.F.
Sales volume:
– Wholesale: 1%. – Retail: 79%. – Restaurants: 10%. – Other: 10% (Copperative).
Sales in France: 99%.
Export sales: 1%.
Main trading partners : Holland.

MENETOU-SALON

DOMAINE DE CHATENOY

Bernard and Pierre Clément
18510 Menetou-Salon
48 64 80 25

Type of vineyard: Agricultural Association. **Vine stocks:** Sauvignon and Pinot Noir. **Soil:** Kimmeridgian limestone. **Exposure:** South. **Average annual production in hectoliters:** 1,500.
Appellation: Menetou-Salon A.O.C. **Type:** Red, rosé, white. **Technique:** Traditional with temperature control of the fermentation. **Maturing:** Red: in Oak casks, 1/3 new. **Alcohol content:** 12.5% to 13%. **Characteristics:** White: typical, delicately fruity, dry. Rosé: dry. Red: good keeping. **Serving temperature:** White and rosé: 10° to 12°. Red: 15° to 16°. **Vintages available in 89:** 1988.

Characteristics of vintages

1988: Good, aromatic whites. Well-made reds, good color and fruity. Average pre-tax, ex-warehouse price: 23 to 28 H.T.
Sales volume:
– Wholesale: 30% (export). – Retail: 35%. – Restaurants: 35%.
Sales in France: 70%.
Export sales: 30%.
Main trading partners : UK, Netherlands.

Abroad

United Kingdom

Findlater, Mackie, Todd & Co., Ltd., 92 Wigmore Street, London W1 HOBP. Tel: 01935264. G.M. Vintners, 7 Wellington Terrace, Truro, Cornwall. Tel: Truro 795809

Germany

Francette Weinhandel-Import, St. Elisabeth Strasse 1, 5400 Koblenz. Tel: 0261 42068.

The Netherlands

Verlinden, Postbus 296, 5201 Ag's, Hertogenbosch. Tel: 073417575.

South Africa

A & F Vintners, P.O. Box 583, Durban 4000. Tel: 304861.

DOMAINE HENRY PELLÉ

Henry and Eric Pellé
18220 Morogues
48 64 42 48

Type of vineyard: Agricultural Association. **Established:** Initially family-owned an Association since 1982. **Number of employees:** 6. **Vine stocks:** Sauvignon Blanc and Pinot Noir. **Soil:** Chalky. **Exposure:** South, Southeast. **Average annual production in hectoliters:** 1,200.
Appellation: Menetou-Salon, Sancerre. **Type:** Red, white, rosé. **Technique:** Red: traditional. White: low temperature fermentation. **Maturing:** Tanks. **Alcohol content:** 12.5%. **Characteristics:** White: dry and fruity. Red: rich and velvety. Rosé: light and distinguished. **Serving temperature:** White: 8° to 12°. Rosé: 8° to 12°. Red: 14° to 16°. **Served with:** White: shellfish, fish, snails, goat cheese. Red: red merat, game, cheese. Rosé: delicatessen, white meat. **Vintages available in 89/90:** 1988.

Characteristics of vintages

1988: Very good quality, fruity and long. Price range (pre-tax, ex-warehouse): Between 25 F.F. and 35 F.F.
Sales volume:
– Retail: 1/3. – Restaurants: 1/3. – Other: 1/3 (export).
Sales in France: 2/3.
Export sales: 1/3.
Main trading partners : UK, Netherlands, Belgium, USA, Germany, Canada.

POUILLY FUMÉ

LE BOUCHOT

Hervé Seguin
58150 Pouilly-sur-Loire
86 39 10 75

Type of vineyard: Family-owned. **Established:** From father to son. **Number of employees:** 2. **Vine stocks:** Chasselas, Sauvignon. **Soil:** Chalky clay. **Exposure:** South, South-West. **Average annual production in hectoliters:** 60.
Appellation: Pouilly-sur-Loire, Pouilly Fumé. **Type:** White. **Technique:** Traditional. **Maturing:** On the estate. **Alcohol content:** 12.8%. **Characteristics:** Dry Pouilly Fumé: round and full-bodied, slight gun flint taste, Pouilly-sur-Loire: light and thirst-quenching. **Serving temperature:** 10°. **Served with:** Fish and shellfish, and as an aperitif. **Vintages available in 89/90:** 1988, 1989.

Characteristics of vintages

1988: Very well balanced, very typical, lingering taste, very good vintage. Price range (pre-tax, ex-warehouse): 20 to 30 F.F.
Sales volume:
– Retail: 20%. – Restaurants: 10%. – Other: 70% (export).
Sales in France: 30%.
Export sales: 70%.
Main trading partners : UK, Belgium, Denmark.

References in France

Restaurants: Le Crocodile, (Strasbourg), Barrier, (Tours).
Shops: Au Vieux Gourmet, (Strasbourg), Cercle de l'Union Interalliée (Paris).

Abroad

United States

Jonathan Palmer.

United Kingdom

Grants of Saint-James – Direct Wines.

Switzerland

Maison Balsiger.

Belgium

Maison Pirard, Genappe.

The Netherlands

Oud Wynjkopers & Hustinx Rest. De Karpendonkse Hoeve Eindhoven.

Comments

Winemakers from father to son for 5 generations, the Seguin family continues the tradition while making use of progress in vinification techniques. Gold Medal at Blayais for the Pouilly Fumé 1984. Gold medal at the Concours Général, Paris 1985.

- *If you find that there are one or more elements missing, so that you are unable to contact a particular proprietor or importer, please write to us at the following address for additional information:*

Gilles Temime, Éditions Vintage,
14, rue Rennéquin - 75017 Paris.

LA MOYNERIE

Michel & Thierry Redde
58150 Pouilly-sur-Loire
86 39 14 71 - Telex: 801 553

Type of vineyard: Corporation. **Established:** 1984. **Number of employees:** 12. **Vine stocks:** Blanc Fumé. **Soil:** chalky clay and silica clay. **Exposure:** South, South-West. **Average annual production in hectoliters:** 60-70 hl/ha.
Appellation: Pouilly Fumé. **Type:** White. **Technique:** traditional. **Maturing:** stainless steel tanks. **Alcohol content:** around 13%. **Vintages available in 89/90:** 1987 & 1988 (Pouilly Fumé la Moynerie) - 1985 (Cuvée Majorum).

Characteristics of vintages

1988: full-bodied, rich, very well-balanced – probably good keeping. **1987:** Pouilly Fumé La Moynerie: delicate, light and elegant. **1986:** Cuvée Majorum: beautiful year, to be aged in the cellar for a while for full development. **1985:** Cuvée Majorum: exceptional lot, honey and woodland aroma – at its best with smoked salmon, fish coocked in sauce or on the grill. Price range (pre-tax, ex-warehouse): 30 – 50 – 80 F.F.
Sales in France: 40%. **Export sales:** 60%.
Main trading partners : USA – UK – Germany.

References in France

Restaurants: Paul Bocuse – Alain Chapel – Georges Blanc – Bernard Loiseau – Jean Bardet – Bernard Robin – Crillon – Le Grand Vefour – Lucas Carton – La Maree.
Shops: Hediard – Kaefer (Germany).

Abroad

United States

Kobrand 134 East 40th Street, New York, Tel: (212) 692 46 90.

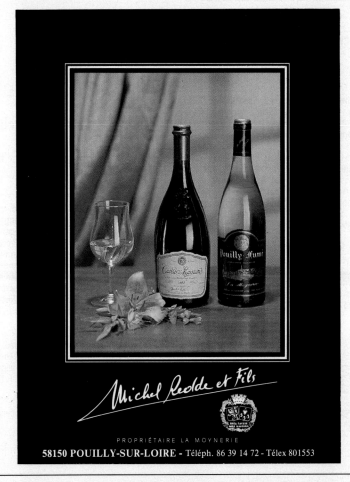

United Kingdom

JBR Reynier – Tachbrook Street – London SW1 1QT – Eldrige Pope, Weymouth Ave – Dorchester.

Belgique

Renglet – Château Bruxelles.

Comments

La Moynerie is a 35 hectare family winegrowing enterprise which has developed over the years and is run by its present owner Michel Redde and his son Thierry, winegrowers from father to son for the 6th and 7th generation. The domaine, ideally situated in the heart of the appellation, extends partly over magnificent plateaux overlooking the Loire, where the chalky clay soil favors harvesting of early maturing grapes providing light and fruity wines, and partly over the Saint-Andain knoll whose sillica clay soil yields lively spicy wines, with a distinct gun flint taste.

CHÂTEAU DE TRACY

Comtessse d'Assay
Château de Tracy-sur-Loire
58150 Pouilly-sur-Loire
86 26 16 55 – Telex: Chamco 800 426 F Château de Tracy

Type of vineyard: Family-owned. **Established:** 1952. **Vine stocks:** Sauvignon. **Soil:** Sandy limon and sandy clay with flint, sub-soil Kimmeridgian rock. **Exposure:** Various. **Average annual production in hectoliters:** 40 to 43 hl/hectare.
Appellation: Pouilly-Fumé Contrôlé. **Type:** White. **Technique:** Traditional with temperature control. **Alcohol content:** 12.5%. **Characteristics:** Dry white wine with a taste of gun flint. **Serving temperature:** Between 8 and 12°, quite cool but not chilled. **Served with:** Shellfish, oysters, fish, blue cheese, Roquefort, goat cheese. **Vintages available in 89/90:** 1986.

Characteristics of vintages

1986: Good year, well-balanced, typical, full. Price range (pre-tax, ex-warehouse): Between 30 F.F. and 50 F.F.
Sales in France: 35%.
Export sales: 65%.
Main trading partners : Belgium, Netherlands, UK, Germany.

SANCERRE

DOMAINE JOSEPH BALLAND-CHAPUIS

Joseph Balland
B.P. 24 – 18300 Sancerre
48 54 06 67 – Telex: 783 431

Type of vineyard: Personal. **Established:** Passed on from father to son since 1650. **Number of employees:** 10. **Vine stocks:** Sauvignon, Pinot. **Soil:** Calcium carbonate and Kirmmeridgian marl. **Exposure:** South and South by Southwest. **Average annual production in hectoliters:** 50 hl/hectare.

Appellation: Sancerre A.O.C. **Type:** Red, white, rosé. **Technique:** Constant temperature. **Maturing:** In enamelled or stainless steel tanks. **Characteristics:** White: dry and fruity. Softer and richer for the Cuvée Prestige "Come Thibault", and very good for ageing. Sancerre (red): light and pleasant (rosé): strong Pinot flavor. **Serving temperature:** Sancerre (white and rosé) and Comte Thibault: 10°. Sancerre (red) to be served in an ice bucket filled with water and 3 or 4 ice cubes to keep it cool. **Vintages available in 89/90:** 1986 and 1985 (only Comte Thibault).

Characteristics of vintages

1986: Very good year. Flowery, dry, well-bred. **1985:** Very good year. **Other:** Must taste the Clos le Chêne marchand and Clos le Vallon: typical Sancerres, fruity, lingering taste. Price range (pre-tax, ex-warehouse): 30-50 F.F. Cuvée Prestige: 80-120 F.F.
Sales volume:
– Wholesale: 5%. – Retail: 10%. – Restaurants: 40%.
– Other: 45% (export).
Sales in France: 55%. **Export sales:** 45%.
Main trading partners : USA, Belgium, Netherlands, Germany, Denmark, UK, Japan.

DOMAINE HENRI BOURGEOIS

Jean-Marie Bourgeois
Chavignol - 18300 Sancerre - Cedex M 72
48 54 21 67 - Telex: 783 490 - TELEFAX: 48 54 14 24

Type of vineyard: Agricultural Association. **Established:** For 10 generations - change of status in 1978. **Number of employees:** 20. **Vine stocks:** Sauvignon, Pinot Noir. **Soil:** Clay, chalk and flint. **Exposure:** South, South-East, South-West. **Average annual production in hectoliters:** 2,000.

Appellation: Sancerre. **Type:** Red, White, Rosé. **Technique:** Traditional, must racking, temperature control. **Maturing:** White: in stainless steel tanks. Red: in new oak casks. **Alcohol content:** 12.5%. **Serving temperature:** White: 8°. Red: 12 to 14°. **Served with:** White: fish, shellfish and goat cheese. Red: beef, veal and cheese. **Vintages available in 89/90:** 1988.

Characteristics of vintages

1988: Full-bodied, good fruit balance. Rather remarkable year. Price range (pre-tax, ex-warehouse): 30 to 50 F.F.
Sales volume:
- Retail: 10%. - Restaurants: 40%.
Sales in France: 50%.
Export sales: 50%.
Main trading partners: UK, Germany, Belgium, USA, Canada, Japan, Hong Kong.

References in France

Restaurants: Hôtel Le Crillon, Hôtel Le Doyen, Le Fouquet's, etc.

Abroad

United Kingdom
Michael Druitt Wines, Ebury Mathiot Wines, Walters S, Siegel Ltd. Jackman Surtees & Dale.

Germany
Kurt Burgard Gmbh. Feinkoft Kafer Gmbh.

Switzerland
Kellerein Movenpick, Tritten.

Belgium
Ets Robert Goffard (Agent).

Canada
Société des Alcools du Québec. Liquor Control Board of Ontario.

The Netherlands
Cees Van Noord, Baarsma Dranken BV.

Far East
Kasho Cie Ltd (Japan). Topsy Trading Co. Ltd & Lucullus Wine & Food Co. Ltd (Hong Kong).

Comments

The village of Chavignol is situated right in the heart of the Sancerre region. It is famous not only for its wines, product of steep, well-exposed slopes, but also for its cheese, the "crottin de Chavignol". The family has been working the vines for 10 generations and has established over the years a domain which now covers 35 hectares, including some of the best slopes in Chavignol.

GITTON
1982
CLOS JOANNE D'ORION
Pouilly-Fumé
1982
LES FOLTIÈRES
GITTON PÈRE ET FILS
1982
SANCERRE
1983
GITTON
Père et Fils
1983
SANCERRE
LES BELLES DAMES
GITTON PÈRE ET FILS
GITTON
Père et Fils
SANCERRE
LES MONTACHINS
APPELLATION CONTROLÉE
GITTON PÈRE ET FILS

GITTON PÈRE ET FILS

Marcel Gitton
Chemin de Lavaud
18300 Menetréol-sous-Sancerre
48 54 38 84 – Telex: 783 440
Fax: 48 54 09 59

Type of vineyard: Family Corporation. **Established:** 1945 – A Corporation since 1981. **Number of employees:** 14. **Vine stocks:** Sauvignon 95%, Pinot Noir 5%. **Soil:** Chalk, marl, flint. **Exposure:** East, West, Southeast. **Average annual production in hectoliters:** 2,000.
Appellation: Sancerre les Belles Dames, Sancerre les Montachins, Sancerre Galinot, Pouilly-Fumé Clos Joanne d'Orion. **Type:** White. **Technique:** Traditional. **Maturing:** Oak casks and stainless steel tanks. **Alcohol content:** 12.5%. **Characteristics:** Les Belles Dames: gun flint taste long. Montachins: fruity, intense aromas. Galinot: animal fragrance, very personalized. Pouilly-Fumé: finesse, elegance, good for ageing. **Serving temperature:** Les Belles Dames, Montachins and Pouilly-Fumé: about 10°. Galinot: 12°. **Served with:** Fish, shellfish, seafood. **Vintages available in 89/90:** 1980, 1983, 1984, 1985, 1986, 1987.

Characteristics of vintages

1988: Fruity and powerfull. **1987:** Floral, fine, delicacy. **1986:** Full bodied. **1985:** With slowly maturing finesse. **1984:** Full with intense honey fragrance. Price range (pre-tax, ex-warehouse): Between 30 and 50 F.F.
Sales volume:
– Retail: 10%. – Restaurants: 90%.
Sales in France: 25%.
Export sales: 75%.
Main trading partners : Sweden, Belgium, UK, Germany, Switzerland, USA, Japan.

References in France

Restaurants: Pic, Chapel, Faugeron, Cagna, Rochedy.

Abroad

United States
Ideal Wines, Medford, Mass. Bacchus, Baltimore, Md. Mayflower, Washington, DC.
Restaurants: Pavillion, D.C.

United Kingdom
Boutinot Wines, Stockport. High Breck Vintners, Headley.

Germany
Weincontor, Weinheim. Weinland, Dortmund.
Restaurants: Ente von Lehel, Wiesbaden. Aubergine and Königshof, Munich.

Canada
LCBO, Toronto. Grape Vine, Vancouver.

The Netherlands
Zeeuwse Wijnimport, Middelburg.

Far East
Foods from France, Hong Kong. Daiei Sangyo, Nagoya, Japan.

Belgium
Branellec, Gand. Caveau France, Anvers.
Restaurants: Snippe, Brugge, Brueghel, Damme.

Switzerland
Fischer & Rihs, Bienne, Coq d'Or, Genève.

Denmark
Millesime Vinhandel, Copenhague.
Restaurants: Cocotte, Copenhague.

CHAUMEAU Jean-Pierre

Jean-Pierre Chaumeau
Bué – 18300 Sancerre
48 54 27 39

Type of vineyard: Family-owned. **Established:** 1982. **Vine stocks:** Sauvignon. **Soil:** Clay with calcium carbonate. **Exposure:** South/South-West. **Average annual production in hectoliters:** 200.
Appellation: Sancerre. **Type:** White. **Technique:** in enamelled tanks at low temperature. **Alcohol content:** 12.8%. **Characteristics:** Dry and fruity. **Serving temperature:** 12-14°. **Served with:** Fish. **Vintages available in 89/90:** 1987.

DOMAINE LA CROIX ST-LAURENT

Maurice and Joël Cirotte
Bué – 18300 Sancerre
48 54 12 49 – Cellar: 48 54 30 95

Type of vineyard: Corporation. **Established:** 1980. **Vine stocks:** Sauvignon, Pinot Noir. **Soil:** CLay with calcium carbonate. Chalk and loam subsoil. **Exposure:** South; Southeast; East. **Average annual production in hectoliters:** 55.
Appellation: Sancerre. **Type:**Red, white, rosé. **Technique:** White and rosé: in tanks. Red: malolactic fermentation in tanks. **Maturing:** in old casks for 6 months. **Characteristics:** White: 2 types – dry and fruity for the grapes grown in limestone soil, and sweeter for the "white soil". Rosé: dry and slightly fruity. Red: fruity, often raspberry aroma. To be kept 7-10 years. **Serving temperature:** White: 10°; Rosé: 8-10°; Red (young): 13-15° (aged): 17-18°. **Served with:** White: fish, seafood. Red: with entire meal. **Vintages available in 89/90:** Red: 1985 & 1986; White: 1986.

Characteristics of vintages

1986: Huge Cuvée – superior to the 1985 – good keeping.
1985: Good year, rich and fragrant wines, good keeping.

THIERRY MERLIN CHERRIER

Thierry Merlin
Bue 18300 Sancerre
48 54 06 31 or 48 54 05 51

Type of vineyard: Family-owned for 3 generations. Corporation since March 1986. **Vine stocks:** Sauvignon. **Soil:** Dry clay and Kimmeridgian marl of glacial origin. **Exposure:** Variable. **Average annual production in hectoliters:** 60 to 65.

Appellation: Sancerre. **Type:** White. **Technique:** Slow fermentation (20°) in enamelled tanks. **Maturing:** First racking in January – bottled in April. **Characteristics:** White: fruity, supple, lingering taste, delicate finish. **Serving temperature:** 10 to 12°. **Served with:** Fish, goat cheese. **Vintages available in 89/90:** 1988.

Characteristics of vintages

1988: Typical Sauvignon, well balanced.
Sales volume:
– Retail: 17%. – Restaurants: 12% – Other: 8% (wine dealers).
Sales in France: 37%.
Export sales: 63%.
Main trading partners : UK, Netherlands, Belgium, Germany.

References in France

Restaurants: Bras, Rostang, Ferrie, Chiorozas, Prouheze, Hiely, Lucullus, Abbaye de Pomier.
Shops: Vernon (Strasbourg, Paris).

Abroad

United Kingdom
David Gummer, Beaconsfield.

Germany
Cord Stehr, Hamburg.

Belgium
Vandenplas Nethen, Vandenhauten, Brussels.

The Netherlands
Vos Wijnimport, Tilburg.

Comments

Mention is made of the Sancerre vineyard in royal and feudal charters as early as the year 582, but its development is mostly due to the Augustine monks. Up until the phylloxera epidemic, 90% of the vineyard was planted in Pinot. Later, the Sauvignon appeared on the scene.

MOULIN DES VRILLÈRES

Christian Lauverjat
S.C.E.A Des Vrillères, Sury-en-Vaux,
18300 Sancerre
48 79 38 28

Type of vineyard: Family Agricultural Association. **Established:** For 2 generations. **Number of employees:** 1. **Vine stocks:** White: Sauvignon. Red and Rosé: Pinot Noir. **Soil:** Chalky clay composed of white soil and pebbles. **Exposure:** Mostly South-East. **Average annual production in hectoliters:** About 420.
Appellation: Sancerre AOC. **Type:** Red, White, Rosé. **Technique:** White and Rosé: slow vinification after destemming with temperature control, 17°. Red: fermentation in bunches, 10 to 15 days followed by devatting with heating for malolactic fermentation, racking. **Alcohol content:** 12.5%. **Characteristics:** White: dry and fruity. Red: easy to drink, but full-bodied because of the soil. **Serving temperature:** White, Rosé: 10°. Red: 14°. **Served with:** White: fish and shellfish. Red: mostly grilled meat. **Vintages available in 89/90:** 1988.

Characteristics of vintages

1988: Well balanced, very fruity, a bit less acid than the 1987. Price range (pre-tax, ex-warehouse): between 30 and 50 F.F.
Sales volume:
– Retail: 80%. – Restaurants: 20%.
Sales in France: 80%.
Export sales: 20%.
Main trading partners : UK, Netherlands, Belgium.

References in France

Restaurants: La Giberne (Paris 15), La Criée (Paris, Bor-

deaux, La Rochelle, Nice), Auberge La Bonne Humeur (18 Belleville), La Mascotte (Paris), Restaurant Saint-Brisson, Le Jeanne d'Arc (45 Gien), La Setaz (73 Valloire), Alidières (15 Saint-Mamet), Beau Rivage (45 Olivet).
Shops: Amour du Vin (Paris 7), Champagne Loisirs (10 Torvilliers), Les Chais de France (Issy-les-Moulineaux), Caveau du Bourg (78 Verneuil), Chais Franco-Monégasques (Monaco), Cellier du Mans (72 Le Mans), Marché aux Vins (51 Lépine).

Abroad

United Kingdom

Cave Direct, Mr. Gillespy, 20 Dawson Mead, Welling, Kent DA 1RU 16 (Tel: 01 303 2261). Pierre Hourlier Quality Wines, 390 Burton Road, Derby DE3 6AD (Tel: Derby 41566).

The Netherlands

Restaurants: Hostellerie du Château, Mr. Huisman, Kapelstraat 48, 5591 Heeze (Tel: 49 07 35 15). (Restaurant chain in the Hague). Hulsink B.V., Verkeersweg 59, 3842 Le Harderwijk. Wijn Kaashuisje, Mr. Kerkvliet, Duindoorn 13, Leidschendam.

Comments

On a small family estate of about 7 hectares, somewhat improved recently, mostly with respect to winemaking equipment, wines are made using established methods while taking advantage of new techniques. Export sales were begun only 3 to 4 years ago. The enterprise is trying hard to keep its family character in spite of the increasing demand, in particular for the Pinot Noir vinestocks. It is open to all market propositions for small and medium quantities of white wines.

SALMON CHRISTIAN

Christian Salmon
18300 Bue
48 54 20 54

Type of vineyard: Family-owned. **Established:** 1974. **Number of employees:** 4. **Vine stocks:** Pinot, Sauvignon. **Soil:** Clay with calcium carbonate. **Exposure:** South. **Average annual production in hectoliters:** 50. **Appellation:** Sancerre Blanc, Sancerre Rouge, Sancerre Rosé, Pouilly Fumé. **Type:** White, red, rosé. **Technique:** Classic. **Maturing:** White in enamelled tanks, red in wooden vats. **Alcohol content:** 12.7%. **Characteristics:** Dry and fruity wines. **Serving temperature:** White: 9°-11°. Rosé: 8°-10°. Red: 10°-12°. **Served with:** Red: lamb, pork, veal, meat in general. White: crayfish, soles, salmon, trout, shellfish, snails. Rosé: soup, delicatessen, white meat, etc. **Vintages available in 89/90:** 1987 in 1988.

Characteristics of vintages

1986: Beautiful white wine, typical, fruity and long. Excellent Pouilly, soft, natural and flowery. Try the reds. Average pre-tax, ex-warehouse price: 30 F.F. Price range (pre-tax, ex-warehouse): Between 30 and 50 F.F.
Sales volume:
– Retail: 10%. – Restaurants: 40%.
Sales in France: 50%.
Export sales: 50%.
Main trading partners : Belgium, Germany, Netherlands, USA.

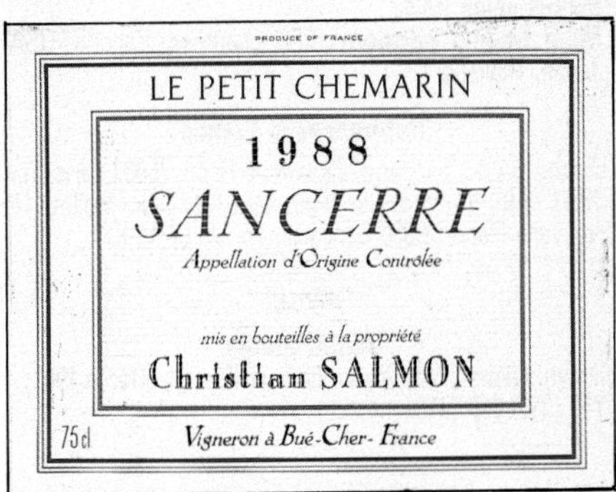

PRODUCE OF FRANCE
LE PETIT CHEMARIN
1988
SANCERRE
Appellation d'Origine Contrôlée
mis en bouteilles à la propriété
Christian SALMON
75cl
Vigneron à Bué-Cher- France

References in France

Restaurants: La Tour (Sancerre), Baumann (Paris), MEE des Officiers (Paris), Relations Extérieures (Paris), La Bonne Table (Clichy), Domaine Ste-Catherine (Créteil), Europ Hotel (Dunkerke).

Abroad

United States

Wines Ltd., 2312 Oerkibs Place, Silver Spring, Maryland 20910 (USA).

Germany

Franz Keller 7818 Vogtsburg Oberbergen/Kaisersthul.

The Netherlands

Sauter's Wijnkelders Rechtstraat 55 Maastricht.

Belgium

Cooremann L. Gillardlaan 3 – Zellik.

DOMAINE DE LA MOUSSIÈRE

Mr. Alphonse Mellot
3, rue Porte César – B.P. 18 18300 Sancerre
48 54 07 41 – Telex: 780 447
Telecopie: 48 54 07 62

Type of vineyard: Family-owned. **Established:** 1513. **Number of employees:** 20. **Vine stocks:** Sauvignon (90%), Pinot Noir (10%). **Soil:** Clay with calcium carbonate. **Exposure:** South/South-West. **Average annual production in hectoliters:** 1,800.
Appellation: Sancerre. **Type:** Red, white, rosé. **Technique:** Traditional. **Alcohol content:** 12.5%. **Vintages available in 89/90:** 1988, 1989.

Characteristics of vintages

1988: Pale color, flowery and fruity nose, rich and seductive. Cuvée Edmond 1988: pale gold color, flowery with oak wood flavors; rich, delicate, beautiful wine. Average pre-tax, ex-warehouse price: 38 F.F. Cuvée Edmond: 65 F.F.
Sales volume:
– Retail: 30%. – Restaurants: 70%.
Sales in France: 55%.
Export sales: 45%.
Main trading partners: EEC countries, Canada, USA, Japan, Thailand.

References in France

Shops: Bar Le Sancerre, 22 avenue Rapp, 75007 Paris. Tel: 45 51 75 91. Auberge La Moussière-Alphonse Mellot, 16, Nouvelle Place, 18300 Sancerre. Tel: 48 54 15 01.

Abroad

United States

Dreyfus Ashby, New York – 60 East 42nd St. (Room 1901) – Tel. (212) 818 0770.

United Kingdom

Thierry's & Tatahm Red deer House, 1 Stockbridge Road, Winchester. Shops: Hants, 5022 6RN. Tel: 0962 66516.

Germany

Mr. Robert Wagner, 25, rue de Schoeneck, 57350 Stiring-Wendel. Tel: 87 85 55 57.

Canada

Charton Hobbs, 9393 Louis-H. Lafontaine, Montreal H1J 1Y8.

The Netherlands

Tilburgse Wijnkoeprij b.v. Gemullehoeckenweg 14 5062 CD-Oisterwijk. Tel: 04242-19139.

Far East

UNEXPA 59, av. Théophile Gautier, 75016 Paris. Tel: 45 27 86 07/45 24 63 63.

Other

(Thaïland): Vanichwathana, 41 Anuwong Road, Bangkok 10100.

ANJOU-SAUMUR

ANJOU

CLOS DE COULAINE

François Roussier
49170 Savennières
41 72 21 06

Type of vineyard: Family-owned. **Established:** For five generations. **Vine stocks:** Chenin Blanc, Cabernet Franc, Cabernet Sauvignon. **Soil:** Schist. **Exposure:** South, South-East. **Average annual production in hectoliters:** 300.
Appellation: Blanc: Savennières. Rouge: Anjou Villages et Anjou. **Type:** Red, White. **Technique:** Traditional, temperature control. **Maturing:** In oak casks. **Alcohol content:** 12.5%. **Served with:** Savennières Blanc: Salmon and other fish.

Characteristics of vintages

1988: Savennières Blanc (dry): wild flower aroma, bitter, can wait. **1987:** Anjou Rouge: rich and well-balanced, red

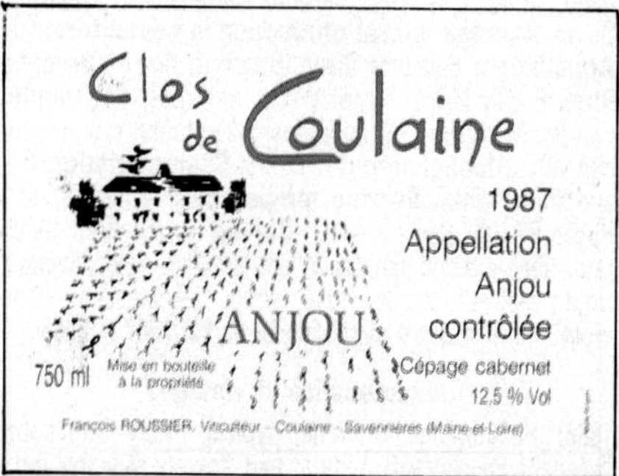

berry aroma. **1986:** Anjou Villages: woodland aroma, lingering taste. Price range (pre-tax, ex-warehouse): 20 to 30 F.F. Anjou Villages Rouge. 30 to 50 F.F. Savennières Blanc.
Sales volume:
– Wholesale: 10%. – Retail: 70%. – Restaurants: 20%.
Sales in France: 70%.
Export sales: 30%.
Main trading partners : UK, Belgium, Netherlands, USA.

Abroad

United Kingdom

Importers: Richards Walford, Pickworth, 222 Stamford. Tel: (078081) 242.

DOMAINE D'AMBINOS

Jean-Pierre Chene
Impasse des Jardins
49190 Beaulieu-sur-Layon
41 78 48 09

Type of vineyard: Family-owned. **Established:** 1945. **Number of employees:** 1. **Vine stocks:** Chenin, Sauvignon White, Cabernet Franc and Sauvignon Grolleau. **Soil:** Muddy, shist and clay. **Exposure:** South. **Average annual production in hectoliters:** 1,000.
Appellation: Anjou Rouge, Coteaux du Layon Beaulieu, Cabernet d'Anjou, Rosé de Loire, Rosé d'Anjou, Anjou Blanc Sec. **Type:** Red, white, rosé. **Technique:** Glass tanks with temperature control. **Maturing:** Slow fermentation at low temperature. **Alcohol content:** Red: 12.5%. Coteaux du Layon Beaulieu between 16° and 18°. **Serving temperature:** Anjou Rouge: 14°. Coteaux du Layon Beaulieu: 10°. **Served with:** Anjou Rouge: red meat or grills. Coteaux du Layon Beaulieu: as an aperitif, pâté, foie, gras, dessert with nuts or almonds. Cabernet d'Anjou: white meat. **Vintages available in 89/90:** 1986, 1985, 1984, 1983, 1982, 1981, 1979, 1978, 1977, 1976, 1975, 1974, 1973, 1969, 1967.

Characteristics of vintages

1988: Great vintage, finesse and elegance. Wait. Very good structure, good alcohol/acid/sugar/tannin balance. **1986:** Finesse and elegance. **1985:** Soft and full, already evolving, great vintage to be aged; Anjou very successful. **1984:** Wait for the Coteaux du Layon, still young. **1983:** Age. **1982:** Developed, very agreeable taste, presisting aromas. **Others:** 1976: Very developed, and very aromatic, honey and quince scents. Price range (pre-tax, ex-warehouse): Between 10 F.F. and 80 F.F.
Sales volume:
– Wholesales: 75%. – Retail: 20 F.F. – Restaurants: 5%.
Sales in France: 90%. **Export sales:** 10%.
Main hading partners: England, Australia.

Abroad

United Kingdom

Robert James Son, 9 Asleet Street, London.

Other

Australia: L. Jesberg.

Comments

To appreciate and taste its real value, the Coteau du Layon Beaulieu, must have a minimum of 10 years in the bottle.

DOMAINE BEAUJEAU

Jacques Beaujeau
49380 Champ sur Layon
41 78 86 19

Type of vineyard: Coporation. **Established:** For 5 generations. **Number of employees:** 12. **Vine stocks:** Chenin Blanc Cabernet, Sauvignon Rouge, Chardonnay Blanc. **Soil:** Gravel and clay. **Average annual production in hectoliters:** 3000.
Appellation: Anjou Rouge, Coteaux du Layon, Rosé d'Anjou. **Type:** Red, white, rosé. **Maturing:** Oak wood 2 years. **Characteristics:** Coteaux du Layon, early harvest, noble grape. Anjou red: vine Cabernet Sauvignon (9 months with Oak). Rosé d'Anjou: from vine Cabernet Franc and Grolleau. Anjou sec: Chardonnay and Chenin varieties (6 months Oak). **Served with:** Coteaux du Layon: foie gras. Roquefort, as an aperitif. Anjou red: cooked meat. Anjou sec: fish. **Vintages available in 89/90:** 1986, 1985, 1983.

Characteristics of vintages

1986: Fruity, supple, great finesse. **1985:** Well structured, rich in aromas, the greatest since '47 and '49. Price range (pre-tax, ex-warehouse): between 10 F.F. and 20 F.F. and 20 F.F. and 30 F.F.
Sales volume:
– Retail: 50%. – Restaurants: 25%.
Sales in France: 75%. **Export sales:** 25%.
Main trading partners : USA.

References in France

Restaurants: Between 300 and 400 restaurants.

Abroad

United States

Importers: New York State; Jason Brooke, California "The Wine House".
Shops: San Francisco; Buffalo, N.Y.

CHÂTEAU DE BRISSAC

Daviau Brothers
Daviau Vignerons – Bablut
49320 Brissac Quince
41 91 22 59

Type of vineyard: Family Agricultural Association. **Vine stocks:** Cabernet Franc, Cabernet Sauvignon, Chenin

Blanc, Chardonnay. **Soil:** Anjou gravel. **Exposure:** South, Southeast. **Average annual production in hectoliters:** 5000.

Appellation: Anjou Villages and Coteaux de l'Aubance (Mellow). **Type:** Red, white. **Technique:** Traditional, plus rousing with nitrogen, temperature control. **Maturing:** 1 year in bulk before bottling. **Alcohol content:** 12% to 12.5% plus 1% to 1.5% surup for the Coteaux de l'Aubance. **Characteristics:** Red: small red fruit fragrance, balance and finesse, to be kept 5 to 10 years. White: Typical Chenin, hazel nut and fig aromas. Mellow: fine and flowery, well-bred, full, aroma of lime and dried fuit, for long ageing. **Serving temperature:** 15°. **Served with:** Red: red meat, game, cheese. Coteaux de l'Aubance: as an aperitif of with foie gras, fish in sauce. **Vintages available in 89/90:** 1986, 1985, 1984, 1983, 1982, 1981 and back to 1953 for the Coteaux de l'Aubance.

Characteristics of vintages

1986: Very good. **1985:** Excellent. **1984:** Average. **1983:** Good. **1982:** Very good. **Other: 1981:** Good. Price range (pre-tax, ex-warehouse): between 10 F.F. and 20 F.F.

Sales volume:
– Retail: 80%. – Restaurants: 20%.

Sales in France: 90%.

Exports sales: 10% (to individuals).

Main trading partners : European Common Market.

References in France

Restaurants: Throughout the West of France.

Comments

Very old Vineyard, in the same Family since 1546. Presently trying to build up their export trade, though they do not have their own exporters yet.

VIGNOBLE LECOINTRE

Vincent Lecointre

La Pierre Blanche 49380 Champ-sur-Layon

41 78 86 34 – Telex: 720 943

Type of vineyard: Family-owned Agricultural Association. **Established:** 1979 as an association – in the family for 2 centuries. **Number of employees:** 5. **Vine stocks:** Chenin, Cabernet. **Soil:** Gravely – schistic sub-soil. **Exposure:** South, South-West. **Average annual production in hectoliters:** 1,500 to 1,800.

Appellation: Anjou Rouge, Anjou Village, Anjou Blanc, Coteaux du Layon Rablay. **Type:** Red, White (dry and mellow). **Characteristics:** Anjou Rouge & Anjou Village: structure due to the Cabernet Franc combined with Cabernet-Sauvignon aromas. Anjou Blanc: firm and fresh (Chenin), dry. Coteaux du Layon Rablay: mellow, exceptionally good ageing during which it acquires delicate aromas. Can also be drunk young (2 to 3 years). Lots of character, very good balance between the acidity due to the Chenin and mellow character of overripe grapes. **Vintages available in 89/90:** Anjou Village: 1988. Anjou Rouge: 1987, 1988. Anjou Blanc: 1986, 1988. Coteaux du Layon Rablay: 1982 to 1988.

Characteristics of vintages

1988: Anjou Rouge: aromatic, light tannins. Anjou Blanc: magnificent. Layon Rablay: "Cuvée Cyrille": excellent. **1987:** Anjou Rouge: supple, fruity finish. C.L. Rablay: typical. **1986:** Anjou Rouge: mellow tannins, good keeping. C.L. Rablay: beautiful year, still undeveloped, wait. **1985:** C.L. Rablay: exceptional year, very long keeping. **Other:** 1984: C.L. Rablay: supple and aromatic, becoming pleasant. 1983: C.L. Rablay: great year, very delicate. 1982: C.L. Rablay: beautiful year, promising, wait. Price range (pre-tax, ex-warehouse): Anjou Rouge & Anjou Blanc 10 to 20 F.F. Coteaux du Layon Rablay 20 to 30 F.F.

Sales volume:
– Wholesale: 30%. – Retail: 35%. – Restaurants: 15%. – Other: 20% (cellars – dealers).

Sales in France: 95%.

Export sales: 5%.

Main trading partners : UK, Denmark, Japan.

Abroad

United Kingdom

The Dedham Fine Wine Company limited – 34 North Station Road, Colchester – Essex CO 11RB.

Others

Denmark: Vinimport Ostjysk Vinforsyning Arhus – Naver-vej 21 – DK 8382 Hinnerup. Japan: Daie, Sangyo Kaisha Ltd. 18,4 Chome, Honjindori, Nakamura-Ku, Nagoya 453.

Comments

The variety of vinestocks in the vineyard makes it possible to produce wines under a number of appellations: Cabernet d'Anjou, Anjou Gamay, Vin de Pays du Jardin de la France, made from Sauvignon and Chardonnay. The enterprise is beginning to develop its foreign sales, the objective being to export 75,000 to 100,000 bottles per year to the various OECD countries.

CHÂTEAU MONTBENAULT

Yves Leduc
49380 Faye d'Avignon
41 78 31 14

Established: 1920. **Vine stocks:** Chenin, Cabernet Franc & Sauvignon, Groslot Gamay. **Soil:** silica and clay. **Exposure:** South. **Average annual production in hectoliters:** 85.

PRODUCE OF FRANCE
Château Montbenault
COTEAUX DU LAYON FAYE D'ANJOU
APPELLATION COTEAUX DU LAYON FAYE D'ANJOU CONTROLÉE
LEDUC, Propriétaire-Viticulteur - 49380 FAYE-D'ANJOU
Mise en bouteille au Château

Appellation: Coteaux du Layon Faye, Anjou (Blanc & Rouge), Cabernet d'Anjou, Anjou-Villages, Coteaux du Layon, Rose de Loire, Rose d'Anjou. **Type:** Red, White. **Technique:** traditional. **Maturing:** Chenin in casks, others in vats.

Characteristics of vintages

1988: exceptional – Coteaux du Layon Faye and Anjou. **1987:** ready right now – very light. **1986:** Coteaux du Layon: good – Anjou (red): good, rich and well-balanced. **1985:** rich and well balanced – to be kept. **Other: 1984:** Coteaux du Layon: good, rich and well-balanced. Anjou (red): very pleasant, drink now. 1983: Coteaux du Layon: good keeping. 1982: Coteaux du Layon: ready for drinking now. Price range (pre-tax, ex-warehouse): 10 to 20 F.F., 20 to 30 F.F., 30 to 50 F.F.

References in France

Restaurants: Grand Monarque, Chartres.
Shops: Legrand – Fauchon – Constant (Perreux – Marne) Aux Négociants – Fief de Vignes (Nantes) Melac (Paris) etc.

Comments

Family enterprise from father to son (for three generations) since 1920. Over the years, the Coteaux du Layon have been awarded a number of Gold Medals at the Concours Agricole of Paris and Mâcon. They have been producing a red Anjou and a red Anjou Villages from a blend of Cabernet Franc and Cabernet Sauvignon for about 10 years.

DOMAINE DE LA MOTTE

André Sorin
31, avenue d'Angers – Rochefort s/Loire 49190
41 78 71 13

Type of vineyard: Family-owned. **Number of employees:** 3. **Vine stocks:** Chenin, Cabernet, Groslot, Gamay, Chardonnay. **Soil:** Silica, clay covered with schist. **Exposure:** North facing the Loire Valley. **Average annual production in hectoliters:** 1,000.
Appellation: Anjou. **Type:** Red, white, rosé. **Technique:** Traditional, with modern methods using glass and enamelled tanks for whites. **Alcohol content:** 12%. **Characteristics:** Supple and digestible for red; robust mellow white which must age. **Served with:** As an aperitif, foie gras, blue cheese. **Vintages available in 89/90:** 1969, 1973, 1974, 1975, 1976, 1977, 1978, 1979, 1980, 1981, 1982, 1983, 1984, 1985, 1986, 1987, 1988.

Characteristics of vintages

1988: Very great year - lots of Botrytis in the mellow wines, tannic reds. **1987:** Pleasant, round, velvety texture. **1986:** Very supple, full of fruit aromas. **1985:** Firm, robust, red for ageing. **1984:** Found of delicacy, light, to be drunk now, marked fragrance. **1983:** Fine still young. **1982:** Mellow, soft, rich butter aroma. Price range (pre-tax, ex-warehouse): Between 20 F.F. and 80 F.F.
Sales volume:
– Retail: 50 %. – Restaurants: 10%. – Other: 40% (export).
Sales in France: 60%.
Export sales: 40%.
Main trading partners : USA, Belgium, UK, Netherlands, Germany, Canada, Asia, Denmark.

References in France

Restaurants: Restaurants de Paris. Loic Martin, Lille. La Chancellerie Erta, Orléans. Le Quère, Angers. Jean Bardet, Tours. Taillevent, Paris.
Shops: Spivinco, 199, rue Faubourg Saint-Honoré, Paris.

Abroad

United States

Classic Wine Import, 1356 Common Wealth Av., Boston, Massachussetts-USA.

United Kingdom

M.F. and E. May 66/69 Great Queen Street, London. Shops: WC2B5 BU/Pennyloaf Wines 96 Station Road Odsey Ashwell Herts. Robin Pallot, Jersey.

Denmark

H.J. Hansen, Vestergade 97-101, DK 5100 Odense.C - Jysk Vinlager, Egegardsves 43, DK 8900 Randers.

Germany

Weindepot Alt-Hürth, Lindenstrasse 25, D.5030 Hürth-Alt-Hürth, RFA.

Canada

HHD Imports P.O. Box 2364 Station B. Kitchener Ontario N 2 H 6 M 2.

The Netherlands

Wijnkoperis HFA Okhuysen BU Gierstraat 343638. Shops: 2011 GE Haarlem.

Belgium

Wijnkeldermeester Broekkantstraat 50 A. B 9821 Gent Afsnee.

Asia-Oceania

Europvin - 65, cours Saint-Louis, 33300 Bordeaux.

Comments

Tasting in the wine cellar at Rochefort s/Loire.

DOMAINE DU SAUVEROY

Pascal Cailleau
49750 Saint Lambert-du-Lattay
41 78 30 59

Type of vineyard: Family-owned. **Established:** 1947. **Number of employees:** 3. **Vine stocks:** Chenin, Chardonnay, Cabernet, Gamay, Pinot Noir. **Soil:** Schistic alluvium, sandy alluvial clay. **Exposure:** South-West, South-East. **Average annual production in hectoliters:** 1,000.

Appellation: Anjou, Coteaux-du-Layon Villages. **Technique:** Maceration with skins, temperature control. **Maturing:** Drawing off and sometimes fining – in vats. **Alcohol content:** 11° and 13°. **Characteristics:** Blanc Sec: very flowery, lemon touch ideally suited to fish in sauce. Coteaux-du-Layon: mellow, very soft and full, rich and long. Rouge: smoky, saddle leather bouquet, its warmth does not stand in the way of harmony and roundness. **Serving temperature:** White and Rosé: 8 to 10°. Red: 16 to 17°. **Served with:** Dry White: fish, grills and first course. Red: white meat, poultry, cheese. Coteaux-du-Layon: foie gras on toast, roquefort cheese. **Vintages available in 89/90:** 1983, 1985, 1987, 1988.

Characteristics of vintages

1988: Great success, long keeping, very aromatic. **1987:** Wines that go down well, very successful, to be drunk in the next few years. **1985:** Good ageing, remarkable quality. **Other:** 1983: Very successful, very good keeping. **Sales volume:** – Retail: 65%. – Other: 15% (small shops) 20% (kept for ageing). **Sales in France:** 70%. **Export sales:** 30%. **Main trading partners :** Belgium, UK, Netherlands, Germany.

References in France

Restaurants: Le Belvédère, (Angers), Restaurant de la Cathédrale, (Chartres).
Shops: Maison du Vin d'Angers, etc.

Abroad

United Kingdom

Grands Vins de France, Carrayol Arch 112, Ratchcoole Gardens, London. Oddbins, London.

Germany

Vinum Weinfachhandel, Bremen.

Belgium

Mr Vermeiren, Place du Chat Botté, Brussels.

The Netherlands

Inter Cave B.V. 8000 Am Zwolle.

Comments

A 20 hectare vineyard, operated from father to son for more than 40 years. Every year, the wines win numerous regional and international awards.

SCEA CHÂTEAU DE PASSAVANT

Jean David
49560 Passavant-sur-Layon
41 59 51 01 and 41 59 53 96

Type of vineyard: Civil Coporation. **Established:** March 1, 1983. **Number of employees:** 4 (+ 2 associating managers). **Vine stocks:** Chenin, Groslot, Cabernet. **Soil:** Schist, schist-clay covered.
Type of vineyard: Civil Corporation. **Established:** Established: March 1, 1983. **Number of employees:** 4 (+ 1 managers). **Grape Varieties:** Chenin, Groslot, Cabernet. **Soil:** Schist, Schist-clay covered. **Exposure:** Hillsides of Layon, the Layon to Passavant: West-East. **Average annual production in hectoliters:** 1,500 in average. **Appellation:** Anjou, Rosé de Loire, Coteaux Layon, Crémant de Loire. **Type:** Red, rosé, white, sparkling. **Alcohol content:** 12%. Rosé de Loire and Anjou blanc: dry, light and aromatic. Crémant de Loire, Champagne Méthod; brut: Coteaux du Layon: sweet and full of Chenin aroma. Anjou rouge: good constitution, with Cabernet Franc character. **Serving temperature:** Cool in general. **Served with:** Hors-d'œuvre, seafood, (Rosé de Loire & Blanc Sec); meat, cheese (Anjou Rouge). As an aperitif (Crémant de Loire, Coteaux du Layon), Foie gras (Coteaux du Layon). **Vintages available in 89/90:** Anjou Rouge 1987, 1988. Coteaux du Layon: since 1975 to 1988.

Characteristics of vintages

1988: very good, typical, fragant wines. Price range (pre-tax, ex-warehouse): between 20 F.F. and 30 F.F, and 50 F.F. and 80 F.F. according to vintages.
Sales volume:
– Retail: 30%. – Restaurants: 50%. – Other: 20% (export).
Sales in France: 80%. **Export sales:** 20%.
Main trading partners : Germany, Belgium and others.

References in France

Restaurants: Around Paris and on the West Coast of France.

DOMAINE RICHOU

Richou father and son
Chauvigne Moze-sur-Louet 49190
41 78 72 13

Type of vineyard: Family-owned. **Established:** 1979. **Number of employees:** 3. **Vine stocks:** Chenin, Cabernet Franc, Cabernet Sauvignon, Gamay, Chardonnay. **Soil:** Clay and shist. **Exposure:** South, Southeast, Northwest. **Appellation:** Anjou Rouge, Anjou Blanc, Rosé de Loire, Anjou, Gamay, Coteaux de l'Aubance. **Type:** Red, white, rosé. **Technique:** Traditional for Anjou Rouge, carbonic maceration for Gamay, tanks and wood (Oak) for Anjou Rouge (Cuvée Special). **Alcohol content:** 12%. **Characteristics:** Anjou Rouge: strawberry nose, slightly spicy, to be aged. Anjou Blanc Sec: apple aroma, to be drunk young, but will be better in 2 years. Coteaux Aubance: wine to keep (10 years), quince and honey aromas. **Serving temperature:** Anjou Rouge: 16°. Anjou Blanc: 7° to 8°. Coteaux Aubance: 7°. **Vintages available in 89/90:** 1986, 1987.

Characteristics of vintages

1986: Good red, fruity, characteristic white clear, very fragrant. Price range (pre-tax, ex-warehouse): Between 10 F.F. and 20 F.F.
Sales volume:
– Retail: 60%. – Restaurants: 20%. – Other: 20%. (export).
Sales in France: 80%. **Export sales:** 20%.
Main trading partners : Holland, Germany, England, USA, Japan.

NOUTEAU CERISIER PÈRE ET FILS

Nouteau Cerisier Father and Son
Le Verger Faye d'Anjou – 49380 Thouarce
41 54 31 40

Type of vineyard: Family-owned. **Established:** Father and son for many Centuries. **Vine stocks:** Chenin Blanc, Cabernet Grolleau Gris et Noir, Pineau Aunis. **Soil:** Clay and sand: with pebbly hillsides: reliable soil. **Exposure:** Midday, south. **Average annual production in hectoliters:** 400 to 500. **Appellation:** Anjou Coteaux Layon Rosé d'Anjou, Cabernet Anjou. **Type:** Red, white, rosé. **Technique:** Drawing for rosé and white; racking. **Maturing:** No laboratory product: no fried yeast added. **Alcohol content:** Degree according to the legislation of each appellation. **Characteristics:** Very fruity wine, agreeable to drink, grape taste present. **Serving temperature:** 8° to 10°. **Served with:** Blanc Coteaux: Foie gras, as an aperitif, or before dessert. Red: for meat. White: throughout the meal. **Vintages available in 89/90:** from 1970 to 1986.

Characteristics of vintages

Price range (pre-tax, ex-warehouse): between 10F.F. and 20 F.F. for young wines.
Sales volume:
– Wholesale: 60%. – Retail: 40%.
Sales in France: 90%.
Export sales: 10% for this time.
Main trading partners : Belgium, Germany and private individuals.

Comments

Since 1970, the Vingeyard is a biologic cultivation with a qualitative contract: no manures, no chemical synthesis treating, no insecticide, no pesticide. The harvested wine never has dried yeast or chemical laboratory products added fruity and agreeable to drink fresh grape taste: no adding aroma.

SCA DOMAINE DE TERREBRUNE

René Renou
Place du Champ de Foire, 49380 Thouarcé
41 54 01 99

Type of vineyard: Agricultural Association. **Established:** 1986. **Number of employees:** 1. **Vine stocks:** Cabernet, Chenin, Grolleau. **Soil:** Schistic clay. **Exposure:** Southwest. **Average annual production in hectoliters:** 2000. **Appellation:** Bonnezeaux, Anjou Blanc Sec, Coteaux du Layon, Anjou Rouge, Rosé de Loire, Rosé Anjou, Cabernet d'Anjou. **Type:** Red, white, rosé. **Technique:** Rosé and white: traditional. Red: semi-carbonic. **Maturing:** Vats. **Alcohol content:** Bonnezeaux: 13% plus 3%. Others between 11% and 12.5%.
Characteristics: Bonnezeaux: finesse, elegance, breed, honey-bearing acacia, old leather. Red: structure, red fruit, flowery. Rosé: fruity, freshness, charm, suppleness. **Serving temperature:** 10° to 12°. **Served with:** Bonnezeaux; foie gras, Roquefort on warm toast, fish. Red: meat, game. Rosé: delicatessen products, fish. **Vintages available in 89/90:** 1985, 1986.

Characteristics of vintages

1986: fine, elegant, seductive, slightly closed. **1985:** Rich, well-balanced, structured, long. Wait for it to age.

COTEAUX DU LAYON

CHÂTEAU BELLERIVE

Jacques Lalanne
49190 Rochefort-sur-Loire
41 78 33 66

Type of vineyard: Family-owned. **Established:** 1975. **Number of employees:** 2. **Vine stocks:** Chenin. **Soil:** Schistic and sandstone. **Exposure:** South. **Average annual production in hectoliters:** 15 to 20. Pruning very short. Cluster thinning in July.
Appellation: A.O.C. Quarts de Chaume. **Type:** White. **Technique:** Traditional in casks. **Maturing:** Very slow fermentation. **Alcohol content:** About 13.5%. **Characteristics:** Great mellow wine, supple, fruity, rich in fragrance, delicate but full, a very particular touch of bitterness, the result of noble rot. Harvest by successive selection of bunches. **Serving temperature:** Young wine: 8° to 10°. Old wine: 10° to 12°. **Served with:** Mostly as an aperitif (a wine for tasting), or with foie gras, fish in cream sauce, guinea hen with Roquefort, Roquefort Tart, chicken in cream sauce, blue cheeses. **Vintages available:** 1980 and 1988.

Characteristics of vintages

1988: Exceptional year. **1986:** Rich in aroma, well-bred, has the touch of acidity and bitterness whcih characterizes wines to be aged. **Others:** 1980: final bouquet supple with character, harmonious wine. Price range (pre-tax, ex-warehouse): Wholesale: between 50 F.F. and 80 F.F. Direct sales to clients: and between 80 and 120 F.F.

CHÂTEAU DE PLAISANCE

Henri Rochais
Chaume Plaisance 49190 Rochefort/Loire
41 78 33 01 and 41 78 49 00

Type of vineyard: Family-owned. **Established:** 1960. Formerly Breyer estate. **Vine stocks:** White: Chenin (Pinot of the Loire region). Red: Cabernet Sauvignon 60%, Cabernet Franc 40%. **Soil:** Schist and chalky clay. **Exposure:** Hillsides facing South. **Average annual production in hectoliters:** 250 Chaume, 200 Anjou Rouge, 280 Anjou Blanc Sec.
Appellation: Chaume, Coteaux du Layon, Anjou Blanc, Anjou Rouge. **Type:** Red, White. **Technique:** Traditional, hand harvesting, successive selection of bunches. **Maturing:** In stainless steel tanks and casks. **Alcohol content:** Red: 12%. White: 13 to 14%. **Characteristics:** Red: beautiful ruby color, red berry aroma. Chaumes (young): golden yellow, lime blossom, banana, pine-apple, fresh honey aroma. Sauternes: amongst the best greatest. **Serving temperature:** White: 10 to 12°. Red: 13 to 14°. **Served with:** Chaume: as an aperitif and with foie gras, fish cooked in sauce, blue cheese: Roquefort, Tourme & Ambert. **Vintages available in 89/90:** 1988 Chaume: 20, 000 bottles. Savennières: 6, 000 bottles.

Characteristics of vintages

1988: Beautiful color, long, soft and full, exotic fruit fragrance. **1987:** Golden color, very delicate, long – Gold Medal (Concours Agricole). **1986:** Beautiful golden color, soft and full, long, concentratred fragrance – Silver Medal, Concours Agricole. **1985:** Great wine but yet undeveloped. **Other:** 1988: White Savennières (Clos des Mauriers) – clear, quite firm due to the schistous soil. Price range (pre-tax, ex-warehouse): 30 F.F. (Savennières), 30 to 50 F.F. (Chaume), 50 to 80 (Chaume more than 3 years old).
Sales volume:
– Wholesale: 10%. – Retail: 70%. – Restaurants: 20%.
Sales in France: 70%.
Export sales: 30%.
Main trading partners : USA, UK, Benelux countries, Canada, Switzerland, Germany.

References in France

Restaurants: Taillevent (Paris), Bardet (Tours), Le Crocodile (Strasbourg), Le Bougainvilliers (Luxembourg), etc.
Shops: Caves Cabanel (Paris), Prunier, Caves de la Madeleine, Nicolas, Arcades Legrand (Issy-les-Moulineaux), etc.

Abroad

United States

May-Flower, Washington. Wine Company, Chicago.

United Kingdom

Sante Wine Warwick.

Belgium

Gaffard, Brussels.

Comments

The Château de Plaisance overlooks the very famous Coteaux de Chaume, the best known of the Coteaux du

Layon which, before the war, belonged to the Breyer group, the biggest French exporter of the Coteaux du Layon wines. Its full South exposure guarantees a maximun of sunshine, favoring the development of Botritys, which after harvesting by successive selection, yields very pronounced aromas. A tasting room that can accomodate 50 to 60 persons is available on a terrace overlooking the hillside. Reservations are accepted for lunch on the terrace.

DOMAINE OGEREAU

Vincent Ogereau
44, rue de la Belle Angevine
49750 Saint-Lambert du Lattay
41 78 30 53

Type of vineyard: Family Coporation. **Established:** 1982, by Ogereau Vincent representing the 4th generation wine maker of the family. **Vine stocks:** Chenin, Cabernet, Groslot, Chardonnay, Sauvignon Blanc. **Soil:** Clay on shits. **Exposure:** Southeast. **Average annual production in hectoliters:** 1,000.
Appellation: Côteaux du Layon St Lambert. **Type:** White. **Technique:** Traditional from grapes harvested by successive sorting. **Characteristics:** Liquoruos wine, beautiful fullness, research of maturing gives it a particular fruity character, excellent wine for ageing. **Serving temperature:** 8° to 10°. **Served with:** Foie gras and all fine pork products, all blue cheeses, white meat. **Vintages available in 89/90:** 1988, 1987, 1983.

Characteristics of vintages

1988: (available as of October 1989). Very beautiful vintage, substantial, good ageing porential. **1987:** Harmonious wine, fruity, very well developed aromas due to maceration on skins. **1983:** Mellow, full of the sap of the vine, a good choice. Price range (pre-tax, ex-warehouse): between 30 F.F. and 50 F.F.

CHÂTEAU DES ROCHETTES

Jean Douet
49700 Concourson sur Layon
41 59 11 51

Type of vineyard: Family-owned. **Established:** For many generations. **Number of employees:** 4. **Vine stocks:** Chenin. **Soil:** Silica, clay cover. **Exposure:** Southwest. **Average annual production in hectoliters:** 30 ha = 200 on 7 ha.
Appellation: Coteaux du Layon. **Type:** White. **Technique:** Traditional. **Maturing:** Casks and large casks. **Characteristics:** Mellow, rich, round, long. **Serving temperature:** 8°. **Served with:** As an aperitif, foie gras, cheese (blue in particular). **Vintages available in 89/90:** 1986, 1985, 1984, 1983, 1982, 1979, 1976, 1975, 1969, 1964.

Characteristics of vintages

1988: Very great vintage. Very well balanced and harmonious, rich and substantial wines. Very long keeping. **1987:** Good vintage. Elegant and fruity, to be enjoyed rather shortly. **1986:** Very good vintage, very successful in '86, very near the 1985. **1985:** A very great, exceptional vintage, very forthcoming, full, fragrant. **1984:** No as rich, not as long, but elegant, average for keeping. **1983:** Another good vintage, very well-balanced. **1982:** A really great wine, but rather quickly evolving. Price range (pre-tax, ex-warehouse): between 20 F.F. and 30 F.F.
Sales volume:
– Restaurants: 10%. – Other: 90%.
Sales in France: 99%.
Export: 1%.

References in France

Restaurants: In Anjou and Touraine, in particular, au Prieuré Chenehutte, Les Truffeaux and the Château d'Artigny, Montbazon.
Shops: Numerous wine cellars in Anjou and Touraine and in the Maisons du Vin de Saumur et d'Angers (Belongs to Wine Trade Union of Angers).

Abroad

Australia

James Halliday, Chez David Jones du Connaisseur Club, Australia.

CHÂTEAU DE LA ROULERIE

Jaudeau
49190 St-Aubin-de-Luigne
41 78 33 02

Established: 1952. **Vine stocks:** White: Chenin, Chardonnay. Red: Cabernet. **Soil:** Schist and clay. **Exposure:** South, Southwest. **Average annual production in hectoliters:** 750 to 800.
Appellation: Anjou, Côteaux-du-Layon, Chaume. **Type:** Red, white. **Technique:** Red and fry white in tanks; mellow white in wood casks. **Characteristics:** Anjou Blanc: very fruity. Anjou Rouge: very beautiful ruby color, red fruit: great body, very long, due to a harvest by successive sorting. **Serving temperature:** Anjou Blanc: 8° to 10°, shellfish, fish. Anjou Rouge: 12° to 13°, red meat. **Served with:** Chourue: 10° to 12°, as an aperitif and foie gras. **Vintages available in 89/90:** 1983, 1986,

Characteristics of vintages

Price range (pre-tax, ex-warehouse): Between 20 F.F. and 30 F.F.
Sales volume:
– Retail: 75%. – Restaurants: 25%.
Sales in France: 90%. **Export sales:** 10%.
Main trading partners : England.

References in France

Restaurants: Jeanne de Lavel, 49350 Les Rosiers-sur-Loire; Le Toussaint, rue Toussaint, 49000 Angers.
Shops: La Truffe Noire, Pl. Parmentier, 92200 Neuilly-sur-Seine; Le Relais, 41250 Bracieux.

Abroad

United States
Ms. Walker, Sommerville, Massachussets 02143 USA.

United Kingdom
Yapp Brothers Ltd. The Olel Brewery Mere Wiltshire.

Far East
Iquo Menka Caicha Ltd. Yokohama Japan.

SAUMUR

CLOS DE L'ABBAYE

Henri Aupy
49260 Puy Notre Dame
41 52 26 71

Type of vineyard: Family-owned. **Established:** 1912. **Number of employees:** 4.**Vine stocks:** Chenin, Chardonnay, Cabernet Franc, Sauvignon. **Soil:** Clay with calcium carbonate. **Exposure:** East. **Average annual production in hectoliters:** 1300.
Appellation: Saumur Rosé de Loire, Crémant de Loire. **Type:** Red, with, rosé. **Technique:** Traditional in truffeau cellar. **Characteristics:** White: finesse, lightness, liveliness and typical of the soil. Red: good color supple but firm, good for ageing. **Serving temperature:** 8° white, rosé, Crémant. 14° red. **Vintages available in 89/90:** 1985, 1986.

Characteristics of vintages

1986: Very good for ageing, full and distinguished, superb aromas. **1985:** Supple, successfull vintage, good for ageing too: combines fullness, fragrance and finesse. Excellent white, marked by the vine and a Rosé de Loire, clear, fresh, very thirst-quenching. Do not hesitate. Price range (pre-tax, ex-warehouse): Between 10 F.F. and 30 F.F.
Sales volume:
– Wholesale: 40%. – Retail: 30%. – Restaurants: 10%. – Other: 20% (export).
Sales in France: 80%.
Export sales: 20%.
Main trading partners : Belgium, Germany, England, Holland.

DOMAINE DES HAUTES VIGNES

André or Alain Fourrier
Rue de la Chapelle 49400 Distre
41 50 21 96 – Telex: 720 183 P 130

Type of vineyard: Family-owned. **Established:** 1961. **Number of employees:** 5. **Vine stocks:** Cabernet Franc & Sauvignon, Chenin Chardonnay. **Soil:** Chalky clay and clay. **Exposure:** South-West. **Average annual production in hectoliters:** 1,800.

Appellation: Saumur, Saumur coteaux, Crémant de Loire. **Type:** Red, white. **Technique:** Red: traditional maceration. White: color extraction. **Maturing:** In temperature controlled stainless steel tanks. **Alcohol content:** 12 to 12.5%. **Characteristics:** Light, fruity, aromatic. **Serving temperature:** Red: 14°. White: 12°. **Served with:** Red: red meat. White: fish. **Vintages available in 89/90:** 1988, 1987, 1986, 1985 and others on demand.

Characteristics of vintages

1988: To be aged, very good year. **1987:** Promising (very aromatic). **1986:** Good year – wait patiently. **1985:** Exceptional. Price range (pre-tax, ex-warehouse): 20 to 30 F.F. – 30 to 50 F.F.
Sales volume:
– Retail: 70%. – Restaurants: 30%.
Sales in France: 95%.
Export sales: 5%.
Main trading partners : Netherlands.

Comments

The vineyard is located in several communes, which results in quite harmonious wines that are full of surprises. They are aged in vats in micaceous chalk caves at constant temperature. Some very good vintages are in stock.

• *A great naturally sweet wine with Roquefort? Try a Sauternes, of course, a Grand Cru from a late Alsacian harvest, a mellow Anjou or a Banyuls.*

CAVE DES VIGNERONS DE SAUMUR

Marcel Neau - Export : Pierre Barast
Saint-Cyr-en-Bourg - 49260 Montreuil-Bellay
33 41 51 61 09 - Telex : 720 181 F
Fax: 33 41 51 98 84

Type of vineyard: Agricultural Association. **Established:** 1957. **Number of employees:** 35. **Vine stocks:** Chenin, Cabernet Franc, Cabernet-Sauvignon, Gamay, Chardonnay. **Soil:** Chalky and micaceous chalk caves. **Exposure:** 860 hectares in 30 communes. **Average annual production in hectoliters:** 55,000.

Appellation: Saumur, Crémant de Loire, Anjou. **Type:** Red, white, rosé. **Technique:** Traditional with temperature control. **Maturing:** Stainless steel tanks. **Alcohol content:** 12%. **Characteristics:** Whites: fruity, firm, well-bred. Reds: deep, ruby color, raspberry and violet bouquet, long. **Serving temperature:** Red: 16°, white and Champagne Method: 6 to 8°. **Served with:** Whites: shellfish and fish. Reds: red meat, small game, cheese. Saumur Champigny: lamb, poultry. Rosé: hors-d'œuvre, delicatessen, poultry, white meat. **Vintages available in 89/90:** 1988, white and red Saumur, Saumur Champigny, Rosé, 1982, 1985 and 1987 for the Champagne Method.

Characteristics of vintages

Price range (pre-tax, ex-warehouse): between 10 and 50 F.F.

Sales in France: 70%.
Export sales: 30%.
Main trading partners : UK, Germany, Benelux, Sweden, Japan, Canada, USA, Australia.

Comments

The Cave des Vignerons de Saumur is known for having taken an active part in the promotion of the Saumur Champigny since the 1960's. Its warehouse is 25 meters underground in the old galleries (7 km) of a micaceous chalk quarry from wich the Châteaux of the Loire and the Duch city of Maastricht are built.

• *Would you like to know to recognize the caracteristic fragrances of certains wines, their woodland, fruity, flowery or leather aromas, the evaluate the level of acidity or the presence of tannins, to ascertain the mellowness or the color of a wine...? See the Chapter entitled "The Art and Manner of Wine Tasting".*

• *Glycerine – wine component responsible for its unctuosity. It appears in the course of the alcoholic fermentation but, in the case of mellow and naturally sweet wines, can also come from the favorable action of noble rot on the grapes. See Sauternes.*

CHÂTEAU DE MONTREUIL-BELLAY

Mr. de Thuy
49260 Montreuil-Bellay
41 52 33 06

Type of vineyard: Family-owned. **Vine stocks:** Red: Cabernet Franc – White: Chenin. **Soil:** Chalky clay. **Average annual production in hectoliters:** 50,000 bottles.

Type: Red, White. **Technique:** Traditional. **Maturing:** For over one year before marketing. **Alcohol content:** 12%. **Characteristics:** Wines for keeping. **Serving temperature:** Red: 16° – White: 10-12°. **Vintages available in 89/90:** Red: 85-87. White: 86-87.

Characteristics of vintages

1987: Light and fruity. **1985:** Great wine for keeping. Price range (pre-tax, ex-warehouse): 20 F.F. to 30 F.F.

Sales volume:
– Wholesale: 30%. – Retail: 30%. – Restaurants: 30%.

Sales in France: 80%.

Export sales: 20%.

Main trading partners : Germany, Switzerland.

Comments

The wines of the Château de Montreuil-Bellay have been more and more in demand in recent years. The 85 is now beautifully mature. Garnet in color, it has the soft aromas of ripe fruit and blackcurrant pointed up with a touch of woodland and bark. The taste of the grapes is very much in evidence, dominating the vanilla aromas of ageing which is at its early stages. Superb Saumur, produced from Cabernet Franc after a short fermentation of 15 to 17 days followed by maturing in vats for the entire winter before being transferred to wooden casks until June. The wine keeps all of its fruitiness, an elegant bouquet of blackcurrant and raspberry which rounds out with age (about 22 F). Careful and attentive vinification. Don't fail to taste the white Saumur, very dry, perfect with seafood. Absolutely no hesitation for the 85 and the 87.

SAUMUR CHAMPIGNY

CHÂTEAU DE TARGÉ

Édouard Pisani-Ferry
49730 Parnay
41 38 11 50

Type of vineyard: Family-owned. **Established:** 1655 – present owner since 1978. **Number of employees:** 5. **Vine stocks:** Cabernet Franc. **Soil:** Sandy alluvium on micaceous chalk. **Average annual production in hectoliters:** 1,000.

Appellation: Saumur Champigny. **Type:** Red. **Technique:** Traditional, in temperature controlled stainless steel tanks. **Maturing:** Partly in stainless steel tanks and partly in oak casks. **Alcohol content:** 12.3% to 12.5%. **Characteristics:** Firm when young, gets rounder in its second year, and after 3 to 4 years of ageing takes on. Some vintages make good keeping wines. **Serving temperature:** 15°. **Served with:** Fine cuisine (grilled fish or poultry cooked with mushrooms). **Vintages available in 89/90:** 1987 and 1988 (as of September).

Characteristics of vintages

1988: Beautiful color, well structured, excellent development, less charming than the 1985, more typical. **1987:** Round, supple, to be consumed sooner. Price range (pre-tax, ex-warehouse): 20 to 30 F.F.

Sales volume:
– Wholesale: 5%. – Retail: 15%. – Restaurants: 65%. – Other: 15%.

Sales in France: 85%. **Export sales:** 15%.

Main trading partners : Belgium, Switzerland, Netherlands, UK, Japan, Canada.

References in France

Restaurants: Pavillon de l'Élysée, Truffe Noire, Méridien-Montparnasse, Aquitaine (Paris). Jean Bardet (Tours). L'Oasis (Bruxelles).

Shops: Caves de Taillevent, Hédiard, Verger de la Madeleine (Paris).

Abroad

United Kingdom

Your Wines Wholesale Ltd. 22 Upper Brook St., London W1 2HD – Tel: 949 5401. Haynes Hanson & Clark, 17 Lettice St., London SW6 4EH.

Switzerland

"Le Cave" J.A. Perrin, 4 Chemin du Port, CH-1298 Céligny. Tel: (022) 776 20 63 – J.-Ph. Bauermeister, rue de Moulins 21, CH-2000 Neuchâtel – Tel: (038) 24 70 70.

Belgium

MM. Goffard, rue Eggerickx, 28. 1150 Brussels. Tél. 02 762 21 37 – Velu Vins, rue Bollinckx, 215. 1070, Brussels. Tél. 02 520 60 68.

Canada

SAQ CP, 1058, place d'Armes, Montreal, Québec.

The Netherlands

De Best Wijnkoperij Dam 36, 1506 Be Zaandam. Tel: 075 35 31 93.

Far East:

Japan – Toyo Menka Kaisha Ltd, Yokohama.

Comments

On the Chinon Road, 8 km from Saumur, can be seen a beautiful dwelling surrounded by four towers nestled into the hillside, overlooking the road on the banks of the Loire. Originally a hunting lodge belonging to a personal secretary of Louis XIV, it has become, in the course of time, the Château de Targé, which is still occupied today by the same family. It has provided rest and relaxation to a number of political personalities: Allain-Targé, Gambetta, Jules and Charles Ferry, Robert and Michel Debré.

CHÂTEAU DE CHAINTRES

B. de Tigny
Domaine Viticole de Chaintre Saumur 49400
41 52 90 54

Type of vineyard: Corporation. **Number of employees:** 13. **Vine stocks:** Cabernet Franc. **Soil:** Clay with calcium carbonate. **Exposure:** South. **Average annual production in hectoliters:** 850.
Appellation: Saumur Champigny A.O.C. **Type:** Red. **Technique:** Large casks. **Maturing:** 1 year. **Alcohol content:** 12.5%. **Characteristics:** Fine, fruity, female, to be drunk between 2 and 5 years +. **Serving temperature:** 13° to 15°. **Served with:** Meat, cheese, fish, red fruit. **Vintages available in 89/90:** 1986.

Characteristics of vintages

1986: Very good standing, supple and fragrant; to be aged. Price range (pre-tax, ex-warehouse): Between 30 F.F. and 50 F.F.

DOMAINE DE VARINELLES

Daheuiller
28 rue de Ruau 49400 Varrains
41 52 90 94

Type of vineyard: Agricultural Association. **Soil:** Chalky clay. **Exposure:** South. **Average annual production in hectoliters:** 1,200.

Appellation: Saumur Champigny and Crémant de Loire. **Type:** Red, white. **Technique:** Red: maceration, fermentation with temperature control. **Maturing:** Several months in casks in deep micaceous chalk caves. **Alcohol content:** 12.5%. **Characteristics:** Saumur Champigny: young, very fruity, round and velvety after the second year. Introducing the feast, the Crémant de Loire sparkles with freshness. **Serving temperature:** Red: 13°. Crémant: 6 to 8°. **Served with:** Saumur Champigny: goes perfectly with light cuisine, all meats. Served a bit cooler, it can go with fish dishes. **Vintages available in 89/90:** 1987, 1988.

Characteristics of vintages

1988: Very rich, quite tannic, will be a wine for keeping. **1987:** Very supple, little acidity, round, very pleasant right now. **1986:** Crémant de Loire: after 2 years it has acquired all of the charm expected of a wine for feasting. Price range (pre-tax, ex-warehouse): Saumur Champigny: between 20 and 30 F.F. Crémant de Loire: between 30 and 50 F.F.
Sales volume:
– Retail: 30%. – Restaurants: 40%. – Other: 20% (winecellars and agents).
Sales in France: 90%.
Export sales: 10%.
Main trading partners : Belgium, United Kingdom, Germany.

References in France

Restaurants: Jean Bardet (Tours), Robuchon (Paris), Les Trois Marches (Versailles).
Shops: Cave Esteve, 10 rue de la Cerisaie, Paris 4e.

Abroad

United Kingdom

Thorman Hunt, 4 Pratt Walk, Lambeth, London SE11 6AR.

Germany

Dr. Kurt Binneberg, Pfarrer Kirchheim d5350 Eurkirchen-Kirchheim.

Belgium

Graffe Lecoq, Place St Aubin, Namur. Lambert, 8 rue de Rome. Ets Delatre, 50 av. de la Pais, Brussels.

Comments

It was in the 1850's that the Daheuiller family began with a few hundred square meters of vines. Family enterprise from father to son for 5 generations. Very well known for its red Saumur Champigny, they also produce the famous Crémant de Loire.

CHÂTEAU DE VILLENEUVE

Mrs. Chevallier
Souzay-Champigny 49400 Saumur
41 51 14 04

Type of vineyard: Agricultural Association. **Established:** 1985. **Vine stocks:** Cabernet Franc and Chenin Blanc. **Soil:** Chalky. **Average annual production in hectoliters:** 1,200.

Appellation: Saumur-Champigny and Saumur Blanc. **Type:** Red, white. **Technique:** Classical with temperature regulation. **Maturing:** In vats, bottling in the Springtime. **Alcohol content:** 12%. **Characteristics:** Saumur-Champigny: rich aromas of red berries, beautiful tannins. Saumur Blanc: lively nose, very floral, supple attack with a certain length. **Serving temperature:** Red: 16°. White: 7 to 8°. **Served with:** Fish in sauce, grilled meat. **Vintages available in 89/90:** 1988.

Characteristics of vintages

1988: Very rich and structured wines. Price range (pre-tax, ex-warehouse): between 20 and 30 F.F.

Sales volume:

– Wholesade: 25%. – Retail: 35%. – Restaurants: 40%.

Sales in France: 90%.

Export sales: 10%.

Main trading partners: United Kingdom, Germany, United States, Italy, Belgium.

Abroad

United States

Importers: Philippi Imports Ltd., 53 West Jackson Blvd., Chicago, Illinois 60604.

United Kingdom

Thorman Hunt & Co., 4 Pratt Walk, Lambeth, London SE11 6AR.

Belgium

Sobelvin S.A., rue Ernest Solvay 7, B4000 Liège. Vantuykom-de-Vadder, 309 rue Vanderkindere, 1180 Uccle-Brussels.

Others

Italy: Enoteca al Ponte Italo "Castelletti", via Roma 7, Ponte San Pietro, Bergamo.

Comments

The oldest of the buildings, of the Château de Villeneuve goes back to 1577. At the time, the Bel Air manor belonged to the Villeneuve family from Allonnes (squires of the Dukes of Luynes). The Bel Air manor was to revert to the eldest son of the Villeneuve family who was killed at the Battle of York, in America, under the command of Lafayette. Subsequently, it became the property of the Foucault, then the Bossoreil family who renovated the Château in 1867. It was bombed on June 13, 1940 and suffered serious damage. It wasn't until 1969 that the Château de Villeneuve, with is vineyard, became the property of the present owners, the Chevallier family who undertook its restoration.

SAUMUR D'ORIGINE

BOUVET LADUBAY

Patrice Monmousseau
Saint-Hilaire, Saint-Florent 49146 Saumur
41 50 11 12 – Telex: 721 181

Vine stocks: Selected through an agreement with 150 wine makers of the Saumur region.
Appellation: Saumur d'Origine. **Type:** White. **Technique:** Champagne method. **Maturing:** New casks and stainless steel tanks with temperature regulation. **Alcohol content:** 12%. **Characteristics:** One of the best examples of the exceptionally successful application of the Champagne method in France. **Serving temperature:** 8°. **Served with:** As an aperitif, with shellfish, fish and desserts. **Vintages available in 89/90:** 1986, 1987.

Characteristics of vintages

1986: Excellent year for all wine lots. Light, fine bubbles. Combines richness and elegance, well-bred and typical, no need to hesitate. Price range (pre-tax, ex-warehouse): between 30 and 50 F.F.

Sales volume:
– Wholesale: 65%. – Retail: 10%. – Restaurants: 25%.

Sales in France: 43%.

Export sales: 57%.

Main trading partners : USA, UK, Canada, Norway, Germany, Belgium, Italy, Australia, New Zealand.

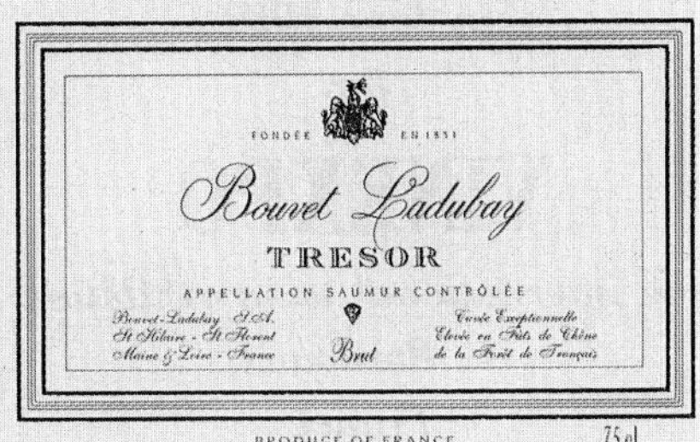

Abroad

United States

Importers: Kobrand, 134 East 40th Street, New York, N.Y 10016 (Telex: 275 852).

United Kingdom

Deinhard, 29 Addington Street, London SE1 7X1 (Tel: 261 11 11).

Germany

La Française d'Exportation, Escher Strasse 23 AO, Koln 71.

Canada

Livico, 2606 Jean Brillant, Ste Foy, Québec GI W 1E6. Restaurants: English Gunn, 49 Wellington Street, East Toronto MSE 1C9.

The Netherlands

La Française d'Exportation, Direnriems 3738, TP Maartensdijk.

Far East

Japan: Mr. Polak Nishiwaki, Gelgique 6 FL, Kojimachi 4 Chome Chiyoda KU, Tokyo 102.

Comments

For the first time in the Loire Valley, Bouvet is offering a blend of Chenin and Chardonnay, vinified in new oak casks from the Tronçay forest, in which it is kept for a year before applying the traditional Champagne method. This wine lot, calling upon techniques used for the greatest French wines, is an exception among sparkling wines. The very limited production is intended for the great restaurants and those amateurs avid for refined sensations. Extremely small bubbles point up the harmonious character of the blend and the new oak underlines the elegance and finesse of the wines whose noble origins, lest we forget, is the "Valley of the Kings".

SAVENNIÈRES

CLOS DE LA COULÉE DE SERRANT, CHÂTEAU DE LA ROCHE AUX MOINES

Mr. et Mrs. Joly
49170 Savennières
41 72 22 32 – Telex: Chamco 720 943 F Att. Coulée de Serrant

Type of vineyard: Agricultural Association. **Established:** 1962. **Number of employees:** 5. **Vine stocks:** Chenin. **Soil:** Schistic. **Exposure:** Hillside facing South. **Average annual production in hectoliters:** 200.
Appellation: Coulée de Serrant, A.O.C. Coulée de Serrant, Château de la Roche aux Moines, A.O.C. Roche aux Moines. **Type:** White. **Technique:** In wood, biodynamically. **Maturing:** Wood. **Alcohol content:** 13%. **Characteristics:** Coulée de Serrant: often considered as one of the 5 best white wines of France at maturity, that is after a minimum of 10 years and up to 30 years or more of ageing. Fragrance of ripe fruit, honey, very long. Don't open before a minimum of 5 years. Château de la Roche aux Moines or Clos de la Bergerie: very mineral, fruity, may be drunk sooner. **Served with:** Coulée de Serrant: white meat, fish in sauce. Château de la Roche aux Moines: all meals. **Vintages available in 89/90:** Older vintages are sold out and can be found in auction sales at very high price.

Characteristics of vintages

Price range (pre-tax, ex-warehouse): Château de la Roche aux Moines: between 50 F.F. and 80 F.F. Coulée de Serrant: between 110 F.F. and 150 F.F.
Sales volume:
– Wholesale: 50%. – Retail: 25 %. – Restaurants: 25 %.
Sales in France: 50%.
Export sales: 50%.
Main trading partners : Europe, Asia, USA, South Ameriac, Australia, New Zeeland.

References in France

Restaurants: In Paris; Tour d'Argent, Taillevent, Laurent, Rebuchon, Beaumanière, Pré Catelan, Le Doyen, George Blanc, (95 % of the 3 and 2 stars Michelin in France), etc.

Comments

La Coulée de Serrant is a vineyard of only 7 hectares. It is the exclusive property of Mrs. Joly and it is cultivated biodynamically, with no chemical products either on horseback, or by hand where the slopes are too steep. Very small yield. Average age of the vines: 35 years availability of the wine is more and more difficult; sales limited to 12 bt per customer in France. Often consider as one of the top 5 best white wines in France.

WINE FROM THE AREA OF TOURAINE

BOURGUEIL

DOMAINE DES GALLUCHES

Jean Gambier
37140 Bourgueil

Type of vineyard: Family-owned. **Established:** reopened in 1960, has existed for 4 generations. **Number of employees:** 1. **Vine stocks:** Cabernet Franc. **Soil:** Gravel. **Exposure:** North, South. **Average annual production in hectoliters:** 400.

Appellation: Bourgueil. **Type:** Red, rosé. **Technique:** Traditional. **Maturing:** in large Oak casks. **Alcohol content:** 12%. **Characteristics:** Fine and fruity with raspberry and blackcurrant fragrance, taking on woodland and mushrom aromas with ageing. **Serving temperature:** 14 to 15°. **Served with:** red meat and goat cheese. Vintages lighter in tannins may be served with fish. **Vintages available in 89/90:** 1985, 1986.

Characteristics of vintages

1986:Very good year. Tannic wine, quite fruity, keeps well, good for ageing. 1985: Very good year. Tanninc and fruity, will age well, blackcurrant fragrance.

DOMAINE DE LA CHANTELEUSERIE

Moïse and Thierry Boucard
Benais 37140 Bourgueil
47 97 30 20

Type of vineyard: Family Agricultural Association. **Established:** 1822. **Number of employees:** 1, **Vine stocks:** Cabernet Franc. **Soil:** 3/4 chalky clay (tufa), 1/4 pebbly sand. **Exposure:** South. **Average annual production in hectoliters:** 750.

Appellation: Bourgueil. **Type:** Red. **Technique:** Traditional. **Maturing:** Stainless steel tanks and oak casks. **Alcohol content:** 12.2%. **Characteristics:** Sandy soil: supple and fruity. Tufa: rich and well-balanced, more tannic, for keeping. **Serving temperature:** 15°. **Served with:** Meat, chicken in wine sauce, eel stew, strawberries and peaches. **Vintages available in 89/90:** 1986, 1987.

Characteristics of vintages

1987: Fruity, supple. **1986:** Fine wine, discreet tannins, pleasant to drink, good evolution. **Other: 1984:** Light. Price range (pre-tax, ex-warehouse): between 10 and 20 F.F.

Sales volume:
– Retail: 70%. – Restaurants: 30%.
Sales in France: 80%.
Export sales: 20%.
Main trading partners : Belgium, Switzerland, U.K., Denmark, Netherlands.

References in France

Restaurants: Ives Thuries (81 Cordes), L'Échauguette (81 Lavaur), Le Petit Robert (75018 Paris), La Truite (78790 Rosay), Auberge de la Rivière (17880 Les Portes en Ré), La Ferme de Montbrun (46460 Cajarc), etc.
Shops: Caves Fauchon (Paris), Caves Saint Clair (Boulogne-Billancourt), Bar aux Négociants (75018 Paris), M. Jarry (78380 Bougival), Cave La Bordelaise (81100 Castres), etc.

Abroad

United Kingdom
Adam Bancroft, Gresham House, 4/7 Great Pulteney Street, London W1R 3DF.

Switzerland
Hédor SA, 15, rue du Général Dufour, 1204 Geneva. Restaurant: Le Grand Alexandre, 1227 Carouge.

Belgium
Leloup SPRL Vinicole, 2, rue Haute, 1438 Bousval.

The Netherlands
Wiertz P.J., Pijnboomstraat 24, 2023 VS Haarlem.

Comments

Origins in 1822. Thierry Boucard is the 7th generation.

DOMAINE JACQUES MORIN

Jacques Morin
Le Vau Godard, Benais – 37140 Bourgueil
47 97 30 17 – Telex: 752 098

Type of vineyard: Family-owned. **Established:** Father to son for more than 7 generations. **Number of employees:** 7. **Vine stocks:** Cabernet Franc. **Soil:** Gravel, clay, alluvium from the Loire. **Exposure:** South. **Average annual production in hectoliters:** 1,000.

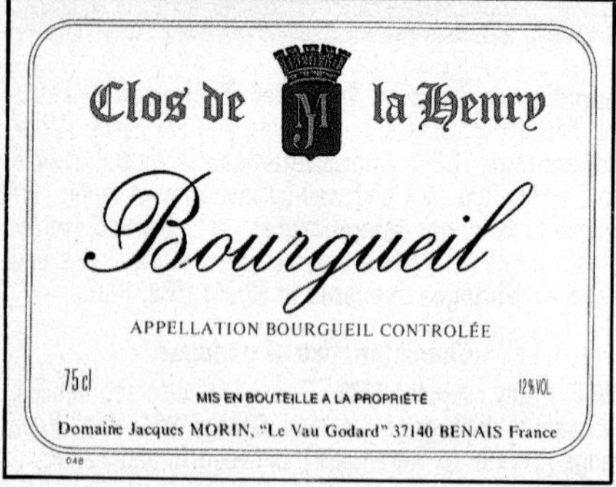

Clos de la Henry
Bourgueil
APPELLATION BOURGUEIL CONTROLÉE
75 cl
12% VOL.
MIS EN BOUTEILLE A LA PROPRIÉTÉ
Domaine Jacques MORIN, "Le Vau Godard" 37140 BENAIS France

Appellation: Bourgueil. **Type:** Red. **Technique:** Traditional, at low temperature to preserve the aromas. **Maturing:** In bottles. **Alcohol content:** 12%. **Characteristics:** Very developed aromas, subtle, red berry fragrance (touch of blackcurrant and raspberry), very round, long, very well-balanced, goes down smoothly, light, flowery, digestive. **Serving temperature:** 15°. **Served with:** White meat, chicken and veal, served chilled with different fish dishes. **Vintages available in 89/90:** 1988, 1985, 1986.

Characteristics of vintages

1988: Full, well balanced, deep aroma, silver medal. **1987:** Fruity, elegant, fine beautiful raspberry aroma. Bronze Medal (Bourgueil). **1986:** Beautiful wine, supple and fragrant, very successful. Gold Medal, Vinexpo (Cuvée Prestige). **1985:** Firmer vintage, full, good color, distinguished, to be aged. Price range (pre-tax, ex-warehouse): 20 to 30 F.F.
Sales volume:
– Retail: 15%. – Restaurants: 80%. – Other: 5%.
Sales in France: 70%.
Export sales: 30%.
Main trading partners : Canada, UK: Averys of Bristol.

References in France

Restaurants Paris: Lucas Carton, Le Vivarois, Le Million, Le Dodin Bouffant. Indre & Loire Region: Le Plaisir Gourmand Chinon, Le Château d'Artigny, Le Domaine de Beauvoir, Le Cheval Rouge.

Abroad

Canada
Société des Alcools du Québec. Alberta Liquor Control Board. Liquor Control Board of Ontario.

CHEVERNY

LE PETIT CHAMBORD

François et Bernard Cazin
Cheverny 41700
54 79 93 75

Type of vineyard: Family-owned. **Established:** Beginning of the Century. **Vine stocks:** Romorantin, Sauvignon, Chardonnay, Pinot Noir, Gamay. **Soil:** Clay with calcium carbonate. Silica and clay top soil. **Exposure:** Northeast, Southwest. **Average annual production in hectoliters:** 600.
Appellation: Cheverny. **Type:** Red, white, Champenoise Method. **Technique:** Traditional at low temperatures (white), carbonic maceration (red). **Maturing:** Tanks and large casks. **Alcohol content:** 12%. **Characteristics:** Romorantin: dry, fruity, white wine, very representative of the appellation Cheverny. Sauvignon: very developped aromas. **Serving temperature:** 12° white, 15° Gamay. **Ser-**

ved with: White wines: fish, shellfish. Gamay: light red and fruity, may accompagny the whole meal. **Vintages available in 89/90:** Romorantin 1985 and 1986.

Characteristics of vintages

1988: Very beautiful year for the red Cheverny. Much richer and more sustained than the 1987, with a beautiful ruby red color. **1984:** Very dry, very representative of the wine. Price range (pre-tax, ex-warehouse): Between 10 F.F. and 20 F.F.
Sales volume:
- Wholesale: 10%. – Retail: 50%. – Restaurants: 40%.
Sales in France: 85%.
Export sales: 15%.
Main trading partners : UK, Belgium.

References in France

Restaurants: Many restaurants in Loir-et-Cher, Allier, Nord, Somme, Pas-de-Calais, and in Paris.
Shops: Caves Pouchet, Paris.

Abroad

United Kingdom

Kfbutler and Co. Ltd., East Grinstead, Sussex RH 19 1XZ. Tempest Slinger and Co. Saffron Walden, Essex CB10 1 NY.

Canada

Liquor Control Board of Ontario 55 Lakeshore. BLVD East Toronto, Ontario, Canada M5E 1 A4.

Belgium

Le Clos du Culot. Le Culot 4, 1300 Wavre.

CHINON

LE LOGIS DE LA BOUCHARDIÈRE

Serge & Bruno Sourdais
Cravant-les-Coteaux 37500 Chinon
47 93 04 27

Type of vineyard: Family-owned. **Established:** In the 1850's (6th generation). **Number of employees:** 4. **Vine stocks:** Cabernet Franc 98%. **Soil:** Silica on clay. **Exposure:** Plateau and hillsides facing full South. **Average annual production in hectoliters:** 1,300.
Appellation: Chinon AOC. **Type:** Red. **Technique:** Traditional, long, temperature control. **Maturing:** Young vines: vats. Old wines: casks. **Alcohol content:** 12 to 12.5%. **Characteristics:** 15 year old vines: light fruity wines that go down well. Old vines: full-bodied, tannic wines, purple color, long, can age for several decades. **Serving temperature:** 14 to 15° (very important). **Served with:** Wines from young vines: delicatessen white meat. Older vines: red meat, and cheese. **Vintages available in 89/90:** 1988, 1987, 1986.

Characteristics of vintages

1988: Deep color, character, slightly tannic, long and round, full-bodied. **1987:** Extremely fragrant, very fruity, lively red color, lingering taste. **1986:** Purple color, very tannic, aromatic (violet and spices), harmonious, and very long. Price range (pre-tax, ex-warehouse): 20 to 30 F.F.
Sales volume:
- Wholesale: 20%. – Retail: 50%. – Restaurants: 20%.
- Other: 10% (cellars).
Sales in France: 95%. **Export sales:** 5%.

Main trading partners : Germany, Netherlands, Belgium, Switzerland.

References in France

Restaurants: Le Moniage Guillaume, (Paris 14e), Les Hautes Roches, (37 Vouvray). L'Aigle d'Or et le Grand Monarque, (37 Azay-le-Rideau), Chalet du Mont d'Arbois, (Megève), le Clos des Bénédictins (49 Saumur), Le Panurge (37 Chinon), Château de Montgoger (37 St Epain).

Abroad

United Kingdom

Charles, Sydney and Philippa Richardson, Lerné 37 France (Tel: 47 95 99 30) (Exporters).

Germany

Wolfgang Hahn, Sandwegs, (Tel: 08207/108H). Académie du Vin, Munich (Tel: 089474434).

Switzerland

Société Diffuvins, M. Murat 1211 Geneva (Tel: 21 39 43 48).

Canada

Maison Norvin, 57, Avenue Beloeil, Outremont, Montreal H2V 2Z1, Québec Province.

The Netherlands

Hubert Schwerzel, 11, rue Alexandre Boers Strate, Amsterdam (Tel: 207116 32).

Comments

The 30 hectare estate has been operated from father to son since 1850. Three quarters of the vineyard is on hillsides yielding wines to be kept. The other quarter, in the valley, on gravelly soil, yields lighter wines that are pleasant to drink young. Wines from different types of soil and from vines of different ages are vinified separately, then aged in wood for 8 to 18 months.

COULY DUTHEIL

Pierre & Jacques Couly
12, rue Diderot 37500 Chinon
47 93 05 84 – Telex: 751 685

Type of vineyard: Family-owned. **Established:** 1921. **Number of employees:** 20. **Vine stocks:** Cabernet Franc. **Soil:** Clay and chalky clay. **Exposure:** South. **Average annual production in hectoliters:** 3,000.

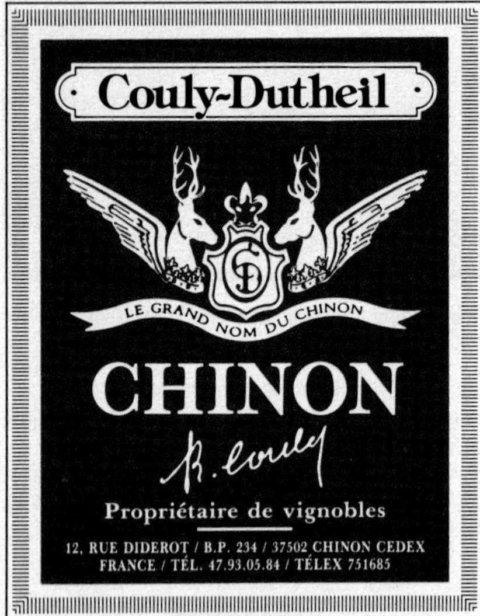

Appellation: Chinon. **Type:** Red, White, Rosé. **Technique:** Traditional. **Maturing:** In casks made of oak from the local forests. **Alcohol content:** 12.5%. **Characteristics:** Young: fruity wines that go down well, red berry flavor. Aged: round tannins, truffle and prune aroma. **Serving temperature:** Young: 14° Aged: 16°. **Served with:** Cold cuts, white meat. **Vintages available in 89/90:** 1979, 1981, 1982, 1983, 1984, 1985, 1986, 1987, 1988.

Characteristics of vintages

1988: Very fruity, excellent year. **1987:** Fine development, improving with age. **1986:** Not yet opened up, but very promising. **1985:** A very great year indeed. Price range (pretax, ex-warehouse): 20 to 50 F.F.

Sales volume:
– Retail: 30%. – Restaurants: 60%. – Other: 10% (export).
Sales in France: 90%. **Export sales:** 10%.
Main trading partners : Belgium, Germany, UK.

References in France

Restaurants: Faugeron, Troisgros, Château d'Artigny, Lucas Carton.
Shops: Fauchon.

Abroad

United Stades

Dreyfus Ashby. 60 East 42 ND. Street, Room 1901 New York. NY 10165

United Kingdom

Reynier, 16/18 Upper Tachmook street.

Germany

Jacques Weindepot. 4000 Dusseldorf

Belgium

Franz Tricot. 6040 Zoning de Jumet

Canada

SAQ – CP 1058 Place d'Armes, Montreal, LCBO, Toronto.

The Netherlands

Verlinden 5201 AG'S Hertogenbosch, Wielinga Leenwarden. Oud 2021 Ka Haarlem.

Comments

The establishment was created in 1921 by B. Dutheil, grandfather of the present owners.

SCI CHÂTEAU DE LA GRILLE

Albert Gosset
B.P. 205 – 37502 Chinon Cedex
47 93 01 95

Type of vineyard: Civil Corporation. **Established:** 1955. **Number of employees:** 6. **Vine stocks:** 95% Cabernet Franc, 5% Cabernet Sauvignon. **Soil:** Muddy, sand with clay sub-soil, tuffeau. **Exposure:** East West. **Average annual production in hectoliters:** 40/ha.
Appellation: A.O.C. Chinon. **Type:** Red. **Technique:** Long fermentation with skins 4 to 5 weeks with temperature control. **Maturing:** Between 12 and 18 months in Oak Merrain Casks (225 l.) and crushing; 25% renewed each year. **Alcohol content:** 12%. **Characteristics:** Wine for keeping necessitates, a certain maturing (after maturing in wood, ageing minimum 1 year in the cellar before the sale) second aroma of cooked fruity (strawberry, blackcurrent), with a touch of spice. **Serving temperature:** 15° to 17°. **Served with:** Game, red, and white meat, cheese. **Vintages available in 89/90:** 1983, 1984, 1982. Presentation: special bottle Gosset XVIII[e] century collection.

Characteristics of vintages

1987: Forthcoming - harvested at perfect maturity. A good vintage with a promising future. **1986:** Well constituted, rich in aromas, soft tannins, combining finesse and complexity. **1985:** Rich and tonic. Has reached excellent maturity level. Perfect with game, red meat and cheese.

1984: Very successful for the year, essential sorting grapes, 30% starting to open in September 1987. Price range (pre-tax, ex-warehouse): Between 30 F.F. and 50 F.F.

CLOS DU SAUT-AU-LOUP

Domaine Dozon
Ligré – 37500 Chinon
47 93 17 67

Type of vineyard: Family Corporation of Saut-au-Loup. **Vine stocks:** Cabernet franc 100%. **Soil:** Silica, clay covered. **Exposure:** Hillsides facing South. **Average annual production in hectoliters:** 800.
Appellation: A.O.C. Chinon. **Type:** Red. **Technique:** Traditional with temperature control. **Maturing:** Wood, casks of 500 and 220 liters. **Characteristics:** Fine, bred, ruby, with woody strawberry and currant fragrances; may be drunk quite young but ages well, too. **Serving temperature:** Young wines: 14 to 15°; when older: around 17°. **Served with:** White meat, poultry, light red meat. **Vintages available in 89/90:** 1986, 1987, 1988.

Characteristics of vintages

1988: Ruby red color, green pepper, small red berry and licorice fragrance, average astringence. Good balance, fruity aromas. Quite typical of its origin. Should be aged. **1987:** Beautiful average ruby color, well developed nose, complex aromas (green pepper, licorice, raspberry), promising. Good balance, but quite astringent, spicy aromas, fruity. Good typical wine. **1986:** Sustained ruby color, rich tannin, truly great vintage to be aged. Price range (pre-tax, ex-warehouse): between 25 F.F. and 35 F.F.
Sales volume:
– Wholesale: 15%. – Retail: 50%. – Restaurants: 20%. – Other: 10% Caves fine shops.
Sales in France: 85%.
Export sales: 10%.
Main trading partners : Germany, Belgium, Canada, Switzerland, England, USA, Netherlands, Japan.

Abroad

United States
Shops: United States Embassy, 2 av. Gabriel, Paris.

Germany
Nothum 72 av. du 10 Septembre, L 2550 Luxemburg. Phone (00352) 45 22 32. Restaurants: Weinkontor Herten Hochstrasse 9 D 4352 Herten.

Canada
Shops: LCBO 55 Lake Shore Toronto. Phone: 416 963 1866.

Belgium
Thorront 1 de la Salandre 8 A 5830 Mazy. Phone: 081 633852.

MONTLOUIS

DOMAINE DES LIARDS

Michel Berger
Montlouis 47 50 67 36

Type of vineyard: Family-owned. **Established:** 1959 at present location but for 3 generations in the village. **Number of employees:** 3. **Vine stocks:** Chenin Blanc. **Soil:** Chalky clay. **Exposure:** South-East, South. **Average annual production in hectoliters:** 750 to 850.

Appellation: Montlouis. **Type:** White. **Technique:** Traditional. **Maturing:** In wooden casks and stainless steel tanks. **Alcohol content:** 11.5%. **Characteristics:** Light and supple with a touch of acidity (characteristic of Chenin) – very good keeping. **Serving temperature:** 6 to 8°. **Served with:** As an aperitif after a few years in the bottle and with delicatessen, or fish in sauce. **Vintages available in 89/90:** 1981, 1985, 1986, 1987, 1988.

Characteristics of vintages

1988: Very well balanced, round and full, fine vintage. **1987:** Light but very typical of the Chenin, good keeping. **1986:** Very aromatic, characterized by a bit of botrytis (noble rot). **1985:** Vendanges tardives: excellent mellow wines. **Other:** 1961: Small yield. Medium-dry extremely fresh, very aromatic, wines harvested after partial drying on the vine. Price range (pre-tax, ex-warehouse): 20 to 30 F.F. – 30 to 50 F.F. for vintage wines.
Sales volume:
– Wholesale: 60%. – Retail: 5%. – Restaurants: 5%. – Other: 30% (export). All in bottles.
Sales in France: 70%.
Export sales: 30%.
Main trading partners : UK, Belgium, Netherlands, Germany, Japan, Australia, USA.

References in France

Restaurants: Roc en Val (Montlouis), Auberge du 12[e]

Siècle (Saché), La Tortinière (37 Montbazon), La Devinière (Boulevard Louis XIV, Lille).
Shops: Arts des Vins (Lille).

Abroad

United Kingdom

Yapp Brothers PLC Mere Wiltshirere Baiz 6DY (Tel: 747 860423).

Germany

Veincontor Postfach 1864 D.6940, Weinheim.

Belgium

Vinea Johny Grootvriendt Stuivenbergstraat 20-B – 1686 Gooik. Gasthof Den Tuin Spoorweghlaan 5, Courtrai.

The Netherlands

Wijnkoperij H.F.A. Okhysen B.V. Gerstraat 36 36 38 2011 GE Haarlem. De Hoop Op D'Swarte Walvis, Kalverringdijk 15, Zaanse Schans, 1509 BT Zaandam.

Far East

Japan: Hatta Shoten Ltd. Ota Ku Tokyo 143.

Others

Australia: Yemisey Pty LTD C/O Franck Cridland P/4 154 Susse Street, Sydney, New South Wales.

Comments

Traditional family type enterprise on ideal soil with perfect exposure. For more than five centuries, the Chenin, cultivated on these hillsides, has benefited from a climate influenced by the confluence of the Cher and the Loire, which can be thought of as a "micro-climate". The wines of the Montlouis appellation have been awarded Medals at the Paris Concours Général more than 20 times in the last 30 years.

SIMIER JAMES & FILS

James Simier

Rue du Moulin – 37270 Saint-Martin-le-Beau

47 50 68 84

Type of vineyard: Family-owned. **Established:** From father to son. **Vine stocks:** Chenin (Pineau de la Loire). **Soil:** Silica and chalk. **Exposure:** Hillsides – very sunny. **Average annual production in hectoliters:** 350 to 400. **Appellation:** Montlouis AOC. **Type:** White. **Technique:** Traditional. **Alcohol content:** 11 to 11.5°. **Characteristics:** Dry and Medium-dry: fruity, straw color, delicate nose, pronounced bouquet, very long. Mellow: very long keeping. **Serving temperature:** 10 to 11°. **Served with:** Champagne method: as an aperitif or with the entire meal. Dry: with fish and seafood. Medium-dry: with delicatessen. Mellow: with foie gras or as an aperitif. **Vintages available in 89/90:** 1988, 1986, 1985, 1981, 1976, 1973, 1970.

Characteristics of vintages

1988: Dry, Medium Dry and Mellow: very fruity, full bodied. **1986:** Champagne method. **1985:** Medium-dry, Mellow: excellent year. **Other: 1981:** Medium-dry. **1976:** Medium-dry. **1973:** Medium-dry, Mellow: exceptional. **1970:** Medium-dry, Mellow. Price range (pre-tax, ex-warehouse): 10 to 40 F.F. depending on the vintage.
Sales volume:
– Wholesale: 30%. – Retail: 30%. – Restaurants: 40%.
Sales in France: 80%. **Export sales:** 20%.
Main trading partners : Belgium.

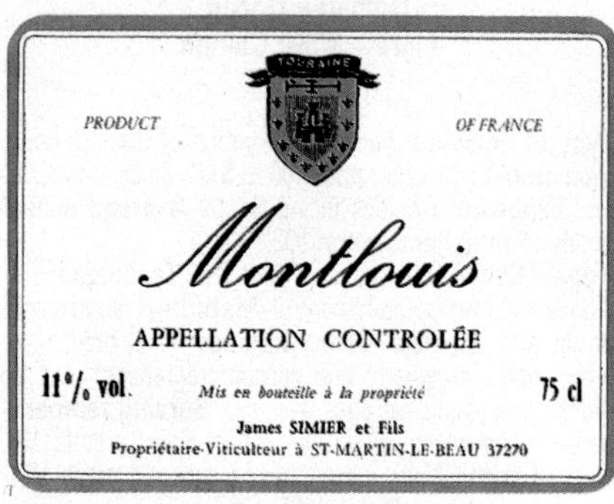

PRODUCT
OF FRANCE
Montlouis
APPELLATION CONTROLÉE
11°/o vol.
Mis en bouteille à la propriété
75 cl
James SIMIER et Fils
Propriétaire-Viticulteur à ST-MARTIN-LE-BEAU 37270

References in France

Restaurants: Bon Accueil (Magne), Chaufour, Hôtel de Strasbourg (Place d'Évreux 27200 Vernon), Le Cappeville (17 rue Cappeville 27140 Gisors).
Shops: De Lescluse & Fils (Route de Delincourt 27140 Gisors), Les Caves de l'Épicerie de Longueil (Maisons-Laffitte 78600).

Abroad

United Kingdom

Esso Abincdon Social Club, Abincdon, Oxon (Tel: 0235-45830).

Belgium

Cercle Royal de la Voile, Grimbergen.

Comments

Family enterprise from father to son, since 1880.

SAINT-NICOLAS DE-BOURGUEIL

"LA CAILLARDIÈRE"

James Morisseau
37140 Saint-Nicolas-de-Bourgueil
47 97 75 40

Type of vineyard: Family-owned. **Established:** 1840. **Vine stocks:** Cabernet Franc. **Soil:** Silica gravel with a small amount of chalky clay. **Exposure:** North-South. **Average annual production in hectoliters:** 700.

Appellation: Saint-Nicolas-de-Bourgueil. **Type:** Red. **Technique:** Traditional, 25-30 days, temperature control, carbonic maceration. **Maturing:** 6 to 18 months in wooden casks. **Alcohol content:** 12%. **Characteristics:** Fruit fragrance (raspberry, blackcurrant, prune), young or aged according to the characteristics of the vintage. **Serving temperature:** 15 to 18° depending on whether served during or between meals. **Served with:** Light meats and cheese. **Vintages available in 89/90:** 1986, 1987, 1988.

Characteristics of vintages

1988: Light, acid. **1987:** Very fragrant, pleasant drinking even between meals. **1986:** Tannic, to be drunk preferably with the meal. Price range (pre-tax, ex-warehouse): 20 to 30 F.F.

Sales volume:
– Wholesale: 20%. – Retail: 40%. – Restaurants: 40%.

Sales in France: 98%. **Export sales:** 2%.

Main trading partners : Belgium.

Comments

"La Caillardière" has been a family enterprise since 1840, producing Bourgueil on the gravelly plateau of Saint-Nicolas, from Cabernet Franc vinestocks. The red wines, with raspberry, blackcurrant and prune fragrances, depending on the vintages, are for keeping. They can be served during or between meals at a temperature between 15 to 18° and go well with light meats and cheese.

DOMAINE DU BOURG

Jean-Paul Mabileau
37140 Saint-Nicolas-de-Bourgueil
47 97 82 02

Type of vineyard: Family-owned. **Established:** 1900. (Jean Paul Mabileau since 1974). **Number of employees:** 1. **Vine stocks:** Cabernet Franc 100%. **Soil:** Sand and gravel – chalky clay hillside. **Exposure:** North, South. **Average annual production in hectoliters:** 650.

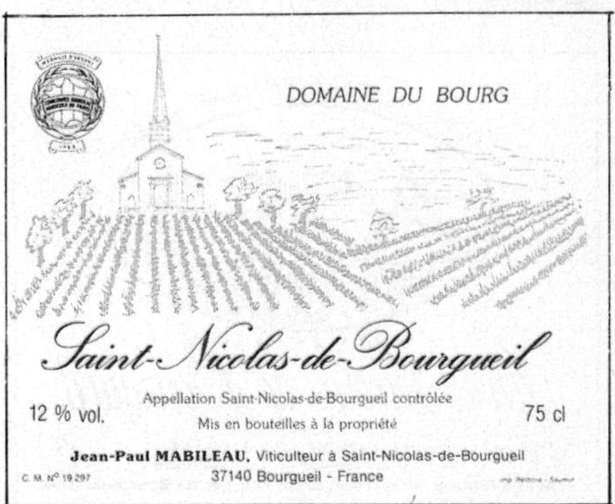

Appellation: St-Nicolas-de-Bourgueil. **Type:** Red. **Technique:** Long vinification, crushing. **Maturing:** In wooden casks (6 to 18 months). **Alcohol content:** Around 12%. **Characteristics:** Supple, fruity, rather tannic, good ageing potentiel. **Serving temperature:** 14 to 16° depending on the vintage. **Served with:** Young: grills, red meat. Aged: more elaborate dishes and cheese. **Vintages available in 89/90:** 1986, 1987, 1988.

Characteristics of vintages

1988: Slightly tannic, supple, fruity, deep color. **1987:** Less tannic, very fruity, ripe fruit fragrance. **1986:** Tannic, rather full, lingering taste, to be aged. Price range (pre-tax, ex-warehouse): 20 to 30 F.F.

Sales volume:
– Retail: 30%. – Restaurants: 70%.

Sales in France: 80%.

Export sales: 20%.

Main trading partners : European community, Benelux countries, UK.

Abroad

United Kingdom

Codi Wines Ltd, 131 Stourbridge road, Broadwaters. Prestige Wintmers, 15 Stucley Place, London. Mabileau, 61 The Cut, London.

Belgium

Poulet 118, rue de Beguines, 1080 Brussels. Verporten Vivier 1024, Malonne 5730.

Others

Luxemburg: St Michel, Bouzonvillier.

DOMAINE DE LA COTELLERAIE - VALLÉE

Claude Vallée
La Cotelleraie - Saint-Nicolas-de-Bourgueil
37140 Bourgueil
47 97 75 53

Type of vineyard: Family-owned. **Established:** From father to son since 1660. **Vine stocks:** Cabernet Franc 90%, Cabernet Sauvignon 10%. **Soil:** Silica with gravel. **Exposure:** North-South. **Average annual production in hectoliters:** 700.

DOMAINE DE LA COTELLERAIE - VALLÉE
Saint Nicolas de Bourgueil
12%vol
PRODUCE OF FRANCE
APPELLATION CONTROLEE
75cl
MIS EN BOUTEILLE A LA PROPRIETE
VALLEE Claude - viticulteur - Saint Nicolas de Bourgueil 37140

Appellation: Saint-Nicolas-de-Bourgueil. **Type:** Red, rosé. **Technique:** Traditional vinification, 18 to 21 days. Rosé: drawing off. **Maturing:** 4 to 6 months in OAK casks. **Alcohol content:** 12%. **Characteristics:** For moderate ageing, dominant red fruit fragrance, sometimes flowery or spicy, slightly tannic, ruby color, well-developed aromas. **Serving temperature:** Young wine: 13° to 15°. 3 to 5 years old or more, 14° to 17° according to the vintage. **Served with:** Young wine: white meat, Quiche Lorraine, sometimes with Plum Pie and game. Rosé: all first courses and, in warm weather, with the entire meal. **Vintages available in 89/90:** 1988.

Characteristics of vintages

1986: Good year, quite tannic, interesting red fruit fragrance. Lovely rosé, typical, robust and fine at the same time, successful. Price range (pre-tax, ex-warehouse): Between 18 and 25 F.F.

Sales volume:
- Retail: 50%. - Restaurants: 50% (restaurants and wholesale).

Sales in France: 95%.
Export sales: 5%.
Main trading partners : Belgium, Germany, Netherlands, Switzerland.

References in France

Restaurants: Château d'Artigny.

DOMAINE DE L'ÉPAISSE

Guy Pontonnier
L'Épaisse - 37140 St-Nicolas de Bourgueil
47 97 84 69

Type of vineyard: Family-owned. **Established:** Father and son. **Vine stocks:** Cabernet Franc. **Soil:** Sand and Tuff gravel. **Exposure:** Slopes of St-Nicolas de Bourgueil. **Average annual production in hectoliters:** 350. **Appellation:** St-Nicolas de Bourgueil and Bourgueil. **Type:** Red. **Technique:** Old. **Alcohol content:** 12%. **Characteristics:** Beautiful, red color, intense, full, red fruit aromas with raspberrry dominance. **Serving temperature:** 16° to 17°. **Served with:** Lighter vintages, with red meat, grilled meat, white meat; others with more body, with game, also goes very well with cheese. **Vintages available in 89/90:** Bronze Medal in Paris 1987. 1986: Bourgueil old vine.

Characteristics of vintages

1986: Light and supple, fresh, good color, well made. Price range (pre-tax, ex-warehouse): Between 20 F.F. and 30 F.F.

Sales volume:
- Wholesale: 24%. - Retail: 75%. - Restaurants: 1%.

Sales in France: 95%. **Export sales:** 5%.
Main trading partners : Belgium.

TOURAINE

CONFRÉRIE DES VIGNERONS DE OISLY ET THÉSÉE

Ph. Angier
Oisly - 41700 Contres
54 79 52 88 - Telex: 750 834 - Fax: 54 79 05 28

Type of vineyard: Cooperative Agricultural Association. **Established:** 10.12.61. **Number of employees:** 18. **Soil:** Clay with calcium carbonate, silica-clay and covered top soil. **Average annual production in hectoliters:** 18,000. **Appellation:** A.O.C. Touraine. **Type:** Red, white, rosé. **Technique:** Temperature control (thermo-regulation of tanks). **Maturing:** Under inert gas. **Alcohol content:** 11,5%/vol. **Characteristics:** White: dry, fruity, light. Red: aromatic, which goes down smoothly. **Serving temperature:** 8° to 15°. **Served with:** Sauvignon: warm fish, game, terrine. Pineau de Loire: shellfish and fish. Gamay: red meat, grills, cooked pork. Cabernet: red meat, game. Touraine rouge: Barronie d'Aignan. **Vintages available in 89/90:** 1988.

Characteristics of vintages

1988: The year '88 without the body of the '85 is full of charm, typical of Loire Wines, finesse, fragrant, fruitiness. Good white wines which are very successful vintages. Price range (pre-tax, ex-warehouse): Between 10 F.F. and 20 F.F.

Sales volume:

– Retail: 7%. – Restaurants: 58%. – Other: Specialized merchants, specialized sales (caves, fine shops).

Sales in France: 73%.

Export sales: 27%.

Main trading partners : Great Britain, Germany, Holland, USA, Singapour, Australia, New-Zeland, Belgium, Hong Kong.

DOMAINE DE MONTIGNY

Jean-Marie Corbin
Montigny
54 79 60 82

Type of vineyard: Family-owned. **Established:** 1976. **Number of employees:** 1. **Vine stocks:** Sauvignon, Gamay, Cabernet, Côt, Pinault d'Aunis. **Soil:** Pebbly clay. **Exposure:** North, South. **Average annual production in hectoliters:** 1,000.

Appellation:AOC Touraine. **Type:** Red, white, rosé. **Technique:** Primeur: carbonic maceration. Traditional, under temperature for the others. **Alcohol content:** 12 to 12.5%. **Characteristics:** Sauvignon, very aromatic dry white wine. Pinault d'Aunis: fresh, slightly spicy wine. Tradition: veruy well-balanced blend of Gamay, Cabernet and Côt. **Serving temperature:** White and rosé: 10 to 12°. Red: 14 to 16°. **Served with:** Sauvignon: fish, asparagus, goat cheese. Red: meat, game.

Characteristics of vintages

1988; Sauvignon: very much appreciated for its fruity and smoky taste. **1987:** Tradition: harmonious marriage of fresh and fruity Gamay and the richer Côt and Cabernet. Beautiful ruby color with black currant fragrance. Price range (pre-tax, ex-warehouse): between 10 F.F. and 20 F.F.

Sales volume:

– Wholesale: 5%. – Retail: 80%. – Restaurants: 15%.

Sales in France: 100%.

References in France

Restaurants: La Vieille Fontaine (78600 Maison Lafitte), Restaurant Panoramique de la Tour Montparnasse (75015 Paris), Géopoly (75002 Paris).

Shops: Les Chais St François (56000 Vannes), La Maison du Vin (29128 Tregunc), Cavis (78000 Versailles).

Comments

Family enterprise for several generations. Collaboration with importers in the UK, Belgium and the Netherlands would be welcome.

DOMAINE DE LA CHARMOISE

Henri Marionnet
Soings – 41230 Mur-de-Sologne
54 98 70 73.

Type of vineyard: Family-owned. **Established:** May 1, 1969, father to son. **Number of employees:** 7. **Vine stocks:** 1/4 Sauvignon, 3/4 Gamay. **Soil:** Clay with flint some sand. **Exposure:** East. **Average annual production in hectoliters:** 3,000.

Appellation: Touraine. **Type:** Red, white, rosé. **Technique:** Very special vinification in all three wines. **Maturing:** Stainless steel tanks. **Alcohol content:** 11.5°. **Characteristics:** To be drunk with in the year; the vinification amount intended to extract the maximum of fruit and aroma, really extraodinary wine. They are so very natural, light fine and so smooth to drink. **Serving temperature:** White and rosé: 7°. Gamay Rouge: 9 to 11°. **Served with:** The red Gamay goes very well with the whole meal, the rosé, too; but especially in the summertime, whole the white goes very well with fish, porr, dry goat cheese and asparagus with cream. **Vintages available in 89/90:** 1986 and above all 1987.

Characteristics of vintages

1987: Flowery, density, extraordinary in white; beautiful and fine red, firm at the same time. Price range (pre-tax, ex-warehouse): Between 20 F.F. and 24 F.F.

Sales volume:

– Retail: 7%. – Restaurants: 50%. – Other: 43% (caves and export).

Sales in France: 83%.

Export sales: 17%.

Main trading partners : Benelux, Germany, England, Japan.

References in France

Restaurants: Guy Savoy, Le Vivarois, Le Bourdonnais, Paris. Robin à Bracieux; Le Quère Angers; Crémaillère, Orléans.

Shops: Hédiard, Legrand, Fief de Vigne, Nantes. Numerous "Bistrots a Vins".

Abroad

United Kingdom

Bibendum Wine Ltd. - Primerose Hill, London NW 1, 8UR.

Germany

Shops: Jacques Wein Depot Bilker, Allee 49, Postfach 260155, 4000 Dusseldorf.

The Netherlands

Sauter Wijnkelders BV, Rechtstraat 55, Po Box 3041 - 6202 NA Maastricht.

Belgium

Les fils de Coninck S.A., rue Middelbourg 66 1170 Bruxelles.

Japan

T.Y. Trading, Naga Building 3F, 8-10-14 Ginza - Chuo-Ku - Tokyo 104.

JM MONMOUSSEAU S.A.

Armand Monmousseau
B.P. 25 F - 41401 Montrichard Cedex
54 32 07 04 - Telex: 751 403

Type of vineyard: Corporation belongs to Champagne Taittinger since 1972. **Established:** 1886. **Number of employees:** 55. **Vine stocks:** Chenin Blanc, Sauvignon, Gamay. **Soil:** Clay with calcium carbonate. **Exposure:** Variable according to each vine variety, in general, very good exposure. **Average annual production in hectoliters:** 3500 to 4000. Wineyard: 50 hectares.
Appellation: Touraine. **Type:** Red, white, rosé. **Technique:** Modern, with a cooling system around the white. **Maturing:** In stainless steel tanks. **Alcohol content:** 11.5% to 12%. **Characteristics:** Mousseux A.O.C. (ever-vescent), harmonious, fine, elegant, well-balanced. Red: fruity, red fruit aromas, subtle and rich tannin. White: fresh, good fruit well structured. **Serving temperature:** Mousseux A.O.C.: 6° to 7°. Red: 12° to 14°. White: 6° to 7°. **Served with:** Mousseux A.O.C.: as an aperitif for hors-d'œuvre or fish in sauce. Red: meat, cheese. White: seafood, pâté, fish, many cooked pork meat. **Vintages available in 89/90:** 1983, 1985, 1986.

Characteristics of vintages

1986: Very successful wines in red and white; color, fruit, to be aged. **1985:** Tannic, rich and well-balanced for red; exceptional for the Vouvray. **1983:** Still Vouvray, ready, full, fruity character. Price range (pre-tax, ex-warehouse): Between 20 F.F. and 30 F.F.
Sales volume: 2 million bottles.
- Wholesale: Exclusively sold by an importer.
Sales in France: 55%.
Export sales: 45%.
Main trading partners: USA, UK, Germany, Norway, Switzerland.

CHÂTEAU DE CHENONCEAU

37150 Chenonceau
47 23 90 07 - Telex: 750 800 - Fax: 47 23 80 88

Type of vineyard: Private wine growing estate. **Established:** 1550. **Number of employees:** 5. **Vine stocks:** Cabernet, Chenin Blanc, Grolleau. **Soil:** Chalky clay. **Exposure:** South.
Appellation: Touraine. **Type:** Red, White, Rosé. **Technique:** Traditional. **For sparkling wine:** Traditional champagne method. **Characteristics:** Excellent, fruity and delicate, well made wines. **Serving temperature:** White & Rosé: cool - Red: room temperature.

Characteristics of vintages

1988: Excellent red (Cabernet), fruity, well made. **1986:** Superb white, concentrated aromas, harmonious.

DOMAINE OCTAVIE

Gaec Barbeillon Jean-Claude
Oisly - 41700 Contres France
54 79 54 57 or 54 79 62 30

Type of vineyard: Family-owned. **Established:** 19th Century. **Vine stocks:** 15 ha: Sauvignon 50%, Chenin 9%, Gamay 22%, Côt 5%, Cabernet 5%, Others 9%. **Soil:** Silica/Clay top soil; clay sub-soil. **Exposure:** South. **Average annual production in hectoliters:** 900.
Appellation: Touraine. **Type:** Red, white, rosé. **Others:** Method Champenoise. Method Traditionnelle. **Technique:** Temperature control: 18° (white, rosé), 25° (red). **Maturing:** In tanks. **Alcohol content:** 12% to 12.5%. **Characteristics:** Sauvignon 1988: dry white, very aromatic, and well-balanced. Gamay 1988: light, fruity and goes down smoothly. Touraine Tradition 1988: full bodied red wine based on Gamay, Cabernet and Côt. Pineau d'Aunis 1988: fruity, fresh and slightly spicy. **Serving temperature:** 10° to 12° for white and rosé; 14° for red. **Served with:** Sauvignon: hors-d'œuvre, shell-fish, fish or as an aperitif. Gamay: white meat, cooked port meat or for the whole meal. Touraine Tradition: red meat, game, cheese. Pineau d'Aunis: Cuisine Indochinoise. **Vintages available in 89/90:** 1988, 1987, 1985.

Characteristics of vintages

1988: White: rich and elegant with a concentrated flavour. Red: fruity, rich, supple and fragant. Price range (pre-tax, ex-warehouse): Between 12 F.F. and 23 F.F.
Sales volume:
- Retail: 20%. - Restaurants & vinothèques: 25%.
- Export: 55%.
Main trading partners: UK, Netherlands, Germany, Belgium.

Abroad

United Kingdom

Majestic Wines Warehouses/Yorkshire Fine Wines. Shops: Sage Resources: Hammond House. Salfords. Surrey RH1 5HB.

Germany

Vinum Weinfachhandel: Wachmannstrasse 39. 2800 Bremen 1. Tel: 0421/34 70 94. - Baus & Provot: Dudweiler Strasse 57. 6603 Sulzbach Neuweiler. Tel: (06897) 42 66. - Stecher & Krahn: Parkstrasse 31. 4000 Düsseldorf 30. Tel: (0211) 49 20 95.

The Netherlands

Wijnkoperij J. Bart: Postbus 231. 1440 AE Purmerend. Tel: 02998 3650. - Wijnkoperij de Oude Warande: Postbus 102. 5056 ZJ Berkel Enschot. Tel: 013.33.38.36.

Belgium

J. Verpoorten: Vivier 27. 5730 Malonne. Tel: 081 44 46 28.

Comments

Family vineyard, run by Mr. and Mrs. Barbeillon, Mr. Noë Rouballay and Patricia Denis Barbeillon who studied œnology at the University of Bordeaux. One usually says that

Loire wines are feminine. These wines nerlly are vinified by women, even with the help of Octavie, Patricia's great-granomother. There is a tasting-room for the reception of the customers.

VIN DE TOURAINE

Jean Louet
3, rue de la Paix – 41120 Monthou-sur-Bièvre
54 44 04 54

Type of vineyard: Family-owned. **Established:** 1960. **Number of employees:** 1. **Vine stocks:** White: Sauvignon, Chenin. Red: Red Gamay, Cabernet, Cot. **Soil:** Relatively light, silica, silica clay covered sub-soil. **Exposure:** Different exposures, leds a good harmony for making reds. **Average annual production in hectoliters:** 450 to 500. **Appellation:** Touraine, plus a Touraine made with the Champenoise method. **Type:** Red, white, rosé. **Technique:** Traditional. **Maturing:** Concrete and enamelled tanks. **Alcohol content:** 11.5%. **Characteristics:** Sauvignon Blanc: agreeable, fruity, goes down smoothly. Blanc sec from Chenin: more robust than the Sauvignon Rosé made by drawing off the Cuvée Red Gamay. Cabernet: dry, but fresh. Eed: made after fermentation and Gamay (60%), Caberent (25%) and Cot (15%). **Served with:** Sauvignon: goes well with fish at the beginning of the meal (10°). Chenin Blanc sec: as an aperitif, "Kir" and with shellfish at 10°. Rosé: between meals with pork cold paltes served at 12/14°. Red: goes as well as with meat at cheese served to 14° to 16°. **Vintages available in 89/90:** 1985, 1986.

Characteristics of vintages

1986: Red: agreeable, rather light, fresh. Rosé: very successful. **1985:** Excellent vintage better in Sauvignon, than in Red, richer, well-balanced, to be aged try the Rosé Champenoise Method, generally wellmade. Price range (pre-tax, ex-wareshouse): Between 10 F.F. and 30 F.F.
Sales volume:
– Wholesale: 40%. – Retail: 40%. – Restaurants: 20%.
Sales in France: 90%.
Export sales: 10%.
Main trading partners : Luxemburg, Belgium.

References in France

Restaurants: La Gallandière, Concarneau. Le Bois d'Amour, Pont Aven. La Tour d'Argent, Lamballe...
Shops: La Cave du Producteur, Lamballe and two other associates soon in the 26 000 region.

Comments

Winner of many competitions and a member of two wine fraternities and Trade Union in Touraine. They are very devote in setting a good example.

AMBOISE MESLAND

DOMAINE DE LA BESNERIE

Mr. & Mrs. François Pironneau
Route de Mesland – 41150 Monteaux
54 70 23 75

Type of vineyard: Family-owned. **Established:** For the third generation. **Vine stocks:** Gamay, Cabernet, Chenin, Sauvignon. **Soil:** Silica clay. **Exposure:** Hillsides. **Average annual production in hectoliters:** 800.

Domaine de la Besnerie
TOURAINE - MESLAND
APPELLATION CONTRÔLÉE
François et Jacqueline PIRONNEAU
Propriétaires - Viticulteurs
Route de Mesland - 41150 MONTEAUX - ☎ 54 70 23 75

Appellation: Touraine Mesland, Touraine, Crémant de Loire. **Type:** Red, White, Rosé. **Other:** Traditional Method & Crémant de Loire. **Technique:** Red: traditional, long maceration. **Maturing:** In stainless steel tanks and wooden vats. **Alcohol content:** 12%. **Characteristics:** Red (Gamay): natural blending Gamay-Cabernet (old vines), long keeping. White and Rosé: wines to be drunk young. **Serving temperature:** Red: 12 to 13°. Rosé & White: 8°. Sparkling wines: 8°. **Served with:** Red: red meat, cheese, game. White & Rosé: fish, delicatessen. **Vintages available in 89/90:** 1986, 1988.

Characteristics of vintages

1988: Very pleasant, can be drunk right now and kept in the cellar for 5 to 6 years. **1986:** Very aromatic, can be drunk now and kept in the cellar for 5 years. **1985:** Same as the 1986. Price range (pre-tax, ex-warehouse): 10 to 20 F.F. (still wine) – 20 to 50 F.F. (sparkling wine & Crémant).
Sales volume:
– Retail: 90%. – Restaurants: 10%.
Sales in France: 100%.

References in France

Restaurants: Charles IX (28 Charleval), Le Réverbère (Pézens), Le Grand Monarque (28 Chartres), Hôtel Restaurant Ibis (Le Mans), etc.
Shops: Vins Fins et Bar à Bière (6, rue Daguerre, 75014 Paris).

Comments

Family enterprise from father to son for three generations. The vineyard is located on the North bank of the Loire, between Blois and Amboise in the region of the Touraine-Mesland appellation and in the heart of the Valley of the Loire Châteaux.

DOMAINE DUTERTRE

Val de Loire
Jacques Dutertre
Limeray 37530 Amboise - France
47 30 10 69

Type of vineyard: Family-owned. **Established:** From father to son for 3 generations. **Vine stocks:** Cabernet, Gamay, Pinot Noir, Chenin, Sauvignon. **Soil:** Flinty clay on clay and sand. **Exposure:** South facing the Loire. **Average annual production in hectoliters:** 1,600.

DOMAINE DUTERTRE
VAL DE LOIRE
TOURAINE-AMBOISE
APPELLATION TOURAINE-AMBOISE CONTROLÉE
PRODUCE OF FRANCE
12 % vol.
750 ml
Mis en bouteille à la propriété par
DUTERTRE - Viticulteurs, place du Tertre à LIMERAY (I.-&-L.) France - Tél. 47.30.10.69

Appellation: Touraine-Amboise, Touraine. **Type:** Red, White, Rosé. **Technique:** Traditional. **Maturing:** In casks and stainless steel tanks. **Alcohol content:** 12%. **Characteristics:** Dry, Gamay: to be drunk young. Cuvée Prestige: good keeping. **Serving temperature:** Red: 15°. White & Rosé: 6 to 8°. **Served with:** Rosé: delicatessen. White: fish. Red: meat. **Vintages available in 89/90:** 1983, 1986, 1987, 1988.

Characteristics of vintages

1988: Very seductive, well balanced, good keeping. **1987:** Light, delicate and elegant. **1986:** Rich and well balanced, lingering taste. Price range (pre-tax, ex-warehouse): 10 to 30 F.F.

Sales volume:
- Wholesale: 25%. – Retail: 60%. – Restaurants: 15%.
- Other: 10% (export).

Main trading partners : UK, Netherlands, Belgium, Germany, Canada, Angleterre.

References in France

Restaurants: Local Restaurants in Amboise, La Baie de Saint-Brieuc.

Comments

From father to son for several generations. 35 hectares of vines. Right bank of the Loire, facing South.

VIGNOBLE DU CLOS CHÂTEAU GAILLARD

Vincent, Béatrice Girault
Mesland - 41150 Onzain
54 70 27 14

Type of vineyard: Family-owned. **Established:** 1978. **Number of employees:** 2. **Vine stocks:** Gamay Noir white juices, Sauvignon, Cabernet Franc, Cot, Chenin. **Soil:** Clay with flint on pebbly soil. **Average annual production in hectoliters:** 800.
Appellation: Touraine, Mesland, Crémant de Loire Champagne Method. **Type:** Red, white, rosé. **Technique:** Traditional (temperature control, pumping over, use of azote). **Maturing:** Traditional, in barrels of (225 liters) for the Touraine Mesland. **Alcohol content:** 12%. **Characteristics:** Touraine Mesland Rouge, Chateau Gaillard & Clos Chateau Gaillard: Harmonious, marked fruity aromas; goes down smothly (100% Gamay). Touraine Mesland Rouge Tration Vieilles Vignes: Hearty, round, rich and well-balanced (Gamay, Cabernet Cot). Touraine Sauvignon, Les 5 Arpents: Characteristics aromas, fine and distinguished. Gris de Touraine Mesland: Rosé, delicately fragrant, with subtle nuances. Crémant de Loire, Les Douciniéres: Extra-Brut. **Served with:** "Grattons", Chopped pork cooked in fat and served cold, meat pies, rabbit with chesnuts, jugged burbot, beef stew, peachs in wine. **Serving temperature:** 8 to 10°; 12° red; 14° tradition. **Vintages available in 89/90:** 1986, 1985, 1987 (Touraine Primeur).

Characteristics of vintages

1986: Good Touraine Sauvignon A.C. **1985:** Touraine Mesland Red A.C. Gold Medal Paris, 1986, Château Gaillard Gamay Tradition, from very old stocks. Price range (pre-tax, ex-warehouse): Between 10 F.F. and 30 F.F.

Sales volume:
– Retail: 20%. – Restaurants: 40%. – Other: 40%.

Sales in France: 65%.

Export sales: 35%.

Main trading partners : Netherlands, Belgium, Germany, England, Canada.

VOUVRAY

DOMAINE DU COTEAU DE LA BICHE

Christophe Pichot
25/32 rue de la Bonne Dame
37210 Vouvray
47 52 62 55 and 47 52 72 45

Type of vineyard: family-owned. **Established:** 1984. **Number of employees:** 1. **Vine stocks:** Chenin. **Soil:** Chalky clay. **Average annual production in hectoliters:** 275.
Appellation: Vouvray AOC. **Type:** White. **Technique:** Traditional. **Maturing:** in wooden casks. **Served with:** Dry: shellfish. Demi-sec: fish in sauce. Mellow: as an aperitif. **Vintages available in 89/90:** Demi-sec: 1985-1986. Dry: 1988. Mellow: 1988.

Characteristics of vintages

1988: Great finesse, fruity (bottled in May). **1987:** Fruity wine (out of stock). **1986:** Fruity, ready to be drunk with a blanquette or chicken in cream sauce. **1985:** Fine and fruity, for keeping. Price range (pre-tax, ex-warehouse): between 20 F.F. and 30 F.F.
Sales volume:
– Retail: 50%. – Restaurants: 30%.
Sales in France: 70%.
Export sales: 30%.
Main trading partners : USA, UK, Belgium.

References in France

Restaurants: Moulin de Maugins (R. Vergès), Château d'Artigny, Auberge Bretonne (J. Thorel), Mariott, Prince de Galles, etc.

Comments

The 26 hectare vineyard, located on the best hillsides of Vouvray since 1786, has been in the family for seven generations. In order to satisfy a demanding clientele and to produce quality wines, only 20 to 25 hectoliters of wine are produced per hectare.

JARRY DANIEL

99, rue de la Vallée Coquette – 37210 Vouvray
47 52 78 75

Type of vineyard: Family-owned. **Established:** 1848, Family succession since 1962. **Number of employees:** 2. **Vine stocks:** Chenin. **Soil:** Clay with calcium carbonate. **Exposure:** South. **Average annual production in hectoliters:** 350 to 400.
Appellation: Vouvray Tranquille (still) and Mousseux (evervescent). **Type:** White. **Others:** Champagne Method. **Technique:** Traditional. **Maturing:** In casks and cellars. **Alcohol content:** 12%. **Characteristics:** Type of wines: dry or semi-dry according to the vintage, a little acidic, may be aged several years. **Serving temperature:** 10° to 12°. **Served with:** Meat, fish, cheese (ex: Ste-Maure). **Vintages available in 89/90:** 1984, 1985, 1986, 1987.

Characteristics of vintages

1988: Excellent year. Dry, demi-sec and some mellow wine. **1986:** Dry and semi-dry; in Vouvray Tranquille: full. **1985:** Rich and well-balanced. Semi-dry. **1982:** Mousseux Brut et "Demi-Sec" (semi-dry): "Pétillant Sec" and "Demi-sec" (semi-dry); very refreshing. Price range (pre-tax, ex-warehouse): Between 20 F.F. and 30 F.F.
Sales volume:
– Retail: 90%. – Restaurants: 10%.
Sales in France: 75%.
Export sales: 25%.
Main trading partners : UK, Germany, Belgium.

References in France

Restaurants: Château d'Artigny in Montbazon, Hôtel du Bon Laboureur in Chenonceaux, Le Grand Monarque in Chartres.

Abroad

United Kingdom
Importers: Yapp Brothers Mere Wiltshire BA12 6DY. Tel: 0747 860 423.

WINE FROM THE AREA OF NANTES

MUSCADET DE SÈVRE ET MAINE

DOMAINE DU BOIS-JOLY

Henri Bouchaud
Le Bois Joly 44330 Le Pallet
40 80 40 83

Type of vineyard: Family-owned. **Established:** 1971. **Vine stocks:** "Melon", Folle Blanche. **Soil:** Metamorphic terrain, alluvium. **Exposure:** South-West. **Average annual production in hectoliters:** 900.

Appellation: Sèvre et Maine. **Type:** White. **Technique:** Fermentation on lees. **Maturing:** Underground in glass-lined tanks or on the surface in stainless steel tanks. **Alcohol content:** Muscadet: 12%. Gros Plant: 11%. **Characteristics:** Supple and fruity. **Serving temperature:** 9°. **Served with:** Fish and seafood.

Characteristics of vintages

1988: Firmer than the 1987 – should improve with ageing. **1987:** Very fruity. **1986:** Ready. Price range (pre-tax, ex-warehouse): 10 to 20 F.F.
Sales volume:
– Wholesale: 80%. – Retail: 18%. – Restaurants: 2%.

DOMAINE BREGEON

A. Michel Bregeon
Les Guisseaux Gorges 44190 Clisson
40 06 93 19

Type of vineyard: Family-owned. **Established:** 1975. **Vine stocks:** Melon de Bourgogne, Folle Blanche. **Soil:** Silica Clay. **Exposure:** South-West. **Average annual production in hectoliters:** 50 hl/ha.

Appellation: Muscadet de Sèvres-et-Maine-sur-Lie, Gros Plant du Pays Nantais. **Type:** White. Other: Sur Lie. **Technique:** Traditional. **Maturing:** In glass lined vats and casks. **Alcohol content:** Muscadet: 12%. Gros Plant: 11%. **Characteristics:** Dry, fruity and very delicate. **Serving temperature:** 8 to 9°. **Served with:** Muscadet: as an aperitif and with fish and sea food. Gros Plant: with shellfish. **Vintages available in 89/90:** 1987, 1988.

Characteristics of vintages

Price range (pre-tax, ex-warehouse): 10 to 20 F.F.
Sales volume:
– Retail: 45%. – Restaurants: 5%. – Other: 50% (export).
Sales in France: 50%.
Export sales: 50%.
Main trading partners : USA, UK, Germany, Belgium, Netherlands.

References in France

Restaurants: Au Marais (46-48, quai Louis-Tardy 79510 Coulon).
Shops: Cellier de Saint-Ouen (144, avenue de Saint-Ouen,

Paris 75008), Gérard Caminot (54, avenue de la Colombette, 31000 Toulouse).

Abroad

Belgium

MV Deryck Ronald SA, Leeuwbrugstraat 20-22, 9470 Denderleeuw.

United States

Importers: Kermit Lynch Wine Merchant, 1605 San Pablo Avenue, Berkeley, California 94702.

United Kingdom

Wodehouse Wine, Gary Williams, 97 Palewell Park, London SW 8 JJ 01 876 0082.

Germany

Heinrich & Heinrich, Wein & Feinkost, Gross & Einzelhandel, Dominikanerstr. 7.8600 Bamberg (Tel: 0951/58057). Inh. Sonja Krebs, Heinrich Sauer & Partner.

The Netherlands

Rijsenus de Frel Grotestraat 6 6711 AM EDE.

Comments

After manual harvesting, the grapes are taken whole to the wine press.

DONATIEN BAHUAUD

Jacques Bahuaud - Jean-Luc Blanchard
44330 La Loge
40 06 70 05 - Telex: 711 448

Type of vineyard: Family-owned. **Established:** 1929. **Vine stocks:** Muscadet. **Average annual production in hectoliters:** 3,500.

Appellation: Muscadet de Sèvre et Maine sur Lie. **Type:** White. **Technique:** Classic. **Alcohol content:** 12%. **Characteristics:** On lees, gives off a bit of natural carbonic gas due to the bottling technique and the cleanliness of the vinification environment. **Serving temperature:** 8°. **Served with:** fish, shellfish. **Vintages available in 89/90:** 1986. **Brand name:** Le Master de Donatien.

Characteristics of vintages

1986: Excellent wines, natural, clean and typical, regular success. Price range (pre-tax, ex-warehouse): between 20 F.F. and 30 F.F.
Sales in France: 60%. **Export sales:** 40%.
Main trading partners: UK, Germany, Belgium, USA, Canada, Japan, Australia.

Abroad

United States

Importers: Donatien Bahuaud Office N.Y.

United Kingdom

Importers: Donatien Bahuaud Office London.

Germany

Importers: Lagenbach, Worms.

Canada

Importers: SAQ Montreal. LCBO Toronto.

Far East

Importers: Suntory Japan.

Others

Importers: Chacalli, Brussels, Belgium.

CHÂTEAU DU CLERAY

Sauvion & Fils
B.P. 3 - 44330 Vallet
Tel: 40 36 22 55 - Telex: 710 147 - Fax: 40 36 34 62

Type of vineyard: Agricultural Association. **Established:** 1965. **Number of employees:** 40. **Vine stocks:** "Melon". **Soil:** Silica clay. **Average annual production in hectoliters:** 250,000 cs × 12.

Appellation: Muscadet AOC S & M sur lie. **Type:** White. **Technique:** Destemming, temperature control. **Maturing:** In casks and vats. **Alcohol content:** 12%. **Characteristics:** Dry and fruity. **Serving temperature:** 6°. **Vintages available in 89/90:** 1988.

Characteristics of vintages

1988: Supple, dry, aromatic. Price range (pre-tax, ex-warehouse): 15 to 30 F.F.
Sales volume:
- Retail: 15%. - Restaurants: 85%.
Sales in France: 30%.
Export sales: 70%.
Main trading partners: 72 countries.

References in France

Restaurants: George V, Pavillon Élysée, La Grande Cascade, Le Ritz, etc.
Shops: Legrand, Hédiard.

Abroad

United States

Importers: William J. Deutsch. Sherry-Lehman 679, Madison NYC. Lutèce - NY - La Côte Basque NY.

CHÂTEAU DES GAUTRONNIÈRES

Claude Fleurance
44330 La Chapelle-Heulin
40 06 74 06 - 40 06 74 02

Type of vineyard: Family-owned. **Established:** Around 1850, 5th generation. **Vine stocks:** 15 hectares devoted to Muscadet Sèvre-et-Maine, 5 hectares for other wines. **Soil:** Silica-clay. **Exposure:** North-East, South. **Average annual production in hectoliters:** 60 hl/ha.

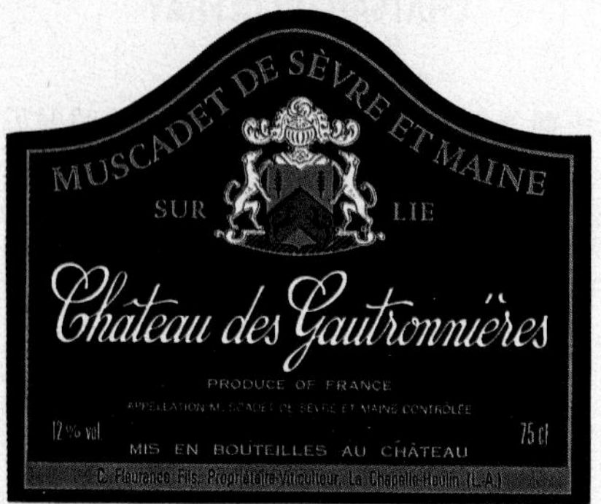

Appellation: Muscadet Sèvre-et-Maine AOC. **Type:** White. **Technique:** Low temperature (19-20°). **Alcohol content:** 12%. **Characteristics:** Light, dry, fruity - slight gun flint taste. **Serving temperature:** 8 to 10°. **Served with:** Seafood and fish. **Vintages available in 89/90:** 1987 and 1988 (after summer).

Characteristics of vintages

1987: Fruity and long. Price range (pre-tax, ex-warehouse): 10 to 20 F.F.

Sales volume:
- Wholesale: 20%. - Retail: 25%. - Restaurants: 5%. - Other: 50% (export).

Abroad

United Kingdom

Paul Boutinot, Wines Ltd Stockport (Tel: 061 477 1171).

The Netherlands

Louis H.A.M. 2011 GE Haarlem (Tel: 023 31 22 40).

DOMAINE DE LA LOUVETRIE

Pierre et Joseph Landron
Les Brandières - 44690 La Haye-Fouassière
40 54 83 27 - Telex: 700 181 F Oceatex Attn. Joseph Landron

Type of vineyard: Family Agricultural Association. **Vine stocks:** Melon de Bourgogne. **Exposure:** Hillsides facing South and Southwest. **Average annual production in hectoliters:** 1,700.

Appellation: Muscadet Sèvre-et-Maine sur Lie. **Type:** White. **Technique;** First juice of the pressing fermented at low temperature (16°), traditional bottling on lees. **Maturing:** Glass-lined tanks. **Characteristics:** A Muscadet, full-bodied beacause of its hillside origine, should be aged a minimum of a year in the bottel. Extra finesse and personality result from ageing two years. **Serving temperature:** 8°. **Served with:** Shell-fish and fine fish, or as an aperitif before meals. **Vintages available in 89/90:** 1987 Cuvée Prestige, 1987 and 1988 Hermine d'Or.

Characteristics of vintages

1988: Very typical Muscadet. Yield 30% less than in 1987. Rich, well-balanced, structured, fine wines. To be drunk in 1990. Gold Medal in Paris. **1987:** Hermine d'Or: Great finesse, fruity, rich and well-balanced, ready to be drunk now. Cuvée Prestige: produced exclusively from old vines from the FIEF DU BREIL (hillsides facing South). Remarkable finesse, quite typical fruitiness because of the schistic soil. To be drunk in 1989 and 1990. A great Muscadet. **1986:** "Hermine d'Or": good selection, fresh, fruity, full. **1985:** Cuvée Prestige (Hillside, old vines) very successful, typical and fragrant. Average pre-tax, ex-warehouse price: 23 F.F. Price range (pre-tax, ex-warehouse): Between 14 F.F. and 30 F.F.

DOMAINE DE GRAS-MOUTONS

Jean Dabin and son
44690 Saint-Fiacre
40 54 81 01

Type of vineyard: Family-owned. **Established:** 1927. **Number of employees:** 6 permanent. **Vine stocks:** Muscadet (known locally as "Melon"). **Soil:** Silica clay. **Exposure:** North-East and South-East. **Average annual production in hectoliters:** 1,000 to 2,000.

Appellation: Muscadet de Sèvres-et-Maine "Sur Lie". **Type:** White. **Technique:** Traditional with temperature control. **Maturing:** 2/3 in oak casks. **Alcohol content:** 12%. **Characteristics:** Lively and gay, like all Muscadet "sur lie", with an extra plus for the aroma particular to the Domaine de Gras-Moutons, and a flavor described as "gun flint" by the old timers. **Serving temperature:** 12 to 14°. **Served with:** It is often said that the Muscadet is the "wine for any time of day". It can be drunk from the beginning to the end of the meal, but, with oysters and sea food it is perfect, with most fish it is very good and with a white butter sauce it is sensational. **Vintages available in 89/90:** 1987 (and 1988 as of June 89).

Characteristics of vintages

1988: Will be bottled in April 89. It should dominate the recent years. **1987:** At the peak of its flavor. Price range (pre-tax, ex-warehouse): between 10 and 20 F.F.

Sales volume:

- Wholesale: 25%. - Retail: 30%. - Restaurants: 25%.
- Other: 20% (winecellars), for sales in France.

Sales in France: 60%.

Export sales: 40% (90% wholesale).

Main trading partners : Germany, Australia, Belgium, United Kingdom, Japan, Netherlands, United States.

References in France

Restaurants: The great restaurants of Paris, Brussels, London and Tokyo.

Comments

A dedicated winemaker, attached to tradition (manual harvesting, no herbicides) who produces excellent wines, notably the Muscadet-sur-Lie.

DOMAINE DE LA GRANGE

Pierre and Rémy Luneau

40 06 43 90 - Telex: 699 559 (Luno 4390)

Established: beginning of the 18th century. **Number of employees:** 6. **Vine stocks:** Nantes, Loire Valley varieties. **Soil:** Light, pebbly soil and old terrain mixed with eruptive rock. **Exposure:** South, South-East. **Average annual production in hectoliters:** 50 hl/hectare.

Appellation: Muscadet de Sèvre et Maine "Sur Lie". **Type:** White. **Technique:** Debourbage, selection of grapes, separate vinification of the "Clos", temperature controlled fermentation. **Maturing:** Cuvée spéciale: in oak casks. **Alcohol content:** 12%. **Characteristics:** Bottling "on lees" is a traditional techiques of the Nantes region. The Muscadet is a fresh, light wine with fine floral aromas. **Serving temperature:** 8 to 12°. **Served with:** As an aperitif or with seafood and fish in "Nantes white butter sauce". **Vintages available in 89/90:** 76, 79, 85, 86, 87, 88.

Characteristics of vintages

1988: More vigorous and lively, fresh. **1987:** Well-structured, long, aroma of the soil. **1985:** Great finesse, elegant and flowery. **Other:** 1979: Very elegant, fine, well-structured. 1976: Very rich, soft and full, persistant aromas. The Cuvée Prestige, awarded medals at the Concours Général Agricole, Paris, or the Prix d'Excellence des Œnologues, is produced annually. Price range (pre-tax, ex-warehouse): between 10 F.F. and 50 F.F.

Sales volume:

- Wholesale: 10%. - Retail: 20%. - Restaurants: 40%.
- Other: 10% (fine winecellars).

Sales in France: 40%.:**Export sales:** 60%.

Main trading partners : UK, Belgium, Netherlands, Germany, USA, Ireland.

Abroad

United States

New Jersey. Tel: (609) 683 5887.

United Kingdom

Grands Vins de France, London. Tel: 01 340 9550.

Belgium

A.R.B.B. Bleuzet, Brussels. Tel: 466 15 000.

The Netherlands

Kertens (Tilburg). Tel: 013 67 82 34.

Comments

Already, at the beginning of the 18th century, the "Melon" vinestock, orginally from Burgundy and known as Muscadet, was planted at the Domaine de la Grange. Each succeeding generation contributed the best of its experience, enthusiasm and love for wine and the vines. Pierre and Rémy Luneau, following 7 generations of winegrowers, continue the family tradition by producing a Muscadet characteristic of the soil. The Luneau family also cultivates the Domaine de la Claretière on the Vallet hillsides.

DOMAINE DE LA FRUITIÈRE
Jean-Joseph Douillard
La Fruitière - Château Thébaud 44690
40 06 53 05

Type of vineyard: Family-owned. **Established:** 1914. **Number of employees:** 2. **Vine stocks:** Melon. **Soil:** Silica clay covered. **Average annual production in hectoliters:** 50.
Appellation: Muscadet de Sèvre et Maine sur Lie. **Type:** White. **Technique:** Selection of first days, racking of the must, temperature control during fermentation. **Maturing:** Underground. **Alcohol content:** 12%. **Characteristics:** Fine, dry, fruity. **Serving temperature:** 10°. **Serving with:** Seafood, fish, as an aperitif. **Vintages available in 89/90:** 1986.

Characteristics of vintages

Price range (pre-tax, ex-warehouse): Between 10 F.F. and 20 F.F.
Sales volume:
- Retail: 5%. - Restaurants: 15%. - Other: 80% (export).
Sales in France: 20 %.
Export sales: 80 %.
Main trading partners: Germany, Belgium, USA, England.

References in France

Shops: Delphin Nantes, restaurant 2 étoiles Michelin.

Abroad

United States
Importers: World Shippers, 1420 Wolmert Street, Philadelphia 19102, Penna.

United Kingdom
Importers: Friarwood Ltd., 26 New Kings Road, London SW 6.

Germany
Importers: Kroté Am Wollershof 5400 Kabluvez 1 RFA.

The Netherlands:
Importers: Prosper Van Nieulande Bariancloan 159 4818 Great Britain.

Comments

Wine-makers: father and son for 4 generations. Medals every years in numerous National Contests.

• Watch out for wines that have lost their authenticity, "with neither soul nor virtue", most often the result of specific vinification techniques (carbonic maceration, too long maturing in casks...). See the various Regions: Bordeaux, Languedoc, South-West, Provence...

DOMAINE DES MORTIERS GOBIN
Robert Brosseau
La Rairie - 44690 La Haie Fouassière
40 54 80 66

Type of vineyard: Family-owned. **Established:** 1957. **Vine stocks:** Melon de Bourgogne 100%. **Soil:** Silica and clay **Exposure:** South, West, East. **Average annual production in hectoliters:** 450.
Appellation: Muscadet de Sèvre-et-Maine sur Lie AOC. **Type:** White. **Technique:** Manually harvested grapes, pressing, fermentation with temperature control (18° to 21°). **Maturing:** In glass tanks until bottling. **Alcohol content:** 12%. **Characteristics:** Dry without excess, very typical and fruity, ages well: 5 to 6 years. **Serving temperature:** 8° to 10°. **Served with:** Perfect with spicy dishes veal, shellfish, fish, white meat; appreciated as an aperitif, with or without Blackcurrant liqueur it's the wine for any hour. **Vintages available in 89/90:** 1985, 1986.

Characteristics of vintages

1986: Clear, dry, lively. **1985:** Perfect wine, ready to be drunk, very fine and fruity. Price range (pre-tax, ex-warehouse): Between 20 F.F. and 30 F.F.
Sales volume:
- Wholesalel: 25%. - Retail: 30%. - Restaurants: 25%. - Other: 20% (export).
Sales in France: 80%.
Export sales: 20%.
Main trading partners: England, USA, Belgium, Germany.

References in France

Restaurants: Hôtel Plaza-Athènée, Paris; Hôtel Restaurant La Croix Verte, Neau (Mayenne); La Ferme du Magnan; La Mole Cogolin.

Abroad

United States
Importers: Idel Wines, 3890 Mystie Valley Parkway, Medford. MA 02155. Tel: 395 3300. Telex: 443 0153 Iwscoing.

United Kingdom
Importers: Hein Wines Ltd. 6 Overdale Avenue New Malden, Surrey KT3 3 UF. Tel: 01 941 2328.

Germany
Importers: Particulars.

Belgium
Importers: Mr. Agresti, La Charette Silicienne Bruxelles. Tel: 021 374 1840.

Comments

Property Mortiers Gobin, vineyard located on hillsides of Sèvre Nantaise, around 15 km form Nantes, towards Clisson Poetiers, tasting and sales to the property; all days by appointment except from the 1st to 22 August.

CHÂTEAU DE L'OISELINIÈRE

Jean Aulanier
Gorges 44190 Clisson
40 06 91 59

Type of vineyard: Agricultural Association. **Established:** In the family since 1762. **Vine stocks:** "Melon", Muscadet. **Soil:** Eruptive rock, silica clay. **Exposure:** East, South, South-West. **Average annual production in hectoliters:** 2,000.

Appellation: Muscadet de Sèvre-et-Maine AOC. **Type:** White. **Technique:** Cold pressing. **Maturing:** Temperature controlled fermentation. **Alcohol content:** 12%. **Characteristics:** Dry, vigorous, intense aromas, long, worthy of its excellent origin. **Serving temperature:** 10 to 12°. **Served with:** All sea food and, in particular, ocean fish, sole and salmon, river trout, fresh cheese.

Characteristics of vintages

1988: At present quite vigorous, very fruity, has good ageing potential. **1987:** Very successful, with aromatic grace and distinction, supple, round, will fulfill its promise. **1986:** Full fragrance, fine and elegant (out of stock). Average pre-tax ex-warehouse price: 14.85 F.F. (on lees), 13.65 F.F. (normal), by carton of 12 bottles.
Sales volume:
- Wholesale: 35%. - Retail: 25%. - Restaurants: 40%.
Sales in France: 50%.
Export sales: 50%.
Main trading partners: United States, Venezuela, UK, Belgium, Germany.

Comments

The Château de l'Oiselinière, stylish historic home, has been in the family since 1762. Vines have been cultivated there since at least the 14th century and the "Vigne Blanche de Muscadet" since 1635, date at which the Muscadet was born, according to an old parchment. Constantly striving for the best, the proprietors adapt to the constraints of their chosen soil, control the yields and exploit the ancien vineyard to guarantee the typical nature of the Muscadet de Sèvre-et-Maine.

CHÂTEAU DU POYET

Bonneau Family - Alain Bonneau
Le Poyet 44330 La Chapelle-Heulin
40 06 74 52 - Telex: 699559 MSMP2652

Type of vineyard: Family-owned. **Established:** 1965. **Number of employees:** 2. **Vine stocks:** "Melon" of Burgundy for the Muscadet. **Soil:** Sandy and pebbly clay – on schistous sub-soil. **Exposure:** Variable. **Average annual production in hectoliters:** 50-55 hl/ha. **Appellation:** Muscadet de Sèvres et Maine. **Type:** White. **Technique:** Selection of grapes for pressing, temperature control. **Maturing:** Fermentation on lees in glass-lined tanks. **Alcohol content:** 12%. **Characteristics:** Very fine, quality wine, carefully made. **Serving temperature:** 12°. **Served with:** Seafood, fish. **Vintages available in 89/90:** 1988.

Characteristics of vintages

1988: Pleasant, clean and fruity. **1987:** Fruity, well balanced, very delicate. Price range (pre-tax, ex-warehouse): 10 to 20 F.F.
Sales volume:
- Wholesale: 40%. - Retail: 15%. - Restaurants: 15%.
- Other: 30% (export).
Sales in France: 40%.
Export sales: 60%.
Main trading partners: UK, Belgium, Denmark.

References in France

Restaurants: Mère Poulard (Mont Saint Michel), Prunier (Paris), Hôtel du Grand Monarque (Chartres).
Shops: Cave Esteve, Paris.

Abroad

Others

Denmark: Taster Wines. Northern Ireland: Findlater, Dublin.

• *Paulée – traditional meal which brings winelovers and winegrowers together after the harvest, particularly in Burgundy.*

CHÂTEAU LA RAGOTIÈRE
CHÂTEAU LA MORINIÈRE
DOMAINE COUILLAUD

Bernard, Michel et François Couillaud
La Regrippière
44330 VALLET - F
40 33 60 56 - Telex: 711381 BMFVIGN

Type of vineyard: Family agricultural association. **Established:** 1979. **Number of employees:** 5.

1. Château La Ragotière: 25 continuous hectares. **Vine stocks:** "Melon" of Burgundy (Muscadet Sèvre & Maine). **Soil:** Metamorphic, vegetal silica clay. **Exposure:** La Ragotière is located on a hilltop, at an average altitude of 78 meters. **Average annual production in hectoliters:** Muscadet Sèvre & Maine 1,400 hl, or 185,000 bottles.

2. Château La Morinière: 20 hectares. **Vine stocks:** "Melon" of Burgundy (Muscadet Sèvre & Maine). **Soil:** Metamorphic rock with veins of granite on the Southern slope, alluvial clay on the plateau. **Exposure:** La Morinière faces full South, with its highest point at 93 meters. **Average annual production in hectoliters:** Muscadet Sèvres & Maine 1,100 hl or 145,000 bottles.

3. Domaine Couillaud: Vine stocks: Chardonnay. **Soil:** Metamorphic rock. **Exposure:** Exceptionnal – full South

on irregular terrain. **Average annual production in hectoliters:** 1,400 hl or 190,000 bottles.

Appellations: Muscadet Sèvres & Maine sur lie, Chardonnay Jardin de France. **Type:** Muscadet: pneumatic pressing, destemming, control of alcoholic fermentation temperature between 18 and 21 °C, bottling on lees in April following the harvest. Chardonnay: pneumatic pressing, destemming, alcoholic fermentation, malolactic fermentation in oak casks (10 to 20% new) and in vats, temperature controlled fermentation. **Characteristics:** Muscadet Ragotière and Morinière: Fine, rich and well-balanced, with a light touch of the soil, they often need a year in the bottle to reach full maturity. To be drunk at any hour of the day, but especially as an aperitif or at table where it goes marvelously well with sea food, shellfish and fish. Chardonnay: Rich and fruity with a good tannic balance. Goes particularly well with fish in sauce or white meat. **Vintages available in 89/90:** Muscadet 1987 & 1988, Chardonnay 1988.

Characteristics of vintages

Price range (pre-tax, ex-warehouse): between 15 and 20 F.F.
Sales volume:
– Wholesale: 20% – Retail: 5% – Restaurants: 5% – Export: 70%.

Comments

For good keeping and great finesse, all of the wines are stabilized at low temperature before bottling. The Muscadets are wines intended for keeping. The proprietors would be pleased to have you discover their little "vinotheque" at the Château de La Ragotière where you can sample the 1969, 1964 and 1947 vintages, which have kept remarkably well.
Last minute news: The Chardonnay Domaine Couillaud 1988 has just been awarded:
1. A silver medal at the Concours général agricole, Paris.
2. A silver "Cépage" prize at the Concours national des vins de cépage.

CLOS DES ROSIERS

Philippe Laure
Les Rosiers – 44330 Vallet
40 33 91 83

Type of vineyard: Family-owned; father and son 3rd generation. **Vine stocks:** Melon de Bourgogne (Muscadet), Folle Blanche (G. Plant). **Soil:** Silica and clay. **Appellation:** Muscadet de Sèvre-et-Maine, Gros plant du Pays Nantais. **Type:** White. **Technique:** Manual harvested grapes, pressing, racking of the must, fermentation control. **Maturing:** Oak casks and underground glass tanks. **Alcohol content:** Muscadet: 12% – fruity, fragrant. Gros plant: 11% – Dry and light, diuretic. **Serving temperature:** 8° for Muscadet: with fish. **Served with:** Gros plant, shellfish and seafood. **Vintages available in 89/90:** 1989.

Characteristics of vintages

1988: Good wine, well-balanced with all the character of its appellation, dry and fruity. Price range (pre-tax, ex-cellar, ex-warehouse): between 10 F.F. and 20 F.F.
Sales volume:
cellar. – Wholesale: 10% – Retail: 60% – Restaurants: 30%.
Sales in France: 70%.
Export sales: 30%.
Main trading partners: England, Germany, Belgium, Holland.

FIEFS VENDÉENS

LA PETITE GROIE

Xavier Coirier
Pissotte – 85200 Fontenay le Comte
51 69 40 98

Type of vineyard: Family Corporation. **Established:** 1890 (3 generations). **Vine stocks:** Chenin, Melon, Chardonnay, Gamay, Pinot Noir, Cabernet (Sauvignon, Franc). **Soil:** Silica clay covered. **Exposure:** South and Southwest. **Average annual production in hectoliters:** 900. **Appellation:** Fiefs Vendeens Pissotte A.O. V.D.Q.S. **Type:** Red, white, rosé. **Technique:** Classic. Research of determinant mixed with temperature control. **Maturing:** Only in tanks. **Alcohol content:** 11.5% to 12%. **Characteristics:** White: rich, fruity: grapes, greeen apples, notes of wisteria. Important long lasting flavor, good suppleness, excellent wine for cooking. Rosé: very beautiful fruity, elegant and a pleasure to taste. Red: light, short fermentation with skins, appreicate after 4 or 5 years ageing. **Serving temperature:**White and rosé: 8° to 10°. Red: around 15°. **Served with:** White shellfish: spider crab, crab; and pork, fish steamed in tinfoil. Rosé: light meal, summer salad, fish in sauce. Red: roast meat (pork, duck). **Vintages available in 89/90:** harvest 1986, Harvest 1985 (Red).

Characteristics of vintages

1986: White and rosé: to be drunk young (around 2 years), even better in the year which follows the Harvest. **1985:** Good red, charming and forthcoming. Price range (pre-tax, ex-warehouse): between 10 F.F. and 20 F.F.
Sales volume:
– Wholesale: 20%. – Retail: 40%. – Restaurants: 10%. – Other: 30% Caves Merchant
Sales in France: 95%.
Export sales: 5%.
Main trading partners: Belgium, England, Germany, Holland private individuals.

References in France

Restaurants: Nantes, La Rochelle, Niort, La Vendée. In Paris: Les Boucholeurs, La Cagouille.
Shops: Legrand Paris, Le Fief de Vigne, Nantes; Le Petit Bacchus, Steven Spurrier Paris, La Rochelle, Niort.
Gold and Silver Medal at the Concours général agricole of Paris 1988-1989.

• *The price scandal, botched up vintages and compromised reputations: the truth and nothing but the truth (see Bordeaux, Provence and Châteauneuf-du-Pape Classifications).*

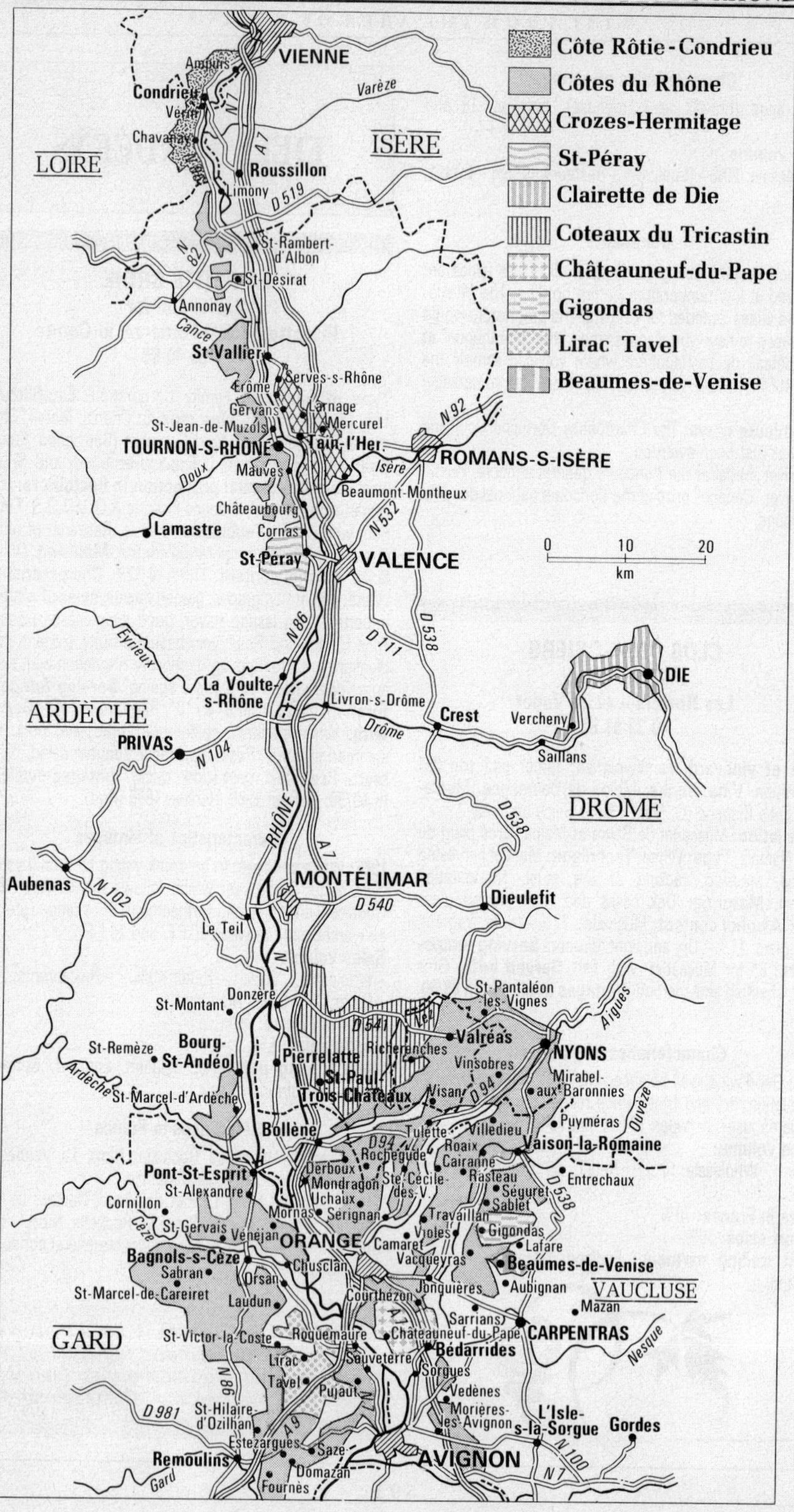

Côte Rôtie - Condrieu
Côtes du Rhône
Crozes-Hermitage
St-Péray
Clairette de Die
Coteaux du Tricastin
Châteauneuf-du-Pape
Gigondas
Lirac Tavel
Beaumes-de-Venise
0 10 20
km
VIENNE
Ampuis
Condrieu
Vérin
Chavanay
LOIRE
ISÈRE
Varèze
Roussillon
Limony
D 519
St-Rambert-d'Albon
St-Désirat
Annonay
Cance
St-Vallier
Serves-s-Rhône
Érôme
Gervans
Larnage
Mercurel
St-Jean-de-Muzols
TOURNON-S-RHÔNE
Tain-l'Her.
Isère
ROMANS-S-ISÈRE
N 92
Doux
Mauves
Beaumont-Montheux
Châteaubourg
Lamastre
Cornas
N 532
St-Péray
VALENCE
D 111
D 538
Eyrieux
La Voulte-s-Rhône
Livron-s-Drôme
Drôme
Crest
Vercheny
DIE
Saillans
ARDÈCHE
PRIVAS
N 104
DRÔME
RHÔNE
A 7
N 86
Aubenas
N 102
MONTÉLIMAR
D 540
Dieulefit
Le Teil
N 7
St-Pantaléon-les-Vignes
Donzère
St-Montant
D 541
Aigues
Valréas
NYONS
St-Remèze
Bourg-St-Andéol
Pierrelatte
Richerenches
Vinsobres
Ardèche
St-Paul-Trois-Châteaux
Visan
D 94
Mirabel-aux-Baronnies
St-Marcel-d'Ardèche
Ouvèze
Puyméras
Bollène
Tulette
Villedieu
Vaison-la-Romaine
Roaix
Rochegude
Cairanne
Pont-St-Esprit
Derboux
Ste-Cécile-des-V.
Rasteau
Entrechaux
St-Alexandre
Mondragon
Séguret
Uchaux
Sablet
D 538
Cornillon
Mornas
Sérignan
Travaillan
Cèze
St-Gervais
Violès
Gigondas
Vénéjan
ORANGE
Camaret
Lafare
Bagnols-s-Cèze
Chusclan
Vacqueyras
Beaumes-de-Venise
Sabran
Orsan
Jonquières
Aubignan
St-Marcel-de-Careiret
Laudun
Courthézon
VAUCLUSE
Mazan
Sarrians
CARPENTRAS
GARD
St-Victor-la-Coste
Roquemaure
Châteauneuf-du-Pape
Bédarrides
Nesque
Lirac
Sauveterre
Sorgues
Tavel
Pujaut
N 86
Vedènes
D 981
St-Hilaire-d'Ozilhan
Morières-les-Avignon
L'Isle-s-la-Sorgue
Gordes
Estezargues
A 9
Saze
N 100
Remoulins
AVIGNON
Domazan
N 7
Gard
Fournès

THE RHÔNE VALLEY

1989 CLASSIFICATION
CHÂTEAUNEUF-DU-PAPE ©

	Red	White
Beyond Classification	Château FORTIA	
First Category Great Wines	Château de Beaucastel Château La Gardine** Domaine de Montredon Château Rayas Domaine du Vieux-Lazaret	Bosquet des Papes Clos des Papes Domaine de Montredon** Château Rayas
Second Category Great Wines	Bosquet des Papes Clos des Papes Domaine de Cabrières* Domaine Riche Domaine Trintignant	Château Fortia* Château La Gardine*
Third Category Great Wines	Domaine de Beaurenard Clos de l'Oratoire des Papes Domaine Diffenty Domaine de Montpertuis Domaine du Père Caboche Domaine de La Roquette* Domaine de la Vieille-Julienne	Domaine de Cabrières* Domaine de Montpertuis* Domaine du Père Caboche
Fourth Category Great Wines	Domaine de La Janasse* Domaine de Nalys	

Beyond Classification: Deserves this distinction, in tribute to the man as well, a standout in the appellation.
(*) Might deserve a better rating in certain vintages - (**) In particular after 1982.
N. B. : To hold on to: Max Chapontier's Châteauneuf-du-Pape La Bernardine, up there with the Greats.

The "Grands Crus" and the others

We have had some of our most delightful wine tastings with the winemakers themselves, in their own vineyards, from Tavel to Châteauneuf (see Classification 89), from the Côtes-du-Rhône-Villages to the great wines of the North (Condrieu, Hermitage...).
In whites as well as reds, even without taking into consideration the great Northern appellations (see "Wine Types"), there are some remarkable bottles in the "modest" Southern Côtes-du-Rhône appellations. An excellent quality/price ratio is associated with good ageing potential. The idea of vintage is much less important than in Burgundy or in the Gironde as indicated by some beautiful successes with the 87 vintage and the superb 88. Don't fail to take advantage of your visits to this (very) great vineyard to take a look at the terrain, study the typical nature of the soils (absolutely fundamental), meet the winegrowers and savor some very surprising nectars.

HISTORICAL BACKGROUND

Of the vast vineyards in the Rhône Valley, legend tells about the famous Hermitage Cru. In 1224, Henry Gaspard de Sterinberg, a knight returning from the crusade against the Albigenses, is said to have climbed to the very top of Mount Hermitage and vowed to lead an exemplary, solitary existence.

Other hermits followed his example and planted vines near the grotto where they lived. They were assisted by monk winegrowers from St. Bernard and St. Bruno, who owned the church and priory of Tain. These monks had proven their wine-growing skills in Burgundy.

The hillside of Hermitage became a popular site where people came to taste its wine. The vineyard grew and the wine from it could be sold only in barrels which carried the stamp of the lord who owned it. Cistercian monks from the Abbey of Aiguebelle showed interest in the wines from Gigondas and Vacqueyras beginning in 1137 and pursued their interest until the Revolution during which time the Abbey was destroyed.

The origin of Châteauneuf-du-Pape dates back to Pope Clement V. He had a summer residence built far enough away from the papal residence in Avignon to discourage intruders. The residence was completed by Clement VII. It was a *châteauneuf* or new chateau as opposed to the old chateau of the pontifical court. When the popes returned permanently to their Italian residence, Avignon sent them wines from the region. Some Avignon residents who followed the popes to Rome were also sent wines from their home region.

Châteauneuf-du-Pape wine is the best known of all Côtes du Rhône wines. It takes its name from the ruins of a summer palace which was destroyed by the Huguenots. But there was never a lack of Carthusian monasteries in the region of Avignon. Bompas is the site of the Knights Templars commandry, which later became the property of the Knights Hospitalers. It was later returned to John XXII who in 1318 donated it to the Carthusian monks.

The right side of the Rhône Valley includes Côte Rôtie, a very old vineyard which is comprised of "Côte Brune" and "Côte Blonde." These names apparently recall a citizen of note of Ampuis, Sire Maurigon. He is said to have divided his land between his two daughters—one was a brunette, the other, a blonde.

A stone's throw away is Condrieu or "Coin du Ruisseau" (a tiny segment of a stream). Condrieu's history preserves traces of the ford and harbor where bargemen were hired. They navigated between the Kingdom and the Empire because under Charlemagne's rule, the Rhône Valley served as a frontier between the right bank or the "Kingdom" and the left bank or the "Empire." If you visit the region, you shouldn't miss the Condrieu Museum which houses the huge crosses that decorated the bows of the bargemen's boats.

Another bit of trivia: in the 9th century the Benedictine monks are said to have won Cornas and St. Perax by betting dinners where the main dish was a plump and juicy local fish.

Bacchus, the vineyards and wines have been hallowed all along the banks of the Rhône. Many statues dedicated to the god of wine have been found among the vestiges of Roman ruins.

THE WINES

RIGHT AND LEFT BANKS, NORTHERN SECTOR

• **COTE ROTIE.** Red wines exclusively, made from Syrah (80% minimum) and Viognier. Appellation approved by decree October 18, 1940. The vineyards are delimited to the communes of Ampuis, Saint Cyr sur le Rhône and Tupin-et-Semons on the right bank of the Rhône, 7 km downstream from Vienne. The land is divided into:
— The "Côte Brune" (clay soil of darkish color) which gives very firm slowly developing red wines that can be aged for many years.
— The "Côte Blonde" (lighter soil) which gives supple wines.

• **CONDRIEU.** White wines made exclusively from Viognier. Appellation approved by decree April 25, 1940. The vineyards are delimited to the communes of Condrieu (in the Rhône district) Chavanay, Malleval, Saint Michel sur Rhône, Saint Pierre de Bœuf and Vérin (in the Ardèche district).
The Condrieu is quite an original wine, very fruity, soft, rich and delicate at the same time, full-bodied and rubust, with a rich bouquet.

• **CHATEAU-GRILLET.** Exclusively white wines made from Viognier, planted on 2,3 hectares plots in the communes of Vérin and Saint Michel sur Rhône. Appellation approved by decree December 8, 1936.

• **HERMITAGE.** Red wines (Syrah, plus a maximum of 15% Marsanne and Roussane). Appellation approved by decree March 4, 1973. Vineyards delimited to the communes of Tain L'Hermitage and Crozes-Hermitage. Wines of deep ruby color, with a scent of violet and hawthorn. Tannic and full-bodied, dense, rich and elegant. Full-bodied, fine whites, with rich bouquet and breed.

• **CROZES-L'HERMITAGE.** Reds (made from Syrah) and whites (made from Marsanne and Roussane). Appellation approved by decree March 4, 1937. Vineyards delimited to the communes of Serves, Érome, Gervais, Larnage, Crozes-L'Ermitage, Mercurol, Chanos-Curson, Beaumont-Monteux, La Roche de Glun and Pont de L'Isère.

• **SAINT JOSEPH.** Red wines (made mostly from Syrah) and whites (from Marsanne and Roussane). Appellation approved by decree June 15, 1956. Satisfactory soil on the right bank of the Rhône from Chavanay, Mallaval and Saint Pierre du Boeuf, in the Loire district and extending to twenty two communes of the Ardèche as far as Châteaubourg, to the south of Tournon. Seductive reds, vigorous, full-bodied, silky texture, beautiful ruby color, marked by an intense blackcurrant aroma, with average ageing potential (10 years).

• **CORNAS.** ("Scorched earth" in Celtic). Red wine made exclusively from Syrah. Appellation approved by decree August 5, 1938. (About 50 hectares for an average annual yield of 1,400 hectoliters). Hard wines of garnet color, rich, strong and well-balanced, with a wild bouquet that must be allowed to develop at least six years.

• **SAINT PERAY.** Still and sparkling white wine made from Roussane and Marsanne. Appellation approved by decree December 8, 1936, covering a region of 50 hectares.

• **CHATEAUNEUF DU PAPE.** Appellation including Châteauneuf du Pape, and projecting to the neighboring Communes of Bédarrides, Courthezon, Sorgues and Orange. The poor soil, mostly large round pebbles, deposited a long time ago by the Rhône glacier, provide exceptional maturing conditions by giving back to the vine during the night the heat accumulated during the day. Another characteristic feature of the appellation is that it is made from thirteen grape varieties. They give rare white wines of a pale yellow color with a tinge of green and a flowery bouquet reminiscent of the vine-flower, the lily and the narcissus.

The reds are deep-colored, predominantly purple and garnet, with a violet tinge in their early years, turning to ruby when fully mature. They present a spectrum of strong fragrances—blackcurrant and plum, sometimes of laurel, coffee and cinnamon. To the taste they unfurl their great architectural dimensions, reminiscent of the old castle and its wine cellars. They are solid, robust, full-bodied and fleshy.

RIGHT AND LEFT BANKS, SOUTHERN SECTOR

- **GIGONDAS.** (1,200 hectares). A.O.C. as of January 6, 1971. Authorized grape varieties: for reds, Grenache Noir (maximum 65%), Syrah, Mourvèdre and Cinsault (minimum 25%); for rosés, Grenache Noir (maximum 60%) and Cinsault (15%).
- **LIRAC.** Good reds, rosés and whites produced on 660 hectares at Lira, Roquemaure, Saint Laurent des Arbes and Sainte Geneviève de Comolas. A.O.C. as of October 14, 1947. Authorized grape varieties: for whites Clairette (minimum 33%) Bourboulenc, Ugni Blanc, Maccabéo, Grenache, Picpoul and Calitor (minimum 25% in each case) and for the reds and rosés Grenache (minimum 40%) Cinsault, Mourvèdre and Syrah (maximum 60% for all three) and Carignan (maximum 10%).
- **The COTES DU RHONE VILLAGES.** Seventeen villages have a right to this general appellation. Produced in different soils with yields limited to 35 hectolitres per hectare, with varying exposures to the sun, the C.D.R. Villages are not very much alike. They can be divided in two categories: the light, fruity, charming, lightly colored and rather easy to drink wines from the Gard, the Drôme and its Vaucluse enclave; and the fuller-bodied wines coming mainly from the Vaucluse, more powerful, better-balanced and for longer keeping.

THE CHARACTERISTICS OF THE VINEYARD

In the Rhône Valley, specifically in the region known as the Côtes du Rhône, vineyards are planted along the right and left banks of the Rhône River, from Vienna to Avignon. The area extends for 200 mi. (322 km) and is split into northern and southern vineyards. The northern vineyards extend from Vienna to the mouth of the Drôme and the southern vineyards, from Montélimar to the mouth of the Durance River.

In the north, the vines are planted on terraced slopes overlooking the Rhône. In the south, they are planted on the hillsides. The northern vineyards of the Côtes du Rhône, France's oldest vineyards, are famed for the production of such vintage wines as Côte-Rôtie, Château Grillet, Condrieu, Hermitage and Saint-Joseph, and other great crus including Saint-Péray and Cornas.

Soil

The soil of the northern Côtes du Rhône is brittle and slightly humid granitic soil. In places, an acidic reaction is found in the soil, in the Côte-Rôtie winegrowing area for example. In the southern Côtes du Rhône, the soil is completely different. It is mostly a mixture of clay and limestone, but in places a mixture of sand and gravel contributes to the production of fine rosé wines.

Climate

The continental climate of the region means sunny, hot summers, but also humidity and frequent periods of fog. The vines face south-southeast and therefore receive a great deal of sun. Rainfall is virtually limited to April and May. The average temperature is 55.4°F (13°C).

RIGHT AND LEFT BANKS NORTHERN SECTOR

CÔTE RÔTIE

BERNARD BURGAUD

Le Champin Ampuis 69420
74 56 11 86

Type of vineyard: Family-owned. **Established:** 1980. **Vine stocks:** Syrah. **Average annual production in hectoliters:** 100.

Appellation: Côte Rotie. **Type:** Red. **Technique:** Crushing. **Maturing:** 15 months in large casks. **Alcohol content:** 12.5%. **Characteristics:** Rich in color, pronounced aromas (venison), very concentrated, lingering taste. **Serving temperature:** 18°. **Served with:** Roasts, game. **Vintages available in 89/90:** 1987, 1988.

Characteristics of vintages

1988: Very rich, long keeping. **1987:** Beautiful color, complex aromas, lingering taste. Price range (pre-tax, ex-warehouse): 50 to 80 F.F.
Sales in France: 60%.
Export sales: 40%.
Main trading partners : USA, UK, Belgium, Switzerland.

References in France

Restaurants: Troisgros, Taillevent, Beau Rivage, Ousto de Baumanière.

Abroad

United States

Martins's Wine – Ideal Wine – Wine Company, etc.

United Kingdom

Yapp Brothers – College Cellar's.

Switzerland

Le Cave.

Belgium

Justin Monar – Les Vins du Rhône.

PIERRE ET GILLES BARGE

Pierre Barge
Route de Boucharet – 69420 Ampuis
74 56 10 80

Type of vineyard: Family-owned. **Established:** 1860. **Vine stocks:** Syrah, Viognier. **Soil:** Meta-schistic. **Exposure:** South, South-East. **Average annual production in hectoliters:** 35 hl/ha.

Appellation: Côte-Rotie. **Type:** Red. **Technique:** Submerged cap (15 to 20 days). **Maturing:** In oak casks (minimum 24 months). **Alcohol content:** 12.5%. **Characteristics:** Good keeping. **Serving temperature:** 16-18°. **Served with:** Game, red meat, cheese. **Vintages available in 89/90:** 1986.

Characteristics of vintages

1986: Beautiful deep color, tannic, promising. Average pre-tax ex-warehouse price: 65 F.F.
Sales volume:
– Wholesale: 50%. – Retail: 20%.

Sales in France: 70%.
Export sales: 30%.
Main trading partners : USA, UK, Australia, Switzerland, Belgium.

Abroad

United States

Agent: Europvin M Cannan 65 Cours Saint Louis 33300, Bordeaux.

United Kingdom

Richard Walford, Manor Hous, Pickworth, Rutland Lincs PE94DJ.

GENTAZ-DERVIEUX

Marius Gentaz
Rue de Vagnot - 69420 Ampuis
74 56 10 83

Type of vineyard: Family-owned. **Established:** 1920. **Vine stocks:** Syrah. **Soil:** Porous soil, very rocky, some clay in sub-soil. **Exposure:** South by Southeast, and South by Southwest. **Average annual production in hectoliters:** 45 to 50.

Appellation: Côte Rôtie. **Type:** Red. **Technique:** Traditional (submerged cap). **Maturing:** Oak casks (18 months to 2 years). **Alchol content:** 12% - 12.8% according to the year. **Characteristics:** Rich and well-balanced wines, tannic, long, with pronounced red fruit aroma - good keeping. **Serving temperature:** 18°. **Served with:** Game, leg of lamb, red meat, guinea-fowl. **Vintages available in 89/90:** 1986 in 1988.

Characteristics of vintages

1986: Very fruity, long, rather supple tannins, should be ready before the 1985 vintage. **Note:** Other vintages are no longer available. The entire 1985 production has been reserved. Price range (pre-tax, ex-warehouse): Between 50 and 80 F.F.
Sales volume:
- Wholesale: 7%. - Retail: 13%. - Restaurants: 20%.
Sales in France: 40%. **Export sales:** 60%.
Main trading partners : USA, UK, Nertherlands, Denmark, Switzerland, Belgium.

References in France

Restaurants: Beau-Rivage (Condrieu); Gagnaire (St-Étienne); Tong Ten (Paris); Willi's Bar (Paris); Paul Chêne (Paris); La Diligence (Chavanay); Troisgros (Roanne), Renaissance (St-Chamond), etc.

Abroad

United States

Kermit Lynch, Berdeley, California. Tel. (415) 524 1524.

United Kingdom

Richard Walford, Lines. Tel. 078081.

The Netherlands

Vos Winymport, Tilbert. Tel. (013) 674918.

J. VIDAL-FLEURY S.A.

La Roche - 69420 Ampuis
74 56 10 18

Vine stocks: Syrah and Viognier. **Soil:** Silica limestone and clay. **Exposure:** East-West. **Average annual production in hectoliters:** 300.
Appellation: Côte Rotie. **Type:** Red. **Technique:** Traditional. **Maturing:** Oak casks. **Alcohol content:** 12.5% to 12.8%. **Characteristics:** To be aged, very fine, elegant, tannic, very typical, fragrant. **Serving temperature:** 16 to 18°. **Served with:** Game, red meat and certain cheeses.
Vintages available in 89/90: 1985.

Characteristics of vintages

1986: Promising vintage which should develop with age.
1985: Really great vintage, excellent for ageing, robust, rich and aromatic. Price range (pre-tax, ex-warehouse): between 50F.F. and 80F.F.
Sales volume:
- Wholesale: 10%. - Retail: 30%. - Restaurants: 60%. - Other: 50% (export).
Sales in France: 50%.
Export sales: 50%.
Main trading partners : USA, UK, Belgium, Switzerland, Netherlands, Denmark, Norway.

References in France

Restaurants: Troisgros, Orsi, Auberge de Noves, Beau Rivage (Condrieu) and many other fine tables with Michelin stars.
Shops: Flo Prestige (Paris and Rungis), Repaire de Bacchus (Paris).

Comments

The oldest and largest vineyard with the best location, (Côte Brune and Côte Blonde).

E. GUIGAL

Marcel Guigal
Ampuis - 69420 Condrieu
74 56 10 22 - Telex: 900 284 F

Type of vineyard: Private Property. **Established:** 1946. **Number of employees:** 23. **Vine stocks:** Syrah (red) and Viognier (white). **Soil:** Silica and calcium carbonate (Côte Blonde), gravel with iron oxide (Côte Brune). **Exposure:** South and Southeast. **Average annual production in hectoliters:** 1 500.

Appellation: Côte Rotie. **Type:** Red. **Technique:** Traditional, long – 3 weeks, pressurized tanks with crushing, temperature control. **Maturing:** 30 month in oak casks. **Alcohol content:** 12.5% - 13%. **Characteristics:** Breed, deep color, tannins refined by prolonged ageing. Vanilla, mulberry and raspberry aromas. **Serving temperature:** 16° - 18°. **Served with:** Meat, game, cheese. **Vintages available in 89/90:** 1984 and 1985.

Characteristics of vintages

1985: Exceptional, beautiful, supple tannins, deep color, dense bouquet. **1984:** Lively, well-structured, a successful vintage. Price range (pre-tax, ex-warehouse): between 80 F.F. and 120 F.F.

Sales volume:
– Wholesale: 50% (only abroad). – Retail: 20%. – Restaurants: 30%.

Sales in France: 40%.

Export sales: 60%.

Main trading partners : USA, UK, Switzerland.

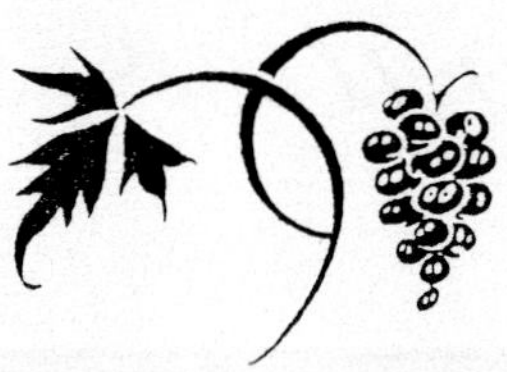

CONDRIEU

CUILLERON YVES

Chavanay - RN 86
42410 Pelussin
74 87 25 00 and 74 87 02 37

Type of vineyard: Family-owned. **Established:** Has always existed. **Number of employees:** 2. **Vine stocks:** Syrah, Viognier, Marsanne. **Soil:** Granitic, not very deep, very sandy. **Exposure:** Hillside South, Southeast. **Average annual production in hectoliters:** 250.

Appellation: Condrieu (white), St. Joseph (red and white), Côte Rôtie (red). **Type:** White. **Technique:** Traditional. **Maturing:** In wooden vats (St. Joseph – red), enamel tanks (white). **Characteristics:** Condrieu: very aromatic. Saint-Joseph and Côte Rôtie: needs to age several years. **Serving temperature:**Condrieu: 10° to 14° – St. Joseph (White) 8° to 12° – St. Joseph (red) + Côte Rôtie 18°. **Served with:** Condrieu: foie gras, dessert, Roquefort. St. Joseph (red): meat, cheese. St. Joseph (white): fish and shellfish. **Vintages available in 89/90:** Condrieu & St. Joseph (white) – 1986. St. Joseph (red) – 1985.

Characteristics of vintages

1988: Very concentrated wines due to small yield (half the usual yield in white, three quarters in red), high alcohol content. **1987:** Good year, well-balanced wines. **1986:** Very aromatic white wines. **1985:** Great year for the red wines, very tannic, to be aged. Price range (pre-tax, ex-warehouse): between 30 F.F. and 50 F.F., between 80 F.F. and 120 F.F.

Sales volume:
– Retail: 40%. – Other: 40%.

Sales in France: 80%.

Export sales: 20%.

Main trading partners : USA, UK, Belgium, Switzerland.

References in France

Restaurants: La Pyramide (Vienne), Beaurivage (Condrieu). *Shops:* Caves de St. Priest, Malleval Cash, Société viticole de Beaumanière.

Abroad

United States

Importers: Rosenthal W – 976 Lexington Avenue, New-York 10021 – USA.

United Kingdom

Importers: Bordeaux Direct – Domaine de la Clairière, Ste. Colombe, Castillon-la-Bataille 33350. Tel. 57 40 09 94 – Bewicke, 6 Greenston Crescent, Knophill, Woking (Surrey).

Others - Switzerland & Belgium

Importers: D.I.V.O., Case postale 145 – 1000 Lausanne.

HERMITAGE

FAMILLE M. CHAPOUTIER

M. Chapoutier
18 avenue du Docteur Paul Durand,
26600 Tain l'Hermitage
75 08 28 65 – Telex: 345 040 F CHAPVIN.
TELEFAX: 75 08 81 70

Type of vineyard: Family owned. **Established:** 1808. **Number of employees:** 64. **Vine stocks:** Correspond to the A.O.C.
Appellation: Hermitage Rouge "M. De La Sizeranne – Grande Cuvée", Hermitage Blanc – Grand Cru "Chante Alouette", La Bernardine – Crozes-Hermitage "Les Meysonniers", Saint-Joseph "Deschants", Côte Rôtie, Châteauneuf-du-Pape – Grande Cuvée. **Type:** Red, white, rosé. **Technique:** Traditional, total alcoholic fermentation in open vats for reds. **Maturing:** Red: Wooden casks. White: Enamelled vats. **Characteristics:** White: Mellow without sweetness, dry but not acid, for keeping. **Serving temperature:** Red and white: 15°. **Served with:** White:

Rich dishes, lobster, fish, white meat (poultry). **Vintages available in 89/90:** 1984, 1985, 1986.

Characteristics of vintages

1988: Côte Rôtie, Hermitage, Châteauneuf-du-Pape: One of the best vintages since 1978. Matured at the right time, harvesting begun 20/09/88, that is, neither too early nor too late. "GRAND CLASSIC" vintage in excellent sanitary condition. Grapes a bit thick. Fermentation without problems yielding rich and well-colored wines that are also delicate and well-balanced. The red Hermitage 1988 is similar to the 1953 which is still a very beautiful bottle. **1987:** Northern sector, climate dry until September, some violent storms during the harvest which left no trace on the grapes because of the topography (steep slope) and the action of the wind. Character, very typical, the wines from the Northern sector are for long keeping. Southern sector are for long keeping. Southern sector: the Châteauneul-du-Pape is light and fruity, sold with the indication "A beautiful little wine" 1987, which has been very well received by our clientele and is now out of stock. **1986:** Remarkable vintage for whites – dense, structure, soft and supple, harmonious, very aromatic. **1985:** Excellent Hermitage. Rich and excellent blends of reds, good color. Superb Hermitage, distinguished and flowery, perfect vinification. Do not hesitate. Price range (pre-tax, ex-warehouse): between 30 an 160 F.F.

Sales volume:
– Retail: 20%. – Restaurant: 80%.
Sales in France: 50%. **Export sales:** 50%.
Main trading partners : USA, Switzerland, UK, Denmark, Belgium, Sweden, Japan, Canada, Netherlands, Austria, Finland, Brasil, Hong Kong, Singapore, Thailand, Australia, New Zeland.

References in France

Restaurants: Most of the great French restaurants with Michelin stars.
Shops: Fauchon.

Abroad

United States

Importers: Paterno Imports Ltd. 2701 S. Western Ave. Chicago IL 60608.

United Kingdom

H. Parrot & Co Ltd. Grants of Ireland, St. Lawrence Road, Chapelizod, Dublin 20, Ireland.
Shops: The Old Customs House, 3 Wapping Pierhead, Wapping High Street, London E1 9PN.

Germany

Frankhof Kellerei GmbH, Burgerstrasse 19, 6203 Hochheim.

Switzerland

Maison M. Berthaudin SA, rue Ferrier, 1211 Geneva. Maison Wymann, Jungfraustrasse 15A, 3600 Thoune. Maison Badoux, 18 Av. du Chamossaire, 1860 Aigle. Maison Zanchi, Ch. de Rionzi 52, 1052 le Mont-s-Lausanne.

Belgium

Ets. Fourcroy, 119 rue Steyls, 1020 Brussels.

Canada

Dumont Vins & Spiritueux, Wine and Spirits, C.P. 40, Rougemont, Quebec.

The Netherlands

Oudwijnkopers & Hustinx, Spaarndamseweg 120, 2021 KA Haarlem.

Far East

Japan: Kanematsu Gosho Ltd., P.P. Box 141, Tokyo 100 91, Attn. TKGE 3 DEPT. Hong Kong: Caves de France Ltd., 2/F First Commercial Bldg, 33-35 Leighton Road. Thailand: Vanichwathana Bangkok Co. Ltd., 41 Anuwong Road, Bangkok 10100. Singapore: Mr. Aloysius ANG HOC TONG BEE PTE LTE, 347 Bukit Timah Road, Singapore 1025. AUSTRALIA: TRIMEX PTY. LTD., 213 Botany Road, Waterloo NSW 2017. NEW ZEELAND: Wilson Neill Wines & Spirits, PO BOX 8555, Symonds Str., Auckland. DENMARK: Better Brands Ltd. A/S, 3/5 Industrivej 3550 Slangerup.

Comments

A marriage of art and wine:
1. Cuvées Anniversaire (see photo), appearing in 1988 in celebration of the 180th anniversary of the establishment.
2. Cuvée Delporte, appearing in 1989.

CROZES-HERMITAGE

DOMAINE DES ENTREFAUX

Messrs. Tardy and Ange
Quartier de la Beaume, Chanos-Curson
26600 Tain-l'Hermitage
75 07 33 38

Type of vineyard: Family-owned. **Established:** 1979. **Vine stocks:** Red: Syrah, White: Marsanne. **Soil:** Chalky clay and Alpine diluvium. **Exposure:** South, South-East. **Average annual production in hectoliters:** 800.

Appellation: Corzes-Hermitage. **Type:** Red, white. **Technique:** Red: traditional, fermentation on skins 12 days, temperature control. **Maturing:** In wood, 1/3 new. **Alcohol content:** 12%. **Characteristics:** Red: aromatic wine, small berry taste, well-colored, tannic but harmonious. White: fruity, dry but soft and full because of slight acidity. **Serving temperature:** Red: 15°. White: 10°. **Served with:** Red: game and red meat. White: Salmon, fatty fish. **Vintages available in 89/90:** Red: 1986, 1987, 1988. White: 1988.

Characteristics of vintages

1988: Red: tannic and fruity, rich and well-balanced. White: soft, full and fruity. **1987:** Red: fruity and fresh. **1986:** Red: fully developed, ready for drinking. Price range (pre-tax, ex-warehouse): Between 20 F.F. and 30 F.F.

Sales volume:
– Wholesale: 40%. – Retail: 20 %. – Restaurants: 40%.
Sales in France: 50%.
Export sales: 50%.
Main trading partners : UK, Belgium, Netherlands, Luxemburg, Germany, USA, Australia, Japan.

References in France

Restaurants: Pic, Nandron.

Abroad

United States

Europvin (under Domaine des Pierrelles label).

United Kingdom

Boutinot, Bibendum, Piper, Byrne.

Germany

Champa Vins.

Belgium

De Coninck.

The Netherlands

Residence Wijnimport.

Comments

The family company was born in 1979 as the result of the association of two brothers-in-law. The average age of the vines is 25 years. Many medals have been won in various competitions.

CAVE DES CLAIRMONTS

Mr. & Mrs. J.M. Borja
Beaumont Monteux 26600 Tain L'Hermitage
75 84 61 91 Telefax: 75 84 56 98

Established: 1972. **Number of employees:** 3, **Vine stocks:** Red: Syrah. White: Marsanne. **Soil:** Rhône terraces, round pebbles on shallow soil. **Exposure:** South-West. **Average annual production in hectoliters:** 4,000.
Appellation: Crozes-Hermitage. **Type:** Red, White. **Technique:** hand harvesting – White: must racking, long fermentation at low temperature, no malolactic fermentation. Red: no crushing, no destemming, vinification in vats equipped with a mechanical crusher, temperature control, ageing in vats for 18 months before bottling. **Alcohol content:** White:12.7%. Red: 12.5%. **Characteristics:** White: very fruity. Round, soft and supple, and yet lively and pleasant when young, acquiring a honey taste with ageing. Red: fruity and yet tannic, no acidity, well-balanced, good ageing potential. **Serving temperature:** White: cool but not iced – Red: 16-17°. **Served with:** White fish in sauce – Red: red meat and game. **Vintages available in 89/90:** Red: 1986-1987. White: 1987-1988.

Characteristics of vintages

1988: White: very fruity, round, soft and full, Paris 1989 Gold Medal. **1987:** Red: lighter color, fruity, supple. **1986:**

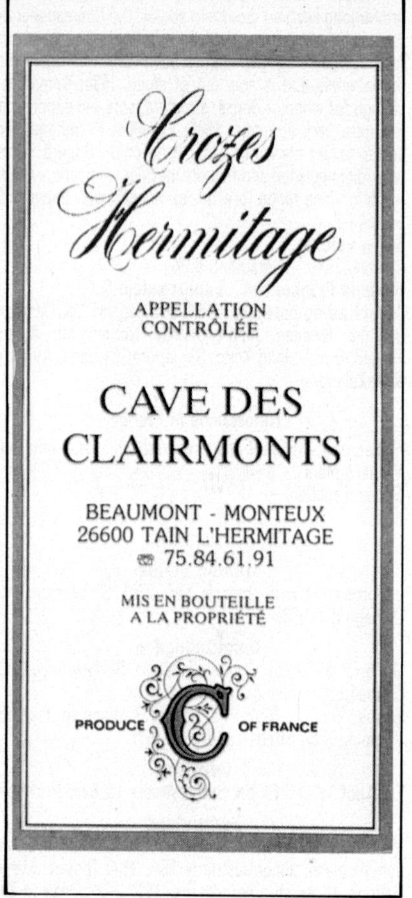

Red: fruity, rather supple, pleasant for drinking now, but can be aged longer. Price range (pre-tax, ex-warehouse): 18 F.F. to 24 F.F.
Sales volume:
– Wholesale: 65%. – Retail: 15%. – Restaurants: 15%.
– Other: 5% (wholesale dealers – wine bars).
Sales in France: 50%.
Export sales: 50%.
Main trading partners : UK, Belgium, Netherlands, Germany, Switzerland.

References in France

Restaurants: Pic (Valence) – Château de Faverge – Chabran (Pont d'Isère).

Comments

Vineyard planted about 25 years also by three families on complemetary soils, which make possible a judicious blending at the time of vinification.

CAVE DE TAIN-L'HERMITAGE

Michel Courtial
B.P. 3, 22, route de Larnage
26600 Tain-l'Hermitage
75 08 20 87 - Telex: 346 107 - Fax: 75 07 15 16

Type of vineyard: Agricultural Cooperative. **Established:** 1933. **Number of employees:** 33. **Vine stocks:** Syrah Rouge and Marsanne Blanc. **Soil:** Granitic, gravel, fluvio-glacial alluvium. **Exposure:** South, East and Souteastd. **Average annual production in hectoliters:** 40,000.
Appellation: Crozes-Hermitage, Hermitage, Cornas, Saint-Joseph, Saint Peray. **Type:** Red, white. Other: Saint-Peray (Champagne Method). **Technique:** Traditional. **Maturing:** Large oak casks, blending. **Alcohol content:** 12%. **Characteristics:** Reds: well balanced, rich in body and extracts, small red fruit flavor, good wine for ageing. Whites: fruity and round, flowery with a honey flavor. **Serving temperature:** Reds: 16° to 18°. Whites: 8 to 10°. **Served with:** Reds: Game and red meat. Whites: fish (cooked in sauce) white meat and dessert. **Vintages available in 89/90:** 1987, 1988.

Characteristics of vintages

Price range (pre-tax, ex-warehouse): between 30 and 50 F.F.
Sales volume: – Wholesale: 50%. – Retail: 25%. – Restaurants: 5%. – Export: 20%.
Sales in France: 90%. **Export sales:** 10%.
Main trading partners : UK, Belgium, Netherlands, Germany, USA.

References in France

Restaurants: Paul Bocuse, Collonges-au-Mont-d'Or: Oustau de Beaumanière, Les Baux-de-Provence: Alain Chapel, Mionnay: Chabran, Pont-de-l'Isère.

Abroad

United States
Importers: Paustic (Minnesota), Arwood (Texas), Atlanta Improvement (Georgia), French Countryside (South Carolina).

United Kingdom
Importers: Peter Hallgarten (London – 1267 2041), Castle Growers (Norwich 603625917), Reynier (London – 1 8342917).

Germany
Importers: Francimport (Heidelbert 62 21 83 4964).
Shops: Jacques Wein Depot (Dusseldorf 21 39 0020).

The Netherlands
Importers: Jean Arnaud (Tilburg – 13 350 255).
Shops: Gastrovino.
Restaurants: Hosman (Schiedam 104 26 40 96).

Others – Belgium
Importers: Andries Merckx (Louvain 1653 44 46). Dewit (Brussels 26 87 84 75). Vimaco (Ternat 2 582 31 96). Flament (Barbençon 71 58 87 88).

SAINT-JOSEPH

PIERRE COURSODON

Place du Marché - Mauves 07300 Tournon
75 08 29 27 or 75 08 18 29

Type of vineyard: Family-owned. **Established:** 1973 – from father to son since 1900. **Number of employees:** 2. **Vine stocks:** Red: Syrah. White: Marsane. **Soil:** Metamorphic schist and granite. **Exposure:** South-East. **Average annual production in hectoliters:** 320.

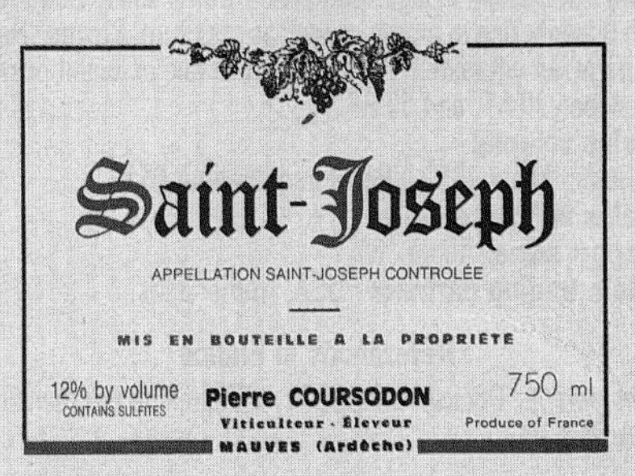

Appellation: Saint Joseph. **Type:** Red, white. **Technique:** Red: in open vats for 2 to 3 weeks. White: Temperature controlled fermentation (18°). Bottled after malolactic fermentation. **Maturing:** Oak casks. **Alcohol content:** 12 to 13%. **Characteristics:** Red: Tannic when young, with intense bouquet of violets, raspberries and red fruit. White: Soft and full with peach and apricot aromas. **Serving temperature:** Red: 16 to 17°. White: 12 to 13°. **Served with:** White: with fish in sauce. **Vintages available in 89/90:** 1987, 1988.

Characteristics of vintages

1988: Complex fragrance, fruity taste. **1987:** Fruit aromas, full. Price range (pre-tax, ex-warehouse): between 30 and 50 F.F.
Sales volume: – Wholesale: 52%. – Retail: 48%.
Sales in France: 70%. **Export sales:** 30%.
Main trading partners : Germany, UK, Belgium, Spain, Norway, Netherlands, Switzerland, USA.

Abroad

United States
Chapon Imports, White Plains, New York.

United Kingdom
Lay and Wheler, J8B, La Reserve.

Belgium
Vinea, B 1686, Gooik.

J. MARSANNE & FILS

Jean Marsanne
25, av. Ozier – 07300 Mauves
75 08 86 26

Type of vineyard: Family-owned. **Vine stocks:** Syrah. **Soil:** Granitic. **Exposure:** St. Joseph: East and South-Crozes l'Hermitage: West. **Average annual production in hectoliters:** 80 hl: St. Joseph.
Appellation: Saint-Joseph – Crozes L'Hermitage. **Type:** Red. **Technique:** No destemming, open vats, crushing twice a day. **Maturing:** 10 months in casks. **Alcohol content:** 11.5% to 12.5%. **Vintages available in 89/90:** St-Joseph 1987 (red), Crozes l'Hermitage 1986 (red).

Characteristics of vintages

1988: St-Joseph Rouge: very good structure and balance. **1987:** St-Joseph Rouge: good, very fruity. **1985:** Good red St. Joseph, rich in aroma as well as structure. Crozes l'Hermitage not yet tasted. Price range (pre-tax, ex-warehouse): between 20 F.F. and 50 F.F.
Sales volume:
– Retail: about 15%. – Restaurants: about 65%.
Sales in France: About 90%.
Export sales: About 10%.
Main trading partners : USA, Netherlands.

References in France

Restaurants: Bocuse, Chapel, Pic, L'Oustan de Baumanière, L'Ambroisie.

Abroad

United States

Crozes L'Hermitages; Kermit Lynch Wine merchant – 1605 San Pablo Avenue, Berkeley – California 94702. Tel: (415) 524 1524.

The Netherlands

Saint Joseph: Wijnkoperif – HFA – Okhuysen B.V. Grestraat 34 36 38 2011 GE Haarlem - Tel. 023 31 22 40. Crozes L'Hermitage: Noordman Frères – Wijnimport Haagned 59 2321 AA Leiden Postbus 1025 – 2302 BA Leiden – Tel: 071 31 04 19 or 071 31 13 84.

LES RAVIÈRES

Maurice & Dominique Courbis
Châteaubourg 07130 Saint-Peray
75 40 32 12

Type of vineyard: Family-owned. **Established:** Since 1587. **Number of employees:** 5. **Vine stocks:** White: Marsanna 95%, Roussane 5%. Red: Syrah 100%. **Soil:** White: middle Jurassic chalky clay. Red: (Saint Joseph): chalk, (Cornas): granite. **Exposure:** Steep slopes South-East, South. **Average annual production in hectoliters:** 450.
Appellation: Saint Joseph Blanc et Rouge, Cornas. **Type:** Red, White. **Technique:** White: pressing, must racking, fermentation at low temperature (16-17°) in enamelled tanks, malolactic fermentation (not systematic) depending on the acidity level. Red: hand harvesting. Little pressing, pumping over twice a day. Fermentation in concrete and stainless steel tanks, with temperature controle 30 to 32° C for maximum color. Maceration (10 days). **Maturing:** White: in stainless steel tanks, fining with bentonite, pressure plate filtration before bottling (in the Spring). Red: in casks (average capacity 20hl) for 14 to 18 months, controlled oxidation, repeated rackings at regular intervals, fining with egg whites before bottling. **Alcohol content:** Saint Joseph: 12.5%, Cornas: 13%. **Characteristics:** 1988: fruity, soft and full, lingering taste. The whites are usually livelier. Saint Joseph 1987 (red): little astringency, should be already pleasant at the end of 1989. Cornas 1986: deep color, still indeveloped, very tannic, excellent quality, to be aged. **Serving temperature:** Red, White, 10 to 11°. 16 to 17°. **Served with:** White: as an aperitif and with fish and shellfish. Red: (Saint Joseph): roasts, poultry, (Cornas) game, strong cheese. **Vintages available in 89/90:** Saint Joseph Rouge: 1987, 1988 (end of 1990). Cornas: 1986, 1987.

Characteristics of vintages

1988: White: white gold color, fruity, touch of peach or apricot, dry and fresh. **1987:** Saint Joseph (red): bright and limpid, purple red color, very round but for average keeping. Saint Joseph Domaine des Roys: deeper color, much more complex nose, spicy, roast coffee aromas, longer, more ageing potential. **1986:** Cornas: typical, very deep color, rich and well balanced, very tannic. Price range (pre-tax, ex-warehouse): Saint Joseph (red and white): 30 to 50 F.F. Cornas: 50 to 80 F.F.
Sales volume:
– Wholesale: 15 %. – Retail: 20 %. – Restaurants: 20 %.
– Other: 10% (export).
Sales in France: 90%. **Export sales:** 10%.
Main trading partners : UK, USA, Switzerland.

References in France

Restaurants: Pic, (Valence), Chabran, (Pont-de-l'Isère), Troisgros, (Roanne), Léon de Lyon, (Lyon).

Abroad

United States

Importers: World Shippers & Importers Co. 1420 Walnut Street, Philadelphia, Pennsylvania 19102. Tel: (215) 732 2018 – Telex: 902 344 Renard PHA. Fourth Street Wine, Berkely, CA.

United Kingdom

Redpath & Tackray Wines, Common lane, Sawston, Cambridge CB2 4HW. Tel: Cambridge (0223) 833 495. Christopher Piper Wines, London.

Switzerland

Masteret & Etter, Zurich.

Comments

Winemakers from father to son since 1587. (Vineyard in

Cornas since 1982). The vineyard, which was planted in the 1930s is located on a hillside facing South and South-East. The modern winecellar (1980) is equipped with temperature regulated vats. The Domaine des Roys is a very beautiful 3 hectare vineyard, located in a valley protected from the North wind. The vines are cultivated on terraces following the curves of the terrains. Regular awards at the Mâcon fair. Gold Medal for white wines in 1985, 1986 and 1987.

CORNAS

MARCEL JUGE

Marcel Juge
Place de la Salle des Fêtes F - 07130 Cornas
75 40 36 68

Type of vineyard: Family-owned. **Established:** From father so son for several generations. **Vine stocks:** Syrah 100%. **Soil:** Sandy, granitic. **Exposure:** East and Southeast. **Average annual production in hectoliters:** 120. **Appellation:** Cornas. **Type:** Red. **Technique:** Traditional. **Maturing:** In oak casks for a minimum or 18 months. **Alcohol content:** 12.8°. **Characteristics:** Tannic and fruity, with the richness and balance of a great wine for ageing. **Serving temperature:** 18°. **Served with:** Red meat, game, cheese. **Vintages available in 89/90:** 1987, 1988.

Characteristics of vintages

1988: Same as the 1987, but a little lighter in color. **1987:** Rich and well-balanced, tannic, fruity, deep red color. **1985:** Tannic, but not excessively; very fruity, blackberry taste. **1984:** Tannic, fruity, blackcurrant taste. Price range (pretax, exwarehouse): between 30 F.F. and 80 F.F.

Sales volume:
– Wholesale: 30%. – Retail: 30%. – Restaurants: 40%.
Sales in France: 75%.
Export sales: 25 %.
Main trading partners : USA.

Abroad

United States
Vineyard Brands, P.O.: Box 160, Chester, Vt. 05143.

RIGHT AND LEFT BANKS SOUTHERN SECTOR

BEAUMES DE VENISE

DOMAINE DE COYEUX

Yves et Catherine Nativelle
84190 Beaumes-de-Venise
90 62 97 96
Telex: 431 529 F - Telefax: 90 65 01 87

Type of vineyard: Family-owned. **Established:** 1976. **Number of employees:** 12. **Vine stocks:** VDN (naturally sweet wine): White Muscat (small grapes). Red: Grenache 50%, Cinsaut 15%, Mourvèdre 15%, Syrah 20%. **Soil:** Triassic. **Exposure:** Full South at an altitude of 260 m. **Average annual production in hectoliters:** 2,500.

Appellation: AOC Muscat de Beaumes-de-Venise, AOC Côtes du Rhône, Beaumes-de-Venise, AOC Gigondas. **Type:** Red – Other: VDN (naturally sweet wine). **Technique:** Traditional, temperature control (VDN: fermentation at very low temperature). **Maturing:** In stainless steel tanks, oak casks (new) and bottles. **Alcohol content:** Red: 13.4%. **Characteristics:** VDN: very delicate, fruity, elegant. Red: full-bodied and fruity. **Serving temperature:** Red: 15 to 17°. VDN: 7°. **Served with:** Red: meat, cheese. VDN: as an aperitif, with foie gras, dessert, and as an after dinner drink. **Vintages available in 89/90:** VDN: 1987, 1988. Red: 1986, 1987.

Characteristics of vintages

1988: VDN: very delicate, fruity, remarkable balance. **1987:** VDN: great finesse, complex aromas, very elegant. **1986:** Red: full-bodied, rich and full, fruity. Price range (pre-tax, ex-warehouse): 20 to 30 F.F. (red) – 30 to 50 F.F. (VDN).
Sales volume:
– Wholesale: 30%. – Retail: 10%. – Restaurants: 60%.
Sales in France: 18%.
Export sales: 82%.
Main trading partners : UK, USA, Canada, Netherlands, Sweden, Belgium, Ireland, Japan, Luxemburg, Australia, New Zealand, Switzerland, Belgium, Hong Kong, Norway, Denmark, etc.

References in France

Restaurants: Négresco, Beaumanière, Pic Blanc, Orsi, Mas d'Artigny, Lucas Carton Fouquet's, Le Grand Vefour, etc.
Shops: Yves Legrand, Paris, Repaire de Bacchus, etc.

Abroad

United States

Importers: Dreyfus Ashby.

United Kingdom

European Cellars.

Belgium

S.P.R.L. Le Millésime.

Canada

L.C.B.O.

The Netherlands

A. Kerstens.

DOMAINE LES GOUBERT

Jean Pierre Cartier
84190 Gigondas
90 65 86 38

Type of vineyard: Family-owned. **Vine stocks:** Grenache 65%, Syrah 25%, Cinsault 10%. **Soil:** Chalky clay. **Exposure:** Beaumes: South-North. Lafare: North-south, micro-climate due to the proximity of the Dentelles de

Montmirail mountains. **Average annual production in hectoliters:** 115.
Appellation: Côtes-du-Rhône village, Beaumes de Venise. **Type:** Red. **Technique:** Traditionnal: crushing without destemming, long fermentation on skins. **Maturing:** 11 months in concrete tanks, bottling in September (one per appellation and per vintage). **Alcohol content:** 13.5°-14°. **Characteristics:** Very masculine – rich and very well balanced, black fruit (blackcurrant, mulberry), rose-wood, toasted bread aroma – wines of a very mysterious character. **Serving temperature:** 16-18°. **Vintages available in 89/90:** 1987.

Characteristics of vintages

Price range (pre-taxe, ex-warehouse): 20 to 30 F.F.
Sales in France: 35%.
Export sales: 65%.
Main trading partners : USA, UK, Australia, Denmark.

References in France

Shops: Bernard Peret, 6, rue Daguerre, (75014 Paris) Cave Michel Marc, 31, rue de la Div. Leclerc (91310 Linas).

CHÂTEAU REDORTIER

Etienne de Menthon
84190 Beaumes de Venise
90 62 96 43

Type of vineyard: Family-owned. **Established:** 1956. **Number of employees:** 2. **Vine stocks:** Grenache 60%, Syrah 20%, Cinsault 20%. **Soil:** Chalky clay. **Exposure:** Full South (terraces). **Average annual production in hectoliters:** 1,000.

Appellation: CDR Village Beaumes de Venise & Gigondas. **Type:** Red Rosé. **Technique:** Traditional. **Maturing:** Cement tanks. **Alcohol content:** 13%. **Characteristics:** Very typical, fruity, well structured, rich and fragrant. **Serving temperature:** 15 to 16°. **Served with:** Red meat, cheese. **Vintage available in 89/90:** 1986, 1987.

Characteristics of vintages

1987: Lighter but very fruity. **1986:** Very fruity, supple and robust at the same time. Price range (pre-tax, ex-warehouse): 10 to 20 F.F. – 20 to 30 F.F.
Sales volume:
– Wholesale: 20%. – Retail: 20%. – Other: 10% (cellars) 50%: (export).
Sales in France: 50%.
Export sales: 50%.

References in France

Restaurants: Lucas Carton, Beauvilliers, Dodin Bouffant.
Shops: Legrand, Pétrissans, Cave Estève.

Comments

Good wines typical of the area. Good wine making technique. Very successful Gigondas (83-86 Vintage).

DOMAINE DE LA FERME SAINT-MARTIN

Guy Julien
Suzette – 84190 Beaumes-de-Venise
90 62 96 40

Type of vineyard: Family-owned. **Established:** 1964. **Number of employees:** 3. **Vine stocks:** Grenache 70%, Cinsault, Syrah. **Soil:** Clay with calcium carbonate and limestone. **Exposure:** Hillside, full South. **Average annual production in hectoliters:** 800.
Appellation: Beaumes-de-Venise (Côtes-du-Rĥne Villages). **Type:** Red. **Technique:** Traditional. **Maturing:** Vats then 1 year in oak casks. **Alcohol content:** 12.5% to 13%. **Characteristics:** Tannic, very fleshy, with a rich and well-balanced aroma of very ripe, red fruit. **Serving temperature:** 18° to 19°. **Served with:** Red meat and cheese. Game and spicy dishes. Bitter chocolate cake for the young Beaumes-de-Venise. **Vintages available in 89/90:** 1985 and 1986.

Characteristics of vintages

1986: Good red, good color, tannins evident. Hold. **1985:** Pretty vintage, fine and robust at the same time, good for ageing. Price range (pre-tax, ex-warehouse): Between 20 an 30 F.F.
Sales volume:
– Wholesale: 20%. – Retail: 60%. – Restaurants: 20%.
Sales in France: 90%.
Export sales: 10%.
Main trading partners : Belgium, Germany, UK.

CAIRANNE

LE CHÂTEAU À CAIRANNE
S.C.E.A. Domaines Rieu-Hérail
Domaine de l'Ameillaud - 84290 Cairanne
90 30 82 02 - Telex: Service SODICOM 431 868

Type of vineyard: Family Agricultural Association. **Established:** 1967. **Number of employees:** 9. **Vine stocks:** Grenache, Syrah, Cinsault, Carignan, Bourboulenc, Clairette. **Soil:** Clay with calcium carbonate and marine terrace. **Exposure:** Hillside and foot hills, East, South and West. **Average annual production in hectoliters:** Cairanne Villages: 200. Côtes-du-Rhône Domaine: 2500. Vin de Pays: 2000.
Appellation: Côtes-du-Rhône and Côtes-du-Rhône Cairanne Villages, Vin de Pays. **Type:** Red. **Technique:** Traditional, fermentation on skins 7 to 12 days. **Maturing:** Cement vats and large oak casks as well as small casks in new wood. **Alcohol content:** 13%. **Characteristics:** Domaine de l'Ameillaud: supple, fruity, to be drunk quite young. Domaine le Château: rich and well-balanced, tannic, will age well. Cairanne: combines suppleness, roundness, bouquet and tannins. **General characteristic:** Spicy (pepper) and liquorice. **Serving temperature:** 16 to 17°. **Served with:** All red meats, game and, of course, cheese. **Vintages available in 89/90:** 1985, 1986.

Characteristics of vintages

1985: Côtes-du-Rhône and Côtes-du-Rhone Cairanne Villages: dense and well-colored. **1984:** Côtes-du-Rhône Cairanne Villages: quite successful. Price range (pre-tax, ex-warehouse): Between 10 and 30F.F.

RABASSE-CHARAVIN Corinne
Corinne Couturier
84290 Cairanne
90 30 70 05 - 90 30 82 27

Type of vineyard: Family-owned for 5 generations. **Established:** Around 1884. **Number of employees:** 2. **Vine stocks:** Grenache 70%, Syrah 15%, Cinsault 5%, Mourvèdre 5%, Carignan 5%. **Soil:** Clay with calcium carbonate. **Exposure:** Hillsides facing full South. **Average annual production in hectoliters:** 900.
Appellation: A.O.C. Côtes-du-Rhône, A.O.C. – C.D.R. Cairanne and Rasteau. **Type:** Red, white, rosé. **Technique:** Traditional – temperature control, harvesting and selection of berries done by hand. **Maturing:** In concrete tanks for the reds, in stainless steel or enamalled tanks for the whites and rosés. **Characteristics:** Red: rich color, well-balanced, very fragrant, firm and supple, good keeping wine. White: fresh and fruity. Rosé: prepared by drawing off, firm, light and supple. **Serving temperature:** White and rosé: 13-14° Red: (young) 17°; (aged) 18°19°. **Served with:** Red: all meats, game. White: fish, seafood. **Vintages available in 89/90:** 1984, 1986, 1987.

Characteristics of vintages

1988: Small harvest, lovely color, very fruity, altogether quite harmonious. Should be kept 7 to 10 years. **1987:** Lighter in color, with very fine tannins and fragrance. Less body than the 85 or 86; rather similar to the 84. The Villages, Cairanne and Rasteau can look forward to a number of beautiful years - 5 to 7. **1986:** A good compromise between 1984 and 1985 – well-balanced, beautiful color, fine and fruity (due to rigorous selection of grapes). **1985:** Very rich in alcohol, well-balanced – should be aged. Price range (pre-tax, ex-warehouse): 10 – 30 F.F.

SABLET

DOMAINE LES GOUBERT
Jean Pierre Cartier
84190 Gigondas
90 65 86 38

Type of vineyard: Family owned. **Vine stocks:** Clairette 60%, Bourboulenc, Roussane 15%. **Soil:** Chalky clay. **Exposure:** East-West. **Average annual production in hectoliters:** 53.
Appellation: Sablet. **Type:** White. **Technique:** Crushing, pressing, must racking. **Maturing:** In stainless steel tanks, bottling in February. **Alcohol content:** 12.4%. **Characteristics:** Subtle fresh grapes and vine peach nose, hazelnut, rose petal aroma. **Serving temperature:** 10°. **Vintages available in 89/90:** 1988.

Characteristics of vintages

Price range (pre-tax, ex-warehouse): 20 to 30 F.F.
Sales in France: 35%.
Export sales: 64%.
Main trading partners : USA, UK, Australia, Denmark.

References in France

Restaurants: Pic (26 Valence), Jenny Jacquet (92 Neuilly/Seine).
Shops: Bernard Peret, 6, rue Daguerre, (75014 Paris), Caves Michel Marc, 31, rue de la Div. Leclerc (91310 Linas).

Comments

There is also a red Côtes-du-Rhône Village, Sablet – a very feminine wine, ideally served at 16-18°.

RASTEAU

LES GIRASOLS

Paul Joyet
84110 Rasteau
90 46 11 70

Type of vineyard: Family-owned. **Established:** 1974 (first wine production in 1978), vineyard dates back to 1914. **Vine stocks:** Grenache 70%, Cinsault 10%, Carignan 8%, Mourvèdre 8%, Syrah. **Exposure:** Hillsides facing south. **Average annual production in hectoliters:** 700-800.
Appellation: Côtes du Rhône & Villages. **Type:** Red, rosé. **Technique:** Semi-carbonic maceration by gravity. **Maturing:** In vats (40hl) and bottles in underground cellar. **Alcohol content:** 13 and 14%. **Characteristics:** Rich spicy aromas, deep and bright color tannic enough for keeping, warm, sunny taste. Rosé: very fruity, taste of English candy, well balanced, supple, vinified by drawing off. **Serving temperature:** Rosé: 13 to 14°. Red: 16 to 17°. **Served with:** 1985: perfect with game. Rosé: oriental cuisine 1986: red meat, terrines. Village 1986-1987: meat cooked in sauce, cheese. **Vintages available in 89/90:** Red: 1985, 1986, 1987 Rosé: 1988.

Characteristics of vintages

1988: Only Rosé Rasteau Village and CDR: good color, fruity lively, no acidity whatsoever. **1987:** Only Red Rasteau Village: aged in casks, rich, long, tannic, spicy aromas – Macon Silver Medal. **1986:** Rasteau Village (limited stock) – superb wine, breed and balance, aged in casks, supple, red berry aroma, very good keeping – Macon Silver Medal. **1985:** 3 wines: One, having spent 6 months in the cask, is excellent to drink now. Medal at Orange. Another, having aged in vats for 18 months and in bottles for 2 years, will go well with game. Cuvée de Lampereuse: more tannic. Aged 9 months in casks. Silver Medal at Mâcon. **Other:** Cuvée de Lampereuse: Macon Silver Medal. Price range (pre-tax, ex-warehouse): 20 to 30 F.F.
Sales volume: – Wholesale: 12%. – Retail: 70%. – Restaurants: 10%. Other: 10% (export).
Sales in France: 90%. **Export sales:** 10%.
Main trading partners: USA, United Kingdom, Denmark, Netherlands, Germany, Belgium.

References in France

Restaurants: Orsi – Leon de Lyon – La Mere Guy – Panorama – Les Trois Maries – L'abbaye (Talloires) 74.
Shops: Delicatessens and specialized wine shops only.

Abroad

United States

Europvin (Bordeaux) – Grand Reserve Ltd. Illinois – Consolidated. Shops: Connoisseur Wines, Chicago.

United Kingdom

Redpath & Thacray Wines – Lancashire – Vessel of Wines.

Switzerland

Cavec St. Denis (Carouges).

The Netherlands

Vinkaelderen (Assens) – Van Geest (Hilversum) – Kok (Rotterdam).

Comments

Marie-Elisabeth and Paul Joyet and their two daughters established themselves at Rasteau in 1974, after leaving Lyon where they were market gardeners. After acquiring the vineyard, they spent 4 years learning the business of winegrowing. They were fortunate to have found a vineyard operated by a single tenant from 1914 until they arrived. It is one the best exposed vineyards of the Rasteau region, entirely on hillsides facing South, overlooking the Ouvèze valley, facing Seguret, Sablet and Gigondas. The Joyets have maintained the family character of their domain which, by its exceptional location and size (15 hectares) is conducive to the cultivation of the vines, the vinification, maturing and commercialization of wine. Thanks to these factors, one finds that the wines produced by the Joyet's an of an exceptional quality - rich and fragrant - easily making them medal winners in all of the competitions.

SAINT-MAURICE

CAVES DES GRANDS VINS DE SAINT-MAURICE

Paul Rouvier
26110 St-Maurice-sur-Eygues
75 27 63 44

Type of vineyard: Cooperative Agricultural Association. **Established:** 1939. **Number of employees:** 7. **Vine stocks:** Grenache, Cinsault, Syrah. **Soil:** Terraces, clay with calcium carbonate, sandy, with round stones, impermeable sub-soil. **Exposure:** Southeast, Northeast, maximum sunshine, sheltered from strong winds (The Mistral). **Average annual production in hectoliters:** 45,000.

Appellation: Côtes-du-Rhône Villages-Communale St-Maurice. **Type:** Red, rosé. **Technique:** Traditional vinification, long maceration - 10 days. **Maturing:** Oak casks and barrels. **Alcohol content:** 13,5%. **Characteristics:** Reds: Brillant ruby color, very delicate bouquet and flavor. Rich, warm, improve with ageing. Refered to as the most elegant of the Côtes-du-Rhône. Rosé: Sumptuous, delicately fruity, persistanct aroma. **Serving temperature:** 17°. **Served with:** Saint-Maurice (red) 1986: red and white meat, Coq au Vin, poultry, leg of lamb. Grande Réserve 1986: (Matured in oak casks) game, truffle omelettes. Cuvée Prestige Marquis Charce, Château Saint-Anne: cheese platter. **Vintages available in 89/90:** St-Maurice (red) 1986, Grande Réserve 1986, Cuvée Prestige Marquis Charce 1986, Cuvée Château Saint-Anne 1986.

Characteristics of vintages

1986: Very elegant, pepper flavor, spices, excellent prospects for development. **1986:** Warm, rich and well-balanced, mixture of flowery fragrances. **1986:** Woody taste, very elegant, vanilla flavor, very subtle with raspberry taste. Price range (pre-tax, ex-warehouse): Between 10 an 28 F.F.

Sales volume:
- Wholesale: 76%. - Retail: 26%. - Restaurants: 1%.

Sales in France: 75%. **Export sales:** 25%.

Main trading partners : Belgium, Netherlands, Scandinavian countries, Switzerland.

SÉGURET

CHÂTEAU LA COURANÇONNE

84150 Violes
90 70 92 16

Type of vineyard: Agricultural Association. **Established:** 1970. **Number of employees:** 24. **Vine stocks:** Grenache, Syrah, Mourvèdre. **Soil:** Chalky clay, gravel and pebbles, clay subsoil. **Average annual production in hectoliters:** 5000.

Appellation: Côtes du Rhône Villages - Séguret Village. **Type:** Red, white, rosé. **Technique:** Traditional for red, low temperature for white. **Maturing:** vats and barrels. **Alcohol content:** 12.5%. **Characteristics:** Red - good structure, very bright color, blackurrant and raspberry aroma. White - finesse and elegance, apple and banana bouquet. **Serving temperature:** Red: 18 - 19° - White: 10°. **Served with:** Red: roasts, game, meat cooked in sauce, cheese. White: fish and shellfish, pastry. **Vintages available in 89/90:** 1981, 1982, 1983, 1984, 1986.

VACQUEYRAS

DOMAINE DE MONTVAC

Jean Dussere
84190 Vacqueyras
90 65 85 51

Type of vineyard: Family-owned. **Established:** 1917. **Number of employees:** 2. **Vine stocks:** Grenache 70%, Syrah 15%, Mourvèdre 9%, Cinsaut 6%. **Soil:** Very variable - chalky clay and round pebbles form ancient river beds. **Exposure:** Hillsides and garrigues. **Average annual production in hectoliters:** 1,000.

Appellation: Vacqueyras, Gigondas. **Type:** Red. **Technique:** Long maceration, strict temperature control. **Maturing:** Partly in oak casks - partly in vats in underground cellars. **Alcohol content:** 13 to 13.5%. **Characteristics:** Very aromatic wines (due to very low temperature vinification), harmonious tannic structure (due to long maceration), spicy aromas (red fruit, violets). **Serving temperature:** 16°. **Served with:** Red meat, meat in sauce, cheese. **Vintages available in 89/90:** 1986, 1987, 1988.

Characteristics of vintages

1988: Very well structured, deep color, clean attack, round. **1987:** Very round and harmonious – classified as best Côtes-du-Rhône Village of the 3 last vintages. **1986:** Rich and well balanced, will be fully developed in 1991-1992. **1985:** Depleted stock. Price range (pre-tax, ex-warehouse): Vacqueyras 10 to 20 F.F. – Gigondas 20 to 30 F.F.
Sales volume:
– Wholesale: 10%. – Retail: 40%. – Restaurants: 10%.
Sales in France: 60%. **Export sales:** 40%.
Main trading partners : Belgium, Germany, Netherlands.

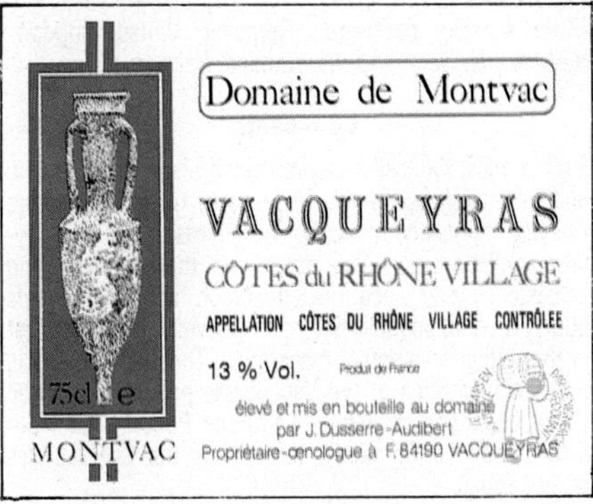

References in France

Restaurants: Pavillon Bellevue (01300, Belley), Le Tisonnier (83 St-Raphaël).

Abroad

Germany

Kurt Burgard Gmbh Dieselstrasse 6604 Gudingen (Tel: 681 874091) La Bonne Cave Haupstrasse 10 6458 Rodenbach, Maison lanz Darmstadter landstrasse 92 6000 Franfurt (Tel: 618453181).

Belgium

Les Caves Clairembourg et Fils 13, rue de la Ferme 5974 Opprebais (Tel: 10 88 87 38) Magasins ROB, Brussels.

The Netherlands

Prosper Van Nieulande Baronielaan 159 4818 PG Breda (Tel: 76 22 63 60).

Others

Denmark: Route du Vin, Frederibsvoerbogade 13 1300 Hillrod (Tel: 225 3662) Togo: Ent. SARL BP 30177 Lomé.

Comments

During the thirties, the domain was one of the first to offer wine for sale in casks. With the construction of new installations in 1980, direct sale made great strides and, presently, 80% of the total production is sold either directly to individual clients or to importers. The modification of the vinestocks with an increase in the proportion of Syrah and complete control of the vinification conditions have led to a substantial qualitative improvement of the Vacqueyras wines which will probably be recognized in a few years by the addition of "Cru" to the appellation.

CHÂTEAU DES ROQUES

Édouard Dusser
Château des Roques, BP 9, 84190 Vacqueyras
Tel: 90 65 85 16 – Telex: 0983 90 65 88 14
Fax: 90 65 88 18

Type of vineyard: Family-owned. **Established:** Between the 2 World Wars. **Number of employees:** 3. **Vine stocks:** Grenache, Syrah, Aubin, Cinsaut, Marsanne, Bourboulenc. **Soil:** Pebbly plateau, chalky clay. **Exposure:** South. **Average annual production in hectoliters:** 1,500.
Appellation: Vacqueyras. Type: Red, white, rosé. **Techniques:** Traditional. **Maturing:** In stainless steel and concrete tanks (225 l). **Alcohol content:** 11.5 – 14%. **Characteristics:** Rich nose, high tannic structure, good keeping. **Serving temperature:** 18 to 20°. **Served with:** Red meat, game and poultry, truffles and cheese. **Vintages available in 89/90:** 1986, 1987, 1988.

Characteristics of vintages

1988: Red: good keeping, very well balanced. Excellent white fine and flowery aroma. **1987:** Fruity, elegant, to be kept 3 to 4 years. Very successful. **1986:** Great elegance. Secondary aromas, very supple, excellent evolution. Price range (pre-tax, ex-warehouse): 20 to 30 F.F.
Sales volume: – Wholesale: 50%. – Retail: 50%.
Sales in France: 70%. **Export sales:** 30%.
Main trading partners : USA, Netherlands, Belgium, Japan.

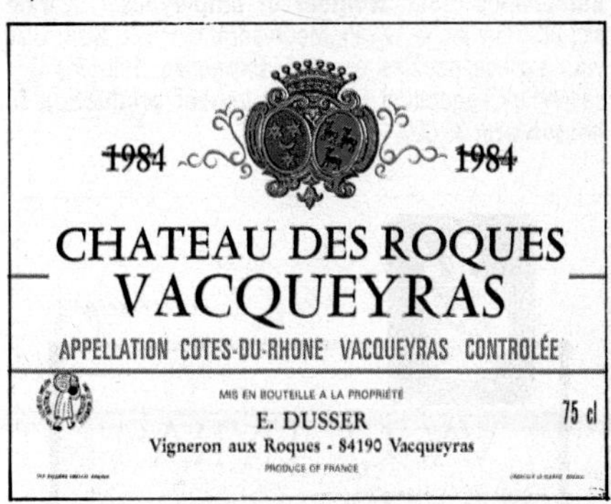

References in France

Shops: Les Comptoirs de la Tour d'Argent.

Comments

Between the two wars, the Dusser and Beraud families undertook to vinify their harvest themselves, using the old château cellars. In 1965, the 35 hectare vineyard, enlarged as a result of extensive land clearing, became a center for Côtes-du-Rhône. In 1979, a modern vinification center was established on the site of an ancient unused sheep-run and used for the conscientious production of wines. Because of a long fermentation, they have a taste highly characteristic of the soil from which they come.

DOMAINE "LE PONT DU RIEU"

Jean-Pierre Faraud
84190 Vacqueyras
90 65 86 03

Type of vineyard: Agricultural Association. **Established:** 1979. **Number of employees:** 1. **Vine stocks:** Grenache, Cinsault, Syrah, Mourvèdre. **Soil:** Clay with calcium carbonate, pebbly. **Exposure:** South, West. **Average annual production in hectoliters:** 600. well-balanced and tannic.
Served temperature: Red: 18°. Rosé: cool. **Servid with:** Vacqueyras and Gigondas: red meat, game. Rosé: first course, fish, shell-fish, light meals. **Vintages available in 89/90:** Gigondas 1982-1983. Vacqueyras 1984-1985.

Characteristics of vintages

1985: Richer and better balanced than the 1984 – quite robust. **1984:**Good, fruity, tannic. Price range (pretax, ex-warehouse): Between 10 F.F. and 30 F.F.

CAVE DES VIGNERONS

Merkl Helmut
84190 Vacqueyras
90 65 84 54 – Telex: 431 353 – FAX: 9065 8132

Established: 1957. **Number of employees:** 15. **Vine stocks:** Grenache, Syrah, Mourvèdre, Cinsault. **Soil:** Clay with surface pebbles or sand. **Exposure:** Hillsides and secondary vegetation. **Average annual production in hectoliters:** 35,000.

Les Vins du Troubadour
VACQUEYRAS
COTES DU RHONE VILLAGES
Appellation Côtes du Rhône Villages Contrôlée
PRODUCE OF FRANCE
MIS EN BOUTEILLE A LA PROPRIETE
e750 ml
CAVE DES VIGNERONS DE VACQUEYRAS VAUCLUSE FRANCE
13% vol.

Appellation: Côtes du Rhône red and white, Vacqueyras red and rosé, Gigondas red and rosé, Muscat de Beaumes de Venise. **Type:** Red, white, rosé. **Technique:** Traditional vinification, carbonic maceration. **Maturing:** Oak casks and cement vats. **Characteristics:** Supple, elegant, well bred wines, with lots of fruitiness and distinction. **Serving temperature:** Red: 16°. White and rosé: 8 to 10°. **Served with:** Everything. **Vintages available in 89/90:** 1986, 1987, 1988.

Characteristics of vintages

1988: Red: Very concentrated inky color, remarkable rich tannins. Superb vintage to keep. **1987:** Red: Light color, neither soft nor full, to be drunk for its freshness and delicate aromas. **1986:** Red: Evolved color but still all right, ripe fruit aroma, very soft tannin, to drink. **1985:** Red: Very deep color with black glints, very aromatic, very agreeable to drink now.
Sales volume:
– Wholesale: 65%. – Retail: 25%. – Restaurants: 10%.
Sales in France: 70%.
Export sales: 30%.
Main trading partners: Germany, United Kingdom, Netherlands, Denmarks, Switzerland, Belgium.

Comments

Built in 1957, this cellar has remained a small cooperative unit producing essentially Vacqueyras on a 700 hectare vineyard, harvested manually. Two thirds of the Vacqueyras appellation is vinified here. From the beginning, and consistently ever since, the orientation has been towards quality production (selection of the harvest). It was the first in the region to practice maceration. This has resulted in the personalization of the Vacqueyras produced by three Côtes du Rhône domains, "Le Grand Prieur", "La Mourielle" and "La Curnière", as well as the Château des Hautes Ribes.

VALRÉAS

DOMAINE DE LA FUZIÈRE

Léo Roussin
84600 Valréas (Enclave des Papes)
90 35 05 15

Type of vineyard: Family-owned. **Established:** For several generations. **Vine stocks:** Grenache – Syrah – Cinsault – Mourvèdre. **Soil:** Clay with calcium carbonate. **Exposure:** Hillsides. **Average annual production in hectoliters:** 900.
Appellation: Côtes-du-Rhône, Côtes-du-Rhône Village "Valréas". **Type:** Red. **Technique:** Traditionnal. **Maturing:** Underground tanks and OAK casks. **Alcohol content:** 13°. **Characteristics:** Rich and well-balanced, tannic, full, round, fruity, with tenacity. Red fruit aroma (balckcurrant). **Serving temperature:** 16°. **Served with:** Red meat – game – cheese. **Vintages available in 89:** 1988 Côtes-du-Rhône, 1985 Village.

Characteristics of vintages

1985: Light and fruity. Very much appreciated for its typical taste. **Others, 1984:** Côtes-du-Rhône Valréas Village: Lots

of character and forthcoming. Aged in OAK casks. Price range (pre-tax, ex-warehouse): between 18 and 25 F.F.
Sales volume:
– Wholesale: 40%. – Retail: 50%. – Restaurant: 5%.
Sales in France: 80%. **Export sales:** 20%.
Main trading partners : Denmark – Belgium – Holland.

References in France

Restaurants: Local and regional restaurants.

DOMAINE DU VAL DES ROIS

Romain Bouchard
84600 Valréas
90 35 04 35 – Telex: 431 919 CIAV

Type of vineyard: Family-owned. **Established:** 1965. **Vine stocks:** Grenache 40%, Syrah 25%, Gamay 10%, Cinsaut 15%, Mourvèdre 3%, Carignan 7%. **Soil:** 3/4 clay, 1/4 silica. **Exposure:** East with the rising sun. **Average annual production in hectoliters:** 550.
Appellation: Côtes du Rhône, Valreas Village. **Type:** Red, rosé. **Technique:** Traditional, submerged cap after destemming. **Maturing:** 11 months in tanks (no wood). **Alcohol content:** 11.5-13.5%.
Characteristics: Red: finesse, length, elegance, can be kept for more than 10 years. Fruit and cereal fragrance, often becoming spicy with age. Rosé: dry, light and supple, flowery and fruity. **Serving temperature:** Red: 16° – Rosé: 12°. **Served with:** As an aperitif, even the reds are appreciated before meals. The lightest (Cuvée des Rois) goes best with fine cuisine. The more robust (Cuvée de la 8° Génération or Valréas Village) go well with spicy food. The Cuvée de la 8° Génération is much appreciated in Canada with buffalo and caribou. **Vintages available in 89/90:** 1987, 1988.

Characteristics of vintages

1988: Balanced and harmonious, rich and well colored, good keeping. **1987:** Fruity, elegant and supple. **1986:** Rich and well balanced, velvety texture, excellent development. **1985:** Very well balanced, rich well colored, lingering flavor. **Other: 1984:** A constitution analogous to that of the Grand Crus de Bourgogne, touch of acidity. 1983: Almost ideal harmony, rich wines, superb, intense, to be kept. 1982: very rich and well balanced, soft and supple, little tannins. Price range (pre-tax, ex-warehouse): 10 to 20 F.F.
Sales volume:
Wholesale: 5%. – Retail: 90%. – Restaurants: 5%.
Sales in France: 64%.
Export sales: 36%.
Main trading partners : United Kingdom, Netherlands, Germany, Belgium, USA, Canada, Switzerland.

References in France

Restaurants: Les restaurants de Valréas (Vaucluse), La Beaugravière (Mondragon), Les Hospitaliers (Poêt Laval) Pizzeria Les Deux Roses (Dieulefit), Le Petit Verdot (Aix-en-Provence).

Shops: L'Amour du Vin, rue St. Dominique 75007 Paris, Tel: 45 56 12 94.

Abroad

United Kingdom
I.E.C.W.S. Wine Society – Tel: (0438) 741177.

Belgium
Equert – Brussel, Tel: (02) 425 66 06.

The Netherlands
Jan van Breda – Rotterdam 010 – 436 52 69.

Comments

Descendant of a family which for 8 generations has distinguished itself in the production and sales of Burgundy wine, Romain Bouchard moved to the Côtes-du-Rhône region and settled on a property which once belonged to the Popes of Avignon and which was the first vineyard in the Enclave of the Popes. There, Romain Bouchard produces a Valréas Village which he guarantees will keep well until its 10th birthday.

VISAN

CAVE LES COTEAUX

Mr. Ordener
Visan 84820
90 41 91 12 - Telex: 432 117 F

Type of vineyard: Cooperative Agricultural Assoc. **Established:** 1937. **Number of employees:** 20. **Vine stocks:** Grenache, Syrah, Mourvèdre, Cinsault, Clairette. **Soil:** Clay with calcium Carbonate. **Exposure:** Hillsides. **Average annual production in hectoliters:** 100000.
Appellation: Côte-du-Rhône, Visan Village A.O.C. **Types:** Red, white, rosé. **Technique:** Traditional. **Alcohol content:** 12-14%. **Characteristics:** Red: beautiful color, fine, fragant, supple. White: well-balanced, supple and vigorous at the same time. Rosé: fruity and robust, a seductive wine. **Serving temperature:** White: 8°. Rosé: 10°. Red: 15°. **Vintages available in 89/90:** 1980, 1986.

Characteristics of vintages

Price range (pre-tax, ex-warehouse): 10-80 F.F.
Sales volume:
- Wholesale: 65%. - Retail: 30%. - Restaurants: 5%.

Sale in France: 50%.
Export sales: 50%.
Main trading partners : Switzerland, Germany, UK, USA, Ireland.

CÔTES DU RHÔNE VILLAGE

CAVE COOPÉRATIVE

André Sode
Route de Nyons
26770 Saint-Pantaléon-les-Vignes
75 27 90 44

Established: 1960. **Number of employees:** 6. **Vine stocks:** Grenache, Cinsault, Mourvèdre, Syrah. **Soil:** Clay with calcium carbonate. **Exposure:** Hillsides and plains. **Average annual production in hectoliters:** 45000 to 50,000.
Appellation: Côtes-du-Rhône, Côtes-du-Rhône Villages. **Types:** Red, white, rosé. **Technique:** Classic. **Maturing:** Vats and casks. **Alcohol content:** Average: 13% to 13.5%. **Characteristics:** Light, fruity wine that goes down well, with a taste of raspberry. **Serving temperature:** White and rosé to be drunk very cool, between 12° and 16°, red between 16° and 18°. **Served with:** Red: game, red meat, cheese. White: fish and shellfish. Rosé: with first courses. **Vintages available in 89/90:** 1983 in 1987, 1985 in 1987 and 1988.

Characteristics of vintages

Average pre-tax ex-warehouse price: Red aged in casks 1983: 16.90 F.F. St-Pantaléon Red 1983: 15.20 F.F. St-Pantaléon Red and Rosé 1985: 14.35 F.F. Rousset Le Vignes 1985: 14.35 F.F.
Sales volume:
- Wholesale: 48%. - Retail, Restaurants: 20%. - Other: 32% (groups).

Sales in France: 95%. **Export sales:** 5%.
Main trading partners : The Cameroons, Netherlands, Germany, Belgium.

CHÂTEAU DE SAINT-GEORGES

André Vignal
Vénéjan - 30200 Bagnols-sur-Cèze
66 79 23 14 - Telex: Cécomex N° 490 981
attention André Vignal

Type of vineyard: Family-owned. **Established:** 1290; by a grant of King Philippe le Bel to P. de Béziers. **Vine stocks:** Grenache, Clairette, Cinsault, Syrah, Mourvèdre, Ugni, Bourboulenc. **Soil:** Ancient terraces of the Rhône Valley round glacial stones. **Exposure:** Good orientation, South and West. **Average annual production in hectoliters:** 1400.
Appellation: Côtes-du-Rhône and Côtes-du-Rhône Villages. **Type:** Red, white and the Syrah Variety. **Technique:** Whole grapes, carbonic maceration. **Maturing:** In vats, then in bottles in a cave hollowed into the rock. **Alcohol content:** 13%. **Characteristics:** Very well-sustained color, fruity, rich and well-balanced, a fine, discreet aroma, but with character. The Côtes-du-Rhône are sustained by good tannins and can age for some time. Fragrance of ripe fruit, blackcurrant, and a trace of animal. **Serving temperature:** 15 to 18°. White: cool. **Served with:** Whites: cool and light, as an aperitif or with shellfish, fish. Red Côtes-du-Rhône: red meat and game. The Côtes-du-Rhône Syrah goes very well with Wild Boar. **Vintages available in 89/90:** Red: 1984, 1985, 1986. White: 1986.

Characteristics of vintages

1986: Red: deep color, rich and complex bouquet. **1985:** Mourvèdre based red: fragant, soft and full, leaves a lasting impression. **1984:** Syrah based red: sustained color, touch of animal and ripe fruit, maturing. Very rich and well-balanced red with well developed blackcurrant aroma. **Other:** Côte-du-Rhône Syrah: sustained ruby color, violet, and hawthorn bouquet, very rich in tannin, will age harmoniously. Price range (pre-tax, ex-warehouse): between 10 F.F. and 30 F.F.

CHÂTEAU SAINT-ESTÈVE D'UCHAUX

Marc Français
Route de Sérignan - Uchaux - 84100 Orange
90 40 62 38 - Telex: 431 919 CIAV

Type of vineyard: Family-owned. **Established:** 1960. **Number of employees:** 12. **Vine stocks:** Red: Syrah, Grenache, Cinsault. White: Rousanne, Wiognier. **Soil:** Ancient alluvium, sandstone, sand. **Exposure:** Southern slopes of the Uchaux Mountain. **Average annual production in hectoliters:** 3,000.
Appellation: A.O.C. Côtes-du-Rhône and Côtes-du-Rhône Villages. **Type:** Red, white, rosé. **Technique:** Traditional, with temperature control. **Maturing:** In underground cave. **Alcohol content:** 12% to 13%. **Characteristics:** Red: fine and robust, velvety, red fruit fragance. White: aromatic, dry and fruity. **Serving temperature:** Red: young - 14°, old - 18°. White: 9°. **Vintages available in 89/90:** 1984, 1985, 1986, 1987, 1988.

Characteristics of vintages

1988: Excellent. **1987:** Good. **1986:** Very good - 11 Prizes and Medals. **1985:** Excellent - 13 Prizes and Medals, very successful wines. **1984:** Good - 10 Prizes and Medals. Do not hesitate. Price range (pre-tax, ex-warehouse): between 10 and 30 F.F.
Sales volume:
- Wholesale: 4%. - Retail: 36%. - Restaurants: 20%.
- Other: 40% (export).
Sales in France: 60%. **Export sales:** 40%.
Main trading partners : Germany, UK, Netherlands, Belgium, Switzerland, Danemark, USA, Japan.

DOMAINE DU VIEUX CHÊNE

Jean-Claude and Dominique Bouche
Rue Buisseron - 84850 Camaret
90 37 25 07

Type of vineyard: Family Corporation (2 brothers). **Established:** Family property since 1700. Cellars in '78. **Vine stocks:** Grenache, Syrah, Cinsault. **Soil:** Clay with calcium carbonate. **Average annual production in hectoliters:** 1800.
Appellation: Côte-du-Rhône Villages, Côte du Rhône, Vin de Pays de Vaucluse. **Type:** Red, white, rosé. **Technique:** Whole grapes (carbonic maceration). **Maturing:** Vats for the Côtes-du-Rhône, casks for the Villages. **Alcohol content:** Côtes-du-Rhônes: 13.5%. Vin de pays: 12.5%. **Characteristics:** Supple, aromatic, rich and well-balanced. **Vintages available in 89/90:** Côtes-du-Rhône Villages - 1986, Côtes-du-Rhône - 1988.

Characteristics of vintages

1988: Excellent year, red good color, round. **1986:** Very good year. Price range (pre-tax, ex-warehouse): between 10 and 20 F.F.

Sales volumes:
- Retail: 70%. - Restaurants: 30%.
Sales in France: 50%.
Export sales: 50%.

Abroad

United States

Importers: Connaisseurs Wines, Chicago, Ill. World Shippers & Importers Co., 1420 Walnut Street, Suite 315, Philadelphia, PA. 19103.

United Kingdom

Importers: Justerini & Brooks, Ltd., 214 Upton Lane, Forest Gate, London E7.

Germany

Importers: Friedrich Klingele, Ravensburgerstrasse 12, 7967 Bad Waldsee. Haus Der Guten Wein, Firma Georg Hack, Schützenstrasse 1, 7758 Meersburg. Gamintchi Winshaus, Decksteinerstrasse 39, 5000 Koln.

The Netherlands

Importers: M. Erick Sauter, Sauter's Wijnkelders bv, Reechstraat 55, 6221 EG Maastricht.

Others - Switzerland

Importers: M. Max A. Sadmeier A.G., CH 4663 Aarburg.

Denmark

J B Vinimport Johan Brinker A/S Gammelgardsvej 96, 3520 Farum.

CAVE DES VIGNERONS

Philippe Martin
Route de l'Ardoise - 30290 Laudun
66 79 49 97

Type of vineyard: Cooperative Agricultural Association. **Established:** 1925. **Number of employees:** 13 to 40 to harvest time. **Vine stocks:** White: Grenache, Clairette, Bourboulenc. Red: Grenache, Syrah, Cinsault, Carignan, Mourvèdre. **Soil:** Terraces, clay with calcium carbonate and stones. **Exposure:** South, Southeast. **Average annual production in hectoliters:** Around 60,000.
Appellation: Côte-du-Rhône and Côtes-du-Rhône Villages Laudun. **Type:** Red, White, rosé. **Technique:** Red: traditional. White: by draining. **Maturing:** Red Laudun: in Oak casks. **Alcohol content:** Côtes-du-Rhône: 12%. Villages: around 13%. **Characteristics:** Red Villages Laudun: robust, rich and well-balanced, subtle fruit aromas, lots of tannin. White: dry and supple, fruity, very aromatic, to be drunk young. **Serving temperature:** Red: about 18°. White: quite coll, 10° to 12°. **Served with:** Red: red meat in sauce. White: seafood. **Vintages available in 89/90:** Red Côtes-du-Rhône: 1985, 1986. Red Villages Laudun: 1984, 1986. White Villages Laudun: 1988.

Characteristics of vintages

1988: Red Côtes-du-Rhône: light, pleasant to drink. Red Villages Laudun: very fruity, rich, well-balanced, promising.

White Villages Laudun: fruity, very supple. **1985:** Red Laudun: Remarkable vintage, wil be recognized as one of the very good years. **1984:** Red Laudun: taste of old wood, tannic. Average pre-tax, ex-warehouse price: Red Côtes-du-Rhône: about 14 F.F. Villages Laudun: about 18 F.F.

CÔTES DU RHÔNE GÉNÉRIQUES

DOMAINE DU BANVIN

Mme Dominique Cumino
84290 Cairanne
90 30 82 38

Type of vineyard: Agricultural Association since 1988. **Established:** 1949. **Number of employees:** 1. **Vine stocks:** Grenache, Cinsault, Syrah, Carignan, Clairette. **Soil:** Sand and chalky clay. **Exposure:** Sunny. **Average annual production in hectoliters:** 35 to 38.

Appellation: Côtes du Rhône. **Technique:** Semi-carbonic maceration. **Maturing:** In vats. **Alcohol content:** 12.5 to 13.5%. **Characteristics:** Fruity, quite clear. **Vintages available in 89/90:** 1984, 1985, 1986, 1987.

Characteristics of vintages

1988: Still in vats – very good year. **1987:** Good year – fruity wine, lighter than the 85 but the Cairanne will be very good. **1986:** Average year, but with selection of the harvest, the Cairanne will be good. **1985:** Very good year – wines stand up well to ageing, will be sold in painted bottles for the two hundredth anniversary of the Revolution. **Other: 1984:** A little "St. Genest", made from 100% Grenache. Price range (pre-tax, ex-warehouse): between 10 and 20 F.F.

Sales volume: – Wholesale: 15%. – Retail: 70%. – Restaurants: 10%. – Other: 5%.
Sales in France: 80%. **Export sales:** 20%.
Main trading partners: United Kingdom, Switzerland, Netherlands, Denmark.

References in France

Restaurants: Côte d'Azur: Le Piano Blanc (Villeneuve-Loubet 06, near the beach), Auberge Franc-Comtoise (Villeneuve-Loubet 06), Restaurant Malausséna (Levens 06), La Crémaillère (Marignane 13), Le Chêne Vert (Bollène 84).

Abroad

United Kingdom

Ets Siegel, London SW11 4JP, 50 Battersea Park Road.

Switzerland

Ets Scherer, Carouge.

The Netherlands

Wijnalliance Vinvins (Mr. De Vos), Culemborg.

Others

Denmark: Vinklub (Mr. Niels Frederiksen), Fyrrebakken 12, Hillerod.

Comments

The origins go back to 1876 at which date the main building of the domain can be found on the land register. The winemaking procedure yields fruity wines (the Cairanne has a taste of raspberries). The Blanc de Blancs is made from 90% Clairette, harvested early for a green and fruity taste.

CAVEAU CHANTECÔTES

Christian Bigey
Côtes du Nord, B.P. 13
84290 Sainte-Cécile-les- Vignes
90 30 83 25 – Telex: 432 675 F

Type of vineyard: Cooperative. **Established:** Cellar in 1927 – tasting cellar in 1973. **Number of employees:** 14. **Vine stocks:** Grenache 70%, Carignan 13%, Syrah 10%, Mourvèdre 6%, Cinsaut 1%. **Soil:** chalky clay, gravel, round pebbles. **Exposure:** South. **Average annual production in hectoliters:** 75,000.
Appellation: Côtes-du-Rhône. **Type:** Red, white, rosé. **Technique:** White: on fine lees, Rosé: drawing off. Red: traditional. **Maturing:** In vats or oak casks depending on the type of wine. **Alcohol content:** 13%. **Characteristics:** White: English candy, exotic fruit and pineapple aromas. Rosé: light and very fruity, lingering fragrance – Red: stewed red fruit, spices, cocoa, truffle aromas, good acidity, tannin and alcohol balance. **Serving temperature:** standart. **Served with:** White: shellfish, fish, fish in sauce, goat cheese. Rosé: delicatessen, quenelles, pasta, truffle omelettes. **Vintages available in 89/90:** 1983 (in 1989), 1985, 1986, 1987.

CAVEAU CHANTECOTES

84290 SAINTE-CÉCILE-LES-VIGNES - Tél. 90.30.83.25

Characteristics of vintages

1987: Chantecôtes Cuvée Cecilia: aromatic, fruity, good texture, now to 1991. **1986:** Chantecôtes Grande Réserve: typical average Côtes du Rhône, ready to drink. **1985:** Chantecôtes Cuvée du Cardinal: stewed red fruit, vanilla aroma, good structure, top quality Côtes du Rhône, better quality/price ratio. **Other: 1983:** Chantecôtes St. Vincent: very great nose, (vanilla, animal, spices). Truffle, red berry and tar flavor. Rich and very well balanced. Tannins still a bit rough. Very long finish. Price range (pre-tax, ex-warehouse): 20 to 30 F.F.

Sales volume:
- Wholesale: 80 %. - Retail: 17 %. - Restaurants: 3 % (cellars and shops).

Sales in France: 55 %. **Export sales:** 45 %.

Main trading partners: Switzerland 95 %, Belgium, Netherlands.

References in France

Restaurants: La Beaugranière (84 Mondragon), Le Vieux Moulin (30 Villeneuve-lès-Avignon), Hôtel Montmirail (84 Vacqueyras).
Shops: L'Amour du Vin, 94, rue Saint-Dominique, 75007 Paris.

Abroad

Switzerland

Hôtel Restaurant du Poisson - 2000 Auvernier - Etb. Hammel - Vins Fins 1180 Rolle - Ets. Dizrad, 94, rue des Eaux Vives, Geneva - Etb. Cavallaro (Ase Postale 202 Genva - 2) - La Vigneronne, 10, route des Falaises, Geneva - Vins Latour, av. de Grandson 39 - 1400 Yverdon-les-Bains - Tel: 24 24 20 84 - Etb. Amann 16 cret Taconnet 2000 Neuchatel.

Belgium

Hotel Delbeccha - Bodegemstraat 180-1710 Dielbeek Tel: 02 56 94 430.

The Netherlands

Etb. Thiessen Grote Gracht 18, Postbus 227-6211SW Maastricht - Etb. Nick Taams - Prisengracht 520 1017 KJ Amsterdam.

Comments

Because of difficult times, the winemakers of Ste. Cécile and Lagarde Paréol, a picturesque neighboring village, decided to get together to survive and founded a cooperative in 1927. Since then, others have joined. The "Coopérative Vinicole Cécilia" has grown considerably and, as a result of the success of its production, vinified according to traditional methods, it was decided to make a special effort to make its wines known to a retail clientele through a direct sales and shipping office. A sales and tasting cellar was created for this purpose and a brand name, Chantecôtes, was assigned to the Côtes du Rhône wine. A very well equipped cellar, very serious, which very carefully matures a number of wines that have an excellent quality/price ratio.

DOMAINE DU CABANON

Yves Payan
5, place de la Fontaine - Saze
30650 Rochefort-du-Gard
90 31 70 74

Type of vineyard: Family-owned. **Established:** 1889. **Vine stocks:** 50% Grenache, 20% Carignan, 20% Cinsault, 10% Syrah. **Soil:** Clay with calcium carbonate. **Exposure:** North South. **Average annual production in hectoliters:** 500.
Appellation: Côtes du Rhône. **Type:** Red. **Technique:** 50% crushing, 50% carbonic maceration. **Maturing:** Concrete and enamel tanks. **Alcohol content: 12.6%. Characteristics:** The light soil yields light, well-balanced wines, and carbonic maceration is responsible for its fruit flavor and aromas. **Serving temperature:** 15°. **Served with:** White meat and goat cheese. **Vintage available 89/90:** 1984 and 1985.

Characteristics of vintages

1985: Good wine for ageing, very fine and fruity. **1984:** has developed with ageing, fragrance and aroma. Price range (pre-tax, ex-warehouse): between 10 and 20 F.F.

CASTAN

Gérard Castan
Mas Chantecler - 30390 Domazan
66 57 00 56

Established: 7 generations. **Vine stocks:** Traditionnal for Côte-du-Rhône. **Soil:** Stones, clay with calcium carbonate. **Exposure:** Hillside. **Average annual production in hectoliters:** 1 200.
Appellation:Côtes-du-Rhône. **Type:** Red, white, rosé. **Technique:** 50% destemming, fermentation for 6 days. White and rosé, by drawing off. **Maturing:** Cement vats lined with stainless steel. **Alcohol content:** 12% to 13%. **Characteristics:** Red: fruity, rich and well-balanced. Rosé: fine and fragant. White: full bodied, fat and rich. **Serving temperature:** Red: 12°. White and rosé: 10°. **Vintages available in 89/90:** Red: 1985, 1986, perhaps 1987. Rosé and white: 1986 and 1987.

Characteristics of vintages

1988: Rosé: Silver Medal (Foire d'Orange) - White - Red and Côtes du Rhône Villages. **1987:** Rosé: Silver Medal (Foire d'Orange), White, Red and Côtes du Rhône Villages. **1986:** Rosé: Gold Medal at the Concours Général Agricole de Paris. Price range (pre-tax, ex-warehouse): Between 10 F.F. and 20 F.F.
Sales volume:
- Wholesale: 50%. - Retail: 20%. - Restaurants: 30%.
Sales in France: 80%.
Export sales: 20%.
Main trading partners : Belgium, Netherlands, UK.

References in France

Restaurants: Avignon, Nîmes, Pont-du-Gard, Vesoul, Lourdes, Nice, Clermont-Ferrand, Sète, etc.

CAVE DES VIGNERONS DE CHUSCLAN

Jean Grandjean
Chusclan 30200, Bagnols-sur-Ceze
66 90 11 03 - Telex 485 301 F

Type of vineyard: Cooperative. **Established:** 1939. **Number of employees:** 20. **Vine stocks:** Grenache, Cinsault, Syrah, Mourvèdre, Carignan, Clairette, Bourboulenc. **Soil:** Sand, round pebbles, chalky clay. **Exposure:** South. **Average annual production in hectoliters:** 50,000.

Appellation: Côtes du Rhône & Côtes du Rhône Villages Chusclan. **Type:** Red, white, rosé. **Technique:** Traditional with carbonic maceration. **Maturing:** Cement lined tanks, stainless steel tanks, oak vats. **Alcohol content:** 12%. **Characteristics:** Aroma of ripe plums, red berries and bay leaves. **Serving temperature:** Rosé and white: cool but not cold. Red 18°. **Vintages available in 89/90:** 1985, 1987, 1988, 1989 harvest (white and rosé).

Characteristics of vintages

1988: Very developed bouquet, fine, deep color, well developed, well made. Price range (pre-tax, ex-warehouse): 10 to 20 F.F.
Sales volume:
- Wholesale: 60%. - Retail: 32%. - Restaurants: 8%.
Sales in France: 65%.
Export sales: 35%.
Main trading partners : Belgium, Luxemburg, Netherlands, United Kingdom, Germany, USA, Canada, Japan, Sweden, Switzerland.

• *For an ideal wine cellar, find out what to do and what not to do (see chapter "Organizing a Wine Cellar")*

CHÂTEAU DE L'ESTAGNOL

Chambovet, Father & Son
26790 Suze-la-Rousse
90 34 21 80

Type of vineyard: Family-owned. **Established:** 1950. **Number of employees:** 8. **Vine stocks:** Grenache, Syrah, Cinsault, Carignan, Mourvèdre, Bourboulenc. **Soil:** Sand. **Average annual production in hectoliters:** 4,000.
Appellation: Côtes-du-Rhône. **Type:** Red, White, rosé. **Technique:** 80% classic, 20% carbonic maceration. **Maturing:** 6 to 12 months in Oak casks. **Alcohol content:** 12.5%. **Characteristics:** Ruby color, mellow, fruity, taste of liquorice. **Served with:** Roasts, game. **Vintages available in 89/90:** 1985 and 1986.

Characteristics of vintages

Price range (pre-tax, ex-warehouse): Between 20 F.F. and 30 F.F.
Sales volume:
- Wholesale: 20%. - Retail: 15%. - Restaurants: 15%. - Other: 50% (export).
Sales in France: 50%.
Export sales: 50%.
Main trading partners : Belgium, Netherlands, UK, Switzerland, USA.

Comments

The Château de l'Estagnol was awarded a Gold Medal with the congratulations of the jury for the Red Côtes-du-Rhône in 1986.
The 1988 vintage has just been awarded a Gold Medal at the Paris National Trade Fair.

CHÂTEAU DE FONSALETTE

Jacques Reynaud
84290 Lagarde-Paréol
90 83 73 09

Vine stocks: Clairette, Grenache, Cinsault, Syrah. **Exposure:** North.
Appellation: Côtes-du-Rhône. **Type:** Red, white, rosé. **Technique:** Traditional. **Maturing:** in casks. **Characteristics:** Full-bodied, fruity, fine bouquet, long finish, finesse. **Serving temperature:** Red: 17° - White: 13°. **Served with:** Red ans rosé: delicatessen products, meat, cheese. White: fish. **Vintages available in 89/90:** 1985.

Characteristics of vintages

1985: Successful year. Excellent red, supple and well-balanced, full flavor, ages well.
Main trading partners : Switzerland, USA, UK, Belgium, Austria, Japan, Netherlands, Germany, Sweden, Italy, Canada, Australia.

DOMAINE DE LA GRAND'RIBE

Abel Sahuc
84290 Sainte-Cécile-les-Vignes
90 30 83 75

Vine stocks: Grenache, Syrah, Mourvèdre, Vieux-Carignan. **Soil:** Clay with calcium carbonate and Mediterranean Garrigue. **Average annual production in hectoliters:** 1 500.
Appellation: Côtes-du-Rhône. **Type:** Red, white. **Technique:** Traditional. **Maturing:** Tanks stored underground. **Characteristics:** Ruby color, developing very slowly with age. Pronounced red fruit fragance when young, later turning to cooked fruit, spice and truffle aroma. Good structural balance, pleasant without being heavy, subtle, lingering farewell. **Serving temperature:** Red (young): 10°-12°; (aged): 14°-15°. White: 8°. Rosé: 10°. **Served with:** Red (young): poultry and delicatessen products. Red (aged): game (feathered), goose preserves. White: fish, truffles. Rosé: poultry (grilled), pastry. **Vintages available in 89/90:** Aged wine: 1981-1986 (Mâcon Gold Medal). Youg wine: 1986 (Mâcon Silver Medal), Rosé 1986 (Mâcon Silver Medal), White 1986.

Characteristics of vintages

1986: Fine, fruity, supple. **1984:** Balance between youthful characteristics and the development of the tertiary aromas of ageing. **Note:** 1981 - full and firm, with the harmonius qualities of an aged wine. Price range (pre-tax, ex-warehouse): 10 F.F.-30 F.F.
Sales volume:
- Wholesale: 50%. - Retail: 40%. - Restaurants: 10%.
Sales in France: 50%.
Export sales: 50%.
Main trading partners : Belgium, Germany, UK.

DOMAINE LES GOUBERT

Jean-Pierre Cartier
84190 Gigondas
90 65 86 38

Type of vineyard: Family-owned. **Vine stocks:** Grenache. **Soil:** Chalky clay. **Average annual production in hectoliters:** 120.
Appellation: Côtes-du-Rhône. **Type:** Red. **Technique:** Traditional - Crushing, no destemming, long fermentation on skins. **Maturing:** 11 months in concrete tanks, bottling in September - One bottling per appellation and vintage. **Alcohol content:** 13%. **Characteristics:** Flowery fragrance, red berry flavor, fresh, goes down well. **Serving temperature:** 16-18°. **Vintages available in 89/90:** 1987.

Characteristics of vintages

Price range (pre-tax, ex-warehouse): 10 to 20 F.F.
Export sales: 35%.
Main trading partners : 65%.

CHÂTEAU DU PRIEURE

Guy Mousset
Les Fines Roches - Châteauneuf du Pape
90 83 70 30
Telefax: 90 83 74 79 - Telex: 431 935

Vine stocks: Grenache, Cinsault, Carignan, Syrah. **Soil:** clay, round pebbles. **Exposure:** very sunny, facing full South. **Average annual production:** 200,000 bottles.

1987
1987
CHATEAU du PRIEURÉ
Côtes du Rhône
e 75 cl
12,5% vol.
APPELLATION COTES-DU-RHONE CONTROLÉE
mis en bouteille au château
PRODUCE OF FRANCE
GUY MOUSSET - PROPRIÉTAIRE-RÉCOLTANT A SORGUES - VAUCLUSE

Appellation: Côtes-du-Rhône. **Type:** Red, Rosé. **Technique:** traditional, destemming, crushing. **Alcohol content:** 12.5%. **Served with:** Red meat, game, cheese. **Vintages available in 89/90:** 1988.

Characteristics of vintages

1988: excellent vintage, rich in color, fragrant, good keeping.
Export sales: 95%.
Main trading partners : UK.

Comments

The Château was erected in the 19th century near Sorgues, in the style of the great manor houses of Provence, in a locality known as the "Grand-Gigognan", on the foundations of an old monastery. The soil is particularly conducive to the cultivation of grape vines which yield a remarkable, balanced and harmonious, beautifully colored wine that ages exceptionally well. The nobility of the vinestocks are responsible for a very typical Côtes-du-Rhône, the sunshine wine.

• Classification of the great Bordeaux wines in 1988. The ratings of Châteaux Lascombes (Margaux), Mazeris-Bellevue (Canon-Fronsac) and Haut-Maco (Côtes-de-Bourg) are improving, as well as those of certain other surprising crus (Châteaux Trocard, Melin, Gazin, Chantegriue, Gloria, La Croix-Saint-André, Fombrauge...). See the 1988 Classification in the Chapter on Bordeaux wines.

CHÂTEAU DE RUTH

Christian Meffre
84290 Sainte-Cécile-les-Vignes
90 65 86 09 - Telex: 431 803

Type of vineyard: Family-owned. **Established:** 1970. **Vine stocks:** Grenache, Cinsault, Syrah, Mourvèdre. **Soil:** Chalky clay, round pebbles. **Exposure:** North-West, South-East. **Average annual production in hectoliters:** 5,000.
Appellation: AOC Côtes-du-Rhône. **Type:** Red. **Technique:** Traditional. **Maturing:** In wooden casks (10 to 15 months). **Alcohol content:** 12.5%. **Characteristics:** Blackcurrant and raspberry aroma. **Serving temperature:** 18°. **Served with:** Red meat, wine sauce and cheese. **Vintages available in 89/90:** 1988.

Characteristics of vintages

1988: Fresh and supple, well-balanced. Price range (pre-tax, ex-warehouse): 20 to 30 F.F.
Sales volume:
- Retail: 25%. - Restaurants: 25%. - Other: 50% - export.
Sales in France: 40%.
Export sales: 40%.
Main trading partners : Belgium, Switzerland, Germany, Netherlands, Japan, USA, Canada, Denmark.

References in France

Restaurants: Pullman, Beaumanière, Armes de Champagne.
Shops: Félix Potin, Marchés aux vins, la Sommelière.

Abroad

United States
Stacole, Miami.

United Kingdom
Hawkins, London.

Germany
Hawesko, Hamburg.

Switzerland
Riotton Gilliéron, Geneva.

Belgium
GB Inno, Goselies.

The Netherlands
Verlinden en Zoon s'Hertogenbosch.

Far East
Jardine Matheson, Tokyo - for South-East Asai.

Comments

The Château de Ruth dates back to 1592. The domain was the property of Fernand Trintignant, father of the automobile racer, Maurice Trintignant, at the beginning of the century before being bought by Nicolas de Beauharnais, a direct descendent of the Empress Joséphine on one side and the Russian Imperial family on the other.

DOMAINE DE TOUT-VENT

Jacques Mousset
Château les Fines Roches
84230 Châteauneuf-du-Pape
90 83 70 30
Telefax: 90 83 74 79 – Telex: 431 935

Vine stocks: Mourvèdre, Syrah, Grenache, Bourboulenc, Clairette, Cinsault, Picpoul. **Soil:** clay, sand and round pebbles. **Exposure:** Sunny slopes to the South, sheltered from the Mistral winds. **Average annual production:** 120,000 bottles.

Produce of France
DOMAINE
DE
TOUT-VENT
1986
Côtes du Rhône
ROSÉ RHONE WINE
VIN ROSÉ
APPELLATION CÔTES DU RHÔNE CONTRÔLÉE
12,5 % ALC VOL
750 ml
MIS EN BOUTEILLE AU DOMAINE
JACQUES MOUSSET, PROPRIÉTAIRE A CHATEAUNEUF-DU-PAPE (VAUCLUSE) FRANCE
75 cl
PRODUIT DE FRANCE

Appellation: Côtes du Rhône. **Type:** Red, Rosé. **Technique:** traditional – Crushing, destemming. **Alcohol content:** 12.5%. **Characteristics:** very typical, forthcoming, spicy aromas. Resembles the neighboring Châteauneuf appellation because of the similar sub-soil and the noble and varied vinestocks. **Serving temperature:** 14°. **Served with:** red meat, cheese. **Vintages available in 89/90:** 1988.

Characteristics of vintages

1988: not yet tasted. Price range (pre-tax, ex-warehouse): 10 F.F. to 20 F.F.
Sales in France: 70%.
Export sales: 30%.
Main trading partners : UK, Canada, USA, Belgium.

Comments

Located on hillsides neighboring the Châteauneuf-du-Pape appellation region, the favorable soil has all of the same characteristics. The reputation of Côtes-du-Rhône has been considerably advanced by the quality of the wines produced here. The variety of the prestigious vinestocks results in a rich, well-balanced, forthcoming wine with a beautiful ruby color.

• *Read labels carefully – An indication to watch out for: "Bottled in the 'region' of production", which often refers to a blend of wines from several producers and not just one.*

DOMAINE DE VERQUIÈRE

Bernard and Denis Chamfort
Rue d'Orange, 84 Sablet
90 46 90 11

Type of vineyard: Agricultural Association. **Established:** 1983. **Number of employees:** 5. **Vine stocks:** 65% Grenache, 15% Syrah, 15% Cinsault/Mourvèdre, 5% Clairette and others. **Soil:** Round stones on terraces, Helvetian sandstone and sand. **Exposure:** Very sunny, climate particularly suitable for winegrowing. **Average annual production in hectoliters:** 2,500.
Appellation: Côtes du Rhône. **Type:** Red, naturally sweet wine. **Technique:** Traditional. **Maturing:** Côtes du Rhône Village: in vats and oak casks. **Alcohol content:** 13%. **Characteristics:** Rich, well balanced, forthcoming, aromatic, spicy, deep ruby color. **Serving temperature:** 16 to 17°. **Served with:** Meats, cheeses. **Vintages available in 89/90:** 1986 C.D.R., 1987 C.D.R. Village Vacqueyras, 1983 C.D.R. Village Sablet.

Characteristics of vintages

1987: Vacqueyras: Tannic, good keeping, supple, fragrant. **1976:** C.D.R.: Good keeping, fruity, long, agreeable. **Other: 1983** Sablet: Purple color, rich well balanced and forthcoming, spicy flavor, lightly tannic. Price range (pre-tax, ex-warehouse): between 10 and 30 F.F..
Sales volume:
– Wholesale: 40%. – Retail: 30%. – Restaurants: 10%. – Other: 20% export.
Sales in France: 40%. **Export sales:** 20%.
Main trading partners : Belgium, Netherlands, Germany, United Kingdom.

DOMAINE de VERQUIERE
e750ml CÔTES-DU-RHÔNE
APPELLATION COTES DU RHONE CONTROLÉE
Mis en bouteille au Domaine
CHAMFORT FRÈRES PROPRIÉTAIRE-RÉCOLTANT - 84110 SABLET
GAEC RECONNU CHAMFORT FRERES A SABLET (Vse) FRANCE
PRODUIT DE FRANCE

References in France

Shops: Au Tastevin and Producer's Cellars (Marseille), Le Tonneau (Montélimar, Orange, Cavaillon).

Abroad

United Kingdom
Pierre Hourlier, 390 Burton Road, Derby DE3 6AD. Richard Spiers, 3 Falcon Road, Guildford, Surrey GU1 4JG.

Germany

Les Vignobles, Mr. Jegers, Mülheimer Str 103, 4100 Duisburg 1. Wahnschaffe Weinimport, 4190 Kleve, Königsallée 173.

Switzerland

Cavallero S & M, 13 bd James-Fazy, CP 202, CH 1211 Geneva 1.

Belgium

Jean Straetmans, Zembstbaan 148, B 2800 Mechelen. Emmanuel De Landtsheer, Mandekenstraat 209, B 9360 Buggenhout. Van Hende, Provinciebaan 108, B 9744 Gavere.

The Netherlands

Verbunt BV, Mr. J de Kock, Ven Vollenhovenstraat 247, Postbus 2035, 5001 CA Tilburg.

Comments

Under the rule of the count of Toulouse, nearly 50 citizens of Sablet, including the mayor, were winegrowers. This, of course, on a much smaller scale than today, however, it is clear that the vineyard was already in place as it had been in the Roman era - a fact as evidenced by the results of excavations. The present Domaine de Verquières is a 50 hectare vineyard extending over three communes.
The wines of the Domaine de Verquière acquire their nobility from the fortunate variety of the vinestocks and by the diversity of the parcels that make up the vineyard. The warm, rocky red soil of the Plan de Dieu, swept by the Mistral winds give them vigor. The well exposed hillsides give them softness and richness. The bouquet, roundness and distinction come from the harmonious mixture of these noble vinestocks.

CHÂTEAUNEUF DU PAPE

CHÂTEAU DE BEAUCASTEL

François Perrin
84350 Courthezon
90 70 70 60 – Telex: PERRINS 432383

Type of vineyard: Family-owned. **Established:** 1909 in its present from. The vineyard existed before the phylloxera epidemic. **Number of employees:** 25. **Vine stocks:** The 13 AOC Châteauneuf-du-Pape vinestocks. **Soil:** Miocene soil covered by Alpine diluvium. **Exposure:** Plateau. **Average annual production in hectoliters:** 2,500.
Appellation: Châteauneuf-du-Pape. **Type:** Red, white. **Technique:** Heating of the harvest, later traditional. **Maturing:** In wooden vats. **Alcohol content:** 13%. **Characteristics:** Young wines: red berry aroma, taking on a gamey character, then with ageing a spicy, woodland and truffle aroma. **Serving temperature:** 15°. **Served with:** Red meat and game. **Vintages available in 89/90:** 1981, 1985, 1986.

Characteristics of vintages

1988: Too early to judge, right now tannic and promising, to be kept. **1987:** Stronger vanilla flavor, more supple, to be drunk sooner. **1986:** Good keeping, tannic, beautiful color. **1985:** Very pleasant. Red berry nose (blackcurrant, huckleberry and vanilla). Mellow tannins, soft and rich. **Other:** 1981: perfect balance, musky touch, very well structured, complex and full-bodied. Very good wine. Price range (pre-tax, ex-warehouse): 50 to 80 F.F.
Sales volume:
– Retail: 70%. – Restaurants: 30%.
Sales in France: 40%.
Export sales: 60%.
Main trading partners: USA, European community countries, Switzerland, Australia, Japan.

References in France

Restaurants: Point, Pic, Troisgros, Le Grand Vefour, Le Vivarois, Rostang, Lucas Carton, Lou Mazuc, Gagnaire, Oustau Beaumanière.
Shops: Legrand (Filles), Fauchon, Steven Spurrier, Willi's Wine Bar, Petit Bacchus, Estèves.

Abroad

United States

Vineyard Brands, Robert Haas Selections, F.F.D. 1, Chester (Vermont).

United Kingdom

Mistral Wines, 5 Junction Mews, Sale Place, London W2 1PN.

Switzerland

Divo S.A., Rue des Terreaux 2, 1003 Lausanne.

Belgium

Divo S.A., Quai au Foin 37, 1000 Brussels. Naud Rullens & Co, Chaussée de Haecht 1387, 1130 Brussels.

Canada

SAQ, Place d'Armes, Montreal. LCBQ 55 Lake Shore Blvd. Toronto, (Ontario).

The Netherlands

Ets Sauter's Wijnkerlers, Rechtstraat 55, Maastricht, 6202 MA.

Far East

Japan: Barclay and CO, Asaka Minato. Thailand: Italthai Industrie, Bangkok.

Others

Australia: Smith and Son Pty, Adelaide. New Zealand: Kitchener Wine, Auckland.

Comments

From time immemorial the Beaucastels have been among the notables of Courthézon. In 1687, Pierre de Beaucastel obtained from King Louis XIV, in recognition of his conversion to Catholicism after the revocation of the Edict of Nantes, the rank of "Captain of the City of Courthézon". Two centuries later, when the phylloxera epidemic broke out, the master of Beaucastel was Elie Dussaud, colleague of Ferdinand de Lesseps who built the Suez Canal. The vineyard was not reconstituted at that time and it was only in 1909 that Pierre Tramier took over the domain and started replanting. He then left it to his son-in-law, Pierre Perrin, a scientist who left his mark on the domain. Jacques Perrin continued the improvements until 1978. Today the torch is in the hands of his sons.

DOMAINE DE BEAURENARD

Paul Coulon
84230 Châteauneuf-du-Pape
90 83 71 79 - Telex: 432.323

Type of vineyard: Agricultural Association. **Number of employees:** 13. **Vine stocks:** Grenache 70%, Syrah 10%, Mourvèdre 10%, Cinsault 10%. **Soil:** Pebbly, chalky clay. **Exposure:** South. **Average annual production in hectoliters:** Châteauneuf: 35 hl/ha Côte du Rhône: 50 hl/ha.

1987
1987
Châteauneuf-du-Pape
APPELLATION CHATEAUNEUF-DU-PAPE CONTRÔLEE
DOMAINE DE BEAURENARD
13% vol.
MIS EN BOUTEILLE AU DOMAINE
75cl e
G.A.E.C. Paul COULON et Fils
PROPRIÉTAIRES-RÉCOLTANTS, 84230 CHATEAUNEUF-DU-PAPE (FRANCE)
PRODUCE OF FRANCE

Appellation: Châteauneuf du Pape (Red & White) - Côte du Rhône (Red & Rosé). **Technique:** Traditional in temperature controlled stainless steel tanks. **Maturing:** In oak casks and vats. **Alcohol content:** Châteauneuf: 13.5%, Côte du Rhône: 12.5%. **Characteristics:** Fruity wine mostly red berry fragrance, pleasant drinking when young, but will age harmoniously without drying out. **Serving temperature:** 17°. **Served with:** Meat, game. **Vintages available in 89/90:** 1986, 1987, 1988.

Characteristics of vintages

1988: Beautiful color, very promising primary and secondary aromas, long, rich and full, balanced, alcoholic, acid and tannic - good ripe grape tannins. **1987:** Very fine, pleasant aromas, to be drunk before the 1986 and 1985 vintages. **1986:** Balanced wine, round, well developed, high tannic content. To be kept more than 10 years. **1985:** Beautiful wine, very harmonious, rich and full, ready to drink or to be kept. Price range (pre-tax, ex-warehouse): Côtes du Rhône 20-30 F.F. - Châteauneuf du Pape 30-50 F.F.
Sales in France: 60%.
Export sales: 40%.
Main trading partners : United Kingdom, Belgium, Germany, Switzerland, Austria, Japan, Canada, USA, Australia.

Abroad

United States

World Shippers - 1420 Wahnut St.-Philadelphia (PA 191103). Transat Trade - 300 East Beach Ave. Inglewood (CA 90302).

United Kingdom

Grants of St Jame's - Eastgate House - Derby 1 3TB.

Germany

Jordan Weinberaeing - Alfredstrasse 345 - Dessen 1.

Switzerland

Mello-Banchet - rue des Vollandes - 1211 Geneva 6.

Belgium

Pirard and Fils - rue du Galbais, B. Genappe 1470.

Canada

Manitoba LCC - PO BOX 1023 - Winnipeg Man R 3C 2X1.

The Netherlands

Fourcroy Nederland - Brockveldselaan 9 - ND 2411 Bodegraven.

Far East

Chesco LTD - Tokyo Ryutsu Center 201 - 1, 2, 6 Chome (Japon). Chome Heiwajima Tokyo (Ohta-Ku).

Others

Australia: Fesq 1 Co. Warehouse 201, Hale Str. Botany (NSW).

Comments

A vineyard at Châteauneuf de Pape, passed down from father to son for 7 generations. The present proprietor strives continually to improve his wines and his installations, as exemplified during the course of 1988 with the creation of new vinification and storage warehouses, and with the restoration of the tasting cellar and improvement of the amenities of the old premises.

BOSQUET DES PAPES

Maurice & Josette Boiron
Route d'Orange, 84230 Châteauneuf-du-Pape
90 83 72 33

Type of vineyard: Family-owned. **Established:** For five generations. **Number of employees:** 3. **Vine stocks:** Grenache 80%, Mourvèdre 8%, Syrah 7%, Cinsaut 3%, Vaccarèse 2%. **Soil:** Pebbly clay.

Appellation: Châteauneuf-du-Pape. **Type:** Red – white. **Technique:** Traditional. **Maturing:** In wooden vasks (18 months to 3 years). **Characteristics:** Tannic, robust, good keeping. **Serving temperature:** Red: 18° – White: 6-8°. **Served with:** Red: red meat, game, cheese. **Vintages available in 89/90:** 1984, 1985, 1986, 1987 – White: 1988.

Characteristics of vintages

1988: Red: superb, tannic, fragrant, well colored, very promising. White: very fragrant, flowery, subtle and elegant. **1987:** Good wine, very fine, beautifully intense fragrance, fruity, woody, will be ready sooner. **1986:** Very good year, beautiful purple color, tannic, robust, very fragrant, to be aged. **1985:** Superb wine, very successful, lively purple color, round and pleasant. Price range (pre-tax, ex-warehouse): 35 to 40 F.F.

Sales volume:
– Wholesale: 10%. – Retail: 45%. – Restaurants: 5%.
Sales in France: 60%.
Export sales: 40%.
Main trading partners : USA, Belgium, Canada, Australia, Germany, Switzerland, Netherlands.

References in France

Restaurants: Willi's Wine Bar (13, rue des Petits Champs, 75001 Paris).

Abroad

United States

Julienne Importing Compagny, 2725 W Coyle, Chicago, Illinois 60645 – Grand Cru Inc., 648 Broadway, New York NY 10002 – Calvert Woodley, 4339 Connecticut, Avenue n.w. Washington DC 20008 – Michel Nathan Wine, Markets International, Syosset New York 11791.

United Kingdom

Sebastopol Wines – Robert Redpath Lancashire.

Germany

Weinland Keller – Dortmund 4600.

Switzerland

J.D. Pilloud – Promovin – Sordet SA Geneve – La Vrille SA Belino Nyon CH.

Belgium

Les Vins du Rhône, 4000 Liège – Vinea B 1686 Gooik.

Canada

Château Imports, Vancouver.

The Netherlands

Wijwkopers Kowing & Sshutte, Heemskerk 1964.

USA

M.S. Walker I.N.C., Somerville Massachussets 02143 – Diamond Wine Merchants, Albany, California 94706 – Left Bank Wine Company, Belleville W.I. 53508 – Lemma Wine Company, Portland, Oregon 97214 – Direct Import Wine Co, Des Plaines I.L. 60018 – Pilgrim of Kentucky, PO. Box 626, Covington Kentucky 41012 – Transatlantic suppliers, Medley, Florida 33166 – Bauer and Foss Inc., PO. Box 238, Groueport, Ohio 43125 – Zephir and Imports, suite 401 Seattle, Washington 98134 – Wine Marketing L.T.D., Slocum RI 02877 – Le Courtier du Vin, Denver Colorado 80205.

Irlande

Mr. Eric Lechmar, Dublin 18 Irelande.

Others

Australia – The De Burgh Day Wine, Melbourne – Wine Bond, Sydney.

Comments

The cellars are located at a short distance from the ruins of the Château des Papes. The vineyard, very much split up (35 lots), is planted on pebbly soil. It has been passed down from father to son for five generations.

DOMAINE LA BASTIDE ST DOMINIQUE

Gérard Bonnet
84350 Courthezon
90 70 85 32

Type of vineyard: Family-owned. **Established:** 1975. **Number of employees:** 1. **Vine stocks:** Grenach, Cinsault, Syrah, Mourvèdre, Clairette. **Soil:** Clay, sand, round pebbles. **Exposure:** Hillside and plateau. **Average annual production in hectoliters:** Châteauneuf: 30-35 Côtes du Rhône: 40-45.
Appellation: Côtes du Rhône – Châteauneuf du Pape. **Type:** Red, white. **Technique:** Very traditional. **Maturing:** In enamelled tanks. **Alcohol content:** 13.5-14.5%. **Characteristics:** White (Châteauneuf): fruity, pale golden color, soft and rich. Red (Châteauneuf): deep color, fruity. **Serving temperature:** White: 5 to 7°. Red: 16 to 17°. **Served with:** White: foie gras, fish. Red: game, red meat. **Vintages available in 89/90:** 1985, 1986, 1988.

Characteristics of vintages

1988: Still too young but very promising. **1986:** More developed wine, stewed fruit aroma, lingering taste. **1985:** Rich and well balanced, forthcoming, to be aged. Price range (pre-tax, ex-warehouse): Côtes du Rhône: 10 to 20 F.F. Châteauneuf du Pape (Red): 30 to 50 F.F. White: 50 to 80 F.F.

Sales volume:
- Wholesale: 30%. - Retail: 50%. - restaurants: 10%.
- Other: 10%.

Sales in France: 90%.
Export sales: 10%.
Main trading partners : UK, Belgium, Netherlands.

BÉRARD PÈRE ET FILS DOMAINE DE TERRE FERME

Robert Dahm
B.P. 30 - 84370 Bédarrides
90 33 02 98 – Telex: 432 548

Type of vineyard: Family-owned. **Established:** 1925, **Number of employees:** 9. **Vine stocks:** Grenache, Syrah, Mourvèdre, Cinsaut, Bourboulenc, Clairette. **Soil:** Alpine diluvium – Briançon pebbles. **Exposure:** 1/3 central plateau, 2/3 setting sun. **Average annual production in hectoliters:** Red: 1,400. White: 300.

Appellation: Châteauneuf-du-Pape. **Type:** Red, white. **Technique:** Partly by carbonic maceration, partly be light crushing. **Maturing:** Casks and enamelled stainless steel tanks. **Alcohol content:** Red: 14%. White: 13.5%. **Characteristics:** White: great bearing and freshness. Red: substantial and elegant. **Serving temperature:** White: 8 to 10°. Red: 15 to 16°. **Served with:** White: as an apéritif or with first courses, foie gras, fish. Red: game, meat in sauce, cheese. **Vintages available in 89/90:** White: 1988. Red: 1986, 1987, 1988.

Characteristics of vintages

1988: White: beautiful bearing, great freshness, exotic fruit taste. Red: less body and more elegant than the 1986 and 1987. **1987:** White: fresh – Gault and Millaud first prize. Red: discreet, good bearing, award at Saint-Marc. **1986:** Red: quite typical of the appellation with a dried fig taste. To be kept. Price range (pre-tax, ex-warehouse): Between 50 and 80 F.F.

Sales volume:
- Wholesale: 20%. - Retail: 50%. - Restaurants: 20%.
- Other: 10% (distributers).

Sales in France: 50%.
Export sales: 50%.
Main trading partners : Germany, UK, Switzerland, Denmark, Belgium, Luxemburg, Netherlands, USA, Canada.

References in France

Restaurants: La Tour d'Argent, Hiely, Baumanière.

Comments

A 58 hectare estate located on one of the best Châteauneuf-du-Pape terrains. Many medals in all of the international competitions.

CLOS DES PAPES

Paul Avril
13, route d'Avignon
84230 Châteauneuf-du-Pape
90 83 70 13

Type of vineyard: Family-owned. **Established:** 1903 – winemakers for 300 years. **Number of employees:** 6. **Vine stocks:** Grenache (red), Syrah (red), Mouvèdre (red), Clairette (white), Roussane (white), Bourboulenc (white). **Soil:** Molasse, clay with calcium carbonate. **Exposure:** Southeast. **Average annual production in hectoliters:** 900.

Appellation: Châteauneuf-du-Pape. **Type:** Red, white. **Technique:** Traditional. **Maturing:** In OAK casks, with temperature control during 12 months. Alcohol content: **13.8%. Characteristics:** Good keeping wine, tannic, quite long, a certain finesse (30% Mourvèdre and Syrah). **Serving temperature:** White: 11 to 12°. Red: 16 to 18°. **Served with:**White: fish (cooked in sauce). Red: game, roasts. **Vintages available in 89/90:** 1984, 1985, 1986.

Characteristics of vintages

1988: Le CLOS DES PAPES Blanc de Blancs - rich and well-balanced, fragrant, dry fruit and flowery aroma, lingering flavor. **1987:** A certain finesse and elegance, rather long, red berry and liquorice aroma. It should develop in 3 to 4 years and reach its peak in a decade. **1986:** Blackcurrant, raspberry, red currant aroma. Finesse and elegance. Tannic. Lingering taste, to be aged. **1985:** Red berry aroma. Peppery, rich and well-balanced. Lingering taste, liquorice finish. For keeping - not to be consumed before 1990. **1984:** Spicy bouquet (truffle, pepper, rosemary). Lingering taste. Can be drunk now, but can also be kept a number of years. **1983:** Great vintage, well-balanced, long. **1982:** Interesting but out of stock for the last two years. Average pre-tax ex-warehouse price: 43 F.F.

Sales volume:
– Retail: 70% (in France). – Restaurants: 30%. – Other: 50% (export).

Sales in France: 50%.
Export sales: 50%.
Main trading partners : Switzerland, Benelux countries, UK, USA, Denmark, Japan, Australia, Germany.

References in France

Restaurants: Jamin, Pic, Bize, Baumanière, Blanc, Côte-Saint-Jacques, Lameloise, Girardet, Faugeron, Le Notre.
Shops: Caves Legrand, Brasserie Lipp. (Paris)

Abroad

United States
Importers: N & T Imports – 3417 NE 12th Terrace – Fort Lauderdale, Florida 33354. World Shippers - Philadelphie.

United Kingdom
Importers: Richards-Walford, Manor House – Pick Worth Rutland, near Stamford Lincs – PE 9 4DJ – Tel: 07 80 81 242.

Germany
Importers: Firme Gstottl – Vogelbeeranweg 39 – D 8011 Kirchheim – Tel: 899 03 1711.

Canada
Importers: Alberta Liquor – Control Board – 50 Corriveau Avenue, St. Albert, Alberta.

The Netherlands
Importers: Noordman Frères – Haagweg 59 – 2321 AA Leiden.

Far East
Importers: Toyo Menko-Kaishe – Yokohama (Japan).

Others
Importers: Australia Richmond Hill Cellars – 132 Bridge Road – Richmond – Victoria 3121.

• *The quality of the 1987 vintage, particularly in Bordeaux, is questionable. Much of the Merlot suffered from coulure and a good bit of the harvesting was done in the rain. Only a few vineyards will produce a good vintage (see the Chapter on Bordeaux wines and the "Vintage Code").*

LES CLEFS D'OR, JEAN DEYDIER ET FILS

Pierre Deydier
Avenue Saint Joseph
84230 Châteauneuf-du-Pape
90 83 71 74

Type of vineyard: Agricultural Association. **Established:** Third generation. **Number of employees:** 6. **Vine stocks:** Grenache, Mourvèdre, Cinsault, Syrah, Muscardin, Bourloulenc, Clairette. **Soil:** Red clay and round pebbles. **Exposure:** Southern part of the Rhône valley. **Average annual production in hectoliters:** 700.

Appellation: Châteauneuf-du-Pape. **Type:** Red, white. **Technique:** Traditional. **Maturing:** In oak casks. **Alcohol content:** About 13.5%. **Characteristics:** Red: rich aroma, full bodied wines, rich and well balanced. White: taste and delicate aromas. **Serving temperature:** Red: 16 to 18°. White: 6 to 8°. **Served with:** Red meat, game, cheese.

Characteristics of vintages

1987: Lovely wine, well colored, fragrant, will evolve well. **1986:** Great year, rich, balanced and harmonious wine to be kept. Price range (pre-tax, ex-warehouse): between 30 and 50 F.F.

Sales volume:
– Wholesale: 30%. – Retail: 50%. – Restaurants: 20%.

Sales in France: 50%.
Export sales: 50%.
Main trading partners : Belgium, Switzerland, Netherlands, United States.

Abroad

United States
World Shippers, Philadelphia. Seggermann, New York.

Switzerland
Raphoz, Chène Bourg, Geneva.

Belgium
Tricot Franz, Zoning de Jumet.

The Netherlands
Wijnimport J. Bart, 1443 AE Purmerend.

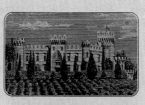

CHÂTEAU DES FINES ROCHES

Louis Mousset
à Châteauneuf-du-Pape
90 83 70 30
Telefax: 90 83 74 79 – Telex: 431 935

Type of vineyard: Family-owned. **Established:** for five generations.
Appellation: Châteauneuf du Pape – Côtes du Rhône.

Abroad

United States

Agents: Yvon Mau Wines Inc, Mr. Alain Urbini, 1302 Madison Avenue, New York N.Y. 10128.

United Kingdom

Agents: Louis Mousset. Mr. Tony Stebbings, 17 Church Street Esher/Surrey KT10 8QS.

Germany

Agent: Mr. Gevaudan. Friedrichstraße 39, 6750 Kaiserslautern.

Canada

Agent: Chase International Wine Merchants Inc., (Mr. Ken Chase). 527 Blenheim CR, Oakville, Ontario, L6J 6P5.

Others

Denmark. Agent: Carl Wandel & Sons. Mr. Willy Falck Olsen, Sollerodvej 90 B, 2840 Holte.

Comments

Two small towers on the road from Châteauneuf-du-Pape to Avignon lead to the majestic turreted building of Château des Fines Roches, which dominates the whole valley. The one-time owner of the domaine, Monsieur Folco de Baroncelli, made this chateau one of the best known cultural centers in Provence with his receptions for such men of letters as Mistral and Daudet... The domaine produces one of the better known crus of the appellation: a fleshy and full-bodied wine with an undisputed elegance and bouquet.

DOMAINE DE NALYS

Route de Courthezon
84230 Châteauneuf-du-Pape
90 83 72 52

Type of vineyard: Real estate enterprise. **Established:** 1778. **Number of employees:** 12. **Vine stocks:** The 13 standart varieties. **Soil:** plateau – round pebbles on Miocene sub-soil. **Exposure:** sunny. **Average annual production in hectoliters:** 2000 (Red: 200,000 bottles – White: 40,000 bottles).
Appellation: Châteauneuf du Pape. **Type:** Red, White. **Technique:** Red: maceration (whole grapes) – White: temperature control – hand harvesting. **Maturing:** Red: 8 to 12 months in oak casks – White: in stainless steel tanks. **Alcohol content:** 13°. **Characteristics:** supple, round, very fragrant. **Serving temperature:** Red: 16° – White:

7°. **Vintages available in 89/90:** Red: 1986-1987. White: 1988.

Characteristics of vintages

Price range (pre-tax, ex-warehouse): 30 F.F. to 50 F.F.
Sales volume:
– Retail: 65%. – Restaurants: 15%. – Other: 20%.
Sales in France: 80%.
Export sales: 20%.
Main trading partners : Switzerland, Belgium, Germany, UK.

References in France

Restaurants: (Paris): Drouant, La Marée, Lasserre, Le Divellec, Le Pré Catelan, Michel Rostang – (Elsewhere in France): La Tour Rosé (69), Alain Chapel (01) etc.

Comments

The entire production is distributed in bottles from the estate. No agents nor exclusive sales. Preference for private clientele and great restaurants. Wines that can be kept 5 to 10 years.

CLOS MONT OLIVET

Jean-Claude, Pierre & Bernard Sabon
15, avenue Saint-Joseph – Châteauneuf-du-Pape
90 83 72 46

Type of vineyard: Family-owned. **Established:** 1979. **Number of employees:** 4. **Vine stocks:** Grenache, Cinsaut, Syrah, Mourvèdre, Clairette, Bourboulenc, Roussanne. **Soil:** Chalky clay. **Exposure:** North-South. **Average annual production in hectoliters:** 750 (Red) - 50 (White).

Appellation: Châteauneuf-du-Pape: Blanc et Rouge, Côtes-du-Rhône: Rouge. **Type:** Red, white. **Technique:** White: direct pressing. Red: traditional in cement vats. **Maturing:** White: in enamelled tanks – Red: about 13.5%. **Characteristics:** Very aromatic and very fruity (red berries, blackcurrant, raspberries, truffles, liquorice) according to the vintage. Very good alcoholic and tannic balance. Beautiful color. **Serving temperature:** Red: 16° – White: 8 to 10°. **Served with:** Red meat, game, cheese, shellfish. **Vintages available in 89/90:** 1986, 1987, 1988.

Characteristics of vintages

1988: Very beautiful color, very aromatic, very promising.
1987: Lighter, very supple, to be consumed within 5 years.
1986: Tannic, very fine color, dominant red berry flavor.
1985: Promising – very beautiful color, good tannic content. **Other:** 1984: a lovely wine, dominant liquorice and red berry flavor, a great bottle. Price range (pre-tax, ex-warehouse): 30 to 50 F.F.
Sales volume:
– Wholesale: 97%. – Retail: 3%.
Sales in France: 80%.
Export sales: 20%.
Main trading partners : USA, United Kingdom, Benelux countries, Switzerland, Germany.

Comments

Fourth generation winemakers who follow traditions with the greatest respect – cultivation of the vines, selection of the harvest, vinification. In 1979, in order to avoid dividing the family enterprise, the sons of Joseph Sabon, all three winemakers, formed an agricultural association for the collective exploitation of the vineyard referred to as Du Clos Mont Olivet.

CHÂTEAU DE LA GARDINE

Brunel
Route de Roquemaure
84230 Châteauneuf-du-Pape
90 83 73 20 – Telex: 431 163 F Gardine
Fax: 90 83 77 24

Type of vineyard: Agricultural Association. **Established:** 1780, Agricultural Association since 1972. **Number of employees:** 24. **Vine stocks:** Grenache, Syrah, Cinsault, Mourvèdre, Bourboulenc, Roussane. **Soil:** Round pebbles and calcium carbonate. **Exposure:** South, Southwest. **Average annual production in hectoliters:** 1,900 hl. Châteauneuf-du-Pape; 1,300 hl. Côtes-du-Rhône Villages. **Appellation:** Châteauneuf-du-Pape. **Type:** Red, white. **Technique:** Red: traditional, 70% crushed. **Maturing:** Large casks for 2 years. **Alcohol content:** 13.3%. **Characteristics:** Typical Châteauneuf, concentration of aroma, deep red color, will age well (6 to 15 years). **Serving temperature:** 17°. **Served with:** Game, red meat, cooked meat, cheese, regional cooking. **Vintages available in 89/90:** 1979, 1980, 1981, 1982, 1984, 1985.

Characteristics of vintages

1986: White: lovely wine, fragrant and structured, full.
1985: Red: excellent wine, well-colored, soft and full with a suggestion of humus, good for ageing. Price range (pre-tax, ex-warehouse): Between 70 F.F. and 160 F.F.

CHÂTEAU FORTIA

84230 Chateauneuf-du-Pape
90 83 72 25 - Telex: Chambre de Commerce d'Avignon

Type of vineyard: Family corporation. **Established:** 1890. **Vine stocks:** Grenache 82%, Syrah 12%, Mourvèdre 6%, Clairette 67%, Roussane 13%, Grenache Blanc 20%. **Soil:** Marine sandstone to the North, Alpine diluvium to the South. **Exposure:** South. **Average annual production in hectoliters:** 700.

Appellation: Chateauneuf du Pape AOC. **Type:** Red, White. **Technique:** Red: traditional. White: modern. **Maturing:** Red: in wooden vats. White: in insulated enamelled tanks. **Alcohol content:** Red 13.8% – White: 13%. **Characteristics:** Red: well colored, structured with age. White: balanced, fresh and aromatic. **Serving temperature:** Red: 17°. White: 10°. **Served with:** Red: red meat, cheese, game. White: as an aperitif or with foie gras, fish, shellfish. **Vintages available in 89/90:** Red: 1981, 1983, 1985. White: 1988.

Characteristics of vintages

1988: White: fleshy and aromatic. **1986:** Will be available in December 89. **1985:** Just like last year, will be ready in 1989. **Other:** 1981: Full, long aromatic. Price range (pre-tax, ex-warehouse): 40 to 50 F.F. (1988 White and 1985 Red) 50 to 80 F.F. (1981 Red).
Sales volume:
- Wholesale: 10% - 12%. - Retail: 30%. -Other: 70% (export).
Sales in France: 30%. **Export sales:** 70%.
Main trading partners : USA, UK, Switzerland, Belgium, Netherlands, Italy, Luxemburg, Canada, Australia.

References in France

Restaurants: Taillevent, Lassere (Paris), some others outside of Paris.
Shops: Hédiard (Paris).

Abroad

United States

Importers: Banfi, Cedar Swamp Road, Old Brookville, New York 11545.

United Kingdom

Hallgarten, Carkers Lane, Hihgate Road, London NW5 1RR.

Belgium

Werco P.V.B.A. hispitaalstraat 5 Ostende - Several Shops in Wallonia.

Canada

LCBQ, Toronto, Ontario.

The Netherlands

Vos Winjimport, Tiburg.

Swiss

Schenk, Rolle, VD.

CHÂTEAU LA NERTHE

Alain Dugas Responsable
Route d'Avignon à Châteauneuf-du-Pape
90 83 70 11

Type of vineyard: Agricultural Association. **Established:** 1985 **Number of employees:** 10. **Vine stocks:** Grenache, Syrah, Mourvèdre, Cinsaut, Clairette, Bourboulenc, Roussane. **Soil:** Chalky caly with round pebbles. **Exposure:** South, South-West. **Average annual production in hectoliters:** 2,000.
Appellation: Côtes-du-Rhône. **Type:** Red, White. **Technique:** Classic. **Maturing:** Partly in casks. **Alcohol content:** 14%. **Characteristics:** Very rich and well balanced wines for keeping. **Serving temperature:** 18°. **Vintages available in 89/90:** 1986, 1988 White and Red.

Characteristics of vintages

1987: Beautiful whites, rich in fruit, soft and supple. Good reds. **1986:** Excellent year. Beautiful red and white wines, well balanced, harmonious, to be kept. Price range (pre-tax, ex-warehouse): between 80 and 90 F.F.
Sales volume:
– Wholesale: 80%. – Retail: 15%. – Restaurants: 5%.
Sales in France: 60%.
Export sales: 40%.
Main trading partners : Switzerland.

Comments

Very few winegrowing properties can pride themselves on so rich an oral written history. Although the written history of the Château-La-Nerthe begins with records in the domain archives as early as 1560, its more distant past is associated with the birth of the vine at Châteauneuf in the 12th century. Some two hundred years later, the presence of the Sovereign Pontiffs gave the village its hours of glory and its name, Châteauneuf-du-Pape.

G.A.E.C. DU DOMAINE MATHIEU

Route de Courthezon
84230 Châteauneuf-du-Pape, B.P. 32
90 83 72 09 – Telex: 431 919 CIAV F
Code Atten. Mathieu

Type of vineyard: Agricultural Association. **Established:** 1988 – Domain exists since 1600. **Vine stocks:** Grenache 85%. **Soil:** Alpine diluvium. **Exposure:** Gently slopping hillsides. **Average annual production in hectoliters:** 550.

Appellation: AOC Châteauneuf-du-Pape. **Type:** Red, white. **Technique:** Traditional, fermentation on skins (15 to 20 days). **Maturing:** In oak casks. **Alcohol content:** 13.8%. **Characteristics:** Good keeping wines, full, complex red berry and coffee aromas. **Serving temperature:** Red: 20°, White: 14°. **Served with:** Red: red meat, game, cheese, White: as an aperitif and with foie gras, fish, cheese, dessert. **Vintages available in 89/90:** Red: 1986-1987, White: 1987, 1988.

Characteristics of vintages

1988: White: very fruity. **1987:** Red: very fruity, to be drunk within 8 years – White: very fruity. **1986:** Red: rich and very well balanced. To be drunk in 5 to 10 years. Price range (pre-tax, ex-warehouse): 30 to 50 F.F.

Sales volume:
– Wholesale: 10%. – Retail: 70%. – Restaurants: 5%.

Sales in France: 85%.

Export sales: 15%.

Main trading partners : USA, United Kingdom, Germany, Switzerland, Belgium.

References in France

Restaurants: La Tassée (Lyon), Jean-Charles et ses amis (Paris), Le Logis d'Arnavel (Châteauneuf), Le Petit Colombier (Paris), Le Bistrot du Sommelier (Paris), Relais du Bois St-Georges (Saintes).

Comments

Winemakers since 1600! The vines have an average age of 50 years and produce a "concentrated nectar", typical and fragrant, which will evolve well.

DOMAINE DE LA PINÈDE

Georges Coulon
84230 Châteauneuf-du-Pape
90 83 71 50

Type of vineyard: Agricultural Association. **Established:** 1880. **Number of employees:** 2. **Vine stocks:** Grenache, Cinsaut, Syrah, Mourvèdre, Muscadin, Clairette. **Soil:** Chalky clay. **Exposure:** South. **Average annual production in hectoliters:** 500 to 600.

Appellation: Châteauneuf-du-Pape. **Type:** Red, white. *Other:* Red and rosé table wine. **Technique:** Semi-carbonic maceration. **Maturing:** In vats. **Alcohol content:** 13.5%. **Characteristics:** Supple, tannic and fruity. Serving temperature: Red: 17° – White: 7°. **Served with:** Red: meat, game. White: fish, soft cheese. **Vintages available in 89/90:** 1986, 1987, 1988.

Characteristics of vintages

1988: White: very well balanced. Red: well colored, concentrated. **1987:** Red: beautiful, fruity, a good year. **1986:** Have been selected among the best. **1985:** Stock depleted. Price range (pre-tax, ex-warehouse): 30 to 50 F.F.

Sales volume:
– Wholesale: 2%. – Retail: 90%. – Restaurants: 8 %.

Sales in France: 80%.

Export sales: 20%.

Main trading partners : USA, Denmark, Belgium.

References in France

Shops: Repère de Bacchus.

Abroad

United States

Prestige Wine Corporation - 21 East 40th Street, New York 10016.

Comments

Georges Coulon took over the family estate in 1975. Bottle sales were introduced in January 1982 and now account for 3/4 of the production. At present, there are from 150-200,000 bottles available and the eventual goal of bottling the entire production will be met before 1992 - without compromising the quality of the product, this due to the competence and attention to detail provided by this small enterprise.

CHÂTEAU MONT-REDON

Familles Abeille - Fabre
84230 Châteauneuf-du-Pape
90 83 72 75 - Telex: 432 350 MT Redon
FAX: 90 83 77 20

Type of vineyard: Agricultural Association. **Established:** 1923. **Number of employees:** About 30. **Vine stocks:** All wine stocks of the Châteauneuf appellation.
Appellation: Châteauneuf-du-Pape, Côtes-du-Rhône (Rouge). **Type:** Red, white. **Technique:** Traditional.
Maturing: Red: 14 to 36 months depending on the year.

Characteristics of vintages

1988: Superb white Châteauneuf, rich and fragrant - Wait.
1987: Successful wines, well made, beautiful color, soft, supple and harmonious, fragrant.
Sales volume:
- Retail: 15%. - Restaurants: 15%. - Other: 70% (export).
Sales in France: 30%.
Export sales: 70%.
Main trading partners : European community countries, USA, Switzerland, Australia, Japan, Bermuda, Brazil, South Africa, Malta, Sweden, Canada, etc.

References in France

Restaurants: Auberge de l'Ile, Frères Troisgros, Paul Bocuse, Pic, Beaumanière, Château d'Artigny, Auberge de Noves, etc.

Comments

"Mouredon" has been known since 1334, at which time the vines were already planted - which means that this part of the papal manor house terrain has been consecrated to the vine for more than six centuries. In 1923, Mont-Redon was acquired by the Plantin family. Henri Plantin then set about regrouping the plots to give the domain its present configuration, 162 hectares in all, of which 95 are planted with grapevines. The Mount-Redon château, in the family for three generations, with its ubiquitous vineyard going back centuries, is well steeped in winemaking tradition.

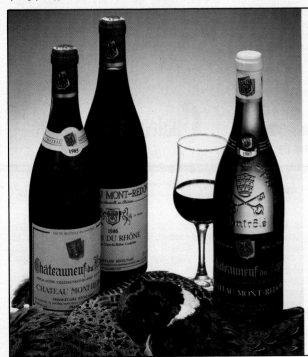

DOMAINE FRANCOIS LAGET ROYER

François and Maurice Laget
19, avenue Saint-Joseph
84230 Châteauneuf-du-Pape
90 83 70 91 or 90 83 71 10

Type of vineyard: Agricultural Association. **Vine stocks:** 70% Grenache, the rest Syrah, Mourvèdre, Cinsault and Counoise. **Average annual production in hectoliters:** 500.
Appellation: Chateauneuf du Pape. **Type:** Red. **Technique:** Traditional, 10 to 12 days of fermentation. **Maturing:** 12 to 18 months in large Oak casks. **Characteristics:** Because most of the vines are old, some more than 60 years, the principal characteristics of the wines are suppleness, elegance, and fragrance, all embellished with subtle tannins which guarantee several years of trouble-free ageing. **Serving temperatur:** 15°. **Served with:** Red meat, cheese game. The red Chateauneuf du Pape is a wine that is savored raher than drunk. **Vintages available in 89/90:** 1984, 1985, 1986 (this last in March 1988). **Vintages available in 89/90:** 1987, 1986, 1985 (small stock), 1984, 1988 (as of Spring 1990).

Characteristics of vintages

1988: Intense purple color. Nose still undeveloped but with noticeable touches of liquorice, coffee, red berry aroma in full evolution. Clean attack, nutmeg aroma, marked presence of tannins, tell-tale structure of a good keeping wine. **1987:** Beautiful color, intense nose, golden tinge associated with very good ageing potential. Still undeveloped but delicate nose, brandy as well as wood and liquorice aroma. Discreet and mellow tannins. Good balance, long, already developing tertiary aromas. **1986:** Very promising, longer than average life. Beautiful color, excellent nose. **1985:** Tannins still young. Beautiful ruby color, flowery fragrance. Good wine for ageing. **Price range (pre-tax, ex-warehouse):** Between 35 F.F. and 55 F.F.

DOMAINE RICHÉ ET DOMAINE DE BABAN

GAEC Riché père et fils
27, rue du Général-de-Gaulle
84230 Châteauneuf-du-Pape
90 83 72 63

Type of vineyard: Family Corporation. **Established:** 1983. **Number of employees:** 2. **Vine stocks:** Grenache, Syrah, Mourvèdre, Cinsault, Clairette et Bourboulenc. **Soil:** Very diversified soil. In particular, large stones specially rolling stones. **Exposure:** North – South, depending upon the soil. **Average annual production in hectoliters:** 32/Châteauneuf-du-Pape – 48/Côtes-du-Rhône.
Appellation: Châteauneuf-du-Pape. Red – Côtes-du-Rhône: Red, white, rosé. **Technique:** Traditional. **Maturing:** In Oak casks, from 18 months to 2 years, before bottling. **Alcohol content:** 13° to 14.5°. **Characteristics:** Robust, rich and well-balanced, good color for the reds (with a touch of aromatic, red fruit, of raspberry and vanilla) Côtes-du-Rhônes is lighter – White and Rosé, young taste. **Serving temperature:** 16° to 18° for reds. White: cool, 6° and 8°. **Served with:** Red: game, red meat, and cheese (strong cheese). White with shellfish, as a fish, bu dessert and as an aperitif too. **Vintages available in 89/90:** 1985 and 1986, perhaps 1984. For white and rosé, vintage of the year.

Characteristics of vintages

1986: Beautiful purple color – agreeable taste. Needs ageing. **1985:** Ruby, brilliant; soft and full, tannic, long. **1984:** Beautiful color, robust, long, with well developped aromas. Price range (pre-tax, ex-warehouse): between 10 F.F. & 20 F.F. (Côtes-du-Rhône). Between 30 F.F. & 50 F.F. (Châteauneuf-du-Pape).
Sales volume:
– Wholesale: 75%. – Retail: 20%. – Restaurants: 5%.
Sales in France: 60%.
Export sales: 40%.
Main trading partners : England, Belgium, Switzerland.

DOMAINE RAYMOND USSEGLIO

Raymond Usseglio
Route de Courthézon
84230 Châteauneuf-du-Pape
90 83 71 85

Type of vineyard: Family-owned. **Established:** 1963. **Number of employees:** 2. **Vine stocks:** Grenache, Mourvèdre, Syrah, Clairette, Bourbelenc. **Soil:** Round pebbles. **Average annual production in hectoliters:** 400.

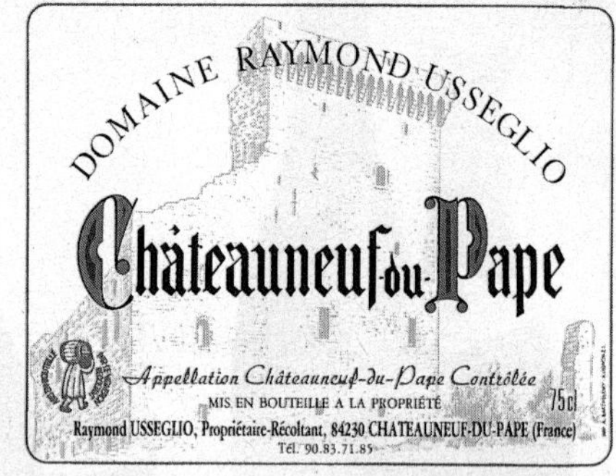

Appellation: Châteauneuf-du-Pape. **Type:** Red, white. **Technique:** Traditional. **Maturing:** Red only – in casks. **Alcohol content:** 13.5%. **Serving temperature:** Red: 16 to 18°. White: 6 to 8°. **Served with:** Red: red meat, cheese. White: fish. **Vintages available in 89/90:** 1986, 1987, 1988.

Characteristics of vintages

1988: Well-balanced and harmonious, for keeping, fragrant, well-structured. **1987:** Dark ruby color, slightly spicy, pleasant, well-made, is ageing well. **1986:** Brilliant color, well-structured and tannic, good keeping. Price range (pre-tax, ex-warehouse): 20 and 30 F.F. – 30 and 50 F.F.

Sales volume:
– Wholesale: 30%. – Retail: 30%. – Restaurants: 10%. – Other: 30% – Export.
Sales in France: 70%.
Export sales: 30%.

References in France

Restaurants: Hôtel Prince de Galles (Paris), Restaurant L'Espérance (Brest), La Taverne du Monchu (72 Aime), Chalet du Lac (39 Les Rousses), Hôtel Diana (67 Molsheim).
Shops: Aux Joies de Bacchus (Toulon), France à la Carte (Poitiers), Breiz Aquitaine (33 Libourne), La Cave du Genevois (74 St. Julien).

Abroad

United Kingdom
Redpath & Thackrays. Lancashire (Tel: 046834 360).

Germany
Weinmmarkt-Korkenzizher. Stuttgart (Tel: 07 11 88 30 80).

Switzerland
Mathieu et Cie. Lausanne (Tel: 21 22 76 67).

Belgium
Bogaart Jean Destelbergen (Tel: 91 28 39 86).

Comments

Family exploitation located at the very heart of the white soil sector of Châteauneuf-du-Pape where winegrowing on a round stone soil dates back to the 14th century. Traditional vinification, bottled at the domain after 18 months in oak casks.

VIEUX TÉLÉGRAPHE

H. Brunier
3, route de Châteauneuf-du-Pape
84370 Bédarrides
90 33 00 31 – Telefax: 90 33 18 47

Type of vineyard: Agricultural Association. **Established:** 1890. **Vine stocks:** Grenache 70%, Syrah 15%, Red: Mourvèdre 15%. **Exposure:** South-East. **Average annual production in hectoliters:** 1,800.
Appellation: Châteauneuf-du-Pape. **Type:** Red, white. **Technique:** Traditional, temperature control, without destemming – stainless steel vats. **Maturing:** Old oak casks (1 year). **Characteristics:** Rich and full, hearty, combining finesse with complexity. Can be tasted after 2 years but will age gracefully for more than 10 years. Rich and well balanced. **Serving temperature:** 17°. **Served with:** Game, red meat, cheese. **Vintages available in 89/90:** Red – 1987.

Characteristics of vintages

1988: Rich and concentrated, promising. **1987:** Very fruity, quite supple – average keeping. Price range (pre-tax, ex-warehouse): 30 to 50 F.F.
Sales volume:
– Wholesale: 85%. – Retail: 5%. – Restaurants: 10%.
Sales in France: 15%.
Export sales: 85%.
Main trading partners : USA, United Kingdom, Switzerland, Canada.

References in France

Restaurants: Pic (Valence), Léon de Lyon (Lyon), Beaumanière, Lucculus (Avignon).
Shops: Fauchon (Paris).

Abroad

United States
Kermit Lynch (Berkeley. Ca.).

United Kingdom
Merchant Wintners – Thorman Hunt (London).

Germany
France Vinicole (Kehl/Rhein).

Switzerland
Ginoux-Vins (Geneva) – Martel (St-Gallen).

Belgium
Van de Wiel.

Canada
Saq – LCBO.

The Netherlands
Delcave (Delft).

Far East
Cave de France (K.K.).

Comments

The estate is located on an extensive pebbly terrace, high point of the appellation. Its name comes from an old optical telegraph relay tower built around 1793, in the middle of the vineyard. Highly traditional vinification techniques (fermentation on stems for about 15 days, complete crusing) are complemented by a new technique (automatic cask filling without pumping conveyor belt or piping, pneumatic pressing, stainless steel temperature controlled tands, use of the carbon dioxide produced).

SCA DES VIGNOBLES DE VAUDIEU

Mrs. Sylvette Brechet
84230 Châteauneuf-du-Pape
90 65 86 09 – Telex: 431 803

Type of vineyard: Agricultural Association. **Vine stocks:** Grenache, Cinsault, Syrah. **Soil:** Sandy marl, clay, chalk. **Exposure:** North-South. **Average annual production in hectoliters:** 2,500.
Appellation: AOC Chateauneuf du Pape. **Type:** Red. **Technique:** Traditional. **Maturing:** In wooden casks (10 to 15 months). **Alcohol content:** 13.5%. **Characteristics:** Typical of the appellation, spice and truffles bouquet. **Serving temperature:** 18°. **Served with:** Red meat, game, cheese. **Vintages available in 89/90:** 1986.

Characteristics of vintages

1986: Purple nuance, truffles and crystallized fruit aroma. Price range (pre-tax, ex-warehouse): 30 to 50 F.F.
Sales volume:
– Retail: 20%. – Restaurants: 15%. – Other: 65 % – Export.
Sales in France: 40%.
Export sales: 60%.
Main trading partners : Belgium, Switzerland, Germany, Netherlands, Japan, Canada, Denmark, USA.

References in France

Restaurants: Pullman, Beaumanière, Armes de Champagne.
Shops: Félix Potin, Marchés aux Vins, La Sommelière.

Abroad

United States
Stacole Miami.

United Kingdom
Hawkins, London.

Germany
Reidemeister, Bremem.

Switzerland
Riotton et Guillieron, Geneva.

Belgium
Cesva – GB Inno Gosselines.

The Netherlands
Verlinden en Zoon s'Hertogenbosch.

Far East
Jardine Matheson, Japan and South East Asia.

Others
Denmark: Irma Vins, Copenhagen.

Comments

The Château de Vaudieu was built, starting in 1767, by the Knight de Guerin, descendant of the Florentine nobility. The domain of Vaudieu owes its name to the fertility of its soil for which it was called Val Dieu (Valley of God). Some good Côtes-du-Rhône Rouget and a very successful Châteauneuf in recent years (83 to 86).

GIGONDAS

ROMANE-MACHOTTE-PIERRE AMADIEU

Jean-Pierre Amadieu
84190 Gigondas
90 65 84 08

Type of vineyard: Family-owned. **Established:** 1930. **Vine stocks:** Grenache 70%, Syrah 25%, Mourvèdre 5%. **Soil:** Chalky clay. **Exposure:** On hillsides. **Average annual production in hectoliters:** 2,500.

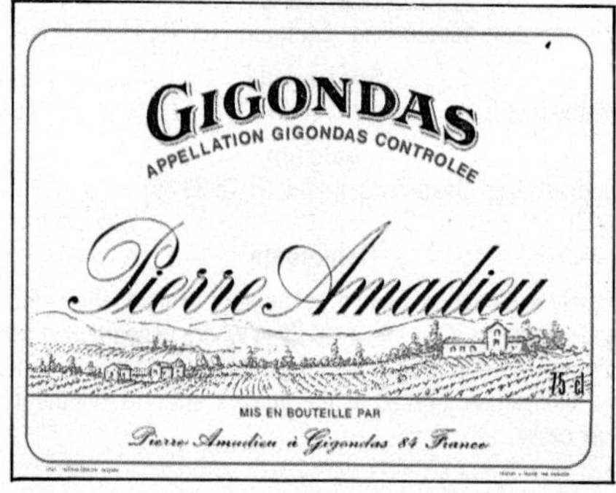

Appellation: Gigondas AOC. **Type:** Red. **Technique:** Traditional. **Maturing:** Oak casks. **Characteristics:** Rich, well balanced wines with the fragrance of fruit with pits and spices. **Serving temperature:** 17 to 18°. **Served with:** Game, meats in sauce, strong cheeses. **Vintages available in 89/90:** 1986, 1988.

Characteristics of vintages

1987: Ruby color, supple and fruity. **1986:** Rich and well balanced, quite tannic, fragrance of fruit with pits and spices. Price range (pre-tax, ex-warehouse): between 20 and 30 F.F.
Sales volume:
– Wholesale: 20%. – Retail: 15%. – Restaurants: 65%.
Sales in France: 85%. **Export sales:** 15%.
Main trading partners : Belgium, Netherlands, Denmark, Ireland, Germany, Switzerland.

References in France

Restaurants: La Marée (Paris), Hôtel Bristol (Paris), Restaurant Gérard Besson (Paris), Restaurant Nandron (Lyon), etc.

Abroad

Germany
M.K. Schoppe, Weberstrasse 28, 6380 Bad Homburg. Tel: (06172) 832 59.

Switzerland

Bujard Fils, SA, Vins Fins, CH 1095 Lutry. Tel: 021/ 39 13 13.

Belgium

Etabl. Charles Van Peteghem, 19 rue Charles Demeer, 1020 Brussels. Tel.: (02) 427 99 20.

Others:

Ireland: Syrah Wines, 11 Rowanbyrn, Blackrock Co., Dublin. Tel: (01) 89 36 70. Denmark: HH Vin, Norregardsvej 81, 2610 Rodovre. Tel: (01) 70 92 20.

Comments

A serious proprietor who carefully vinifies his Gigondas to make a typical, very fragrant wine, worth keeping.

DOMAINE DE CASSAN

Paul Croset
Lafare 84190 Beaumes de Venise
90 65 87 65 - 90 62 96 12

Type of vineyard: Family-owned. **Vine stocks:** Grenache, Syrah, Mourvèdre. **Soil:** Chalky clay. **Exposure:** South. **Average annual production in hectoliters:** 950.

Appellation: Gigondas, Côtes du Rhône Village, Beaumes de Venise, Côtes du Rhône Régional. **Type:** Red, rosé. **Technique:** Traditional. **Maturing:** In oak vats. **Alcohol content:** 12-14%. **Characteristics:** Excellent bouquet, round, beautifully balanced, long keeping (up to 10 years). **Serving temperature:** Red 14-15°. Rosé: 5°. **Vintages available in 89/90:** 1986 to 1988.

Characteristics of vintages

1988: Very well structured, excellent bouquet – to be aged. **1987:** Good average quality. **1986:** Good vintage – cooked fruit aroma. Price range (pre-tax, ex-warehouse): 10 to 20 F.F. (Côte du Rhône) 20 to 30 F.F. (Gigondas) 30 to 50 F.F. (special "Cuvées").

Sales volume:
- Wholesale: 15%. – Retail: 25%. – Restaurants: 10%.
- Other: 55% (retail and wholesale).

Sales in France: 65%.
Export sales: 35%.

Main trading partners : The Netherlands, Belgium, Denmark, USA.

References in France

Restaurants: A number of restaurants in Lyon, Marseille, in and around Nice and in the Cévennes.

Abroad

United States

World Shipper and Importer Co. Philadelphia.

Germany

Pierre-Philippe D 5202 Hennef-Sieg.

Belgium

Sodexran (Waterloo) – La Capucina – Vinum (Geel).

The Netherlands

Vos Vijnimport (Tilburg).

Others

Denmarks: G.S. (Skorping) – C.B. Vinimport (Koge).

DOMAINE DU CAYRON

Michel Faraud
84190 Gigondas
90 65 87 46

Type of vineyard: Family-owned. **Established:** 1936. **Vine stocks:** Grenache 2/3, Cinsaut, Syrah. **Soil:** Chalky sandstone, alluvium. **Exposure:** South-West. **Average annual production in hectoliters:** 200-300.

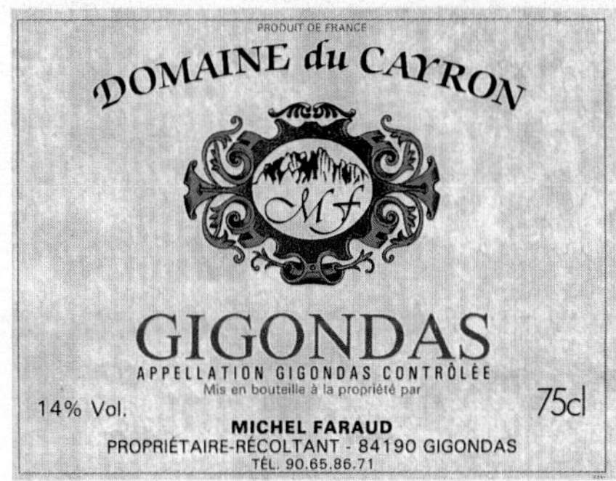

Appellation: AOC Gigondas. **Type:** Red. **Technique:** Traditional – hydraulic pressing. **Maturing:** In oak casks (minimum 2 years). **Alcohol content:** 13.5%. **Characteristics:** Fruity, rich and well balanced, purple color. **Serving temperature:** 16 to 18°. **Served with:** Red meat, game, cheese. **Vintages available in 89/90:** 1985, 1986, 1987.

Characteristics of vintages

1988: Promising, well colored and dense wines, good keeping. **1987:** Good wines, more supple, fruity. **1986:** Rich

and fragrant. Price range (pre-tax, ex-warehouse): 30 to 50 F.F.
Sales in France: 70%.
Export sales: 30%.
Main trading partners : USA, UK, Belgium, Switzerland.

References in France

Restaurants: Bocuse.

Comments

Wines produced from vines 20 to 50 years old yielding a harvest of 15 to 30 hl per hectare (no fining, no filtering).

DOMAINE LES GOUBERT

Jean Pierre Cartier
84190 Gigondas
90 65 86 38

Type of vineyard: Family owned. **Vine stocks:** Grenache 85%, Syrah 15%. **Soil:** Chalky clay. **Exposure:** North-South. Micro-climate due to the proximity of the Dentelles de Montmirail mountains. **Average annual production in hectoliters:** 62.

Appellation: Gigondas "Cuvée Florence". **Type:** Red. **Technique:** Traditional: crushing without destemming, long fermentation on skins. **Maturing:** 11 months in new wooden barrels (bois des Vosges and bois de Nevers), selection, blending and bottling in November. **Characteristics:** Wine for keeping – rich, very good tannic balance (new wood and wine tannins), vanilla, cinnamon, liquorice and red berry (cherry, blackcurrant, raspberry) flavor. **Serving temperature:** 16-18°. **Vintages available in 89/90: 1987.**

Characteristics of vintages

Price range (pre-tax, ex-warehouse): 50 to 80 F.F.
Sales in France: 35%.
Export sales: 65%.
Main trading partners : USA, UK, Australia, Denmark.

References in France

Restaurants: Georges Blanc (01 Vonnas), Jenny Jacquet (92 Neuilly/sur-Seine).
Shops: Bernard Peret, 6 Rue Daguerre (75014 Paris), Cave Michel Marc, 31 rue de la Div. Leclerc, (91310 Linas).

DOMAINE DU GOUR DE CHAULE

Aline Bonfils
SCEA Beaumet Bonfils 84190 Gigondas
90 65 85 62

Type of vineyard: Agricultural Association. **Established:** 1901. **Vine stocks:** Grenache, Syrah, Mourvèdre. **Soil:** Sandy alluvial clay. **Exposure:** Semi hillsides – South, South-West. **Average annual production in hectoliters:** 330.

Appellation: A.O.C. Gigondas. **Type:** Red. **Technique:** Traditional maceration, temperature control. **Maturing:** Old casks. **Alcohol content:** 14%. **Characteristics:** Tannic, well balanced, good keeping, high alcoholic content, acquires tile-red color with age, woodland aroma with a gamey touch, lingering flavor. **Serving temperature:** 17%. **Served with:** Game, leg of lamb, cheese. **Vintages available in 89/90:** 1983, 1985, 1986, 1987, 1988.

Characteristics of vintages

1988: Intense color, tannic, well balanced, very well structured and full-bodied. **1987:** Garnet color, elegant aromas (red berries and spices), supple and forthcoming. **1986:** Deep garnet color, woody and spicy bouquet, full-bodied, structured. **1985:** Deep garnet color, rich aromas, well balanced, high and alcoholic content or high in alcohol, robust, very complete wine. **Other:** 1983: garnet color, tile-red tinge, remarkable spicy bouquet, gamey, supple, robust, and well bred. Price range (pre-tax, ex-warehouse): 30 to 50 F.F.
Sales volume:
– Wholesale: 35%. – Retail: 30%. – Restaurants: 5%. – Other: 30% – Cellars, cafés, retailers in France and abroad.
Sales in France: 65%. **Export sales:** 35%.
Main trading partners : United Kingdom, USA, Netherlands.

References in France

Restaurants: La Regalido (13 Fontvieille), Les Bories (84 Gordes), Les Florets (84 Gigondas).
Shops: La Cave de Gnafron (69 St Genis Laval).

Abroad

United States

Neal Rosenthal 56-31 56th Drive. Maspeth, NY (Tel: 718 326 7990) and Los Angeles (Tel: 213 834 5755).

United Kingdom

Justerini & Brooks 214 Upton Lane Forest Gate, London, E7 – Ellis, Son & Vidler Cliffe Cellars 12/13 Cliffe Estate, Lewes East Sussex BN8 6JL.

Germany

Rosenfelder Karl Linde Strat 13 6700 Ludwigshafen (Tel: 621 65 20 33) – E Kleine Homann Freiheitsstr.l. 4270 Dorsten Holsterhausen (Tel: 23 62 62 573).

Belgium

Ets. Deridder Avenue de Marouset 109 7490 Braine Le Conte (Tel: 65 55 57 95).

The Netherlands

Intercaves BV. Marsweg 43 Postbus 517 8000 Am Zwolle (Tel: 38 69 69 69).

Comments

The family domain is currently run by three generations of winemakers who combine their know-how with their love of the vines, the grapes and the wines. The winestocks are 80% Grenache, complemented harmoniously by Syrah and Mourvèdre. The grape harvest is lightly crushed and macerated on the marc with temperature control of the fermentation. The wine is then aged for twelve months in old oak casks before being bottled on the domain. The red APPELLATION GIGONDAS, characterized by its bouquet, richness and balance, is a forthcoming wine that will age with elegance, providing pleasure to the senses and the table. Also, good Côtes-du-Rhône.

DOMAINE DE LONGUE TOQUE

Serge Chapalain
84190 Gigondas
90 65 86 88

Type of vineyard: family-owned. **Established:** 1919 – enlarged in 1957 and 1975. **Number of employees:** 3. **Vine stocks:** Grenache 65%, Syrah: 20%, Cinsault 10%, Mourvèdre 5%. **Soil:** hillsides, gravelly chalk and clay, or rocky, depending on the altitude. **Exposure:** hillsides facing South-East and South-West. **Average annual production in hectoliters:** 600.
Appellation: Gigondas. **Type:** Red. **Technique:** traditional long fermentation on skins (15 to 20 days). **Maturing:** 12 to 15 months in oak casks (40 hl). **Alcohol content:** 13.5%. **Characteristics:** tannic, full-bodied but quite supple due to very little crushing and destemming and long fermentation on skins. Very regular even in less "appreciated" years, red berry, liquorice and spicy nose. **Serving temperature:** 17°. **Served with:** red meat, meat cooked in sauce, game, cheese. **Vintages available in 89/90:** 1986-1987-1988.

Characteristics of vintages

1988: excellent year, intense color, rich aromas, full-bodied, good keeping. **1987:** good year, supple and well balanced wine, delicate nose, pleasant, to be drunk rather young (within 4 to 6 years). **1986:** very good year, very good balance between nose, color and taste, to be kept. **1985:** almost out of stock – only a few magnums left. **Other:** 1984: average year to start with but has developed quite well into a very typical Gigondas worthy of much more highly esteemed vintages. Price range (pre-tax, ex-warehouse): 30 F.F. to 50 F.F.
Sales volume:
– Wholesale: 20%. – Retail: 75%. – Restaurants: 5%.
Sales in France: 90%.
Export sales: 10%.
Main trading partners : UK, Belgium, Denmark, Netherlands, Germany, Switzerland, Canada, USA.

Abroad

United States

New England Wine Distributors, Norwood, Ma.

United Kingdom

Barwell and Jones, Ipswich Tel: (0473) 231723 – Vessel du Vin, Tunstall Tel: (046) 834 360.

Switzerland

"Oeno" Dardagny Tel: (22) 541606.

Belgium

De Gauw Gebr., Leuven-Wisele – Tel (16) 445328 – "T. Wynhuis", Merelbeke Tel: (91) 307056 – Winjnhandel Boon Pvba, Bornem Tel: (3) 8890635.

Canada

Vin Conseil, Montreal.

The Netherlands

Augusta Polling Wijnen, Amsterdam Tel: (20) 420101.

Others

Denmark – Viola Vine, Kvissel, Frederikshavn Tel: (848) 4429.

Comments

Originally a small family-estate of the 19th century, the

domain has been extended by successive generations, ending up at its present size and with its present name in 1962, at which time the sale of the production in bulk to dealers was discontinued and replaced by direct sales in bottles. The domain encompasses hillsides in three of the main vineyards of Gigondas: Montmirail, Les Florets as well as hillsides bordering the Village. Each year, the best "Cuvées" are selected for bottling, and sold under the "Domaine de Longue Toque" appellation, thus ensuring a great regularity of quality.

SCEA Les Fils de Hilarion Roux
DOMAINE LES PALLIERES

Pierre Roux
Gigondas 84190 Beaumes de Venise
90 65 85 07

Type of vineyard: Agricultural Association. **Established:** For 250 years (same family). **Number of employees:** 4. **Vine stocks:** Grenache, Syrah, Mourvèdre, Cinsault. **Soil:** Sandy and chalky sandstone – slightly pebbly with clay. **Exposure:** West, North-West. **Average annual production in hectoliters:** 855.

Appellation: A.O.C. Gigondas "Les Pallières". **Type:** Red Rosé. **Technique:** Traditional. **Maturing:** Vats and casks. **Alcohol content:** 13.5 – 14%. **Characteristics:** Tannic – good keeping (10 years). **Serving temperature:** 16 – 17°. **Served with:** Red meat, game, strong cheeses. **Vintages available in 89/90:** Red: 1984 (until depletion of stock).

Characteristics of vintages

1988: Very tannic, good color and acidity. **1987:** Lighter, but very aromatic. **1986:** Beautiful wine, breed, rather rich and well balanced for the year. **1985:** Great vintage, long keeping. Price range (pre-tax, ex-warehouse): 30 to 50 F.F.
Sales volume:
– Retail: 50%. – Restaurants: 50%.
Sales in France: 70%.
Export sales: 30%.
Main trading partners: United Kingdom, Germany, Netherlands, Switzerland, Belgium, USA.

References in France

Restaurants: L'Oustau de Beaumanière (Les Baux), Au Chapon Fin (Thoissy), Le Gray d'Albion (Cannes), Table du Combat Séguret, Legrand, La Tassée (Lyon).

Abroad

United States

Martine's Wines 1201 Andersen Drive, San Rafael, San Francisco – World Shippers 1420 Walnut Street, Philadelphia, Pennsylvannia Grand Cru 648 Broadway, New York, N.Y. 10012.

United Kingdom

Thorman Hunt 4 Pratt Walk, Lambeth, London SE11 6 AR.

Germany

Guy Foglino 79 Trinzrigentenstrasse 8000 Munich.

Switzerland

E. Raphoz 12 Chemin de la Trousse 1225 Chêne Bourg.

Belgium

A. Théran 66 rue Eugène Vandenhoff, Grèvegnée B 4030.

The Netherlands

Noordman Frères 59 Haagweg 2321 AA Leiden.

CHÂTEAU DE MONTMIRAIL

Maurice Archimbaud,
Jacques, Monique Bouteiller
B.P. 12 – 84190 Vacqueyras
90 65 86 72

Type of vineyard: Family-owned. **Established:** Since the 15th Century in this commune. **Number of employees:** 12. **Vine stocks:** Grenache 65%, Syrah 15%, Mourvèdre 10%, Cinsault 5%, Clairette 5%. **Soil:** Clay with calcium carbonate. **Exposure:** South, Southwest. **Average annual production in hectoliters:** 2,000.
Appellation: A.O.C. Gigondas, Côtes-du-Rhône Vacqueyras, Côtes-du-Rhône Blanc and Rosé. **Type:** Red, white, rosé. **Technique:** Red: traditional vinification, long maceration, little destemming. **Maturing;** Traditional cement vats, short stay in wood. **Alcohol content:** 13.5 to 14%. **Characteristics:** Deep colors. Rich and well-balanced, finesse, long. To be aged a long time: 7 to 10 years for the Vacqueyras, 15 to 20 years for the Gigondas. **Serving temperature:** 14 to 16°. **Served with:** Meat and cheese. Goes particularly well with game and meat in sauce. **Vintages available in 89/90:** 1984, 1985, 1986, 1987, 1988 (as of Autumn 89).

Characteristics of vintages

1988: A very great vintage. Beautiful deep color, tannic, rich, long and balanced. Very promising for drinking in 3 to 20 years. **1987:** Early harvest, fine elegant, fragrant wines, less hard than previous years, to be drunk within 6 years. **1986:** Very good year, average for ageing. **1985:** Exceptional year, rich and highly colored wines. **1984:** Good balance and taste in spite of the lack of Grenache. **1983:**

Exceptional vintage for wines to be aged. **Other:** 1981; Great year for ageing. 1980: Mature wines, may be drunk now. Average pre-tax, ex-warehouse price : 30 F.F. Price range (pre-tax, ex-warehouse): Between 20 F.F. and 30 F.F.

CHÂTEAU RASPAIL

Christian Meffre
84190 Gigondas
90 65 86 09 - Telex: 431 803

Type of vineyard: Family-owned. **Established:** 1979. **Vine stocks:** Grenache, Syrah. **Soil:** Jurassic marl, chalk. **Exposure:** North-South. **Average annual production in hectoliters:** 700.
Appellation: AOC Gigondas. **Type:** Red. **Technique:** Traditional. **Maturing:** In wooden casks (10 to 15 months).

Alcohol content: 13%. **Characteristics:** Rich and full, full-bodied, typical of the appellation. **Serving temperature:** 18°. **Served with:** Red meat, game, cheese. **Vintages available in 89/90:** 1985.

Characteristics of vintages

1985: Tannic and forthcoming, dried fruit and kirsch aroma. Price range (pre-taxe, ex-warehouse): 30 to 50 F.F.
Sales volume:
- Retail: 20%. - Restaurants: 15%. - Others: 65% Export.
Sales in France: 40%.
Export sales: 60%.
Main trading partners : Belgium, Switzerland, Germany, Netherlands, Japan, USA, Canada, Denmark.

References in France

Restaurants: Pullman Hôtels, Beaumanière, Armes de Champagne.
Shops: Marchés aux vins - La Sommelière.

Abroad

United States

Stacole, Miami.

United Kingdom

Pechiney, London.

Switzerland

Riotton et Gilliéron, Geneva.

The Netherlands

Verlinden en Zoon s'Hertogenbosch.

Far East

Jardine Matheson, Tokyo for South-East Asia.

Comments

Located in the center of political and winemaking history of Gigondas, the Château Raspail derives its name from Eugène Raspail who had it built in 1866. As of 1870, Eugène Raspail gave a new impetus to the Gigondas vineyards which was already well known abroad at the beginning of the century. Its re-known is easy to understand when one tastes the very successful 83 and 85 vintages.

• *Would you like to know to recognize the caracteristic fragrances of certains wines, their woodland, fruity, flowery or leather aromas, the evaluate the level of acidity or the presence of tannins, to ascertain the mellowness or the color of a wine...? See the Chapter entitled "The Art and Manner of Wine Tasting".*

• *In 1985, the wines of the following regions received the A.O.C. (Appellation d'Origine Contrôlée) classification: Minervois, Coteaux-des-Baux, Coteaux-d'Aix-en-Provence, Coteaux-du-Lyonnais and Coteaux-du-Languedoc.*

CAVES DES VIGNERONS DE GIGONDAS

84190 Gigondas
90 65 86 27 - Telex: 432 311 F

Président: Jean-Pierre Palon. **Type of vineyard:** Cop-perative Agricultural Association. **Established:** 1955. **Number of employees:** 12. **Cépages:** Grenache 80%, Mourvèdre-Syrah 15%, Cinsault etc. 5%. **Average annual production in hectoliters:** 10,000.
Appellation: Gigondas A.O.C. and Côtes-du-Rhône (Red & White). **Type:** Red. **Technique:** Traditional with carbonic maceration. **Maturing:** Ageing for 3 years (18 months in Oak casks for Gigondas). **Characteristics:** Gigondas Rouge: Dark red color, marvelous bouquet of spices and red berries, soft, rich and forthcoming. Gigondas (rosé): luminous pink color, wild grasses fragrance, seductive, dry and fruity. **Serving temperature:** Reds - room temperature (17°-18°). Rosés - coll (8°-10°). **Served with:** Gigondas Rouge: game, red meat, strong cheeses. Gigondas Rosé: superb wity delicatessen products and fish. **Vintages available in 89/90:** Gigondas Rouge Traditionnel Signature 1985-1986-1988; Gigondas Cuvée du Président 1988; Gigondas rosé Signature 1988-1989; Blanc de Blancs '87; Côtes-du-Rhône 1988, Roucassier.

Characteristics of vintages

1988: Beautiful purple color, spice and raspberry fragrance. A wine that will be remembered. **1986:** Subtle red berry bouquet, very pleasant, Price range (pre-tax, ex-warehouse): 20 F.F. - 30 F.F.
Sales volume:
- Wholesale: 50%. - Retail: 40%. - Restaurants: 10%.
Sales in France: 85%.
Export sales: 15%.
Main trading partners : Belgium, Swtizerland, Germany, Denmark, Netherlands, UK, luxemburg.

References in France

Restaurants: Le Petit Colombier - Paris; Beau Rivage - Condrieu; Boule d'Or-Fleurs; Hôtel de Grignan - Vichy.
Shops: "La Taste" chain stores, Verot-St-Étienne, Les Toques Gourmandes - Port Marly. Cellars: Bourgogne (Paris); Camus (Paris); Grands Vins de France (Paris); St-Vincent; Cave Besson (Paris); etc.

Abroad

United Kingdom
Importers: Lynden Vintners 4-6, Chandos Park Estate, Chandos Road park Royal - London.

Germany
Importers: Muller Sons Gmbh Postfach 25 6601 Saarbrucken Bubigen - 506805) 8021/22. Shops: Der Gallier Postfach 1223, 7333 Ebersbach.

The Netherlands
Importers: 1. Mr Keilbert B.V. Wijnkoperij J. Baas & Zoon Spoorlaan 1 3735 MV Bosch en Duin - Tel: 03404-31468 - 2 JJC Kwast Wijnkopers Haverstraat 18, Nieuw Vennep 2150 AA.

Others
Switzerland - Belgium - Denmark - Luxemburg.

DOMAINE DU TERME

Rolland Gaudin
84190 Gigondas
90 65 86 75

Type of vineyard: Family-owned. **Established:** 1918. **Number of employees:** 4. **Vine stocks:** 80% Grenache, 10% Mourvèdre, 10% Syrah. **Soil:** Chalky soil on clay subsoil. **Exposure:** East - West. **Average annual production in hectoliters:** 33 hl per hectare. Gigondas: 380 hl, Sablet Villages: 42 hl, Côtes du Rhône: 299 hl.

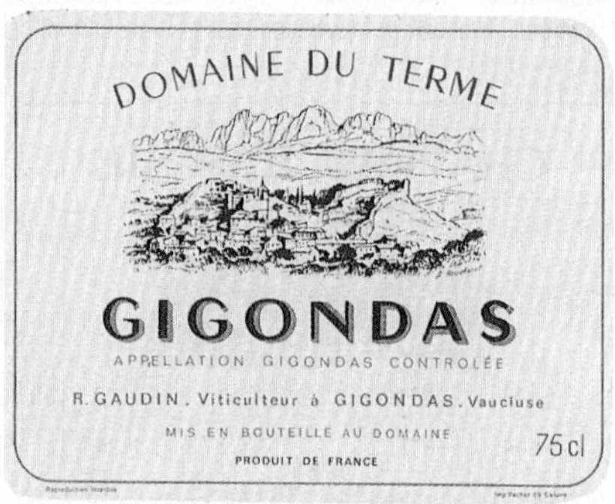

Appellation: AOC Gigondas, Sablet Villages, Côtes du Rhône. **Type:** Red, rosé. **Technique:** Traditional. **Maturing:** Oak casks, 12 to 18 months. **Alcohol content:** Gigondas: 14%, Sablet Villages: 13%, Côtes du Rhône: 13 %. **Characteristics:** Wines for keeping. **Serving temperature:** Gigondas: 17°, Sablet and Côtes du Rhône: 16°. **Served with:** Red Gigondas: game, red meats, cheese. **Vintages available in 89/90:** 1986 (some 1985).

Characteristics of vintages

1986: Very fruity, less tannic than the 1985, very fine. **1985:** Very characteristic of the Gigondas, tannic, well balanced, long, for keeping. **Other:** Sablet Villages red: very harmonious, less alcoholic than the Gigondas. Côtes du Rhône red: fruity, very pleasant to drink now.
Sales volume:
- Retail: 60%. - Restaurants: 40%.
Sales in France: 60%. **Export sales:** 40%.
Main trading partners : United States, Germany, Belgium, United Kingdom, Netherlands.

Comments

Family enterprise for three generations. The domain is located just within the limits of an ancient territory of the Principality of Orange, which explains the name "du Terme" (terminus). Galerie d'Art et Caveau Domaine du Terme, place de Gigondas.

TAVEL

DOMAINE DE LA GENESTIÈRE

Andrée Bernard
30126 Tavel
66 50 07 03

Type of vineyard: Privately owned. **Established:** 1960. **Number of employees:** 9. **Vine stocks:** Grenaches, Cinsaults, Syrahs, Carignans, Clairettes, et. **Exposure:** Various. **Average annual production in hectoliters:** 1,300.
Appellation: Tavel. **Type:** Rosé. **Technique:** Traditional. **Alcohol content:** 12.5%. **Served with:** Goes with everything. **Vintages available in 89/90:** 1986, 1987.

Characteristics of vintages

1988: Very elegant, very developed aromas. Good rosé, fine, rich, well-balanced at the same time, very pleasant. Price range (pre-tax, ex-warehouse): 25 F.F.

LES VIGNERONS DE TAVEL

R. Barrelet
B.P. 3 – 30126 Tavel
66 50 03 57

Type of vineyard: Producer's Association. **Established:** 1938. **Vine stocks:** Grenache, Cinsault, Clairette, Bourbonlenc, Mourvèdre, Picpoul. **Soil:** Silica-Clay, round stones. **Exposure:** North/South. **Average annual production in hectoliters:** 18,000.
Appellation: Tavel. **Type:** Rosé. **Techique:** Classic, cold maceration for 24 hours controlled temperature. **Alcohol content:** 13%. **Characteristics:** Warm and round, rich and very well balanced. **Serving temperature:** 12 to 14°. **Served with:** Throughout the meal except with red meat and dessert. **Vintages available in 89/90:** 1987 and 1988.

Characteristics of vintages

1988: Long, great finesse, aromatic. **1987:** Warm, round, quite robust, a better ageing wines. Price range (pre-tax, ex-warehouse): between 20 F.F. and 30 F.F.
Sales volume:
– Wholeslaer: 30% – Retail: 30%. – Ohter: 30%.
Sales in Fracnce: 70%.
Export sales: 30%.
Main trading partners : EEC, Northern Europe, Japan, USA.

SOCIÉTÉ CIVILE AGRICOLE JEAN OLIVIER

M. Vincent de Bez
Château d'Aqueria – 30126 Tavel
66 50 04 56 – Telex: 431 919 F

Type of vineyard: Family Corporation. **Established:** 1920. **Number of employees:** 7. **Vine stocks:** Grenache, Cinsault, Clairette, Mourvèdre, Bourboulecn. **Soil:** Sand, and clay with round stones under skeletal soil. **Exposure:** Hillsides. **Average annual production in hectoliters:** 2200.
Appellation: Tavel. **Type:** Rosé. **Technique:** Short maceration and fermentation at low temperature. **Maturing:** In stainless steel tanks. **Alcohol content:** 13%. **Characteristics:** Light ruby color, good alcohol/acidity balance, red fruit aroma, flowery flavor. **Serving temperature:** 12°. **Served with:** Veal sauteed, saddle of lamb. **Vintages available in 89/90:** 1986.

Characteristics of vintages

1986: Light ruby color, red fruit aroma, good alcohol/acidity balance, long, full flavor. Average pre-tax, ex-warehouse price: between 20 F.F and 28 F.F. Price range (pre-tax, ex-warehouse): between 10 F.F. and 30 F.F.
Sales volume:
– Retail: 10%. – Restaurants: 40% and specialized shops.
– Other: 50% importers.
Sales in France: 50%.
Export sales: 50%.
Main trading partners : USA, Germany, Switzerland, Japan.

LIRAC

DOMAINES J.C. ASSÉMAT

J.C. Assémat
30150 Roquemaure
66 82 65 52 or 66 82 86 75 –
Telex: 43 19 19 Code 007

Type of vineyard: Family-owned. **Established:** 1963. **Vine stocks:** Grenache, Cinsault, Syrah, Mourvèdre. **Soil:** Silica-clay covered with stones. **Exposure:** Southwest. **Average annual production in hectoliters:** 2,000.
Appellation: Lirac, "Rouge Été" (a Summer Red), "Réserve Syrah". **Type:** Red, white, rosé. **Technique:** Destemming, pressing, for the white, drawing off for the rosé, long maceration for the red. **Characteristics:** Dry and fruity, long, round. **Vintages available in 89/90:** 1986.

Characteristics of vintages

1988: Sound grapes has made possible the production of clean wines, round, soft, full and fruity. **1987:** Red wines whose qualities have been recognized by 2 Gold Medals at Orange. Part of the wine has subsequently been matured in casks made of Allier oak. Price range (pre-tax, ex-warehouse): Between 20 F.F. and 30 F.F.
Sales volume:
- Wholesale: 75%. - Retail: 10%. - Restaurants: 5%.
- Other: 10% (winecellars).
Sales in France: 15%. **Export sales:** 85%.
Main trading partners : Germany.

Comments

Sold in bottles since 1980. 18 Medals at the Concours of Mâcon and Paris. The Château is located on RN. 580, 500 meters after the Roquemaure Exit of the Autoroute (Highway), direction Bagnols.

GAEC LOMBARDO "DOMAINE DU DEVOY"

Lombardo Brothers
Saint-Laurent-des-Arbres - 30126 Tavel
66 50 01 23 - Telex: Telex publi A 490 730 F

Type of vineyard: Agricultural Association. **Established:** 1964. **Vine stocks:** Grenache, Mourvedre, Syrah, Cinsault, Grenache Blanc, Bourboulenc, Roussane, Clairette. **Soil:** Pebbles and astian sand. **Exposure:** South. **Average annual production in hectoliters:** 1,700.

MIS EN BOUTEILLE AU DOMAINE
Domaine du Devoy
LIRAC
750 ml.
APPELLATION LIRAC CONTROLÉE
LOMBARDO F^res, PROPRIETAIRES A St-LAURENT-DES-ARBRES (30126)
Produce of France

Appellation: Lirac. **Type:** Red, white, rosé. **Technique:** Traditional. **Maturing:** 2 years. **Alcohol content:** 12.8%. **Characteristics:** Generally recognized as feminine wines, their alcohol is not agressive. They are pleasant and delicate wines. The delicacy of their tannins go perfectly with an active life. **Serving temperature:** Red: 16°. Rosé and white: 12°. **Served with:** Red: all meats. Rosé: poultry in cream and sweetbreads. White: fish in general. **Vintages available in 89/90:** Red: 85, 86, 88. Rosé: 88. White: 87, 88.

Characteristics of vintages

1988: Rich, well balanced and fruity, promising. **1986:** Tannic and very aromatic, excellent ageing potential. **1985:** Very good balance, harmonious. Price range (pre-taxe, ex-warehouse): between 20 and 30 F.F.
Sales volumes:
- Wholesale: 60%. - Retail: 15%. - Restaurants: 25%.
Sales in France: 40%.
Export sales: 60%.
Main trading partners: United Kingdom, Netherlands, Canada, Switzerland, Germany.

References in France

*Restaurants:*Gray d'Albion, etc...

Abroad

United Kingdom
Majestic Wine, London.

Canada
S.A.Q. BP No. 1058 Place d'Armes, Montreal.

The Netherlands
Van der Linden, Rotterdam.

Comments

A domain of 40 hectares, planted in 1964, near St-Laurent-des-Arbres, marvelously located on the hills which overlook the royal Lirac road. The various vinestocks are vinified separately, and their blending at the end of the harvest is done, after tasting by the producer, in scrupulously studied proportions, to provide the Lirac du Devoy with its own very special personality. Typical of the beautiful successes of the appellation, the 83 to 88 vintages.

DOMAINE DUSEIGNEUR

Jean Duseigneur
Route de Saint-Victor
30126 Saint Laurent des Arbres
66 50 02 57 or 66 82 85 01

Type of vineyard: Family-owned. **Established:** 1968. **Number of employees:** 3. **Vine stocks:** Noble varieties. **Soil:** Chalky clay. **Exposure:** Hillsides. **Average annual production in hectoliters:** 1,100.
Appellation: Lirac. **Type:** Red, white, rosé. **Technique:** Traditional. **Maturing:** Red: in casks - White and Rosé: in cement vats and stainless steel tanks. **Alcohol content:** 12.7%. **Characteristics:** Very fruity (blackcurrant, raspberry, faded rose...) and particularly long. Takes on woody and mushroom flavors with ageing. **Serving temperature:** White and Rosé: 8 to 10° - Red: 16°. **Served with:** Red: meat in sauce - Rosé: delicatessen - White: fish, seafood. **Vintages available in 89/90:** Red: 1983, 1984, 1986, 1987 - White and Rosé: 1988.

Characteristics of vintages

1988: Exceptional, good keeping red wine, beautiful white. **1987:** Very good (Mâcon Silver Medal). **1986:** Exceptional

(Paris Gold Medal). **1985:** Very good (Paris Bronze Medal). **Other:** 1983 – very good (Paris Silver Medal). Price range (pre-tax, ex-warehouse): 20 to 30 F.F.
Sales volume:
Lirac
– Wholesale: 40%. – Retail: 25%. – Restaurants: 15%. – Other: 20%.
Côte-du-Rhône
– Wholesale: 10%.
Sales in France: 80%.
Export sales: 20%.
Main trading partners : United Kingdom, Belgium.

MIS EN BOUTEILLE AU DOMAINE
DOMAINE DUSEIGNEUR
LIRAC
Appellation Lirac Controlée
75 cl
JEAN DUSEIGNEUR – PROPRIÉTAIRE A St LAURENT-DES-ARBRES (GARD)

References in France

Restaurants: A number of restaurants in the Avignon region (Gard, Hérault, Drôme, Alpes-de-Haute-Provence).

Abroad

United Kingdom

Michael Harrison Wines, 27 Hillside Av. Thore St. Andrew – Norwich NR 7 OQW – Tel: 0603 33773 – Mayor Sworder & Co, Ltd, 21 Duke St. Hill, London Bridge, SE1 2SW – Tel: 01 407 5111.

Belgium

J.P. Nauters, 29, avenue du Griffon B – 7498 Hennuyeres TVA: 669 204 879 (Tel: 067 64 68 00) – Raphael Verbaeys, 29, rue de l'Enfer, B 7081 Estinne-au-Val (Tel: 064 33 33 01).

Comments

Created on this virgin ground as of 1968 by Jean Duseigneur, the domain produces red, white and rosé wines of remarkable grace and delicacy due to the very ancient soil (800 million years), the pebbly soil, the hillside location and a special micro-climate due to its location on the banks of the Rhône. Forthcoming and fruity, the red is a good keeping wine (10 years). The rosé has a clear ruby color with topaz glints which are accentuated with age. As for the white, fine and fragrant, it is made mostly from Clairette and Bourboulenc grapes.

> • *Watch out for wines that lose their authenticity, most often because of carbonic maceration (see Roussillon, Southwest, Périgord...).*

MARIE PONS-MURE

Mrs. Pons-Mure
Domaines de Castel Oualou – 30150 Roquemaure
66 82 82 64 – Telex: 431 919 F CIAV
abonnée Mme Pons-Mure

Type of vineyard: Privately owned. **Established:** 1961. **Vine stocks:** Grenaches, Syrah, Mourvèdres, Cinsault, Ugny Blanc, Clairette, Picpoult. **Soil:** Red, pebbly, large round stones. **Exposure:** Very sunny. **Average annual production in hectoliters:** about 2000.
Appellation: A.O.C. Lirac. **Type:** Red, white, rosé. **Technique:** Long fermentation (15 days) for the red, low temperature vinification for the rosé. **Maturing:** In a special cellar. The vats are stored 3 meters below ground to protect the wines from temperature variations. **Characteristics:** Red: rich and well-balanced, very full, long, violet-raspberry fragrance. Keeps for 5 to 7 years or more. Rosé: sustained color, long, fruity with finesse due to the large percentage of Cinsault. White: dry, gun flint taste. **Serving temperature:** Red: 15 to 17°. White and rosé: 10°. **Served with:** Red: stews (made with Lirac wines). Roasts, game, cheese. Rosé: spicy cooking, brochettes, exotic cooking, can be drunk agreeably throughout the meal. White: fish, shelffish, cooking with cream and for that excellent aperitif, the Kir. **Vintages available in 89/90:** Red: 85, 86. Rosé and white: 87, 88.

Characteristics of vintages

1986: Rosé: sustained color, fruity, finesse due to the large percentage of Cinsault. White: fruity, fresh, gun flint taste. **1985:** Classic, fine, supple, lovely color.

DOMAINE ROUSSEAU

Alexis Rousseau
Les Charmettes – 30290 Laudun
66 79 44 20 – Telex: 480 148

Established: 1963. **Number of employees:** 6. **Vine stocks:** 40% Grenache, 20% Cinsault Couché, 10% Syrah, 30% Mourvèdre. **Soil:** Pebbly, silica-clay, sometimes covered with large stones. **Average annual production in hectoliters:** 1000.
Appellation: Lirac A.O.C. **Type:** Red, rosé. **Maturing:** Vats. **Alcohol content:** 12.5%. **Vintages available in 89/90:** 1985, 1986.

Characteristics of vintages

1985: Good red, good color, quite supple. Gold Medal at Mâcon. Price range (pre-tax, ex-warehouse): Between 20 F.F. and 30 F.F.
Sales volume:
– Other: 80% (export).
Sales in France: 20%.
Export sales: 80%.
Main trading partners : UK, Germany, Netherlands, Belgium, Denmark, Canada.

CHÂTEAU DE SÉGRIÈS

Comte de Régis
30126 Lirac
66 21 85 35

Type of vineyard: Family-owned. **Established:** 1930. **Vine stocks:** Red: Grenache, Cinsault, Syrah, Carignan – White: Clairette, Bourboulenc, Ugni Blanc, Picpoul Blanc. **Soil:** Clay with calcium carbonate. **Average annual production in hectoliters:** 35.
Appellation: Lirac. **Type:** Red, white, rosé. **Technique:** Traditionnal – Rosé, by drawing off. **Maturing:** 12 to 24 months for the reds, in cement vats. **Characteristics:** Rosé: salmon color, vervain aroma. White: dry, light and fragrant. Red: Good color, rich and well-balanced, supple. **Vintage available 89/90:** Lirac red: 1985; Lirac rosé: 1987; Lirac white: 1985-1988.

Characteristics of vintages

1985: Successful vintage for white as well as red, quite supple. Price range (pre-tax, ex-warehouse): between 20 and 30 F.F.
Sales volume:
- Wholesale: 60%. - Retail: 15%. - Restaurants: 15%. - Other: 10% (export to EEC Countries + Switzerland + U.S.A.).

Sales in France: 65%.
Export sales: 35%.
Main trading partners : UK, Luxemburg, Germany, Switzerland, U.S.A.

References in France

Restaurants: "Le Magister", Nîmes – Le Carré des Feuillants – Les Vendanges à Nîmes – Restaurant Lucien Vanel à Toulouse – La Beaugravière à Mondragon (Vaucluse) – Restaurant "Provence" à Lymington (Hampshire) (G.-B.).
Shops: Maison Malleval, 11, rue Émile Zola, Lyon.

Abroad

Germany
R. and I. Buhler – Wicheimer Strasse 82, 5 köln 80. Tel: (0221) 83 13 04.

Switzerland
Kurt Gehring – 3175- Flamatt (Suisse). Tel.: 031 94 02 13

Luxemburg
Asbach & Co – 296, route de Thionville – 5884 Luxembourg Howald – Tél. 49 02 24.

Comments

Other wines for sale: Château Braquety: Bandol Rosé 1986. A.O.C. Château du Chêne: Mâcon Rouge, 1987 – Bourgogne Passetoutgrains 1987 – Marc de Bourgogne.

CÔTES DU VENTOUX

DOMAINE DE CHAMP-LONG

Gely father and son.
Ancienne Route de Malaucene, 84340 Entrechaux
90 46 01 58

Type of vineyard: Family-owned. **Established:** Several generations. **Vine stocks:** Grenache, Syrah, Cinsault, Carignan, Clairette. **Soil:** Very variable, from sand to clay. **Exposure:** South, South-East. **Average annual production in hectoliters:** 1,200.

1985
Domaine Champ-Long
Côtes du Ventoux
APPELLATION CÔTES DU VENTOUX CONTRÔLÉE
cuvée spéciale
GAEC du DOMAINE DE CHAMP-LONG
M. GÉLY et Fils, vignerons-récoltants
84340 Entrechaux FRANCE
Mis en bouteille à la Propriété
75 cl
12,5% Vol.

Appellation: Côtes du Ventoux. **Type:** Red, rosé. **Technique:** Traditional (no destemming, temperature control). **Maturing:** Rosé, in vats. Red: vats and wood. **Alcohol content:** 12 to 12.5%. **Serving temperature:** Rosé: 8 to 10°. Red: 14 to 16°. **Served with:** Rosé: Pizza, delicatessen, first courses. Red: Red meat, game, cooked cheeses. **Vintages available in 89/90:** 1986, 1987, 1988.

Characteristics of vintages

1988: Well colored wines, rich and well balanced with lingering aromas. Good keeping. **1987:** Very fruity, supple wines that go down well. Lots of distinction. Remarkable rosé. **1986:** Well balanced wine, round and forthcoming. Good keeping. Price range (pre-tax, ex-warehouse): between 10 and 20 F.F.

Sales volume:
– Wholesale: 10%. – Retail: 75%. – Restaurants: 15%.
Sales in France: 75%.
Export sales: 25%.
Main trading partners : Belgium, Germany.

Comments

Excellent winegrowing property for a number of generations and producers with their own cellars since 1964. The Gely family produces excellent red wines, rich and supple, that evolve extremely well as well as one of the best rosé wines of the region.

CAVE LES VIGNERONS DE CANTEPERDRIX

Marc Masinsky
B.P. N° 15 – F. Mazan 84380
90 69 70 31 – Telex: 432 931 GDA for Canteperdrix

Type of vineyard: Cooperative. **Established:** 1927. **Number of employees:** 10 employees, 430 members. **Vine stocks:** Red: Grenache, Syrah, Cinsault, Carignan. **Soil:** Chalky clay on cobalt blue rocks. **Exposure:** South, South-East, South-West. **Average annual production in hectoliters:** 90,000.
Appellation: Côtes du Ventoux. **Type:** Red, White, Rosé. **Technique:** Traditional. **Maturing:** Cement and lined steel tanks. **Alcohol content:** 12.5% (AOC). **Characteristics:** Fruity, vigorous, fragrant, typical. **Serving temperature:** White: 8 to 10°. Rosé: 10 to 12°. Red: 12 to 15°. **Served with:** White: First courses, shellfish, fish and sea food. Rosé: all refined dishes. Red: From roast to cheese, all dishes, hot or cold. **Vintages available in 89/90:** Perhaps still some 1988 in (1990), but surely some 1989.

Characteristics of vintages

Price range (pre-tax, ex-warehouse): between 13 and 14 F.F.
Sales volume:
– Wholesale: 95% (in bulk). – Retail: 2%. – Restaurants: 3%.
Sales in France: 80% (Aoc). **Export sales:** 20% (Aoc).
Main trading partners : Switzerland, Belgium, Germany, Japan, Netherlands.

Comments

The largest and most important of the "Cotes du Ventoux" terrains extend to the South of the "Geant de Provence". The Mazan parcels occupy a major position with its 1,800 hectares divided into more than 200 individual family vineyards. The great variety of soils has made it possible to optimize the planting of the major vinestocks of the appellation. The winecellar with the musical name "Les Vignerons de Canteperdrix" is one of the most modern. It has succeeded in maintaining secular tradition while sensibly using high-performance equipment, compatible with its production level.

COTEAUX DU VIVARAIS

DOMAINE GALLETY

Alain Gallety
La Montagne – 07220 Saint-Montan
75 52 63 18

Type of vineyard: Family-owned. **Vine stocks:** Grenache, Syrah, Cinsault, Clairette. **Soil:** Clay with calcium carbonate. **Exposure:** South, Southeast.**Average annual production in hectoliters:** 500.
Appellation: V.D.Q.S. Côtes-du-Vivarais. **Type:** Red, white, rosé. **Technique:** Carbonic maceration. **Maturing:** 1 year in new Oak casks for the "cuvée spéciale" (red). **Alcohol content:** 13%. **Characteristics:** Supple, fruity, rich and well-balanced, goes down smoothly. **Vintage available 89/90:** 1986.

Characteristics of vintages

1986: Pleasant white and seductive red, fresh and fragrant.
Sales volume:
– Retail: 90%. – Restaurants: 10%.
Sales in France: 90%.
Export sales: 10%.
Main trading partners : Germany, Netherlands.

CLAIRETTE DE DIE

DOMAINE DE LA MURE

Jean-Claude Raspail
26340 Saillans
75 21 55 99

Type of vineyard: Family-owned. **Established:** 1942. **Number of employees:** variable. **Vine stocks:** Clairette, Muscat. **Soil:** Chalky Clay. **Exposure:** Hillsides and plateaux. **Average annual production in hectoliters:** 50.
Appellation: Clairette de Die AOC. **Type:** white. Other: White mousseux (Sparkling). **Technique:** Champagne Method. **Maturing:** Casks, fermentation in bottles at constant temperature. **Alcohol content:** 12%. **Characteristics:** Brut: fine, subtle, fruity and elegant, creamy foam. Demi-sec: Strong Muscat aroma, natural and seductive,

creamy foam. Vaunière 87 and Domaine de la Mûre 87 (dry white): same character as the Brut, young fruit, still. **Serving temperature:** 6-8°. **Served with:** As an aperitif and with shellfish, foie gras, white meat, and dessert or during the entire meal. **Vintages available in 89/90:** Extra Brut 1986, Dry white 1986, 1985, Semi-dry 1987 and 1988.

Characteristics of vintages

1987: Demi-sec 1987. Gold Medal at the Concours général Agricole de Paris (1989). Very great wine, marked by Muscat, flowery, long, creamy and lingering foam. Vaunière 1987: dry still wine). Very fruity, soft and full, great finesse. Domaine de la Mûre 1987: Gold Medal at Macon and Blayais-Bourgeois 1988. Matured in oak casks, very aromatic, velvety texture, lingering taste, on sale in the best restaurants of the region. Served as an aperitif or with fish and foie gras. **1986:** Brut-extra: Gold Medal at Blayais-Borugeais 1988. Subtle, elegant, fruity, creamy, foam.
Price range (pre-tax, ex-warehouse): 25 to 36 F.F. (Tax included).

COTEAUX DU TRICASTIN

DOMAINE DE GRANGENEUVE

O. Bour and family
Roussas - 26230
75 98 50 22 - Telex : 345 260

Type of vineyard: Family-owned. **Established:** 1964. **Number of employees:** 20. **Vine stocks:** Syrah - Grenache - Cinsault - Mourvèdre. **Soil:** Pebbly, old alluvial deposits. **Exposure:** South. **Average annual production in hectoliters:** 5000.
Appellation: Coteaux du Tricastin. **Type:** Red, rosé. **Technique:** Traditional with temperature control. **Alcohol content:** 12.8%. **Characteristics:** Very fruity, long, red fruit fragrance. Very good color. **Serving temperature:** Young wines should be drunk cool, older wines at room temperature. **Served with:** Pure Syrah with meat. The others with the entire meal. **Vintages available 89/90:** 85-86.

Characteristics of vintages

1986: Very fruity. Well-balanced rosé. Soft and rich, still very fresh. **1985:** Very good balance between body and fragrance. **1984:** Very round - at its best. Full flavor. Price range (pre-tax, ex-warehouse): 20 F.F.-50 F.F.
Sales volume:
- Retail: 20%. - Restaurants: 10%. - Other: 70% (Export).
Sales in France: 30%.
Export sales: 70%.
Main trading partners: USA, Japan, Denmark, UK, Switzerland, Germany, Netherlands, Belgium, Costa Rica, Austria.

References in France

Restaurants: Le Bistrot de Léon - Le Pré bossu - Le Grand Écuyer (Cordes). Dutournier - Chabran - Michel Rostan - L'Espérance (Vézelay). La Bone Étape (Châteaux-Arnoux). *Shops:* Les Caves de la Madeleine - Les Toques gourmandes.

CHÂTEAU GRILLET

CHÂTEAU GRILLET

Neyret-Gachet
42410 Verin
74 59 51 56

Type of vineyard: Family-owned. **Established:** 1830. **Number of employees:** 3. **Vine stocks:** Exclusively Viognier. **Soil:** Quartz sand covering a granite projection towards the Rhône. **Exposure:** Full South. **Average annual production in hectoliters:** 90 (in good years). **Appellation:** Château Grillet A.O.C. **Type:** White. **Technique:** Traditional. **Maturing:** Oak casks. **Alcohol content:** Approx. 12%. Characteristics: very aromatic, soft and supple, good for ageing. **Serving temperature:** Very cool. **Served with:** White meat, lamb. **Vintages available 89/90:** 1985 - previous vintages are out of stock. **Vintages available in 1989-90:** 1985, 1987 (to be bottled in 1989).

Characteristics of vintages

1985: Excellent year, finesse, very subtle, aromatic, soft and full, very successful. Do not hesitate. **Price:** 115 to 135 F.F. (tax included).

SPIRITS

COGNAC

Cognac, today, is above all a question of brand. Who isn't familiar with those beautiful golden bottles with prestigious names, Hennessy, Courvoisier, Rémy Martin, Camus and so many others, striving to outdo each other with their fancy labels? Cognac is a "star" in its own right. It has been surrounded by an aura of luxury and festivity that gives it an untouchable, unrivalled character. However, behind this flashy display organized by the great trade houses of the Cognac region and run by marketing specialists under the watchful eye of financiers, one finds a wonderful product, an honest to goodness product of nature, tamed and civilized by man. Cognac is at its best, in its natural state, without make up.

Cognac is the fruit of a unique convergence between man's intelligence and a bountiful nature, and is the result of an extraordinary combination of circumstances, offering a perfect example of symbiosis between man and earth.

The Charentes: a paradise in miniature

The Charentes has a more or less chalky soil, reasonably well drained, and is planted with 85,000 hectares of vines (100,000 five years ago) which produce on the average one billion liters of white wine, rather acid and of low alcoholic content (8 to 9%). The Charentes region is ideally suited to the production, after two consecutive distillations, of the best brandy in the world, which has to be aged in oak casks for a number of years before it can rightfully claim the Cognac appellation.

Coming from the North, what is most striking is the omnipresence of light, intense and yet subtle: a pale blue sky often speckled with small white clouds brings harmony to this slightly undulated and always calm landscape: a complex mosaic in pastel shades that no artist has ever been able to capture.

The Cognac region is a kind of no-man's land, separating Northern and Southern climates. Bordered on the West by the Atlantic Ocean and on the East by the ancient volcanoes of the Massif Central, it is a haven of peace, protected from the clash of influences from both North and South.

The land of Cognac fits into a circle of about 100 km in diameter, whose center is located midway between Cognac and Jarnac. In its heart one finds the best Cognac cru, the Grande Champagne, and around are scattered concentrically, the five other lesser crus: Petite Champagne, Borderies, Bons Bois, Fin Bois and Bois Ordinaires. One single criterion has been used for the delimitation of these regions: the high quality of the brandies produced. But this quality level is not a matter of chance; it can today be explained by the nature of the soil and subsoil: the more chalk, the better the brandy.

This oasis of calm and light has been marked by the taste and skill of the Charentes builders who have given it an architectural design that blends harmoniously with the landscape: the

Roman style churches, and the small chapels that stand out by their stature and purity of design in the greenery are not there by accident. No more so than the large farm houses and the old bourgeois mansions, all inward-looking, without any other opening on the outside world than a stately wooden gate.

The Charentes resident is secretive by nature. A conservative and an individualist, he lives a simple life, but a good one, in a natural environment that has been good to him. The vineyards are planted, at about 95%, with Saint-Emilion des Charentes, a grape variety better known as Ugni Blanc. This Mediterranean vinestock reputed for its excellent white wines from the Cassis region, near Marseille, or for the Italian whites (known as Trebbiano) has recently been implanted in California, giving, on the other side of the Atlantic, a rather pleasant white wine. But the Charentes is the Northern limit for the cultivation of this grape variety: this explains why the Ugni Blanc grapes never reach full maturity in the Cognac region.

The less ripe the grape, the lower the alcohol content of the wine, the more wine you need for a given quantity of brandy, and the better the brandy because of it higher aromatic content.

The winegrower of the Charentes is well aware of this, since he is at the same time cultivator, harvester, winemaker and distiller. Traditionally, the producer in this region is the complete master of the product up to, and including, the distillation process. In Charentes there is no super-industry for the production of Cognac; each and everyone of the 30,000 proprietors makes his wine just after the harvest, and starts distillation as of the 15th of December of the same year. During two or three winter months he will remain, day and night, close to his boiler, to oversee the distillation process.

The Charentes white wines are distilled when young, on their lees, without filtration or racking. After a first heating cycle, a distillate called brouillis (about 30% alcohol) is obtained; a second heating is necessary to produce a young brandy (of around 70% alcohol). Each producer uses all his know-how in the distillation process, which sometimes forces him to remain all night at a few meters from his still: he will eliminate more or less of the first and last runnings of the distillate, keeping more or less of the heart. In order to make a good brandy one needs to start with a good wine, but one needs also a great deal of experience and technique and, above all, intuition. No wonder then that the Charentes farmer is such an individualist, so at one with his land, so set in his ways, living so close and intense a relationship with his vines, his wine, his still and his Cognac.

But this is only the beginning. It will take a lot of work and patience for this young Cognac to reach full maturity and to be ready for drinking.

The art of patience

Once out of the still, the brandy is immediately placed into 250 to 350 liter oak casks. The size of the cask is of importance since the aim is to obtain a good ratio between the volume of liquid and the wooden surface of the cask. Another decisive factor is the cask's age: a new cask releases more tannin more rapidly, and will thus age a young brandy faster. On the other hand, if you want a lighter brandy, you should use 5 to 6 year old casks, as excess tannin could be detrimental to the subtlety and finesse of the brandy. During this long wait, the young brandy will acquire maturity, finesse, and roundness. The wood acts as a filter between the brandy and the surrounding atmosphere so that it will eventually lose a part of its volume and alcoholic content each year—this is called "la part des anges" (the angels' share). The ageing process will depend on the humidity in the warehouse. In a hayloft, under the roof, brandy loses more volume than alcohol, while in a humid cellar on the banks of the Charentes, the loss in alcohol will occur faster than the loss in volume. The ideal solution is to transfer the casks from the hayloft to the cellar, and then from the cellar to the hayloft, according to the evolution of the ageing process. If there is too much humidity, the softness and richness will soon turn to flabbiness and, if the atmosphere is too dry, it might very well become too hard because of its high alcohol content.

The location of the vineyard, the year, the vinification technique, the distillation process, the casking, the warehouse and the ageing time are all decisive factors, and it is not surprising that each Cognac, each cask, has its own individuality and that you won't ever find two identical brandies. This is a major problem for dealers handling various qualities of Cognac.

The House Stamp

Each dealer has his own style, and his own criteria for the selection of young brandies, as well as rules for ageing, blending procedures, etc.

The cellar master, for each wine merchant, is responsible for the selection of the crus. His experience with brandies will lead him to choose Fin Bois, which ages rapidly, for his three star brandy, while, for his prestige crus, he will buy Grandes Champagnes crus that he will place in old casks (called "fûts roux") for long ageing (several decades). Each cru has its own specific characteristics: very chalky hills and slopes are less productive, thus they give better brandy than the low-lying land that has a better yield. Moreover, if there is a hierachy of crus, and characteristics peculiar to each of them, the cellar master must also take into consideration the different vintages—the good years and the less good—since a bad Cognac will never be good, even after ageing. Blending several vintages is often a successful procedure which helps produce a more balanced and harmonious brandy.

Is it then shameful to blend an excellent vintage with a lesser one?

This is a good question with which to lead into a discussion of Cognac vintages.

Vintages Forbidden

Vintage existed in Cognac until 1914, but it is presently outlawed by the Bureau National du Cognac (an inter-professional organization responsible for enforcing the regulations directly derived from an allocations bureau) established in 1940 and closely connected with the Kommandantur of the dreary days of the Occupation.

Thus, in order to put a stop to any attempted fraud (a grower is said to have sold 4 times his harvest in 1906!) regulations have been set up and enforced. Would it be a good idea to return to vintages for Cognac? There are those who think that Cognac could thus regain a certain specificity, and particularly, that exceptionnal years should be awarded their own vintage: remember the 1914, 1939 or 1949 which all deserve accolades. As it is, the notion of vintage in Cognac concerns only the first Cognac cru, the Grande Champagne, where certain estates, belonging to a single grower, have the best opportunities for producing vintage Cognacs. But seductive though it is, this idea fails to take into account the harsh reality that over 85% of Cognacs are marketed as "three stars" or V.S.O.P. (Very Superior Old Pale) products, that is to say after a relatively short ageing time. On the other hand, the bulk of Cognac sales goes through dealers who have no interest whatsoever in having these vintages reestablished, because this would be much too long a process (today's vintages could not be put on the market before the turn of the century) hence the necessity to set up a marginal stock, a regulation system, etc.

For the last twenty years or so, the older cellar masters have been paying no attention to vintages, and attach much more importance to blendings, ageing behavior, etc.

It is also said that there are no longer any very bad years as in the old days, because the growing technique has improved. Yields too have changed, it seems. Last, but not least, people are wary of the much talked about harvesting machine which is replacing the manual harvester in 60 to 80% of French vineyards: these machines pick up not only the grapes, but leaves, and a good many snails as well. . . (these well known "cagouilles" of the Charentes).

"Cagouilles are all right in their place" says an old cellar master "but not in wine. . ."

No one can tell how machine harvested Cognac will age in 20 to 30 years. Fortunately, in Grande Champagne, harvesting is still done by hand, in keeping with the best traditions. It's matter of prestige!

THE BEST COGNACS

Traditional Cognac is a strong and elegant spirit, supple and fruity as well as soft and rich.

Tastes having changed are tending to lean now towards lighter and more refined spirits, certain brands have developed qualities bound to seduce even the most incorruptible.

Château De Fontpinot Grande Champagne "Réserve du Château"

A Grand Cru of great finesse, subtle, very flowery, with a clean and velvety taste.

Delamain Grande Champagne Pale and Dry

A beautiful blend derived from five Grande Champagne estates. Refined, soft and rich, lively and fruity, very aromatic.

Hennessy, V.S.O.P. Fine Champagne

Excellent blend of Grande and Petite Champagne, rather strong nose, light and vigorous to the taste.

Among the traditional Grands Cognacs, that are well made, soft and rich, very velvety and well aged we recommend:

Courvoisier X.O.

An exceptional Cognac for important occasions and for connoisseur friends.

Centaure Extra Fine Champagne de Rémy Martin.

One of the best of the prestigious crus, for very special evenings.

Camus X.O.

Without reproach. For experienced wine lovers.

Martell Extra

A very harmonious blend of traditional Cognac for connoisseurs. Rich and well-balanced.

Six crus ready for tasting

The best Cognacs come from three major growing areas: Grande Champagne, Petite Champagne, and Borderies.

Grande Champagne is a Cognac of great distinction, which ages better and longer than the other crus. It distinguishes itself by its flowery aroma reminiscent of the vine flower and dried lime-blossom. Not unduly heavy, it can be described as slightly vinous. To the taste, Grande Champagne has plenty of finesse, and is supple, natural and delicate, with lingering aroma and flavor.

Petite Champagne is to be enjoyed in the same way as Grande Champagne, but is less flowery and somewhat more fruity. To the taste, it is quite similar to Grande Champagne though lighter and with a somewhat less persistent flavor.

Fine Champagne is not a cru but a blend of at least 50% Grande Champagne, the remainder being Petite Champagne.

Borderies produces Cognacs of deeper color than those of the Champagnes, with scents of iris and violet. Heavier on the palate than both Champagnes, but with lighter aroma, which makes them somewhat more neutral.

The other Cognac crus are called "Les Bois" and are divided into Fins Bois, Bons Bois and Bois Ordinaires (or Bois Communs). Less fine and heavier than the first three, they are characterized by their fruitiness and typical character. They age more quickly.

The Fins Bois are comparable to the Champagnes but are heavier, more vinous, and have a much shorter aftertaste.

The Bons Bois are less natural and heavier than the Fins Bois. They are more astringent on the palate, with a pronounced ethyl alcohol aftertaste.

The Bois Ordinaires give very heavy brandies, high in alcohol, rather coarse to the taste, typical of the area.

DOUBLE DISTILLATION IN A CHARENTES STILL

Cognac is produced by distillation, that is to say by separation. Wine is heated in a pot (above, left) on an open fire. According to the principles of physics, alcohol boils, and thus evaporates, at a lower temperature than water. The vapors are then captured in the still cover, concentrated in the swan's neck and condensed in the coil immersed in cold water (above, right). The onion shaped vase in the center is for pre-heating the wine which will be distilled during the next cycle.

Two consecutive distillations are necessary to obtain a young Cognac, that will be aged for a long time, after several blendings.

COGNAC LHERAUD

M. Guy Lheraud
Angeac - 16120 Châteauneuf/Charente
45 97 12 33 - Telex: 791 020 - Fax: 45 62 51 96

Type of vineyard: Corporation. **Established:** 1971. **Number of employees:** 10. **Vine stocks:** Ugni Blanc, Colombar. **Soil:** Calcium carbonate. **Exposure:** Southwest. **Average annual production in hectoliters:** 90. **Technique:** Liqueurs: maceration of fruit for a year. **Alcohol content:** Cognac 40%, Pineau 17%, Liqueurs 25%. **Vintages available in 89/90:** Cognac aged for 3, 5, 10, 20 and 50 years available. Also a limited quantity of Cognac 112 years old. Pineau aged for 7 years.

Characteristics of vintages

Average pre-tax, ex-warehouse price: Cognac 110 F.F., Pineau 50 F.F., Liqueurs 70 F.F.
Sales volume:
- Retail: 60%. - Restaurants: 20%. - Other: 20% (Cellars, delicatessens).
Sales in France: 45%.
Export sales: 55%.
Main trading partners : UK, Germany, USA, Switzerland, Canada.

References in France

Restaurants: Château Nieul.
Shops: Fauchon, Daloyau, Paris.

Abroad

United States

Importers: Langdon.

United Kingdom

Importers: Maison Lheraud. Shops: Harrods. Restaurants: Frères Roux.

Germany

Importers: Stahlhut. Shops: Dallmayr.

Canada

Importers: Vinette.

The Netherlands

Importers: ISPC.

Others

Importers: Le Cellier du Richemond, Switzerland.

WHERE TO GET YOUR BRANDY

• **Petrissans:** 30 bis, avenue Niel, 75017 Paris.
Tel: 42 27 83 84. Closed Sundays and Mondays.
This cellar, well known to Parisians, is a real family affair. Taste its Raspberry Brandy, Blackberry or Blackcurrant Liqueurs. Absolutely delicious!

• **L'Oenothèque:** 20, rue Saint-Lazare, 75009 Paris. Closed Sundays.
The ideal place for tasting excellent Cognacs direct from the producer.

• **L'Oenophile:** 30, boulevard Voltaire, 75011 Paris. Tel: 47 00 69 45. Closed Sunday afternoons and all day Monday.
Brandies selected by Michel Renaud. Particularly noteworthy are the old brandies, such as the wild raspberry or the 1936 Greengage Plum Brandy, as well as some superb Armagnacs.

• **Spécialités Antillaises (Jean et Brassac):** 16, boulevard de Belleville, 75020 Paris.
Tel: 43 58 31 30. Closed Mondays.
A huge variety of rhums from all over. For the "educated consumer": "le cœur de chauffe"—a West Indian specialty. Good selection of punches, syrups and exotic fruit juices.

• **Verger de la Madeleine:** 4, boulevard Malesherbes, 75008 Paris. Tel: 42 65 51 99. Closed Sundays.
The treasure cave of Ali Baba, alias Jacques Legras! One of the best collections in Paris, particularly for excellent vintage Ports. And you're sure to find there at least one "King" of alcohol from every country in the world.

• **King Henry:** 44, rue des Boulangers, 75004 Paris. Tel: 43 54 54 37. Closed Sundays. No less than 200 Whiskeys! But also an impressive selection of fruit brandies—cherry plum, raspberry, gentian, and a marvelous muscat made from hybrid plums.

• **Aux Caves Royales:** 6, rue Royale, 78000 Versailles. Tel: 49 50 14 10. Closed Mondays. Under the direction of the "Maistre-échanson" (Master Cupbearer) of France, Roger Després, the proprietor, you will choose from a selection of beautiful alcohols, perhaps an old Calvados or an Armagnac from 1893!

• **Jean-Baptiste Besse:** 48, rue de la Montagne Sainte Geneviève, 75005 Paris. Tel: 43 25 35 80. Closed Mondays.
A fine 16th century cellar. Incredible disorder, but you'll be greeted by a warm and fascinating character, Jean-Baptiste Besse. He will choose brandies for you from another age, or, if you prefer, a hundred year old Port.

• **Jean Danflou:** 36, rue du Mont-Thabor, 75001 Paris. Tel: 42 61 51 09. Closed Saturdays and Sundays.
A specialist in fruit brandies: Old Kirsch grande réserve, raspberry and pear brandies, Burgundy Marc, Cognacs and Armagnacs. Beautifully displayed, and you can taste before buying. Excellent selection.

• **François Clerch:** 18, rue de Poissy, 78100 Saint-Germain-en-Laye. Tel: 41 15 17 29. Closed Mondays.
Very good selection of Bas-Armagnac.

• **Cave Sainte-Avoye:** 10, rue Rambuteau, 75003 Paris. Tel: 42 72 99 78. Closed Sunday afternoons and all day Monday.
Specializing in Bas-Armagnac, vintage Burgundy Vieux Marcs, and Calvados.

• **Lucien Legrand:** 1, rue de la Banque, 75002 Paris. Tel: 42 60 07 12. Closed Sundays and Mondays.
Lucien Legrand is an engaging personality of great competence. His Armagnacs and Calvados are well worth trying, as well as his marvellous vintage Ports.

• **Comptoir du Chocolat et des Alcools:** 103, rue de Turenne, 75003 Paris. Tel: 42 60 07 12. Closed Sundays and Mondays. (Several other addresses in Paris its suburbs).
Interesting price/quality ratio, especially for whiskeys and Cognacs.

• **Mannevy:** 50, boulevard Richard Wallace, 92800 Puteaux. Tel: 45 06 07 75. Closed Sunday afternoons and all day Monday.
Extensive selection of vintage Armagnacs (some from 1893) and Burgundy Vieux Marcs, Champagne and fruit brandies, such as elderberry of bilberry.

• **La Cognathèque:** 10, place Jean Tlomet, 16100 Cognac. Tel: 45 82 43 31. Closed Mondays. The only place in Cognac offering an extensive and interesting selection, representative of the entire production. Very good selection, good advice, warm welcome.

• **Malleval:** 11, rue Emile Zola, 69002 Lyon. Tel: 78 42 02 07. Closed Mondays.
Fine Armagnacs and a superb collection of old Ports.

ARMAGNAC

Armagnac is a remote province, the scene of a love story between the rough and hospitable men of Gascony, and their soil, their vines, their stills and their great Armagnacs.

Making Armagnac is a passion! A passion for the land and for nature, because life is good in the land of the Gascons. You'll find no industry, no machines, no robots there. One lives according to the seasons, as did grandfather—and great grandfather.

Producers know how to put time on their side, how to cool down the ardor of young Armagnacs by putting them to rest for a number of years in oak casks in wine warehouses with hard-packed clay floors, neither too humid nor too dry.

Grandfather never placed the casks against the wall, because this causes the wines to lose alcohol and acquire less body than if they were left in the middle of the room. Too close to the ground isn't good either. The best Armagnacs come from casks placed higher up.

This is artisanship in the etymological sense of the term (arte: art), the artisan being above all an artist, a person who knows, who creates.

The great old Armagnacs have not adapted to the light asepticized cuisine now in fashion. Their powerful aroma and their Gascon temperament are in strict opposition. They are unique and their authenticity commands respect.

ARMAGNAC, AND WHERE TO FIND IT

Domaine de Jouanda
Bas Armagnac 1966
Domaine de Jouanda, M. de Poyferre,
40190 Artez-d'Armagnac,
Tel.: 58 45 21 41

Château de Maillac
Bas Armagnac "Folle Blance" 1966
Château de Malliac
32250 Montréal-du-Gers
Tel.: 62 28 44 87

Bas Armagnac Sempé 1968
Armagnacs Sempé,
32290 Aignan-en-Armagnac
Tel.: 62 09 24 24

Armagnac veuve Goudoulin 1959
Courrensan, 32330 Gondrin
Tel.: 62 06 35 02

Armagnac Castarède 1968
J. Nisme-Delclou
Pont de Bordes
47230 Lavardac
Tel.: 53 65 50 06

Château de Mariban, Bas Armagnac,
Mauléon d'Armagnac
32240 Estang
Tel.: 62 09 66 80

And for very old Armagnacs:
(1829-1838-1878-1893-1900)

Maison Dartigalongue
32110 Nogaro
Tel.: 62 09 03 01

S.A.H. DARTIGALONGUE & FILS
ARMAGNAC CROIX DE SALLES

32110 Nogaro
62 09 03 01 – Telex: 530 566

Type of vineyard: Corporation. **Established:** 1838. **Number of employees:** 11.
Appellation: Bas-Armagnac. **Technique:** Traditional. **Maturing:** Numerous years in oak casks 400 liters. **Vintages available in 89/90:** 1848, 1900, 1939, 1945, 1959, 1962, 1968.

Characteristics of vintages

A serious property (five generations of the same family) which proposes exceptional Armagnac.
Sales in France: 30%.
Export sales: 70%.

Abroad

United Kingdom, Germany, Canada, The Netherlands, Italy, Spain, Denmark, Sweden.

Comments

Very old Armagnac Collection: 1829-1848-1852-1878. In 1978, inauguration of the Musée of the House where the records are since 1838.

ARMAGNAC VVE GOUDOULIN

Christian Faure
32330 Courrensan, Bas-Armagnac
62 06 35 02 – Telex: 520 306 Goulin

Established: 1935. **Average annual production in hectoliters:** 1,000 hl. in stock.
Vintages available in 89/90: Traditional vintages plus 1964 and 1962 (excellent) in addition to 1953, 1948, 1942 and 1934 still ageing in casks, as well as small quantities of old vintages (various years). (1929-1914...)

Characteristics of vintages

Sales in France: 50%.
Export sales: 50%.
Main trading partners : Germany, Switzerland, Austria, Belgium, Netherlands, UK, USA.

References in France

Shops: Fauchon, Corcellet, Ducs de Gascogne Boutiques.

Abroad

United States
Importers: Tastevin Wines, California.

United Kingdom
Importers: May, London.

Germany
Importers: Segnitz Bremen.

The Netherlands
Importers: Bart Purmerend.

Others
Importers: (Switzerland) Reichmuth Zurich. (Austria) Gottardi Innsbruck.

ARMAGNAC LACAVE FRANCIS

Francis Lacave
Bretagne d'Armagnac, 32800 Eauze
62 09 90 09

Type of vineyard: Family-owned. **Established:** For over 40 years. **Number of employees:** 5-6 depending on the season of the year. **Average annual production in hectoliters:** 2,300.
Appellation: Armagnac and Floc de Gascogne. Vin de Pays des Côtes de Gascogne. **Serving temperature:** Armagnac (at room temperature), Floc (very cool). **Served with:** Armagnac as an after dinner drink – Floc (red and white) as an aperitif. Red: with melon, strawberries and in sauces. White: with foie grs. **Vintages available in 89/90.** Armagnac – 1983-1980-1975-1973-1962 and ofthers on demand. Floc: no vintages available.

Characteristics of vintages

Prices: Floc: 33.20 F.F/33.73 F.F. Armagnac (depending on the year): from 60.71 F.F. to 244.52 F.F. Vin de Pays des Côtes de Gascogne, white and red: 11.38 F.F., in cartons of 12.
Sales volume:
– Retail: 25%. – Restaurants: 25%. – Other: 50% (fairs, exhibitions, etc).
Sales in France: 100%.

References in France

Restaurants: A Gascon Restaurant in Paris.

CALVADOS

ONCE MORE ON THE MARCH

Quite surprisingly, Calvados, that pure product of Normandy, has a Spanish name. After the wreck on the Norman coast, in 1583, of a ship of the invincible Armada, El Calvador, the locality was given the name of Calvados. This name was later to be given to the entire department by the Constituent Assembly. It was only in the 19th century that the name was applied to the brandy made from cider.

It must, however, be recalled that the Gauls of the Western regions used to ferment wild apples to make a kind of beverage which they later distilled in a rather rudimentary way. The Calvados appellation itself dates from the middle of the 16th century and is associated with Gilles de Gouberville, who is considered as one of the first agronomists.

THE FRUIT OF THE ORCHARD

The entire orchard consists of approximately 15,000,000 apple trees, with a 15 year average yield. Harvesting is done over a period of three months, starting in October. Cider making is the first step in the preparation of Calvados.

Yet, in order to be distilled, after a natural fermentation of at least one month, the cider must present a certain number of characteristics: it must be at least 40% alcohol, with a volatile acidity lower than 2.5 parts per 1,000, no sugar should have been added and it should be suitable for drinking as is.

THE IMPORTANCE OF THE SOIL

The question of appellations and quality is always a matter of controversy. Yet, this is, for the consumer, an indispensable criterion for selection. The geographical allocation of appellations and the different techniques used are defined by the law of January 1941. The first appellation, the "Appellation Pays d'Auge contrôlée," strictly corresponds to the Pays d'Auge. All the apples must be grown and harvested in that region. Moreover, the preparation of Calvados involves a double distillation. The "petites eaux" (light alcohol content of 25%) are extracted from the cider during a first distillation cycle and then distilled a second time. The second appellation, "Appellation Calvados réglementée," applies to six delimited wine areas: Cotentin, Mortainais, Calvados, Avranchin, Dufrontais (in the Orne valley), Pays de Risle, Perche, and Pays de Bray. Establishing a hierarchy among these six appellations is no easy matter. Unfortunately they do not often compare with the Appellation Pays d'Auge Contrôlée as far as quality is concerned. The price, of course, is correspondingly lower. It should be kept in mind that the very basis of Calvados production is continuous column distillation.

TASTING A CALVADOS: A DIFFERENT EXPERIENCE

Calvados is unquestionably, one of the brandies with the strongest personality. Except for a small number of white brandies, few of the well known spirits more closely reflect the aroma of the fruit from which they are made. This is particularly true, of course, of old Calvados, so it is wise to check the labels carefully. **Trois étoiles or Trois pommes:** a Calvados or a brandy aged in the cask for at least a year (minimum required for commercialization). It is then in its second year. They are not for those who like fruity, fragrant and colorful spirits. The same for the **Vieux** or **Réserve** which are two years old and are still, in my opinion, not ready. Three to four years old **V.O..** . . . or **Vieille Réserve**, as well as four to five years old cask-aged **V.S.O.P..** . . . are beginning to be ready to be appreciated, depending on the producer. But it is only after six years of ageing in the cask that Calvados really comes into its own and can qualify for the **hors âge** or **extra** category. However, prices then become a deterrent and do not permit regular consumption. You can always hope to fall on a Norman proprietor, distilling for his own consumption and ready to let you have one of his old bottles.

A PRODUCT NOT YET FULLY EXPLOITED

Young Calvados and even older categories are not exploited to the extent that they might be. A number of aperitifs, (Pommeau for one) cocktails or sherbets can be made with Calvados.

There are also a number of recipes prepared with Calvados such as "truite normande" (Normandy trout) "poulet Vallée d'Auge" (chicken, style Vallée d'Auge) or snails in Calvados sauce, absolutely delicious according to connoisseurs.

A BRILLIANT FUTURE AHEAD

In France, the general pattern of Calvados consumption is changing rapidly. Only a few years ago, sales of low quality Calvados were far ahead of the others. Even today, more than half of the Calvados is sold young, so that it does not have a chance to acquire the reputation of a quality product. The market seems, however, to be developing in favor of a more important consumption of Calvados A.O.C. (35% of the market) with Calvados réglementé retaining only 65%. At the same time, figures seem to indicate an increase in the sales of **Vieux Calvados** (approximately 30% of total sales). One would be pleased indeed to see this trend confirmed in restaurants which, at present, offer only a meager stock of old Calvados.

THE NEED TO EXPORT

Export figures remain relatively low (between 10 to 20% of total sales). They will have to increase to help meet the cost of production of Vieux Calvados. Cask ageing is an expensive process which cannot be done at affordable prices if consumption is limited to the local market.

THE ROLE OF THE CALVADOS LOVER

While it is the producer's responsability to produce quality Calvados, it is up to the real lover of Calvados to control market prices. Like other spirits, Calvados should be tasted in a particular way, and perhaps even in a more special context. Calvados is undeniably one of Normandy's most important resources. Still inadequately exploited, it has, because of its orginality, a brilliant future. A good Calvados can only be found in Normandy. The region would do well to realize it.

EVERYTHING THERE IS TO KNOW ABOUT WINE

The Chemistry of Wine

Did you know that the favorite drink of the French is also one of the most extraordinary foods that has ever existed? Red wine and white wine are both liquids composed of water (800-950 grams per liter) containing, either when dissolved or in suspension, most of the major organic substances the human body needs. Phosphates and lipids are found along with vitamins, glucides and ethers, making this fermented product (known long before the fermentation of bread or cheese) an elixir that gives long life and helps regulate our body functions. That is, provided it is consumed in moderation rather than indiscriminately or to excess.

Wine is a most unusual nectar which for centuries has enjoyed the luxury of possessing its own language. It is an international vocabulary of chemistry terms, poetic words, colors, aromas and a host of adjectives. True wine lovers know wine deserves the same respect as other great creations.

The main component of wine is ethyl alcohol (C_2H_5OH), which is formed during fermentation. We will also discover the organic mineral substances and mixtures that accompany it.

THE NATURE OF WINE

— **Glucides.** The glucose and levulose in the grape juice disappear during fermentation. A very well made wine should not contain traces of reducing sugar. However, certain very rich and sweet white wines, Sauternes, for example, contain a considerable quantity. The sugar is retained as glycogen in the liver where it is transformed into glucose, in which form it serves, little by little, the needs of the organism. Burned in the tissues and muscles, it serves in the production of animal heat and, above all, to produce the energy necessary for muscular effort.

— **Aldehydes** (acetic, vinic and ethyl).

— **Acids.** There are two kinds: volatile acids and fixed acids. Among the volatile acids, the most important are acetic acid and butic acid. The fixed acids are tartric, succinic. . . and the color of the wines depend on their acidity, both quantitatively and qualitatively. Because of their bactericidal action, the acids stimulate the smooth muscles of the stomach, increasing their tonicity and contractibility. Added to the naturel acidity of the stomach chyme, they accelerate the digestion of starchy and albuminoid substances. The tannin—or tannic acid—acts above all as an astringent; it excites the smooth fibers and, by provoking regular energetic contractions of the stomach, helps with the mixing and breakdown of the stomach content.

— Lipids consist of fatty materials such as glycerides and lipoids.

— **Protides:** mature grape juice contains nitrogen.

— **Ethers.** They are, for the most part, formed by the combination of fatty acids with ethyl alcohol. While the total acidity of ripe grape juice is equivalent to 7 to 9 grams of sulfuric acid per liter, it decreases to 4.5 to 5 grams as the juice is transformed into wine. With time, this acidity decreases even further (3 to 4 grams in the red Bordeaux).

— **Phosphates.** Kept in solution by the acids, calcium and magnesium phosphates are found in wine.

— **Sulfates** (of calcium, magnesium and potassium).

— **Sulfurous acid.** It is found in wine because it is necessary to add sulfur dioxide.

Not to be forgotten are oxygen, which acts slowly on the tannins, carbon dioxide, vitamins and the radioactivity, discovered in wine in 1896 by Henri Becquerel. . . .

THE LANGUAGE OF WINE

— **Acescence:** A disease produced by bacteria. It makes the wine acid.

— **Aggressivity:** It is due to an excess of acidity or tannin and is perceived as a "tingling" of the taste buds.

— **Alcohol:** The natural sugar of the grape juice is transformed into alcohol during fermentation.

— **Allaceous:** Refers to a strong odor of garlic resulting from a combination of an excess of sulfur dioxide and alcohol. Sometimes referred to as an odor of mercaptan.

— **Amber-colored:** Not to be confused with "maderized".

— **Beeswing:** Can be found in suspension in clear wines in the form of deposits made up of clumps of yeast, tartar crystals or cork debris. An incompetent sommelier once swore to us that these deposits (at the bottom of a glass) were traces of sugar.

— **Bentonite:** Clay which converts dissolved proteins into a flocculent precipitate. It often provides an excellent method of keeping track of fining operations.

— **Blending:** Method consisting of mixing different wines coming from different vats or, even, different years, in order to obtain a more homogeneous product.

— **Blue casse:** Mostly in white or rosé wine, it is prevented by the use of potassium ferrocyanide. A wine containing more than 10 mg of iron per liter is in danger of developing blue casse.

— **Body:** Consistency.

— **Bouquet:** Olfactive sensation produced by the flower and fruit aromas given off by the wine. The primary bouquet (aroma) is that of the fruit. The secondary bouquet is due to the action of the yeast during fermentation. The tertiary bouquet develops as a result of contact with air during ageing in the cask and blossoms out (without further contact with the air) during subsequent ageing in the bottle.

— **Carbonic maceration:** Winemaking method in which the bunches are not crushed. Fermentation thus takes place inside the skin of the grape. It produces fragrant wines than can be drunk young.

— **Cask:** Its capacity varies from 225 to 232 liters according to the winegrowing region.

— **Chaptalization (addition of sugar):** Named after Chaptal. Addition of sugary substances (concentrated must, cane or beet sugar) to the must when it is not sufficiently rich, in order to improve the quality of the wine. Often employed illegally where it is not allowed (Beaujolais, Burgundy), it is unfortunate that it is not authorized in all regions.

— **"Charpenté":** Said of a wine that keeps well, combining richness in alcohol and harmony between the elements that enter into its composition.

— **Color:** Comes from the colored material in the grapes, dissolved during alcoholic fermentation.

— **Corky:** Very characteristic odor and taste due either to parasites which live in the bark of the cork-oak or to mildew of the cork. If the taste is not too pronounced, it may disappear after a good aeration of the wine.

— **Crown-cork or seal:** Made of wax, lead or aluminum, it guarantees the authenticity of the wine and protects it against parasites which sometimes lay their eggs in corks.

— **Cru:** Indicates the place where the vine grows.

— **Crystal-clear:** Brilliant and entirely transparent wine.

— **Decanting:** Too often used unnecessarily, decanting consists in transferring the wine from its bottle to a carafe in order to separate it from its tannin deposits and to let it "BREATHE". It is really only necessary for defective wines or for very old vintages (fifty to sixty years), and should be done just before tasting.

— **Destemming:** Separation of the grapes from the stems, either by hand or by mechanical crusher. It tends to diminish the tannic astringence of the must, producing more supple wines with a higher alcohol content.

— **Diseases of the vine:** Caused by insects (phylloxera, cochylis, red spider) or molds (mildew, black-rot, oidium), prevented by treatment with copper sulfate or dusting with flowers of sulfur.

— **Esters:** Volatile substances in the bouquet produced by the action of acids on alcohols.

— **Fat:** Fleshy, soft and supple.

— **Fermentation:** Operation by which the must is transformed into wine.

— **Filtration:** Generally used as part of the fining operation to assure the limpidity of the wine by removing the ferments and deposits.

— **Fining:** Operation which consists of clarifying the wine by adding protein (egg whites, gelatin, fish glue...) to the tannin.

— **Firm:** Full-bodied and vigorous.

— **Fixed acidity:** All of the fixed acids (see "The composition of wine"), both organic and mineral. It is arrived at by calculating the difference between the total acidity and the volatile acidity.

— **Flabby:** Said of wine that is not sufficiently acid.

— **Flat:** Results from the wine being in contact with air, in particular, after bottling. It is sometimes called "bottle sickness".

— **Fresh:** Said of a wine that has a good harmony between acidity and alcohol, particularly applied to whites and rosés.

— **Fruity:** When the young wine has the aroma and the taste of the grape: wild strawberry, muscat, raspberry, violet. . . .

— **Glycerin:** Component of wine responsible for its unctuousity. It appears at the time of alcoholic fermentation but, in soft, sweet wines, also comes from the favorable action of noble rot on the grapes. See Sauternes.

— **Green:** Wine resulting from an immature harvest.

— **Hard:** When the wine is too tannic or too acid.

— **Harshness or astringence:** When the wine has a rough taste produced by an excess of tannin, it is often a sign of good ageing potential for red wines.

— **Heady:** Wine rich in alcohol. If it is badly made, watch out for headaches.

— **Lees:** Deposit in wine in casks that is eliminated by racking.

— **Maderized:** Wine (particularly white and rosé) that is a bit oxidized, whose taste of "Madeira" is very characteristic. Certain vinestocks, notably Clairette, are often responsible.

— **Marc:** Residue of the pressed grapes. Often used to produce famous brandies by distillation.

— **Must:** Unfermented grape juice.

— **Oenologist:** Specialist in wine and winemaking.

— **Oenophilist:** Ardent lover of the "divine bottle". We are to be counted among them.

— **Onion peel:** Pink tint with a slight golden glint, comparable to the skin of certain onions. It is not a wine brand name—watch out for misleading labels.

— **Oxidasic casse:** Produces a thin film at the surface of the wine and causes the precipitation of coloring agents. It is caused by the oxidase normally present in the grapes which develops rapidly in wines produced from crops contaminated by grey (Botrytis) rot. It is prevented by adding sulfur dioxide or by heating the wine to 65°C.

— **Pale wine (clairet):** Very light colored red wine, but not rosé.

— **"Paulée":** Traditional dinner for œnophilists and winemakers after the harvest, particularly in Burgundy.

— **Phylloxera:** Plant louse that destroyed the French vinestocks at the end of the last century.

— **Piquette:** Product resulting from the addition of water to the must which, after having been removed from the press, is put back into the vat.

— **Primeur:** Freshly made wine, often pleasant to drink and (normally) authorized to be distributed towards the month of December (November for Beaujolais).

— **Racking:** Operation which consists of separating the lees from the wine.

— **Robust:** Used for a wine with a good, fleshy structure.

— **Ruby:** Beautiful bright red color.

— **"Séveux":** Term used for a solid wine, full-blown, thanks to its aromas and its richness in alcohol.

— **Sound:** Clean, natural.

— **Sterilization of the must:** Operation which consists of stopping the fermentation of the must by introducing ethyl alcohol. The natural sweet wines (Roussillon...), for example, receive almost pure (90%) alcohol.

— **Sulfur dioxide (SO_2):** Antiseptic used in winecellars at bottling time. Its use—quite proper—prevents the oxidation of the wine and a possible resumption of fermentation in the bottle.

— **Tannin:** Group of organic products that come essentially from the skin and the seeds of the grape. Its importance varies according to the grape variety and the vinification technique.

— **Total acidity:** All of the free acids in the wine.

— **Troubled:** Said of a wine that has been badly fermented or attacked by a microbial disease.

— **"Tuilé":** Term applied to oxidized red wine.

— **Veraison:** Condition of the bunch of grapes at the beginning of maturity.

— **"Viné":** Sweet wine which, as a result of dosing with alcohol, conserves some of the sugar from the must (see Sterilization).

— **Volatile acidity:** All of the fatty acids.

Wine and Foods

Naturally there is a wine for every dish. But general statements like fish deserves a white wine and a Burgundy must be served with game run counter to the philosophy of wine. Any given dish can be served with several wines and vice versa. What happens afterwards, including choice of colors, is a matter of taste.

Foods

Hors-d'œuvre, salads (without salad dressing), *crudités* (dishes of raw vegetables), pâtés, mussels, herring, mackerel, sardines, seafood and shellfish.

Accompanying Dry White Wines

Gros Plant: from the area of Nantes in the Loire. Light. Perfect aroma and taste. Excellent with shellfish.

Muscadet: from the Loire. Fruity and refreshing. *Muscadet de Sèvre-et-Maine* wines have even more bouquet.

Pouilly Fumé: also from the area of Nantes in the Loire. A special taste, lively and fragrant; smoked aromas and the smell of flint.

Sancerre: lively, well-balanced. Subtle fruitiness and a pale yellow color are characteristics of this superb wine from the region of Berry.

Savennières: a superb wine from the region of Anjou. Elegant and subtle at the same time. The best Savennières is *Coulée de Serrant*, which can be kept for many, many years.

Vouvray: a wine from Touraine. Pleasant and fragrant.

Entre-Deux-Mers: a white Bordeaux. A fresh, fruity wine. From vineyards located between the Dordogne and Garonne rivers.

Gaillac: from the Southwest. Light in body and style. Its bouquet is the result of blending with the Mauzac grape variety.

Jurançon: another Southwest wine. Fragrant, lively, with a character of its own. It can be served as a light wine to accompany foie gras.

Pacherenc de Vic Bihl: another fruity wine from the Southwest where Sauvignon is the main grape variety. Wise money goes on this wine.

Crozes-Hermitage: the Marsanne grape variety boosts this Côtes du Rhône appellation wine which has good bouquet.

Lirac: from the famed Côtes du Rhône winegrowing region. Flowery, pure and natural.

Chablis: synonymous with very great vintage wines. But there are also more common Chablis that are pleasant to drink. Truly great Chablis wines like *Blanchots* and *Les Clos* have remarkable liveliness and fragrance.

Condrieu: made from Viognier grapes. An unusual wine with a fruity fragrance.

Mercurey Blanc: from the Côte Chalonnaise area. An exquisitely fruity wine with a strong flowery scent.

Puligny-Montrachet and **Chassagne-Montrachet:** great vintages from the Côte de Beaune. Wines with intense bouquet and full taste.

Saint-Véran: from the Mâconnais region. Not as good as *Pouilly-Fuissé* but nonetheless light and delicate.

Gewurztraminer: one of the best known Alsatian wines. Fine, supple, with good body. Remarkably well-balanced and fruity.

Pinot Blanc or **Klevner:** another Alsatian wine. Supple and fragrant.

Riesling: the most characteristic Alsatian wine. Fragrant, vigorous and subtle. The choice wine to accompany shellfish.

Sylvaner: pleasant to drink. Dry, light, with bouquet.

Pinot Gris (also called **Tokay d'Alsace**): full-bodied. The French describe it as "a wine with breeding".

Crépy Wines: from the Thonon-les-Bains and Geneva regions of the Savoie wine country. Mostly Chasselas vintages that are cool and fruity.

Foods

Hors-d'œuvre, fresh vegetable salads, vegetable soufflés, quiches, dishes with sauce, white meats and shellfish.

Accompanying Rosé Wines

Cabernet: from Anjou. The scent of raspberries and violets. Light and natural.

Clairet: a Bordeaux wine. Very pale red in color. Light and very fragrant.

Rosés from Provence: the best known rosé wines, especially those from Bandol. Fine, supple, with bouquet.

Tavel: a blend of several varieties of grapes. The result is a great Côtes du Rhône rosé.

Marsannay: produced in the Mâconnais region. This Burgundy wine made from Pinot Noir grapes has a delicate bouquet.

Rosés from the Jura: among the best, they are elegant and pleasant to drink.

Foods

Pâtés, cold cuts, grilled red meats, white meats, poultry, lightly-cooked game and soft cheeses.

Accompanying Light Red Wines

Anjou Rouge: made from Cabernet grapes. Full-bodied and fruity.

Sancerre Rouge: made from the Pinot Noir grape variety. The result is good tannin and pleasant fruitiness for this wine from the region of Nantes in the Loire.

Saumur-Champigny: from Anjou. Good body, with a pleasant scent of violets.

Cahors: made principally from the Malbec and Merlot grape varieties. A fruity yet strong wine.

Corbières: from Languedoc. Supple, fruity and structured.

Côtes de Bourg: full-bodied, distinctive, supple.

Gaillac: from the Southwest. As a red wine it is pleasant, fine and has good body.

Madiran: of all the wines from the Southwest, probably the most vigorous and most consistent. Balanced and full-bodied.

Premières Côtes de Bordeaux: a rich fragrance. Strong and supple at the same time.

Tursan: from the Southwest. Firm and fruity.

Cornas: a wine with character. A Côtes du Rhône with bouquet.

Côtes du Rhône: supple, fruity and full-bodied.

Lirac: from the Côtes du Rhône. Full-bodied and fragrant.

Saint-Joseph: also from the Côtes du Rhône. Made from the Syrah grape variety. With age, this wine develops the fragrance of blackcurrant.

Beaujolais-Villages: made from Gamey Noir grapes. A robust, supple wine.

Brouilly: a Beaujolais cru. Light and fruity.

Chiroubles: also from the Beaujolais region. Fruity.

Côte de Beaune: a pleasant, fruity Burgundy wine.

Côte de Nuits: a Burgundy wine that is supple to the taste.

Givry: a robust Burgundy made from Pinot Noir grapes.

Marsannay: a light, fruity wine from the Mâconnais region. Made from Pinot Noir grapes.

Mercurey: the consistent full-body of Burgundy wines. The aroma of red berries.

Morgon: a robust Beaujolais that ages well.

Nuits-Saint-Georges: from the Côte d'Or. Vigorous and with bouquet.

Rully: from the Côte Chalonnaise. A warm, vigorous wine with a generous taste.

Foods

Red meats in sauce, beef bourguignon, liver, large game and firm cheeses.

Accompanying Full-bodied Red Wines

Fronsac: from the hills near the town of Libourne. Fruity, supple and pleasantly structured.

Graves: from south of the Médoc. Balanced tannin, bouquet. Full-bodied but well balanced.

Lalande-de-Pomerol: from near the town of Libourne. Mostly made from the Merlot grape variety. Tannic, full-bodied, with bouquet.

Listrac: among the hardest of Médoc wines, but with bouquet and generous taste.

Margaux: one of the great Bordeaux wines. Sharply tannic, elegant and full-bodied.

Médoc: tannic therefore should be set aside to age. Fruity, velvety. Made from Cabernet Sauvignon and Merlot grapes.

Moulis: made from Cabernet, Merlot and Petit Verdot grapes. A soft, aromatic wine.

Pauillac: a great wine from the Médoc. Vigorous, full-bodied and rich.

Pomerol: a superb wine of great class. Elegant and velvety.

Saint-Émilion: the pride of the Bordeaux wine region. Full-bodied, supple in taste. The fragrance of red berries and the scent of undergrowth.

Saint-Estèphe: from the commune of Saint-Estèphe in the Médoc. Tannic and full-bodied. Great *sève.*

Châteauneuf-du-Pape: deep purple in color. Exquisitely aromatic, well balanced and full-bodied.

Côte-Rôtie: a Côtes du Rhône. Mostly made from the Syrah grape variety but also from Viogniers grapes which provide a good tannic balance and excellent fruitiness.

Crozes-Hermitage: from the Côtes du Rhône. Made exclusively from the Syrah grape variety. Fruity. Not as hard as Hermitage wines.

Gigondas: from the mountains in the Côtes du Rhône. Made from several grape varieties including Grenache Noir, Syrah, Mourvèdre, and Cinsault. This blending makes Gigondas wine strong, astringent and vigorous, yet infinitely elegant.

Hermitage: a blend of the Syrah, Roussane and Marsanne grape varieties give this wine from the Côtes du Rhône a very strong color. A tannic, fragrant wine that can be sumptuous.

Aloxe-Corton: a fine wine with a long-lasting fragrance.

Chambolle-Musigny: probably the fruitiest, most vigorous and most delicate wine of Burgundy.

Chassagne-Montrachet: from the Côte de Beaune. Full-bodied taste, soft and supple.

Clos-de-Vougeot: another Burgundy wine from the Côte de Nuits. All the qualities of Vougeot and a delicate fragrance make it totally unique.

Gevrey-Chambertin: another wine from the Côte de Nuits. Firm, with the aroma of red berries. A taste that lingers pleasantly.

Pommard: from the Côte de Beaune. It has bouquet, and is concentrated and supple.

Puligny-Montrachet: also from the Côte de Beaune. The same characteristics as *Chassagne-Montrachet*, but even more fragrant.

Santenay: from the Côte de Beaune. Refined, very round and with good body.

Volnay: another superb wine from the Côte de Beaune. Delicate. A rainbow of aromas.

Vosne-Romanée: one of the best known wines from the Côte de Nuits. Perfectly balanced; among the most fragrant of Burgundy wines. Of incomparable finesse.

Foods

Fresh fruit pies, fruit, blue cheeses, pâtés and *foie gras.*

Accompanying Sweet White Wines

Bonnezeaux: from Anjou. Round, soft and supple, a blend of many fragrances.

Coteaux du Layon: also from Anjou. Delicately fruity and soft.

Quarts-de-Chaume: the most delicately fragrant dessert wines from Anjou.

Loupiac: a Bordeaux wine. Sweet and fruity.

Sauternes: the best known dessert wine. Justifiably so—it is aromatic, elegant and has personality. It may be kept for many, many years and still remains full-bodied.

Last But Far From Least

Auxey-Duresses: a Burgundy wine. Soft, subtle, fragrant. Similar to *Meursault.* A dry wine.

Meursault: better known within Burgundy itself. An aromatic, full-bodied, perfectly balanced wine. A dry wine but rich and full enough to accompany cheeses and foie gras.

Buying Wines *en Primeur*

Buying wines *en primeur*, that is, shortly after the grapes have been harvested, is a new thing. Until recently this type of purchase arrangement was restricted to people in the wine business but now it is commonly available for consumers who are knowledgeable about wines and who, according to their financial means and expertise, may select the vintage of their choice before the wine is even bottled.

But what exactly is buying wine en primeur and what are the rules of the game? The quality of a new year is a subjective issue; whether a harvest will be a good one or a bad one can be determined very early—as early as a few months after the grapes have been picked. The availability of some years, though, is dropping rapidly because there is a growing demand for great wines, especially from foreign buyers who appreciate the French winegrowing heritage and who are from countries that have strong currencies.

The law of supply and demand inevitably has an immediate effect on wine prices. For the consumer, buying wines en primeur is protection against subsequent price hikes which may come into effect from the moment the wine leaves the countryside. It is also an assurance that some quantities of wine which otherwise would be sold out as soon as they are put on the market are still available.

Investments of any king generate speculation. To an extent, therefore, en primeur wine purchases can be considered speculative. One golden rule for minimizing risk is to buy good years and have them cared for by professionals whose reputation is beyond reproach. Between the buyer and the seller there is a real contract, which the buyer signs as much as two years before delivery of the wines ordered. This is why it is absolutely necessary that the supplier's reputation be irreproachable.

For the 1982 wine year there was an explosion of speculative transactions. People with ownership certificates for 1982 wines will of course have a good return on their investment; these wines are assured a fabulous future. 1983 wine is expected to follow the same trend since it was an equally good year. The procedure is easy; the problem is making a choice. That is where advice and "miracles" come into the picture because for good years, less highly rated vintages may turn out to be good bets. Whenever there is any doubt about the exact quality of a year, selection should be based on buying the best (top quality and good quality). Even an average year may become remarkable, so its wines, when purchased en primeur, should be more affordable.

THE PROCEDURE

Buying wines "en primeur" means buying "futures" that are still in casks and that are delivered only once they are bottled on the winery property itself, that is, at the estate or "château." Château bottling is mandatory for Bordeaux *crus classés*—officially designated crus. The wines are delivered 18 months later.

FOUR GOLDEN RULES

1. Don't try to speculate, simply buy wines at reasonable prices.
2. Buy only from winehouses whose seriousness is recognized and whose reputation is proven.
3. Never buy mediocre or average years.
4. Buy only great vintages (or vintages from small wine-producing regions).

A FEW ADDRESSES FOR BUYING WINES EN PRIMEUR

M. Duclot
3-21, rue Macau, BP 79
33027 Bordeaux Cedex
France

Bordeaux Millésimés
42, rue de Rivière, BP 23
33029 Bordeaux
France

M. Delestrée
14, quai Jean-Fleuret, BP 66
33250 Pauillac
France

A SUCCINCT WINE CALENDAR

September-October 1987: harvesting.
June-July 1988: 1987 primeur wines go on sale.
January-February 1989: delivery.

French sales tax (T.V.A.) of 18.6% and freight charges are generally billed at the time of delivery.

THE BEST BETS

Over the last fourteen years (1970-1983), there have been three exceptional years—1970, 1975 and 1982. The wine year 1982 is probably the greatest year since 1961. Six remarkable years are 1971, 1976, 1978, 1979, 1981 and 1983. Two good years are 1973 and 1974. Four average years are 1972, 1977, 1980 and 1984.

Price trends clearly show that 1972, 1977 and 1980 were not good years to buy en primeur. 1973 and 1974 were good bets and 1971, 1976, 1978, 1979 and 1981 were sure bets. 1983 was definitely a year to buy. It was a cardinal sin to let 1970, 1975 or 1982 slip by.

Organizing a Wine Cellar

A wine cellar is very important for those of us who are wine lovers. It can be the poetic refuge we share with close friends. It can also be a room for storing ordinary wines as well as vintage wines that will have a peaceful place in which to age. But to acquire this kind of material "art de vivre," you will have to conform to a number of rules.

— **Darkness**: Rule No. 1: Your wine cellar must be dark. There should be no openings that allow bright, artificial light or daylight to filter through. Better wine cellars are visited candle-in-hand, or, in a more practical vein, with a flashlight.

— **Temperature**: Ideally, the range is from 50°F (10°C) to 53.6°F (12°C) but in any case there should be no sharp variations in temperature. Be careful of heating and hot water pipes, especially if you make a wine cellar in your apartment. If need be, insulate the pipes with fiberglass. Below 48.2°F (9°C), aging slows down and little by little the aromas of wine may be hidden as a result of the formation of sediment. Above 57.2°F (14°C), wine matures more rapidly as a result of the action of yeasts and bacteria.

— **Humidity**: A cellar should be neither too dry nor too humid. The humidity level should be around 70%. Wines are living substances, and, like us, they need a pure, aerated environment—but no drafts!

— **Tranquility**: Whatever you do, don't move your bottles every six months and watch out for vibrations that are so common, especially in cities (the subway passing underground, drilling in the street, etc.). Sand or gravel lining the floor will help absorb such vibrations.

A cellar should also be clean and tidy. Remove all cobwebs and any old tools which may be lying around. If you bottle your own wine, be sure to thoroughly clean both the bottles and the funnel you use.

Unnecessary odors

Please don't store fermenting cheeses in your cellar, or cans of gasoline you are preciously keeping in case there is another oil crisis. Your wine cellar should contain only wines and alcohols.

What you will need

- A thermometer and a hydrometer used to check the temperature and humidity in your cellar.
- A cellar book, which is a (confidential) register of your purchases of wine, price paid, date purchased and name of winegrower. A cellar book is very useful when you decide to replace certain bottles.

• If you prefer to bottle your own wines you will need the longest, best-quality corks you can find. You can of course use old bottles (but not old corks) provided they are cleaned throughly and allowed to dry on a porcupine roller. You will also need a funnel (cubitainers do not always have a pour spout), and, most important of all, a hand-operated corking machine. A corking machine is much more practical than a bat or a hammer for forcing the cork into the neck of the bottle. And don't forget to ask your wine dealer to send you the appropriate labels.

• If your pocketbook and your taste permit you might consider a wine cabinet, which will insure a constant temperature and a proper level of humidity. Wine cabinets lack heart and soul, but they are nonetheless practical.

Labeling

MANDATORY LABELING REQUIRED FOR A.O.C. AND V.D.Q.S. WINES

- Name of the particular region where the wine has been produced (Corbières, Bordeaux, etc.).
- The labeling A.O.C.—Appellation d'Origine Contrôlée (controlled appellation of origin)—or V.D.Q.S.—Vin Délimité de Qualité Supérieure (wines guaranteed to be of superior quality). All V.D.Q.S. wines have been stringently checked and carry an inspection number.
- Name and address of the bottler.
- Fluid content (75 cl, 37.5 cl, etc.).

Optional, approved labeling indications include:

- Name and address of the proprietor (winegrower, cooperative, etc.).
- The *château*, *clos* or *domaine* which has produced and bottled the wine.
- The year. Serious proprietors never fail to mention it.
- Information on the unique features of the wine (*primeur*, *cru classé*, including those classified in 1855).
- The mention "Product of France" or "France," which is mandatory if the wine is intended for export.

DECEPTIVE LABELING

- The indication "Bottled in the 'Region' of Production". This often means that the wine is a blend of wines from several producers rather than from a single producer.
- Indications such as "Great Wine," "Personally Selected," "Personal Stock," "noble grapes/variety of vine," and "cask aged" (some wines are cask aged for no more than one week).
- You will also need to pay special attention to the awards and other medals attributed to some wines at fairs. They should stand up to the wine in the bottle. For instance, on a bottle of 1980 wine, you may find mention or a picture of a medal awarded to the producer for their 1976 or 1978 wine. So, the wine you are buying is not the one that received the award. Often there is just a thin line between truth and deception.

LABELING TO AVOID

The indication "Wine from the countries of the Economic Community" is clearly intended to define a red, white or rosé wine from different regions or countries. You will be doing the French wine industry a great service if you simply refuse to purchase such wines sold by mega-winehouses for the sole purpose of promoting non-French wines.

The Appellations

From simple local wines to the finest Grand Cru Classé, here is a list of all the appellations of French wines.

APPELLATIONS D'ORIGINE CONTRÔLÉES

(A.O.C.)

R: **red wine (rouge),** ***r:*** **rosé,** ***W:*** **white wine (blanc),** ***g:*** **vin gris,**
j: **vin jaune,** ***p:*** **vin de paille**

Regions - Appellations	Color		
ALSACE			
Alsace or Vin d'Alsace	R	r	W
Alsace or Vin d'Alsace followed by:			
Gewurztraminer			W
Riesling			W
Pinot gris or Tokay d'Alsace			W
Muscat			W
Pinot or Klevner			W
Sylvaner			W
Chasselas or Gutedel			W
Pinot noir	R		
Vins d'Alsace Edelzwicker			W
Alsace Grand Cru			W
Alsace Grand Cru followed by the name of the locality			W
Crémant d'Alsace		r	W
BORDELAIS			
Barsac			W
Blaye or Blayais	R		W
Bordeaux	R		W
Bordeaux Clairet		r	
Bordeaux-Côtes de Castillon	R		
Bordeaux-Côtes de Francs	R		W
Bordeaux-Haut-Benauge			W
Bordeaux Mousseux		r	W
Bordeaux Rosé		r	
Bordeaux Supérieur	R		W
Bordeaux Supérieur clairet		r	
Bordeaux Supérieur-Côtes de Castillon	R		
Bordeaux Supérieur rosé		r	

Bourg ou Bourgeais	R		W
Cadillac			W
Cérons			W
Côtes-de-Canon-Fronsac ou Canon-Fronsac	R		
Côtes-de-Bourg	R		W
Côtes-de-Blaye			W
Côtes-de-Bordeaux-Saint-Macaire			W
Entre-Deux-Mers			W
Entre-Deux-Mers-Haut-Benauge			W
Fronsac	R		
Graves	R		W
Graves Supérieurs			W
Graves de Vayres	R		W
Haut-Médoc	R		
Lalande-de-Pomerol	R		
Listrac	R		
Loupiac			W
Lussac-Saint-Émilion	R		
Margaux	R		
Médoc	R		
Montagne-Saint-Émilion	R		
Moulis ou Moulis-Médoc	R		
Nérac	R		
Parsac-Saint-Émilion	R		
Pauillac	R		
Pomerol	R		
Premières-Côtes-de-Blaye	R		W
Premières-Côtes-de-Bordeaux	R		W
Premières-Côtes-de-Bordeaux. *See localities or crus*	R		
Puisseguin-Saint-Émilion	R		
Sainte-Croix-du-Mont			W
Saint-Émilion Grand Cru	R		
Saint-Émilion Grand Cru Classé	R		
Saint-Émilion Premier Grand Cru Classé	R		
Saint-Estèphe	R		
Sainte-Foy-Bordeaux	R		W
Saint-Georges-Saint-Émilion	R		
Saint-Julien	R		
Sauternes			W

BOURGOGNE

Aloxe-Corton	R		W
Auxey-Duresses	R		W
Bâtard-Montrachet			W
Beaujolais	R	r	W
Beaujolais. *See localities or crus which have the right to add their names to that of the appellation d'origine.*			
Beaujolais Supérieur	R	r	W
Beaujolais-Villages	R	r	W
Beaune	R		W
Bienvenues-Bâtard-Montrachet			W
Blagny	R		
Bonnes-Mares	R		
Bourgogne	R		W
Bourgogne Aligoté			W

Bourgogne Clairet		r	
Bourgogne Clairet-Hautes-Côtes-de-Beaune		r	
Bourgogne Clairet-Hautes-Côtes-de-Nuits		r	
Bourgogne Clairet-Marsannay		r	
Bourgogne Grand Ordinaire	R		W
Bourgogne Grand Ordinaire Clairet		r	
Bourgogne Grand Ordinaire Rosé		r	
Bourgogne-Hautes-Côtes-de-Beaune	R		
Bourgogne-Hautes-Côtes-de-Nuits	R		
Bourgogne-Irancy	R		
Bourgogne Clairet-Irancy		r	
Bourgogne Rosé-Irancy		r	
Bourgogne-Marsannay ou Bourgogne-Marsannay-la-Côte	R		
Bourgogne Mousseux	R	r	W
Bourgogne Ordinaire	R		W
Bourgogne Ordinaire Clairet		r	
Bourgogne Ordinaire Rosé		r	
Bourgogne Passetoutgrain	R	r	
Bourgogne Rosé		r	
Bourgogne Rosé-Hautes-Côtes-de-Beaune		r	
Bourgogne Rosé-Hautes-Côtes-de-Nuits		r	
Bourgogne Rosé-Marsannay		r	
Brouilly	R		
Chablis. *See producing localities having a right to the appellation*			W
Chablis Grand Cru		W	
Chambertin	R		
Chambertin-Clos de Bèze	R		
Chambolle-Musigny	R		
Chapelle-Chambertin	R		
Charlemagne			W
Chassagne-Montrachet	R		W
Cheilly-lès-Maranges	R		W
Chénas	R		
Chevalier-Montrachet			W
Chiroubles	R		
Chorey-lès-Beaune	R		W
Clos de la Roche	R		
Clos de Tart	R		
Clos Saint-Denis	R		
Clos-Vougeot	R		
Corton	R		W
Corton-Charlemagne			W
Côtes-de-Beaune	R		W
Côtes-de-Beaune preceded by the name of the locality of origin	R		
Côtes-de-Beaune-Villages	R		
Côtes-de-Brouilly	R		
Côtes-de-Nuits-Villages	R		W
Crémant de Bourgogne		r	W
Criots-Bâtard-Montrachet			W
Dezize-lès-Maranges	R		W
Échezeaux	R		
Fixin	R		W
Fleurie	R		
Gevrey-Chambertin	R		
Givry	R		W
Grands-Échezeaux	R		
Griotte-Chambertin	R		

Juliénas	R		
Ladoix	R		W
Latricières-Chambertin	R		
Mâcon	R	r	W
Mâcon-Villages			W
Mâcon Supérieur	R	r	W
Mâcon. *See localities or crus which have the right to add their names to that of the appellation d'origine*	R	r	W
Mazis-Chambertin	R		
Mazoyères-Chambertin	R		
Mercurey	R		W
Meursault	R		W
Montagny			W
Monthélie	R		W
Montrachet			W
Morcy-Saint-Denis	R		W
Morgon	R		
Moulin-à-Vent	R		
Musigny	R		W
Nuits ou Nuits-Saint-Georges	R		W
Pernand-Vergelesses	R		W
Petit Chablis. *See producing localities having a right to the appellation*			W
Pinot-Chardonnay-Mâcon			W
Pommard	R		
Pouilly-Fuissé			W
Pouilly-Loché			W
Pouilly-Vinzelles			W
Puligny-Montrachet	R		W
Richebourg	R		
Romanée (La)	R		
Romanée-Conti	R		
Romanée-Saint-Vivant	R		
Ruchottes-Chambertin	R		
Rully	R		W
Saint-Amour	R		
Saint-Aubin	R		W
Saint-Romain	R		W
Saint-Véran			W
Sampigny-lès-Maranges	R		W
Santenay	R		W
Savigny ou Savigny-lès-Beaune	R		W
Tâche (La)	R		
Vins fins de la Côtes-de-Nuits	R		W
Volnay	R		
Volnay-Santenots	R		
Vosne-Romanée	R		
Vougeot	R		W

CHAMPAGNE

Champagne		r	W
Coteaux Champenois	R	r	W
Rosé des Riceys		r	

CÔTES-DU-RHÔNE

Château-Grillet			W
Châteauneuf-du-Pape	R		W

Châtillon-en-Diois				R	r	W
Clairette de Die						W
Clairette de Die Mousseux						W
Condrieu						W
Cornas				R		
Côtes-Rôtie				R		
Coteaux du Tricastin				R	r	W
Côtes-du-Rhône. ***See localities or crus which have the right to add their names to that of the appellation d'origine.***				R	r	W
Côtes-du-Rhône-Villages				R	r	W
Côtes-du-Ventoux				R	r	W
Crozes-l'Hermitage ou Crozes-Ermitage				R		W
Gigondas				R	r	
Hermitage ou Ermitage				R		W
Liras				R	r	W
Saint-Joseph				R		W
Saint-Péray						W
Saint-Péray Mousseux			W			
Tavel		r				
CORSE						
Vin de Corse				R	r	W
Vin de Corse-Patrimonio				R	r	W
Vin de Corse-Coteaux d'Ajaccio ou Ajaccio				R	r	W
Vin de Corse-Sartène				R	r	W
Vin de Corse-Calvi				R	r	W
Vin de Corse-Coteaux du Cap Corse				R	r	W
Vin de Corse-Figari				R	r	W
Vin de Corse-Porto-Vecchio				R	r	W
JURA						
Arbois	R	r	W	g	j	p
Arbois Mousseux			W			
Arbois Pupillin	R	r	W		j	p
Château-Chalon					j	
Côtes-du-Jura	R	r	W	g	j	p
Côtes-du-Jura Mousseux			W			
L'Étoile			W		j	p
L'Étoile Mousseux			W			
LANGUEDOC-ROUSSILLON						
Clairette de Bellegarde						W
Clairette du Languedoc						W
Collioure				R		
Corbières				R	r	W
Côtes-du-Roussillon				R	r	W
Côtes-du-Roussillon-Villages-Caramany				R		
Côtes-du-Roussillon-Villages-Latour-de-France				R		
Côtes-du-Roussillon-Villages				R		
Fitou				R		
Minervois				R	r	W
Saint-Chinian				R	r	W

PROVENCE			
Bandol	R	r	W
Bellet	R	r	W
Cassis	R	r	W
Coteaux d'Aix, des Baux	R	r	W
Côtes-de-Provence	R	r	W
Palette	R	r	W
Vin de Bandol	R	r	W
Vin de Bellet	R	r	W

SAVOIE			
Crépy			W
Mousseux de Savoie			W
Pétillant de Savoie			W
Roussette de Savoie			W
Roussette de Savoie. *See localities or crus which have the right to add their names to that of the appellation d'origine*			
Seyssel			W
Seyssel Mousseux			W
Vin de Savoie	R	r	W
Vins de Savoie. *See localities or crus which have the right to add their names to that of the appellation d'origine*	R	r	W
Vin de Savoie Mousseux			W
Vin de Savoie Pétillant			W
Vin de Savoie-Ayze Mousseux			W
Vin de Savoie-Ayze Pétillant			W

SUD-OUEST			
Béarn	R	r	W
Bergerac	R	r	W
Bergerac Sec			W
Blanquette de Limoux			W
Cahors	R		
Côtes-de-Bergerac	R		
Côtes-de-Bergerac Moelleux			W
Côtes-de-Bergerac-Côtes de Saussignac			W
Côtes-de-Buzet	R	r	W
Côtes-de-Duras	R		W
Côtes-du-Frontonnais	R	r	
Côtes-du-Montravel			W
Gaillac	R	r	W
Gaillac Premières Côtes			W
Gaillac Doux			W
Gaillac Mousseux		r	W
Haut-Montravel			W
Irouléguy	R	r	W
Jurançon			W
Jurançon Sec			W
Limoux Nature			W
Madiran	R		
Monbazillac			W
Montravel			W
Pacherenc-du-Vic-Bilh			W
Pécharmant	R		
Rosette			W
Vin de Blanquette			W

VAL DE LOIRE			
• *Nivernais et Berry*			
Blanc Fumé de Pouilly			W
Menetou-Salon	R	r	W
Pouilly Fumé			W
Pouilly-sur-Loire			W
Quincy			W
Reuilly	R	r	W
Sancerre	R	r	W
• *Touraine*			
Bourgueil	R	r	
Chinon	R	r	W
Coteaux du Loir	R	r	W
Jasnières			W
Montlouis			W
Montlouis Mousseux			W
Montlouis Pétillant			W
Saint-Nicolas-de-Bourgueil	R	r	
Touraine	R	r	W
Touraine-Amboise	R	r	W
Touraine-Azay-le-Rideau			W
Touraine-Mesland	R	r	W
Touraine Mousseux	R	r	W
Touraine Pétillant	R	r	W
Vouvray			W
Vouvray Mousseux			W
Vouvray Pétillant			W
• *Anjou*			
Anjou	R		W
Anjou-Coteaux de la Loire			W
Anjou-Gamay	R		
Anjou Mousseux		r	W
Anjou Pétillant		r	W
Bonnezeaux			W
Cabernet		r	
Coteaux de l'Aubance			W
Coteaux de Layon			W
Coteaux du Layon. *See localities or crus which have the right to add their names to that of the appellation d'origine*			W
Coteaux du Layon-Chaume			W
Coteaux de Saumur			W
Quarts-de-Chaume			W
Rosé d'Anjou		r	
Rosé d'Anjou Pétillant		r	
Saumur	R		W
Saumur-Champigny	R		
Saumur Pétillant			W
Saumur Mousseux		r	W
Savennières			W
Savennières-Coulée-de-Serrant			W
Savennières-Roche-aux-Moines			W
• *In the region of the Anjou, Saumur and Touraine appellations*			
Crémant de Loire		r	W
Rosé de Loire		r	

• *Nantes region*			
Muscadet			W
Muscadet des Coteaux de la Loire			W
Muscadet de Sèvres-et-Maine			W

"VINS DOUX NATURELS" NATURALLY SWEET WINES			
Banyuls	R	r	W
Banyuls Rancio			
Banyuls Grand Cru	R		
Banyuls Grand Cru Rancio			
Frontignan			
Grand Roussillon	R	r	W
Grand Roussillon Rancio			
Maury	R	r	W
Maury Rancio			
Muscat de Beaumes-de-Venise			
Muscat de Frontignan			
Muscat de Lunel			
Muscat de Mireval			
Muscat de Rivesaltes			
Muscat de Saint-Jean-de-Minervois			
Rasteau	R	r	W
Rasteau Rancio			
Rivesaltes	R	r	W
Rivesaltes Rancio			
Vin de Frontignan			

VINS DÉLIMITÉS DE QUALITÉ SUPÉRIEURE

(V.D.Q.S.)

R: red wine, *r:* rosé, *W:* white wine, *g:* vin gris

LANGUEDOC-ROUSSILLON			
Cabrières		r	
Cabardès	R	r	
Costières du Gard	R	r	W
Coteaux du Languedoc	R	r	
Coteaux du Languedoc accompanied by an appellation	R	r	
Coteaux de la Méjanelle	R	r	W
Coteaux de Saint-Christol	R	r	
Coteaux de Vérargues	R	r	
Côtes du Cabardès et de l'Orbiel	R	r	
Côtes de la Malepère	R	r	
Montpeyroux	R	r	
Picpoul-de-Pinet			W
Pic-Saint-Loup	R	r	W
Quatourze	R	r	W
Saint-Drezery	R		
Saint-Georges-d'Orques	R		
Saint-Saturnin	R	r	
Vin Noble du Minervois			W

LORRAINE			
Côtes de Toul	R	r	W
Vins de Moselle	R		W

PROVENCE ET CÔTES-DU-RHÔNE			
Coteaux de Pierrevert	R	r	W
Côtes-du-Lubéron	R	r	W
Côtes-du-Vivarais	R	r	W
Côtes-du-Vivarais followed by the name of the cru : Orgnac, Saint-Montant, Saint-Remèze	R	r	W
Haut-Comtat	R	r	

SAVOIE - BUGEY - BOURGOGNE			
Coteaux du Lyonnais	R	r	W
Mousseux du Bugey			W
Pétillant du Bugey			W
Roussette du Bugey			W
Roussette du Bugey, followed by the name of the cru: Anglefort, Arbignieu, Chanay, Lagnieu, Montagnieu, Virieu-le-Grand			W
Sauvignon de Saint-Bris			W
Vin du Bugey	R	r	W
Vin du Bugey, followed by the name of the cru: Virieu-le-Grand, Montagnieu, Manicle, Machuraz, Cerdon	R	r	W
Vin du Bugey-Cerdon Pétillant			W
Vin du Bugey-Cerdon Mousseux			W
Vin du Bugey Mousseux			W
Vin du Bugey Pétillant			W
Vin du Lyonnais	R	r	W

SUD-OUEST			
Côtes du Marmandais	R	r	W
Tursan	R	r	W
Vin d'Entraygues et du Fel	R	r	W
Vin d'Estaing	R	r	W
Vin de Lavilledieu	R		
Vin de Marcillac	R	r	

VAL DE LOIRE			
Châteaumeillant	R	r	W
Cheverny	R	r	W
Coteaux d'Ancenis, which must be followed by the name of the vinestock used : Pineau de la Loire, Chenin Blanc, Malvoisie, Pinot Beurot, Gamay, Cabernet	R	r	W
Coteaux du Vendômois		r	
Côte-Roannaise	R	r	
Côtes-d'Auvergne	R	r	W
Côtes-d'Auvergne followed by the name of the cru: Boudes, Chanturgue, Corent-Châteaugay, Mendargues			
Côtes de Forez	R	r	
Côtes de Gien	R	r	W
Gros-Plant or Gros-Plant du Pays Nantais			W
Valençay	R	r	W

Vin des Coteaux du Giennois	R	r	W
Vins du Haut-Poitou	R	r	W
Vins de l'Orléanais	R	r	W
Vins de Saint-Pourçain-sur-Sioule	R	r	W
Vins du Thouarsais	R	r	W

LOCAL WINES

Regions	Appellations
Ardèche	Coteaux de l'Ardèche
Département de l'Aude	Coteaux de la Cabrerisse
	Coteaux Cathares
	Coteaux de la Cité de Carcassonne
	Coteaux du Lézignanais
	Coteaux de Miramont
	Coteaux de Peyriac
	Coteaux du Termenès
	Côtes-de-Pérignan
	Cucugnan
	Hauterive du Pays d'Aude
	Haute Vallée de l'Aude
	Val de Cesse
	Val de Dagne
	Val d'Orbieu
	Val du Torgan
	Vallée du Paradis
Département des Bouches-du-Rhône	Petite Crau
	Sables du Golfe du Lion
Département de la Drôme	Coteaux de Baronnies
Département du Gard	Coteaux Cévenoles
	Coteaux de Cèze
	Coteaux Flaviens
	Coteaux du Pont-du-Gard
	Coteaux du Salavès
	Coteaux du Vidourle
	Mont Bouquet
	Sables du Golfe du Lion
	Serre de Coiran
	Uzège
	Val de Montferrand
	Vistrenque
Département du Gers	Côtes-du-Condomois
	Côtes-de-Gascogne
	Côtes-de-Montestruc
	Côtes-de-Saint-Mont
Département de l'Hérault	Bassan
	Caux
	Cessenon
	Collines de la Moure

	Coteaux d'Enserune **Coteaux de Laurens** **Coteaux du Libron** **Coteaux de Murviel** **Coteaux de Peyriac** **Coteaux du Salagou** **Côtes-du-Brian** **Côtes-du-Céressou** **Côtes-de-Thau** **Côtes-de-Thongue** **Gorges de l'Hérault** **Haute Vallée de l'Orb** **Mont Baudile** **Sables du Golfe du Lion** **Val de Montferrand** **Vicomté d'Aumelas**
Département de l'Isère	**Balmes Dauphinoises** **Coteaux du Grésivaudan**
Département de la Loire-Atlantique	**Marches de Bretagne** **Pays de Retz**
Département du Lot	**Coteaux de Glanes** **Coteaux du Quercy**
Département du Lot-et-Garonne	**Agenais** **Côtes-du-Condomois**
Département du Maine-et-Loire	**Marches de Bretagne**
Département des Pyrénées-Orientales	**Coteaux des Fenouillèdes** **Côtes-Catalanes** **Pays Catalan** **Val d'Agly**
Département de la Savoie	**Balmes Dauphinoises** **Coteaux du Grésivaudan**
Départements de Savoie et Haute-Savoie	**Allobrógie**
Département du Tarn	**Côtes-du-Tarn**
Département du Tarn-et-Garonne	**Agenais** **Coteaux du Quercy** **Côtes-du-Brulhois** **Saint-Sardos**
Département du Var	**Coteaux Varois** **Les Maures**
Département de la Vendée	**Fiefs Vendéens** **Marches de Bretagne**

The French Vinestocks

• ALSACE - LORRAINE

Alsace A.O.C.		**(Commercialized under the name of the vinestock or various appellations)**
	(W)	**Gewurztraminer, Riesling, Pinot Gris, Muscat (S), Pinot Blanc, Auxerrois, Chasselas, Sylvaner**
	(R)	**Pinot Noir**
Côtes de Toul V.D.Q.S.	**(W)**	**Aubin, Aligoté**
	(R)	**Pinot Noir, Pinot Meunier**
Vins de Moselle V.D.Q.S.	**(W)**	**Auxerrois, Sylvaner, Riesling, Elbing, Gewurztraminer**
	(R)	**Pinot Noir, Pinot Meunier, Gamay**

• BOURGOGNE - BEAUJOLAIS

Bourgogne A.O.C.		***Grands Crus, White :*** **Montrachet, Meursault, etc.**
	(W)	**Chardonnay, Pinot Blanc**
Bourgogne A.O.C.		***Grands Crus, Red :*** **Pommard, Vougeot, Chambertin, Côtes-de-Nuits, Vosne-Romanée, etc.**
	(R)	**Pinot Noir**
Bourgogne A.O.C.	**(W)**	**Chardonnay, Pinot Blanc, Aligoté, Melon**
	(R)	**Pinot Noir, Gamay**
Bourgogne Passetoutgrain A.O.C.	**(W)**	**Pinot Blanc, Chardonnay**
	(R)	**Pinot Noir, Gamay**
Chablis A.O.C.	**(W)**	**Chardonnay**
Beaujolais A.O.C.		**Fleurie, Chiroubles, Brouilly, Saint-Amour, Juliénas, etc.**
	(R)	**Gamay, Pinot Noir**
Pouilly-Fuissé A.O.C.	**(W)**	**Chardonnay**
Mâcon A.O.C.	**(W)**	**Chardonnay, Pinot Blanc**
	(R)	**Gamay, Pinot Noir**
Mercurey A.O.C.	**(W)**	**Pinot Chardonnay**
	(R)	**Pinot Noir, Beurot**
Vins du Lyonnais V.D.Q.S.	**(W)**	**Chardonnay, Aligoté, Melon**
	(R)	**Gamay**
Sauvignon de Saint-Bris V.D.Q.S.	**(W)**	**Sauvignon**

• BORDELAIS ET VIGNOBLES SATELLITES

Bordelais A.O.C.	(W)	Sauvignon, Sémillon, Muscadelle
	(R)	Merlot, Cabernet Franc, Cabernet-Sauvignon, Petit Verdot, Cot Malbec
Predominant vinestocks		
Médoc	(R)	Cabernet-Sauvignon
Saint-Emilion	(R)	Merlot, Cabernet Franc
Pomerol	(R)	Merlot, Cabernet Franc
Sauternais	(W)	Sauvignon, Sémillon
Barsac	(W)	Sauvignon, Sémillon
Bergerac A.O.C.	(W)	Sémillon, Sauvignon, Muscadelle, Chenin
	(R)	Cabernet (S), Merlot, Cot Malbec
Pécharmant A.O.C.	(R)	Cabernet (S), Merlot, Cot Malbec
Montbazillac A.O.C.	(W)	Sémillon, Sauvignon, Muscadelle
Côtes de Duras A.O.C.	(W)	Sémillon, Sauvignon, Muscadelle, Mauzac, Chenin
	(R)	Cabernet (S), Merlot, Cot Malbec

• CHAMPAGNE

Champagne A.O.C.	(W)	Chardonnay
	(R)	Pinot Noir, Pinot Meunier
Coteaux Champenois	(W)	Chardonnay
Still wines	(R)	Pinot Noir, Pinot Meunier
Rosés des Riceys A.O.C.		
Still wines	(R)	Pinot Noir

• JURA

Artois - Côtes du Jura A.O.C.	(W)	Savagnin, Chardonnay
	(R)	Poulsard, Trousseau, Pinot Noir
Château-Chalon A.O.C.	(W)	Savagnin
(Château Chalon) Vins de Paille		

• LANGUEDOC-ROUSSILLON

Blanquette de Limoux A.O.C.	(W)	Mauzac, Chenin, Clairette, Chardonnay
Fitou A.O.C.	(R)	Carignan, Grenache, Syrah, Mourvèdre
Collioure A.O.C.	(R)	Grenache, Carignan, Mourvèdre, Syrah
Clairette du Languedoc A.O.C.	(W)	Clairette
Aspiran		
Clairette de Bellegarde A.O.C.	(W)	Clairette
Côtes-du-Roussillon A.O.C.	(W)	Maccabéo, Grenache, Clairette, Muscat
Céret	(R)	Grenache, Carignan, Mourvèdre, Cinsaut, Syrah, Lladoner Pelut
Corbières A.O.C.	(W)	Grenache Maccabéo, Terret
	(R)	Carignan, Grenache, Cinsault, Mourvèdre, Syrah
Coteaux du Languedoc A.O.C.	(W)	Ugni Blanc, Terret, Carignan, Picpoul, Clairette
Minervois A.O.C.	(R)	Grenache, Carignan, Cinsault, Mourvèdre, Syrah, Œillade
Costières du Gard A.O.C.		
Picpoul du Pinet V.D.Q.S.	(W)	Picpoul, Terret, Clairette
Pinet		

• PROVENCE-COTE D'AZUR - CORSE

Bandol A.O.C.	**(W)**	**Ugni Blanc, Clairette, Bourboulenc**
	(R)	**Mourvèdre, Grenache, Cinsault, Calitor, Syrah**
Cassis A.O.C.	**(W)**	**Ugni Blanc, Sauvignon, Marsanne, Pascal**
	(R)	**Grenache, Carignan, Mourvèdre, Barbaroux**
Bellet A.O.C.	**(W)**	**Rolle, Roussan, Mayorquin**
	(R)	**Grenache, Folle Noire, Cinsault, Braquet**
Palette A.O.C.	**(W)**	**Clairette (S), Picardan, Ugni Blanc, Muscat (S)**
Meyreuil	**(R)**	**Mourvèdre, Grenache, Cinsault**
Vins de Corse A.O.C.	**(W)**	**Vermentino, Ugni Blanc**
Patrimonio	**(R)**	**Nielluccio, Sciacarello, Barbarosa**
Coteaux d'Ajaccio A.O.C.		
Corse Sartène A.O.C.	**(W)**	**Vermentino, Ugni Blanc**
Cap Corse A.O.C.		
Corse Figari A.O.C.	**(R)**	**Nielluccio, Sciacarello + Codivarta (Blanc) for the appellation Coteaux**
Corse Porto-Vecchio A.O.C.		**Cap Corse**
Coteaux d'Aix A.O.C.	**(W)**	**Bourboulenc, Clairette, Ugni Blanc**
Côtes-de-Provence A.O.C.	**(R)**	**Cinsault, Counoise, Grenache, Mourvèdre, Syrah, Cabernet-Sauvignon**
Coteaux de Pierrevert V.D.Q.S.	**(W)**	**Clairette, Picpoul, Marsanne, Roussanne, Ugni Blanc**
Albiose	**(R)**	**Cinsault, Grenache, Mourvèdre, Carignan, Œillade**
Côtes-du-Lubéron V.D.Q.S.	**(W)**	**Bourboulenc, Clairette, Ugni Blanc**
Pertuis	**(R)**	**Grenache, Syrah, Mourvèdre, Counoise, Cinsault, Carignan, Gamay**

LOCAL WINES : ***Same vinestocks + Cabernet (S), Merlot, Alicante Bouchet***
TABLE WINES : ***Same vinestocks + Aramon, Tempranillo***

• SAVOIE

Seyssel A.O.C.	**(W)**	**Roussette**
Vins mousseux	**(W)**	**Roussette, Chasselas (Fendant)**
Crépy A.O.C.	**(W)**	**Chasselas**
Vins de Savoie A.O.C.	**(W)**	**Altesse, Jacquère, Chardonnay, Bergeron**
(Apremont Chiguin)	**(R)**	**Mondeuse, Gamay, Pinot Noir**
Vins du Bugey V.D.Q.S.	**(W)**	**Chardonnay, Pinot gris, Altesse, Aligoté, Jacquère**
Ambérieu	**(R)**	**Gamay, Pinot Noir, Poulsard, Mondeuse**

• SUD-OUEST - MIDI-PYRÉNÉES

Armagnac ***Eaux-de-vie*** **A.O.C.**	**(W)**	**Ugni Blanc, Folle Blanche, Colombard, Baco A 22**
Côtes du Buzet A.O.C.	**(W)**	**Sémillon, Sauvignon, Muscadelle**
	(R)	**Cabernet (S), Merlot, Cot Malbec**
Cahors A.O.C.	**(R)**	**Cot Malbec, Merlot, Jurançon Noir, Tannat, Syrah**

Gaillac A.O.C.	(W)	Mauzac, Len de l'En, Sémillon, Sauvignon, Muscadelle
	(R)	Fer Servadou, Duras, Syrah, Cabernet (S), Jurançon noir
Côtes du Frontonnais A.O.C.	(R)	Négrette, Cabernet (S), Cot Malbec, Fer Servadou, Syrah, Gamay
Madiran - Pacherenc-du-Vic-Bilh A.O.C.	(W)	Gros Manseng, Raffiat de Moncade, Courbu, Sauvignon, Sémillon
	(R)	Cabernet (S), Fer Servadou, Tannat
Jurançon A.O.C.	(W)	Gros Manseng, Petit Manseng, Courbu
Irouléguy A.O.C.	(W)	Gros Manseng, Courbu
	(R)	Tannat, Cabernet (S)
Côtes du Marmandais A.O.C.	(W)	Sémillon, Ugni Blanc, Sauvignon, Muscadelle
	(R)	Cabernet (S), Merlot, Abouriou, Fer Servadou, Syrah, Cot Malbec, Gamay Noir "à jus blanc" (yeilding white juice)
Vins de Marcillac V.D.Q.S.	(R)	Fer Servadou, Cabernet (S), Gamay, Merlot, Cot Malbec
Tursan V.D.Q.S.	(W)	Barroque, Manseng, Sauvignon, Clairette
	(R)	Tannat, Fer Servadou, Cabernet (S)
Vins de Lavilledieu V.D.Q.S.	(W)	Mauzac, Sémillon, Sauvignon, Muscadelle, Blanquette
	(R)	Négrette, Gamay, Syrah, Fer Servadou
Vins d'Estaing V.D.Q.S.	(W)	Chenin, Mauzac
	(R)	Fer Servadou, Gamay, Abouriou, Cabernet (S), Pinot Noir
Vins d'Entraygues et de Fel V.D.Q.S.	(W)	Chenin, Mauzac
	(R)	Fer Servadou, Cabernet (S), Gamay, Merlot, Négrette, Pinot Noir

• VAL DE LOIRE - CENTRE

Vins du Haut-Poitou V.D.Q.S.	(W)	Chardonnay, Sauvignon, Chenin, Pinot Blanc vrai (true Pinot Blanc)
	(R)	Gamay (S), Pinot Noir, Cabernet Franc, Cabernet-Sauvignon, Grolleau, Merlot Rouge, Cot Malbec
Pays Nantais A.O.C.	(W)	Melon, Folle Blanche
Coteaux d'Ancenis A.O.C.	(W)	Melon, Chenin, Folle Blanche, Pinot Gris
	(R)	Gamay (S), Cabernet Franc, Cabernet-Sauvignon
Retz region, Local Wine, Table Wine	(W)	Melon, Folle Blanche, Malvoisie
	(R)	Gamay (S), Grolleau, Abourlou, Cabernet Franc, Cabernet-Sauvignon, Pinot Noir
Anjou et Saumur A.O.C.		
Natural wine	(W)	Chenin Blanc, Chardonnay, Sauvignon
Natural wine	(R)	Cabernet Franc, Cabernet-Sauvignon, Grolleau, Cot Malbec, Pineau d'Aunis, Pinot Noir, Gamay (S), (Saumur region excepted)
Local wine		The same vinestock + Abouriou (R)
Table wine	(W)	Pinot Blanc vrai (true Pinot Blanc)
Crémants et Vins mousseux	(W)	Chenin Blanc, Chardonnay
	(R)	Cabernet Franc, Cabernet Sauvignon,

Appellation		Colour	Varieties
			Grolleau Noir, Pineau d'Aunis, Gamay, Pinot Noir, (Saumur region only)
Bourgueil - Chinon A.O.C.		**(R)**	**Cabernet Franc, Cabernet-Sauvignon**
	Local wine	**(R)**	**Same wine varieties + Gamay (S)**
		(W)	**Chenin, Chardonnay**
Vouvray - Montlouis A.O.C.	*(Natural and sparkling)*	**(W)**	**Chenin**
Touraine A.O.C.		**(W)**	**Chenin Blanc, Artois, Sauvignon, Chardonnay**
		(R)	**Gamay (S), Cabernet Franc, Cabernet-Sauvignon, Cot Malbec, Pineau d'Aunis, Pinot Noir, Grolleau, Pinot Gris, Pinot Meunier**
	Local wine		**Same wine varieties +**
	Table wine	**(W)**	**Pinot Blanc vrai (true)**
		(R)	**Abouriou**
Coteaux du Loir A.O.C.		**(W)**	**Chenin Blanc**
Jasnières		**(R)**	**Pineau d'Aunis, Cabernet (S), Cot Malbec, Gamay, Grolleau**
Sancerre A.O.C.		**(W)**	**Sauvignon**
		(R)	**Pinot Noir**
Pouilly-sur-Loire A.O.C.	*Pouilly*	**(W)**	**Chasselas, Sauvignon**
	Pouilly fumé	**(W)**	**Sauvignon**
Menetou-Salon A.O.C.		**(W)**	**Sauvignon**
		(R)	**Pinot Noir**
Quincy A.O.C.		**(W)**	**Sauvignon**
Reuilly A.O.C.		**(W)**	**Sauvignon**
		(R)	**Pinot Noir, Pinot Gris**
Coteaux du Vendômois V.D.Q.S.		**(R)**	**Pineau d'Aunis, Gamay Noir à jus blanc (white grape juice)**
Vins de l'Orléanais V.D.Q.S.		**(W)**	**Chardonnay, Sauvignon**
		(R)	**Pinot Meunier, Pinot Noir, Cabernet Franc, Cabernet-Sauvignon, Gamay (S)**
Cheverny V.D.Q.S.		**(W)**	**Chenin Blanc, Chardonnay, Romorantin, Sauvignon**
		(R)	**Gamay (S), Cabernet-Sauvignon, Cabernet Franc, Pinot Noir, Cot Malbec**
Coteaux du Giennois V.D.Q.S.		**(W)**	**Sauvignon, Chenin**
		(R)	**Gamay Noir à jus blanc (white grape juice), Pinot noir**
Valençay V.D.Q.S.		**(W)**	**Arbois, Chardonnay, Sauvignon, Chenin**
		(R)	**Cabernet (S), Cot Malbec, Gamay (S), Pinot Noir**
Saint-Pourçain-sur-Sioule V.D.Q.S.		**(W)**	**Tressalier, Chardonnay, Sauvignon, Aligoté**
		(R)	**Gamay, Pinot Noir**
Châteaumeillant V.D.Q.S.		**(R)**	**Gamay Noir à jus blanc (white grape juice), Pinot Noir, Pinot Gris**
Côtes d'Auvergne V.D.Q.S.		**(R)**	**Gamay, Pinot Noir**
Côtes du Forez V.D.Q.S.		**(R)**	**Gamay Noir à jus blanc (white grape juice)**
Côtes Roannaise V.D.Q.S.		**(R)**	**Gamay Noir à jus blanc (white grape juice)**
Vendée	*Local wine*	**(W)**	**Colombard, Chenin, Sauvignon, Chardonnay, Pinot Blanc vrai (true Pinot Blanc)**
	and from Vendée dependencies	**(R)**	**Négrette, Gamay (S), Cabernet (S), Pinot Noir, Cot Malbec**

• VALLÉE DU RHÔNE

Châteauneuf-du-Pape A.O.C.	**(W)**	**Roussanne, Clairette, Bourboulenc**
Gigondas	**(R)**	**Syrah, Mourvèdre, Grenache, Cinsault**
Laudun - Lirac - Tavel A.O.C.	**(W)**	**Clairette, Bourboulenc**
	(R)	**Grenache, Syrah, Cinsault, Carignan**
Coteaux-du-Tricastin A.O.C.	**(W)**	**Picpoul, Clairette, Bourboulenc, Ugni Blanc, Grenache**
Donzère	**(R)**	**Grenache Noir, Cinsault, Mourvèdre, Syrah, Carignan**
Clairette de Die A.O.C.	**(W)**	
Vins Mousseux		**Clairette, Muscat à petits grains (white small grape clusters)**
Saint-Péray* A.O.C. *Vins Mousseux	***(W)***	***Roussette, Marsanne***
Cornas A.O.C.	**(R)**	**Syrah**
Crozes-l'Hermitage		
Hermitage A.O.C.	**(W)**	**Roussanne, Marsanne**
Tain-l'Hermitage	**(R)**	**Syrah**
Saint-Joseph A.O.C.	**(W)**	**Roussanne, Marsanne**
	(R)	**Syrah**
Condrieu - Château-Grillet A.O.C.	**(W)**	**Viognier**
Côte-Rôtie A.O.C.	**(W)**	**Viognier**
	(R)	**Syrah**
Châtillon-en-Diois A.O.C.	**(W)**	**Aligoté, Chardonnay**
	(R)	**Gamay Noir à jus blanc (white grape juice), Syrah, Pinot Noir**

Local and Table Wines : Similar vinestocks

• NATURAL SWEETS WINES

Banyuls A.O.C.	**(W)**	**Grenache Blanc, Maccabéo, Muscat à petits grains (with small grape clusters), Tourbat, Muscat d'Alexandrie**
	(R)	**Grenache Noir, Cinsault, Syrah**
Rivesaltes A.O.C.	**(R)**	**Muscat à petits grains (with small grape clusters), Muscat d'Alexandrie**
Maury A.O.C.	**(W)**	**Grenache Blanc, Maccabéo, Tourbat, Muscat d'Alexandrie Muscat à petits grains (with small grape clusters)**
	(R)	**Grenache Noir, Cinsault, Syrah**
Saint-Jean-de-Minervois A.O.C.	**(W)**	**Muscat Doré**
Frontignan A.O.C.	**(W)**	**Muscat Doré de Frontignan**
Mireval A.O.C.	**(W)**	**Muscat à petits grains (with small grape clusters)**
Lunel A.O.C.	**(W)**	**Muscat à petits grains (with small grape clusters)**
Rasteau A.O.C.	**(W)**	**Grenache Blanc, Clairette, Roussanne**
	(R)	**Grenache Noir, Syrah, Picpoul, Terret**
Beaumes-de-Venise A.O.C.	**(W)**	**Muscat à petits grains (with small grape clusters)**

INDEX

C

M

TABLE DES MATIÈRES

Translated by Ellen Chase
Photos: Phototheque I.T.V.-Mackiewicz
Marketing: Guy Lunal, Laurence Mergny
Map of the vineyards from
the "Guide des vins de France", Albin Michel
Lay-out: Atelier Rosier
Phototypeset: Points de repère Photogravure, Montreuil
Printer: Mame - APS Tours
Dépôt légal : juillet 1989

EDITION VINTAGE
14, rue Rennéquin
75017 Paris
Tél. (1) 46 22 72 20